I dedicate this book to Sgt. Lawrence Martin Carlson, who gave his life in service to his country on November 19, 2006, and to his mother, Charlotte Carlson, to his sister and brother, Andrea and Douglas, to his children, Savannah, and Ezra, and to his nieces, Helana, Anna, Eva Rose, and Emily.

William L. Carlson

I dedicate this book to my husband, Jim, and to our family, Jennie, Ann, Renee, Jon, Chris, Jon, Hannah, Leah, Christina, Jim, Wendy, Marius, Mihaela, Cezara, Anda, and Mara Iulia.

Betty M. Thorne

Dr. Bill Carlson is professor emeritus of economics at St. Olaf College, where he taught for 31 years, serving several times as department chair and in various administrative functions, including director of academic computing. He has also held leave assignments with the U.S. government and the University of Minnesota in addition to lecturing at many different universities. He was elected an honorary member of Phi Beta Kappa. In addition, he spent 10 years in private industry and contract research prior to beginning his career at St. Olaf. His education includes engineering degrees from Michigan Technological University (BS) and from the Illinois Institute of Technology (MS) and a PhD in quantitative management from the Rackham Graduate School at the University of Michigan. Numerous research projects related to management, highway safety, and statistical education have produced more than 50 publications. He received the Metropolitan Insurance Award of Merit for Safety Research. He has previously published two statistics textbooks. An important goal of this book is to help students understand the forest and not be lost in the trees. Hiking the Lake Superior trail in Northern Minnesota helps in developing this goal. Professor Carlson led a number of study-abroad programs, ranging from 1 to 5 months, for study in various countries around the world. He was the executive director of the Cannon Valley Elder Collegium and a regular volunteer for a number of community activities. He is a member of both the Methodist and Lutheran disaster-relief teams and a regular participant in the local Habitat for Humanity building team. He enjoys his grandchildren, woodworking, travel, reading, and being on assignment on the North Shore of Lake Superior.

Dr. Betty M. Thorne, author, researcher, and award-winning teacher, is professor of statistics and director of undergraduate studies in the School of Business Administration at Stetson University in DeLand, Florida. Winner of Stetson University's McEniry Award for Excellence in Teaching, the highest honor given to a Stetson University faculty member, Dr. Thorne is also the recipient of the Outstanding Teacher of the Year Award and Professor of the Year Award in the School of Business Administration at Stetson. Dr. Thorne teaches in Stetson University's undergradaute business program in DeLand, FL and also in Stetson's summer program in Innsbruck, Austria; Stetson University's College of Law; Stetson University's Executive MBA program; and Stetson University's Executive Passport program. Dr. Thorne has received various teaching awards in the JD/MBA program at Stetson's College of Law" in Gulfport, Florida. She received her BS degree from Geneva College and MA and PhD degrees from Indiana University. She has co-authored statistics textbooks which have been translated into several languages and adopted by universities, nationally and internationally. She serves on key school and university committees. Dr. Thorne, whose research has been published in various refereed journals, is a member of the American Statistical Association, the Decision Science Institute, Betal Alpha Psi, Beta Gamma Sigma, and the Academy of International Business. She and her husband, Jim, have four children. They travel extensively, attend theological conferences and seminars, participate in international organizations dedicated to helping disadvantaged children, and do missionary work in Romania.

Business statistics has continued to evolve as a discipline and has become an increasingly important part of business education programs. It is crucial *how* business statistics gets taught and *what* gets taught. *Statistics for Business and Economics, ninth edition*, has been written to meet the need for an introductory text that provides a strong introduction to business statistics, develops understanding of concepts, and emphasizes problem solving using realistic examples that use real data sets and computer based analysis. These examples highlight business and economics examples for the following:

- MBA or undergraduate business programs that teach business statistics
- Graduate and undergraduate economics programs
- Executive MBA programs
- Graduate courses for business statistics

Designed to build a strong foundation in applied statistical procedures, *Statistics for Business and Economics* enables individuals to perform solid statistical analysis in many business and economic situations. We have emphasized an understanding of the assumptions that are necessary for professional analysis. In particular we have greatly expanded the number of applications that utilize data from applied policy and research settings. These data and problem scenarios have been obtained from business analysts, major research organizations, and selected extractions from publicly available data sources. With data analysis software like Microsoft Excel, JMP, and Minitab, that illustrate how software can assist decision making process, it is now easy to compute, from the data, the output needed for many statistical procedures. It is tempting to merely apply simple "rules" using these outputs—an approach used in many textbooks. Our approach is to provide instruction through a combination of examples and exercises, supported by relevant software that show how understanding of methods and their assumptions lead to useful understanding of business and economic problems.

NEW TO THIS EDITION

The ninth edition of this book has been revised and updated to provide students with improved problem contexts for learning how statistical methods can improve their analysis and understanding of business and economics.

The objective of this revision is to provide a strong core textbook with new features and modifications that will provide an improved learning environment for students entering a rapidly changing technical work environment. This edition has been carefully revised to improve the clarity and completeness of explanations. This revision recognizes the globalization of statistical study and in particular the global market for this book.

1. Improvement in clarity and relevance of discussions of the core topics included in the book.
2. Addition of large databases developed by public research agencies, businesses, and databases from the authors' own works.
3. An extensive number of new end-of-section or end-of-chapter problems.

CONTINUING FEATURES

1. Addition of a number of case studies, with both large and small sample sizes. Students are provided the opportunity to extend their statistical understanding to the context of research and analysis conducted by professionals. These studies include

data files obtained from on-going research studies, which reduce for the student, the extensive work load of data collection and refinement, thus providing an emphasis on question formulation, analysis, and reporting of results.

2. Careful revision of text and symbolic language to ensure consistent terms and definitions and to remove errors that accumulated from previous revisions and production problems.

3. Major revision of the discussion of Time Series both in terms of describing historical patterns and in the focus on identifying the underlying structure and introductory forecasting methods.

4. Integration of the text material, data sets, and exercises into new online applications including MyLab Statistics.

5. Expansion of descriptive statistics to include percentiles, z-scores, and alternative formulae to compute the sample variance and sample standard deviation.

6. Addition of a significant number of new examples based on real world data.

7. Greater emphasis on the assumptions being made when conducting various statistical procedures.

8. Reorganization of sampling concepts.

9. More detailed business-oriented examples and exercises incorporated in the analysis of statistics.

10. Improved chapter introductions that include business examples discussed in the chapter.

11. Good range of difficulty in the section ending exercises that permit the professor to tailor the difficulty level to his or her course.

12. Improved suitability for both introductory and advanced statistics courses for undergraduate and graduate students.

13. Decision Theory, which is covered in other business classes such as operations management or strategic management, has been moved to an online location for access by those who are interested (www.pearsonglobaleditions.com).

This edition devotes considerable effort to providing an understanding of statistical methods and their applications. We have avoided merely providing rules and canned computer routines for analyzing and solving statistical problems. This edition contains a complete discussion of methods and assumptions, including computational details expressed in clear and complete formulas. Through examples and extended chapter applications, we provide guidelines for interpreting results and explain how to determine if additional analysis is required. The development of the many procedures included under statistical inference and regression analysis are built on a strong development of probability and random variables, which are a foundation for the applications presented in this book. The foundation also includes a clear and complete discussion of descriptive statistics and graphical approaches. These provide important tools for exploring and describing data that represent a process being studied.

Probability and random variables are presented with a number of important applications, which are invaluable in management decision making. These include conditional probability and Bayesian applications that clarify decisions and show counterintuitive results in a number of decision situations. Linear combinations of random variables are developed in detail, with a number of applications of importance, including portfolio applications in finance.

The authors strongly believe that students learn best when they work with challenging and relevant applications that apply the concepts presented by dedicated teachers and the textbook. Thus the textbook has always included a number of data sets obtained from various applications in the public and private sectors. In the eighth edition we have added a number of large data sets obtained from major research projects and other sources. These data sets are used in chapter examples, exercises, and case studies located at the end of analysis chapters. A number of exercises consider individual analyses that are typically part of larger research projects. With this structure, students can deal with important detailed questions and can also work with case studies that require them to identify the detailed questions that are logically part of a larger research project. These large data sets can also be used by the teacher to develop additional research and case study projects that are custom designed for local course environments. The opportunity to custom design new research questions for students is a unique part of this textbook.

A number of major data sets containing Taiwan's real estate measures, automobile fuel consumption, health data, the HEI Cost Data Variable Subset (which Includes the Healthy Eating Index, a measure of diet quality developed by the Economic Research Service and computed for each individual in the survey), New York's air quality index, and more are described in detail at the end of the chapters where they are used in exercises and case studies. A complete list of the data files and where they are used is located at the end of this preface. Data files are also shown by chapter at the end of each chapter.

The book provides a complete and in-depth presentation of major applied topics. An initial read of the discussion and application examples enables a student to begin working on simple exercises, followed by challenging exercises that provide the opportunity to learn by doing relevant analysis applications. Chapters also include summary sections, which clearly present the key components of application tools. Many analysts and teachers have used this book as a reference for reviewing specific applications. Once you have used this book to help learn statistical applications, you will also find it to be a useful resource as you use statistical analysis procedures in your future career.

A number of special applications of major procedures are included in various sections. Clearly there are more than can be used in a single course. But careful selection of topics from the various chapters enables the teacher to design a course that provides for the specific needs of students in the local academic program. Special examples that can be left out or included provide a breadth of opportunities. The initial probability chapter, Chapter 3, provides topics such as decision trees, overinvolvement ratios, and expanded coverage of Bayesian applications, any of which might provide important material for local courses. Confidence interval and hypothesis tests include procedures for variances and for categorical and ordinal data. Random-variable chapters include linear combination of correlated random variables with applications to financial portfolios. Regression applications include estimation of beta ratios in finance, dummy variables in experimental design, nonlinear regression, and many more.

As indicated here, the book has the capability of being used in a variety of courses that provide applications for a variety of academic programs. The other benefit to the student is that this textbook can be an ideal resource for the student's future professional career. The design of the book makes it possible for a student to come back to topics after several years and quickly renew his or her understanding. With all the additional special topics, that may not have been included in a first course, the book is a reference for learning important new applications. And the presentation of those new applications follows a presentation style and uses understandings that are familiar. This reduces the time required to master new application topics.

APPLYING CONCEPTS

We understand how important it is for students to know statistical concepts and apply those to different situations they face everyday or will face as managers of the future. Almost all sections include examples that illustrate the application of the concepts or methods of that section to a real-world context (even though the company or organization may be hypothetical). Problems are structured to present the perspective of a decision maker and the analysis provided is to help understand the use of statistics in a practical way.

PROMOTING PROBLEM ANALYSIS

This book includes section Exercises and chapter Exercises and Applications. The section exercises for each chapter begin with straightforward exercises targeted at the topics in each section. These are designed to check understanding of specific topics. Because they appear after each section, it is easy to turn back to the chapter to clarify a concept or review a method. The Chapter Exercises and Applications are designed to lead to conclusions about the real world and are more application-based. They usually combine concepts and methods from different sections.

ACKNOWLEDGMENTS

We appreciate the following colleagues who provided feedback about the book to guide our thoughts on this revision: Valerie R. Bencivenga, University of Texas at Austin; Burak Dolar, Augustana College; Zhimin Huang, Adelphi University; Stephen Lich-Tyler, University of North Carolina; Tung Liu, Ball State University; Leonard Presby, William Paterson University; Subarna K. Samanta, The College of New Jersey; Shane Sanders, Nicholls State University; Harold Schneider, Rider University; Sean Simpson, Westchester Community College.

The authors thank Dr. Andrea Carlson, Economic Research Service (ERS), U. S. Department of Agriculture, for her assistance in providing several major data files and for guidance in developing appropriate research questions for exercises and case studies. We also thank Paula Dutko and Empharim Leibtag for providing an example of complex statistical analysis in the public sector. We also recognize the excellent work by Annie Puciloski in finding our errors and improving the professional quality of this book.

We extend appreciation to two Stetson alumni, Richard Butcher (RELEVANT Magazine) and Lisbeth Mendez (mortgage company), for providing real data from their companies that we used for new examples, exercises, and case studies.

In addition, we express special thanks for continuing support from our families. Bill Carlson especially acknowledges his best friend and wife, Charlotte, their adult children, Andrea and Doug, and grandchildren, Ezra, Savannah, Helena, Anna, Eva Rose, and Emily. Betty Thorne extends special thanks to her best friend and husband, Jim, and to their family Jennie, Ann, Renee, Jon, Chris, Jon, Hannah, Leah, Christina, Jim, Wendy, Marius, Mihaela, Cezara, Anda, and Mara Iulia. In addition, Betty acknowledges (in memory) the support of her parents, Westley and Jennie Moore.

The authors acknowledge the strong foundation and tradition created by the original author, Paul Newbold. Paul understood the importance of rigorous statistical analysis and its foundations. He realized that there are some complex ideas that need to be developed, and he worked to provide clear explanations of difficult ideas. In addition, he realized that these ideas become useful only when used in realistic problem-solving situations. Thus, many examples and many applied student exercises were included in the early editions. We have worked to continue and expand this tradition in preparing a book that meets the needs of future business leaders in the information age.

GLOBAL ACKNOWLEDGEMENTS

We would like to thank the people who have contributed towards developing this book for the global markets and who have put in effort to update this global edition for students across the world.

Roland Baczur, PhD student at the University of Pécs

Alicia Tan Yiing Fei, Taylor's University Malaysia

Višnja Juric, Zagreb School of Economics and Management

Daniel Kehl, University of Pecs

Patricia Ramos, Nova School of Business and Economics

We would also like to thank the individuals who reviewed the text and whose feedback has made this a better book.

Dogan Serel, Bilkent University

Manfred Soeffky, Berlin School of Economics and Law

Get the Most Out of
MyLab Statistics

MyLab™ Statistics is the leading online homework, tutorial, and assessment program for teaching and learning statistics, built around Pearson's best-selling content. MyLab Stats helps students and instructors improve results; it provides engaging experiences and personalized learning for each student so learning can happen in any environment. Plus, it offers flexible and time-saving course management features to allow instructors to easily manage their classes while remaining in complete control, regardless of course format.

Preparedness

One of the biggest challenges in many mathematics and statistics courses is making sure students are adequately prepared with the prerequisite skills needed to successfully complete their course work. Pearson offers a variety of content and course options to support students with just-in-time remediation and keyconcept review.

- Build homework assignments, quizzes, and tests to support your course learning outcomes. From Getting Ready (GR) questions to the Conceptual Question Library (CQL), we have your assessment needs covered from the mechanics to the critical understanding of Statistics. The exercise libraries include technology-led instruction and learning aids to reinforce your students' success.

Resources for Success
MyLab Statistics Online Course

for Statistics for Business and Economics, Ninth Edition, by Newbold/Carlson/Thorne
(access code required)

MyLab™ Stats is available to accompany Pearson's market leading text offerings. To give students a consistent tone, voice, and teaching method each text's flavor and approach is tightly integrated throughout the accompanying MyLab Statistics course, making learning the material as seamless as possible.

StatCrunch

StatCrunch, a powerful, web-based statistical software, is integrated into MyLab, so students can quickly and easily analyze datasets from their text and exercises. In addition, MyLab includes access to **www.StatCrunch.com**, the full webbased program

where users can access tens of thousands of shared datasets, create and conduct online surveys, interact with a full library of applets, and perform complex analyses using the powerful statistical software.

Technology Tutorials

Excel® tutorials provide brief video walkthroughs and step-by-step instructional study cards on common statistical procedures such as Confidence Intervals, ANOVA, Simple & Multiple Regression, and Hypothesis Testing. Tutorials will capture methods in Microsoft Windows Excel® 2010, 2013, and 2016 versions.

pearson.com/mylab/statistics

Resources for Success

Instructor Supplements

Online Test Bank (download only)**:** The test-item files contain true/false, multiple-choice, and short-answer questions based on concepts and ideas developed in each chapter of the text. Available to qualified instructors through Pearson's online catalog at **www.pearsonglobaleditions.com** or within MyLab Statistics.

Instructor's Solutions Manual (download only)**:** Contains worked-out solutions for end-of-section and end-of-chapter exercises and applications. The Instructor's Solutions Manual is available to qualified instructors through Pearson's online catalog at **www .pearsonglobaleditions.com** or within MyLab Statistics.

TestGen® Computerized Test Bank (**www.pearsoned .com/testgen**)**:** Enables instructors to build, edit, print, and administer tests using a computerized bank of questions developed to cover all the objectives of the text. TestGen is algorithmically based, allowing instructors to create multiple but equivalent versions of the same question or test with the click of a button. Instructors can also modify test bank questions or add new questions. The software and test bank are available for download from Pearson's online catalog at **www.pearsonglobaleditions.com**.

PowerPoint Lecture Slides: Free to qualified adopters, this set of chapter-by-chapter PowerPoint slides provides an instructor with individual lecture outlines to accompany the text. The slides include key figures and tables from the text, which can easily be modified, and help bring the statistical concepts alive in the classroom. These files are available to qualified instructors through Pearson's online catalog at **www.pearsonglobaleditions.com** or within MyLab Statistics.

Learning Catalytics™: A web-based engagement and assessment tool. As a "bring-your-own-device" direct response system, Learning Catalytics offers a diverse library of dynamic question types that allow students to interact with and think critically about statistical concepts. As a real-time resource, instructors can take advantage of critical teaching moments both in the classroom and through assignable and gradable homework.

Student's Solutions Manual, provides detailed, worked-out solutions to odd-numbered exercises. This item is available within MyLab Statistics and can be shared by the instructor only.

Student Resources

Online Resources: These resources include data files and answers to select even-numbered exercises. These files are available through Pearson's online catalog at **www.pearsonglobaleditions.com**.

Technology Resources

MyLab Statistics Online Course (access code required) MyLab™ Statistics is the teaching and learning platform that empowers you to reach every student. By combining trusted author content with digital tools and a flexible platform, MyLab Statistics personalizes the learning experience and improves results for each student. With MyLab Statistics and StatCrunch®, an integrated web-based statistical software program, students learn the skills they need to interact with data in the real world. Learn more about MyLab Statistics at **pearson.com/mylab/statistics**.

Used by nearly one million students a year, MyLab Statistics is the world's leading online program for teaching and learning statistics. MyLab Statistics delivers assessment, tutorials, and multimedia resources that provide engaging and personalized experiences for each student, so learning can happen in any environment. Each course is developed to accompany Pearson's best-selling content, authored by thought leaders across the statistics curriculum, and can be easily customized to fit any course format.

Methods for teaching statistics are continuously evolving to provide today's students with the skills they need to interact with data in the real world. In addition, statistics students are coming to the classroom with a wide range of backgrounds and learner styles. The flexibility to build a course that fits instructors' individual course formats and every student's needs—with a variety of content options and multimedia resources all in one place—has made MyLab Statistics the market-leading solution for teaching and learning statistics since its inception.

Thanks to feedback from instructors and students from more than 10,000 institutions, MyLab Statistics continues to transform—delivering new content, innovative learning resources, and platform updates to support students and instructors, today and in the future.

Deliver Trusted Content

You deserve teaching materials that meet your own high standards for your course. That's why Pearson partners with highly respected authors to develop interactive content and course-specific resources that you can trust—and that keep your students engaged.

Tutorial Exercises with Multimedia Learning Aids: The homework and practice exercises in MyLab Statistics align with the exercises in the textbook, and they regenerate algorithmically to give students unlimited opportunity for practice and mastery. Exercises offer immediate helpful feedback, guided solutions, sample problems, animations, videos, and eText clips for extra help at point-of-use.

StatCrunch: MyLab Statistics integrates the web-based statistical software, StatCrunch, within the online assessment platform so that students can easily analyze datasets from exercises and the text. In addition, MyLab Statistics includes access to **www.StatCrunch.com**, a website where users can access tens of thousands of shared datasets, conduct online surveys, perform complex analyses using the powerful statistical software, and generate compelling reports.

Business Insight Videos: Engaging videos show managers at top companies using statistics in their everyday work. Assignable questions encourage debate and discussion.

StatTalk Videos: Fun-loving statistician Andrew Vickers takes to the streets of Brooklyn, New York, to demonstrate important statistical concepts through interesting stories and real-life events. This series of videos includes available assessment questions and an instructor's guide.

Empower Each Learner

Each student learns at a different pace. Personalized learning pinpoints the precise areas where each student needs practice, giving all students the support they need—when and where they need it—to be successful.

- **Study Plan:** Acts as a tutor, providing personalized recommendations for each of your students based on his or her ability to master the learning objectives in your course. This allows students to focus their study time by pinpointing the precise areas they need to review, and allowing them to use customized practice and learning aids—such as videos, eText, tutorials, and more—to get them back on track. Using the report available in the Gradebook, you can tailor course lectures to prioritize the content where students need the most support, offering you better insight into classroom and individual performance.

- With the **Companion Study Plan Assignments** you can now assign the Study Plan as a prerequisite to a test or quiz, guiding students through the concepts they need to master.

- **Getting Ready for Statistics:** A library of questions now appears within each MyLab Statistics course to offer the developmental math topics students need for the course. These can be assigned as a prerequisite to other assignments, if desired.

Conceptual Question Library: In addition to algorithmically regenerated questions that are aligned with your textbook, there is a library of 1,000 Conceptual Questions available in the assessment manager that require students to apply their statistical understanding.

Teach the Course Your Way

Your course is unique. So whether you'd like to build your own assignments, teach multiple sections, or set prerequisites, MyLab gives you the flexibility to easily create *your* course to fit *your* needs.

- **Learning Catalytics:** Generate class discussion, guide your lecture, and promote peer-to-peer learning with real-time analytics. MyLab Statistics now provides Learning Catalytics™—an interactive student response tool that uses students' smartphones, tablets, or laptops to engage them in more sophisticated tasks and thinking.

- **LMS Integration:** You can now link Blackboard Learn™, Brightspace® by D2L®, Canvas™, or Moodle® to the MyLabs. Access assignments, rosters, and resources, and synchronize grades with your LMS gradebook. For students, single sign-on provides access to all the personalized learning resources that make studying more efficient and effective.

Improve Student Results

When you teach with MyLab, student performance improves. That's why instructors have chosen MyLab for over 15 years, touching the lives of more than 50 million students.

StatCrunch

Integrated directly into MyLab Statistics, StatCrunch® is powerful web-based statistical software that allows users to perform complex analyses, share datasets, and generate compelling reports of their data.

The vibrant online community offers tens of thousands of shared datasets for students to analyze.

- **Collect.** Users can upload their own data to StatCrunch or search a large library of publicly shared datasets, spanning almost any topic of interest. Datasets from the text and from online homework exercises can also be accessed and analyzed in StatCrunch. An online survey tool allows users to quickly collect data via web-based surveys.

- **Crunch.** A full range of numerical and graphical methods allows users to analyze and gain insights from any dataset. Interactive graphics help users understand statistical concepts, and are available for export to enrich reports with visual representations of data.

- **Communicate.** Reporting options help users create a wide variety of visually appealing representations of their data.

StatCrunch is also available by itself to qualified adopters. It can be accessed on your laptop, smartphone, or tablet when you visit the StatCrunch website from your device's browser. For more information, visit the StatCrunch website at **www.StatCrunch.com** or contact your Pearson representative.

TestGen

TestGen® (**www.pearsoned.com/testgen**) enables instructors to build, edit, print, and administer tests using a computerized bank of questions developed to cover all the objectives of the text. TestGen is algorithmically based, allowing instructors to create multiple but equivalent versions of the same question or test with the click of a button. Instructors can also modify test bank questions or add new questions. The software and test bank are available for download from Pearson's Instructor Resource Center at **www.pearsonglobaleditions.com**.

PowerPoint Lecture Slides

PowerPoint® Lecture Slides provide an outline to use in a lecture setting, presenting definitions, key concepts, and figures from the text. These slides are available within MyLab Statistics and in the Instructor Resource Center at **www .pearsonglobaleditions.com**.

Foster student engagement and peer-to-peer learning

Generate class discussion, guide your lecture, and promote peer-to-peer learning with real-time analytics. MyLab™ Math and MyLab Statistics now provide Learning Catalytics™—an interactive student response tool that uses students' smartphones, tablets, or laptops to engage them in more sophisticated tasks and thinking.

Instructors, you can:

- Pose a variety of open-ended questions that help your students develop critical thinking skills.

- Monitor responses to find out where students are struggling.

- Use real-time data to adjust your instructional strategy and try other ways of engaging your students during class.

- Manage student interactions by automatically grouping students for discussion, teamwork, and peer-to-peer learning.

pearson.com/mylab/statistics

CHAPTER 1

Describing Data: Graphical

Introduction

What are the projected sales of a new product? Will the cost of Google shares continue to increase? Who will win the 2020 UEFA Champions League? How satisfied were you with your last purchase at Starbucks, on alibaba.com, or at IKEA? If you were hired by the National Nutrition Council of your country, how would you determine if the Council's guidelines on consumption of fruit, vegetables, snack foods, and soft drinks are being met? Do people who are physically active have healthier diets than people who are not physically active? What factors (perhaps disposable income or grants) are significant in forecasting the aggregate consumption of durable goods? What effect will a 2% increase in interest rates have on residential investment? Do credit scores, current balance, or outstanding maintenance balance contribute to an increase in the percentage of a mortgage company's delinquent accounts increasing? Answers to questions such as these come from an understanding of statistics, fluctuations in the market, consumer preferences, trends, and so on.

Statistics are used to predict or forecast sales of a new product, construction costs, customer-satisfaction levels, the weather, election results, university enrollment figures, grade point averages, interest rates, currency-exchange rates, and many other variables that affect our daily lives. We need to absorb and interpret substantial amounts of data. Governments, businesses, and scientific researchers spend billions of dollars collecting data. But once data are collected, what do we do with them? How do data impact decision making?

In our study of *statistics* we learn many tools to help us process, summarize, analyze, and interpret data for the purpose of making better decisions in an uncertain environment. Basically, an understanding of statistics will permit us to make sense of all the data.

In this chapter we introduce tables and graphs that help us gain a better understanding of data and that provide visual support for improved decision making. Reports are enhanced by the inclusion of appropriate tables and graphs, such as frequency distributions, bar charts, pie charts, Pareto diagrams, line charts, histograms, stem-and-leaf displays, or ogives. Visualization of data is important. We should always ask the following questions: What does the graph suggest about the data? What is it that we see?

1.1 DECISION MAKING IN AN UNCERTAIN ENVIRONMENT

Decisions are often made based on limited information. Accountants may need to select a portion of records for auditing purposes. Financial investors need to understand the market's fluctuations, and they need to choose between various portfolio investments. Managers may use surveys to find out if customers are satisfied with their company's products or services. Perhaps a marketing executive wants information concerning customers' taste preferences, their shopping habits, or the demographics of Internet shoppers. An investor does not know with certainty whether financial markets will be buoyant, steady, or depressed. Nevertheless, the investor must decide how to balance a portfolio among stocks, bonds, and money market instruments while future market movements are unknown.

For each of these situations, we must carefully define the problem, determine what data are needed, collect the data, and use statistics to summarize the data and make inferences and decisions based on the data obtained. Statistical thinking is essential from initial problem definition to final decision, which may lead to reduced costs, increased profits, improved processes, and increased customer satisfaction.

Random and Systematic Sampling

Before bringing a new product to market, a manufacturer wants to arrive at some assessment of the likely level of demand and may undertake a market research survey. The manufacturer is, in fact, interested in *all* potential buyers (the population). However, populations are often so large that they are unwieldy to analyze; collecting complete information for a population could be impossible or prohibitively expensive. Even in circumstances where sufficient resources seem to be available, time constraints make the examination of a subset (sample) necessary.

Population and Sample

A **population** is the complete set of all items that interest an investigator. Population size, N, can be very large or even infinite. A **sample** is an observed subset (or portion) of a population with sample size given by n.

Examples of populations include the following:

- All potential buyers of a new product
- All stocks traded on the London Stock Exchange (LSE)
- All registered voters in a particular city or country
- All accounts receivable for a corporation

Our eventual aim is to make statements based on sample data that have some validity about the population at large. We need a sample, then, that is representative of the population. How can we achieve that? One important principle that we must follow in the sample selection process is randomness.

Random Sampling

Simple random sampling is a procedure used to select a sample of n objects from a population in such a way that each member of the population is chosen strictly by chance, the selection of one member does not influence the selection of any other member, each member of the population is equally likely to be chosen, and every possible sample of a given size, n, has the same chance of selection. This method is so common that the adjective *simple* is generally dropped, and the resulting sample is called a **random sample**.

Another sampling procedure is systematic sampling (stratified sampling and cluster sampling are discussed in Chapter 17).

Systematic Sampling

Suppose that the population list is arranged in some fashion unconnected with the subject of interest. **Systematic sampling** involves the selection of every jth item in the population, where j is the ratio of the population size N to the desired sample size, n; that is, $j = N/n$. Randomly select a number from 1 to j to obtain the first item to be included in your systematic sample.

Suppose that a sample size of 100 is desired and that the population consists of 5,000 names in alphabetical order. Then $j = 50$. Randomly select a number from 1 to 50. If your number is 20, select it and every 50th number, giving the systematic sample of elements numbered 20, 70, 120, 170, and so forth, until all 100 items are selected. A systematic sample is analyzed in the same fashion as a simple random sample on the grounds that, relative to the subject of inquiry, the population listing is already in random order. The danger is that there could be some subtle, unsuspected link between the ordering of the population and the subject under study. If this were so, bias would be induced if systematic sampling was employed. Systematic samples provide a good representation of the population if there is no cyclical variation in the population.

Sampling and Nonsampling Errors

Suppose that we want to know the average age of registered voters in the United States. Clearly, the population size is so large that we might take only a random sample, perhaps 500 registered voters, and calculate their average age. Because this average is based on sample data, it is called a *statistic*. If we were able to calculate the average age of the entire population, then the resulting average would be called a *parameter*.

Parameter and Statistic

A **parameter** is a numerical measure that describes a specific characteristic of a population. A **statistic** is a numerical measure that describes a specific characteristic of a sample.

Throughout this book we will study ways to make decisions about a population parameter, based on a sample statistic. We must realize that some element of uncertainty will always remain, as we do not know the exact value of the parameter. That is, when a sample is taken from a population, the value of any population parameter will not be able to be known *precisely*. One source of error, called **sampling error**, results from the fact that information is available on only a subset of all the population members. In Chapters 6, 7, and 8 we develop statistical theory that allows us to characterize the nature of the sampling error and to make certain statements about population parameters.

In practical analyses there is the possibility of an error unconnected with the kind of sampling procedure used. Indeed, such errors could just as well arise if a complete census of the population were taken. These are referred to as **nonsampling errors**. Examples of nonsampling errors include the following:

1. *The population actually sampled is not the relevant one.* A celebrated instance of this sort occurred in 1936, when *Literary Digest* magazine confidently predicted that Alfred Landon would win the presidential election over Franklin Roosevelt. However, Roosevelt won by a very comfortable margin. This erroneous forecast resulted from the fact that the members of the *Digest's* sample had been taken from telephone directories and other listings, such as magazine subscription lists and automobile registrations. These sources considerably underrepresented the poor, who were predominantly Democrats. To make an inference about a population (in this case the U.S. electorate), it is important to sample that population and not some subgroup of it, however convenient the latter course might appear to be.
2. *Survey subjects may give inaccurate or dishonest answers.* This could happen because questions are phrased in a manner that is difficult to understand or in a way that appears to make a particular answer seem more palatable or more desirable. Also, many questions that one might want to ask are so sensitive that it would be foolhardy to expect uniformly honest responses. Suppose, for example, that a plant manager wants to assess the annual losses to the company caused by employee thefts. In principle, a random sample of employees could be selected and sample members asked, What have you stolen from this plant in the past 12 months? This is clearly not the most reliable means of obtaining the required information!
3. *There may be no response to survey questions.* Survey subjects may not respond at all, or they may not respond to certain questions. If this is substantial, it can induce additional sampling and nonsampling errors. The sampling error arises because the achieved sample size will be smaller than that intended. Nonsampling error possibly occurs because, in effect, the population being sampled is not the population of interest. The results obtained can be regarded as a random sample *from the population that is willing to respond*. These people may differ in important ways from the larger population. If this is so, a bias will be induced in the resulting estimates.

There is no general procedure for identifying and analyzing nonsampling errors. But nonsampling errors could be important. The investigator must take care in such matters as identifying the relevant population, designing the questionnaire, and dealing with non-response in order to minimize the significance of nonsampling errors. In the remainder of this book it is assumed that such care has been taken, and our discussion centers on the treatment of sampling errors.

To think statistically begins with problem definition: (1) What information is required? (2) What is the relevant population? (3) How should sample members be selected? (4) How should information be obtained from the sample members? Next we will want to know how to use sample information to make decisions about our population of interest. Finally, we will want to know what conclusions can be drawn about the population.

After we identify and define a problem, we collect data produced by various processes according to a design, and then we analyze that data using one or more statistical procedures. From this analysis, we obtain information. Information is, in turn, converted into knowledge, using understanding based on specific experience, theory, literature, and additional statistical procedures. Both descriptive and inferential statistics are used to change data into knowledge that leads to better decision making. To do this, we use descriptive statistics and inferential statistics.

Descriptive and Inferential Statistics

Descriptive statistics focus on graphical and numerical procedures that are used to summarize and process data. **Inferential statistics** focus on using the data to make predictions, forecasts, and estimates to make better decisions.

1.2 CLASSIFICATION OF VARIABLES

A variable is a specific characteristic (such as age or weight) of an individual or object. Variables can be classified in several ways. One method of classification refers to the type and amount of information contained in the data. Data are either categorical or numerical. Another method, introduced in 1946 by American psychologist Stanley Smith Stevens is to classify data by levels of measurement, giving either qualitative or quantitative variables. Correctly classifying data is an important first step to selecting the correct statistical procedures needed to analyze and interpret data.

Categorical and Numerical Variables

Categorical variables produce responses that belong to groups or categories. For example, responses to yes/no questions are categorical. Are you a business major? and Do you own a car? are limited to yes or no answers. A health care insurance company may classify incorrect claims according to the type of errors, such as procedural and diagnostic errors, patient information errors, and contractual errors. Other examples of categorical variables include questions on gender or marital status. Sometimes categorical variables include a range of choices, such as "strongly disagree" to "strongly agree." For example, consider a faculty-evaluation form where students are to respond to statements such as the following: The instructor in this course was an effective teacher (1: strongly disagree; 2: slightly disagree; 3: neither agree nor disagree; 4: slightly agree; 5: strongly agree).

Numerical variables include both discrete and continuous variables. A **discrete numerical variable** may (but does not necessarily) have a finite number of values. However, the most common type of discrete numerical variable produces a response that comes from a counting process. Examples of discrete numerical variables include the number of students enrolled in a class, the number of university credits earned by a student at the end of a particular semester, and the number of Microsoft stocks in an investor's portfolio.

A **continuous numerical variable** may take on any value within a given range of real numbers and usually arises from a measurement (not a counting) process. Someone might say that he is 6 feet (or 72 inches) tall, but his height could actually be 72.1 inches, 71.8 inches, or some other similar number, depending on the accuracy of the instrument used to measure height. Other examples of continuous numerical variables include the weight of a cereal box, the time to run a race, the distance between two cities, or the temperature. In each case the value could deviate within a certain amount, depending on the precision of the measurement instrument used. We tend to truncate continuous variables in daily conversation and treat them as though they were the same as discrete variables without even giving it a second thought.

Measurement Levels

We can also describe data as either *qualitative* or *quantitative*. With **qualitative data** there is no measurable meaning to the "difference" in numbers. For example, one football player is assigned the number 7 and another player has the number 10. We cannot conclude that the first player plays twice as well as the second player. However, with **quantitative data** there is a measurable meaning to the difference in numbers. When one student scores 90 on an exam and another student scores 45, the difference is measurable and meaningful.

Qualitative data include nominal and ordinal levels of measurement. Quantitative data include interval and ratio levels of measurement.

Nominal and ordinal levels of measurement refer to data obtained from categorical questions. Responses to questions on gender, country of citizenship, political affiliation, and ownership of a mobile phone are nominal. **Nominal data** are considered the lowest or weakest type of data, since numerical identification is chosen strictly for convenience and does not imply ranking of responses.

The values of nominal variables are words that describe the categories or classes of responses. The values of the gender variable are male and female; the values of Do you own a car? are yes and no. We arbitrarily assign a code or number to each response. However, this number has no meaning other than for categorizing. For example, we could code gender responses or yes/no responses as follows:

1 = Male; 2 = Female
1 = Yes; 2 = No

Ordinal data indicate the rank ordering of items, and similar to nominal data the values are words that describe responses. Some examples of ordinal data and possible codes are as follows:

1. Product quality rating (1: poor; 2: average; 3: good)
2. Satisfaction rating with your current Internet provider (1: very dissatisfied; 2: moderately dissatisfied; 3: no opinion; 4: moderately satisfied; 5: very satisfied)
3. Consumer preference among three different types of soft drink (1: most preferred; 2: second choice; 3: third choice)

In these examples the responses are ordinal, or put into a rank order, but there is no measurable meaning to the "difference" between responses. That is, the difference between your first and second choices may not be the same as the difference between your second and third choices.

Interval and ratio levels of measurement refer to data obtained from numerical variables, and meaning is given to the *difference* between measurements. An interval scale indicates rank and distance from an arbitrary zero measured in unit intervals. That is, data are provided relative to an arbitrarily determined benchmark. Temperature is a classic example of this level of measurement, with arbitrarily determined benchmarks generally based on either Celsius degrees or Fahrenheit. Suppose that in March 2019, it is 30°C in Pune, India, and only 10°C in Tokyo, Japan. We can conclude that the difference in temperature is 20°, but we cannot say that it is three times as warm in Pune as it is in Tokyo. The year is another example of an interval level of measurement, with benchmarks based most commonly on the Gregorian calendar.

Ratio data indicate both rank and distance from a natural zero, with ratios of two measures having meaning. A person who weighs 200 pounds is twice the weight of a person who weighs 100 pounds; a person who is 40 years old is twice the age of someone who is 20 years old.

After collecting data, we first need to classify responses as categorical or numerical or by measurement scale. Next, we assign an arbitrary ID or code number to each response. Some graphs are appropriate for categorical variables, and others are used for numerical variables.

Note that data files usually contain "missing values." For example, respondents to a questionnaire may choose not to answer certain questions about gender, age, income, or some other sensitive topic. Missing values require a special code in the data entry stage. Unless missing values are properly handled, it is possible to obtain erroneous output. Statistical software packages handle missing values in different ways.

EXERCISES

 Visit **www.MyStatLab.com** or **www.pearson globaleditions.com** to access the data files.

Basic Exercises

1.1 State whether each of the following variables is categorical or numerical. If categorical, give the level of measurement. If numerical, is it discrete or continuous?

a. Size of a vanilla chai (small to extra-large)
b. The number of shares of a stock purchased by a broker
c. The weight (in pounds, ounces, etc.) of a newborn baby
d. The nationality of a state's incumbent governor

1.2 Upon visiting a newly opened Starbucks store, customers were given a brief survey. Is the answer to each of the following questions categorical or numerical? If categorical, give the level of measurement. If numerical, is it discrete or continuous?

a. Is this your first visit to this Starbucks store?
b. On a scale from 1 (very dissatisfied) to 5 (very satisfied), rate your level of satisfaction with today's purchase?
c. What was the actual cost of your purchase today?

1.3 The Budapest Airport managers circulated a form to find out passengers' level of satisfaction with the lounges and VIP services. The passengers who frequented the lounges and used the services were asked to indicate how much they spent on such services in a year. They were also asked to indicate their level of satisfaction on a scale from 1 (very satisfied) to 5 (very dissatisfied). Is a passenger's response to each question numerical or categorical? If numerical, is it discrete or continuous? If categorical, give the level of measurement.

1.4 Faculty at one university were asked a series of questions in a recent survey. State the type of data for each question.

a. Indicate your level of satisfaction with your teaching load (very satisfied, moderately satisfied, neutral, moderately dissatisfied, or very dissatisfied).
b. How many of your research articles were published in refereed journals during the last 5 years?
c. Did you attend the last university faculty meeting?
d. Do you think that the teaching evaluation process needs to be revised?

1.5 Tourists visiting Croatia are asked to participate in a survey, consisting of various questions regarding their experience during their trip, which have been provided below. For each question, describe the type of data obtained.

a. Which of the following areas did you visit?
   Coast
   Islands
   Mountains
   Zagreb (Croatia's capital)
b. Did you rent the sailing boat?
   Yes
   No
c. What was the average amount you spent on food per day?
d. What is the optimal number of days you would recommend a tourist spends in Croatia?
e. How often would you recommend visiting Croatia?
   a. every year   **b.** once in a five years   **c.** once in a lifetime   **d.** never

1.6 Residents in one housing development were asked a series of questions by their homeowners' association. Identify the type of data for each question.

a. Did you play golf during the last month on the development's new golf course?
b. How many times have you eaten at the country club restaurant during the last month?
c. Do you own a camper?
d. Rate the new security system for the development (very good, good, poor, or very poor).

Application Exercises

1.7 A survey of students at one college was conducted to provide information to address various concerns about the college's library. This information and other data about the students are stored in the data file **Library Survey**.

a. Give an example of a categorical variable with ordinal responses.
b. Give an example of a categorical variable with nominal responses.
c. Give an example of a numerical variable with discrete responses.

1.8   The U.S. Department of Agriculture (USDA) Center for Nutrition Policy and Promotion (CNPP) developed and administered the Healthy Eating Index–2005 to measure how well the population follows the recommendations of the 2005 Dietary Guidelines for Americans. The data are contained in the data file **HEI Cost Data Variable Subset**.

a. Give an example of a categorical variable with ordinal responses.
b. Give an example of a categorical variable with nominal responses.
c. Give an example of a numerical variable with continuous responses.
d. Give an example of a numerical variable with discrete responses.

1.3 GRAPHS TO DESCRIBE CATEGORICAL VARIABLES

We can describe categorical variables using frequency distribution tables and graphs such as bar charts, pie charts, and Pareto diagrams. These graphs are commonly used by managers and marketing researchers to describe data collected from surveys and questionnaires.

Frequency Distribution

A **frequency distribution** is a table used to organize data. The left column (called classes or groups) includes all possible responses on a variable being studied. The right column is a list of the frequencies, or number of observations, for each class. A **relative frequency distribution** is obtained by dividing each frequency by the number of observations and multiplying the resulting proportion by 100%.

Tables and Charts

The classes that we use to construct frequency distribution tables of a categorical variable are simply the possible responses to the categorical variable. Bar charts and pie charts are commonly used to describe categorical data. If our intent is to draw attention to the *frequency* of each category, then we will most likely draw a **bar chart**. In a bar chart the height of a rectangle represents each frequency. There is no need for the bars to touch.

Example 1.1 Healthy Eating Index 2005 (HEI-2005): Activity Level (Frequency Distribution and Bar Chart)

The U.S. Department of Agriculture (USDA) Center for Nutrition Policy and Promotion (CNPP) and the National Center for Health Statistics (NCHS), part of the Centers for Disease Control and Prevention (CDC), conduct surveys to assess the health and nutrition of the U.S. population. The CNPP conducts the Healthy Eating Index (Guenther et al. 2007) and the NCHS conducts the National Health and Nutrition Examination Survey (CDC 2003–2004). The Healthy Eating Index (HEI) monitors the diet quality of the U.S. population, particularly how well it conforms to dietary guidance. The HEI–2005 measures how well the population follows the recommendations of the 2005 *Dietary Guidelines for Americans* (Guenther et al.). In particular it measures, on a 100-point scale, the adequacy of consumption of vegetables, fruits, grains, milk, meat and beans, and liquid oils.

The data file **HEI Cost Data Variable Subset** contains considerable information on randomly selected individuals who participated in two extended interviews and medical examinations. Data for the first interview are identified by daycode = 1; data for the second interview are identified by daycode = 2. Other variables in the data file are described in the data dictionary in the Chapter 10 Appendix.

One variable in the HEI–2005 study is a participant's activity level coded as 1 = sedentary, 2 = active, and 3 = very active. Set up a frequency distribution and relative frequency distribution and construct a simple bar chart of activity level for the HEI–2005 participants during their first interview.

Solution Table 1.1 is a frequency distribution and a relative frequency distribution of the categorical variable "activity level." Figure 1.1 is a bar chart of this data.

Table 1.1 HEI–2005 Participants' Activity Level: First Interview

	PARTICIPANTS	PERCENT
Sedentary	2,183	48.9
Active	757	17.0
Very active	1,520	34.1
Total	4,460	100.0

Figure 1.1 HEI–2005 Participants' Activity Level: First Interview (Simple Bar Chart)

Cross Tables

There are situations in which we need to describe relationships between categorical or ordinal variables. Market-research organizations describe attitudes toward products, measured on an ordinal scale, as a function of educational levels, social status measures, geographic areas, and other ordinal or categorical variables. Personnel departments study employee evaluation levels versus job classifications, educational levels, and other employee variables. Production analysts study relationships between departments or production lines and performance measures to determine reasons for product change, reasons for interruption of production, and quality of output. These situations are usually described by cross tables and pictured by component or cluster bar charts. These bar charts are useful extensions of the simple bar chart in Figure 1.1.

Cross Table

A **cross table**, sometimes called a crosstab or a contingency table, lists the number of observations for every combination of values for two categorical or ordinal variables. The combination of all possible intervals for the two variables defines the cells in a table. A cross table with r rows and c columns is referred to as an $r \times c$ cross table.

Example 1.2 illustrates the use of cross tables, component bar charts, and cluster bar charts to describe graphically two categorical variables from the HEI–2005 study.

Example 1.2 HEI–2005: Activity Level and Gender (Component and Cluster Bar Charts)

Consider again the data in Table 1.1. Sometimes a comparison of one variable (activity level) with another variable (such as gender) is of interest. Construct component and cluster bar charts that compare activity level and gender. Use the data coded daycode = 1 in the data file **HEI Cost Data Variable Subset**.

Solution Table 1.2 is a cross table of activity levels (1 = sedentary; 2 = active; and 3 = very active) and gender (0 = male; 1 = female) obtained from the first interview for HEI–2005 participants.

Table 1.2 HEI–2005 Participants' Activity Level (First Interview) by Gender (Component Bar Chart)

	MALES	FEMALES	TOTAL
Sedentary	957	1,226	2,183
Active	340	417	757
Very active	842	678	1,520
Total	2,139	2,321	4,460

Figure 1.2 displays this information in a *component* or *stacked bar chart*. Figure 1.3 is a *cluster*, or *side-by-side*, bar chart of the same data.

Figure 1.2 HEI–2005 Participants' Activity Level (First Interview) by Gender (Component Bar Chart)

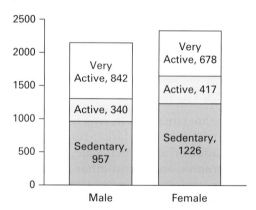

Figure 1.3 HEI–2005 Participants' Activity Level (First Interview) by Gender (Cluster Bar Chart)

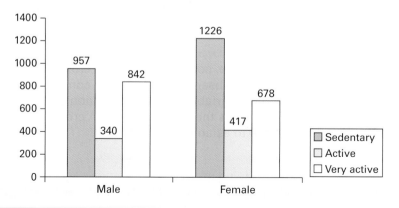

Pie Charts

If we want to draw attention to the *proportion* of frequencies in each category, then we will probably use a **pie chart** to depict the division of a whole into its constituent parts. The circle (or "pie") represents the total, and the segments (or "pieces of the pie") cut from its center depict shares of that total. The pie chart is constructed so that the area of each segment is proportional to the corresponding frequency.

Example 1.3 Windows Wars: Market Shares (Pie Chart)

In the competition for market share by desktop Windows versions, StatCounter Global Stats, the research arm of StatCounter Stats reported that in January 2019, for the first time Windows 7 was not the lead operating system for Microsoft. However, we note that in January 2017 Windows 7's market share of 41.86% does not appear to be significantly different from Windows 10's market share of 42.78%. The data file **Windows Wars** contains market-share data for Win7, Win10, WinXP, WinVista, Win2003, and others for a 13-month period from January 2017 through January 2018 (StatCounter Global Stats Desktop Windows Version Market Share Worldwide, Jan 2017 - Jan 2018). Construct pie charts of the market shares for January 2017 and January 2018. In Section 1.4 we develop a graphical procedure to show the trend in market share over a period of time.

Solution Table 1.3 lists the market shares for Microsoft's various operating systems during January 2017 and January 2018. Figure 1.4 is a pie chart of the January 2017 market shares, and Figure 1.5 is a pie chart of the January 2018 market shares.

Table 1.3 Market Shares (Pie Chart)

	JANUARY 2017	*JANUARY 2018*
Win7	47.46	41.86
Win10	32.84	42.78
WinXP	5.72	3.36
WinVista	1.20	0.74
Win2003	0.08	0.07
Others	0.03	0.02

SOURCE: http://gs.statcounter.com

Figure 1.4 Windows Wars: January 2017 Market Share (Pie Chart)

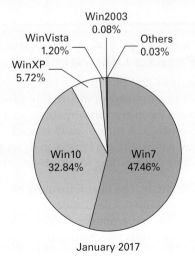

January 2017

Figure 1.5 Windows Wars: January 2018 Market Share (Pie Chart)

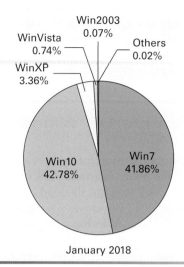

January 2018

Pareto Diagrams

Managers who need to identify major causes of problems and attempt to correct them quickly with a minimum cost frequently use a special bar chart known as a *Pareto diagram*. The Italian economist Vilfredo Pareto (1848–1923) noted that in most cases a small number of factors are responsible for most of the problems. We arrange the bars in a Pareto diagram from left to right to emphasize the most frequent causes of defects.

Pareto Diagram

A **Pareto diagram** is a bar chart that displays the frequency of defect causes. The bar at the left indicates the most frequent cause and the bars to the right indicate causes with decreasing frequencies. A Pareto diagram is used to separate the "vital few" from the "trivial many."

Pareto's result is applied to a wide variety of behavior over many systems. It is sometimes referred to as the 80–20 rule. A cereal manufacturer may find that most of the packaging errors are due to only a few causes. A student might think that 80% of the work on a group project was done by only 20% of the team members. The use of a Pareto diagram can also improve communication with employees or management and within production teams.

Example 1.4 illustrates the Pareto principle applied to a problem in a health insurance company.

Example 1.4 Insurance Claims Processing Errors (Pareto Diagram)

Analysis and payment of health care insurance claims is a complex process that can result in a number of incorrectly processed claims leading to an increase in staff time to obtain the correct information, an increase in costs, or a negative effect on customer relationships. A major health insurance company set a goal to reduce errors by 50%. Show how we would use Pareto analysis to help the company determine the most significant factors contributing to processing errors. The data are stored in the data file **Insurance**.

Solution The health insurance company conducted an intensive investigation of the entire claims' submission and payment process. A team of key company personnel was selected from the claims processing, provider relations and marketing, internal auditing, data processing, and medical review departments. Based on their experience and a review of the process, the team members finally agreed on a list of possible errors. Three of these errors (procedural and diagnostic, provider information, and patient information) are related to the submission process and must be checked by reviewing patient medical records in clinics and hospitals. Three possible errors (pricing schedules, contractual applications, and provider adjustments) are related to the processing of claims for payment within the insurance company office. The team also identified program and system errors.

A complete audit of a random sample of 1,000 claims began with checking each claim against medical records in clinics and hospitals and then proceeded through the final payment stage. Claims with errors were separated, and the total number of errors of each type was recorded. If a claim had multiple errors, then each error was recorded. In this process many decisions were made concerning error definition. If a child were coded for a procedure typically used for adults and the computer processing system did not detect this, then this error was recorded as error 7 (Program and System Errors) and also as error 3 (Patient Information). If treatment for a sprain were coded as a fracture, this was recorded as error 1 (Procedural and Diagnostic Codes). Table 1.4 is a frequency distribution of the categories and the number of errors in each category.

Next, the team constructed the Pareto diagram in Figure 1.6.

Table 1.4 Errors in Health Care Claims Processing

CATEGORY	ERROR TYPE	FREQUENCY
1	Procedural and Diagnostic Codes	40
2	Provider Information	9
3	Patient Information	6
4	Pricing Schedules	17
5	Contractual Applications	37
6	Provider Adjustments	7
7	Program and System Errors	4

Figure 1.6 Errors in Health Care Claims Processing (Pareto Diagram)

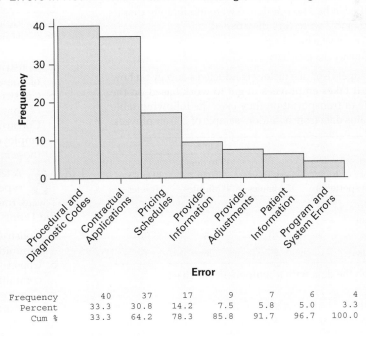

Frequency	40	37	17	9	7	6	4
Percent	33.3	30.8	14.2	7.5	5.8	5.0	3.3
Cum %	33.3	64.2	78.3	85.8	91.7	96.7	100.0

From the Pareto diagram the analysts saw that error 1 (Procedural and Diagnostic Codes) and error 5 (Contractual Applications) were the major causes of error. The combination of errors 1, 5, and 4 (Pricing Schedules) resulted in nearly 80% of the errors. By examining the Pareto diagram in Figure 1.6, the analysts could quickly determine which causes should receive most of the problem correction effort. Pareto analysis separated the vital few causes from the trivial many.

Armed with this information, the team made a number of recommendations to reduce errors.

EXERCISES

 Visit www.MyStatLab.com or www.pearson globaleditions.com to access the data files.

Basic Exercises

1.9 A university administrator requested a breakdown of travel expenses for faculty to attend various professional meetings. It was found that 41% of the travel expenses was spent for transportation costs, 20% was spent for lodging, 15% was spent for food, 8% for conference fees, and 16% was spent for conference registration fees; the remainder was spent for miscellaneous costs.
   a. Construct a pie chart.
   b. Construct a bar chart.

1.10 A company has determined that there are seven possible defects for one of its product lines. Construct a Pareto diagram for the following defect frequencies:

Defect Code	A	B	C	D	E	F	G
Frequency	10	70	15	90	8	4	3

1.11 Bank clients were asked to indicate their level of satisfaction with the service provided by the bank's tellers. Responses from a random sample of customers were as follows: 67 were very satisfied, 53 were moderately satisfied, 8 had no opinion, 5 were moderately dissatisfied, and 3 were very dissatisfied.
   a. Construct a bar chart.
   b. Construct a pie chart.

1.12 The supervisor of a factory conducted a survey on how long it takes employees to get to work based on the mode of transportation they use. The following table contains data from a random sample of 230 employees:

Mode of Transportation	Less Than 15 Minutes	15 to Less Than 30 Minutes	30 to 45 Minutes
Bus	20	14	7
Train	11	8	27
Car	31	45	19
Walk	17	26	5

Graph the data with a component bar chart.

Application Exercises

1.13 Suppose that an estimate of a certain country's federal spending showed that 45% was for entitlements, 19% was for defense, 15% was for grants to various regions, 13% was for interest on debt, 5% was for other federal operations, and 3% was for deposit insurance. Construct a pie chart to show this information.

1.14 The European Central Bank (ECB) published a reliable and complete statistics of annual structural financial indicators for the banking sector in the European Union (EU). It comprises statistics on the number of employees of domestic credit institutions. The 2014 data highlighted that bank employees in the region declined by about 74,000. The following table gives a partial list of the number of employees of domestic credit institutions in certain countries (Table 1, *EU Structural Financial Indicators*, 2014):

Country	Number of Employees of Domestic Credit Institutions	
	2012	2013
Belgium	60,068	58,237
Bulgaria	33,527	32,756
Czech Republic	40,147	39,742
Denmark	44,900	36,367
Germany	659,100	655,600

SOURCE: Based on data from European Central Bank website, "EU Structural Financial Indicators: 2014," SSI Table, July 1, 2015

   a. Construct a bar chart on the number of employees of domestic credit institutions in 2012.
   b. Construct a bar chart on the number of employees of domestic credit institutions in 2013.
   c. Construct a bar chart to compare the number of employees of domestic credit institutions in 2012 to those in 2013.

1.15 A tennis coach kept a record of the most serious type of errors made by each player during a 1-week training camp. The data are stored in the data file **Tennis**.
   a. Construct a Pareto diagram of total errors committed by all players.
   b. Construct a Pareto diagram of total errors committed by male players.
   c. Construct a Pareto diagram of total errors committed by female players.
   d. Construct a component bar chart showing type of error and gender of the player.

1.16 On what social media platform do you spend the most time? The responses from a random sample of 1,200 Internet users were Instagram, 382; Facebook, 226; LinkedIn, 350; Twitter, 85; Tumblr, 56; and Google+, 101. Describe the data graphically.

1.17 A random sample of 100 business majors was asked a series of demographic questions including major, gender, age, year in school, and current grade point average (GPA). Other questions were also asked for their levels of satisfaction with campus parking, campus housing, and campus dining. Responses to these satisfaction questions were measured on a scale from 1 to 5, with 5 being the highest level of satisfaction. Finally, these students were asked if they planned to attend graduate school within 5 years of their college graduation (0: no; 1: yes). These data are contained in the data file **Finstad and Lie Study**.
   a. Construct a cluster bar chart of the respondents' major and gender.
   b. Construct a pie chart of their majors.

1.18 The Healthy Eating Index–2005 measures how well the population follows the recommendations of the 2005 *Dietary Guidelines for Americans*. Table 1.2 is a frequency distribution of males and females in each of three activity level lifestyles: sendentary, active, and very active. This activity level was taken at the first interview (daycode = 1).

a. Use the data in Table 1.2 or data (coded daycode = 1) contained in the data file **HEI Cost Data Variable Subset** to construct a pie chart of the percent of males in each of the activity level categories.
b. Use the data in Table 1.2 or data (coded daycode = 1) contained in the data file **HEI Cost Data Variable Subset** to construct a pie chart of the percent of females in each of the activity level categories.

1.19 Internet Explorer (IE) dropped below 50% of the worldwide market for the first time in September 2010 (StatCounter Global Stats Microsoft 2010). IE's worldwide market share continued to decrease over the next several months. Worldwide market share data from January 2010 through February 2011 for IE, Firefox, Chrome, Safari, and Opera are contained in the data file **Browser Wars.**

a. Depict the worldwide market shares for February 2011 for the data contained in the data file **Browser Wars** using a pie chart.
b. Use a pie chart to depict the current market shares for these Internet browsers (Source: gs.statcounter.com).
c. Select a country or region from the list provided by StatCounter Global Stats and depict the market shares for the current time period with a pie chart (Source: gs.statcounter.com).

1.4 GRAPHS TO DESCRIBE TIME-SERIES DATA

Suppose that we take a random sample of 100 boxes of a new variety of cereal. If we collect our sample at one point in time and weigh each box, then the measurements obtained are known as *cross-sectional* data. However, we could collect and measure a random sample of 5 boxes every 15 minutes or 10 boxes every 20 minutes. Data measured at successive points in time are called *time-series* data. A graph of time-series data is called a *line chart* or *time-series plot*.

Line Chart (Time-Series Plot)
A **time series** is a set of measurements, ordered over time, on a particular quantity of interest. In a time series the sequence of the observations is important. A **line chart**, also called a **time-series plot**, is a series of data plotted at various time intervals. Measuring time along the horizontal axis and the numerical quantity of interest along the vertical axis yields a point on the graph for each observation. Joining points adjacent in time by straight lines produces a time-series plot.

Examples of time-series data include annual university enrollment, annual interest rates, the gross domestic product over a period of years (Example 1.5), daily closing prices for shares of common stock, daily exchange rates between various world currencies (Example 1.6), government receipts and expenditures over a period of years (Example 1.7), monthly product sales, quarterly corporate earnings, and social network weekly traffic (such as weekly number of new visitors) to a company's Web site (Example 1.8). In Chapter 16 we consider four components (trend, cyclical, seasonal, and irregular) that may affect the behavior of time-series data, and we present descriptive procedures for analyzing time-series data.

Example 1.5 Gross Domestic Product (Time-Series Plot)

One of the world's most prominent providers of economic statistics is the Bureau of Economic Analysis (BEA), an agency of the U.S. Department of Commerce. The BEA provides economic data such as the annual (or quarterly or monthly) Gross Domestic Product (GDP), as well as many other regional, industrial, national, and international economic statistics. These data are valuable to government officials, business executives, and individuals in making decisions in the face of uncertainty. The annual GDP from 1929 through 2009 (in billions) is contained in the data file **Macro 2009**. GDP and other data provided by Bureau of Economic Analysis are available online at www.bea.gov. Graph GDP from 1929–2009 with a time-series plot.

Solution The time-series plot in Figure 1.7 shows the annual GDP data growing rather steadily over a long period of time from 1929 through 2009. This pattern clearly shows a strong upward trend component that is stronger in some periods than in others. This time plot reveals a major trend component that is important for initial analysis and is usually followed by more sophisticated analyses (Chapter 16).

Figure 1.7 Gross Domestic Product by Time: 1929–2009 (Time-Series Plot)

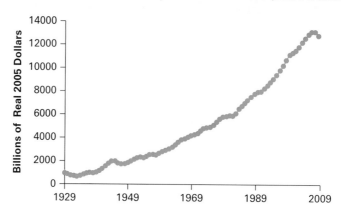

Example 1.6 Currency Exchange Rates (Time-Series Plot)

Investors, business travelers, tourists, and students studying abroad are all aware of the fluctuations in the exchange rates between various world currencies. Exchange rates between U.S. dollars (USD) and the euro (EUR) as well as the exchange rates between USD and the British pound (GBP) for the 6-month period from August 22, 2010, through February 17, 2011, are contained in the data file **Currency Exchange Rates**. Plot these data with time-series plots.

Solution Figure 1.8 shows the currency conversion from USD to 1 EUR. Figure 1.9 is a time series plot of the currency exchange rate from USD to 1 GBP.

Figure 1.8 Currency Exchange Rates: USD to EUR (Time-Series Plot)

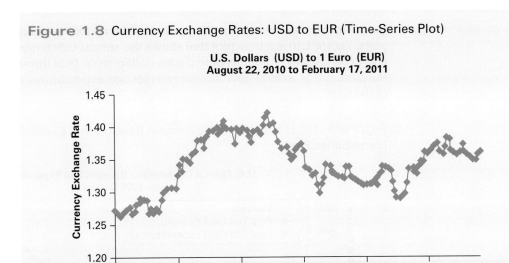

U.S. Dollars (USD) to 1 Euro (EUR)
August 22, 2010 to February 17, 2011

Figure 1.9 Currency Exchange Rates: USD to GBP (Time-Series Plot)

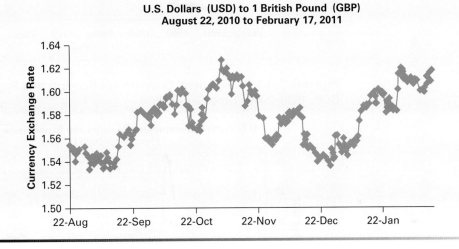

U.S. Dollars (USD) to 1 British Pound (GBP)
August 22, 2010 to February 17, 2011

Example 1.7 and Example 1.8 illustrate that sometimes a time-series plot is used to compare more than one variable over time

Example 1.7 Federal Government Receipts and Expenditures: 1929–2009 (Time-Series Plot)

The state of the economy is important to each of us. It is not just a topic for government officials. The data file **Macro 2009** contains information such as the gross domestic product, personal consumption expenditure, gross private domestic investment, imports, exports, personal savings in 2005 dollars, and many other variables from 1929 through 2009. Graph the annual U.S. federal government receipts and expenditures from 1929 to 2009.

Solution From the data in the data file **Macro 2009** we construct two time-series plots. Figure 1.10 is a time plot that shows the annual U.S. federal government receipts and expenditures in billions of real 2005 dollars from 1929 through 2009. In Figure 1.11 the annual U.S. federal government receipts and expenditures are plotted as a percent of the GDP.

Figure 1.10 U.S. Federal Government Receipts and Expenditures: 1929–2009 (Time-Series Plot)

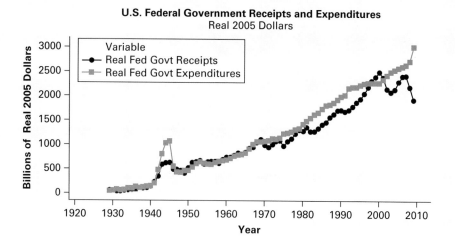

Figure 1.11 U.S. Federal Government Receipts and Expenditures as Percent of GDP: 1929–2009 (Time-Series Plot)

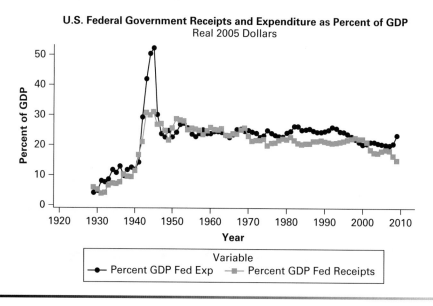

Example 1.8 Social Network Traffic (Time-Series Plot)

RELEVANT Magazine keeps records of traffic (such as the number of weekly new visitors) to its Web site from various social networks such as Facebook and Twitter (Butcher 2011). This information may be helpful to Richard Butcher, Marketing Assistant of *RELEVANT Magazine*. Plot the number of weekly new visitors for a recent

9-week period from both Facebook and Twitter. Use a time-series plot. The data are stored in the data file **RELEVANT Magazine**.

Solution From the data file **RELEVANT Magazine** we obtain the number of weekly new visitors for a recent 9-week period from both Facebook and Twitter. This information is given in Table 1.5. The time series plot in Figure 1.12 shows the trend over this same time period.

Table 1.5 Social Network Traffic: Weekly New Visitors to *RELEVANT Magazine* Web Site

WEEK	TWITTER	FACEBOOK
1	5,611	20,499
2	6,799	22,060
3	6,391	21,365
4	6,966	17,905
5	6,111	17,022
6	8,101	20,572
7	7,370	22,201
8	7,097	17,628
9	7,531	24,256

Figure 1.12 *RELEVANT Magazine:* Social Network Traffic of Weekly New Visitors (Time-Series Plot)

EXERCISES

Visit www.MyStatLab.com or www.pearson globaleditions.com to access the data files.

Basic Exercises

1.20 Construct a time-series plot for the following number of customers shopping at a new mall during a given week.

Day	Number of Customers
Monday	516
Tuesday	534
Wednesday	451
Thursday	487
Friday	558
Saturday	641

1.21 The number of male and female Indian tourists visiting Korea from March 2018 to December 2018 is given in the following table. Graphically present these data with a time-series plot.

Number of Tourists From India (2018)	Males	Females
March	5,457	1,142
April	5,748	1,467
May	6,056	1,433
June	5,498	1,383
July	5,724	1,156
August	5,752	1,384
September	6,400	1,281
October	7,023	1,482
November	5,978	1,309
December	4,895	1,093

SOURCE: Korea, Monthly Statistics of Tourism, 2018, Korea Tourism Organization, https://kto.visitkorea.or.kr/eng/tourismStatics/keyFacts/KoreaMonthlyStatistics.kto

Application Exercises

1.22 From the data file **Macro 2009** use a time plot to graph both gross domestic investment and gross private savings in billions of real 2005 dollars.

1.23 Information about GDP (Gross domestic product), which is a measure of the economic activity and is important to business owners and economists.

a. Use a time-series plot to graph real GDP growth rate for the category EU (28 countries) from 2011 to 2017. Data are in percentages. (Source: Table tec00115. 2017, Eurostat).

b. Use a time-series plot to graph real GDP growth rate for Malta from 2011 to 2017. Data are in percentages. (Source: Table: tec00115. 2018. Eurostat).

1.24 In Example 1.6 we plotted the USD to 1 EUR for a 6-month time period.

a. Use a time-series plot to graphically display the currency conversion from the EUR to 1 USD. The data are contained in the data file **Currency Exchange Rates**.

b. Use a time-series plot to graphically display the currency conversion from the GBP to 1 USD. The data are contained in the data file **Currency Exchange Rates**.

c. Compare your currency with an appropriate world currency for the last 30 days.

1.25 Market shares for a period of 14 months for various Internet providers are contained in the data file **Browser Wars**.

a. Use a time-series plot to graphically display the worldwide market shares of IE, Firefox, Chrome, Safari, and Opera.

b. Use a time-series plot to graphically display the European market shares of IE, Firefox, Chrome, Safari, and Opera.

c. Use a time-series plot to graphically display the North American market shares of IE, Firefox, Chrome, Safari, and Opera.

1.26 Select annual returns on a stock market index over 14 years from the Internet. Graph the data with a time-series plot.

1.27 The data file **Gold Price** shows the year-end price of gold (in dollars) over 14 consecutive years. Graph the data with a time-series plot.

1.28 The data file **Housing Starts** shows private housing units started per thousand persons in the U.S. population over a period of 24 years. Describe the data with a graph.

1.29 Earnings per share of a corporation over a period of 28 years are stored in the data file **Earnings per Share**. Graph the series and comment on the plot.

1.5 GRAPHS TO DESCRIBE NUMERICAL VARIABLES

In this section we briefly present histograms, ogives, and stem-and-leaf displays that summarize and describe numerical data. First, we consider a frequency distribution for numerical data.

Frequency Distributions

Similar to a frequency distribution for categorical data (Section 1.3), a frequency distribution for numerical data is a table that summarizes data by listing the classes in the left column and the number of observations in each class in the right column. However, the classes, or intervals, for a frequency distribution of numerical data are not as easily identifiable.

Determining the classes of a frequency distribution for numerical data requires answers to certain questions: How many classes should be used? How wide should each class be? There are some general rules (such as Equation 1.1) for preparing frequency distributions that make it easier for us to answer these types of questions, to summarize data, and to communicate results.

Construction of a Frequency Distribution

Rule 1: Determine k, the number of classes.
Rule 2: Classes should be the same width, w; the width is determined by the following:

$$w = \text{Class Width} = \frac{\text{Largest Observation} - \text{Smallest Observation}}{\text{Number of Classes}} \qquad (1.1)$$

Always round class width, w, upward.
Rule 3: Classes must be inclusive and nonoverlapping.

Rule 1: Number of Classes

The number of classes used in a frequency distribution is decided in a somewhat arbitrary manner.

Quick Guide to Approximate Number of Classes for a Frequency Distribution

SAMPLE SIZE	NUMBER OF CLASSES
Fewer than 50	5–7
50 to 100	7–8
101 to 500	8–10
501 to 1,000	10–11
1,001 to 5,000	11–14
More than 5,000	14–20

Practice and experience provide the best guidelines. Larger data sets require more classes; smaller data sets require fewer classes. If we select too few classes, the patterns and various characteristics of the data may be hidden. If we select too many classes, we will discover that some of our intervals may contain no observations or have a very small frequency.

Rule 2: Class Width

After choosing the number of classes, the next step is to choose the class width:

$$w = \text{Class Width} = \frac{\text{Largest Observation} - \text{Smallest Observation}}{\text{Number of Classes}}$$

The class width must always be rounded upward in order that all observations are included in the frequency distribution table.

Rule 3: Inclusive and Nonoverlapping Classes

Classes must be inclusive and nonoverlapping. Each observation must belong to one and only one class. Consider a frequency distribution for the ages (rounded to the nearest year) of a particular group of people. If the frequency distribution contains the classes "age 20 to age 30" and "age 30 to age 40," to which of these two classes would a person age 30 belong?

The *boundaries*, or endpoints, of each class must be clearly defined. To avoid overlapping, the age classes could be defined as "age 20 *but less than* age 30," followed by "age 30 *but less than* age 40" and so on. Another possibility is to define the age classes as 20–29, 30–39, and so forth. Since age is an integer, no overlapping occurs. Boundary selection is subjective. Simply be sure to define class boundaries that promote a clear understanding and interpretation of the data.

In Section 1.3 we defined a *frequency distribution* and a *relative frequency distribution*. Now we introduce two special frequency distributions, the *cumulative frequency distribution* and the *relative cumulative frequency distribution*.

Cumulative and Relative Cumulative Frequency Distributions

A **cumulative frequency distribution** contains the total number of observations whose values are less than the upper limit for each class. We construct a cumulative frequency distribution by adding the frequencies of all frequency distribution classes up to and including the present class. In a **relative cumulative frequency distribution**, cumulative frequencies can be expressed as cumulative proportions or percents.

Example 1.9 Employee Completion Times (Statistical Thinking)

The supervisor of a very large plant obtained the time (in seconds) for a random sample of $n = 110$ employees to complete a particular task. The goal is to complete this task in less than 4.5 minutes. Table 1.6 contains these times (in seconds). The data are stored in the data file **Completion Times**. What do the data indicate?

Table 1.6 Completion Times (seconds)

271	236	294	252	254	263	266	222	262	278	288
262	237	247	282	224	263	267	254	271	278	263
262	288	247	252	264	263	247	225	281	279	238
252	242	248	263	255	294	268	255	272	271	291
263	242	288	252	226	263	269	227	273	281	267
263	244	249	252	256	263	252	261	245	252	294
288	245	251	269	256	264	252	232	275	284	252
263	274	252	252	256	254	269	234	285	275	263
263	246	294	252	231	265	269	235	275	288	294
263	247	252	269	261	266	269	236	276	248	299

Solution Table 1.6 by itself offers little guidance to the supervisor. We can find some information in Table 1.6, such as the quickest time that the task was completed by an employee was 222 seconds, and the maximum time used was 299 seconds. However, we need more information than this before submitting any report to senior-level executives. To better understand what the data in Table 1.6 indicate, we first develop a frequency distribution.

From the Quick Guide we develop a frequency distribution with eight classes for the data in Table 1.6. From Equation 1.1, the width of each class is

$$w = \frac{299 - 222}{8} = 10 \ (rounded \ up)$$

Since the smallest value is 222, one choice for the first class is 220 but less than 230. Subsequent classes of equal width are added to the frequency distribution, as well as the number of seconds that belong to each class. Table 1.7 is a frequency distribution for the mobile phone data in Table 1.6.

Table 1.7 Frequency and Relative Frequency Distributions for Completion Times

COMPLETION TIMES (IN SECONDS)	FREQUENCY	PERCENT
220 less than 230	5	4.5
230 less than 240	8	7.3
240 less than 250	13	11.8
250 less than 260	22	20.0
260 less than 270	32	29.1
270 less than 280	13	11.8
280 less than 290	10	9.1
290 less than 300	7	6.4

Table 1.8 is a cumulative frequency distribution and a cumulative percent distribution.

Table 1.8 Cumulative Frequency and Relative Cumulative Frequency Distributions for Completion Times

COMPLETION TIMES (IN SECONDS)	CUMULATIVE FREQUENCY	CUMULATIVE PERCENT
Less than 230	5	4.5
Less than 240	13	11.8
Less than 250	26	23.6
Less than 260	48	43.6
Less than 270	80	72.7
Less than 280	93	84.5
Less than 290	103	93.6
Less than 300	110	100.0

The frequency distributions in Table 1.7 and Table 1.8 are an improvement over the original list of data in Table 1.6. We have at least summarized 110 observations into eight classes and are able to tell the supervisor that less than three-fourths (72.7%) of the employees sampled completed the task within the desired goal. The supervisor may initiate an extra training session for the employees who failed to meet the time constraint.

Histograms and Ogives

Once we develop frequency distributions, we are ready to graph this information. In this section we discuss two graphs, *histograms* and *ogives*.

Histogram

A **histogram** is a graph that consists of vertical bars constructed on a horizontal line that is marked off with intervals for the variable being displayed. The intervals correspond to the classes in a frequency distribution table. The height of each bar is proportional to the number of observations in that interval. The number of observations can be displayed above the bars.

Ogive

An **ogive**, sometimes called a *cumulative line graph*, is a line that connects points that are the cumulative percent of observations below the upper limit of each interval in a cumulative frequency distribution.

Figure 1.13 is a histogram of the completion times in Table 1.7. Figure 1.14 is an ogive that describes the cumulative relative frequencies in Table 1.8.

Figure 1.13
Completion Times (Histogram)

Figure 1.14
Completion Times (Ogive)

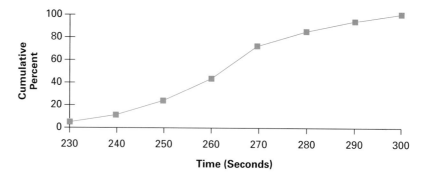

Shape of a Distribution

We can describe graphically the shape of the distribution by a histogram. That is, we can visually determine whether data are evenly spread from its middle or center. Sometimes the center of the data divides a graph of the distribution into two "mirror images," so that the portion on one side of the middle is nearly identical to the portion on the other side. Graphs that have this shape are *symmetric*; those without this shape are asymmetric, or *skewed*.

Symmetry
The shape of a distribution is said to be **symmetric** if the observations are balanced, or approximately evenly distributed, about its center.

Skewness
A distribution is **skewed**, or asymmetric, if the observations are not symmetrically distributed on either side of the center. A *skewed-right* distribution (sometimes called *positively skewed*) has a tail that extends farther to the right. A *skewed-left* distribution (sometimes called *negatively skewed*) has a tail that extends farther to the left.

Figure 1.15(a), Figure 1.15(b), and Figure 1.15(c) illustrate a histogram for a continuous numerical unimodal variable with a symmetric distribution, a skewed-right distribution and a skewed-left distribution, respectively.

Figure 1.15(a) Symmetric Distribution

Figure 1.15(b) Skewed-right Distribution

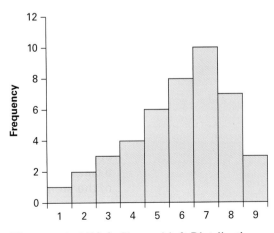

Figure 1.15(c) Skewed-left Distribution

Distribution of incomes is often skewed-right because incomes tend to contain a relatively small proportion of high values. A large proportion of the population has relatively modest incomes, but the incomes of, say, the highest 10% of all earners extend over a considerable range. An example of a skewed-left distribution is given in Example 1.10.

Example 1.10 Grade Point Averages (Skewed Left)

Describe the distribution of grade point averages contained in the data file **Grade Point Averages**.

Solution The data file **Grade Point Averages** contains a random sample of 156 grade point averages for students at one university. Figure 1.16 is a histogram of the data. Notice the long tail to the left, indicating that the shape of this distribution is skewed-left.

Figure 1.16 Grade Point Averages (Skewed-left Distribution)

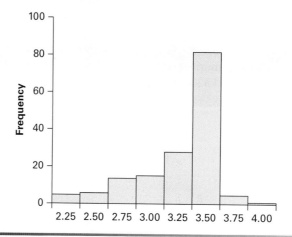

Although histograms may provide us with insight about the shape of a distribution, it is important to remember that poorly designed histograms may be misleading. In Section 1.7 we provide some warnings about histograms that distort the truth. In Chapter 2 we discuss a numerical measure to determine the skewness of a distribution.

Stem-and-Leaf Displays

Exploratory data analysis (EDA) consists of procedures used to describe data in simple arithmetic terms with easy-to-draw pencil-and-paper pictures. One such procedure, the *stem-and-leaf display*, is a quick way to identify possible patterns when you have a small data set.

Stem-and-Leaf Display

A **stem-and-leaf display** is an EDA graph that is an alternative to the histogram. Data are grouped according to their leading digits (called stems), and the final digits (called leaves) are listed separately for each member of a class. The leaves are displayed individually in ascending order after each of the stems.

The number of digits in each class indicates the class frequency. The individual digits indicate the pattern of values within each class. Except for extreme *outliers* (data values that are much larger or smaller than other values in the data set), all stems are included, even if there are no observations (leaves) in the corresponding subset. We illustrate a stem-and-leaf display in Example 1.11.

Example 1.11 Grades on an Accounting Final Exam (Stem-and-Leaf Display)

Describe the following random sample of 10 final exam grades for an introductory accounting class with a stem-and-leaf display.

88   51   63   85   79   65   79   70   73   77

Solution In constructing a stem-and-leaf display, each final exam grade is separated into two parts. For example, the grade of 63 is separated as 6 | 3, where 6 is called a stem; it appears on the left side of the straight line. The number 3 is called a leaf and appears on the right side of the straight line. From Figure 1.17 we see that the lowest grade was 51, the hightest grade was 88, and most of the students in the sample earned a grade of C on the accounting final exam.

Figure 1.17 Accounting Final-exam Grades (Stem-and-Leaf Display)

Stem-and-Leaf Display
$n = 10$

Stem	Leaves
5	1
6	3 5
7	0 3 7 9 9
8	5 8

Scatter Plots

In Section 1.3 we discussed graphs (bar chart, pie chart, Pareto diagram) to describe a single categorical variable, and we also discussed graphs (component bar chart and cluster bar chart) to describe the relationship between two categorical variables. In this section we presented histograms, ogives, and stem-and-leaf displays as graphs to describe a single numerical variable. We now extend graphical measures to include a *scatter plot*, which is a graph used to investigate possible relationships between two numerical variables.

Business and economic analyses are often concerned about relationships between variables. What is the effect of advertising on total profits? What is the change in quantity sold as the result of a change in price? How are total sales influenced by total disposable income in a geographic region? What is the change in infant mortality in developing countries as per capita income increases? How does one asset perform in relation to another asset? Do higher SAT mathematics scores predict higher college GPAs?

In these examples we notice that one variable may depend to a certain extent on the other variable. For example, the quantity of an item sold may depend on the price of the commodity. We then call the quantity sold the *dependent variable* and label it Y. We call the price of the commodity the *independent variable* and label it X.

To answer these questions, we gather and analyze random samples of data collected from relevant populations. A picture often provides insight as to the relationship that may exist between two variables. Our analysis begins with constructing a graph called a scatter plot (or scatter diagram). A more extensive study of possible relationships between numerical variables is considered in Chapters 11–13.

Scatter Plot

We can prepare a **scatter plot** by locating one point for each pair of two variables that represent an observation in the data set. The scatter plot provides a picture of the data, including the following:

1. The range of each variable
2. The pattern of values over the range
3. A suggestion as to a possible relationship between the two variables
4. An indication of outliers (extreme points)

We could prepare scatter plots by plotting individual points on graph paper. However, all modern statistical packages contain routines for preparing scatter plots directly from an electronic data file. Construction of such a plot is a common task in any initial data analysis that occurs at the beginning of an economic or business study. In Example 1.12 we illustrate a scatter plot of two numerical variables.

Example 1.12 Entrance Scores and College GPA (Scatter Plots)

Are SAT mathematics scores a good indicator of college success? All of us have taken one or more academic aptitude tests as part of a college admission procedure. The admissions staff at your college used the results of these tests to determine your admission status. Table 1.9 gives the SAT math scores from a test given before admission to college and the GPAs at college graduation for a random sample of 11 students at one small private university in Denmark. Construct a scatter plot and determine what information it provides.

Table 1.9 SAT Math Versus GPA

SAT MATH	GPA
450	3.25
480	2.60
500	2.88
520	2.85
560	3.30
580	3.10
590	3.35
600	3.20
620	3.50
650	3.59
700	3.95

Solution Using Excel, we obtain Figure 1.18, a scatter plot of the dependent variable, college GPA, and the independent variable, SAT math score.

We can make several observations from examining the scatter plot in Figure 1.18. GPAs range from around 2.5 to 4, and SAT math scores range from 450 to 700. An interesting pattern is the positive upward trend—GPA scores tend to increase directly with increases in SAT math scores. Note also that the relationship does not provide an exact prediction. Some students with low SAT math scores have higher GPA scores than do students with higher SAT math scores. We see that the basic pattern appears to indicate that higher entrance scores predict higher grade point averages, but the results are not perfect.

Figure 1.18 GPA vs. SAT Math Scores (Scatter Plot)

EXERCISES

 Visit www.MyStatLab.com or www.pearson globaleditions.com to access the data files.

Basic Exercises

1.30 Use the Quick Guide to find an approximate number of classes for a frequency distribution for each sample size.

    a. $n = 47$ b. $n = 80$ c. $n = 150$
    d. $n = 400$ e. $n = 650$

1.31 Determine an appropriate interval width for a random sample of 370 observations that fall between and include each of the following:

    a. 30 to 75   b. 40 to 200
    c. 50 to 240   d. 180 to 400

1.32 Consider the following data:

17	62	15	65
28	51	24	65
39	41	35	15
39	32	36	37
40	21	44	37
59	13	44	56
12	54	64	59

    a. Construct a frequency distribution.
    b. Construct a histogram.
    c. Construct an ogive.
    d. Construct a stem-and-leaf display.

1.33 Construct a stem-and-leaf display for the price (in dollars) of 20 cryptocurrencies that is spent to make international money transfers.

5.2	5.0	3.6	3.6	3.5	3.9	4.4	3.0	3.3	4.8
2.6	2.2	2.1	6.2	1.6	5.5	1.4	4.5	1.8	3.3

1.34 Consider the following frequency distribution for a random variable x:

Class	Frequency
$0 \le x < 10$	10
$10 \le x < 20$	12
$20 \le x < 30$	16
$30 \le x < 40$	15
$40 \le x < 50$	11

    a. Construct a relative frequency distribution.
    b. Construct a cumulative frequency distribution.
    c. Construct a cumulative relative frequency distribution.

1.35 Prepare a scatter plot of the following data:

    $(4, 54)$ $(20, 66)$ $(14, 49)$ $(12, 66)$ $(8, 47)$ $(3, 57)$
    $(8, 54)$ $(20, 56)$ $(18, 50)$ $(15, 66)$ $(8, 54)$ $(6, 57)$
    $(10, 54)$ $(20, 53)$ $(14, 50)$ $(15, 56)$ $(8, 59)$ $(3, 57)$

Application Exercises

1.36 The following table shows the age of the faculty members of the largest university in Lithuania who have obtained a PhD degree.

Age	Percent
26–28	18.48
29–32	23.12
33–40	30.51
41–45	12.09
46–50	9.11
51+	6.69

    a. Construct a relative cumulative frequency distribution.
    b. What percent of faculty members who obtained a PhD are under the age of 32 years?
    c. What percent of faculty members who obtained a PhD are 46 years or older?

1.37 The demand for bottled water increases during the hurricane season in Florida. The manager at a plant that bottles drinking water wants to be sure that the process to fill 1-gallon bottles (approximately 3.785 liters) is operating properly. Currently, the company is testing the volumes of 1-gallon bottles. A random sample of 75 bottles is tested. Study the filling process for this product and submit a report of your findings to the operations manager. Construct a frequency distribution, cumulative frequency distribution, histogram, and a stem-and-leaf display. Incorporate these graphs into a well-written summary. How could we apply statistical thinking in this situation? The data are stored in the data file **Water**.

1.38 Percentage returns for the 25 largest U.S. common stock mutual funds for a particular day are stored in the data file **Returns**.

  a. Construct a histogram to describe the data.
  b. Draw a stem-and-leaf display to describe the data.

1.39 Ann Thorne, the operations manager at a suntan lotion manufacturing plant, wants to be sure that the filling process for 8-oz (237 mL) bottles of SunProtector is operating properly. Suppose that a random sample of 100 bottles of this lotion is selected, the contents are measured, and the volumes (in mL) are stored in the data file **Sun**. Describe the data graphically.

1.40 Eight different regions in Croatia set different prices for renting a three bedroom holiday house or apartment. The accompanying table shows the number of apartments rented and the corresponding prices per day (in euros). Plot the data using a scatter plot with number of apartments rented as the dependent variable and price per day as the independent variable.

Price per day	104	135	80	200	98	206	141	109
Number of apartments	220	380	350	100	440	185	250	120

1.41 A corporation administers an aptitude test to all new sales representatives. Management is interested in the possible relationship between test scores and the sales representatives' eventual success. The accompanying table records average weekly sales (in thousands of dollars) and aptitude test scores for a random sample of eight representatives. Construct a scatter plot with weekly sales as the dependent variable and test scores as the independent variable.

Weekly sales	11	13	30	26	19	15	13	11
Test score	54	58	84	77	79	84	66	58

1.42 Doctors are interested in the possible relationship between the dosage of a medicine and the time required for a patient's recovery. The following table shows, for a sample of 10 patients, dosage levels (in grams) and recovery times (in hours).

These patients have similar characteristics except for medicine dosages. Describe the data graphically with a scatter plot.

Dosage level	1.2	1.3	1.0	1.4	1.5	1.8	1.2	1.3	1.4	1.3
Recovery time	25	28	40	38	10	9	27	30	16	18

1.43 Bishop's supermarket records the actual price for consumer food products and the weekly quantities sold. Use the data file **Bishop** to obtain the scatter plot for the actual price of a gallon of orange juice and the weekly quantities sold at that price. Does the scatter plot follow the pattern from economic theory?

1.44 Sixteen transport companies offer a bus transportation from a local city in Croatia, Split, to Croatia's capital, Zagreb. Croatia's transportation department wants to estimate whether the number of delays of each company during a six-month period affects the number of passengers traveling between the two cities. The following data show the number of delays, x, and the number of passengers traveling, y, in (x, y) pairs for the six month period.

(6; 21,350) (8; 31,200) (9; 40,321) (3; 52,980) (7; 45,970)

(5; 35,900) (8; 36,987) (2; 44,519),

(4; 35 980) (3; 37,500) (8; 43,000) (3; 25,160) (6; 59,329)

(4; 54,000) (2; 42,981) (6; 32,989)

Prepare a scatter plot of the points and comment on the relationship between the number of delays and the number of passengers transported.

1.45 Sales revenue totals (in dollars) by day of the week are contained in the data file **Stordata**. Prepare a cross table that contains the days of the week as rows and the four sales quartile intervals as columns.

  a. Compute the row percentages.
  b. What are the major differences in sales level by day of the week as indicated by the row percentages?
  c. Describe the expected sales volume patterns over the week based on this table.

1.46 Many small cities make significant efforts to attract commercial operations such as shopping centers and large retail stores. One of the arguments is that these facilities will contribute to the property that can be taxed and thus provide additional funds for local government needs. The data stored in the data file **Citydatr** come from a study of municipal revenue-generation capability. Prepare a scatter plot of "taxbase"—the assessed value of all city property in millions of dollars—versus "comper"—the percent of assessed property value that is commercial property. What information does this scatter plot provide about the assessable tax base and percent of commercial property in the city?

Poorly designed graphs can easily distort the truth. Used sensibly and carefully, graphs can be excellent tools for extracting the essential information from what would otherwise be a mere mass of numbers. Unfortunately, it is not invariably the case that an attempt at data summarization is carried out either sensibly or carefully. In such circumstances one can easily be misled by the manner in which the summary is presented. We must draw from data as clear and accurate a picture as possible. Improper graphs can produce a distorted picture, yielding a false impression. It is possible to convey the wrong message without being deliberately dishonest.

Accurate graphic design is essential in today's global markets. Cultural biases may influence the way people view charts. For example, in Western cultures people read from left to right and will automatically do so when reading bar charts or time-series plots. In this situation, you should aim to place your most important information on the right-hand side of the chart. Charts and graphs must be persuasive, clear, and truthful.

In this section we present some examples of misleading graphs, the intent being not to encourage their use but to caution against their dangers. Example 1.13 shows that distortions in histograms can lead to incorrect conclusions. Example 1.14 illustrates that different choices for the vertical axis in time-series plots can lead to different conclusions.

Misleading Histograms

We know that the width of all intervals should be the same. Suppose a data set contains many observations that fall into a relatively narrow part of the range, whereas others are widely dispersed. We might be tempted to construct a frequency distribution with narrow intervals where the bulk of the observations are and broader ones elsewhere. Even if we remember that it is the areas, rather than the heights, of the rectangles of the histogram that must be proportional to the frequencies, it is still never a desirable option to construct such a histogram with different widths because it may easily deceive or distort the findings. We include this section simply to point out potential errors that we might find in histograms. In Example 1.13 we illustrate the construction of a histogram when interval widths are not all the same.

Example 1.13 Grocery Receipts (Unequal Interval Widths)

The euro amounts of a random sample of 692 grocery receipts are summarized in the frequency distribution given in Table 1. 10.

One possible error in constructing a histogram is to make the *heights* of the rectangles, and not the *areas* of the rectangles, proportional to the frequencies. We see this misleading histogram in Figure 1.19. Inspection of this incorrect histogram gives us the mistaken impression of a very large proportion of observations in the highest class. *Under no circumstance should we ever construct a histogram with this error. We illustrate this mistake only as a warning against deceptive graphs.*

With continuous upgrades in software packages has come an increase in the use and misuse of computer-generated graphs. Figure 1.20 illustrates a computer-generated histogram with equal interval widths, even though three of the classes vary in width. Again, *under no circumstance should we ever construct a histogram with this error. We illustrate this mistake only as a warning against deceptive graphs.*

Table 1.10 Grocery Receipts (Dollar Amounts)

EURO AMOUNT	NUMBER OF RECEIPTS	PROPORTIONS
€ 0 < €10	84	84/692
€10 < €20	113	113/692
€20 < €30	112	112/692
€30 < €40	85	85/692
€40 < €50	77	77/692
€50 < €60	58	58/692
€60 < €80	75	75/692
€80 < €100	48	48/692
€100 < €200	40	40/692

To construct a histogram, we should observe that the quantities in Table 1.10 are interpreted in the usual way. Thus, of all these receipts, 113/692, or 16.3%, were in the range from €10 to under €20. We need to draw a histogram with the areas of the rectangles drawn over the intervals proportional to their frequencies. Since each of the first 6 intervals has a width of 10, we can draw rectangles of heights 84, 113, 112, 85, 77, and 58 over these intervals. The next two intervals have a width of 20, that is, twice the width of each of the first six. Thus, in order for their areas to be proportional to the frequencies, the rectangles drawn over these intervals should have heights that are one-half of the corresponding frequencies—that is, 37.5 and 24.

Finally, the last interval has a width of 100, or 10 times the width of each of the first 6 intervals. It follows that the height of the rectangle drawn over this last interval should be one-tenth of the frequency. That is, the height of the last rectangle should be 4. The reason that we make the areas of these rectangles proportional to the frequencies is that visually we associate area with size. We see in Figure 1.21 a histogram that avoids the errors illustrated in Figure 1.19 and Figure 1.20.

Figure 1.19 Misleading Histogram of Grocery Receipts **(Error: Heights Proportional to Frequencies for Distribution with Varying Interval Widths)**

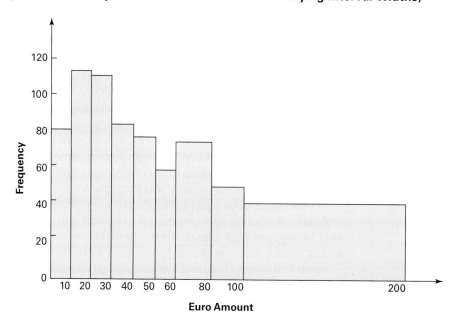

Figure 1.20 Misleading Histogram of Grocery Receipts **(Error: Bars of Equal Width for Distribution with Varying Interval Widths)**

Figure 1.21 Grocery Receipts (Histogram)

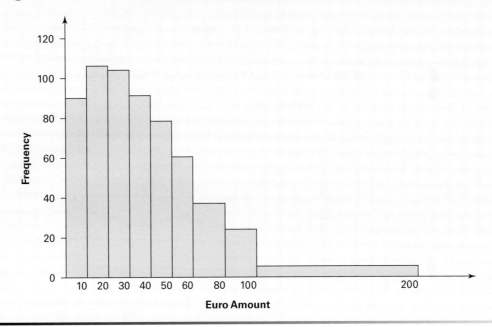

Misleading Time-Series Plots

By selecting a particular scale of measurement, we can, in a time-series plot, create an impression either of relative stability or of substantial fluctuation over time.

Example 1.14 SAT Math Scores 1989–2009 (Choice of Scale for Time-Series Plot)

The average SAT mathematics scores for the incoming first-year students at one university over a 20-year period are contained in the data file **SAT Math**. Graph these data with a time-series plot.

Solution Here we show two possible time-series plots for the SAT math scores contained in the data file **SAT Math**. Figure 1.22 suggests quite wide fluctuations in average scores. Precisely the same information is graphed in Figure 1.23, but now with a much coarser scale on the vertical axis. The resulting picture in Figure 1.23 is much flatter, suggesting considerably less variability in average scores over time.

There is no "correct" choice of scale for any particular time-series plot. Rather, the conclusion from Example 1.14 is that looking at the shape of the plot alone is inadequate for obtaining a clear picture of the data. It is also necessary to keep in mind the scale on which the measurements are made.

Figure 1.22 SAT Math Scores: First-Year Students (Time-Series Plot)

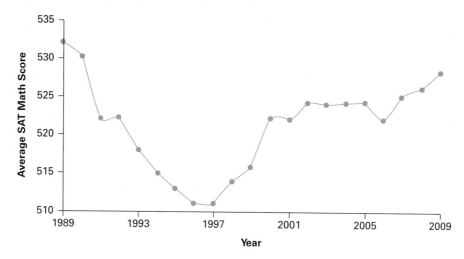

Figure 1.23 SAT Math Scores: First-Year Students (Revised Time-Series Plot)

EXERCISES

 Visit www.MyStatLab.com or www.pearson globaleditions.com to access the data files.

Basic Exercises

1.47 A supervisor of a plant kept records of the time (in seconds) that employees needed to complete a particular task. The data are summarized as follows:

Time	$30 < 40$	$40 < 50$	$50 < 60$	$60 < 80$	$80 < 100$	$100 < 120$
Number	12	13	22	34	24	22

a. Graph the data with a histogram.
b. Discuss possible errors.

1.48 The following table lists the number of tickets sold in a local theater in Germany during the 2018.

Month	Number of Tickets	Month	Number of Tickets
1	5,230	7	5,702
2	5,120	8	5,190
3	5,880	9	5,760
4	5,050	10	5,570
5	5,430	11	5,250
6	5,812	12	5,100

a. Graph the data with a time-series plot using a vertical scale from 5,000 to 5,900.

b. Graph the data with a time-series plot using a vertical scale from 4,000 to 7,000.

c. Comment on the difference between these two time-series plots.

Application Exercises

1.49 The data file **Exchange Rate** shows an index of the value of the U.S. dollar against trading partners' currencies over 12 consecutive months.

a. Construct a time-series plot of this data using a vertical axis that ranges from 92 to 106.

b. Construct a time-series plot of this data using a vertical axis that ranges from 75 to 120.

c. Comment on these two time-series plots.

1.50 The data file **Inventory Sales** shows the inventory-sales ratio for manufacturing and trade in the United States over a period of 12 years. Construct two time-series plots for this series with different vertical ranges. Comment on your findings.

KEY WORDS

- bar chart, 32
- categorical variables, 29
- continuous numerical variable, 30
- cross table, 33
- cumulative frequency distribution, 46
- descriptive statistics, 29
- discrete numerical variable, 29
- frequency distribution, 32
- histogram, 48
- inferential statistics, 29
- line chart, 39
- nominal data, 30

- nonsampling errors, 28
- numerical variables, 29
- ogive, 48
- ordinal data, 30
- parameter, 28
- Pareto diagram, 36
- pie chart, 35
- population, 27
- qualitative data, 30
- quantitative data, 30
- random sample, 27
- relative frequency distribution, 32

- relative cumulative frequency distribution, 46
- sample, 27
- sampling error, 28
- scatter plot, 52
- simple random sampling, 27
- skewed, 49
- statistic, 28
- stem-and-leaf display, 50
- symmetric, 49
- systematic sampling, 27
- time series, 39
- time-series plot, 39

DATA FILES

- Apple Stock Prices, 61
- Bishop, 54
- Browser Wars, 39, 44
- Citydatr, 54
- Completion Times, 46
- Currency Exchange Rates, 40, 44
- Earnings per Share, 44
- Exchange Rate, 59
- Finstad and Lie Study, 39
- Florin, 61

- Gold Price, 44
- Grade Point Averages, 50, 61
- HEI Cost Data Variable Subset, 32, 34, 39
- Housing Starts, 44
- Insurance, 36
- Inventory Sales, 59
- Library Survey, 31
- Macro 2009, 40, 41, 42, 44
- RELEVANT Magazine, 43, 61

- Returns, 54
- SAT Math, 57
- Shopping Times, 61
- Snappy Lawn Care, 61
- Stordata, 54
- Sun, 54
- Tennis, 38
- Water, 54
- Windows Wars, 35

CHAPTER EXERCISES AND APPLICATIONS

Visit www.MyStatLab.com or www.pearson globaleditions.com to access the data files.

1.51 Describe graphically the average amount of money a person spends on movie tickets each month (in € per month).

6.0 5.3 4.0 5.7 4.3 6.8 4.1 3.4 3.9 5.0 6.5

4.7 6.2 2.5 1.9 4.5 3.1 2.4 3.5 2.3 3.1 5.5

1.52 A financial analyst has recorded a random sample of stock price return over the last 30 days. The observations are summarized in the following table:

Stock Price (€)	Number of Days
19.95 < 20.45	2
20.45 < 30.95	3
30.95 < 41.45	12
41.45 < 51.95	8
51.95 < 62.45	4
62.45 < 73.95	1

a. Construct the histogram.

b. Determine the relative frequencies.

c. Determine the cumulative frequencies.

d. Determine and interpret the relative cumulative frequencies.

1.53 In one region it was found that 32% of shoppers with incomes less than €50,000 shop online; 48% of those with incomes between €50,000 and €74,999 shop online; and 20% of those with incomes of at least €75,000 prefer to shop online. Use a pie chart or a bar chart to plot this data.

1.54 Management of a British firm recognize that statistics is useful for business decisions, but do not think it is important to have an in-depth knowledge of it. The firm decides to conduct a survey to determine how usefule statistics are for its business activities. A random sample of managers of levels 1, 2, and 3 are selected from small, medium, and large firms and their use of statistical methods (in percentages) are recorded in the following table:

Management Level	Small Firms	Medium Firms	Large Firms
1 and 2	18	14	7
3	14	42	23

Construct a cluster bar chart of these findings.

1.55 How familiar are consumers with ecommerce? Suppose a survey is conducted among consumers who had recently shopped online for the first time. The survey found that 89% were able to use the Internet to place their orders; 81% were able to download an app and place their orders; and 57% were able to use PayPal. The survey also found that 45% had basic Internet skills and 8% had basic computer skills. Present this data graphically.

1.56 A team of undergraduate business students was asked to recommend improvement to the data entry process at the county appraiser's office. The team identified several types of errors, such as posting an incorrect name or entering an incorrect parcel number. The deed abstractors were asked to keep a record of the errors in data entry that were sent to them. The following table is a frequency distribution of errors:

Defect	Total
Posting error in name	23
Posting error in parcel	21
Property sold after tax bills were mailed	5
Inappropriate call transfer (not part of deeds/mapping)	18
Posting error in legal description/incomplete legal description	4
Deeds received after tax bills printed	6
Correspondence errors	2
Miscellaneous errors	1

a. Construct a Pareto diagram of these defects in data entry.
b. What recommendations would you suggest to the county appraiser?

1.57 Groupon, an online Web site, offers its subscribers at least one special deal per day to local businesses in their cities such as places to eat, health-related activities (spas or fitness centers), places to see (museums), a variety of activities such as golfing or sky diving, or other specials (such as a Gap Groupon or a gourmet fruit basket). Since December 2008, the number of subscribers has increased from 400 to more than 50 million in more than 400 markets, in over 40 countries (Groupon Hits 50m Subscribers, 2011). To date, Groupon claims that more than 30 million Groupons have been sold, saving subscribers nearly $1.3 billion. From a survey of students at one university, it was found that during the past week, the following number and category of Groupons were purchased: 230 (activities); 80 (food); 90 (health-related items), and 50 (other).

a. Graph these purchases with a pie chart.
b. Graph these purchases with a bar chart.

1.58 For the random sample of Groupon purchases by the university students in Exercise 1.57, the following breakdown by gender was obtained:

	Male	Female	Total
Activities	140	90	230
Food	45	35	80
Health related	20	70	90
Other	10	40	50
Total	215	235	450

a. Graphically depict the type of purchase by gender with a component bar chart.
b. Graphically depict the type of purchase by gender with a cluster bar chart.

1.59 Management of a supermarket wants to find the relationship between the £ price of milk and the average daily demand for milk. A random sample of (price, quantity) data for eight days of operation was obtained. Construct a plot and describe the relationship between quantity and price, with emphasis on any unusual observations.

$(25; 1,104)$ $(20; 1,401)$ $(18; 2,202)$ $(17; 2,430)$ $(29; 985)$ $(19; 1,618)$ $(16; 1,573)$

1.60 A consumer goods company has been studying the effect of advertising on total profits. As part of this study, data on advertising expenditures (1,000s) and total sales (1,000s) were collected for a 5-month period and are as follows:

$(10, 100)$ $(15, 200)$ $(7, 80)$ $(12, 120)$ $(14, 150)$

The first number is advertising expenditures and the second is total sales. Plot the data.

1.61 The CEO of *tradeindia.com* wants information concerning the relationship between the age of an individual (in years) and weekly sales (in hundreds of rupees). He obtained the following random sample of age and weekly sales:

$(19, 32)$ $(24, 101)$ $(33, 89)$ $(46, 192)$ $(53, 65)$ $(15, 132)$ $(36, 214)$ $(52, 42)$

The first number for each observation is age (years) and the second is weekly sales. Plot the data.

1.62 The coach of a rowing team wants to know if working with a sport nutritionist will improve the performance of the elite rowers. A random sample of eight members of his crew took part in a year-long program. The following ordered pairs show the amount of fiber (in grams) each individual added to their daily intake and the corresponding improvement in their muscle mass percentage.

(19, 2.31) (26, 4.62) (15, 1.70) (38, 5.12) (18, 2.42)

(29, 5.82) (16, 3.32) (20, 4.32)

Plot the data and state whether you think the nutrition program was successful in improving the elite rowers' performance.

1.63 Four types of checking accounts are offered by one bank. Suppose that recently a random sample of 300 bank customers was surveyed and asked several questions. It was found that 60% of the respondents preferred Easy Checking; 12%, Intelligent Checking; 18%, Super Checking; and the remainder, Ultimate Checking. Of those who selected Easy Checking, 100 were females; one-third of the respondents who selected Intelligent Checking were males; half of the respondents who selected Super Checking were males; and 80% of respondents who selected Ultimate Checking were males.

  a. Describe the data with a cross table.
  b. Describe the data graphically.

1.64 How did people first learn about a new product? A random sample of 200 shoppers at a particular store was asked their age and whether they heard about the product from a friend or through a local newspaper advertisement. The results indicated that 50 respondents were under 21 years of age, 90 people were in the age group between 21 and 35, and 60 respondents were older than 35 years of age. Of those under 21 years old, 30 heard about the product from a friend, and the remainder learned about the product through an advertisement in the local paper. One-third of the people in the age category from 21 to 35 first learned about the product from the local newspaper advertisement; the remainder of this age group learned about the product from a friend. A friend informed 30% of the people in the over-35 age category about the product; the remainder learned about it from the local newspaper advertisement.

  a. Describe the data with a cross table.
  b. Describe the data graphically.

1.65 A random sample of customers was asked to select their favorite soft drink from a list of five brands. The results showed that 30 preferred Brand A, 50 preferred Brand B, 46 preferred Brand C, 100 preferred Brand D, and 14 preferred Brand E.

  a. Construct a pie chart.
  b. Construct a bar chart.

1.66 The owner of Snappy Lawn Care thinks that the time it takes to mow a yard may be related to the temperatures at the time of mowing. He randomly sampled several yards of the same size and collected data on temperature and time it takes to mow. The data are in the data file **Snappy Lawn Care.** Plot the data with a scatter plot and comment on your findings.

1.67 Construct a time-series plot of population growth for the state of New York from 2002 to the present. (*Hint:* Check www.census.gov.)

1.68 Florin, owner of Florin's Flower Mart, randomly sampled 124 customers in order to obtain data such as a customer's method of payment (Visa, MasterCard, American Express, cash, or some other method) and the day of the week that the customer made the purchase (except for when the store is closed on Sundays). The data are contained in the data file **Florin.** Construct the following:

  a. A cross table of the variables method of payment and day of purchase
  b. A pie chart of day of purchase

1.69 A supermarket developer has conducted a large study to determine alcohol preferences based on the type of vehicle typically driven to a shopping center. A random sample of 100 car drivers and a second random sample of 100 pickup truck drivers were interviewed and asked to indicate their preference for beer or wine. The results indicated that 68% of car drivers preferred wine, whereas 71% of pickup truck drivers preferred beer. Construct a cross table and bar chart of this information.

1.70 The closing costs of shares of Apple Inc. (AAPL) stock from January 3, 2011, through February 21, 2011, are contained in the data file **Apple Stock Prices**.

  a. Construct a time series plot of the closing costs.
  b. Obtain closing costs of Apple stock for the most recent 30-day period.

1.71 *RELEVANT Magazine* keeps records of traffic (such as the weekly number of new visitors) to its Web site from various social networks, such as Facebook and Twitter (Butcher 2011). Use a time-series plot to graph the number of unique page views by weekly new visitors to *RELEVANT Magazine*'s Web site by Facebook users over a recent 9-week period. The data are stored in the data file **RELEVANT Magazine.**

1.72 How much time (in minutes) do people spend on a typical visit to a local mall? A random sample of $n = 104$ shoppers was timed and the results (in minutes) are stored in the data file **Shopping Times.**

  a. Construct a histogram of these shopping times.
  b. Construct a stem-and-leaf display of these shopping times.

1.73 The data file **Grade Point Averages** contains a random sample of 156 grade point averages for students at one university. Construct a stem-and-leaf display of the data.

1.74 A professor wants to explore the relationship between the grades students receive on their first classroom quiz (*X*) and the grade they receive on their first aptitude test (*Y*). Aptitude test scores range from 0 to 30 with greater scores indicating a higher aptitude. The first quiz and test scores for a random sample of eight students reveal the following results:

Quiz Score, X	10	29	16	25	14	27	25	20
Test Score, Y	19	60	28	49	20	60	56	31

Construct a scatter plot of the quiz scores and test scores for a random sample of 8 students.

REFERENCES

1. Butcher, Richard, Marketing Assistant. *RELEVANT Magazine*. 2011. www.RELEVANTmagazine.com.

2. Centers for Disease Control and Prevention (CDC). 2003–2004. "National Health and Nutrition Examination Survey Data." Hyattsville, MD: U.S. Department of Health and Human Services, Centers for Disease Control and Prevention. http://www.cdc.gov/nchs/nhanes/nhanes2003-2004/nhanes03_04.htm (accessed March 6, 2011).

3. Final Report of the Advisory Committee on Smaller Public Companies to the U.S. Securities and Exchange Commission, April 23, 2006). http://www.sec.gov/info/smallbus/acspc/acspc-finalreport.pdf (accessed July 19, 2011).

4. "Groupon Hits 50m Subscribers." 2011. http://www.socialshopping.com/Groupon/news/Groupon-hits-50m-Subscribers-Shopping-site-sensation-201101210398/ (accessed February 20, 2011).

5. Guenther, P. M., J. Reedy, S. M. Krebs-Smith, B. B. Reeve, and P. P. Basiotis. 2007. *Development and Evaluation of the Healthy Eating Index–2005: Technical Report.* Center for Nutrition Policy and Promotion, U.S. Department of Agriculture. Available at http://www.cnpp.usda.gov/Healthy-EatingIndex.htm. (accessed March 9, 2011).

6. Michelson, Stuart, J. Stryker, and B. Thorne. 2009. The Sarbanes-Oxley Act of 2002: What impact has it had on small business firms? *Managerial Auditing Journal/Emerald Group Publishing Limited*, 24(8): 743–766. To read the complete research paper visit http://www.pearsonglobaleditions.com.

7. StatCounter Global Stats Press Release "Firefox overtakes Internet Explorer in Europe in browser wars." 2011. Boston, USA and Dublin, Ireland, January 4, 2011. http://gs.statcounter.com/press/firefox-overtakes-internet-explorer-in-europe-in-browser-wars (accessed February 25, 2011).

8. StatCounter Global Stats Press Release "Microsoft's Internet Explorer browser falls below 50% of worldwide market share for first time." 2010. Boston, USA and Dublin, Ireland, October 5, 2010. http://gs.statcounter.com/press/microsoft-internet-explorer-browser-falls-below-50-perc-of-worldwide-market-for-first-time (accessed August 27, 2011).

9. StatCounter Global Stats "Top 5 Browsers from Jan 10 to Feb 11." 2011. http://gs.statcounter.com/#browser-eu-monthly-201001-201102 (accessed February 25, 2011) and http://gs.statcounter.com/#browser-na-monthly-201001-201102 (accessed February 25, 2011).

10. Table 275. College Enrollment by Selected Characteristics. 2011. Source: U.S. National Center for Education Statistics, Digest of Education Statistics. Reprinted in the 2011 *Statistical Abstract of the United States*. Education. Data available at http://www.census.gov/compendia/statab/ (accessed February 12, 2011). Internet Release December 10, 2010.

11. Table 383. Threatened and Endangered Wildlife and Plant Species. 2010. Source: U.S. Fish and Wildlife Service, *Endangered Species Bulletin*. Reprinted in the 2011 *Statistical Abstract of the United States*, Geography and Environment. Data available at http://www.census.gov/compendia/statab/cats/geography_environment.html (accessed February 12, 2011).

12. Table 1002. Gross Domestic Product in Current and Real 2005 Dollars by Industry. Source: U.S. Bureau of Economic Analysis, *Survey of Current Business*, January 2011. Reprinted in the 2011 *Statistical Abstract of the United States*, U.S. Census Bureau, Statistical Abstract of the United States: 2011 (130th ed.) Washington, DC, 2010. Data available at http://www.census.gov/compendia/statab/ (accessed February 12, 2011).

CHAPTER 2

Describing Data: Numerical

Introduction

In Chapter 1 we described data graphically, noting that different graphs are used for categorical and numerical variables. In this chapter we describe data numerically and observe that different numerical measures are used for categorical and numerical data. In addition, we discuss measures for grouped data and measures of the direction and strength of relationships between two variables.

2.1 MEASURES OF CENTRAL TENDENCY AND LOCATION

One of the first and basic questions asked by researchers, economists, corporate executives, government officials, and anyone with sample data is whether the data in their sample tend to be centered or located around a particular value. In Chapter 1 we considered a graphical response to this question and learned that histograms give us a visual picture of the shape of a distribution as well as provide us with an idea of whether our data tend to center or cluster around some value. In this section, we present numerical measures—the mean, median, and mode—in response to questions concerning the location of the center of a data set. We also study a special type of mean called the geometric mean. These numerical measures provide information about a "typical" observation in the data and are referred to as *measures of central tendency.*

Often we ask questions that concern the location or position of a value relative to the *entire* set of data. We answer this type of query by examining such measures of location as percentiles and quartiles. Most of us are somewhat familiar with percentiles from standardized test scores (such as the SAT). Another measure of location, called a z-score, examines the location or position of a value relative to the *mean* of the distribution; z-scores are addressed in Section 2.2.

Mean, Median, and Mode

In Chapter 1 we introduced the terms *parameter* and *statistic.* A parameter refers to a specific population characteristic; a statistic refers to a specific sample characteristic. Measures of central tendency are usually computed from sample data rather than from population data. One measure of central tendency that quickly comes to mind is the *arithmetic mean,* usually just called the *mean,* or average.

Arithmetic Mean

The **arithmetic mean** (or simply *mean*) of a set of data is the sum of the data values divided by the number of observations. If the data set is the entire population of data, then the *population mean, μ,* is a *parameter* given by

$$\mu = \frac{\sum_{i=1}^{N} x_i}{N} = \frac{x_1 + x_2 + \cdots + x_N}{N} \tag{2.1}$$

where N = population size and Σ means "the sum of."

If the data set is from a sample, then the *sample mean, $\bar{x}$,* is a *statistic* given by

$$\bar{x} = \frac{\sum_{i=1}^{n} x_i}{n} \tag{2.2}$$

where n = sample size. The mean is appropriate for numerical data.

To locate the *median*, we must arrange the data in either increasing or decreasing order.

Median

The **median** is the middle observation of a set of observations that are arranged in increasing (or decreasing) order. If the sample size, n, is an odd number, the median is the middle observation. If the sample size, n, is an even number, the median is the average of the two middle observations. The median will be the number located in the

$$0.50(n + 1)\text{th ordered position.} \tag{2.3}$$

Mode

The **mode**, if one exists, is the most frequently occurring value. A distribution with one mode is called unimodal; with two modes, it is called bimodal; and with more than two modes, the distribution is said to be multimodal. The mode is most commonly used with categorical data.

Example 2.1 Demand for Bottled Water (Measures of Central Tendency)

The demand for bottled water increases during the hurricane season in Florida. The number of 1-gallon bottles of water sold for a random sample of $n = 12$ hours in one store during hurricane season is:

60 84 65 67 75 72

80 85 63 82 70 75

Describe the central tendency of the data.

Solution The average or mean hourly number of 1-gallon bottles of water demanded is found as follows:

$$\bar{x} = \frac{\sum_{i=1}^{n} x_i}{n} = \frac{60 + 84 + \cdots + 75}{12} = 73.17$$

Next, we arrange the sales data from least to greatest sales:

60 63 65 67 70 72 75 75 80 82 84 85

and find that the median sales is located in the $0.5(12 + 1) = 6.5$th ordered position; that is, the median number of 1-gallon bottles of water is midway between the 6th and 7th ordered data points: $(72 + 75)/2 = 73.5$ bottles. The mode is clearly 75 bottles.

The decision as to whether the mean, median, or mode is the appropriate measure to describe the central tendency of data is context specific. One factor that influences our choice is the type of data, categorical or numerical, as discussed in Chapter 1.

Categorical data are best described by the median or the mode, not the mean. If one person strongly agrees (coded 5) with a particular statement and another person strongly disagrees (coded 1), is the mean "no opinion"? An obvious use of median and mode is by clothing retailers considering inventory of shoes, shirts, and other such items that are available in various sizes. The size of items sold most often, the mode, is then the one in heaviest demand. Knowing that the mean shirt size of European men is 41.13 or that the average shoe size of American women is 8.24 is useless, but knowing that the modal shirt size is 40 or the modal shoe size is 7 is valuable for inventory decisions. However, the mode may not represent the true center of numerical data. For this reason, the mode is used less frequently than either the mean or the median in business applications.

Example 2.2 Percentage Change in Earnings per Share (Measures of Central Tendency)

Find the mean, median, and mode for a random sample of eight Asian corporations with the following percentage changes in earnings per share in the current year compared with the previous year:

5% 5% 8.1% 13.6% 23.2% 20.7% 12.0% 14.2%

Solution The mean percentage change in earnings per share for this sample is

$$\bar{x} = \frac{\sum_{i=1}^{n} x_i}{n} = \frac{5 + 5 + 8.1 + 13.6 + \cdots + 14.2}{8} = 12.73 \text{ or } 10.73\%$$

and the median percentage change in earnings per share is 12.8%. The mode is 5%, since it occurs twice and the other percentages occur only once. But this modal percentage rate does not represent the center of this sample data.

Numerical data are usually best described by the mean. However, in addition to the type of data, another factor to consider is the presence of outliers—that is, observations that are unusually large or unusually small in comparison to the rest of the data. The median is not affected by outliers, but the mean is. Whenever there are outliers in the data, we first need to look for possible causes. One cause could be simply an error in data entry. The mean will be greater if unusually large outliers are present, and the mean will be less when the data contain outliers that are unusually small compared to the rest of the data.

Shape of a Distribution

In Chapter 1 we described graphically the shape of a distribution as symmetric or skewed by examining a histogram. Recall that if the center of the data divides a graph of the distribution into two mirror images, so that the portion on one side of the middle is nearly identical to the portion on the other side, the distribution is said to be symmetric. Graphs without this shape are asymmetric.

We can also describe the shape of a distribution numerically by computing a measure of skewness. In nearly all situations, we determine this measure of skewness with Excel or a statistical software package such as SPSS, SAS, or Minitab. Skewness is positive if a distribution is skewed to the right, negative for distributions skewed to the left, and 0 for distributions, such as the bell-shaped distribution, that are mounded and symmetric about their mean. Manual computation of skewness is presented in the chapter appendix.

For continuous numerical unimodal data, the mean is usually less than the median in a skewed-left distribution and the mean is usually greater than the median in a skewed-right distribution. In a symmetric distribution the mean and median are equal. This relationship between the mean and the median may not be true for discrete numerical variables or for some continuous numerical variables (von Hippel 2005).

Example 2.3 Grade Point Averages (Skewed-Left Distribution)

Describe the shape of the distribution of grade point averages stored in the data file **Grade Point Averages.**

Solution The data file **Grade Point Averages** contains a random sample of 156 grade point averages for students at one university. In Chapter 1, we described the shape of this distribution graphically with a histogram. In Figure 1.16 we saw that the shape of the distribution appears to be skewed left. Figure 2.1 gives the descriptive measures of the data using Excel. The value of the mean is approximately 3.14 and is less than the median of 3.31. Also, the median is less than the mode of 3.42. The graph, the negative value of skewness, and the comparison of the mean and the median suggest that this is a skewed-left distribution.

Figure 2.1 Grade Point Average

Grade Point Average

Mean	3.141154		Skewness	−1.1685
Standard Error	0.029144		Range	1.73
Median	3.31		Minimum	2.12
Mode	3.42		Maximum	3.85
Standard Deviation	0.364006		Sum	490.02
Sample Variance	0.132501		Count	156
Kurtosis	0.609585			

The median is the preferred measure to describe the distribution of incomes in a city, state, or country. Distribution of incomes is often right skewed since incomes tend to contain a relatively small proportion of high values. A large proportion of the population has relatively modest incomes, but the incomes of, say, the highest 10% of all earners extend over a considerable range. As a result, the mean of such distributions is typically quite a bit higher than the median. The mean, which is inflated by the very wealthy, gives too optimistic a view of the economic well-being of the community. The median is then preferred to the mean.

We do *not* intend to imply that the median should *always* be preferred to the mean when the population or sample is skewed. There are times when the mean would still be the preferred measure even if the distribution were skewed. Consider an insurance company that most likely faces a right-skewed distribution of claim sizes. If the company wants to know the most typical claim size, the median is preferred. But suppose the company wants to know how much money needs to be budgeted to cover claims. Then, the mean is preferred.

In spite of its advantage in discounting extreme observations, the median is used less frequently than the mean. In Chapter 7 we discuss certain properties of the mean that make it more attractive than the median in many situations. The reason is that the theoretical development of inferential procedures based on the mean, and measures related to it, is considerably more straightforward than the development of procedures based on the median.

Geometric Mean

Another measure of central tendency that is important in business and economics, but often overlooked, is the *geometric mean*.

Geometric Mean
The **geometric mean**, $\bar{x}_g$, is the nth root of the product of n numbers:

$$\bar{x}_g = \sqrt[n]{(x_1 x_2 \cdots x_n)} = (x_1 x_2 \cdots x_n)^{1/n} \qquad (2.4)$$

The **geometric mean rate of return**, $\bar{r}_g$,

$$\bar{r}_g = (x_1 x_2 \cdots x_n)^{1/n} - 1 \qquad (2.5)$$

gives the mean percentage return of an investment over time.

Consider the two numbers 20 and 5. The arithmetic mean is 12.5, but the geometric mean of the numbers 20 and 5 is $\sqrt{100} = 10$.

Business analysts and economists who are interested in growth over a number of time periods use the geometric mean. Applications of the geometric mean in finance include compound interest over several years, total sales growth, and population growth. An important question concerns the average growth each year that will result in a certain total growth over several years.

Example 2.4 Annual Growth Rate (Geometric Mean)

Find the annual growth rate if sales have grown 25% over 5 years.

Solution The intuitive but naive temptation is simply to divide total growth, 25%, by the number of time periods, 5, and conclude that the average annual growth rate is 5%. This result is incorrect because it ignores the compound effect of growth.

Suppose that the annual growth rate is actually 5%; then the total growth over 5 years will be

$$(1.05)(1.05)(1.05)(1.05)(1.05) = 1.2763$$

or 27.63%. However, the annual growth rate, r, that would yield 25% over 5 years must satisfy this equation:

$$(1 + r)^5 = 1.25$$

First, solve for the geometric mean:

$$\bar{x}_g = 1 + r = (1.25)^{1/5} = 1.046$$

The geometric mean growth rate is $\bar{r}_g = 0.046$, or 4.6%.

Percentiles and Quartiles

Percentiles and quartiles are measures that indicate the location, or position, of a value relative to the entire set of data. Suppose you are told that you scored in the 92nd percentile on your SAT mathematics exam. This means that approximately 92% of the students who took this exam scored lower than you and approximately 8% of the students who took this exam scored higher than you. Percentiles and quartiles are generally used to describe large data sets, such as sales data, survey data, or even the weights of newborn babies. Pediatricians will measure a baby's weight in terms of percentiles. A newborn who weighs in the 5th percentile is quite small in comparison to a newborn in the 95th percentile in weight (Grummer-Strawn, Reinold, and Krebs 2010).

Statisticians do not agree on one best method to calculate percentiles and quartiles and propose different ways to calculate these measures (Langford 2006). Slightly different values for percentiles and quartiles are found using various computer software packages (such as SPSS, SAS, MINITAB, JMP) or using Excel or with the use of different calculators. In this book we rely on linear interpolation between ranked values and identify the location of percentiles and quartiles, as given in Equations 2.6, 2.7, and 2.8.

Percentiles and Quartiles

To find percentiles and quartiles, data must first be arranged in order from the smallest to the largest values.

The Pth **percentile** is a value such that approximately $P\%$ of the observations are at or below that number. **Percentiles** separate large ordered data sets into 100ths. The 50th percentile is the median.

The Pth percentile is found as follows:

$$P\text{th percentile} = \text{value located in the } (P/100)(n + 1)\text{th ordered position} \tag{2.6}$$

Quartiles are descriptive measures that separate large data sets into four quarters. The **first quartile**, Q_1, (or 25th *percentile*) separates approximately the smallest 25% of the data from the remainder of the data. The **second quartile**, Q_2, (or 50th *percentile*) is the median (see Equation 2.3).

The **third quartile**, Q_3, (or 75th *percentile*), separates approximately the smallest 75% of the data from the remaining largest 25% of the data.

$$Q_1 = \text{the value in the } \mathbf{0.25}(n + 1)\text{th ordered position} \qquad (2.7)$$

$$Q_2 = \text{the value in the } \mathbf{0.50}(n + 1)\text{th ordered position}$$

$$Q_3 = \text{the value in the } \mathbf{0.75}(n + 1)\text{th ordered position} \qquad (2.8)$$

In describing numerical data, we often refer to the five-number summary. In Section 2.2 we present a graph of the five-number summary called a box-and-whisker plot.

Five-Number Summary

The **five-number summary** refers to the five descriptive measures: minimum, first quartile, median, third quartile, and maximum.

$$\text{minimum} < Q_1 < \text{median} < Q_3 < \text{maximum}$$

To illustrate the use of Equations 2.7 and 2.8, we include Example 2.5 with only $n = 12$ observations. For such a small sample size, one would rarely compute these values in practice. Percentiles and quartiles are generally used to describe large data sets. Example 2.6 has $n = 104$ observations and Example 2.7 has $n = 4{,}460$ observations.

Example 2.5 Demand for Bottled Water (Quartiles)

In Example 2.1 we found the measures of central tendency for the number of 1-gallon bottles of water sold in a sample of 12 hours in one store in Florida during hurricane season. In particular, the median was found to be 73.5 bottles. Find the five-number summary.

Solution We arrange the data from Example 2.1 in order from least to greatest.

$$60 \quad 63 \quad 65 \quad 67 \quad 70 \quad 72 \quad 75 \quad 75 \quad 80 \quad 82 \quad 84 \quad 85$$

Using Equation 2.7, we find the first quartile, Q_1, as follows:

$$Q_1 = \text{the value located in the } 0.25(12 + 1)\text{th ordered position}$$

$$Q_1 = \text{the value located in the } 3.25\text{th ordered position}$$

The value in the third ordered position is 65 bottles, and the value in the 4th ordered position is 67 bottles. The first quartile is found as follows:

$$Q_1 = 65 + 0.25(67 - 65)$$

$$Q_1 = 65 + 0.50 = 65.5 \text{ bottles}$$

Using Equation 2.8, the third quartile, Q_3, is located in the $0.75(12 + 1)$th ordered position—that is, the value in the 9.75th ordered position. The value in the 9th ordered position is 80 bottles and the value in the 10th ordered position is 82 bottles. The third quartile is calculated as follows:

$$Q_3 = 80 + 0.75(82 - 80)$$

$$Q_3 = 80 + 0.75(2) = 81.5 \text{ bottles}$$

The five-number summary for this data is as follows:

$$\text{Minimum} < Q_1 < \text{median} < Q_3 < \text{maximum}$$

$$60 < 65.5 < 73.5 < 81.5 < 85$$

Example 2.6 Shopping Times at a Mall (Percentiles)

In an endeavor to increase sales at a local mall, the management gathered data on the amount of time that current shoppers spend in the mall. A random sample of $n = 104$ shoppers were timed, and the results (in minutes) are given in Table 2.1. Find the 25th and 85th percentiles. The data is listed in Table 2.1 and contained in the data file **Shopping Times**.

Table 2.1 Shopping Times

18	34	42	37	19	37	30	40	28	34	71	18
46	42	34	30	21	23	40	37	57	69	73	47
45	38	34	25	34	23	37	20	63	57	73	52
20	31	18	42	25	40	21	40	57	69	71	55
33	38	30	41	18	31	34	18	63	57	70	25
33	21	48	34	25	45	34	21	31	70	69	
21	37	51	50	25	51	42	52	67	18	68	
31	37	52	52	43	45	43	18	25	70	64	
23	30	19	50	59	60	60	68	69	70	59	

Solution The first step is to sort the data in the data file **Shopping Times** from smallest to largest. Using Equation 2.6, we find the 25th percentile as follows:

25th percentile = the value located in the $0.25(n + 1)$th ordered position

25th percentile = the value located in the $0.25(104 + 1)$th ordered position

25th percentile = the value located in the 26.25th ordered position

The value in the 26th ordered position is 28 minutes, and the value in the 27th ordered position is 30 minutes. The 25th percentile is found as follows:

$$25\text{th percentile} = 28 + 0.25(30 - 28) = 28.5$$

Similarly, we use Equation 2.6 to locate the 85th percentile as follows:

85th percentile = the value located in $0.85(104 + 1)$th ordered position

85th percentile = the value located in the 89.25th ordered position

Since the value in the 89th ordered position is 64 minutes and the value in the 90th ordered position is 67 minutes, the value in the 89.25th ordered position is 25% of the distance between 67 and 64. The 85th percentile is found as follows:

$$64 + 0.25(67 - 64) = 64 + 0.75 = 64.75 \text{ minutes}$$

Approximately 85% of the shoppers in our sample spend less than 64.75 minutes at the mall.

Statistical software packages are useful to describe data when the sample size is very large. In Chapter 1 we developed bar charts to graph one of the categorical variables, activity level, from the Healthy Eating Index–2005 (Figure 1.1 to Figure 1.3). Now, in Example 2.7 we find the five-number summary for the HEI–2005 data using Minitab.

Example 2.7 Healthy Eating Index–2005 (Five-Number Summary)

The HEI–2005 measures how well the population follows the recommendations of the 2005 *Dietary Guidelines for Americans* (Guenther et al. 2007). The HEI measures, on a 100-point scale, the adequacy of consumption of vegetables, fruits, grains, milk, meat and beans, and liquid oils. This scale is titled HEI2005 in the data file **HEI Cost Data Variable Subset**.

We saw in Example 1.1 that the data file **HEI Cost Data Variable Subset** contains considerable information on randomly selected individuals who participated in an extended interview and medical examination. Recall that there are two interviews for each person in the study. Results for the first interview are identified by daycode = 1, and data for the second interview are identified by daycode = 2. Other variables in the data file are described in the data dictionary in the Chapter 10 appendix. Find the five-number summary of the HEI scores taken during the first interview for both males (code = 0) and females (code = 1).

Solution Since the data file contains $n = 4,460$ observations, we use Minitab to obtain the measures in the five-number summary (Figure 2.2).

Figure 2.2 Healthy Eating Index–2005 Scores: First Interview (Five-Number Summary)

Descriptive Statistics: HEI2005 (Females; First Interview)

Variable	N	Minimum	Q_1	Median	Q_3	Maximum
HEI2005	2,321	11.172	42.420	53.320	63.907	92.643

Descriptive Statistics: HEI2005 (Males; First Interview)

Variable	N	Minimum	Q_1	Median	Q_3	Maximum
HEI2005	2,139	13.556	39.644	49.674	59.988	99.457

EXERCISES

 Visit www.MyStatLab.com or www.pearson globaleditions.com to access the data files.

Basic Exercises

2.1 A random sample of 5 weeks showed that a cruise agency received the following number of weekly specials to the Caribbean:

17 71 78 80 84

a. Compute the mean, median, and mode.
b. Which measure of central tendency best describes the data?

2.2 Israel's Ministry of Transport and Road Safety is interested in the number of cars passing through the Wadi Araba crossing between Israel and Jordan. Records over a 5-day period show the following number of cars for each day:

16 21 12 19 1 2

a. Compute the mean number of cars passing through the Wadi Araba crossing.

b. Calculate the median number of the cars passing through the Wadi Araba crossing.
c. Find the mode.

2.3 The records of a university in Berlin over a 12-year period show the following percentage increase in the number of students enrolled:

4.1 3.5 3.2 4.6 5.1 3.8

3.2 5.7 4.4 3.8 2.9 3.2

a. Compute the mean increase in the number of students enrolled.
b. Compute the median increase in the number of students enrolled.
c. Find the mode.

2.4 Alpha Yatching, a yatch charter in Greece, reviewed its finances at the end of 2018. The records over the last 10 years show that the following amount (in €000) was spent on maintenance and repairs of yatchs during the summer season:

2.51 3.74 4.15 5.33 6.18

6.65 7.18 6.92 6.95 7.54

a. Calculate the mean amount spent on maintenance and repairs.

b. Calculate the median.

2.5 A manager at the Norinchukin Bank, a Japanese cooperative bank, randomly sampled 12 overdrawn bank accounts. The following overdrafts are found (in 000 yen):

1.2   3.15   2.33   4.15   3.1   2.74

3.1   2.63   1.8   1.5   4.18   5.23

a. Compute the sample median.

b. Compute the sample mean.

2.6 During the last couple years many countries faced depopulation. Ten counties of a certain country are selected and the number of elementary schools closed are found:

10   6   13   5   11   5   6   3   7   9

a. Find the mean, median, and mode of the number of schools closed.

b. Find the five-number summary.

2.7 A textile manufacturer obtained a sample of 50 bolts of cloth from a day's output. Each bolt is carefully inspected and the number of imperfections is recorded as follows:

Number of imperfections	0	1	2	3
Number of bolts	33	12	4	1

Find the mean, median, and mode for these sample data.

2.8 Private rented sector is showing strong *growth* due to an increase number of tourists. A tourist office wants to examine the number of 4-bedroom apartments available for rent in the local city over the last twelve years. The number of apartments are listed below:

2,351   2,574   3,571   3,532   4,871   5,952

5,735   5,821   6,025   6,100   6,250   6,310

a. What is the mean number of apartments available for rent?

b. Calculate the median number of apartments available for rent.

c. Find the mode.

Application Exercises

2.9 A random sample of 156 grade point averages for students at one university is stored in the data file **Grade Point Averages**.

a. Compute the first and third quartiles.

b. Calculate the 30th percentile.

c. Calculate the 80th percentile.

2.10 A sample of 33 accounting students recorded the number of hours spent studying the course material during the week before the final exam. The data are stored in the data file **Study Data.**

a. Compute the sample mean.

b. Compute the sample median.

c. Comment on symmetry or skewness.

d. Find the five-number summary for this data.

2.11 The data file **Sun** contains the volumes for a random sample of 100 bottles (237 mL) of a new suntan lotion.

a. Find and interpret the mean volume.

b. Determine the median volume.

c. Are the data symmetric or skewed? Explain.

d. Find the five-number summary for this data.

2.2 MEASURES OF VARIABILITY

The mean alone does not provide a complete or sufficient description of data. In this section we present descriptive numbers that measure the variability or spread of the observations from the mean. In particular, we include the range, interquartile range, variance, standard deviation, and coefficient of variation.

No two things are exactly alike. Variation exists in all areas. In the UEFA Euro 2020, a star football player might score three goals in one match and none in the next or play 20 minutes in one game and only 6 minutes in the next. The weather varies greatly from day to day and even from hour to hour; grades on a test differ for students taking the same course with the same instructor; a person's blood pressure, pulse, cholesterol level, and caloric intake will vary daily. In business, variation is seen in sales, advertising costs, the percentage of product complaints, the number of new customers, and so forth.

While two data sets could have the same mean, the individual observations in one set could vary more from the mean than do the observations in the second set. Consider the following two sets of sample data:

Sample A:	1	2	1	36
Sample B:	8	9	10	13

Although the mean is 10 for both samples, clearly the data in sample A are farther from 10 than are the data in sample B. We need descriptive numbers to measure this spread.

Range and Interquartile Range

Range
Range is the difference between the largest and smallest observations.

The greater the spread of the data from the center of the distribution, the larger the range will be. Since the range takes into account only the largest and smallest observations, it is susceptible to considerable distortion if there is an unusual extreme observation. Although the range measures the *total* spread of the data, the range may be an unsatisfactory measure of variability (spread) because outliers, either very high or very low observations, influence it. One way to avoid this difficulty is to arrange the data in ascending or descending order, discard a few of the highest and a few of the lowest numbers, and find the range of those remaining. Sometimes the lowest 25% of the data and the highest 25% of the data will be removed. To do this, we define quartiles and the *interquartile range*, which measures the spread of the middle 50% of the data.

Interquartile Range
The **interquartile range (IQR)** measures the spread in the *middle 50%* of the data; it is the difference between the observation at Q_3, the third quartile (or 75th percentile), and the observation at Q_1, the first quartile (or 25th percentile). Thus,

$$IQR = Q_3 - Q_1 \qquad (2.9)$$

In Example 2.6 we considered a random sample of times (in minutes) spent by $n = 104$ people shopping at a mall, and we found the 25th percentile, or the first quartile, to be 28.5 minutes. Similarly, it can be shown that the 75th percentile, or the third quartile, is 56.5 minutes. It follows that the interquartile range for the data contained in the data file **Shopping Times** is as follows:

$$IQR = Q_3 - Q_1 = 56.5 - 28.5 = 28 \text{ minutes}$$

Box-and-Whisker Plots

In Chapter 1, we introduced one of Tukey's exploratory data analysis graphs called a stem-and-leaf display. We now include another one of Tukey's exploratory data analysis graphs called a box-and-whisker plot. Both types of graphs reveal information about the shape of the distribution. A box-and-whisker plot also provides some insight into the spread of the data.

Box-and-Whisker Plot
A **box-and-whisker plot** is a graph that describes the shape of a distribution in terms of the five-number summary: the minimum value, first quartile (25th percentile), the median, the third quartile (75th percentile), and the maximum value. The inner box shows the numbers that span the range from the first to the third quartile. A line is drawn through the box at the median. There are two "whiskers." One whisker is the line from the 25th percentile to the minimum value; the other whisker is the line from the 75th percentile to the maximum value.

Example 2.8 Gilotti's Pizzeria (Box-and-Whisker Plot)

Gilotti's Pizzeria has 4 locations in one large metropolitan area. Daily sales (in hundreds of dollars) from a random sample of 10 weekdays from each of the 4 locations are given in Table 2.2. Plot the data with a box-and-whisker plot. The data are contained in the data file **Gilotti's Pizzeria**.

Table 2.2 Gilotti's Pizzeria Sales (in $100s)

LOCATION 1	LOCATION 2	LOCATION 3	LOCATION 4
6	1	2	22
8	19	3	20
10	2	25	10
12	18	20	13
14	11	22	12
9	10	19	10
11	3	25	11
7	17	20	9
13	4	22	10
11	17	26	8

Solution We can easily compute the five-number summary using the equations in this chapter, or we can obtain the results using a software package such as Minitab. Table 2.3 lists mean sales and the values of each of the five-number summary measures for each of the four pizzeria locations.

Table 2.3 Gilotti's Pizzeria Sales

VARIABLE	MEAN	MIN.	Q_1	MEDIAN	Q_3	MAX.	IQR	RANGE
Location 1	10.1	6.0	7.75	10.5	12.25	14.0	4.5	8.0
Location 2	10.2	1.0	2.75	10.5	17.25	19.0	14.5	18.0
Location 3	18.4	2.0	15.00	21.0	25.00	26.0	10.0	24.0
Location 4	12.5	8.0	9.75	10.5	14.75	22.0	5.0	14.0

A quick look at Table 2.3 and Figure 2.3 shows that Location 1, Location 2, and Location 4 all have the same median sales of $1,050. We even note that Location 1 and Location 2 have nearly identical mean sales, with $1,010 for Location 1 and $1,020 for Location 2. However, a closer examination of the range and IQR of Location 1 and Location 2 reveals that the sales in Location 2 are spread over a wider interval than the sales for Location 1. Note that Location 3 has the highest mean sales, $1,840, but it also has the largest range, or overall spread.

Using Minitab, we see in Figure 2.3 the shapes of the distribution of sales for these four locations.

Figure 2.3 Gilotti's Pizzeria Sales (Box-and-Whisker Plots)

Boxplots of Gilotti's Pizzeria Sales in Four Locations

Notice that the distribution of sales for Location 3 is skewed left, which indicates the presence of days with sales less than most of the other days ($200 and $300) or perhaps a data-entry error. Similarly, the distribution of sales in Location 4 is skewed right indicating the presence of sales higher than most of the other days ($2,200 and $2,000) or the possibility that sales were incorrectly recorded.

The management of Gilotti's Pizzeria will want to know more about the variation in sales, both within a given location as well as between these four locations. This information will assist Gilotti's Pizzeria in their decision-making process.

Variance and Standard Deviation

Although range and interquartile range measure the spread of data, both measures take into account only two of the data values. We need a measure that would *average* the total (Σ) distance between each of the data values and the mean. But for *all* data sets, this sum will *always equal zero* because the mean is the center of the data. If the data value is less than the mean, the difference between the data value and the mean would be negative (and distance is not negative). If each of these differences is squared, then each observation (both above and below the mean) contributes to the sum of the squared terms. The average of the sum of squared terms is called the *variance.*

Variance

With respect to **variance**, the *population variance*, σ^2, is the sum of the squared differences between each observation and the population mean divided by the population size, N:

$$\sigma^2 = \frac{\sum_{i=1}^{N}(x_i - \mu)^2}{N} \tag{2.10}$$

The *sample variance*, s^2, is the sum of the squared differences between each observation and the sample mean divided by the sample size, n, minus 1:

$$s^2 = \frac{\sum_{i=1}^{n}(x_i - \bar{x})^2}{n - 1} \tag{2.11}$$

Notice that, for sample data, variance in Equation 2.11 is found by dividing the numerator by $(n - 1)$ and not n. Since our goal is to find an average of squared deviations about the mean, one would expect division by n. So why is the denominator of sample variance given as $(n - 1)$ in Equation 2.11? If we were to take a very large number of samples, each of size n, from the population and compute the sample variance, as given in Equation 2.11 for each of these samples, then the average of all of these sample variances would be the population variance, σ^2. In Chapter 6 we see that this property indicates that the sample variance is an "unbiased estimator" of the population variance, σ^2. For now, we rely on mathematical statisticians who have shown that if the population variance is unknown, a sample variance is a better estimator of the population variance if the denominator in the sample variance is $(n - 1)$ rather than n.

To compute the variance requires squaring the distances, which then changes the unit of measurement to square units. The *standard deviation*, which is the square root of variance, restores the data to their original measurement unit. If the original measurements were in feet, the variance would be in feet squared, but the standard deviation would be in feet. The standard deviation measures the *average* spread around the mean.

Standard Deviation

With respect to **standard deviation**, the population *standard deviation*, σ, is the (positive) square root of the population variance and is defined as follows:

$$\sigma = \sqrt{\sigma^2} = \sqrt{\frac{\sum_{i=1}^{N}(x_i - \mu)^2}{N}} \tag{2.12}$$

The *sample standard deviation*, s, is as follows:

$$s = \sqrt{s^2} = \sqrt{\frac{\sum_{i=1}^{n}(x_i - \bar{x})^2}{n - 1}} \tag{2.13}$$

In Example 2.8 we found the range of daily sales in Location 1 to be $800, smaller than the range of the other three locations (Table 2.3). These differences in the ranges are clearly seen in the box-and-whisker plots in Figure 2.3. However, since only the maximum and minimum values are used to find the range, it is better to calculate the variance and standard deviation, as these measures take into account the difference of each daily sale from its mean.

Example 2.9 Gilotti's Pizzeria Sales (Variance and Standard Deviation)

Calculate the standard deviation of daily sales for Gilotti Pizzeria, Location 1. From Table 2.3 the daily sales for Location 1 are:

6	8	10	12	14	9	11	7	13	11

Solution To calculate sample variance and standard deviation follow these three steps:

Step 1: Calculate the sample mean, $\bar{x}$, using Equation 2.2. It is equal to 10.1.
Step 2: Find the difference between each of the daily sales and the mean of 10.1.
Step 3: Square each difference. The result is Table 2.4.

Table 2.4 Gilotti's Pizzeria Sales

SALES ($100s), x_i	DEVIATION ABOUT THE MEAN, $(x_i - \bar{x})$	SQUARED DEVIATION ABOUT THE MEAN, $(x_i - \bar{x})^2$
6	−4.1	16.81
8	−2.1	4.41
10	−0.1	0.01
12	1.9	3.61
14	3.9	15.21
9	−1.1	1.21
11	0.9	0.81
7	−3.1	9.61
13	2.9	8.41
11	0.9	0.81

$$\sum_{i=1}^{10} x_i = 101 \qquad \sum_{i=1}^{10}(x_i - \bar{x}) = 0 \qquad \sum_{i=1}^{10}(x_i - \bar{x})^2 = 60.9$$

$$\bar{x} = \frac{\sum x_i^2}{n} = 10.1 \qquad\qquad s^2 = \frac{\sum_{i=1}^{n}(x_i - \bar{x})^2}{n - 1} = \frac{60.9}{9} = 6.7\overline{6}$$

$$s = \sqrt{s^2} = \sqrt{6.7\overline{6}} \approx 2.6$$

Equations 2.14 and 2.15 are sometimes referred to as shortcut formulas to calculate sample variance. We include these equations for statisticians who prefer these methods of computation. The value of sample variance is the same using Equation 2.11, 2.14, or 2.15. We illustrate this in Example 2.10.

Shortcut Formulas for Sample Variance, s^2

Sample variance, s^2, can be computed as follows:

$$s^2 = \frac{\sum_{i=1}^{n} x_i^2 - \frac{\left(\sum x_i\right)^2}{n}}{n - 1} \qquad (2.14)$$

Alternatively, sample variance, s^2, can be computed as follows:

$$s^2 = \frac{\sum_{i=1}^{n} x_i^2 - n\bar{x}^2}{n - 1} \qquad (2.15)$$

Example 2.10 Gilotti's Pizzeria Sales (Variance by Alternative Formula)

Calculate the variance in daily sales for Gilotti Pizzeria, Location 1, using the alternative shortcut formulas found in Equations 2.14 and 2.15. From Table 2.3 daily sales for Location 1 are:

6	8	10	12	14	9	11	7	13	11

Solution From Table 2.4 we have the following calculations for the $n = 10$ daily sales:

$$\sum_{i=1}^{10} x_i = 101 \qquad \bar{x} = 10.1$$

All we need is to find the sum of the squares of each daily sale. This is found as follows:

$$\sum x_i^2 = (6)^2 + (8)^2 + (10)^2 + \cdots + (11)^2 = 1{,}081$$

Substituting into Equation 2.14, sample variance, s^2 is calculated as follows:

$$s^2 = \frac{\sum_{i=1}^{n} x_i^2 - \dfrac{\left(\sum x_i\right)^2}{n}}{n-1} = \frac{1{,}081 - \left[\dfrac{(101)^2}{10}\right]}{9} = \frac{1{,}081 - 1{,}020.1}{9} = \frac{60.9}{9} = 6.7\overline{6}$$

Using Equation 2.15, sample variance, s^2 is calculated as follows:

$$s^2 = \frac{\sum_{i=1}^{n} x_i^2 - n\bar{x}^2}{n-1} = \frac{1{,}081 - 10(10.1)^2}{9} = \frac{1{,}081 - 1{,}020.1}{9} = \frac{60.9}{9} = 6.7\overline{6}$$

There are numerous applications of standard deviation in business. For example, investors may want to compare the risk of different assets. In Example 2.11 we look at two assets that have the same mean rates of return. In Example 2.12 we consider an investment in stocks with different mean closing prices over the last several months.

Example 2.11 Comparing Risk of Two Assets with Equal Mean Rates of Return (Standard Deviation)

Fillippa and Elin Kihlborg, owners of an accessory store in Stockholm, Sweden, are considering two investment alternatives, asset A and asset B. They are not sure which of these two single assets is better, and they ask Linnéa Karlsson, a financial planner, for some assistance.

Solution Linnéa knows that the standard deviation, s, is the most common single indicator of the risk or variability of a single asset. In financial situations the fluctuation around a stock's actual rate of return and its expected rate of return is called the *risk* of the stock. The standard deviation measures the variation of returns around an asset's mean. Linnéa obtains the rates of return on each asset for the last 5 years and calculates the means and standard deviations of each asset. Her results are given in Table 2.5.

Table 2.5 Rates of Return: Asset A and Asset B

	ASSET A	ASSET B
Mean Rate of Return	12.2%	12.2%
Standard Deviation in Rate of Return	0.63	3.12

Since each asset has the same average rate of return of 12.2%, Linnéa compares the standard deviations and determines that asset B is a more risky investment.

Coefficient of Variation

Since the mean rates of return for asset A and asset B were the same in Example 2.11, a comparison of standard deviations was appropriate to determine which asset was more risky. Now let's consider another investment opportunity. We have two stocks, and the mean closing prices of these stocks over the last several months are not equal. We need to compare the coefficient of variation for both stocks rather than the standard deviations. The *coefficient of variation* expresses the standard deviation as a percentage of the mean.

> ### Coefficient of Variation
> The **coefficient of variation, CV**, is a measure of relative dispersion that expresses the standard deviation as a percentage of the mean (provided the mean is positive).
>
> The *population coefficient of variation* is
>
> $$CV = \frac{\sigma}{\mu} \times 100\% \qquad \text{if } \mu > 0 \qquad\qquad (2.16)$$
>
> The *sample coefficient of variation* is
>
> $$CV = \frac{s}{\bar{x}} \times 100\% \qquad \text{if } \bar{x} > 0 \qquad\qquad (2.17)$$

If the standard deviations in sales for large and small stores selling similar goods are compared, the standard deviation for large stores will almost always be greater. A simple explanation is that a large store could be modeled as a number of small stores. Comparing variation using the standard deviation would be misleading. The coefficient of variation overcomes this problem by adjusting for the scale of units in the population.

Example 2.12 Stock Purchase Comparison (Coefficient of Variation)

In Example 2.11 two different investments with the same mean rate of return were considered. Now, Fillippa and Elin are considering purchasing shares of stock A or shares of stock B, both listed on Nasdaq Stockholm, the Stockholm Stock Exchange. From the closing prices (Swedish krona or kr) of both stocks over the last several months, the standard deviations were found to be considerably different, with $s_A = 2.00$ kr and $s_B = 8.00$ kr. Should stock A be purchased, since the standard deviation of stock B is larger?

Solution We might think that stock B is more volatile than stock A. However, the mean closing price for stock A is 4.00 kr and the mean closing price for stock B is 80.00 kr. Next, the coefficients of variation are computed to measure and compare the risk of these competing investment opportunities:

$$CV_A = \frac{2.00 \text{ kr}}{4.00 \text{ kr}} \times 100\% = 50\% \quad \text{and} \quad CV_B = \frac{8.00 \text{ kr}}{80.00 \text{ kr}} \times 100\% = 10\%$$

Notice that the market value of stock A fluctuates more from period to period than does that of stock B. The coefficient of variation tells us that for stock A the sample standard deviation is 50% of the mean, and for stock B the sample standard deviation is only 10% of the mean.

Chebyshev's Theorem and the Empirical Rule

A Russian mathematician, Pafnuty Lvovich Chebyshev (1821–1894), established data intervals for any data set, *regardless* of the shape of the distribution.

Chebyshev's Theorem

For any population with mean μ, standard deviation σ, and $k > 1$, the percent of observations that lie within the interval $[\mu \pm k\sigma]$ is

$$at\ least\ 100[1 - (1/k^2)]\% \tag{2.18}$$

where k is the number of standard deviations.

To see how Chebyshev's theorem works in practice, we construct Table 2.6 for selected values of k.

Suppose that the mean grade on an exam is 72, with a standard deviation of 4. According to Chebyshev's theorem, at least 75% of the scores are in the interval between 64 and 80, and at least 88.9% of the scores are in the interval between 60 and 84. Or, suppose that the mean salary for a sample of employees is €33,500 and the standard deviation is €1,554. By Chebyshev's theorem at least 55.6% of the salaries must fall within (1.5) (€1,554) = €2,331 around the mean—that is, within the range €31,169–€35,831. Similarly, at least 75% of the salaries in this population must fall within $\pm$€3,108 around the mean—that is, within the range €30,392–€36,608.

Table 2.6
Chebyshev's Theorem for Selected Values of k

Selected Values of $k > 1$	1.5	2	2.5	3
$[1 - (1/k^2)]\%$	55.56%	75%	84%	88.89%

The advantage of Chebyshev's theorem is that its applicability extends to any population. However, it is within this guarantee that its major drawback lies. For many populations the percentage of values falling in any specified range is much higher than the *minimum* assured by Chebyshev's theorem. In the real world many large populations provide mounded data that are at least approximately symmetric, with many of the data points clustered around the mean. We often think of this as the bell-shaped distribution. In Chapter 5 we give a much more detailed explanation as the empirical rule and its more exact formula are one of the main focus points of statistics.

Empirical Rule (68%, 95%, or Almost All)

For many large populations (mounded, bell-shaped) the **empirical rule** provides an estimate of the approximate percentage of observations that are contained within one, two, or three standard deviations of the mean:

- Approximately **68%** of the observations are in the interval $\mu \pm 1\sigma$.
- Approximately **95%** of the observations are in the interval $\mu \pm 2\sigma$.
- Almost all of the observations are in the interval $\mu \pm 3\sigma$.

Consider a very large number of students taking a college entrance exam such as the SAT. Suppose the mean score on the mathematics section of the SAT is 550 with a standard deviation of 50.

Then, by the empirical rule, we estimate that roughly 68% of the scores are between 500 and 600 and that approximately 95% fall within the range 450 to 650. There is only a relatively small chance that an observation will differ from the mean by more than $\pm 2\sigma$; any observation that differs from the mean by more than $\pm 3\sigma$ is an outlier.

Example 2.13 Lifetimes of Lightbulbs (Chebyshev's Theorem and Empirical Rule)

A company produces lightbulbs with a mean lifetime of 1,200 hours and a standard deviation of 50 hours.

    a. Describe the distribution of lifetimes if the shape of the population is unknown.
    b. Describe the distribution of lifetimes if the shape of the distribution is known to be bell-shaped.

Solution Using the mean of 1,200 and the standard deviation of 50, we find the following intervals:

$$\mu \pm 1\sigma = 1,200 \pm 50 = (1,150, 1,250)$$
$$\mu \pm 2\sigma = 1,200 \pm 2(50) = (1,100, 1,300)$$
$$\mu \pm 3\sigma = 1,200 \pm 3(50) = (1,050, 1,350)$$

    a. Assuming that the shape of the distribution is unknown, we apply Chebyshev's theorem. But be aware that $k > 1$. Therefore, we cannot make any conclusions about the percentage of bulbs that last between 1,150 hours and 1,250 hours. We can conclude that at least 75% of the lightbulbs will last between 1,100 hours and 1,300 hours and that at least 88.89% of the lightbulbs will last between 1,050 hours and 1,350 hours.
    b. If the shape of the distribution is bell-shaped, then we can conclude that approximately 68% of the lightbulbs will last between 1,150 hours and 1,250 hours; that approximately 95% of the lightbulbs will last between 1,100 hours and 1,300 hours; and that almost all the bulbs will last between 1,050 hours and 1,350 hours. It would be very unusual for a lightbulb to burn out in, say, 600 hours or 1,600 hours. Such values are possible but not very likely. These lifetimes would definitely be outliers.

z-Score

In Section 2.1 we discussed percentiles and quartiles as a measure of location or position of a value relative to the *entire* set of data. Now we consider a measure called a z-score that examines the location or position of a value relative to the *mean* of the distribution. Throughout this book you will learn much more about z-scores because they play a major role in business statistics.

z-Score

A **z-score** is a standardized value that indicates the number of standard deviations a value is from the mean. A z-score greater than zero indicates that the value is greater than the mean; a z-score less than zero indicates that the value is less than the mean; and a z-score of zero indicates that the value is equal to the mean.

    If the data set is the entire population of data and the population mean, μ, and the population standard deviation, σ, are known, then for each value, x_i, the corresponding z-score associated with x_i is defined as follows:

$$z = \frac{x_i - \mu}{\sigma} \tag{2.19}$$

Example 2.14 Lifetimes of Lightbulbs (z-Score)

Consider the company in Example 2.13, which produces lightbulbs with a mean lifetime of 1,200 hours and a standard deviation of 50 hours.

    a. Find the z-score for a lightbulb that lasts only 1,120 hours.
    b. Find the z-score for a lightbulb that lasts 1,300 hours.

Solution Since 1,120 is less than the mean of 1,200 hours, we know that the corresponding z-score will be negative. Using Equation 2.19, the z-score for 1,120 hours is as follows:

$$z = \frac{x_i - \mu}{\sigma} = \frac{1,120 - 1,200}{50} = -1.6$$

Similarly, the z-score for a lightbulb that lasts 1,300 hours is found as follows:

$$z = \frac{x_i - \mu}{\sigma} = \frac{1,300 - 1,200}{50} = 2$$

The standardized z-score is often used with admission tests for colleges and universities.

Example 2.15 College Entrance Exams (z-scores)

Consider a very large number of students taking a college entrance exam such as the SAT. And suppose the mean score on the mathematics section of the SAT is 570 with a standard deviation of 40.

    a. Find the z-score for a student who scored 600.
    b. A student is told that his z-score on this test is −1.5. What was his actual SAT math score?

Solution The corresponding z-score for the SAT math score of 600 is found using Equation 2.19 as follows:

$$z = \frac{x_i - \mu}{\sigma} = \frac{600 - 570}{40} = 0.75$$

If the student knows that his or her z-score is −1.5, then the student also knows that his or her score is less than the mean of 570.

$$z = \frac{x_i - \mu}{\sigma} \Rightarrow -1.5 = \frac{x_i - 570}{40}$$

Solving algebraically, the student realizes that his or her test score is found as:

$$40(-1.5) = x_i - 570$$

or

$$x_i = 510$$

EXERCISES

Basic Exercises

2.12 Compute the variance and standard deviation of the following sample data:

5   9   10   2   7   9   14

2.13 Compute the variance and standard deviation of the following sample data:

5   −3   0   2   −1   7   4

2.14 Calculate the coefficient of variation for the following sample data:

13   15   12   14   11

2.15 The number of cars that pass through a payment point on an A1-highway toll road during a period of 35 days are as follows:

60	70	74	56	84	54	50
47	80	71	50	95	121	90
75	84	70	61	110	64	80
85	85	43	76	60	91	90
60	87	110	85	44	94	69

a. Find the mean number of cars.
b. Find the standard deviation.
c. Find the coefficient of variation.

2.16 Construct a stem-and-leaf display of the number of cars that pass through the payment point mentioned in Exercise 2.15. Then find the interquartile range.

2.17 A random sample of data has a mean of 77 and a variance of 9.

a. Use Chebyshev's theorem to determine the percent of observations between 68 and 86.
b. If the data are mounded, use the empirical rule to find the approximate percent of observations between 68 and 86.

2.18 If the mean of a population is 190 and its standard deviation is 15, approximately what proportion of observations is in the interval between each pair values?

a. 145 and 235
b. 160 and 220

2.19 A set of data is mounded, with a mean of 300 and a variance of 144. Approximately what proportion of the observations is

a. greater than 288?
b. less than 324?
c. greater than 336?

Application Exercises

2.20 The daily EUR to USD exchange rates converting from February 5 to 14, 2019 (business days only) were as follows:

1.1410   1.1363   1.1351   1.1324   1.1276   1.1332   1.1266

Over the same period, the daily USD to JPY exchange rates were as follows:

109.95   109.96   109.80   109.77   110.41   110.48   111.00

a. Compare the means of these two population distributions.
b. Compare the standard deviations of these two population distributions.

2.21 Navigating through an airport can be quite chaotic. You could instead choose to spend your waiting time at one of the *airport lounges*—hospitality areas where you can relax and enjoy food and beverages before you jet off. A random sample of 10 airport lounges are selected and the following entry fees are listed below (in euros):

15   30   25   32   40   18   22   28   25   35

a. Find the mean entry fee.
b. Calculate the standard deviation using Equation 2.13.
c. Calculate the standard deviation using Equation 2.14.
d. Calculate the standard deviation using Equation 2.15.
e. Find the coefficient of varaition.

2.22 The operations manager at a plant that bottles natural spring water wants to be sure that the filling process for 1-gallon bottles (1 gallon is approximately 3.785 liters) is operating properly. A random sample of 75 bottles is selected and the contents are measured. The volume of each bottle is contained in the data file **Water**.

a. Find the range, variance, and standard deviation of the volumes.
b. Find and interpret the interquartile range for the data.
c. Find the value of the coefficient of variation.

2.23 In Chapter 1 we described graphically, with a frequency distribution and histogram, the time (in seconds) for a random sample of $n = 110$ employees to complete a particular task. Describe the data in Table 1.6 numerically. The data are stored in the data file **Completion Times**.

a. Find the mean time.
b. Find the variance and standard deviation.
c. Find the coefficient of variation.

2.24 The assessment rates (in percentages) assigned to a random sample of 40 commercially zoned parcels of land in the year 2012 are stored in the data file **Rates**.

a. What is the standard deviation in the assessment rates?
b. Approximately what proportion of the rates will be within ± 2 standard deviations of the mean?

2.25 Calculate the mean Croatian kuna (kn) amount and the standard deviation for the kuna amounts charged to the Master Card account at Pristavi Kavu, a local cafe in Croatia, for the coffee sold. Data are stored in the data file **Croatian Coffee**.

Some situations require a special type of mean called a *weighted mean*. Applications of weighted means include, but are not limited to, calculating GPA, determining average stock recommendation, and approximating the mean of grouped data.

Weighted Mean

The **weighted mean** of a set of data is

$$\bar{x} = \frac{\sum w_i x_i}{n} \tag{2.20}$$

where w_i = weight of the ith observation and $n = \sum w_i$.

One important situation that requires the use of a weighted mean is the calculation of grade point average (GPA).

Example 2.16 Grade Point Average (Weighted Mean)

Suppose that a student who completed 15 credit hours during his first semester of college received one A, one B, one C, and one D. Suppose that a value of 4 is used for an A, 3 for a B, 2 for a C, 1 for a D, and 0 for an F. Calculate the student's semester GPA.

Solution If each course were given the same number of credit hours, the student's semester GPA would equal the following:

$$\bar{x} = \frac{\sum_{i=1}^{n} x_i}{n} = \frac{x_1 + x_2 + \cdots + x_n}{n} = \frac{4 + 3 + 2 + 1}{4} = 2.5$$

However, each course is not worth the same number of credit hours. The A was earned in a 3-credit-hour English course, and the B was earned in a 3-credit-hour math course, but the C was earned in a 4-credit-hour biology lab course, and the D grade, unfortunately, was earned in a 5-credit-hour Spanish class. Computation of the mean is

$$\bar{x} = \frac{(4 + 4 + 4) + (3 + 3 + 3) + (2 + 2 + 2 + 2) + (1 + 1 + 1 + 1 + 1)}{15} = \frac{34}{15} = 2.267$$

where the numerator is the sum of $(4 + 4 + 4)$ representing the three English credits plus $(3 + 3 + 3)$ for the three math credits plus $(2 + 2 + 2 + 2)$ for the four biology lab credits plus $(1 + 1 + 1 + 1 + 1)$ for the five Spanish credits. Using Equation 2.20 the computation of the GPA is given in Table 2.7.

$$\bar{x} = \frac{\sum_{i=1}^{n} w_i x_i}{n} = \frac{w_1 x_1 + w_2 x_2 + \cdots + w_n x_n}{n} = \frac{12 + 9 + 8 + 5}{15} = \frac{34}{15} = 2.267$$

Table 2.7 Semester Academic Record

COURSE	GRADE	CREDIT HOURS, w_i	VALUE, x_i	CREDIT HOURS × VALUE, $w_i x_i$
English	A	3	4	12
Math	B	3	3	9
Biology lab	C	4	2	8
Spanish	D	5	1	5
Total		15		34

Example 2.17 Stock Recommendation (Weighted Mean)

Mekhi Kodjoe's African Investment Research (AIR) is a leading investment research firm in South Africa. AIR will make one of the following recommendations with corresponding weights for a given stock: Strong Buy (1), Moderate Buy (2), Hold (3), Moderate Sell (4), or Strong Sell (5). Suppose that on a particular day, 10 analysts recommend Strong Buy, 3 analysts recommend Moderate Buy, and 6 analysts recommend Hold for a particular stock. Based on AIR's weights, find the mean recommendation.

Solution Table 2.8 shows the weights for each recommendation and the computation leading to a recommendation based on the following weighted mean recommendation conversion values: if the weighted mean is 1, Strong Buy; 1.1 through 2.0, Moderate Buy; 2.1 through 3.0, Hold; 3.1 through 4.0, Moderate Sell; 4.1 through 5, Strong Sell.

Table 2.8 Computation of African Investment Research (AIR) Average Brokerage Recommendation

ACTION	NUMBER OF ANALYSTS, w_i	VALUE, x_i	$w_i x_i$
Strong Buy	10	1	10
Moderate Buy	3	2	6
Hold	6	3	18
Moderate Sell	0	4	0
Strong Sell	0	5	0

$$\bar{x} = \frac{\sum_{i=1}^{n} w_i x_i}{n} = \frac{10 + 6 + 18 + 0 + 0}{19} = 1.79$$

The weighted mean of 1.79 yielded a Moderate Buy recommendation.

A survey may ask respondents to select an age category such as 20–29 rather than giving their specific age. Or respondents may be asked to select a cost category such as €4.00 to under €6.00 for a purchase at a local coffee shop in France. In these situations *exact* values of the mean and variance are not possible. However, we are able to approximate the mean and the variance.

Approximate Mean and Variance for Grouped Data

Suppose that data are grouped into K classes, with frequencies $f_1, f_2, \ldots, f_K$. If the midpoints of these classes are $m_1, m_2, \ldots, m_K$, then the sample mean and sample variance of grouped data are approximated in the following manner:
   The mean is

$$\bar{x} = \frac{\sum_{i=1}^{K} f_i m_i}{n} \tag{2.21}$$

where $n = \sum_{i=1}^{K} f_i$, and the variance is

$$s^2 = \frac{\sum_{i=1}^{K} f_i (m_i - \bar{x})^2}{n - 1} \tag{2.22}$$

Example 2.18 Cost of Coffee Shop Purchase (Mean and Variance for Grouped Values)

Coffee shop customers in France were randomly surveyed and asked to select a category that described the cost of their recent purchase. The results were as follows:

Cost (in EUR)	$0 < 2$	$2 < 4$	$4 < 6$	$6 < 8$	$8 < 10$
Number of Customers	2	3	6	5	4

Find the sample mean and standard deviation of these costs.

Solution The frequencies are the number of customers for each cost category. The computations for the mean and the standard deviation are set out in Table 2.9.

Table 2.9 Cost of Purchase (Grouped Data Computation)

Costs (€)	Frequency, f_i	Midpoint, m_i	$(f_i m_i)$	$(m_i - \bar{x})$	$(m_i - \bar{x})^2$	$f_i(m_i - \bar{x})^2$
$0 < 2$	2	1	2	−4.6	21.16	42.32
$2 < 4$	3	3	9	−2.6	6.76	20.28
$4 < 6$	6	5	30	−0.6	0.36	2.16
$6 < 8$	5	7	35	1.4	1.96	9.80
$8 < 10$	4	9	36	3.4	11.56	46.24
	20		112			120.80

$$n = \sum_{i=1}^{K} f_i = 20 \quad \text{and} \quad \sum_{i=1}^{K} f_i m_i = 112$$

The sample mean is estimated by

$$\bar{x} = \frac{\sum_{i=1}^{K} f_i m_i}{n} = \frac{112}{20} = 5.6$$

Since these are sample data, the variance is estimated by

$$s^2 = \frac{\sum_{i=1}^{K} f_i (m_i - \bar{x})^2}{n - 1} = \frac{120.8}{19} = 6.3579$$

Hence, the sample standard deviation is estimated as

$$s = \sqrt{s^2} = \sqrt{6.3579} = 2.52$$

Therefore, the mean coffee shop purchase price is estimated as €5.60, and the sample standard deviation is estimated to be €2.52.

EXERCISES

 Visit www.MyStatLab.com or www.pearson globaleditions.com to access the data files.

Basic Exercises

2.26 Consider the following sample of five values and corresponding weights:

x_i	w_i
4.7	8
3.8	7
5.7	4
2.6	3
5.5	2

a. Calculate the arithmetic mean of the x_i values without weights.
b. Calculate the weighted mean of the x_i values.

2.27 Consider the following frequency distribution for a sample of 40 observations:

Class	Frequency
$0 < 5$	5
$5 < 10$	6
$10 < 15$	12
$15 < 20$	10
$20 < 25$	7

a. Calculate the sample mean.
b. Calculate the sample variance and sample standard deviation.

Application Exercises

2.28 A drive-through fast-food chain obtained the following pick-up times (number of minutes between the time an order is placed and the time the order is picked up at the drive-through window). A random sample of 30 orders along with the corresponding duration is given in the following table:

Number of Minutes, x_i	Number of Orders, f_i
$2 < 4$	11
$4 < 6$	8
$6 < 8$	6
$8 < 10$	5

a. What is the approximate mean pick-up time?
b. What is the approximate variance and standard deviation?

2.29 An *online-grocery* market is growing fast. A sample of 40 customers is selected and the number of online orders over the last month are listed in the following table.

Number of Orders	0	1	2	3
Number of Customers	12	13	9	6

Calculate the standard deviation.

2.30 Frequent-flyer programs are customer loyalty programs used by many passenger airlines. The following table shows the number of award trips offered to 60 passengers during the last year.

Number of Award Trips	0	1	2	3	4	5
Number of Passengers	21	12	8	9	6	4

a. Find the mean number of the award trips offered to the passengers over the last year.
b. Find the sample variance and standard deviations.

2.31 A survey was conducted to find the amount of money university students spend during Valentine's day. A random sample of 28 students was selected from a local university in Brussels and their responses are recorded in the following table:

Money Spent (€)	20	13	10	5	0
Number of students	2	8	8	6	4

a. Estimate the sample mean money (€) spent on Valentine's day.
b. Estimate the sample standard deviation.

2.32 For predicting credit default, a sample of 20 financial data analysts was asked to provide forecasts of credit scores for next year. The results are summarized in the following table:

Forecast (£ 000)	Number of Clients
$10.95 < 11.45$	5
$11.45 < 12.95$	18
$12.95 < 13.45$	16
$13.45 < 14.95$	23
$14.95 < 15.45$	11

a. Estimate the sample mean forecast.
b. Estimate the sample standard deviation.

2.33 The number of problems solved on the entrance exam is given in the table:

Number of Exams	0	1	2	3	4
Number of Problems	100	110	130	50	10

Find the mean and standard deviation of the number of problems per exam.

2.34 In Chapter 1, we described graphically using a frequency distribution table and a histogram the time (in seconds) for a random sample of $n = 110$ employees to complete a particular task. Describe the data numerically based on the frequency distribution given in Table 1.7. The data is stored in the data file **Completion Times**.

a. Compute the mean using Equation 2.21.
b. Compute the variance using Equation 2.22.
c. Compare your answers to the mean and variance calculated in Exercise 2.23.

We introduced scatter plots in Chapter 1 as a graphical way to describe a relationship between two variables. In this section we introduce *covariance* and *correlation*, numerical ways to describe a linear relationship; we give more attention to these concepts in Chapters 11 to 13. Covariance is a measure of the *direction* of a linear relationship between two variables.

Covariance

Covariance (*Cov*) is a measure of the linear relationship between two variables. A positive value indicates a direct or increasing linear relationship, and a negative value indicates a decreasing linear relationship.

A *population covariance* is

$$Cov(x, y) = \sigma_{xy} = \frac{\sum_{i=1}^{N} (x_i - \mu_x)(y_i - \mu_y)}{N} \tag{2.23}$$

where x_i and y_i are the observed values, μ_x and μ_y are the population means, and N is the population size.

A *sample covariance* is

$$Cov(x, y) = s_{xy} = \frac{\sum_{i=1}^{n} (x_i - \bar{x})(y_i - \bar{y})}{n - 1} \tag{2.24}$$

where x_i and y_i are the observed values, $\bar{x}$ and $\bar{y}$ are the sample means, and n is the sample size.

The value of the covariance varies if a variable such as height is measured in feet or inches or weight is measured in pounds, ounces, or kilograms. Also, covariance does not provide a measure of the strength of the relationship between two variables. The most common measure to overcome these shortcomings is called Pearson's product-moment correlation coefficient, Pearson's r, or simply the correlation coefficient. Although this measure is named after Karl Pearson, it was Sir Francis Galton who first introduced the concept in the late 1800s (Salsburg 2002). This correlation coefficient will give us a standardized measure of the linear relationship between two variables. It is generally a more useful measure because it provides both the *direction* and the *strength* of a relationship. The covariance and corresponding correlation coefficient have the same sign (both are positive or both are negative). There are other measures of correlation, such as Spearman's rank correlation coefficient, which we discuss in Chapter 14.

Correlation Coefficient

The **correlation coefficient** is computed by dividing the covariance by the product of the standard deviations of the two variables.

A *population correlation coefficient*, ρ, is

$$\rho = \frac{Cov(x, y)}{\sigma_x \sigma_y} \tag{2.25}$$

A *sample correlation coefficient*, r, is

$$r = \frac{Cov(x, y)}{s_x s_y} \tag{2.26}$$

A useful rule to remember is that a relationship exists if

$$|r| \geq \frac{2}{\sqrt{n}} \tag{2.27}$$

It can be shown that the correlation coefficient ranges from −1 to +1. The closer r is to +1, the closer the data points are to an increasing straight line, indicating a *positive* linear relationship. The closer r is to −1, the closer the data points are to a decreasing straight line, indicating a *negative* linear relationship. When $r = 0$, there is no *linear* relationship between x and y—but not necessarily a lack of relationship. In Chapter 1 we presented scatter plots as a graphical measure to determine relationship. Figure 2.4 presents some examples of scatter plots and their corresponding correlation coefficients. Figure 2.5 is a plot of quarterly sales for a major retail company.

Note that sales vary by quarter of the year, reflecting consumers' purchasing patterns. The correlation coefficient between the time variable and quarterly sales is zero. However, we can see a very definite seasonal relationship, but the relationship is not linear.

Figure 2.4 Scatter Plots and Correlation

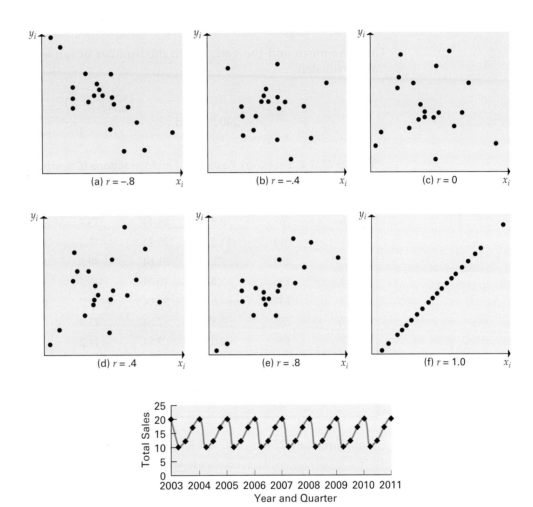

Figure 2.5 Retail Sales by Quarter

Example 2.19 Facebook Posts and Interactions (Covariance and Correlation Coefficient)

RELEVANT Magazine (a culture magazine) keeps in touch and informs their readers by posting updates through various social networks. These updates take up a large part of both the marketing and editorial teams' time. Because these updates take so much time, marketing is interested in knowing whether reducing posts (updates) on Facebook (a specific site) will also lessen their fan interaction; if not, both departments may pursue using their time in more productive ways. The weekly number of posts (updates) and fan interactions for Facebook during a 9-week period are recorded in Table 2.10. Compute the covariance and correlation between Facebook posts (site updates) and fan interactions. The data are stored in the data file **RELEVANT Magazine**.

Table 2.10 Facebook Posts (site updates) and Fan Interactions

Facebook posts (updates), x	16	31	27	23	15	17	17	18	14
Fan interactions, y	165	314	280	195	137	286	199	128	462

Solution The computation of covariance and correlation between Facebook posts (site updates) and fan interactions are illustrated in Table 2.11. The mean and the variance in the number of Facebook posts are found to be approximately

$$\bar{x} = 19.8 \quad \text{and} \quad s_x^2 = \frac{\sum_{i=1}^{n}(x_i - \bar{x})^2}{n-1} = 34.694$$

and the mean and the variance in the number of fan interactions are found to be approximately

$$\bar{y} = 240.7 \quad \text{and} \quad s_y^2 = \frac{\sum_{i=1}^{n}(y_i - \bar{y})^2}{n-1} = 11{,}369.5$$

Table 2.11 Facebook Posts and Fan Interactions (Covariance and Correlation)

x	y	$(x_i - \bar{x})$	$(x_i - \bar{x})^2$	$(y_i - \bar{y})$	$(y_i - \bar{y})^2$	$(x_i - \bar{x})(y_i - \bar{y})$
16	165	−3.8	14.44	−75.7	5,730.49	287.66
31	314	11.2	125.44	73.3	5,372.89	820.96
27	280	7.2	51.84	39.3	1,544.49	282.96
23	195	3.2	10.24	−45.7	2,088.49	−146.24
15	137	−4.8	23.04	−103.7	10,753.69	497.76
17	286	−2.8	7.84	45.3	2,052.09	−126.84
17	199	−2.8	7.84	−41.7	1,738.89	116.76
18	128	−1.8	3.24	−112.7	12,701.29	202.86
14	462	−5.8	33.64	221.3	48,973.69	−1,283.54
$\bar{x} = 19.8$	$\bar{y} = 240.7$					$\Sigma = 652.34$

From Equation 2.24,

$$Cov(x, y) = s_{xy} = \frac{\sum_{i=1}^{n}(x_i - \bar{x})(y_i - \bar{y})}{n-1} = \frac{652.34}{8} = 81.542$$

From Equation 2.26,

$$r = \frac{Cov(x, y)}{s_x s_y} = \frac{81.542}{\sqrt{34.694}\sqrt{11{,}369.5}} = 0.1298$$

From Equation 2.27

$$|0.1298| < \frac{2}{\sqrt{9}} = 0.67$$

We conclude that there is not sufficient data to think that there is a strong linear relationship between Facebook posts and fan interaction.

Minitab, Excel, SPSS, SAS, and many other statistical packages can be used to compute descriptive measures such as the sample covariance and the sample correlation coefficient. Consider Example 2.19. Figure 2.6 shows the Minitab output for computing covariance and correlation, and Figure 2.7 shows the Excel output for the same data.

Special care must be taken if we use Excel to compute covariance. In Example 2.19 the covariance between Facebook posts and fan interactions was found to be 81.542 (the same value as in the Minitab output in Figure 2.6). But the covariance of 72.4815 given in the Excel output is the population covariance, not the sample covariance. That is, Excel automatically calculates the population covariance as well as the population variance for the X and Y variables. To obtain the sample covariance, we must multiply the population covariance by a factor of $n/(n-1)$.

Figure 2.6
Covariance and Correlation: Facebook Posts, Fan Interactions (Minitab)

Covariances: Facebook Posts, Fan Interactions

	Facebook Posts	Fan Interactions
Facebook Posts	34.694	
Fan Interactions	81.542	11,369.500

Correlations: Facebook Posts, Fan Interactions

Pearson Correlation of Facebook Posts and Fan Interactions = 0.130

Figure 2.7
Covariance and Correlation: Facebook Posts, Fan Interactions (Excel)

Covariance	Facebook Posts	Fan Interactions
Facebook Posts	30.8395	
Fan Interactions	72.4815	10106.2222

Correlation	Facebook Posts	Fan Interactions
Facebook Posts	1	
Fan Interactions	0.1298	1

From the Excel output, the sample covariance between Facebook posts and fan interactions is found as follows:

$$Cov(x, y) = 72.4815\left(\frac{9}{8}\right) = 81.542$$

More formal procedures to determine if two variables are linearly related are discussed in Chapters 11 and 12. Also, we consider another measure of correlation in Chapter 14.

Example 2.20 Analysis of Stock Portfolios (Correlation Coefficient Analysis)

Christina Bishop, financial analyst for Integrated Securities, is considering a number of different stocks for a new mutual fund she is developing. One of her questions concerns the correlation coefficients between prices of different stocks. To determine the patterns of stock prices, she prepared a series of scatter plots and computed the sample correlation coefficient for each plot. What information does Figure 2.8 provide?

Figure 2.8 Relationships Between Various Stock Prices

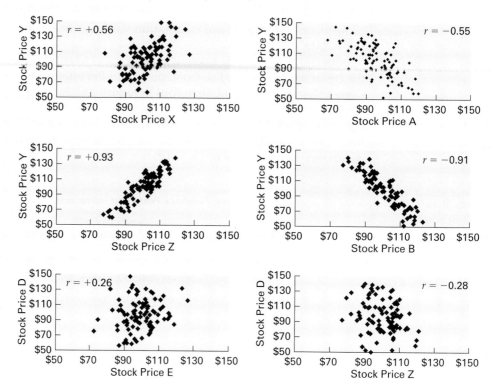

Solution Christina sees that it is possible to control the variation in the average mutual fund price by combining various stocks into a portfolio. The portfolio variation is increased if stocks with positive correlation coefficients are included because the prices tend to increase together. In contrast, the portfolio variation is decreased if stocks with negative correlation coefficients are included. When the price of one stock increases, the price of the other decreases, and the combined price is more stable. Experienced observers of stock prices might question the possibility of very large negative correlation coefficients. Our objective here is to illustrate graphically the correlation coefficients for certain patterns of observed data and not to accurately describe a particular market. After examining these correlation coefficients, Christina is ready to begin constructing her portfolio. Correlation coefficients between stock prices affect the variation of the entire portfolio.

It is important to understand that correlation does not imply causation. It is possible for two variables to be highly correlated, but that does not mean that one variable causes the other variable. We need to be careful about jumping to conclusions based on television news reports, newspaper articles, online Web sites, or even medical studies that claim that A causes B.

EXERCISES

 Visit www.MyStatLab.com or www.pearson globaleditions.com to access the data files.

Basic Exercises

2.35 Following is a random sample of 11 (x, y) pairs of data points:

$(15, 45) \ (6, 18) \ (11, 33) \ (12, 36) \ (16, 48) \ (14, 42)$
$(5, 15) \ (17, 51) \ (4, 12) \ (19, 57) \ (7, 21)$

a. Compute the covariance.
b. Compute the correlation coefficient.

2.36 Following is a random sample of seven (x, y) pairs of data points:

$(11, 102) \ (15, 51) \ (6, 25) \ (14, 30) \ (10, 21) \ (8, 56)$
$(13, 30)$

a. Compute the covariance.
b. Compute the correlation coefficient.

2.37 According to the Office for National Statistics (ONS), the monthly growth rate in the quantity of goods bought in Great Britain increased by 1.0% in January 2019, after a 0.7% decline in December 2018.

Source: Office for National Statistics, "Retail sales, Great Britain: January 2019," February 15, 2019.

Following is a random sample of price per piece (£), X, and quantity sold, Y (in thousands):

Price (x)	Thousands of Pieces Sold (y)
£6	90
8	60
10	70
9	30
20	100

a. Compute the covariance.
b. Compute the correlation coefficient.

Application Exercises

2.38 According to Statista, in 2016, global retail sales of chocolate amounted to approximately $98.2 billion, making choclates one of the most popular snacks in the world. A random sample of 15 consumers were given varying quantities of chocolates for four weeks. The following (x, y) data shows the number of chocolate cups, X, and the number of days required for recovering, Y, for each consumer:

$(3, 23)$ $(1, 11)$ $(10, 24)$ $(8, 33)$ $(4, 42)$
$(8, 35)$ $(8, 27)$ $(5, 42)$ $(9, 38)$ $(7, 29)$
$(1, 14)$ $(2, 22)$ $(11, 26)$ $(2, 31)$ $(3, 36)$

a. Compute the covariance.
b. Compute the correlation coefficient.

2.39 Travel Shaw is an agency based in Bulgaria that employs a group of travel reporters who publish stories based on exciting destinations from around the world. Travel Shaw also offers three destination tours: Asia, Europe, and the United States. One of the agents at Travel Shaw wants to determine the relationship between the price of a tour and the number of sales arrangements. Over a 15-day period, the agent records the number of sales made for each of the three tours. The following data show the tour's price ($000), X, and the number tours sold, Y, during the period:

$(3, 8), (5, 6), (9, 3), (4, 10), (6, 6), (11, 4), (3, 5), (4, 2),$
$(10, 1), (2, 9), (6, 7), (10, 1), (2, 4), (6, 7), (9, 2)$

a. Describe the data numerically with their covariance and correlation.
b. Discuss the relationship between the price and number of travel tours sold.

2.40 The manager of a used-car dealership is very interested in the resale price of used cars. The manager feels that the age of the car is important in determining the resale value. He collects data on the value of the car (in thousands of dollars) as the dependent variable and the age of the car (in years) as the independent variable.

Age	Value (Thousands of €)
3	50
5	43
7	35
8	40
11	15

a. Compute the covariance.
b. Compute the correlation coefficient.

2.41 A professor at the University of Oulu, Finland, keeps records of the number of hours each student studies and the grades they receive. A random sample of hours studied and test grades for $n = 11$ contracts is stored in the data file **Oulu Grades.**

a. Compute the covariance.
b. Compute the correlation coefficient.

2.42 The farmer based in Gujarat, India, wants to determine the relationship between the number of rainy days in August and the amount of rice (kg) sold per month. Data was collected for a 5-year period are as follows:

$(1, 40)$ $(0, 32)$ $(3, 36)$ $(8, 44)$ $(5, 41)$

The first number indicates the number of rainy days in August and the second is the amount of rice sold. Plot the data and compute the correlation coefficient.

2.43 The president of World Aircraft Association wants to determine if there is a relationship between the number of vacation days provided to cabin crew members of eight airline companies and their monthly salaries (in thousands of euros). He obtained the following random sample on the number of vacation days and monthly salaries:

$(5, 7) (6, 4) (3, 5.5) (6, 5) (8, 7.5) (5, 8) (6, 6.8) (2, 8.4)$

The first number for each observation is vacation days per month, and the second number is monthly salaries. Plot the data and compute the covariance and the correlation coefficient.

KEY WORDS

- arithmetic mean, 64
- box-and-whisker plot, 73
- coefficient of variation, CV, 79
- correlation coefficient, 88
- covariance (Cov), 88
- empirical rule, 80
- first quartile, 68
- five-number summary, 69
- geometric mean, 67
- geometric mean rate of return, 67
- interquartile range (IQR), 73
- median, 64
- mode, 64
- percentiles, 68
- Pth percentile, 68
- quartiles, 68
- range, 73
- second quartile, 68
- skewness, 95
- standard deviation, 76
- third quartile, 69
- variance, 75
- weighted mean, 84
- z-score, 81

DATA FILES

- Completion Times, 83, 87, 94
- Croatian Coffee, 83
- Gilotti's Pizzeria, 74, 94
- Grade Point Averages, 66, 72
- HealthTech, 94
- HEI Cost Data Variable Subset, 71
- Mendez Mortgage, 95
- Oulu Grades, 93
- Rates, 83
- RELEVANT Magazine, 89
- Shopping Times, 70, 73, 95
- Student GPA, 94
- Study Data, 72
- Sun, 72
- Water, 83

CHAPTER EXERCISES AND APPLICATIONS

 Visit www.MyStatLab.com or www.pearson globaleditions.com to access the data files.

2.44 A local bus company wants to estimate if the major travel line from a local city to the capitol is a profitable route. The number of passengers and the number of corresponding trips made during a two-month period are recorded in the following table:

Passengers	0 < 10	10 < 20	20 < 30	30 < 40	40 < 50	50 < 60
Trips	23	21	2	6	5	4

a. Estimate the mean number of passengers.
b. Estimate the sample variance and standard deviation.

2.45 AI Heatlthtech, a growing startup in Sweden, keeps records of charges for its various health-care services. A random sample of $n = 40$ charges is stored in the data file **HealthTech**. Describe the data numerically.

a. Compute the mean charge.
b. Compute the standard deviation.
c. Compute the five-number summary.

2.46 In Example 2.9 we calculated the variance and standard deviation for Location 1 of Gilotti's Pizzeria restaurants. Use the data in the data file **Gilotti's Pizzeria** to find the variance and the standard deviation for Location 2, Location 3, and Location 4.

2.47 The following data represents the age of the students enrolled at a music school and the scores obtained by them in an entrance exam. The scores ranged from 0 to 70. Describe the data numerically.

(5, 40) (9, 65) (12, 48) (9, 66) (8, 46) (6, 56)
(7, 64) (10, 57) (11, 42) (12, 69) (9, 53) (7, 55)
(8, 51) (7, 52) (10, 56) (9, 66) (5, 31) (9, 43)

2.48 Only 67 students in the data file **Student GPA** have SAT verbal scores.

a. Construct the scatter plot of GPAs and SAT scores for these 67 students.
b. Calculate the correlation between GPAs and SAT scores for these 67 students.

2.49 Consider the following four populations:

- 2, 3, 4, 5, 5, 6, 7, 8
- 1, 1, 1, 4, 5, 7, 7, 14
- 2, 4, 4, 5, 5, 8, 8, 4
- −9, −3, 0, 3, 9, 12, 13, 15

All these populations have the same mean. *Without doing the calculations*, arrange the populations according to the magnitudes of their variances, from smallest to largest. Then calculate each of the variances manually.

2.50 Babbel is a language learning app with around one million users worldwide. The central principle behind Babbel's language learning method is that people should spend a mean of 15 minutes per day studying a new language and a standard deviation of 3 minutes.

a. In what interval can you guarantee that 60% of these people will be in?
b. In what interval can you guarantee that 84% of these people will be in?

2.51 The Audit Bureau of Circulations of South Africa a nonprofit company that provides accurate and comparable circulation figures, has released newspaper-circulation statistics for the period October—December 2017. In one year, earnings growth averaged 8.2%; the standard deviation was 2.5%.

a. It can be guaranteed that 84% of these earnings growth will be in what interval?
b. Using the empirical rule, it can be estimated that approximately 68% of these earnings growth will be in what interval?

2.52 In April 2018, a study was conducted to understand the role of Twitter. The study showed that Twitter helps business by illustrating the practical implications of a decision, connecting businesses to prominent technologies and trends—eWom, big data, and smart cities—and identifying possible future directions. The practical implications of the study have a mean of 686 results and a standard deviation 66.

a. It can be guaranteed that 75% of businesses being connected to prominent technologies and trends will be in what interval?
b. Using the empirical rule, it can be estimated that approximately 95% of businesses being connected to prominent technologies and trends will be in what interval?

2.53 The supervisor of a very large plant obtained the time (in seconds) for a random sample of $n = 110$ employees to complete a particular task. The data is stored in the data file **Completion Times**.

a. Find and interpret the IQR.
b. Find the five-number summary.

2.54 How much time (in minutes) do people spend on a typical visit to a local mall? A random sample of $n = 104$ shoppers was timed and the results (in minutes) are stored in the data file **Shopping Times**. You were asked to describe graphically the shape of the distribution of shopping times in Exercise 1.72 (Chapter 1). Now describe the shape of the distribution numerically.

a. Find the mean shopping time.
b. Find the variance and standard deviation in shopping times.
c. Find the 95th percentile.
d. Find the five-number summary.
e. Find the coefficient of variation.
f. Ninety percent of the shoppers completed their shopping within approximately how many minutes?

2.55 To explore the relationship between the grades students receive on their first quiz (X) and their first exam (Y). The first quiz and exam scores for a sample of students reveal the following data:

Quiz Scores (x)	4	3.4	3	5	1.1
Exam Scores (y)	78	66	82	80	30

a. Compute the covariance.
b. Compute the correlation coefficient.

2.56 Management of a local retail outlet in Australia wants to predict weekly online shopping sales. It administers an aptitude test to all sales people, where test scores range from 0 to 10 with greater scores indicating a higher aptitude. Test scores and weekly sales (in AU$000) are as follows:

Test Score (x)	10	9	8	8	7	9	6	5	9	7
Weekly Sales (y)	23	61	17	30	21	20	51	44	31	17

a. Compute the covariance.
b. Compute the correlation between test score and weekly sales.

CASE STUDY: MORTGAGE PORTFOLIO

Within the past months, the management team of Mendez Mortgage Company expressed concern about the company's rapidly increasing deterioration of its portfolio which was causing the company to lose significant amounts of money. At the end of a particular month the mortgage portfolio consisted of $45,060,059. Of this amount, $38,706,788 was from active accounts (accounts that are 30–119 days delinquent). The active delinquency in that month closed at 6.21% (the goal was 5.30%). The portfolio represents more than 6,000 accounts, mostly families who purchased a week of Timeshare in the company's resort in Myrtle Beach, SC.

You have been asked to assist Lizbeth Mendez, CEO, with a study of this problem. A random sample of $n = 350$ accounts of the company's total portfolio was selected and data concerning numerous variables on these accounts (like the purchaser's original and latest credit scores, state of residence, amount of down payment) were obtained. The data are stored in the data file **Mendez Mortgage**. Prepare a well-written report that describes both graphically and numerically a selected number of variables from this portfolio file. Be sure to explain how this data might benefit the management team in their investigation of the portfolio's deterioration.

Appendix

SKEWNESS

In nearly all situations, we would compute skewness with a statistical software package or Excel. If skewness is zero or close to zero, then the distribution is symmetric or approximately symmetric. A negative skewness value tells us that the distribution is skewed to the left. Similarly, a positive skewness value tells us that the distribution is skewed to the right.

Skewness
Skewness is calculated as follows:

$$\text{skewness} = \frac{1}{n} \frac{\sum_{i=1}^{n} (x_i - \bar{x})^3}{s^3}$$

(2.28)

The important part of this expression is the numerator; the denominator serves the purpose of standardization, making units of measurement irrelevant. Positive skewness results if a distribution is skewed to the right, since average cubed discrepancies about the mean are positive. Skewness is negative for distributions skewed to the left and 0 for distributions such as the bell-shaped distribution that is mounded and symmetric about its mean.

In Example 2.3 we found that the mean grade point average for a random sample of 156 students was 3.14 and the median grade point average was 3.31, thus indicating negative skewness. From the Excel output in Figure 2.1, the measure of skewness is −1.17, again indicating negative skewness. The same skewness value is obtained using Equation 2.28.

REFERENCES

1. Grummer-Strawn, L., C. Reinold, and N. Krebs. 2010. "Use of World Health Organization and CDC Growth Charts for Children Aged 0–59 Months in the United States." Recommendations and Reports, September 10, 2010/59(rr09): 1–15. http://www.cdc.gov/mmwr/preview/mmwrhtml/rr5909a1.htm (accessed March 10, 2011).

2. Guenther, P. M., J. Reedy, S. M. Krebs-Smith, B. B. Reeve, and P. P. Basiotis. 2007. *Development and Evaluation of the Healthy Eating Index–2005: Technical Report.* Center for Nutrition Policy and Promotion, U.S. Department of Agriculture. http://www.cnpp.usda.gov/HealthyEatingIndex.htm (accessed March 9, 2011).

3. Langford, E. 2006. Quartiles in Elementary Statistics. *Journal of Statistics Education* (online), 14(3). www.amstat.org/publications/jse/v14n3/langford.html (accessed March 11, 2011).

4. Strasburg, David. 2002. *The Lady Tasting Tea: How Statistics Revolutionized Science in the Twentieth Century.* New York: Henry Holt and Company.

5. von Hippel, P. T. 2005. Mean, Median, and Skew: Correcting a Textbook Rule. *Journal of Statistics Education* (online), 13(2). www.amstat.org/publications/jse/v13n2/vonhippel.html (accessed March 11, 2011).

CHAPTER

3

Probability

Introduction

In his classic Financial Times Best Business Book of the Year, *Fooled by Randomness*, Nassim Nicholas Taleb—a successful trader in London and New York and professor of finance—presents a clear analysis of why all persons in business and economics should understand probability. From selected passages: "This book is about luck disguised and perceived as nonluck (that is, skills) and, more generally, randomness disguised and perceived as non-randomness (that is, determinism). . . . more generally, we underestimate the share of randomness in about everything. . . . Probability theory is a young arrival in mathematics; probability applied to practice is almost nonexistent as a discipline. . . . we seem to have evidence that what is called 'courage' comes from an underestimation of the share of randomness in things rather than the more noble ability to stick one's neck out for a given belief" (Taleb 2005).

In this and the following two chapters, we develop an understanding of probability and thus help you avoid the pitfalls discussed by Taleb. It will be important for you to understand first that the world in which your future occurs is not deterministic. Second, if you can construct and use probability models by involving the understandings developed in the following chapters, you will have a greater chance of success. But, finally, it is also important to know that there are future outcomes where a probability model cannot be developed—the popular term "Black Swans." One could not have known the probability that underdogs Greece would pull off one of the biggest shocks in UEFA history and win the UEFA Euro 2004 final, that the Voyager 2 probe launched in 1977 would be NASA's longest running mission, that an earthquake and a tsunami would cause the Fukushima Daiichi nuclear disaster in 2011, or that a series of financial decisions made in September 2008 will lead to the greatest world financial collapse since the 1930s. And, of course, these events have seriously influenced business and economic outcomes. But understanding probability can also help you realize that in fact there are Black Swans. If you understand probability, your future business decisions are more likely to be successful. We will show how probability models are used to study the variation in observed data so that inferences about the underlying process can be developed. Our objective is to understand probabilities, how they can be determined and how they can be used.

3.1 RANDOM EXPERIMENT, OUTCOMES, AND EVENTS

For a manager the probability of a future event presents a level of knowledge. The manager could know with certainty that the event will occur—for example, a legal contract exists. Or the manager may have no idea if the event will occur—for example, the event could occur or not occur as part of a new business opportunity. In most business situations we cannot be certain about the occurrence of a future event, but if the probability of the event is known, then we have a better chance of making the best possible decision, compared to having no idea about the likely occurrence of the event. Business decisions and policies are often based on an implicit or assumed set of probabilities.

To help you develop a clear and rigorous understanding of probability, we will first develop definitions and concepts that provide a structure for defining probabilities. These definitions and concepts—such as sample space, outcomes, and events—are the basic building blocks for defining and computing probabilities. Probability begins with the concept of a *random experiment* that can have two or more outcomes, but we do not know which will occur next.

Random Experiment

A **random experiment** is a process leading to two or more possible outcomes, without knowing exactly which outcome will occur.

Examples of random experiments include the following:

1. A coin is tossed and the outcome is either a head or a tail.
2. A company has the possibility of receiving 0–5 contract awards.
3. The number of persons admitted to a hospital emergency room during any hour cannot be known in advance.
4. A customer enters a store and either purchases a shirt or does not.
5. The daily change in an index of stock market prices is observed.
6. A bag of cereal is selected from a packaging line and weighed to determine if the weight is above or below the stated package weight.
7. A baseball batter has a number of different outcomes—such as a hit, walk, strikeout, fly ball out, and more—each time he or she is at bat.

In each of the random experiments listed, we can specify the possible outcomes, defined as *basic outcomes*. We do not know in advance which outcome will occur.

Sample Space
The possible outcomes from a random experiment are called the **basic outcomes**, and the set of all basic outcomes is called the **sample space**. We use the symbol S to denote the sample space.

We must define the basic outcomes in such a way that no two outcomes can occur simultaneously. In addition, the random experiment must necessarily lead to the occurrence of one of the basic outcomes.

Example 3.1 Professional Baseball Batter (Sample Space)

What is the sample space for a professional baseball batter? A high-quality professional baseball player, when at bat, could have the listed outcomes occur that are shown in the sample space displayed in Table 3.1. The sample space consists of six basic outcomes. No two outcomes can occur together, and one of the seven must occur. The probabilities were obtained by examining baseball batters' data.

Table 3.1 Outcomes for a Baseball Batter

	SAMPLE SPACE, S	PROBABILITY
O_1	Safe hit	0.30
O_2	Walk or hit by pitcher	0.10
O_3	Strikeout	0.10
O_4	Groundball out	0.30
O_5	Fly ball out	0.18
O_6	Reach base on an error	0.02

Example 3.2 Investment Outcomes (Sample Space)

An investor follows the Dow Jones Industrial index. What are the possible basic outcomes at the close of the trading day?

Solution The sample space for this experiment is as follows:

$$S = [\{1. \text{ The index is higher than at yesterday's close}\},$$
$$\{2. \text{ The index is not higher than at yesterday's close}\}]$$

One of these two outcomes must occur. They cannot occur simultaneously. Thus, these two outcomes constitute a sample space.

In many cases we are interested in some subset of the basic outcomes and not the individual outcomes. For example, we might be interested in whether the batter reached the base safely—that is, safe hit, walk, or reach base on an error. This subset of outcomes is defined as an event.

Event

An **event**, E, is any subset of basic outcomes from the sample space. An event occurs if the random experiment results in one of its constituent basic outcomes. The null event represents the absence of a basic outcome and is denoted by $\varnothing$.

In some applications we are interested in the simultaneous occurrence of two or more events. In the batter example we might be interested in two events: "the batter reaches base safely" (Event A [O_1, O_2, O_6]) and "the batter hits the ball" (Event B [O_1, O_4, O_5, O_6]). One possibility is that specific outcomes in both events occur simultaneously. This will happen for outcomes that are contained in both events—that is, safe hit, O_1, or reach base on an error, O_6. This later set of outcomes is the intersection $A \cap B$[O_1, O_6]. Thus, in the batter example the outcomes, safe hit, O_1, or reach base on an error, O_6, belong to both of these two events: "the batter reaches base safely" (Event A [O_1, O_2, O_6]) and "the batter hits the ball" (Event B [O_1, O_4, O_5, O_6]). Note that the probability of this intersection is 0.32 ($0.30 + 0.02$).

Intersection of Events

Let A and B be two events in the sample space S. Their **intersection**, denoted by $A \cap B$, is the set of all basic outcomes in S that belong to both A and B. Hence, the intersection $A \cap B$ occurs if and only if both A and B occur. We use the term **joint probability** of A and B to denote the probability of the intersection of A and B.

More generally, given K events $E_1, E_2, \ldots, E_K$, their intersection, $E_1 \cap E_2 \cap \ldots \cap E_K$, is the set of all basic outcomes that belong to every $E_i (i = 1, 2, \ldots, K)$.

It is possible that the intersection of two events is the empty set. In the hitter example, if we had defined an event C, "batter is out," then the intersection of events A, "batter reaches base safely," and C would be an empty set, so A and C are *mutually exclusive*.

Mutually Exclusive

If the events A and B have no common basic outcomes, they are called **mutually exclusive**, and their intersection, $A \cap B$, is said to be the empty set, indicating that $A \cap B$ has no members.

More generally, the K events $E_1, E_2, \ldots, E_K$ are said to be mutually exclusive if every pair (E_i, E_j) is a pair of mutually exclusive events.

In the batter example Events A and C from above are mutually exclusive.

Figure 3.1 illustrates intersections using a Venn diagram. In part (a) of Figure 3.1, the rectangle S represents the sample space, and the two closed figures represent the events A and B. Basic outcomes belonging to A are within the circle labeled A, and basic outcomes belonging to B are in the corresponding B circle. The intersection of A and B, $A \cap B$, is indicated by the shaded area where the figures intersect. We see that a basic outcome is in $A \cap B$ if and only if it is in both A and B. Thus, in the batter example outcomes, safe hit, O_1, or reach base on an error, O_6, belong to both events: "the batter reaches base safely" (Event A [O_1, O_2, O_6]) and "the batter hits the ball" (Event B [O_1, O_4, O_5, O_6]). In Figure 3.1(b) the figures do not intersect, indicating that events A and B are mutually exclusive. For example, if a set of accounts is audited, the events "less than

5% contain material errors" and "more than 10% contain material errors" are mutually exclusive.

Figure 3.1 Venn Diagrams for the Intersection of Events A and B: (a) $A \cap B$ is the Shaded Area; (b) A and B are Mutually Exclusive

 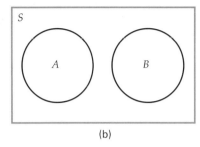

(a)　　　　　　　　　　　　(b)

Tables 3.2(a) and 3.2(b) can also be used to demonstrate the same conditions. The entire table represents S the sample space. Basic outcomes belonging to A are in the first row labeled A, and basic outcomes belonging to B are in the first column labeled B. The second row designates basic outcomes not in A as $\overline{A}$, and outcomes not in B as $\overline{B}$. The intersection of A and B, $A \cap B$, is indicated by the upper left table cell. A basic outcome is in $A \cap B$ if and only if it is in both A and B. Thus, in the batter example—Table 3.2(a)—outcomes safe hit, O_1, and reach base on an error, O_6, belong to the two events: "the batter reaches base safely" (Event A [O_1, O_2, O_6]) and "the batter hits the ball" (Event B [O_1, O_4, O_5, O_6]), the result shown in Figure 3.1(a). In Table 3.2(b) the figures do not intersect, indicating that events A and B are mutually exclusive, the same as Figure 3.1(b). When we consider several events jointly, another possibility of interest is that at least one of them will occur. This will happen if the basic outcome of the random experiment belongs to at least one of the events. The set of basic outcomes belonging to at least one of the events is called their *union*. For the batter example the two events, "the batter reaches base safely" (Event A [O_1, O_2, O_6]) and "the batter hits the ball" (Event B [O_1, O_4, O_5, O_6]), the events [O_1, O_2, O_4, O_5, O_6] are included in at least one of the events. This is an example of the union of two events.

Table 3.2 Intersection of and Mutually Exclusive Events

(a) Intersection of Events		
	B	$\overline{B}$
A	$A \cap B$	$A - (A \cap B)$
$\overline{A}$	$B - (A \cap B)$	$\overline{A} \cap \overline{B}$

(b) Mutually Exclusive Events		
	B	$\overline{B}$
A	$\varnothing$	A
$\overline{A}$	B	$\overline{A} \cap \overline{B}$

Union

Let A and B be two events in the sample space, S. Their **union**, denoted by $A \cup B$, is the set of all basic outcomes in S that belong to at least one of these two events. Hence, the union $A \cup B$ occurs if and only if either A or B or both occur.

More generally, given the K events $E_1, E_2, \ldots, E_K$, their union, $E_1 \cup E_2 \cup \ldots \cup E_K$, is the set of all basic outcomes belonging to at least one of these K events.

The Venn diagram in Figure 3.2 shows the union, from which it is clear that a basic outcome will be in $A \cup B$ if and only if it is in either A or B or both.

Figure 3.2 Venn
Diagram for the
Union of Events A
and B

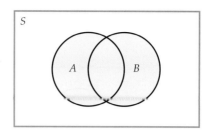

If the union of several events covers the entire sample space, S, we say that these events are *collectively exhaustive*. Since every basic outcome is in S, it follows that every outcome of the random experiment will be in at least one of these events. In the baseball example, the events "the batter gets on base" and "batter makes an out" are collectively exhaustive.

Collectively Exhaustive

Given the K events $E_1, E_2, \ldots, E_K$ in the sample space, S, if $E_1 \cup E_2 \cup \ldots \cup E_K = S$, these K events are said to be **collectively exhaustive**.

We can see that the set of all basic outcomes contained in a sample space is both mutually exclusive and collectively exhaustive. We have already noted that these outcomes are such that one must occur, but no more than one can simultaneously occur.

Next, let A be an event. Suppose that our interest is all of the basic outcomes not included in A.

Complement

Let A be an event in the sample space, S. The set of basic outcomes of a random experiment belonging to S but not to A is called the **complement** of A and is denoted by $\overline{A}$.

Clearly, events A and $\overline{A}$ are mutually exclusive—no basic outcome can belong to both—and collectively exhaustive—every basic outcome must belong to one or the other. Figure 3.3 shows the complement of A using a Venn diagram. We have now defined three important concepts—intersection, union, and complement—that will be important in our development of probability.

Figure 3.3 Venn
Diagram for the
Complement of
Event A

Example 3.3 Batter Performance Showing Unions, Intersections, and Complements

The following examples help to illustrate these concepts. When a batter is up, two events of interest are "the batter reaches base safely" (Event A $[O_1, O_2, O_6]$) and "the batter hits the ball"(Event B $[O_1, O_4, O_5, O_6]$), using the definitions from Example 3.1.

1. The complements of these events are, respectively, "the batter does not reach base safely" ($\overline{A}$) and "the batter does not hit the ball" ($\overline{B}$)

$$\overline{A} = [O_3, O_4, O_5] \quad \overline{B} = [O_2, O_3]$$

2. The intersection of A and B is the event "batter reaches base safely as the result of hitting the ball," and so,

$$A \cap B = [O_1, O_6] \tag{3.1}$$

3. The union is the event "the batter reaches base safely or the batter hits the ball," and so,

$$A \cup B = [O_1, O_2, O_4, O_5, O_6] \tag{3.2}$$

4. Note that the events $A[O_1, O_2, O_6]$ and $\overline{A}[O_3, O_4, O_5]$ are mutually exclusive since their intersection is the empty set and collectively exhaustive since their union is the sample space S, that is,

$$A \cup \overline{A} = [O_1, O_2, O_3, O_4, O_5, O_6]$$

The same statements apply for $B[O_1, O_4, O_5, O_6]$ and $\overline{B}[O_2, O_3]$.

Consider also the intersection of events $\overline{A}[O_3, O_4, O_5]$ and $B[O_1, O_4, O_5, O_6]$. The events O_4, "ground ball out," and O_5, "fly ball out," represent the condition where the batter hits the ball but makes an out.

Example 3.4 Dow Jones Industrial Average (Unions, Intersections, and Complements)

We designate four basic outcomes for the Dow Jones Industrial average over two consecutive days:

O_1: The Dow Jones average rises on both days.
O_2: The Dow Jones average rises on the first day but does not rise on the second day.
O_3: The Dow Jones average does not rise on the first day but rises on the second day.
O_4: The Dow Jones average does not rise on either day.

Clearly, one of these outcomes must occur, but more than one cannot occur at the same time. We can, therefore, write the sample space as $S = [O_1, O_2, O_3, O_4]$. Now, we consider these two events:

A: "The Dow Jones average rises on the first day."
B: "The Dow Jones average rises on the second day."

Find the intersection, union, and complement of A and B.

Solution We see that A occurs if either O_1 or O_2 occurs, and B occurs if either O_1 or O_3 occurs; thus,

$$A = [O_1, O_2] \quad \text{and} \quad B = [O_1, O_3]$$

The intersection of A and B is the event "the Dow Jones average rises on the first day and rises on the second day." This is the set of all basic outcomes belonging to both A and B, $A \cap B = [O_1]$.

The union of A and B is the event "the Dow Jones average rises on at least one of the two days." This is the set of all outcomes belonging to either A or B or both. Thus,

$$A \cup B = [O_1, O_2, O_3]$$

Finally, the complement of A is the event "the Dow Jones average does not rise on the first day." This is the set of all basic outcomes in the sample space, S, that do not belong to A. Hence,

$$\overline{A}[O_3, O_4] \quad \text{and, similarly,} \quad \overline{B}[O_2, O_4]$$

Figure 3.4 shows the intersection of events $\overline{A}$ and B. This intersection contains all outcomes that belong in both $\overline{A}$ and B. Clearly, $\overline{A} \cap B = [O_3]$.

Figure 3.4 Venn Diagram for the Intersection of $\overline{A}$ and B

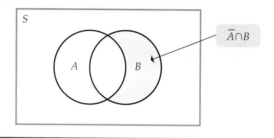

Additional results are shown in the chapter appendix.

EXERCISES

Basic Exercises

3.1 The sample space $S = [E_1, E_2, E_3, E_4, E_5, E_6, E_7, E_8, E_9, E_{10}, E_{11}]$. Given $A = [E_5, E_6, E_7, E_8]$ and $B = [E_5, E_7, E_9, E_{11}]$

a. What is A intersection B?
b. What is the union of A and B?
c. Is the union of A and B collectively exhaustive?

For Exercises 3.2–3.4 use the sample space S defined as follows:
$$S = [E_1, E_2, E_3, E_4, E_5, E_6, E_7, E_8, E_9, E_{10}]$$

3.2 Given $A = [E_1, E_3, E_6, E_9]$, define $\overline{A}$.

3.3 Given $\overline{A} = [E_1, E_4, E_5, E_7]$ and $\overline{B} = [E_2, E_3, E_5, E_8]$

a. What is A intersection $\overline{B}$?
b. What is A intersection B?
c. What is the union of A and B?
d. Is the union of A and B collectively exhaused?

3.4 Given $A = [E_3, E_5, E_7, E_{10}]$ and $B = [E_3, E_4, E_5, E_9]$

a. What is the intersection of A and B?
b. What is the union of A and B?
c. Is the union of A and B collectively exhaustive?

Application Exercises

3.5 A corporation takes delivery of some new machinery that must be installed and checked before it becomes available to use. The corporation is sure that it will take no more than 10 days for this installation and check to take place. Let A be the event "it will be more than 3 days before the machinery becomes available" and B be the event "it will be less than 7 days before the machinery becomes available."

a. Describe the event that is the complement of event A.
b. Describe the event that is the intersection of events A and B.
c. Describe the event that is the union of events A and B.
d. Are events A and B mutually exclusive?
e. Are events A and B collectively exhaustive?
f. Show that $(A \cap B) \cup (\overline{A} \cap B) = B$.
g. Show that $A \cup (\overline{A} \cap B) = A \cup B$.

3.6 Consider Example 3.4, with the following four basic outcomes for the Dow Jones Industrial Average over two consecutive days:

O_1: The Dow Jones average rises on both days.
O_2: The Dow Jones average rises on the first day but does not rise on the second day.

O_3: The Dow Jones average does not rise on the first day but rises on the second day.

O_4: The Dow Jones average does not rise on either day.

Let events A and B be the following:

A: The Dow Jones average rises on the first day.
B: The Dow Jones average rises on the second day.

a. Show that $(A \cap B) \cup (\overline{A} \cap B) = B$.
b. Show that $A \cup (\overline{A} \cap B) = A \cup B$.

3.7 Florin Frenti operates a small, used car lot that has three Mercedes (M_1, M_2, M_3) and two Toyotas (T_1, T_2). Two customers, Cezara and Anda, come to his lot, and each selects a car. The customers do not know each other, and there is no communication between them. Let the events A and B be defined as follows:

A: The customers select at least one Toyota.
B: The customers select two cars of the same model.

a. Identify all pairs of cars in the sample space.
b. Define event A.
c. Define event B.
d. Define the complement of A.
e. Show that $(A \cap B) \cup (\overline{A} \cap B) = B$.
f. Show that $A \cup (\overline{A} \cap B) = A \cup B$.

3.2 PROBABILITY AND ITS POSTULATES

Now, we are ready to use the language and concepts developed in the previous section to determine how to obtain an actual probability for a process of interest. Suppose that a random experiment is to be carried out and we want to determine the probability that a particular event will occur. Probability is measured over the range from 0 to 1. A probability of 0 indicates that the event will not occur, and a probability of 1 indicates that the event is certain to occur. Neither of these extremes is typical in applied problems. Thus, we are interested in assigning probabilities between 0 and 1 to uncertain events. To do this, we need to utilize any information that might be available. For example, if incomes are high, then sales of luxury automobiles will occur more often. An experienced sales manager may be able to establish a probability that future sales will exceed the company's profitability goal based on past experience. In this section we consider three definitions of probability:

1. Classical probability
2. Relative frequency probability
3. Subjective probability

Classical Probability

Classical Probability
Classical probability is the proportion of times that an event will occur, assuming that all outcomes in a sample space are equally likely to occur. Dividing the number of outcomes in the sample space that satisfy the event by the total number of outcomes in the sample space determines the probability of an event. The probability of an event A is

$$P(A) = \frac{N_A}{N} \tag{3.3}$$

where N_A is the number of outcomes that satisfy the condition of event A, and N is the total number of outcomes in the sample space. The important idea here is that one can develop a probability from fundamental reasoning about the process.

The classical statement of probability requires that we count outcomes in the sample space. Then we use the counts to determine the required probability. The following example indicates how classical probability can be used in a relatively simple problem.

Example 3.5 Tablet Purchase Selection (Classical Probability)

As graduation gifts, Andrei Zhukov decides to buy his daughter and son a tablet each. Suppose that Andrei visits a retailer in Belgium and sees a number of options. Andrei is not concerned about which brand he purchases—to him they all have the similar specifications—so Andrei selects the tablets purely by chance: Any tablet on the shelf is equally likely to be selected. What is the probability that Andrei will purchase one Apple and one Samsung tablet?

Solution The answer can be obtained using classical probability. To begin, the sample space is defined as all possible pairs of two tablets that can be selected from the store. The number of pairs is then counted, as is the number of outcomes that meet the condition—one Apple and one Samsung. Define the three Apple iPads as H_1, H_2, and H_3 and the two Samsung tablets as D_1 and D_2. The sample space, S, contains the following pairs of computers:

$$S = \{H_1D_1, H_1D_2, H_2D_1, H_2D_2, H_3D_1, H_3D_2, H_1H_2, H_1H_3, H_2H_3, D_1D_2\}$$

The number of outcomes in the sample space is 10. If A is the event "one Apple and one Samsung tablet are chosen," then the number, N_A, of outcomes that have one Apple and one Samsung tablet is 6. Therefore, the required probability of event A—one Apple and one Samsung—is

$$P(A) = \frac{N_A}{N} = \frac{6}{10} = 0.6$$

Counting all the outcomes would be very time consuming if we first had to identify every possible outcome. However, from previous courses many of you may have learned the basic formula to compute *the number of combinations* of n items taken x at a time.

Formula for Determining the Number of Combinations

The counting process can be generalized by using the following equation to compute the **number of combinations** of n items taken x at a time:

$$C_x^n = \frac{n!}{x!(n-x)!} \qquad 0! = 1 \tag{3.4}$$

The following section develops combinations, and you should study this section if you need to learn about or review your understanding of combinations.

Permutations and Combinations

A practical difficulty that sometimes arises in computing the probability of an event is counting the numbers of basic outcomes in the sample space and the event of interest. For some problems the use of *permutations* or *combinations* can be helpful.

1. Number of Orderings

We begin with the problem of ordering. Suppose that we have some number x of objects that are to be placed in order. Each object may be used only once. How many different sequences are possible? We can view this problem as a requirement to place one of the objects in each of x boxes arranged in a row.

Beginning with the left box in Figure 3.5, there are x different ways to fill it. Once an object is put in that box, there are $(x - 1)$ objects remaining, and so $(x - 1)$ ways to fill the second box. That is, for each of the x ways to place an object in the first box, there are $(x - 1)$ possible ways to fill the second box, so the first two boxes can be filled in a total of $x(x - 1)$ ways. Given that the first two boxes are filled, there are now $(x - 2)$ ways of filling the third box, so the first three boxes can be filled in a total of $x(x - 1)(x - 2)$ ways. When we arrive at the last box, there is only one object left to put in it. Finally, we arrive at the number of possible orderings.

Figure 3.5 The Orderings of x Objects

| x | $(x-1)$ | $(x-2)$ | $\cdots$ | 2 | 1 |

Number of Possible Orderings
The total number of possible ways of arranging x objects in order is given by

$$x(x - 1)(x - 2) \cdots (2)(1) = x!$$

where $x!$ is read "x factorial."

2. Permutations
Suppose that now we have a number n of objects with which the x *ordered* boxes could be filled (with $n > x$). Each object may be used only once. The number of possible orderings is called the number of *permutations* of x objects chosen from n and is denoted by the symbol P_x^n.

We can argue precisely as before, except that there will be n ways to fill the first box, $(n - 1)$ ways to fill the second box, and so on, until we come to the final box. At this point there will be $(n - x + 1)$ objects left, each of which could be placed in that box, as illustrated in Figure 3.6.

Figure 3.6 The Permutations of x Objects Chosen From n Objects

| n | $(n-1)$ | $(n-2)$ | $\cdots$ | $(n-x+2)$ | $(n-x+1)$ |

$(n - x)$ objects left over

Permutations
The total number of **permutations** of x objects chosen from n, P_x^n, is the number of possible arrangements when x objects are to be selected from a total of n and arranged in order.

$$P_x^n = n(n - 1)(n - 2) \cdots (n - x + 1)$$

Multiplying and dividing the right hand side by

$$(n - x)(n - x - 1) \cdots (2)(1) = (n - x)!$$

gives

$$P_x^n = \frac{n(n - 1)(n - 2) \cdots (n - x + 1)(n - x)(n - x - 1) \cdots (2)(1)}{(n - x)(n - x - 1) \cdots (2)(1)}$$

$$= \frac{n!}{(n - x)!}$$

Example 3.6 Five Letters (Permutations)

Suppose that two letters are to be selected from A, B, C, D, and E and arranged in order. How many permutations are possible?

Solution The number of permutations, with $n = 5$ and $x = 2$, is as follows:

$$P_2^5 = \frac{5!}{3!} = 20$$

These are

AB	AC	AD	AE	BC
BA	CA	DA	EA	CB
BD	BE	CD	CE	DE
DB	EB	DC	EC	ED

3. Combinations

Finally, suppose that we are interested in the number of different ways that x objects can be selected from n (where no object may be chosen more than once) but *order is not important*. Notice in Example 3.6 that the entries in the second and fourth rows are just rearrangements of those directly above them and may, therefore, be ignored. Thus, there are only 10 possibilities for selecting two objects from a group of 5 if order is not important. The number of possible selections is called the number of **combinations** and is denoted by C_x^n; here x objects are to be chosen from n. To find this number, note first that the number of possible permutations is P_x^n. However, many of these will be rearrangements of the same x objects and, therefore, are irrelevant. In fact, since x objects can be ordered in $x!$ ways, we are concerned with only a proportion $1/x!$ of the permutations. This leads us to a previously stated outcome—namely, Equation 3.5.

Number of Combinations

The number of combinations, C_x^n, of x objects chosen from n is the number of possible selections that can be made. This number is

$$C_x^n = \frac{P_x^n}{x!}$$

or, simply,

$$C_x^n = \frac{n!}{x!(n - x)!} \tag{3.5}$$

In some applications the notation

$$\binom{n}{x} = C_x^n = \frac{n!}{x!(n - x)!}$$

is used.

We illustrate the combination equation, Equation 3.5, by noting that in Example 3.5 the number of combinations of the 5 tablets taken 2 at a time is the number of elements in the sample space:

$$C_2^5 = \frac{5!}{2!(5 - 2)!} = \frac{5 \cdot 4 \cdot 3 \cdot 2 \cdot 1}{2 \cdot 1(3 \cdot 2 \cdot 1)} = 10$$

Example 3.7 Probability of Employee Selection (Combinations)

A personnel officer has 8 candidates to fill 4 similar positions. 5 candidates are men, and 3 are women. If, in fact, every combination of candidates is equally likely to be chosen, what is the probability that no women will be hired?

Solution First, the total number of possible combinations of 4 candidates chosen from 8 is as follows:

$$C_4^8 = \frac{8!}{4!4!} = 70$$

Now, in order for no women to be hired, it follows that the 4 successful candidates must come from the available 5 men. The number of such combinations is as follows:

$$C_4^5 = \frac{5!}{4!1!} = 5$$

Therefore, if at the outset each of the 70 possible combinations was equally likely to be chosen, the probability that one of the 5 all-male combinations would be selected is $5/70 = 1/14$.

Example 3.8 Tablet Selection Revised (Classical Probability)

Suppose that retail outlet in Belgium now contains 10 Apple iPads, 5 Samsung tablets, and 5 Huawei tablets. Andrei enters the store and wants to purchase 3 tablets. The tablets are selected purely by chance from the shelf. Now what is the probability that he selects 2 Apple iPads and 1 Samsung tablet?

Solution The classical definition of probability will be used. But in this example the combinations formula will be used to determine the number of outcomes in the sample space and the number of outcomes that satisfy the condition A: [2 Apple iPads and 1 Samsung tablet].

The total number of outcomes in the sample space is as follows:

$$N = C_3^{20} = \frac{20!}{3!(20-3)!} = 1,140$$

The number of ways that we can select 2 Applie iPads from the 10 available is computed by the following:

$$C_2^{10} = \frac{10!}{2!(10-2)!} = 45$$

Similarly, the number of ways that we can select 1 Samsung tablet from the 5 available is 5 and, therefore, the number of outcomes that satisfy event A is as follows:

$$N_A = C_2^{10} \times C_1^5 = 45 \times 5 = 225$$

Finally, the probability of $A = $ [2 Apple and 1 Samsung] is as follows:

$$P_A = \frac{N_A}{N} = \frac{C_2^{10} \times C_1^5}{C_3^{20}} = \frac{45 \times 5}{1,140} = 0.197$$

Relative Frequency

We often use relative frequency to determine probabilities for a particular population. The *relative frequency probability* is the number of events in the population that meet the condition divided by the total number in the population. These probabilities indicate how often an event will occur compared to other events. For example, if event A has a probability of 0.40, we know that it will occur 40% of the time. This is more often than event B if event B has only a 0.30 probability of occurrence. But we do not know which event, A or B, will occur next.

Relative Frequency Probability

The **relative frequency probability** is the limit of the proportion of times that event A occurs in a large number of trials, n,

$$P(A) = \frac{n_A}{n} \tag{3.6}$$

where n_A is the number of A outcomes and n is the total number of trials or outcomes. The probability is the limit as n becomes large (or approaches infinity).

The probabilities for the baseball batter in Example 3.1 were computed from baseball statistical files using the definition of relative frequency.

Example 3.9 Probability of Incomes Above €75,000 (Relative Frequency Probability)

Franka Brühl is considering an opportunity to establish a new-car dealership in Paderborn, a county in Germany that has a population of about 150,000 people. Experience from many other dealerships indicates that in similar areas a dealership will be successful if at least 40% of the households have annual incomes above €75,000. She has asked Karl Klatten, a marketing consultant, to estimate the proportion of family incomes above €75,000, or the probability of such incomes.

Solution After considering the problem, Karl decides that the probability should be based on the relative frequency. He first examines the most recent census data and finds that there were 51,617 households in Paderborn and that 29,245 had incomes above €75,000. Karl computed the probability for event A, "family income greater than €75,000" as follows:

$$P(A) = \frac{n_A}{n} = \frac{29{,}245}{51{,}617} = 0.566$$

Since Karl knows that there are various errors in census data, he also consulted a recent population data source on the Web to which his company subscribes. From this source he found 52,800 households, with 30,108 having incomes above €75,000. Karl computed the probability of event A from this source as follows:

$$P(A) = \frac{n_A}{n} = \frac{30{,}108}{52{,}800} = 0.570$$

Since these numbers are close, he could report either. Karl chose to report the probability as 0.57.

This example shows that probabilities based on the relative frequency approach often can be obtained using existing data sources. It also indicates that different results can and do occur and that experienced analysts and managers will seek to verify their results by using more than one source. Experience and good judgment are needed to decide if confirming data is close enough.

> ### Subjective Probability
> **Subjective probability** expresses an individual's degree of belief about the chance that an event will occur. These subjective probabilities are used in certain management decision procedures.

We can understand the subjective probability concept by using the concept of fair bets. For example, if I assert that the probability of a stock price rising in the next week is 0.5, then I believe that the stock price is just as likely to increase as it is to decrease. In assessing this subjective probability, I am not necessarily thinking in terms of repeated experimentation, but instead I am thinking about a stock price over the next week. My subjective probability assessment implies that I would view as fair a bet in which I paid $1 if the price decreased and I received $1 if the price increased. If I would receive more than $1 for a price increase, then I would regard the bet as being in my favor. Similarly, if I believe that the probability of a horse winning a particular race is 0.4, then I am asserting the personal view that there is a 40-to-60 chance of it winning. Given this belief, I would regard as fair a bet in which I would gain $3 if the horse won and lose $2 if the horse lost.

We emphasize that subjective probabilities are personal. There is no requirement that different individuals arrive at the same probabilities for the same event. In the stock price example we would conclude that the appropriate probability of a stock increase is 0.50. However, an individual with more information about the stock might believe otherwise. In the horse race example, it is likely that two bettors will reach different subjective probabilities. They may not have the same information, and, even if they do, they may interpret the information differently. We know that individual investors do not all hold the same views on the future behavior of the stock market. Their subjective probabilities depend on their knowledge and experience and the way they interpret it. Managers of different firms have different subjective probabilities about the potential sales opportunities in a given regional market, and, thus, they make different decisions.

Probability Postulates

We need to develop a framework for assessing and manipulating probabilities. To do this, we will first set down three rules (or postulates) that probabilities will be required to obey and show that these requirements are "reasonable."

> ### Probability Postulates
> Let S denote the sample space of a random experiment, O_i the basic outcomes, and A, an event. For each event A of the sample space, S, we assume that $P(A)$ is defined and we have the following **probability postulates**:
>
> **1.** If A is any event in the sample space, S,
> $$0 \leq P(A) \leq 1$$
>
> **2.** Let A be an event in S and let O_i denote the basic outcomes. Then,
> $$P(A) = \sum_A P(O_i)$$
> where the notation implies that the summation extends over all the basic outcomes in A.
>
> **3.** $P(S) = 1$.

The first postulate requires that the probability lie between 0 and 1. The second postulate can be understood in terms of relative frequencies. Suppose that a random experiment is repeated N times. Let N_i be the number of times the basic outcome O_i occurs, and let N_A be the number of times event A occurs. Then, since the basic outcomes are mutually exclusive, N_A is just the sum of N_i for all basic outcomes in A; that is,

$$N_A = \sum_A N_i$$

and, on dividing by the number of trials, N, we obtain

$$\frac{N_A}{N} = \sum_A \frac{N_i}{N}$$

But under the relative frequency concept of probability, N_A/N tends to $P(A)$, and each N_i/N tends to $P(O_i)$ as N becomes infinitely large. Thus, the second postulate can be seen as a logical requirement when probability is viewed in this way.

The third postulate can be paraphrased as, When a random experiment is carried out, something has to happen. Replacing A by the sample space, S, in the second postulate gives

$$P(S) = \sum_S P(O_i)$$

where the summation extends over all the basic outcomes in the sample space. But since $P(S) = 1$ by the third postulate, it follows that

$$\sum_S P(O_i) = 1$$

That is, the sum of the probabilities for all basic outcomes in the sample space is 1.

Consequences of the Postulates

We now list and illustrate some immediate consequences of the three postulates.

1. If the sample space, S, consists of n equally likely basic outcomes, $O_1, O_2, \ldots, O_n$, then

$$P(O_i) = \frac{1}{n} \qquad \text{where } i = 1, 2, \ldots, n$$

   This follows because the n outcomes cover the sample space and are equally likely. For example, if a fair die is rolled, the probability for each of the six basic outcomes is $1/6$.

2. If the sample space, S, consists of n equally likely basic outcomes and event A consists of n_A of these outcomes, then

$$P(A) = \frac{n_A}{n}$$

   This follows from consequence 1 and postulate 2. Every basic outcome has the probability $1/n$, and, by postulate 2, $P(A)$ is just the sum of the probabilities of the n_A basic outcomes in A. For example, if a fair die is rolled and A is the event "even number results," there are $n = 6$ basic outcomes, and $n_A = 3$ of these are in A. Thus, $P(A) = 3/6 = 1/2$.

3. Let A and B be mutually exclusive events. Then the probability of their union is the sum of their individual probabilities—that is,

$$P(A \cup B) = P(A) + P(B)$$

In general, if $E_1, E_2, \ldots, E_K$ are mutually exclusive events,

$$P(E_1 \cup E_2 \cup \cdots \cup E_K) = P(E_1) + P(E_2) + \cdots + P(E_K)$$

This result is a consequence of postulate 2. The probability of the union of A and B is

$$P(A \cup B) = \sum_{A \cup B} P(O_i)$$

where the summation extends over all basic outcomes in $A \cup B$. But since A and B are mutually exclusive, no basic outcome belongs to both, so

$$\sum_{A \cup B} P(O_i) = \sum_A P(O_i) + \sum_B P(O_i) = P(A) + P(B)$$

4. If $E_1, E_2, \ldots, E_K$ are collectively exhaustive events, the probability of their union is

$$P(E_1 \cup E_2 \cup \cdots \cup E_K) = 1$$

Since the events are collectively exhaustive, their union is the whole sample space, S, and the result follows from postulate 3.

Example 3.10 Web Advertising (Probability)

The Web site for a specialty clothing retailer receives 1,000 hits on a particular day. From past experience it has been determined that every 1,000 hits results in 10 large sales of at least $500 and 100 small sales of less than $500. Assuming that all hits have the same probability of a sale, what is the probability of a large sale from a particular hit? What is the probability of a small sale? What is the probability of any sale?

Solution Over many days with 1,000 hits there will be 10 large sales, 100 small sales, and 890 will result in no sales. Our single hit is selected from the 1,000 total hits. Let A be the event "selected hit results in a large sale" and let B be the event "selected hit results in a small sale." The probabilities are as follows:

$$P(A) = \frac{10}{1,000} = 0.01$$

$$P(B) = \frac{100}{1,000} = 0.10$$

The event "hit results in a sale" is the union of events A and B. Since these events are mutually exclusive,

$$P(A \cup B) = P(A) + P(B) = 0.01 + 0.10 = 0.11$$

Example 3.11 Dow Jones Revisited (Probability)

In Example 3.4 we considered the course of the Dow Jones Industrial Average over 2 days and defined four basic outcomes:

O_1: The Dow Jones average rises on both days.
O_2: The Dow Jones average rises on the first day but does not rise on the second day.
O_3: The Dow Jones average does not rise on the first day but rises on the second day.
O_4: The Dow Jones average does not rise on either day.

Suppose that we assume these four basic outcomes are equally likely. In that case what is the probability that the market will rise on at least 1 of the 2 days?

Solution The event of interest, "market rises on at least 1 of the 2 days," contains 3 of the 4 basic outcomes—O_1, O_2, and O_3. Since the basic outcomes are all equally likely, it follows that the probability of this event is 3/4, or 0.75.

Example 3.12 Oil Well Drilling (Probability)

In the early stages of the development of the Hibernia oil site in the Atlantic Ocean, the Petroleum Directorate of Newfoundland estimated the probability to be 0.1 that economically recoverable reserves would exceed 2 billion barrels. The probability for reserves in excess of 1 billion barrels was estimated to be 0.5. Given this information, what is the estimated probability of reserves between 1 and 2 billion barrels?

information through the mail, and 0.3 of no expression of interest. Information is mailed to all people requesting it, and it is estimated that 20% of these people will eventually donate. An operator makes a sequence of calls, the outcomes of which can be assumed to be independent.

    a. What is the probability that no immediate credit-card donation will be received until at least four unsuccessful calls have been made?

    b. What is the probability that the first call leading to any donation (either immediately or eventually after a mailing) is preceded by at least four unsuccessful calls?

3.40 A mail-order firm considers three possible events in filling an order:

    A: The wrong item is sent.
    B: The item is lost in transit.
    C: The item is damaged in transit.

    Assume that *A* is independent of both *B* and *C* and that *B* and *C* are mutually exclusive. The individual event probabilities are $P(A) = 0.02, P(B) = 0.01$, and $P(C) = 0.04$. Find the probability that at least one of these foul-ups occurs for a randomly chosen order.

3.41 A coach recruits for a college team a star player who is currently a high school senior. In order to play next year, the senior must both complete high school with adequate grades and pass a standardized test. The coach estimates that the probability the athlete will fail to obtain adequate high school grades is 0.02, that the probability the athlete will not pass the standardized test is 0.15, and that these are independent events. According to these estimates, what is the probability that this recruit will be eligible to play in college next year?

3.42 Market research in a particular city indicated that during a week, 18% of all adults watch a television program oriented to business and financial issues, 12% read a publication oriented to these issues, and 10% do both.

    a. What is the probability that an adult in this city who watches a television program oriented to business and financial issues reads a publication oriented to these issues?

    b. What is the probability that an adult in this city who reads a publication oriented to business and financial issues watches a television program oriented to these issues?

3.43 An inspector examines items coming from an assembly line. A review of his record reveals that he accepts only 8% of all defective items. It was also found that 1% of all items from the assembly line are both defective and accepted by the inspector. What is the probability that a randomly chosen item from this assembly line is defective?

3.44 A football fan wants to predict who would win the Premier League. There is a choice of 4 English and 3 German football clubs. She is asked to predict, in order, the 2 clubs of each league that will score the best results over the next year. Suppose that these predictions are made randomly and independently of each other. What is the probability that the football fan will be successful in at least 1 of the 2 leagues?

3.45 A bank classifies borrowers as high risk or low risk. Only 15% of its loans are made to those in the high-risk category. Of all its loans, 5% are in default, and 40% of those in default were made to high-risk borrowers. What is the probability that a high-risk borrower will default?

3.46 A conference began at noon with two parallel sessions. The session on portfolio management was attended by 40% of the delegates, while the session on chartism was attended by 50%. The evening session consisted of a talk titled "Is the Random Walk Dead?" This was attended by 80% of all delegates.

    a. If attendance at the portfolio management session and attendance at the chartism session are mutually exclusive, what is the probability that a randomly chosen delegate attended at least one of these sessions?

    b. If attendance at the portfolio management session and attendance at the evening session are statistically independent, what is the probability that a randomly chosen delegate attended at least one of these sessions?

    c. Of those attending the chartism session, 75% also attended the evening session. What is the probability that a randomly chosen delegate attended at least one of these two sessions?

3.47 A stock market analyst claims expertise in picking stocks that will outperform the corresponding industry norms. This analyst is presented with a list of 5 high-technology stocks and a list of 5 airline stocks, and she is invited to nominate, in order, the 3 stocks that will do best on each of these 2 lists over the next year. The analyst claims that success in just 1 of these 2 tasks would be a substantial accomplishment. If, in fact, the choices are made randomly and independently, what is the probability of success in at least 1 of the 2 tasks merely by chance? Given this result, what do you think of the analyst's claim?

3.48 A traffic analyst supervisor wants to examine the worst day and time during a week to commute. He finds that 35% of accidents happen on a Friday and that 23% of the accidents occur at around 2 p.m. He also finds that 5% of accidents occur on Friday at around 2 p.m.

    a. What is the probability that an accident that occurs on Friday does not occur around 2 p.m.?

    b. Are the events "accident occurs on Friday" and "accident occurs around 2 p.m." statistically independent?

3.49 A corporation was concerned with the basic educational skills of its workers and decided to offer a selected group of them separate classes in reading and practical mathematics. Of these workers, 40% signed up for the reading classes and 50% for the practical mathematics classes. Of those signing up for the reading classes 30% signed up for the mathematics classes.

a. What is the probability that a randomly selected worker signed up for both classes?
b. What is the probability that a randomly selected worker who signed up for the mathematics classes also signed up for the reading classes?
c. What is the probability that a randomly chosen worker signed up for at least one of these two classes?
d. Are the events "signs up for the reading classes" and "signs up for the mathematics classes" statistically independent?

3.50 A lawn-care service makes telephone solicitations, seeking customers for the coming season. A review of the records indicates that 15% of these solicitations produce new customers and that, of these new customers, 80% had used some rival service in the previous year. It is also estimated that, of all solicitation calls made, 60% are to people who had used a rival

service the previous year. What is the probability that a call to a person who had used a rival service the previous year will produce a new customer for the lawn-care service?

3.51 An editor may use all, some, or none of three possible strategies to enhance the sales of a book:

a. An expensive prepublication promotion
b. An expensive cover design
c. A bonus for sales representatives who meet predetermined sales levels

In the past, these three strategies have been applied simultaneously to only 2% of the company's books. Twenty percent of the books have had expensive cover designs, and, of these, 80% have had expensive prepublication promotion. A rival editor learns that a new book is to have both an expensive prepublication promotion and an expensive cover design and now wants to know how likely it is that a bonus scheme for sales representatives will be introduced. Compute the probability of interest to the rival editor.

3.4 BIVARIATE PROBABILITIES

In this section we introduce a class of problems that involve two distinct sets of events, which we label $A_1, A_2, \ldots, A_H$ and $B_1, B_2, \ldots, B_K$. These problems have broad application in business and economics. They can be studied by constructing two-way tables that develop intuition for problem solutions. The events A_i and B_j are mutually exclusive and collectively exhaustive within their sets, but intersections $(A_i \cap B_j)$ can occur between all events from the two sets. These intersections can be regarded as basic outcomes of a random experiment. Two sets of events, considered jointly in this way, are called *bivariate*, and the probabilities are called *bivariate probabilities*. It is possible to apply the methods of this section to trivariate and higher-level probabilities, but with added complexity.

We also consider situations where it is difficult to obtain desired conditional probabilities, but where alternative conditional probabilities are available. It may be difficult to obtain probabilities because the costs of enumeration are high or because some critical, ethical, or legal restriction prevents direct collection of probabilities.

Table 3.6 illustrates the outcomes of bivariate events labeled $A_1, A_2, \ldots, A_H$ and $B_1, B_2, \ldots, B_K$. If probabilities can be attached to all intersections $(A_i \cap B_j)$, then the whole probability structure of the random experiment is known, and other probabilities of interest can be calculated.

Table 3.6
Outcomes for
Bivariate Events

	B_1	B_2	$\ldots$	B_K
A_1	$P(A_1 \cap B_1)$	$P(A_1 \cap B_2)$	$\ldots$	$P(A_1 \cap B_K)$
A_2	$P(A_2 \cap B_1)$	$P(A_2 \cap B_2)$	$\ldots$	$P(A_2 \cap B_K)$
.	.	.	.	.
.	.	.	.	.
.	.	.	.	.
A_H	$P(A_H \cap B_1)$	$P(A_H \cap B_2)$	$\ldots$	$P(A_H \cap B_K)$

As a discussion example, consider a potential advertiser who wants to know both income and other relevant characteristics of the audience for a particular television show. Families may be categorized, using A_i, as to whether they regularly, occasionally, or never watch a particular series. In addition, they can be categorized, using B_j, according to low-, middle-, and high-income subgroups. Then the nine possible cross-classifications can be set out in the form of Table 3.7, with $H = 3$ and $K = 3$. The subsetting of the population can also be displayed using a tree diagram, as shown in Figure 3.8. Beginning at the left, we have the entire population of families. This population is separated into three branches, depending on their television-viewing frequency. In turn, each of these branches is separated into three subbranches, according to the family income level. As a result, there are nine subbranches corresponding to all combinations of viewing frequency and income level.

Table 3.7 Probabilities for Television Viewing and Income Example

Viewing Frequency	High Income	Middle Income	Low Income	Totals
Regular	0.04	0.13	0.04	0.21
Occasional	0.10	0.11	0.06	0.27
Never	0.13	0.17	0.22	0.52
Totals	0.27	0.41	0.32	1.00

Figure 3.8 Tree Diagram for Television Viewing and Income Example

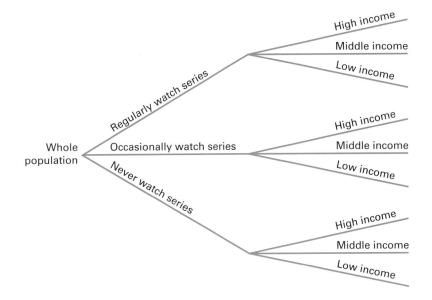

Now it is necessary to obtain the probabilities for each of the event intersections. These probabilities, as obtained from viewer surveys, are all presented in Table 3.7. For example, 10% of the families have high incomes and occasionally watch series. These probabilities are developed using the relative frequency concept of probability, assuming that the survey is sufficiently large so that proportions can be approximated as probabilities. On this basis, the probability that a family chosen at random from the population has a high income and occasionally watches the show is 0.10.

Joint and Marginal Probabilities
In the context of bivariate probabilities the intersection probabilities, $P(A_i \cap B_j)$, are called joint probabilities. The probabilities for individual events, $P(A_i)$ or $P(B_j)$, are called **marginal probabilities**. Marginal probabilities are at the margin of a table such as Table 3.7 and can be computed by summing the corresponding row or column.

To obtain the marginal probabilities for an event, we merely sum the corresponding mutually exclusive joint probabilities:

$$P(A_i) = P(A_i \cap B_1) + P(A_i \cap B_2) + \cdots + P(A_i \cap B_K)$$

Note that this would be equivalent to summing the probabilities for a particular row in Table 3.7. An analogous argument shows that the probabilities for B_j are the column totals.

Continuing with the example, define the television-watching subgroups as A_1, "regular"; A_2, "occasional"; and A_3, "never." Similarly define the income subgroups as B_1, "high"; B_2, "middle"; and B_3, "low." Then the probability that a family is an occasional viewer is as follows:

$$P(A_2) = P(A_2 \cap B_1) + P(A_2 \cap B_2) + P(A_2 \cap B_3) = 0.10 + 0.11 + 0.06 = 0.27$$

Similarly, we can add the other rows in Table 3.7 to obtain $P(A_1) = 0.21$ and $P(A_3) = 0.52$. We can also add the columns in Table 3.7 to obtain

$$P(B_1) = 0.27 \quad P(B_2) = 0.41 \quad \text{and} \quad P(B_3) = 0.32$$

Marginal probabilities can also be obtained from tree diagrams like Figure 3.9, which has the same branches as Figure 3.8. The right-hand side contains all of the joint probabilities, and the marginal probabilities for the three viewing-frequency events are entered on the main branches by adding the probabilities on the corresponding sub-branches. The tree-branch model is particularly useful when there are more than two events of interest. In this case, for example, the advertiser might also be interested in the age of the head of household or the number of children. The marginal probabilities for the various events sum to 1 because those events are mutually exclusive and mutually exhaustive.

Figure 3.9 Tree Diagram for the Television Viewing–Income Example, Showing Joint and Marginal Probabilities

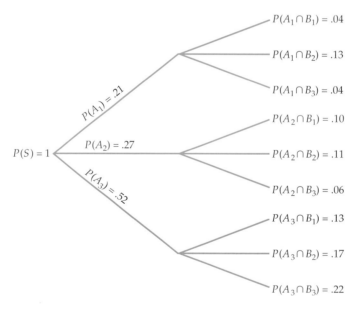

In many applications we find that the conditional probabilities are of more interest than the marginal probabilities. An advertiser may be more concerned about the probability that a high-income family is watching than the probability of any family watching. The conditional probability can be obtained easily from the table because we have all the joint probabilities and the marginal probabilities. For example, the probability of a high-income family regularly watching the show is as follows:

$$P(A_1|B_1) = \frac{P(A_1 \cap B_1)}{P(B_1)} = \frac{0.04}{0.27} = 0.15$$

Table 3.8 shows the probability of the viewer groups conditional on income levels. Note that the conditional probabilities with respect to a particular income group always add up to 1, as seen for the three columns in Table 3.8. This will always be the case, as seen by the following:

$$\sum_{i=1}^{H} P(A_i|B_j) = \sum_{i=1}^{H} \frac{P(A_i \cap B_j)}{P(B_j)} = \frac{P(B_j)}{P(B_j)} = 1$$

The conditional probabilities for the income groups, given viewing frequencies, can also be computed, as shown in Table 3.9, using the definition for conditional probability and the joint and marginal probabilities.

To obtain the conditional probabilities of income given viewing frequency in Table 3.7, we divide each of the joint probabilities in a row by the marginal probability in the right-hand column. For example,

$$P(\text{low income} \,|\, \text{occasional viewer}) = \frac{0.06}{0.27} = 0.22$$

Table 3.8 Conditional Probabilities of Viewing Frequencies, Given Income Levels

VIEWING FREQUENCY	HIGH INCOME	MIDDLE INCOME	LOW INCOME
Regular	0.15	0.32	0.12
Occasional	0.37	0.27	0.19
Never	0.48	0.41	0.69

Table 3.9 Conditional Probabilities of Income Levels, Given Viewing Frequencies

VIEWING FREQUENCY	HIGH INCOME	MIDDLE INCOME	LOW INCOME
Regular	0.19	0.62	0.19
Occasional	0.37	0.41	0.22
Never	0.25	0.33	0.42

We can also check, by using a two-way table, whether or not paired events are statistically independent. Recall that events A_i and B_j are independent if and only if their joint probability is the product of their marginal probabilities—that is, if

$$P(A_i \cap B_j) = P(A_i)P(B_j)$$

In Table 3.7 joint events A_2 ("occasionally watch") and B_1 ("high income") have a probability of

$$P(A_2 \cap B_1) = 0.10$$

and

$$P(A_2) = 0.27 \quad P(B_1) = 0.27$$

The product of these marginal probabilities is 0.0729 and, thus, not equal to the joint probability of 0.10. Hence, events A_2 and B_1 are not statistically independent.

Independent Events

Let A and B be a pair of events, each broken into mutually exclusive and collectively exhaustive event categories denoted by labels $A_1, A_2, \ldots, A_H$ and $B_1, B_2, \ldots, B_K$. If every event A_i is statistically independent of every event B_j, then A and B are **independent events**.

Since A_2 and B_1 are not statistically independent, it follows that the events "viewing frequency" and "income" are not independent.

In many practical applications the joint probabilities will not be known precisely. A sample from a population is obtained, and estimates of the joint probabilities are made from the sample data. We want to know, based on this sample evidence, if these events are independent of one another. We will develop a procedure for conducting such a test later in the book.

Odds

Odds are used to communicate probability information in some situations. For example, a sports analyst might report that the odds in favor of team A winning over team B are 2 to 1. Odds can be converted directly to probabilities, and probabilities can be converted to odds using the following equations.

Odds

The **odds** in favor of a particular event are given by the ratio of the probability of the event divided by the probability of its complement. The odds in favor of A are as follows:

$$\text{Odds} = \frac{P(A)}{1 - P(A)} = \frac{P(A)}{P(\overline{A})} \tag{3.12}$$

Therefore, the odds of 2 to 1 can be converted to the probability of A winning,

$$\frac{2}{1} = \frac{P(A)}{1 - P(A)}$$

and by basic algebra

$$2 \times (1 - P(A)) = P(A)$$

giving

$$P(A) = 0.67$$

Similarly, if the odds in favor of winning are 3 to 2, then the probability of winning is 0.60. Note that $0.60/0.40$ is equal to $3/2$.

Overinvolvement Ratios

There are a number of situations where it is difficult to obtain desired conditional probabilities, but alternative conditional probabilities are available. For example, the costs of enumeration might be high, or some critical, ethical, or legal restriction prevents direct collection of probabilities. In some of those cases it may be possible to use basic probability relationships to derive desired probabilities from available probabilities. In this section we develop one such approach based on the use of overinvolvement ratios (Carlson and Thorne 1997).

We start by considering a simple example. Suppose that we know 60% of the purchasers of our product have seen our advertisement, but only 30% of the nonpurchasers have seen the advertisement. The ratio of 60% to 30% is the overinvolvement of the event "seen our advertisement" in the purchasers group, compared to the nonpurchasers group. In the analysis to follow, we show how an overinvolvement ratio greater than 1.0 provides evidence that, for example, advertising influences purchase behavior.

An overinvolvement ratio, Equation 3.13, is the ratio of the probability of an event—such as viewing an advertisement—that occurs under two mutually exclusive and complementary outcome conditions, such as a product sale or not a product sale. If the ratio of the conditional probabilities is not equal to 1.0, then the event has an influence on the outcome condition. These ratios have applications in a number of business situations, including marketing, production, and accounting. In this section we develop the theory and application of *overinvolvement ratios*.

Overinvolvement Ratios

The probability of event A_1, conditional on event B_1, divided by the probability of A_1, conditional on event B_2, where B_1 and B_2 are mutually exclusive and complementary, is defined as the **overinvolvement ratio**:

$$\frac{P(A_1|B_1)}{P(A_1|B_2)} \tag{3.13}$$

An overinvolvement ratio greater than 1,

$$\frac{P(A_1|B_1)}{P(A_1|B_2)} > 1.0$$

implies that event A_1 increases the conditional odds ratio in favor of B_1:

$$\frac{P(B_1|A_1)}{P(B_2|A_1)} > \frac{P(B_1)}{P(B_2)}$$

Consider a company that wishes to determine the effectiveness of a new advertisement. An experiment is conducted in which the advertisement is shown to one customer group and not to another, followed by observation of the purchase behavior of both groups. Studies of this type have a high probability of error; they can be biased because people who are watched closely often behave differently than they do when not being observed. It is possible, however, to measure the percentage of buyers who have seen an ad and to measure the percentage of nonbuyers who have seen the ad. Let us consider how those study data can be analyzed to determine the effectiveness of the new advertisement.

Advertising effectiveness is determined using the following analysis. The population is divided into the following categories:

B_1: Buyers
B_2: Nonbuyers

and

A_1: Those who have seen the advertisement
A_2: Those who have not seen the advertisement

The odds in favor of the buyer in this problem are as follows:

$$\frac{P(B_1)}{P(B_2)}$$

Similarly, we can define the conditional odds, in which we use the ratio of the probabilities that are both conditional on the same event. For this problem the odds of a buyer being conditional on the event "have seen an advertisement" are as follows:

$$\frac{P(B_1|A_1)}{P(B_2|A_1)}$$

If the conditional odds are greater than the unconditional odds, the conditioning event is said to have an influence on the event of interest. Thus, advertising would be considered effective if

$$\frac{P(B_1|A_1)}{P(B_2|A_1)} > \frac{P(B_1)}{P(B_2)}$$

The left-hand terms are equal to the following:

$$P(B_1|A_1) = \frac{P(A_1|B_1)P(B_1)}{P(A_1)}$$

$$P(B_2|A_1) = \frac{P(A_1|B_2)P(B_2)}{P(A_1)}$$

By substituting these later terms, the conditional odds ratio equation becomes the following:

$$\frac{P(A_1|B_1)P(B_1)}{P(A_1|B_2)P(B_2)} > \frac{P(B_1)}{P(B_2)}$$

Dividing both sides by the right-hand ratio, we obtain the following:

$$\frac{P(A_1|B_1)}{P(A_1|B_2)} > 1.0$$

This result shows that, if a larger percent of buyers have seen the advertisement, compared to nonbuyers, then the odds in favor of purchasing being conditional on having seen the advertisement are greater than the unconditional odds. Therefore, we have evidence that the advertising is associated with an increased probability of purchase.

From the original problem, 60% of the purchasers and 30% of the nonpurchasers had seen the advertisement. The overinvolvement ratio is 2.0 (60/30), and, thus, we conclude that the advertisement increases the probability of purchase. Market researchers use this result to evaluate the effectiveness of advertising and other sales promotion activities. Purchasers of products are asked whether they have seen certain advertisements. This is combined with random sample surveys of households from which the percentage of nonpurchasers who have seen an advertisement is determined.

Consider another situation in which it is difficult, illegal, or unethical to obtain probability results (Carlson 1972).

Example 3.22 Alcohol and Highway Crashes (Overinvolvement Ratios)

Researchers at the National Highway Traffic Safety Administration in the U.S. Department of Transportation wished to determine the effect of alcohol on highway crashes. Clearly, it would be unethical to provide one group of drivers with alcohol and then compare their crash involvement with that of a group that did not have alcohol. However, researchers did find that 10.3% of the nighttime drivers in a specific county had been drinking and that 32.4% of the single-vehicle-accident drivers during the same time and in the same county had been drinking. Single-vehicle accidents were chosen to ensure that any driving error could be assigned to only one driver, whose alcohol usage had been measured. Based on these results they wanted to know if there was evidence to conclude that accidents increased at night when drivers had been drinking. Use the data to determine if alcohol usage leads to an increased probability of crashes (Carlson 1972).

Solution Using the overinvolvement ratios can help solve this problem. First, the events in the sample space need to be defined:

A_1: The driver had been drinking.
A_2: The driver had not been drinking.
C_1: The driver was involved in a crash.
C_2: The driver was not involved in a crash.

We know that alcohol, A_1, increases the probability of a crash if

$$\frac{P(A_1|C_1)}{P(A_1|C_2)} > 1.0$$

From the research the conditional probabilities are as follows:

$$P(A_1|C_1) = 0.324$$
$$P(A_1|C_2) = 0.103$$

Using these results, the overinvolvement ratio is as follows:

$$\frac{P(A_1|C_1)}{P(A_1|C_2)} = \frac{0.324}{0.103} = 3.15$$

Based on this analysis, there is evidence to conclude that alcohol increases the probability of automobile crashes.

The overinvolvement ratio is a good example of how mathematical manipulations of probabilities can be used to obtain results that are useful for business decisions. The wide usage of automated methods of data collection, including bar code scanners, audience segmentation, and census data on tapes and disks, provides the possibility to compute many different probabilities, conditional probabilities, and overinvolvement ratios. As a result, analyses similar to those presented in this chapter have become part of the daily routine for marketing analysts and product managers.

EXERCISES

Basic Exercises

Basic Exercises 3.52–3.58 refer to Table 3.10.

3.52 What is the joint probability that a Doctoral student prefers Movies /Series?

3.53 What is the joint probability that a Doctoral student prefers Documentaries?

3.54 What is the joint probability that a Masters student prefers watching News?

3.55 What is the joint probability that a Bachelors student prefers Documentaries?

3.56 What is the conditional probability that a student who prefers watching News is a Bachelors student?

3.57 What is the conditional probability a student who prefers Movies/Series is a Bachelors student?

3.58 What is the conditional probability that a Masters student prefers Documentaries?

3.59 The probability of a sale is 0.80. What are the odds in favor of a sale?

3.60 The probability of a sale is 0.50. What are the odds in favor of a sale?

3.61 Consider two groups of students: B_1, students who received high scores on tests, and B_2, students who received low scores on tests. In group B_1, 60% study more than 25 hours per week, and in group B_2, 35% study more than 25 hours per week. What is the overinvolvement ratio for high study levels in high test scores over low test scores?

3.62 Consider two groups of athletes: A_1, athletes who excel at football, and A_2, the athletes who do not excel at football. In A_1, 55% of the athletes jog in the morning for more than three days a week, and in A_2, 23% jog in the morning for more than three days a week. What is the over-involvement ratio for an athlete to excel at football for A_1 over A_2?

3.63 Consider two groups of students: B_1, students who received high scores on tests, and B_2, students who received low scores on tests. In group B_1, 20% study more than 25 hours per week, and in group B_2, 40% study more than 25 hours per week. What is the over-involvement ratio for high study levels in high test scores over low test scores?

Table 3.10 Probabilities for Television Preferences and Degree Programs:

TV PREFERENCES	BACHELORS	MASTERS	DOCTORAL	TOTALS
News	0.15	0.21	0.09	0.45
Movies/Series	0.14	0.07	0.05	0.26
Documentaries	0.08	0.15	0.06	0.29
Totals	0.37	0.43	0.20	1.00

Application Exercises

3.64 A survey carried out for a supermarket classified customers according to whether their visits to the store are frequent or infrequent and whether they often, sometimes, or never purchase generic products. The accompanying table gives the proportions of people surveyed in each of the six joint classifications.

Frequency of Visit	Purchase of Generic Products		
	Often	Sometimes	Never
Frequent	0.14	0.42	0.16
Infrequent	0.08	0.04	0.09

a. What is the probability that a customer both is a frequent shopper and often purchases generic products?
b. What is the probability that a customer who never buys generic products visits the store frequently?
c. Are the events "never buys generic products" and "visits the store frequently" independent?
d. What is the probability that a customer who infrequently visits the store often buys generic products?
e. Are the events "often buys generic products" and "visits the store infrequently" independent?
f. What is the probability that a customer frequently visits the store?
g. What is the probability that a customer never buys generic products?
h. What is the probability that a customer either frequently visits the store or never buys generic products or both?

3.65 An analyst at an airline company wants to predict whether the number of passengers for the various cabin classes will decrease, remain the same, or increase over the next year. The following table shows predictions based on the past records.

	Prediction		
	Decrease	Remains the same	Increase
Economy class	0.14	0.30	0.05
Business class	0.09	0.12	0.04
First class	0.10	0.02	0.14

a. What is the probability that the number of passengers in the economy class remains the same?
b. What is the probability that the number of passengers decrease?
c. If the number of passengers increased, what is the probability that this would happen for business class passengers?
d. If the number of passengers for first class is considered, what is the probability that it will decrease?

3.66 Subscribers to a local newspaper were asked whether they regularly, occasionally, or never read the business section and also whether they had traded common stocks (or shares in a mutual fund) over the last year. The table shown here indicates the proportions of subscribers in six joint classifications.

Traded Stocks	Read Business Section		
	Regularly	Occasionally	Never
Yes	0.18	0.10	0.04
No	0.16	0.31	0.21

a. What is the probability that a randomly chosen subscriber never reads the business section?
b. What is the probability that a randomly chosen subscriber has traded stocks over the last year?
c. What is the probability that a subscriber who never reads the business section has traded stocks over the last year?
d. What is the probability that a subscriber who traded stocks over the last year never reads the business section?
e. What is the probability that a subscriber who does not regularly read the business section traded stocks over the last year?

3.67 A corporation regularly takes deliveries of a particular sensitive part from three subcontractors. It found that the proportion of parts that are good or defective from the total received were as shown in the following table:

Part	Subcontractor		
	A	B	C
Good	0.27	0.30	0.33
Defective	0.02	0.05	0.03

a. If a part is chosen randomly from all those received, what is the probability that it is defective?
b. If a part is chosen randomly from all those received, what is the probability it is from subcontractor B?
c. What is the probability that a part from subcontractor B is defective?
d. What is the probability that a randomly chosen defective part is from subcontractor B?
e. Is the quality of a part independent of the source of supply?
f. In terms of quality, which of the three subcontractors is most reliable?

3.68 A form was circulated among the employees at the Sinopec Group, one of the world's largest oil refining, gas and petrochemical conglomerate, asking them if they are planning to apply for leaves in August (Yes/No) and their preferred location. The following table gives proportions of employees and their preferences.

Response	Destination Type			
	Coastal Resort	Mountain Resort	Thermal Spa	Rural Cottage
Yes	0.11	0.13	0.07	0.01
No	0.25	0.32	0.08	0.03

a. Find the probability that the preferred destination for a randomly chosen employee is a rural Cottage.

b. What is the probability that a randomly chosen employee will apply for leave in August?

c. Find the probability that the preferred destination for a randomly chosen employee who will not apply for leave in August is a coastal resort.

d. If a randomly chosen employee's preferred destination is a rural cottage, what is the probability that they will take apply for leave in August?

e. If a randomly chosen employee plans to apply for leave in August, what is the probability that their preferred destination is not a mountain resort?

f. Are the "vacation time" and "destination type" statistically independent?

3.69 The accompanying table shows proportions of computer salespeople classified according to marital status and whether they left their jobs or stayed over a period of 1 year.

	Time on job	
Marital Status	≥ one year	< one year
Married	0.64	0.13
Single	0.17	0.06

a. What is the probability that a randomly chosen salesperson was married?

b. What is the probability that a randomly chosen salesperson left the job within the year?

c. What is the probability that a randomly chosen single salesperson left the job within the year?

d. What is the probability that a randomly chosen salesperson who stayed in the job over the year was married?

3.70 The accompanying table shows proportions of adults in metropolitan areas, categorized as to whether they are public-radio contributors and whether or not they voted in the last election.

Voted	Contributors	Noncontributors
Yes	0.63	0.13
No	0.14	0.10

a. What is the probability that a randomly chosen adult from this population voted?

b. What is the probability that a randomly chosen adult from this population contributes to public radio?

c. What is the probability that a randomly chosen adult from this population did not contribute and did not vote?

3.71 At a business school in London, a student club distributes material about membership to new students attending an orientation meeting. Of those receiving this material 66% were women and 42% were men. Subsequently, it was found that 10% of the women and 8% of the men who received this material joined the club.

a. What is the probability that a randomly chosen new student who receives the membership material will join the club?

b. What is the probability that a randomly chosen new student who joins the club after receiving the membership material is a woman?

3.72 An analyst attempting to predict a corporation's earnings next year believes that the corporation's business is quite sensitive to the level of interest rates. He believes that, if average rates in the next year are more than 1% higher than this year, the probability of significant earnings growth is 0.1. If average rates next year are more than 1% lower than this year, the probability of significant earnings growth is estimated to be 0.8. Finally, if average interest rates next year are within 1% of this year's rates, the probability for significant earnings growth is put at 0.5. The analyst estimates that the probability is 0.25 that rates next year will be more than 1% higher than this year and 0.15 that they will be more than 1% lower than this year.

a. What is the estimated probability that both interest rates will be 1% higher and significant earnings growth will result?

b. What is the probability that this corporation will experience significant earnings growth?

c. If the corporation exhibits significant earnings growth, what is the probability that interest rates will have been more than 1% lower than in the current year?

3.73 Fourty-four percent of a corporation's blue-collar employees were in favor of a modified health care plan, and 24% of its blue-collar employees favored a proposal to change the work schedule. Thirty percent of those favoring the health care plan modification, favored the work schedule change.

a. What is the probability that a randomly selected blue-collar employee is in favor of both the modified health care plan and the changed work schedule?

b. What is the probability that a randomly chosen blue-collar employee is in favor of at least one of the two changes?

c. What is the probability that a blue-collar employee favoring the work schedule change also favors the modified health care plan?

3.74 Suppose the students at the Lebanese University, Beirut, can attend advanced math (precalculus) classes during their final year. Records show that among the students who took precalculus during their final year, 65% of them were at the top of the University's math class, and 45% were in the middle quarter, and 35% were in the bottom of the math class.

a. What is the probability that a randomly chosen student took the precalculus during the final year?

b. What is the probability that a randomly chosen student who attended the precalculus classes will be a toper of the class?

c. What is the probability that a randomly chosen student who did not attend the precalculus classes will not be a top quarter of the class?

3.75 Before books aimed at preschool children are marketed, reactions are obtained from a panel of preschool children. These reactions are categorized as favorable, neutral, or unfavorable. Subsequently, book sales are categorized as high, moderate, or low, according to the norms of this market. Similar panels have evaluated 1,000 books in the past. The accompanying table shows their reactions and the resulting market performance of the books.

Sales	Panel Reaction		
	Favorable	Neutral	Unfavorable
High	173	101	61
Moderate	88	211	70
Low	42	113	141

a. If the panel reaction is favorable, what is the probability that sales will be high?
b. If the panel reaction is unfavorable, what is the probability that sales will be low?
c. If the panel reaction is neutral or better, what is the probability that sales will be low?
d. If sales are low, what is the probability that the panel reaction was neutral or better?

3.76 A manufacturer produces boxes of candy, each containing 10 pieces. Two machines are used for this purpose. After a large batch has been produced, it is discovered that one of the machines, which produces 40% of the total output, has a fault that has led to the introduction of an impurity into 10% of the pieces of candy it makes. The other machine produced no defective pieces. From a single box of candy, one piece is selected at random and tested. If that piece contains no impurity, what is the probability that the faulty machine produced the box from which it came?

3.77 A student feels that 70% of her college courses have been enjoyable and the remainder have been boring. This student has access to student evaluations of professors and finds out that professors who had previously received strong positive evaluations from their students have taught 60% of his enjoyable courses and 25% of his boring courses. Next semester the student decides to take three courses, all from professors who have received strongly positive student evaluations. Assume that this student's reactions to the three courses are independent of one another.

a. What is the probability that this student will find all three courses enjoyable?
b. What is the probability that this student will find at least one of the courses enjoyable?

3.5 Bayes' Theorem

In this section we introduce an important result that has many applications to management decision making. Bayes' theorem provides a way of revising conditional probabilities by using available information. It also provides a procedure for determining how probability statements should be adjusted, given additional information.

Reverend Thomas Bayes (1702–1761) developed Bayes' theorem, originally published in 1763 after his death and again in 1958 (Bayes 1958). Because games of chance—and, hence, probability—were considered to be works of the devil, the results were not widely publicized. Since World War II a major area of statistics and a major area of management decision theory have developed based on the original works of Thomas Bayes. We begin our development with an example problem, followed by a more formal development.

Example 3.23 Drug Screening (Bayes' Theorem)

A number of amateur and professional sports organizations use routine screening tests to determine if athletes are using performance-enhancing drugs. Jennifer Smith, president of an amateur athletic union, has asked you to determine the feasibility of screening athletes to determine if they are using performance-enhancing drugs. Amateur athletes are increasingly denied participation or deprived of victories if they are found to be users.

As part of the study, you propose the following scenario for analysis. Suppose that 10% of the athletes seeking participation in the athletic union have used performance-enhancing drugs. In addition, suppose that a test is available that correctly identifies an athlete's drug usage 90% of the time. If an athlete is a drug user, the probability is 0.90 that the athlete is correctly identified by the test as a drug user. Similarly, if the athlete is not a drug user, the probability is 0.90 that the athlete is correctly identified as not using performance-enhancing drugs.

We should note that there are potential ethical and possible legal questions concerning the use of these tests. Here, we are concerned about the feasibility of using such a test if one has decided that such a test is proper, given the legal and value systems.

Solution The first step in the analysis is to identify the events in the sample space:

D_1: The athlete is a user of performance-enhancing drugs.
D_2: The athlete is not a user of performance-enhancing drugs.

The proposed test indicates positive or negative results:

T_1: Test says that the athlete is a user of performance-enhancing drugs.
T_2: Test says that the athlete is not a user of performance-enhancing drugs.

From the information provided, the following probabilities can be defined:

$$P(D_1) = 0.10 \qquad P(D_2) = 0.90$$
$$P(T_1|D_1) = 0.90 \quad P(T_2|D_1) = 0.10$$
$$P(T_1|D_2) = 0.10 \quad P(T_2|D_2) = 0.90$$

Using these probabilities, a two-way table, Table 3.11, containing the joint probabilities can be constructed:

$$P(D_1 \cap T_1) = P(T_1|D_1)P(D_1) = 0.90 \times 0.10 = 0.09$$
$$P(D_1 \cap T_2) = P(T_2|D_1)P(D_1) = 0.10 \times 0.10 = 0.01$$
$$P(D_2 \cap T_1) = P(T_1|D_2)P(D_2) = 0.10 \times 0.90 = 0.09$$
$$P(D_2 \cap T_2) = P(T_2|D_2)P(D_2) = 0.90 \times 0.90 = 0.81$$

Table 3.11 Drug Test Subgroups

	T_1 (TEST SAYS DRUG USER)	T_2 (TEST SAYS NOT A DRUG USER)	TOTAL
D_1 (Drug User)	0.09	0.01	0.10
D_2 (Not a Drug User)	0.09	0.81	0.90
Total	0.18	0.82	1.0

From Table 3.11 we can easily determine the conditional probability of a drug user, given that the test says drug user, by dividing the joint probability of D_1 and T_1 (0.09) by the marginal probability of T_1 (0.18):

$$P(D_1|T_1) = \frac{P(D_1 \cap T_1)}{P(T_1)} = \frac{0.09}{0.18} = 0.50$$

Similarly, the probability of not a drug user, given that the test says not a drug user, can be obtained from the second column:

$$P(D_2|T_2) = \frac{P(D_2 \cap T_2)}{P(T_2)} = \frac{0.81}{0.82} = 0.988$$

From these results we see that, if the test says an athlete is not a drug user, the probability is very high that the test result is correct. However, if the test says that the athlete is a drug user, the probability is only 0.50 that the athlete is a drug user. This is a large increase over a probability of 0.10 for a randomly selected athlete. However, it is clear that the athletic association would not want to reject athletes merely on the results of this screening test. The potential for unethical actions and serious legal challenge would be too great. The best strategy would be to use a second independent test to further screen the athlete identified as a drug user by the first test. We stress again that there may be serious ethical and medical concerns if athletes are rejected on the basis of only the first test!

Given this background, we now provide a more formal development of Bayes' theorem. To begin, we first review the multiplication rule, Equation 3.10:

$$P(A_1 \cap B_1) = P(A_1|B_1)P(B_1) = P(B_1|A_1)P(A_1)$$

Bayes' theorem follows from this rule.

Bayes' Theorem

Let A_1 and B_1 be two events. Then **Bayes' theorem** states that

$$P(B_1|A_1) = \frac{P(A_1|B_1)P(B_1)}{P(A_1)} \tag{3.14}$$

and

$$P(A_1|B_1) = \frac{P(B_1|A_1)P(A_1)}{P(B_1)}$$

Solution Steps for Bayes' Theorem

1. Define the subset events from the problem.
2. Define the probabilities and conditional probabilities for the events defined in Step 1.
3. Compute the complements of the probabilities.
4. Formally state and apply Bayes' theorem to compute the solution probability.

Here, we apply these solution steps to a problem that requires careful analysis. Consider Example 3.23 again. The first task is to identify the events in the sample space. The sample space in Example 3.23 consists of athletes separated into D_1, users of performance-enhancing drugs, and D_2, nonusers of the drugs. This required an independent diagnosis to determine which athletes were actually drug users and which were not. These events cover the sample space. Athletes were also identified by their test classification, T_1, the test indicates drug user, and T_2, the test indicates not a drug user. These events also cover the sample space. Note that a test result T_1, which indicates drug user, does not guarantee that the person is a drug user.

After the events have been defined, we need to determine the capability of the procedure to predict, using the data. Thus, in Example 3.23 the test was given to a group of known users of performance-enhancing drugs and to a group of known non–drug users. These test results provided the conditional probabilities of the test results, given either drug user or not. The data were converted to information concerning the quality of the screening test predictions by using Bayes' theorem. The final task is to express one or more questions in the form of Bayes' theorem. In Example 3.23 we were interested in the probability that an athlete was a drug user, given that the athlete obtained a positive result on the test. We also realized that it was important to know the probability that an athlete was not a drug user, given a positive test result.

Bayes' theorem is often expressed in a different, but equivalent, form that uses more detailed information. Let $E_1, E_2, \ldots, E_K$ be K mutually exclusive and collectively exhaustive events, and let A_1 be some other event. We can find the probability of E_i, given A_1, by using Bayes' theorem:

$$P(E_i|A_1) = \frac{P(A_1|E_i)P(E_i)}{P(A_1)}$$

The denominator can be expressed in terms of the probabilities of A_1, given the various E_is, by using the intersections and the multiplication rule:

$$P(A_1) = P(A_1 \cap E_1) + P(A_1 \cap E_2) + \cdots + P(A_1 \cap E_K)$$
$$= P(A_1|E_1)P(E_1) + P(A_1|E_2)P(E_2) + \cdots + P(A_1|E_K)P(E_K)$$

These results can be combined to provide a second form of Bayes' theorem.

Bayes' Theorem (Alternative Statement)

Let $E_1, E_2, \ldots, E_K$ be K mutually exclusive and collectively exhaustive events, and let A be some other event. The conditional probability of E_i, given A, can be expressed as Bayes' theorem:

$$P(E_i|A_1) = \frac{P(A_1|E_i)P(E_i)}{P(A_1)}$$

$$P(E_i|A_1) = \frac{P(A_1|E_i)P(E_i)}{P(A_1|E_1)P(E_1) + P(A_1|E_2)P(E_2) + \cdots + P(A_1|E_K)P(E_K)} \quad (3.15)$$

where

$$P(A_1) = P(A_1 \cap E_1) + P(A_1 \cap E_2) + \cdots + P(A_1 \cap E_K)$$
$$= P(A_1|E_1)P(E_1) + P(A_1|E_2)P(E_2) + \cdots + P(A_1|E_K)P(E_K)$$

The advantage of this restatement of the theorem lies in the fact that the probabilities it involves are often precisely those that are directly available.

This process for solving conditional probability and/or Bayes' problems is summarized in Example 3.24.

Example 3.24 Automobile Sales Incentive (Bayes' Theorem)

A car dealership knows from past experience that 10% of the people who come into the showroom and talk to a salesperson will eventually purchase a car. To increase the chances of success, you propose to offer a free dinner with a salesperson for all people who agree to listen to a complete sales presentation. You know that some people will do anything for a free dinner, even if they do not intend to purchase a car. However, some people would rather not spend a dinner with a car salesperson. Thus, you wish to test the effectiveness of this sales promotion incentive. The project is conducted for 6 months, and 40% of the people who purchased cars had a free dinner. In addition, 10% of the people who did not purchase cars had a free dinner.

The specific questions to be answered are the following:

a. Do people who accept the dinner have a higher probability of purchasing a new car?
b. What is the probability that a person who does not accept a free dinner will purchase a car?

Solution

Step 1. Define the subset events from the problem:

D_1: The customer has dinner with the salesperson.
D_2: The customer does not have dinner with the salesperson.

P_1: The customer purchases a car.
P_2: The customer does not purchase a car.

Step 2. Define the probabilities for the events defined in Step 1:

$$P(P_1) = 0.10 \quad P(D_1|P_1) = 0.40 \quad P(D_1|P_2) = 0.10$$

Step 3. Compute the complements of the probabilities:

$$P(P_2) = 0.90 \quad P(D_2|P_1) = 0.60 \quad P(D_2|P_2) = 0.90$$

Step 4. Apply Bayes' theorem to compute the probability for the problem solution.

a. We know that the sales promotion plan has increased the probability of a car purchase if more than 10% of those that had dinner purchased a car. Specifically, we ask if

$$P(P_1|D_1) > P(P_1) = 0.10$$

Using Bayes' theorem, we find that

$$P(P_1|D_1) = \frac{P(D_1|P_1)P(P_1)}{P(D_1|P_1)P(P_1) + P(D_1|P_2)P(P_2)}$$
$$= \frac{0.40 \times 0.10}{0.40 \times 0.10 + 0.10 \times 0.90}$$
$$= 0.308$$

Therefore, the probability of purchase is higher, given the dinner with the salesperson.

b. This question asks that we compute the probability of purchase, P_1, given that the customer does not have dinner with the salesperson, D_2. We again apply Bayes' theorem to compute the following:

$$P(P_1|D_2) = \frac{P(D_2|P_1)P(P_1)}{P(D_2|P_1)P(P_1) + P(D_2|P_2)P(P_2)}$$
$$= \frac{0.60 \times 0.10}{0.60 \times 0.10 + 0.90 \times 0.90}$$
$$= 0.069$$

We see that those who refuse the dinner have a lower probability of purchase. To provide additional evaluation of the sales program, we might also wish to compare the 6-month sales experience with that of other dealers and with previous sales experience, given similar economic conditions.

We have presented a logical step-by-step or linear procedure for solving Bayes' problems. This procedure works very well for persons experienced in solving this type of problem. The procedure can also help you to organize Bayes' problems. However, most real problem solving in new situations does not follow a step-by-step, or linear, procedure. Thus, you are likely to move back to previous steps and revise your initial definitions. In some cases you may find it useful to write out Bayes' theorem before you define the probabilities. The mathematical form defines the probabilities that must be obtained from the problem description. Alternatively, you may want to construct a two-way table, as we did in Example 3.23. As you are learning to solve these problems, use the structure, but learn to be creative and willing to go back to previous steps.

Example 3.25 Market Research (Bayes' Throrem)

Blue Star United, a major electronics distributor, has hired Southwest Forecasters, a market research firm, to predict the level of demand for its new product that combines cell phone and complete Internet capabilities at a price substantially below its major competitors. As part of its deliverables, Southwest provides a rating of Poor, Fair, or Good, on the basis of its research. Prior to engaging Southwest Blue Star, management concluded the following probabilities for the market-demand levels:

$$P(\text{Low}) = P(s_1) = 0.1 \quad P(\text{Moderate}) = P(s_2) = 0.5 \quad P(\text{High}) = P(s_3) = 0.4$$

Southwest completes its study and concludes that the market potential for this product is poor. What conclusion should Blue Star reach based on the market-study results?

Solution A review of the market-research company's records reveals the quality of its past predictions in this field. Table 3.12 shows, for each level of demand outcome, the proportion of Poor, Fair, and Good assessments that were made prior to introducing the product to the market.

Table 3.12 Proportion of Assessments Provided by a Market-Research Organization Prior to Various Levels of Market Demand (Conditional Probabilities)

	MARKET DEMAND THAT ACTUALLY OCCURRED AFTER ASSESSMENT WAS PROVIDED		
Assessment	*Low Demand* (s_1)	*Moderate Demand* (s_2)	*High Demand* (s_3)
Poor	0.6	0.3	0.1
Fair	0.2	0.4	0.2
Good	0.2	0.3	0.7

For example, on 10% of occasions that demand was high, the assessment prior to market introduction was Poor. Thus, in the notation of conditional probability, denoting *Low*, *Moderate*, and *High* demand levels by s_1, s_2, and s_3, respectively, it follows that

$$P(\text{Poor}|s_1) = 0.6 \quad P(\text{Poor}|s_2) = 0.3 \quad P(\text{Poor}|s_3) = 0.1$$

Given this new information, the prior probabilities

$$P(s_1) = 0.1 \quad P(s_2) = 0.5 \quad P(s_3) = 0.4$$

for the three demand levels can be modified using Bayes' theorem. For a low level of demand, the posterior probability is as follows:

$$P(s_1|\text{Poor}) = \frac{P(\text{Poor}|s_1)P(s_1)}{P(\text{Poor}|s_1)P(s_1) + P(\text{Poor}|s_2)P(s_2) + P(\text{Poor}|s_3)P(s_3)}$$

$$= \frac{(0.6)(0.1)}{(0.6)(0.1) + (0.3)(0.5) + (0.1)(0.4)} = \frac{0.06}{0.25} = 0.24$$

Similarly, for the other two demand levels, the posterior probabilities are as follows:

$$P(s_2|\text{Poor}) = \frac{(0.3)(0.5)}{0.25} = 0.6 \quad P(s_3|\text{Poor}) = \frac{(0.1)(0.4)}{0.25} = 0.16$$

Based on this analysis we see that the probability for high demand is now reduced to 0.16, and the most likely outcome is moderate demand with a posterior probability of 0.6.

Subjective Probabilities in Management Decision Making

An interesting interpretation of Bayes' theorem has been developed in the context of subjective probabilities. Suppose that an individual is interested in event B and forms a subjective view of the probability that B will occur; in this context the probability $P(B)$ is called a *prior* probability. If the individual then acquires an additional piece of information—namely, that event A has occurred—this may cause a modification of the initial judgment as to the likelihood of the occurrence of B. Since A is known to have happened, the relevant probability for B is now the conditional probability of B, given A, and is termed the *posterior* probability. Viewed in this way, Bayes' theorem can be thought of as a mechanism for updating a prior probability to a posterior probability when the information that A has occurred becomes available. The theorem then states that the updating is accomplished through the multiplication of the prior probability $P(B)$ by $P(A \mid B)/P(A)$.

We know that people commonly form and subsequently modify subjective probability assessments. For example, an important part of an auditor's work is to determine whether or not the account balances are correct. Before examining a particular account, the auditor will have formed an opinion, based on previous audits, of the probability that there is an error. However, if the balance is found to be substantially different from what might be expected on the basis of the last few years' figures, the auditor will believe that the probability of an error is higher and, therefore, give the account particularly close attention. Here, the prior probability has been updated in the light of additional information.

Example 3.26 Auditing Business Records (Bayes' Theorem)

Based on an examination of past records of a corporation's account balances, an auditor finds that 15% have contained errors. Of those balances in error, 60% were regarded as unusual values based on historical figures. Of all the account balances, 20% were unusual values. If the figure for a particular balance appears unusual on this basis, what is the probability that it is in error?

Solution Let A_1 be "error in account balance" and B_1 be "unusual value based on historical figures." Then, from the available information,

$$P(A_1) = 0.15 \quad P(B_1) = 0.20 \quad P(B_1 \mid A_1) = 0.60$$

Using Bayes' theorem,

$$P(A_1 \mid B_1) = \frac{P(B_1 \mid A_1) P(A_1)}{P(B_1)} = \frac{(0.60)(0.15)}{0.20} = 0.45$$

Thus, given the information that the account balance appears unusual, the probability that it is in error is modified from the prior 0.15 to the posterior 0.45.

EXERCISES

Basic Exercises
The following basic exercises use a sample space defined by events A_1, A_2, B_1, and B_2.

3.78 Given $P(A_1) = 0.38, P(B_1 \mid A_1) = 0.87$, and $P(B_1 \mid A_2) = 0.42$, what is the probability of $P(A_1 \mid B_1)$?

3.79 Given $P(A_1) = 0.60, P(B_1 \mid A_1) = 0.40$, and $P(B_1 \mid A_2) = 0.30$, what is the probability of $P(A_1 \mid B_1)$?

3.80 Given $P(A_1) = 0.50, P(B_1 \mid A_1) = 0.40$, and $P(B_1 \mid A_2) = 0.70$, what is the probability of $P(A_1 \mid B_2)$?

3.81 Given $P(A_1) = 0.40, P(B_1 \mid A_1) = 0.60$, and $P(B_1 \mid A_2) = 0.70$, what is the probability of $P(A_2 \mid B_2)$?

3.82 Given $P(A_1) = 0.60, P(B_1 \mid A_1) = 0.60$, and $P(B_1 \mid A_2) = 0.40$, what is the probability of $P(A_1 \mid B_1)$?

Application Exercises

3.83 A publisher sends advertising material for an accounting text to 60% of all the professors teaching the appropriate accounting course in the Netherlands. Twenty percent of the professors who received this material adopted the book, as did 5% of the professors who did not receive the material. What is the probability that a professor who adopts the book has received the advertising material?

3.84 A cryptocurrency market analyst investigated the performance of a large number of cryptocurrencies listed on CoinMarketCap, a website that tracks cryptocurrencies by market captialization. The analyst found that of all the cryptocurrencies 15% performed much better (that is, the price rose) in comparison to the previous year, 23% performed much worse (that is, the price fell) in comparison to the previous year, and the others performed about the same as the last year. Of the cryptocurrencies that were rated as "best buys," 30% were those that had performed much better than the previous year, 17% were those that performed about the same, and 5% were those that had performed much worse. What is the probability that a cryptocurrency rated as "best buy" performed much better than the previous year?

3.85 The Watts New Lightbulb Corporation ships large consignments of lightbulbs to big industrial users. When the production process is functioning correctly, which is 90% of the time, 10% of all bulbs produced are defective. However, the process is susceptible to an occasional malfunction, leading to a defective rate of 50%. If a defective bulb is found, what is the probability that the process is functioning correctly? If a nondefective bulb is found, what is the probability that the process is operating correctly?

3.86 You are the meat products manager for Gigantic Foods, a large retail supermarket food distributor who is studying the characteristics of its whole chicken product mix. Chickens are purchased from both Free Range Farms and Big Foods Ltd. Free Range Farms produces chickens that are fed with natural grains and grubs in open feeding areas. In their product mix, 10% of the processed chickens weigh less than 3 pounds. Big Foods Ltd. produces chickens in cages using enriched food grains for rapid growth. They note that 20% of their processed chickens weigh less than three poounds. Gigantic Foods purchases 40% of its chickens from Free Range Farms and mixes the products together with no identification of the supplier. Suppose you purchase a chicken that weighs more than three pounds. What is the probability the chicken came from Free Range Farms? If you purchase 5 chickens, what is the probability that at least 3 came from Free Range Farms?

3.87 You are evaluating the player selection process used by a major league baseball team. The team gives a bonus to 10% of the players that it signs to a contract, 30% of the players who were obtained through a trade, and the remainder did not receive a bonus. Examination of the player records for the past five years indicates that 40% of the players who were on the major league roster for at least one year received an initial signing bonus. In addition, 30% of the players on the major league roster for at least one year did not receive an initial signing bonus. The remaining players were obtained from trades. For those players who were signed and did not make the major league roster, 20% had received bonuses and 70% had not, with the remainder coming from trades. Of all players signed or obtained in trades, 20% are on the major league roster for at least one year.

a. What is the probability that a player who received a bonus is on the major league roster for at least one year?

b. What is the probability that a player who did not receive a bonus is on the major league roster for at least one year?

c. Should a player insist on a signing bonus because this will increase his probability of being on the major league roster?

KEY WORDS

- addition rule of probabilities, 116
- basic outcomes, 99
- Bayes' theorem, 138
- Bayes' theorem (alternative statement), 139
- classical probability, 105
- collectively exhaustive, 102
- combinations, 108
- complement, 102
- complement rule, 115
- conditional probability, 117
- event, 100
- independent events, 129
- intersection, 100
- joint probability, 100
- marginal probabilities, 127
- multiplication rule of probabilities, 118
- mutually exclusive, 100
- number of combinations, 106
- odds, 130
- overinvolvement ratio, 131
- permutations, 107
- probability postulates, 111
- random experiment, 98
- relative frequency probability, 110
- sample space, 99
- solution steps for Bayes' theorem, 138
- statistical independence, 120
- subjective probability, 111
- union, 101

3.88 Suppose that you have an intelligent friend who has not studied probability. How would you explain to your friend the distinction between mutually exclusive events and independent events? Illustrate your answer with suitable examples.

3.89 State, with evidence, whether each of the following statements is true or false:

a. The complement of the union of two events is the intersection of their complements.

b. The sum of the probabilities of collectively exhaustive events must equal 1.

c. The number of combinations of x objects chosen from n is equal to the number of combinations of $(n - x)$ objects chosen from n, where $1 \leq x \leq (n - 1)$.

d. If A and B are two events, the probability of A, given B, is the same as the probability of B, given A, if the probability of A is the same as the probability of B.

e. If an event and its complement are equally likely to occur, the probability of that event must be 0.5.

f. If A and B are independent, then $\overline{A}$ and $\overline{B}$ must be independent.

g. If A and B are mutually exclusive, then $\overline{A}$ and $\overline{B}$ must be mutually exclusive.

3.90 Explain carefully the meaning of conditional probability. Why is this concept important in discussing the chance of an event's occurrence?

3.91 Bayes' theorem is important because it provides a rule for moving from a prior probability to a posterior probability. Elaborate on this statement so that it would be well understood by a fellow student who has not yet studied probability.

3.92 State with evidence, whether each of the following statements is true or false:

a. If two events are mutually exclusive, the probability of their union is the sum of their probabilities.

b. The sum of the probabilities of two events cannot be more than 2.

c. The sum of the probabilities of an event and its complement cannot be more than 2.

d. An event and its complement are collectively exhaustive and mutually exclusive.

e. The probability of the intersection of two events is always smaller than the individual probability of each event.

3.93 Distinguish among joint probability, marginal probability, and conditional probability. Provide some examples to make the distinctions clear.

3.94 State with evidence, whether each of the following statements is true or false:

a. If events A and B are mutually exclusive, the conditional probability of A, given B, is equal to the probability that event A occurs times the probability that event B occurs.

b. If events A and B are independent, the conditional probability of A given B is equal to the probability that event A occurs times the probability that event B occurs,

c. The conditional probability of A given B is equal to the probability of event A if events A and B are independent.

d. When two events are independent, the probability of both occurring is the sum of the probabilities of the individual events.

3.95 Show that the probability of the union of events A and B can be written as follows:

$$P(A \cup B) = P(A) + P(B)[1 - P(A|B)]$$

3.96 An insurance company estimated that 30% of all automobile accidents were partly caused by weather conditions and that 20% of all automobile accidents involved bodily injury. Further, of those accidents that involved bodily injury, 40% were partly caused by weather conditions.

a. What is the probability that a randomly chosen accident both was partly caused by weather conditions and involved bodily injury?

b. Are the events "partly caused by weather conditions" and "involved bodily injury" independent?

c. If a randomly chosen accident was partly caused by weather conditions, what is the probability that it involved bodily injury?

d. What is the probability that a randomly chosen accident both was not partly caused by weather conditions and did not involve bodily injury?

3.97 Suppose a student needs to apply for a loan to enroll at the University of Melbourne, Australia. She believes that there is a 0.8 probability that the loan will be approved within the next three months if the bank interest rate remains the same, and a 0.4 probability that the loan will be approved within the next three months if the interest rates change. A bank manager believes that there is 0.65 probability that the interest rate will remain the same in the next three months.

a. What is the probability that the student's loan will be approved by the bank within the next three months?

b. If there is a 0.75 probability to get the loan, what is the probability that the bank interest rate will remain the same?

3.98 Staff, Inc., a management consulting company, is surveying the personnel of Acme Ltd. It determined that 35% of the analysts have an MBA and that 40% of all analysts are over age 35. Further, of those who have an MBA, 30% are over age 35.

a. What is the probability that a randomly chosen analyst both has an MBA and also is over age 35?

b. What is the probability that a randomly chosen analyst who is over age 35 has an MBA?

c. What is the probability that a randomly chosen analyst has an MBA or is over age 35?

d. What is the probability that a randomly chosen analyst who is over age 35 does not have an MBA?

e. Are the events MBA and over age 35 independent?

f. Are the events MBA and over age 35 mutually exclusive?

g. Are the events MBA and over age 35 collectively exhaustive?

3.99 In a campus restaurant it was found that 35% of all customers order vegetarian meals and that 50% of all customers are students. Further, 25% of all customers who are students order vegetarian meals.

a. What is the probability that a randomly chosen customer both is a student and orders a vegetarian meal?

b. If a randomly chosen customer orders a vegetarian meal, what is the probability that the customer is a student?

c. What is the probability that a randomly chosen customer both does not order a vegetarian meal and is not a student?

d. Are the events "customer orders a vegetarian meal" and "customer is a student" independent?

e. Are the events "customer orders a vegetarian meal" and "customer is a student" mutually exclusive?

f. Are the events "customer orders a vegetarian meal" and "customer is a student" collectively exhaustive?

3.100 Suppose in Greece it is known that 75% of all properties in the country is privately held and 35% is located along the coast. Of all the properties located along the coast, 57% is privately owned.

a. What is the probability that a randomly chosen property in Greece is privately held and located along the coast?

b. What is the probability that a property is privately held or is located along the coast

c. What is the probability that a privately owned property is located along the coast?

d. Are ownership and location statistically independent?

3.101 In a large corporation, 80% of the employees are men and 20% are women. The highest levels of education obtained by the employees are graduate training for 10% of the men, undergraduate training for 30% of the men, and high school training for 60% of the men. The highest levels of education obtained are also graduate training for 15% of the women, undergraduate training for 40% of the women, and high school training for 45% of the women.

a. What is the probability that a randomly chosen employee will be a man with only a high school education?

b. What is the probability that a randomly chosen employee will have graduate training?

c. What is the probability that a randomly chosen employee who has graduate training is a man?

d. Are gender and level of education of employees in this corporation statistically independent?

e. What is the probability that a randomly chosen employee who has not had graduate training is a woman?

3.102 A large corporation organized a ballot for all its workers on a new bonus plan. It was found that 65% of all night-shift workers favored the plan and that 40% of all female workers favored the plan. Also, 50% of all employees are night-shift workers and 30% of all employees are women. Finally, 20% of all night-shift workers are women.

a. What is the probability that a randomly chosen employee is a woman in favor of the plan?

b. What is the probability that a randomly chosen employee is either a woman or a night-shift worker (or both)?

c. Is employee gender independent of whether the night shift is worked?

d. What is the probability that a female employee is a night-shift worker?

e. If 50% of all male employees favor the plan, what is the probability that a randomly chosen employee both does not work the night shift and does not favor the plan?

3.103 A jury of 12 members is to be selected from a panel consisting of 8 men and 8 women.

a. How many different jury selections are possible?

b. If the choice is made randomly, what is the probability that a majority of the jury members will be men?

3.104 A consignment of 12 electronic components contains 1 component that is faulty. Two components are chosen randomly from this consignment for testing.

a. How many different combinations of 2 components could be chosen?

b. What is the probability that the faulty component will be chosen for testing?

3.105 A Turkish blogger posts many diabetic-friendly and gluten-free recipes on his "Healthy Cooking" blog. As the blog administrator, he decides which healthy food advertisements should be allowed on his blog. The criteria for selection include that the product advertised needs to increase sale by 10% in the first three months. Of all the products advertised on the blog, 40% see an increase in sale in the first three months. Reviewing the yearly income, the blogger found that he earns a certain amount from 70% of the products that increased in sale in the first three months and from 30% of the products that did not. What is the probability that the product will increase in sale by 10% in the next three months given that the blogger received the compensation?

3.106 Of 100 patients with a certain disease, 10 were chosen at random to undergo a drug treatment that increases the cure rate from 50% for those not given the treatment to 75% for those given the drug treatment.

a. What is the probability that a randomly chosen patient both was cured and was given the drug treatment?
b. What is the probability that a patient who was cured had been given the drug treatment?
c. What is the probability that a specific group of 10 patients was chosen to undergo the drug treatment? (Leave your answer in terms of factorials.)

3.107 Subscriptions to a particular magazine are classified as gift, previous renewal, direct mail, and subscription service. In January 8% of expiring subscriptions were gifts; 41%, previous renewal; 6%, direct mail; and 45%, subscription service. The percentages of renewals in these four categories were 81%, 79%, 60%, and 21%, respectively. In February of the same year, 10% of expiring subscriptions were gift; 57%, previous renewal; 24%, direct mail; and 9%, subscription service. The percentages of renewals were 80%, 76%, 51%, and 14%, respectively.

a. Find the probability that a randomly chosen subscription expiring in January was renewed.
b. Find the probability that a randomly chosen subscription expiring in February was renewed.
c. Verify that the probability in part (b) that is higher than that in part (a). Do you believe that the editors of this magazine should view the change from January to February as a positive or negative development?

3.108 The Customs Inspection agency at international airports has developed a traveler profiling system (TPS) to detect passengers who are trying to bring more liquor into the country than is allowed by present regulations. Long-term studies indicate that 20% of the passengers are carrying more liquor than is allowed. Tests on the new TPS scheme has shown that of those carrying illegal amounts of liquor, 80% will be identified and subject to complete luggage search. In addition 20% of those not carrying illegal amounts of liquor will also be identified by TPS and subject to a complete luggage search.

If a passenger is identified by TPS, what is the probability that the passenger is carrying an illegal amount of liquor? Comment on the value of this system.

3.109 In a large city, 8% of the inhabitants have contracted a particular disease. A test for this disease is positive in 80% of people who have the disease and is negative in 80% of people who do not have the disease. What is the probability that a person for whom the test result is positive has the disease?

3.110 A life insurance salesman finds that, of all the sales he makes, 70% are to people who already own policies. He also finds that, of all contacts for which no sale is made, 50% already own life insurance policies.

Furthermore, 40% of all contacts result in sales. What is the probability that a sale will be made to a contact who already owns a policy?

3.111 A traffic safety service found that only 30% of drivers take the highway to coastal destinations due to the costly highway toll. Of those who do take the highway, 80% use the central traffic information center to obtain traffic information and road conditions. It was also found that 14% of the drivers who take local routes to coastal destinations use the central traffic information service for assistance. What is the probability that a driver who uses the central traffic information service will use the highway to reach the coast?

3.112 The accompanying table shows, for 1,000 forecasts of earnings per share made by financial analysts, the numbers of forecasts and outcomes in particular categories (compared with the previous year).

| | Forecast | | |
| | | About the | |
Outcome	Improvement	Same	Worse
Improvement	210	82	66
About the same	106	153	75
Worse	75	84	149

a. Find the probability that if the forecast is for a worse performance in earnings, this outcome will result.
b. If the forecast is for an improvement in earnings, find the probability that this outcome fails to result.

3.113 A dean has found that 62% of entering freshmen and 78% of community college transfers eventually graduate. Of all entering students, 73% are entering freshmen and the remainder are community college transfers.

a. What is the probability that a randomly chosen entering student is an entering freshman who will eventually graduate?
b. Find the probability that a randomly chosen entering student will eventually graduate.
c. What is the probability that a randomly chosen entering student either is an entering freshman or will eventually graduate (or both)?
d. Are the events "eventually graduates" and "enters as community college transfer" statistically independent?

3.114 A market-research group specializes in providing assessments of the prospects of sites for new children's toy stores in shopping centers. The group assesses prospects as good, fair, or poor. The records of assessments made by this group were examined, and it was found that for all stores that had annual sales over $1,000,000, the assessments were good for 70%, fair for 20%, and poor for 10%. For all stores that turned out to be unsuccessful, the assessments were good for 20%, fair for 30%, and poor for 50%. It is known that 60% of new clothing stores are successful and 40% are unsuccessful.

a. For a randomly chosen store, what is the probability that prospects will be assessed as good?

b. If prospects for a store are assessed as good, what is the probability that it will be successful?

c. Are the events "prospects assessed as good" and "store is successful" statistically independent?

d. Suppose that five stores are chosen at random. What is the probability that at least one of them will be successful?

3.115 A restaurant manager classifies customers as regular, occasional, or new, and finds that of all customers 50%, 40%, and 10%, respectively, fall into these categories. The manager found that wine was ordered by 70% of the regular customers, by 50% of the occasional customers, and by 30% of the new customers.

a. What is the probability that a randomly chosen customer orders wine?

b. If wine is ordered, what is the probability that the person ordering is a regular customer?

c. If wine is ordered, what is the probability that the person ordering is an occasional customer?

3.116 A record-store owner assesses customers entering the store as high school age, college age, or older, and finds that of all customers 30%, 50%, and 20%, respectively, fall into these categories. The owner also found that purchases were made by 20% of high school age customers, by 60% of college age customers, and by 80% of older customers.

a. What is the probability that a randomly chosen customer entering the store will make a purchase?

b. If a randomly chosen customer makes a purchase, what is the probability that this customer is high school age?

3.117 Note that this exercise represents a completely imaginary situation. Suppose that a tourist agency wants to offer four free trips aboard a Caribbean cruise line. The Agency considers 10 women and 7 men, all of whom are randomly selected from the customers who frequently book trips with this agency. Since the agency wants to make an unbiased selection, they use a free Internet software to assign the four trips randomly. What is the probability that all four free trips will be awarded to female customers?

3.118 A survey of auto consumers shows the buying preferences of consumers in Asia. Out of 120 cars included in the survey, 75 are brand new and the rest are used cars. Of the new cars, 12 are MAZDAs, 25 BMWs, 27 KIAs, and rest is Citroens. Of the used cars, 14 are MAZDAs, 13 are BMWs, and the rest of them are Citroens. Based on this data, calculate the following:

a. The probability that a buyer purchases a used car.

b. The probability that a buyer purchases a Citroen.

c. The probability that a buyer does not purchase BMW.

d. The probability that a buyer purchases a used car that is a MAZDA.

3.119 Several insurance companies are trying to promote additional health insurance coverage. In order to offer complete information, insurance providers connect with customers via phone or email. It is estimated that approximately 87% of total customers are contacted by phone, half of whom purchase the additional health insurance coverage, and 12% of the customers who are not contacted by phone purchase the additional coverage anyway. Given the information about the purchase patterns of additional health insurance coverage, what is the probability that a phone call is received by a customer who purchases additional health insurance coverage?

3.120 After meeting with the regional sales managers, Lauretta Anderson, president of Cowpie Computers, Inc., you find that she believes that the probability that sales will grow by 10% in the next year is 0.70. After coming to this conclusion, she receives a report that John Cadariu of Minihard Software, Inc., has just announced a new operating system that will be available for customers in 8 months. From past history she knows that in situations where growth has eventually occurred, new operating systems have been announced 30% of the time. However, in situations where growth has not eventually occurred, new operating systems have been announced 10% of the time. Based on all these facts, what is the probability that sales will grow by 10%?

3.121 Sally Firefly purchases hardwood lumber for a custom furniture-building shop. She uses three suppliers, Northern Hardwoods, Mountain Top, and Spring Valley. Lumber is classified as either clear or has defects, which includes 20% of the pile. A recent analysis of the defect lumber pile showed that 30% came from Northern Hardwoods and 50% came from Mountain Top. Analysis of the clear pile indicates that 40% came from Northern and 40% came from Spring Valley. What is the percent of clear lumber from each of the three suppliers? What is the percent of lumber from each of the three suppliers?

3.122 Robert Smith uses either regular plowing or minimal plowing to prepare the cornfields on his Minnesota farm. Regular plowing was used for 40% of the field acreage. Analysis after the crop was harvested showed that 50% of the high-yield acres were from minimal-plowing fields and 40% of the low yield fields were from fields with regular plowing. What is the probability of a high yield if regular plowing is used? What is the probability that a field with high yield had been prepared using regular plowing?

Appendix: Unions and Intersections of Events

The Venn diagrams in Figures 3.10, 3.11, and 3.12 illustrate three results involving unions and intersections of events.

Result 1

Let A and B be two events. Then the events $A \cap B$ and $\overline{A} \cap B$ are mutually exclusive, and their union is B, as illustrated in the Venn diagram in Figure 3.10. Clearly,

$$(A \cap B) \cup (\overline{A} \cap B) = B \tag{3.16}$$

Figure 3.10 Venn Diagram for Result 1: $(A \cap B) \cup (\overline{A} \cap B) = B$

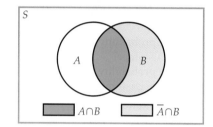

Result 2

Let A and B be two events. The events A and $\overline{A} \cap B$ are mutually exclusive, and their union is $A \cup B$, as illustrated in the Venn diagram in Figure 3.11—that is,

$$A \cup (\overline{A} \cap B) = A \cup B \tag{3.17}$$

Figure 3.11 Venn Diagram for Result 2: $A \cup (\overline{A} \cap B) = A \cup B$

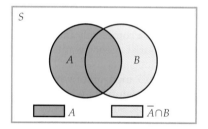

Result 3

Let $E_1, E_2, \ldots, E_K$ be K mutually exclusive and collectively exhaustive events, and let A be some other event. Then the K events $E_1 \cap A, E_2 \cap A, \cdots, E_K \cap A$ are mutually exclusive, and their union is A—that is,

$$(E_1 \cap A) \cup (E_2 \cap A) \cup \cdots \cup (E_K \cap A) = A \tag{3.18}$$

We can better understand the third statement by examining the Venn diagram in Figure 3.12. The large rectangle indicates the entire sample space and is divided into smaller rectangles depicting K mutually exclusive and collectively exhaustive events $E_1, E_2, \ldots, E_K$. The event A is represented by the closed figure. We see that the events composed of the intersection of A and each of the E events are indeed mutually exclusive and that their union is simply the event A. We can, therefore, write the following:

$$(E_1 \cap A) \cup (E_2 \cap A) \cup \cdots \cup (E_K \cap A) = A$$

Figure 3.12
Venn Diagram for
Result 3

	E_1	E_2	E_3	E_4	E_5	....	E_K
A	$E_1 \cap A$	$E_2 \cap A$	$E_3 \cap A$	$E_4 \cap A$	$E_5 \cap A$	....	$E_K \cap A$
$\overline{A}$							

Example 3.27 Single Die (Results 1 and 2)

Consider a die-rolling experiment with $A = [2,4,6]$ and $B = [4,5,6]$. Show the following:

    a. $(A \cap B) \cup (\overline{A} \cap B) = B$
    b. $A \cup (\overline{A} \cap B) = A \cup B$

Solution We know that

$$\overline{A} = [1,3,5]$$

It follows that

$$A \cap B = [4,6] \text{ and } \overline{A} \cap B = [5]$$

    a. Then, $A \cap B$ and $\overline{A} \cap B$ are mutually exclusive, and their union is $B = [4,5,6]$—that is,

$$(A \cap B) \cup (\overline{A} \cap B) = [4,5,6] = B$$

    b. Also, A and $\overline{A} \cap B$ are mutually exclusive, and their union is

$$A \cup (\overline{A} \cap B) = [2,4,5,6] = A \cup B$$

Example 3.28 Single Die (Result 3)

Consider a die-rolling experiment with events A, E_1, E_2, and E_3 given by the following:

$$A = [2,4,6] \quad E_1 = [1,2] \quad E_2 = [3,4] \quad E_3 = [5,6]$$

Show that $E_1 \cap A$, $E_2 \cap A$, and $E_3 \cap A$ are mutually exclusive and that their union is A.

Solution First, we notice that E_1, E_2, and E_3 are mutually exclusive and collectively exhaustive. Then,

$$E_1 \cap A = [2] \quad E_2 \cap A = [4] \quad E_3 \cap A = [6]$$

Clearly, these three events are mutually exclusive, and their union is as follows:

$$(E_1 \cap A) \cup (E_2 \cap A) \cup (E_3 \cap A) = [2,4,6] = A$$

REFERENCES

1. Bayes, T. 1958. Essay Towards Solving a Problem in the Doctrine of Chance. *Biometrika* 45: 293–315 (reproduction of 1763 paper).
2. Carlson, W. L. 1972. Alcohol Usage of the Night Driver. *Journal of Safety Research* 4 (1): 12–29.
3. Carlson, W. L., and B. Thorne. 1997. *Applied Statistical Methods for Business and Economics*. Upper Saddle River, NJ: Prentice Hall.
4. Taleb, N. N. 2005. *Fooled by Randomness*. New York: Random House.

4

CHAPTER OUTLINE

Discrete Random Variables and Probability Distributions

Introduction

In Chapter 3 we began our development of probability to represent situations with uncertain outcomes. In this chapter we use those ideas to develop probability models with an emphasis on discrete random variables. In Chapter 5 we develop probability models for continuous random variables.

Probability models have extensive application to a number of business problems, and many of these applications are developed here. Suppose that you have a business that rents a variety of equipment. From past experience—relative frequency—you know that 30% of the people who enter your store want to rent a trailer. Today you have three trailers available. Five completely unrelated people enter your store (the probability of one of them renting a trailer is independent of that of the others). What is the probability that these five people are seeking to rent a total of four or five trailers? If that happens, rental opportunities will be missed and customers will be disappointed. The probability of the events (number of trailers desired) can be computed using the binomial model that is developed in this chapter.

The preceding trailer problem is an example of a problem whose probability can be computed using a standard probability model, which simplifies problem solving and the computation of probabilities. However, in order to use a standard model certain important assumptions must be satisfied. We begin with some important definitions and then move to developing several important models that are used extensively in business and economic applications.

4.1 RANDOM VARIABLES

Probabilities can be conveniently summarized by using the notion of a *random variable*.

Random Variable

A **random variable** is a variable that takes on numerical values realized by the outcomes in the sample space generated by a random experiment.

It is important to distinguish between a random variable and the possible values that it can take. Using notation, this is done with capital letters, such as X, to denote the random variable and the corresponding lowercase letter, x, to denote a possible value. For example, a store has five computers on the shelf. From past experience we know that the probabilities of selling one through five computers are equal and at least one computer will be sold. We can use the random variable X to denote the outcome. This random variable can take the specific values $x = 1, x = 2, \ldots, x = 5$, each with probability 0.2 and the random variable X as a discrete random variable.

Discrete Random Variable

A random variable is a **discrete random variable** if it can take on no more than a countable number of values.

It follows from the definition that any random variable that can take on only a finite number of values is discrete. For example, the number of sales resulting from 10 customer contacts is a discrete random variable. Even if the number of possible outcomes is infinite but countable, the random variable is discrete. An example is the number of customer contacts needed before the first sale occurs. The possible outcomes are 1, 2, 3, . . . , and a probability can be attached to each. (A discrete random variable that can take a countably infinite number of values is discussed in Section 4.5, "Poisson Distribution.") Some other examples of discrete random variables are as follows:

1. The number of defective items in a sample of 20 items from a large shipment
2. The number of students attending a statistics class on a Friday
3. The number of errors detected in a corporation's accounts
4. The number of claims on a medical insurance policy in a particular year

By contrast, suppose that we are interested in the day's high temperature. The random variable, temperature, is measured on a continuum and so is said to be *continuous*.

Continuous Random Variable

A random variable is a **continuous random variable** if it can take any value in an interval.

For continuous random variables we can assign probabilities only to a range of values. The probabilities can be determined for ranges, using a mathematical function, so that one could compute the probability for the event "today's high temperature will be between 75° and 76°."

Some other examples of continuous random variables include the following:

1. The yearly income for a family
2. The time it takes to get to work
3. The amount of oil exported by Saudi Arabia in a particular month
4. The length of a Skype call to your mother
5. The percentage of impurity in a batch of chemicals

We develop continuous random variables and their associated methodology in Chapter 5.

The distinction that we have made between discrete and continuous random variables may appear rather artificial. After all, rarely is anything actually measured on a continuum. For example, we cannot report today's high temperature more precisely than the measuring instrument allows. Moreover, a family's income in a year will be some integer number of cents. However, we will find that it is convenient to act as if measurements had truly been made on a continuum when the differences between adjacent values are of no importance. The difference between families' incomes of $35,276.21 and $35,276.22 is not important, and the attachment of probabilities to each would be a tedious and worthless exercise.

For practical purposes we treat random variables as discrete when probability statements about the individual possible outcomes have worthwhile meaning; all other random variables are regarded as continuous. We treat these two types separately, and useful models have been developed for each type. Discrete random variables are developed in this chapter and continuous random variables are developed in Chapter 5.

EXERCISES

Basic Exercises

4.1 An ornithologist is studying and recording the number of boreal owl eggs found in south-central Sweden. Is the number of eggs a discrete or continuous random variable?

4.2 As a part of the school health services offered at Alderwood Primary School, London, the weight of students are recorded. Is the weight of students a discrete or continuous random variable?

4.3 For each of the following, indicate if a discrete or a continuous random variable provides the best definition:

  a. The amount of oil exported by Saudi Arabia in January 2019
  b. The number of newspapers published by *The Copenhagen Post*
  c. The number of rainy days in July at a beach resort
  d. The level of pressure in the tires of an automobile

4.4 After studying the queueing theory, Samara learnt that messages in a network are broken into packets that are routed to a destination server. Is the waiting time until the next packet arrives at the server a discrete or random variable?

Application Exercises

4.5 List four examples of discrete random variables that could be observed in education.

4.6 List three continuous random variables that a portfolio manager at an investment firm should regularly examine.

4.7 A presidential election poll contacts 2,000 randomly selected people. Should the number of people that support candidate A be analyzed using discrete or continuous probability models?

4.8 The Embassy of Vietnam in India receives a number of visa applications. Should the number of visas issued per day be analyzed using discrete or continuous probability models?

4.2 PROBABILITY DISTRIBUTIONS FOR DISCRETE RANDOM VARIABLES

Suppose that X is a discrete random variable and that x is one of its possible values. The probability that random variable X takes specific value x is denoted $P(X = x)$. The *probability distribution function* of a random variable is a representation of the probabilities for all the possible outcomes. This representation might be algebraic, graphical, or tabular.

For discrete random variables, one simple procedure is to list the probabilities of all possible outcomes according to the values of x.

Probability Distribution Function

The **probability distribution function**, $P(x)$, of a discrete random variable X represents the probability that X takes the value x, as a function of x. That is,

$$P(x) = P(X = x), \text{ for all values of } x$$

We use the term *probability distribution* to represent probability distribution functions in this book, following the common practice.

Once the probabilities have been calculated, the probability distribution function can be graphed.

Example 4.1 Number of Product Sales (Probability Distribution Graph)

Define and graph the probability distribution function for the number of waffles sold by a bakery in the Netherlands. This shop offers waffles that have a price of €4.00 each.

Solution Let the random variable X denote the number of sales during a single hour of business from 3 to 5 P.M. The probability distribution of sales is given by Table 4.1, and Figure 4.1 is a graphical picture of the distribution.

Table 4.1 Probability Distribution for Example 4.1

x	$P(x)$
0	0.10
1	0.30
2	0.20
3	0.40

Figure 4.1 Graph of Probability Distribution for Example 4.1

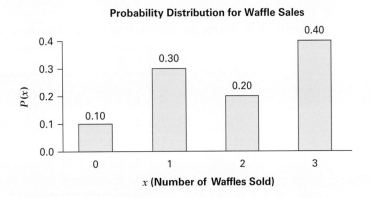

From the probability distribution function, we see that, for example, the probability of selling one waffle is 0.30 and the probability of selling two or more is $0.60(0.20 + 0.40)$.

The probability distribution function of a discrete random variable must satisfy the following two properties.

Required Properties of Probability Distribution for Discrete Random Variables

Let X be a discrete random variable with probability distribution $P(x)$. Then,

1. $0 \le P(x) \le 1$ for any value x, and
2. the individual probabilities sum to 1, that is,

$$\sum_x P(x) = 1 \tag{4.1}$$

where the notation indicates summation over all possible values of x.

Property 1 merely states that probabilities cannot be negative or exceed 1. Property 2 follows from the fact that the events "$X = x$," for all possible values of x, are mutually exclusive and collectively exhaustive. The probabilities for these events must, therefore, sum to 1. It is simply a way of saying that when a random experiment is to be carried out, something must happen.

Another representation of discrete probability distributions is also useful.

Cumulative Probability distribution

The **cumulative probability distribution**, $F(x_0)$, of a random variable X, represents the probability that X does not exceed the value x_0, as a function of x_0. That is,

$$F(x_0) = P(X \le x_0) \tag{4.2}$$

where the function is evaluated at all values of x_0.

Example 4.2 Automobile Sales (Probabilities)

Olaf Motors, Inc., is a car dealer in a small southern town. Based on an analysis of its sales history, the managers know that on any single day the number of Prius cars sold can vary from 0 to 5. How can the probability distribution function shown in Table 4.2 be used for inventory planning?

Table 4.2 Probability Distribution Function for Automobile Sales

x	$P(x)$	$F(x)$
0	0.15	0.15
1	0.30	0.45
2	0.20	0.65
3	0.20	0.85
4	0.10	0.95
5	0.05	1.00

Solution The random variable, X, takes on the values of x indicated in the first column, and the probability distribution, $P(x)$, is defined in the second column. The third column contains the cumulative distribution, $F(x)$. This model could be used for planning the inventory of cars. For example, if there are only four cars in stock, Olaf Motors could satisfy customers' needs for a car 95% of the time. But if only two cars are in stock, then 35% $[(1 - 0.65) \times 100]$ of the customers would not have their needs satisfied.

It can be seen from the definition that as x_0 increases, the cumulative probability distribution will change values only at those points x_0 that can be taken by the random variable with positive probability. Its evaluation at these points can be carried out in terms of the probability distribution.

Derived Relationship Between Probability Distribution and Cumulative Probability Distribution

Let X be a random variable with probability distribution $P(x)$ and cumulative probability distribution $F(x_0)$. Then we can show that

$$F(x_0) = \sum_{x \leq x_0} P(x) \tag{4.3}$$

where the notation implies that summation is over all possible values of x that are less than or equal to x_0.

The result in Equation 4.3 follows, since the event "$X \leq x_0$" is the union of the mutually exclusive events "$X = x$," for all possible values of x less than or equal to x_0. The probability of the union is then the sum of these individual event probabilities.

Derived Properties of Cumulative Probability Distributions for Discrete Random Variables

Let X be a discrete random variable with cumulative probability distribution $F(x_0)$. Then we can show that

1. $0 \leq F(x_0) \leq 1$ for every number x_0; and
2. if x_0 and x_1 are two numbers with $x_0 < x_1$, then $F(x_0) \leq F(x_1)$.

Property 1 simply states that a probability cannot be less than 0 or greater than 1. For example, note the probabilities for automobile sales in Table 4.2. Property 2 implies that the probability that a random variable does not exceed some number cannot be more than the probability that it does not exceed any larger number.

EXERCISES

Basic Exercises

4.9 What is the probability distribution function of the number of prime numbers when a number between 1 and 25, inclusive, is randomly selected?

4.10 Show the probability distribution function of the face values of a single die when a fair die is rolled.

4.11 Show the probability distribution function of the number of heads when three fair coins are tossed independently.

4.12 Let the random variable represent the number of flight delays during a day at the large airport. Prepare a table that shows the probability distribution and the cumulative probability distribution?

Application Exercises

4.13 The number of computers sold per day at Dan's Computer Works is defined by the following probability distribution:

x	0	1	2	3	4	5	6
$P(x)$	0.03	0.11	0.15	0.22	0.19	0.26	0.04

a. $P(3 \leq x < 6) = ?$
b. $P(x > 3) = ?$
c. $P(x \leq 4) = ?$
d. $P(2 < x \leq 5) = ?$

4.14 A local grocery store has asked you to examine the probability of choosing a product based on the height of shelf on which the product is placed. The random variable X is the height of the shelf from the floor. The customers' choice of products is defined by the following probability distribution:

Height (x)	0–20	20–40	40–60	60–80	80–100
$P(x)$	0.08	0.12	0.22	0.34	0.24

a. What is the cumulative probability distribution of X?
b. What is the probability of choosing an article from a shelf equal to or higher than 60 cm?
c. What is the probability of choosing an article from the shelf smaller than or equal to 40 cm?

4.3 PROPERTIES OF DISCRETE RANDOM VARIABLES

The probability distribution contains all the information about the probability properties of a random variable, and graphical inspection of this distribution can certainly be valuable. However, it is desirable to have some summary measures of the distribution's characteristics.

Expected Value of a Discrete Random Variable

In order to obtain a measure of the center of a probability distribution, we introduce the notion of the *expectation* of a random variable. In Chapter 2 we computed the sample mean as a measure of central location for sample data. The *expected value* is the corresponding measure of central location for a random variable. Before introducing its definition, we show the fallacy of a superficially attractive alternative measure.

Consider the following example: A review of textbooks in a segment of the business area found that 81% of all pages of texts were error free, 17% of all pages contained one error, and the remaining 2% contained two errors. We use the random variable X to denote the number of errors on a page chosen at random from one of these books, with possible values of 0, 1, and 2, and the probability distribution function

$$P(0) = 0.81 \quad P(1) = 0.17 \quad P(2) = 0.02$$

We could consider using the simple average of the values as the central location of a random variable. In this example the possible numbers of errors on a page are 0, 1, and 2. Their average is, then, one error. However, a moment's reflection will convince the reader that this is an absurd measure of central location. In calculating this average, we paid no attention to the fact that 81% of all pages contain no errors, while only 2% contain two errors. In order to obtain a sensible measure of central location, we *weight* the various possible outcomes by the probabilities of their occurrence.

Expected Value

The **expected value**, $E[X]$, of a discrete random variable X is defined as

$$E[X] = \mu = \sum_x xP(x) \tag{4.4}$$

where the notation indicates that the summation extends over all possible values of x.

The expected value of a random variable is also called its **mean** and is denoted μ.

We can express expected value in terms of long-run relative frequencies. Suppose that a random experiment is repeated N times and that the event "$X = x$" occurs in N_x of these trials. The average of the values taken by the random variable over all N trials will then be the sum of xN_x/N over all possible values of x. Now, as the number of replications, N, becomes infinitely large, the ratio N_x/N tends to the probability of the occurrence of the event "$X = x$"—that is, to $P(x)$. Hence, the quantity xN_x/N tends to $xP(x)$. Thus, we can view the expected value as the long-run average value that a random variable takes over a large number of trials. Recall that in Chapter 2 we used the *mean* for the average of a set of numerical observations. We use the same term for the expectation of a random variable.

Example 4.3 Errors in Textbooks (Expected Value)

Suppose that the probability distribution for the number of errors, X, on pages from business textbooks is as follows:

$$P(0) = 0.81 \quad P(1) = 0.17 \quad P(2) = 0.02$$

Find the mean number of errors per page.

Solution We have

$$\mu_x = E[X] = \sum_x xP(x) = (0)(0.81) + (1)(0.17) + (2)(0.02) = 0.21$$

From this result we conclude that over a large number of pages, the expectation would be to find an average of 0.21 error per page. Figure 4.2 shows the probability distribution, with the location of the mean indicated.

Figure 4.2 Probability Distribution for Number of Errors per Page in Business Textbooks for Example 4.3

Variance of a Discrete Random Variable

In Chapter 2 we found that the sample variance was one useful measure of the dispersion of a set of numerical observations. The sample variance is the average of the squared discrepancies of the observations from their mean. We use this same idea to measure dispersion in the probability distribution of a random variable. We define the *variance* of a random variable as the weighted average of the squares of its possible deviations, $(x - \mu)$, from the mean; the weight associated with $(x - \mu)^2$ is the probability that the random variable takes the value x. The variance can then be viewed as the average value that will be taken by the function $(X - \mu)^2$ over a very large number of repeated trials, as defined by Equation 4.5.

Variance and Standard Deviation of a Discrete Random Variable

Let X be a discrete random variable. The expectation of the squared deviations about the mean, $(X - \mu)^2$, is called the **variance**, denoted as σ^2 and given by

$$\sigma^2 = E[(X - \mu)^2] = \sum_x (x - \mu)^2 P(x) \tag{4.5}$$

The variance of a discrete random variable X can also be expressed as

$$\sigma^2 = E[X^2] - \mu^2 = \sum_x x^2 P(x) - \mu^2 \tag{4.6}$$

The **standard deviation**, σ, is the positive square root of the variance.

In some practical applications the alternative, but equivalent, formula for the variance is preferable for computational purposes. That alternative formula is defined by Equation 4.6, which can be verified algebraically (see the chapter appendix).

The concept of variance can be very useful in comparing the dispersions of probability distributions. Consider, for example, viewing as a random variable the daily return over a year on an investment. Two investments may have the same expected returns but will still differ in an important way if the variances of these returns are substantially different. A higher variance indicates that returns substantially different from the mean are more likely than if the variance of returns amount is small. In this context, then, variance of the return can be associated with the concept of the risk of an investment—the higher the variance, the greater the risk.

Taking the square root of the variance to obtain the standard deviation yields a quantity in the original units of measurement, as noted in Chapter 2.

Example 4.4 Expected Value and Variance of Automobile Sales (Expected Value and Variance)

In Example 4.2 Olaf Motors, Inc., determined that the number of Prius cars sold daily could vary from 0 to 5, with the probabilities given in Table 4.2. Find the expected value and variance for this probability distribution.

Solution Using Equation 4.4, the expected value is as follows:

$$\mu_X = E[X] = \sum_x xP(x) = 0(0.15) + 1(0.30) + \cdots + 5(0.05) = 1.95$$

Using Equation 4.5, the variance is as follows:

$$\sigma_X^2 = (0 - 1.95)^2(0.15) + (1 - 1.95)^2(0.3) + \cdots + (5 - 1.95)^2(0.05) = 1.9475$$

For more complex probability distributions, Excel, Minitab, SPSS, or another statistical package can be used for these computations.

Table 4.3 contains an alternative probability distribution function for car sales. We will examine the effect of this alternative probability distribution on the mean and variance. Note the higher probabilities for 0 and 5 cars sold and smaller probabilities for intermediate daily sales. In Table 4.3 we see the detailed calculations that are used to compute the mean and variance of sales.

Table 4.3 Probability Distribution Function for Olaf Motors Automobile Sales

x	$P(x)$	MEAN	VARIANCE
0	0.30	$(0.30)(0)$	$(0.30)(0 - 2.15)^2$
1	0.20	$(0.20)(1)$	$(0.20)(1 - 2.15)^2$
2	0.10	$(0.10)(2)$	$(0.10)(2 - 2.15)^2$
3	0.05	$(0.05)(3)$	$(0.05)(3 - 2.15)^2$
4	0.15	$(0.15)(4)$	$(0.15)(4 - 2.15)^2$
5	0.20	$(0.20)(5)$	$(0.20)(5 - 2.15)^2$
	1.0	2.15	3.83

COMMENTS

- In Table 4.3 there is a higher probability of 0 sales (0.30 rather than 0.15 in Table 4.2). Also there is a higher probability of selling all 5 cars (0.20 rather than 0.05 from Table 4.2).

- We expect a larger variance because the probabilities of extreme values 0 and 5 are larger. Note that the mean has increased from 1.95 to 2.15, while the variance has increased from 1.95 to 3.83, reflecting the higher probabilities of more extreme values of X.

Mean and Variance of Linear Functions of a Random Variable

The notion of expectation is not restricted to the random variable itself but can be applied to any function of the random variable. For example, a contractor may be uncertain of the time required to complete a contract. This uncertainty could be represented by a random variable whose possible values are the number of days elapsing from the beginning to the completion of work on the contract. However, the contractor's primary concern is not with the time taken but rather with the cost of fulfilling the contract. This cost will be a function of the time taken, so in determining expected value of the random variable "cost," we need to find the expectation of a function of the random variable "time to completion."

Expected Value of Functions of Random Variables
Let X be a discrete random variable with probability distribution $P(x)$, and let $g(X)$ be some function of X. Then the expected value, $E[g(X)]$, of that function is defined as follows:

$$E[g(X)] = \sum_x g(x)P(x) \tag{4.7}$$

We define the expectation of a function of a random variable X by Equation 4.7. That is, the expectation can be thought of as the average value that $g(X)$ would take over a very large number of repeated trials. In general

$$E[g(x)] \neq g(\mu_x) \tag{4.8}$$

as shown in the chapter appendix. However, if $g(x)$ is a linear function of x, there are some simple results for the mean and variance. These results are very useful for business and economics because many applications can be approximated by a linear function.

We now consider the expected value and variance for linear functions of a random variable using the linear function $a + bX$, where a and b are constant fixed numbers. Let X be a random variable that takes the value x with probability $P(x)$, and consider a new random variable Y, defined by the following:

$$Y = a + bX$$

When random variable X takes the specific value x, Y must take the value $a + bx$. The mean and variance of such variables are frequently required. The mean, variance, and standard deviation for a linear function of a random variable are derived in the chapter appendix. The results are summarized in Equations 4.9 and 4.10.

Summary of Properties for Linear Functions of a Random Variable
Let X be a random variable with mean μ_X and variance σ_X^2, and let a and b be any constant fixed numbers. Define the random variable Y as $a + bX$. Then, the **mean** and **variance of** Y are

$$\mu_Y = E[a + bX] = a + b\mu_X \tag{4.9}$$

and

$$\sigma_Y^2 = Var(a + bX) = b^2\sigma_X^2 \qquad (4.10)$$

so that the **standard deviation of Y** is

$$\sigma_Y = |b|\sigma_X$$

Example 4.5 Total Project Cost (Computations for Functions of Random Variables)

A contractor is interested in the total cost of a project on which she intends to bid. She estimates that materials will cost $25,000 and that her labor will be $900 per day. If the project takes X days to complete, the total labor cost will be 900X dollars, and the total cost of the project (in dollars) will be as follows:

$$C = 25,000 + 900X$$

Using her experience the contractor forms probabilities (Table 4.4) of likely completion times for the project.

a. Find the mean and variance for completion time X.
b. Find the mean, variance, and standard deviation for total cost C.

Table 4.4 Probability Distribution for Completion Times

COMPLETION TIME x (DAYS)	10	11	12	13	14
Probability	0.1	0.3	0.3	0.2	0.1

Solution

a. The mean and variance for completion time X can be found using Equations 4.4 and 4.5.

$$\mu_X = E[X] = \sum_x xP(x)$$
$$= (10)(0.1) + (11)(0.3) + (12)(0.3) + (13)(0.2) + (14)(0.1) = 11.9 \text{ days}$$

And

$$\sigma_x^2 = E[(X - \mu_x)^2] = \sum_x (x - \mu_x)^2 P(x)$$
$$= (10 - 11.9)^2(0.1) + (11 - 11.9)^2(0.3) + \cdots + (14 - 11.9)^2(0.1) = 1.29$$

b. The mean, variance, and standard deviation of total cost, C, are obtained using Equations 4.9 and 4.10.

The mean is as follows:

$$\mu_C = E[25,000 + 900X] = (25,000 + 900\mu_X) = 25,000 + (900)(11.9) = \$35,710$$

The variance is as follows:

$$\sigma_C^2 = Var(25,000 + 900X) = (900)^2\sigma_X^2 = (810,000)(1.29) = 1,044,900$$

The standard deviation is as follows:

$$\sigma_C = \sqrt{\sigma_C^2} = \$1,022.20$$

Three special examples of the linear function $W = a + bX$ are important. The first example considers a constant function, $W = a$, for any constant a. In this situation the coefficient $b = 0$. In the second example $a = 0$, giving $W = bX$. The expected value and the variance for these functions are defined by Equations 4.11 and 4.12. The third example is significant in later chapters. The mean and variance of this special linear function are defined by Equations 4.13 and 4.14. Thus, subtracting its mean from a random variable and dividing by its standard deviation yields a random variable with mean 0 and standard deviation 1.

Summary Results for the Mean and Variance of Special Linear Functions

a. Let $b = 0$ in the linear function $W = a + bX$. Then let $W = a$ (for any constant a).

$$E[a] = a \quad \text{and} \quad Var(a) = 0 \tag{4.11}$$

If a random variable always takes the value a, it will have a mean a and a variance 0.

b. Let $a = 0$ in the linear function $W = a + bX$. Then let $W = bX$.

$$E[bX] = b\mu_X \quad \text{and} \quad Var(bX) = b^2\sigma_X^2 \tag{4.12}$$

c. To find the mean and variance of

$$Z = \frac{X - \mu_X}{\sigma_X}$$

let $a = -\mu_X/\sigma_X$ and $b = 1/\sigma_X$ in the linear function $Z = a + bX$. Then

$$Z = a + bX = \frac{X - \mu_X}{\sigma_X} = \frac{X}{\sigma_X} - \frac{\mu_X}{\sigma_X}$$

so that

$$E\left[\frac{X - \mu_X}{\sigma_X}\right] = \frac{\mu_X}{\sigma_X} - \frac{1}{\sigma_X}\mu_X = 0 \tag{4.13}$$

and

$$Var\left(\frac{X - \mu_X}{\sigma_X}\right) = \frac{1}{\sigma_X^2}\sigma_X^2 = 1 \tag{4.14}$$

EXERCISES

Basic Exercises

4.15 Consider the probability distribution function.

x	0	1
Probability	0.30	0.70

a. Graph the probability distribution function.
b. Calculate and graph the cumulative probability distribution.
c. Find the mean of the random variable X.
d. Find the variance of X.

4.16 Given the probability distribution function:

x	0	1	2
Probability	0.25	0.50	0.25

a. Graph the probability distribution function.
b. Calculate and graph the cumulative probability distribution.
c. Find the mean of the random variable X.
d. Find the variance of X.

4.17 Consider the probability distribution function.

X	0	1
Probability	0.40	0.60

a. Graph the probability distribution function.
b. Calculate the cumulative probability distribution function.
c. Find the mean of the random variable X.
d. Find the variance of X.

4.18 An automobile dealer calculates the proportion of new cars sold that have been returned a various numbers of times for the correction of defects during the warranty period. The results are shown in the following table.

Number of returns	0	1	2	3	4
Proportion	0.28	0.36	0.23	0.09	0.04

a. Graph the probability distribution function.
b. Calculate and graph the cumulative probability distribution.
c. Find the mean of the number of returns of an automobile for corrections for defects during the warranty period.
d. Find the variance of the number of returns of an automobile for corrections for defects during the warranty period.

4.19 A company specializes in installing and servicing central-heating furnaces. In the prewinter period, service calls may result in an order for a new furnace. The following table shows estimated probabilities for the numbers of new furnace orders generated in this way in the last two weeks of September.

Number of orders	0	1	2	3	4	5
Probability	0.10	0.14	0.26	0.28	0.30	0.05

a. Graph the probability distribution function.
b. Calculate and graph the cumulative probability distribution.
c. Find the probability that at least 3 orders will be generated in this period.
d. Find the mean of the number of orders for new furnaces in this 2-week period.
e. Find the standard deviation of the number of orders for new furnaces in this 2-week period.

Application Exercises

4.20 Forest Green Brown, Inc., produces bags of cypress mulch. The weight in pounds per bag varies, as indicated in the accompanying table.

Weight in pounds	44	45	46	47	48	49	50
Proportion of bags	0.04	0.13	0.21	0.29	0.20	0.10	0.03

a. Graph the probability distribution.
b. Calculate and graph the cumulative probability distribution.
c. What is the probability that a randomly chosen bag will contain more than 45 and less than 49 pounds of mulch (inclusive)?
d. Two packages are chosen at random. What is the probability that at least one of them contains at least 47 pounds?
e. Compute—using a computer—the mean and standard deviation of the weight per bag.
f. The cost (in cents) of producing a bag of mulch is $75 + 2X$, where X is the number of pounds per bag. The revenue from selling the bag, regardless of weight, is $2.50. If profit is defined as the difference between revenue and cost, find the mean and standard deviation of profit per bag.

4.21 A municipal bus company has started operations in a new subdivision. Records were kept on the numbers of riders on one bus route during the early-morning weekday service. The accompanying table shows proportions over all weekdays.

Number of riders	20	21	22	23	24	25	26	27
Proportion	0.02	0.12	0.23	0.31	0.19	0.08	0.03	0.02

a. Graph the probability distribution.
b. Calculate and graph the cumulative probability distribution.
c. What is the probability that on a randomly chosen weekday there will be at least 24 riders from the subdivision on this service?
d. Two weekdays are chosen at random. What is the probability that on both of these days there will be fewer than 23 riders from the subdivision on this service?
e. Find the mean and standard deviation of the number of riders from this subdivision on this service on a weekday.
f. If the cost of a ride is $1.50, find the mean and standard deviation of the total payments of riders from this subdivision on this service on a weekday.

4.22 a. A very large shipment of parts contains 10% defectives. Two parts are chosen at random from the shipment and checked. Let the random variable X denote the number of defectives found. Find the probability distribution of this random variable.
b. A shipment of 20 parts contains 2 defectives. Two parts are chosen at random from the shipment and checked. Let the random variable Y denote the number of defectives found. Find the probability distribution of this random variable. Explain why your answer is different from that for part (a).
c. Find the mean and variance of the random variable X in part (a).
d. Find the mean and variance of the random variable Y in part (b).

4.23 A student needs to know details of a class assignment that is due the next day and decides to call fellow class members for this information. She believes that for any particular call, the probability of obtaining the necessary information is 0.40. She decides to continue calling class members until the information is obtained. But her cell phone battery will not allow more than 8 calls. Let the random variable X denote the number of calls needed to obtain the information.

a. Find the probability distribution of X.
b. Find the cumulative probability distribution of X.
c. Find the probability that at least three calls are required.

4.24 Amazon's third-largest market is the United Kingdom. In 2019, the employees at a local firm in London received their salary and decided to spend a portion of it on making online purchases from Amazon. The probability that the online purchases will be shipped on time to each employee is 0.68. Determine the following:

a. The probability that three products will be shipped on time.

b. The probability that out of three, two products will be shipped on time.

4.25 One of the leading retail banks in China is the Postal Savings Bank of China, located in Beijing. Suppose the number of arrivals per minute at the bank, which has around 40,000 outlets, was recorded over a period of 200 minutes with the results shown in the table below.

Arrivals	0	1	2	3	4	5	6	7	8
Frequency	22	41	44	37	26	16	8	4	2

Find the mean and standard deviation of the number of arrivals at the bank.

4.26 The manager at a firm in Tokyo wants to organize a trip for his team in the summer of 2020, but some employees have already applied for leave. To be better prepared, he estimates the probabilities of the employees who are taking day(s) off during the summer season in the following table.

Number of days off	0	1	2	3	4	5
Probability	0.05	0.30	0.45	0.10	0.07	0.03

Find the mean and the standard deviation of the number of days off.

4.27 A store owner stocks an out-of-town newspaper that is sometimes requested by a small number of customers. Each copy of this newspaper costs her 70 cents, and she sells them for 90 cents each. Any copies left over at the end of the day have no value and are destroyed. Any requests for copies that cannot be met because stocks have been exhausted are considered by the store owner as a loss of 5 cents in goodwill. The probability distribution of the number of requests for the newspaper in a day is shown in the accompanying table. If the store owner defines total daily profit as total revenue from newspaper sales, less total cost of newspapers ordered, less goodwill loss from unsatisfied demand, what is the expected profit if four newspapers are order?

Number of requests	0	1	2	3	4	5
Probability	0.12	0.16	0.18	0.32	0.14	0.08

4.28 A factory manager is considering whether to replace a temperamental machine. A review of past records indicates the following probability distribution for the number of breakdowns of this machine in a week.

Number of breakdowns	0	1	2	3	4
Probability	0.10	0.26	0.42	0.16	0.06

a. Find the mean and standard deviation of the number of weekly breakdowns.

b. It is estimated that each breakdown costs the company $1,500 in lost output. Find the mean and standard deviation of the weekly cost to the company from breakdowns of this machine.

4.29 An investor is considering three strategies for a €1,200 investment. The probable returns are estimated as follows:

- **Strategy 1:** A certain profit of €200.
- **Strategy 2:** A profit of €12,000 with probability 0.15 and a loss of €1,200 with probability 0.85
- **Strategy 3:** A profit of €5,00 with probability 0.50, a profit of €250 with probability 0.30, and a loss of €250 with probability 0.20

Which strategy has the highest expected profit? Explain why you would or would not advise the investor to adopt this strategy.

4.4 BINOMIAL DISTRIBUTION

We now develop the binomial probability distribution, which is used extensively in many applied business and economic problems. Our approach begins with the Bernoulli model, which is a building block for the binomial. Consider a random experiment that can give rise to just two possible mutually exclusive and collectively exhaustive outcomes, which for convenience we label "success" and "failure." Let P denote the probability of success, and, the probability of failure $(1 - P)$. Then, define the random variable X so that X takes the value 1 if the outcome of the experiment is success and 0 otherwise. The probability distribution of this random variable is then

$$P(0) = (1 - P) \quad \text{and} \quad P(1) = P$$

This distribution is known as the *Bernoulli distribution*. Its mean and variance can be found by direct application of the equations in Section 4.3.

Derivation of the Mean and Variance of a Bernoulli Random Variable

The **mean** is

$$\mu_X = E[X] = \sum_x xP(x) = (0)(1 - P) + (1)P = P \qquad (4.15)$$

and the **variance** is

$$\sigma_X^2 = E[(X - \mu_X)^2] = \sum_x (x - \mu_X)^2 P(x)$$

$$= (0 - P)^2(1 - P) + (1 - P)^2 P = P(1 - P) \qquad (4.16)$$

Example 4.6 Contract Sale (Compute Bernoulli Mean and Variance)

Shirley Ferguson, an insurance broker, believes that for a particular contact the probability of making a sale is 0.4. If the random variable X is defined to take the value 1 if a sale is made and 0 otherwise, then X has a Bernoulli distribution with probability of success P equal to 0.4. Find the mean and the variance of the distribution.

Solution The probability distribution of X is $P(0) = 0.6$ and $P(1) = 0.4$. The mean of the distribution is $P = 0.40$, and the variance is $\sigma^2 = P(1 - P) = (0.4)(0.6) = 0.24$.

Developing the Binomial Distribution

An important generalization of the Bernoulli distribution concerns the case where a random experiment with two possible outcomes is repeated several times and the repetitions are independent. We can determine these probabilities by using the binomial probability distribution. Suppose again that the probability of a success in a single trial is P and that n independent trials are carried out, so that the result of any one trial has no influence on the outcome of any other. The number of successes, X, resulting from these n trials could be any whole number from 0 to n, and we are interested in the probability of obtaining exactly $X = x$ successes in n trials.

Suppose that Shirley in Example 4.6 seeks a total of, $x = 3$ sales and to do this she contacts four $n = 4$ potential customers. She would like to know the probability of exactly 3 sales out of the 4 contacts. If we label a sale as (S) and a nonsale as (F), one possible sequence that results in 3 sales would be [S, S, S, F]. Given that each customer contact is independent, the probability of this particular event is as follows:

$$(0.40 \times 0.40 \times 0.40 \times 0.60) = 0.40^3 0.60^1 = 0.0384$$

The sequences of S and F can be arranged in combinations of 4 outcomes taken 3 at a time, as developed in Chapter 3, and thus there are

$$C_3^4 = \frac{4!}{3!(4 - 3)!} = 4$$

possible ways that she can obtain 3 sales, and thus the probability of exactly 3 sales would be 4 times 0.0384, or 0.1536; expressed in equation form,

$$C_3^4 0.40^3 0.60^1 = 4 \times 0.0384 = 0.1536$$

Continuing from this specific example we develop the result in two stages. First, observe that the n trials will result in a sequence of n outcomes, each of which must be either success (S) or failure (F). One sequence with x successes and $(n - x)$ failures is as follows:

$$S, S, \ldots, S \qquad F, F, \ldots, F$$
$$(x \text{ times}) \qquad (n - x \text{ times})$$

In other words, the first x trials result in success, while the remainder result in failure. Now, the probability of success in a single trial is P, and the probability of failure is $(1 - P)$. Since the n trials are independent of one another, the probability of any particular sequence of outcomes is, by the multiplication rule of probabilities (Chapter 3), equal to the product of the probabilities for the individual outcomes. Thus, the probability of observing the specific sequence of outcomes just described is as follows:

$$[P \times P \times \cdots \times P] \times [(1 - P) \times (1 - P) \times \cdots \times (1 - P)] = P^x (1 - P)^{(n-x)}$$
$$(x \text{ times}) \qquad\qquad (n - x \text{ times})$$

This line of argument establishes that the probability of observing *any specific sequence* involving x successes and $(n - x)$ failures is $P^x(1 - P)^{n-x}$. For example, suppose that there are 5 independent trials, each with probability of success $P = 0.60$, and the probability of exactly 3 successes is required. Using $+$ to designate a success and 0 to indicate a nonsuccess, the desired outcomes could be designated as follows:

$$+++00 \quad \text{or} \quad +0+0+$$

The probability of either of these specific outcomes is $(0.6)^3(0.4)^2 = 0.03456$.

The original problem concerned the determination not of the probability of occurrence of a particular sequence, but of the probability of precisely x successes, regardless of the order of the outcomes. There are several sequences in which x successes could be arranged among $(n - x)$ failures. In fact, the number of such possibilities is just the number of combinations of x objects chosen from n, since any x locations can be selected from a total of n in which to place the successes and the total number of successes can be computed using Equation 4.17. Returning to the example of three successes in five trials ($P = 0.60$), the number of different sequences with three successes would be as follows:

$$C_3^5 = \frac{5!}{3!(5 - 3)!} = 10$$

The probability of 3 successes in 5 independent Bernoulli trials is, therefore, 10 times the probability of each of the sequences that has 3 successes; thus,

$$P(X = 3) = (10)(0.03456) = 0.3456$$

Next, we generalize this result for any combination of n and x.

Number of Sequences with x Successes in n Trials
The number of sequences with x successes in n independent trials is

$$C_x^n = \frac{n!}{x!(n - x)!} \tag{4.17}$$

where $n! = n \times (n - 1) \times (n - 2) \times \cdots \times 1$ and $0! = 1$.

These C_x^n sequences are mutually exclusive, since no two of them can occur at the same time. This result was developed in Chapter 3.

The event "x successes resulting from n trials" can occur in C_x^n mutually exclusive ways, each with probability $P^x(1 - P)^{n-x}$. Therefore, by the addition rule of probabilities (Chapter 3) the probability required is the sum of these C_x^n individual probabilities. The result is given by Equation 4.18.

The Binomial Distribution

Suppose that a random experiment can result in two possible mutually exclusive and collectively exhaustive outcomes, "success" and "failure," and that P is the probability of a success in a single trial. If n independent trials are carried out, the distribution of the number of resulting successes, x, is called the **binomial distribution**. Its probability distribution function for the binomial random variable $X = x$ is as follows:

$$P(x \text{ successes in } n \text{ independent trials})$$

$$= P(x) = \frac{n!}{x!(n-x)!} P^x (1-P)^{(n-x)} \text{ for } x = 0, 1, 2, \ldots, n \qquad (4.18)$$

The mean and variance are derived in the chapter appendix, and the results are given by Equations 4.19 and 4.20.

Mean and Variance of a Binomial Probability Distribution

Let X be the number of successes in n independent trials, each with probability of success P. Then X follows a binomial distribution with **mean**

$$\mu = E[X] = nP \qquad (4.19)$$

and **variance**

$$\sigma_X^2 = E[(X - \mu_X)^2] = nP(1-P) \qquad (4.20)$$

The derivation of the mean and variance of the binomial is shown in Section 4 of the chapter appendix.

The binomial distribution is widely used in business and economic applications involving the probability of discrete occurrences. Before using the binomial, the specific situation must be analyzed to determine if the following occur:

1. The application involves several trials, each of which has only two outcomes: yes or no, on or off, success or failure.
2. The probability of the outcome is the same for each trial.
3. The probability of the outcome on one trial does not affect the probability on other trials.

In the following examples typical applications are provided.

Binomial distribution probabilities can be obtained using the following:

1. Equation 4.18 (good for small values of n); see Example 4.7
2. Tables in the appendix (good for selected values of n and P); see Example 4.8
3. Computer-generated probabilities (Example 4.9)

Example 4.7 Multiple Contract Sales

Suppose that a real estate agent, Jeanette Nelson, has 5 contacts, and she believes that for each contact the probability of making a sale is 0.40. Using Equation 4.18, do the following:

a. Find the probability that she makes at most 1 sale.
b. Find the probability that she makes between 2 and 4 sales (inclusive).
c. Graph the probability distribution function.

Solution

a. $P(\text{at most 1 sale}) = P(X \le 1) = P(X = 0) + P(X = 1)$
$= 0.078 + 0.259 = 0.337$ since

$$P(0 \text{ sales}) = P(0) = \frac{5!}{0!5!}(0.4)^0(0.6)^5 = (0.6)^5 - 0.078$$

$$P(1 \text{ sale}) = P(1) = \frac{5!}{1!4!}(0.4)^1(0.6)^4 = 5(0.4)(0.6)^4 = 0.259$$

b. $P(2 \le X \le 4) = P(2) + P(3) + P(4) = 0.346 + 0.230 + 0.077 = 0.653$, since

$$P(2) = \frac{5!}{2!3!}(0.4)^2(0.6)^3 = 10(0.4)^2(0.6)^3 = 0.346$$

$$P(3) = \frac{5!}{3!2!}(0.4)^3(0.6)^2 = 10(0.4)^3(0.6)^2 = 0.230$$

$$P(4) = \frac{5!}{4!1!}(0.4)^4(0.6)^1 = 5(0.4)^4(0.6)^1 = 0.077$$

c. The probability distribution function is shown in Figure 4.3.

Figure 4.3 Graph of Binomial Probability Distribution for Example 4.7

Comments

- This shape is typical for binomial probabilities when *P* is neither very large nor very small.
- At the extremes (0 or 5 sales), the probabilities are quite small.

Unless the number of trials n is very small, the calculation of binomial probabilities, using Equation 4.18, is likely to be extremely cumbersome. Therefore, binomial probabilities can also be obtained from tables in the appendix.

Example 4.8 College Admissions

Early in August an undergraduate college discovers that it can accommodate a few extra students. Enrolling those additional students would provide a substantial increase in revenue without increasing the operating costs of the college; that is, no new classes would have to be added. From past experience the college knows that the frequency of enrollment given admission for all students is 40%.

a. What is the probability that at most 6 students will enroll if the college offers admission to 10 more students?
b. What is the probability that more than 12 will actually enroll if admission is offered to 20 students?
c. If the frequency of enrollment given admission for all students was 70%, what is the probability that at least 12 out of 15 students will actually enroll?

Solution

a. We assume that the additional students admitted have the same probability of enrolling as the previously admitted students.

b. The probability can be obtained using the cumulative binomial probability distribution from Table 3 in the appendix. The probability of at most 6 students enrolling if $n = 10$ and $P = 0.40$ is as follows:

$$P(X \leq 6 | n = 10, P = 0.40) = 0.945$$

c. $P(X > 12 | n = 20, P = 0.40) = 1 - P(X \leq 12) = 1 - 0.979 = 0.021$

d. The probability that at least 12 out of 15 students enroll is the same as the probability that at most 3 out of 15 students do not enroll (the probability of a student not enrolling is $1 - 0.70 = 0.30$).

$$P(X \geq 12 | n = 15, P = 0.70) = P(X \leq 3 | n = 15, P = 0.30) = 0.297$$

Most good computer packages can compute binomial and other probabilities for various probability distribution functions. Example 4.9 presents a probability table computed using Minitab, but other packages have similar capabilities.

Example 4.9 Sales of Airline Seats

Have you ever agreed to give up your airplane ticket in return for a free ticket? Have you ever searched for the cheapest flight so that you could visit a special friend? This example provides some of the analysis that leads to results such as overbooked flights and reduced fares on certain flights.

Suppose that you are in charge of marketing airline seats for a major carrier. Four days before the flight date you have 16 seats remaining on the plane. You know from past experience data that 80% of the people that purchase tickets in this time period will actually show up for the flight.

a. If you sell 20 extra tickets, what is the probability that you will overbook the flight or have at least 1 empty seat?
b. If you sell 18 extra tickets, what is the probability that you will overbook the flight or have at least 1 empty seat?

Solution

a. To find $P(X > 16)$, given $n = 20$ and $P = 0.80$, use the cumulative probability distribution in Table 4.5 that was computed using Minitab. You will find that all quality statistical packages have a capability to computer similar cumulative probability distributions.

Table 4.5 Cumulative Binomial Probabilities Obtained from Minitab for $n = 20, P = 0.80$.

x	$P(X \leq x)$
10	0.0026
11	0.0100
12	0.0321
13	0.0867
14	0.1958
15	0.3704
16	0.5886
17	0.7939
18	0.9308
19	0.9885
20	1.0000

The probability of overbooking is

$$P(X > 16) = 1 - P(X \le 16) = 1 - 0.589 = 0.411$$

and we see that the probability of overbooking when 20 seats are sold is 41.1%. If 20 tickets are sold, this also means that the probability that 15 or fewer people will arrive is

$$P(X \le 15) = 0.37$$

so there is a 37% chance that selling 20 tickets results in at least one empty seat.

b. To find the chance that you overbook the flight by selling 18 tickets, compute the cumulative probability distribution using $n = 18$. The chance that you overbook the flight will be only 10%, but the probability of at least one empty seat will increase to 72.9%.

The airline management then must evaluate the cost of overbooking (providing free tickets) versus the cost of empty seats that generate no revenue. Airlines analyze data to determine the number of seats that should be sold at reduced rates to maximize the ticket revenue from each flight. This analysis is complex, but it has its starting point in analyses such as the example presented here.

EXERCISES

Basic Exercises

4.30 For a Bernoulli random variable with probability of success $P = 0.8$, compute the mean and variance.

4.31 For a binomial probability distribution with $P = 0.4$ and $n = 10$, find the probability that the number of successes is equal to 5 and the probability that the number of successes is fewer than 2.

4.32 For a binomial distribution probability with $P = 0.42$ and $n = 18$, find the probability that:

a. The number of successes is equal to 7.

b. The number of successes is fewer than 10.

4.33 For a binomial distribution probability with $P = 0.87$ and $n = 23$, find the probability that:

a. The number of successes is equal to 11.

b. The number of successes is fewer than 15.

4.34 For a binomial probability distribution with $P = 0.7$ and $n = 18$, find the probability that the number of successes is equal to 12 and the probability that the number of successes is fewer than 6.

Application Exercises

4.35 A production manager knows that 5% of components produced by a particular manufacturing process have some defect. Six of these components, whose characteristics can be assumed to be independent of each other, are examined.

a. What is the probability that none of these components has a defect?

b. What is the probability that one of these components has a defect?

c. What is the probability that at least two of these components have a defect?

4.36 A state senator believes that 25% of all senators on the Finance Committee will strongly support the tax pro-posal she wishes to advance. Suppose that this belief is correct and that 5 senators are approached at random.

a. What is the probability that at least 1 of the 5 will strongly support the proposal?

b. What is the probability that a majority of the 5 will strongly support the proposal?

4.37 A public interest group in Belgium hires students to solicit donations by telephone. After a brief training period, the students call potential donors and are paid on a commission basis. Experience indicates that these students tend to have only modest success early on and that 85% of them quit the job within the first two weeks of employment. The group hires 7 students, which can be viewed as a random sample.

a. What is the probability that at least 2 of the 7 will give up in the first two weeks?

b. What is the probability that at least 2 of the 7 will not give up in the first two weeks?

4.38 À la Mère de Famille had opened in 1761 and is the old-est chocolate store in Paris, France. Suppose you visit the store and find that 30% of the truffles are made of white chocolate, 25% of a dark chocolate, and the rest of the milk chocolate. You decide to pick a random sample of five truffles from a shelf. Find the probability that:

a. All five are made of milk chocolate.

b. Three of them are made of white chocolate.

c. At least two of them are made of white chocolate.

4.39 SparkSolutions, a video surveillance systems producer in Italy, installs new security cameras and has found that for 17% of all installations, a return visit is needed to make some modifications. Five installations were made in a particular week. Assume independence of outcomes for these installations.

a. What is the probability that a return visit will be needed in all these cases?

b. What is the probability that a return visit will be needed in none of these cases?

c. What is the probability that a return visit will be needed in more than 1 of these cases?

4.40 The rise of cultured pearls or pearl farms have made natural pearls are very rare and have limited pearl fishing. However, a significant number of natural pearls can still be found in the Australian Indian Ocean waters from wild oysters. Of the 5 kinds of pearls, the probability of encountering pink pearls in the wild is 0.05; white pearls is 0.41; purple pearls is 0.04; blue pearls is 0.27; and black pearls is 0.07. Calculate each likelihood of the following events.

a. The probability of not encountering a black pearl.

b. The probability of encountering a black pearl.

c. The probability of not encountering a purple pearl.

4.41 A small commuter airline flies planes that can seat up to 8 passengers. The airline has determined that the probability that a ticketed passenger will not show up for a flight is 0.2. For each flight the airline sells tickets to the first 10 people placing orders. The probability distribution for the number of tickets sold per flight is shown in the accompanying table. For what proportion of the airline's flights does the number of ticketed passengers showing up exceed the number of available seats? (Assume independence between the number of tickets sold and the probability that a ticketed passenger will show up.)

Number of tickets	6	7	8	9	10
Probability	0.25	0.35	0.25	0.10	0.05

4.42 A football fan is analyzing the number of people interested in purchasing tickets for Europe's biggest football championship, the UEFA Euro 2020. The fan's survey tells her that out of 10 tickets, registered once a month, 70% of them are likely to be from the host city of Dublin, Republic of Ireland. Assume that a random variable follows a binomial distribution.

a. What is the standard deviation of the random variable?

b. What is the probability that all the tickets to the championship will be sold?

c. What is the probability that no tickets will be sold?

4.43 A local car dealer in Germany is mounting a new cross-divisional promotional campaign. Purchasers of new caes may, if dissatisfied for any reason, return the vehicle within 2 days of purchase and receive a full refund. The cost to the dealer of such a refund is €300. The dealer estimates that 18% of all purchasers will indeed return cars purchased and obtain refunds. Suppose that 80 cars are purchased during the campaign period.

a. Find the mean and standard deviation of the number of these cars that will be returned for refunds.

b. Find the mean and standard deviation of the total refund costs that will accrue as a result of these 80 purchases.

4.44 A family of mutual funds maintains a service that allows clients to switch money among accounts through a telephone call. It was estimated that 3.2% of callers either get a busy signal or are kept on hold so long that they may hang up. Fund management assesses any failure of this sort as a $10 goodwill loss. Suppose that 2,000 calls are attempted over a particular period.

a. Find the mean and standard deviation of the number of callers who will either get a busy signal or may hang up after being kept on hold.

b. Find the mean and standard deviation of the total goodwill loss to the mutual fund company from these 2,000 calls.

4.45 We have seen that for a binomial distribution with n trials, each with probability of success P, the mean is as follows:

$$\mu_X = E[X] = nP$$

Verify this result for the random variable "number of heads" in an experiment tossing three coins by calculating the mean directly from

$$\mu_X = \sum xP(x)$$

showing that for the binomial distribution, the two formulas produce the same answer.

4.46 A campus finance officer finds that, for all parking tickets issued, fines are paid for 78% of the tickets. The fine is $2. In the most recent week, 620 parking tickets have been issued.

a. Find the mean and standard deviation of the number of these tickets for which the fines will be paid.

b. Find the mean and standard deviation of the amount of money that will be obtained from the payment of these fines.

4.47 A company receives a very large shipment of mobile phones. A random sample of 22 of these mobile phones will be checked, and the shipment will be accepted if only one or none of these components do not meet the required specifications. What is the probability of accepting a shipment containing each of the following number of defectives?

a. 2%

b. 5%

c. 3%

4.48 The following two acceptance rules are being considered for determining whether to take delivery of a large shipment of components:

• A random sample of 10 components is checked, and the shipment is accepted only if none of them is defective.

• A random sample of 20 components is checked, and the shipment is accepted only if no more than 1 of them is defective.

Which of these acceptance rules has the smaller probability of accepting a shipment containing 20% defectives?

4.49 A company receives large shipments of parts from two sources. Seventy percent of the shipments come from a supplier whose shipments typically contain 10% defectives, while the remainder are from a supplier whose shipments typically contain 20% defectives. A manager receives a shipment but does not know the source. A random sample of 20 items from this shipment is tested, and 1 of the parts is found to be defective. What is the probability that this shipment came from the more reliable supplier? (*Hint:* Use Bayes' theorem.)

4.5 POISSON DISTRIBUTION

The **Poisson probability distribution** was first proposed by Simeon Poisson (1781–1840) in a book published in 1837. The number of applications began to increase early in the 20th century, and the availability of the computer has brought about further applications. The Poisson distribution is an important discrete probability distribution for a number of applications, including the following:

1. The number of failures in a large computer system during a given day
2. The number of replacement orders for a part received by a firm in a given month
3. The number of ships arriving at a loading facility during a 6-hour loading period
4. The number of delivery trucks to arrive at a central warehouse in an hour
5. The number of dents, scratches, or other defects in a large roll of sheet metal used to manufacture various component parts
6. The number of customers to arrive for flights during each 10-minute time interval from 3:00 p.m. to 6:00 p.m. on weekdays
7. The number of customers to arrive at a checkout aisle in your local grocery store during a particular time interval

We can use the Poisson distribution to determine the probability of each of these random variables, which are characterized as the number of occurrences or successes of a certain event in a given continuous interval (such as time, surface area, or length).

A Poisson distribution is modeled according to certain assumptions.

Assumptions of the Poisson Distribution
Assume that an interval is divided into a very large number of equal subintervals so that the probability of the occurrence of an event in any subinterval is very small. The assumptions of a Poisson distribution are as follows:

1. The probability of the occurrence of an event is constant for all subintervals.
2. There can be no more than one occurrence in each subinterval.
3. Occurrences are independent; that is, an occurrence in one interval does not influence the probability of an occurrence in another interval.

We can derive the equation for computing Poisson probabilities directly from the binomial probability distribution by taking the mathematical limits as $P \rightarrow 0$ and $n \rightarrow \infty$. With these limits, the parameter $\lambda = nP$ is a constant that specifies the average number of occurrences (successes) for a particular time and/or space. We can see intuitively that the Poisson is a special case of the binomial obtained by extending these limits. However, the mathematical derivation is beyond the scope of this book. The interested reader is referred to page 258 of Hogg and Craig (1995). The Poisson probability distribution function is given in Equation 4.21.

The Poisson Distribution Function, Mean, and Variance

The random variable X is said to follow the Poisson distribution if it has the probability distribution

$$P(x) = \frac{e^{-\lambda}\lambda^x}{x!}, \text{ for } x = 0, 1, 2, \ldots \tag{4.21}$$

where

$P(x)$ = the probability of x successes over a given time or space, given λ

λ = the expected number of successes per time or space unit, $\lambda > 0$

$e \cong 2.71828$ (the base for natural logarithms)

The mean and variance of the Poisson distribution are

$$\mu_x = E[X] = \lambda \quad \text{and} \quad \sigma_x^2 = E[(X - \mu_x)^2] = \lambda$$

The sum of Poisson random variables is also a Poisson random variable. Thus, the sum of K Poisson random variables, each with mean λ, is a Poisson random variable with mean $K\lambda$.

Two important applications of the Poisson distribution in the modern global economy are the probability of failures in complex systems and the probability of defective products in large production runs of several hundred thousand to a million units. A large worldwide shipping company such as Federal Express has a complex and extensive pickup, classification, shipping, and delivery system for millions of packages each day. There is a very small probability of handling failure at each step for each of the millions of packages handled every day. The company is interested in the probability of various numbers of failed deliveries each day when the system is operating properly. If the number of actual failed deliveries observed on a particular day has a small probability of occurring, given proper targeted operations, then the management begins a systematic checking process to identify and correct the reason for excessive failures.

Example 4.10 System Component Failure (Poisson Probabilities)

Andrew Whittaker, computer center manager, reports that his computer system experienced three component failures during the past 100 days.

   a. What is the probability of no failures in a given day?
   b. What is the probability of one or more component failures in a given day?
   c. What is the probability of at least two failures in a 3-day period?

Solution A modern computer system has a very large number of components, each of which could fail and thus result in a computer system failure. To compute the probability of failures using the Poisson distribution, assume that each of the millions of components has the same very small probability of failure. Also assume that the first failure does not affect the probability of a second failure (in some cases, these assumptions may not hold, and more complex distributions would be used). In particular, for this problem we assume that the past 100 days have been a good standard performance for the computer system and that this standard will continue into the future.

From past experience the expected number of failures per day is $3/100$, or $\lambda = 0.03$.

   a. $P(\text{no failures in a given day}) = P(X = 0 | \lambda = 0.03) = \dfrac{e^{-0.03}\lambda^0}{0!} = 0.970446$

b. The probability of at least one failure is the complement of the probability of 0 failures:

$$P(X \geq 1) = 1 - P(X = 0) = 1 - \left[\frac{e^{-\lambda}\lambda^x}{x!}\right] = 1 - \left[\frac{e^{-0.03}\lambda^0}{0!}\right]$$

$$= 1 - e^{-0.03} = 1 - 0.970446 = 0.029554$$

c. $P(\text{at least two failures in a 3-day period}) = P(X \geq 2 \mid \lambda = 0.09)$, where the average over a 3-day period is $\lambda = 3(0.03) = 0.09$:

$$P(X \geq 2 \mid \lambda = 0.09) = 1 - P(X \leq 1) = 1 - [P(X = 0) + P(X = 1)]$$

$$= 1 - [0.913931 + 0.082254]$$

and, thus,

$$P(X \geq 2 \mid \lambda = 0.09) = 1 - 0.996185 = 0.003815$$

The Poisson distribution has been found to be particularly useful in *waiting line*, or *queuing*, problems. These important applications include the probability of various numbers of customers waiting for a phone line or waiting to check out of a large retail store. These queuing problems are an important management issue for firms that draw customers from large populations. If the queue becomes too long, customers might quit the line or might not return for a future shopping visit. If a store has too many checkout lines, then there will be personnel idle waiting for customers, resulting in lower productivity. By knowing the probability of various numbers of customers in the line, management can balance the trade-off between long lines and idle customer service associates. In this way the firm can implement its strategy for the desired customer service level—shorter wait times imply higher customer-service levels but have a cost of more idle time for checkout workers.

Example 4.11 Customers at a Photocopying Machine (Poisson Probability)

Customers arrive at a photocopying machine at an average rate of 2 every five minutes. Assume that these arrivals are independent, with a constant arrival rate, and that this problem follows a Poisson model, with X denoting the number of arriving customers in a 5-minute period and mean $\lambda = 2$. Find the probability that more than two customers arrive in a 5-minute period.

Solution Since the mean number of arrivals in five minutes is 2, then $\lambda = 2$. To find the probability that more than 2 customers arrive, first compute the probability of at most 2 arrivals in a five-minute period, and then use the complement rule.

These probabilities can be found in Table 5 in the appendix or by using a computer:

$$P(X = 0) = \frac{e^{-2}2^0}{0!} = e^{-2} = 0.135335$$

$$P(X = 1) = \frac{e^{-2}2^1}{1!} = 2e^{-2} = 0.27067$$

$$P(X = 2) = \frac{e^{-2}2^2}{2!} = 2e^{-2} = 0.27067$$

Thus, the probability of more than 2 arrivals in a five-minute period is as follows:

$$P(X > 2) = 1 - P(X \leq 2) = 1 - [0.135335 + 0.27067 + 0.27067] = 0.323325$$

Example 4.12 Ship Arrivals at a Dock

The Canadian government has built a large grain-shipping port at Churchill, Manitoba, on the Hudson Bay. Grain grown in southern Manitoba is carried by rail to Churchill during the open-water shipping season. Unfortunately the port is open only 50 days per year during July and August. This leads to some critical crew staffing decisions by management. The port has the capacity to load up to 7 ships simultaneously, provided that each loading bay has an assigned crew. The remote location and short shipping season results in a very high labor cost for each crew assigned, and management would like to minimize the number of crews. Ships arrive in a random pattern that can be modeled using the Poisson probability model. If a ship arrives and all available loading bays are filled, the ship will be delayed, resulting in a large cost that must be paid to the owner of the ship. This penalty was negotiated to encourage ship owners to send their ships to Churchill.

Results of an initial analysis indicate that each ship requires six hours for loading by a single crew. The port can remain open only 50 days per year, and 500 ships must be loaded during this time. Each additional crew costs $180,000, and each boat delay costs $10,000. How many crews should be scheduled?

Solution The final decision is based on the probability of ship arrivals during a 6-hour period and the cost of additional crews versus the penalty cost for delayed ships. The first step is to compute the probabilities of various numbers of ships arriving during a 6-hour period and then the cost of ship delays. Then, we compute the cost of crews and the cost of ship delays for various levels of crew assignment.

Ship arrivals can be modeled by assuming that there are thousands of ships in the world and each has a small probability of arriving during a 6-hour loading period. An alternative model assumption is that during six hours there are a large number of small time intervals—say, 0.1 second—in this case, 216,000 such intervals. We also need to assume that ships do not travel in convoys. With 500 ships arriving over 50 days, we have a mean of 10 ships per day, or $\lambda = 2.5$ ship arrivals during a 6-hour period. The probability of x arrivals during a 6-hour period is computed using the following:

$$P(X = x \mid \lambda = 2.5) = \frac{e^{-2.5}2.5^x}{x!}$$

If four crews are scheduled, the probabilities of delaying ships are as follows:

$$P(\text{delay 1 ship}) = P(\text{5 ships arrive}) = \frac{e^{-2.5}2.5^5}{5!} = 0.0668$$

$$P(\text{delay 2 ships}) = P(\text{6 ships arrive}) = \frac{e^{-2.5}2.5^6}{6!} = 0.0278$$

$$P(\text{delay 3 ships}) = P(\text{7 ships arrive}) = \frac{e^{-2.5}2.5^7}{7!} = 0.0099$$

The probabilities of idle crews are as follows:

$$P(\text{1 crew idle}) = P(\text{3 ships arrive}) = \frac{e^{-2.5}2.5^3}{3!} = 0.2138$$

$$P(\text{2 crews idle}) = P(\text{2 ships arrive}) = \frac{e^{-2.5}2.5^2}{2!} = 0.2565$$

$$P(\text{3 crews idle}) = P(\text{1 ship arrive}) = \frac{e^{-2.5}2.5^1}{1!} = 0.2052$$

$$P(\text{4 crews idle}) = P(\text{0 ship arrive}) = \frac{e^{-2.5}2.5^0}{0!} = 0.0821$$

With four crews scheduled, the expected number of boats delayed during a 6-hour period would be as follows:

$$(1 \times 0.0668 + 2 \times 0.0278 + 3 \times 0.0099) = 0.1521$$

With a 50-day shipping season there are 200 6-hour periods, and thus the delay cost is as follows:

$$(0.1521)(200)(10,000) = \$304,200$$

Following the same computational form, we would find that with 5 crews scheduled, the expected cost of delays would be $95,200 and, thus, the extra crew would save $209,000. Since the cost of an extra crew is $180,000 the scheduling of 5 crews would be the correct decision.

We note that scheduling an additional crew would also lead to increased crew idle time. However, the higher service level makes it economically sensible to have crews idle in order to reduce ship delays.

Poisson Approximation to the Binomial Distribution

Previously, we noted that the Poisson distribution is obtained by starting with the binomial probability distribution with P approaching 0 and n becoming very large. Thus, it follows that the Poisson distribution can be used to approximate the binomial probabilities when the number of trials, n, is large and at the same time the probability, P, is small (generally such that $\lambda = nP \leq 7$). Examples of situations that would satisfy these conditions include the following:

- An insurance company will hold a large number of life policies on individuals of any particular age, and the probability that a single policy will result in a claim during the year is very low. Here, we have a binomial distribution with large n and small P.
- A company may have a large number of machines working on a process simultaneously. If the probability that any one of them will break down in a single day is small, the distribution of the number of daily breakdowns is binomial with large n and small P.

Poisson Approximation to the Binomial Distribution

Let X be the number of successes resulting from n independent trials, each with probability of success P. The distribution of the number of successes, X, is binomial, with mean nP. If the number of trials, n, is large and nP is of only moderate size (preferably $nP \leq 7$), this distribution can be **approximated by the Poisson distribution** with $\lambda = Np$. The probability distribution of the approximating distribution is then

$$P(x) = \frac{e^{-nP}(nP)^x}{x!} \text{ for } x = 0, 1, 2, \ldots \qquad (4.22)$$

Example 4.13 Probability of Bankruptcy (Poisson Probability)

An analyst predicted that 3.5% of all small corporations would file for bankruptcy in the coming year. For a random sample of 100 small corporations, estimate the probability that at least 3 will file for bankruptcy in the next year, assuming that the analyst's prediction is correct.

Solution The distribution of X, the number of filings for bankruptcy, is binomial with $n = 100$ and $P = 0.035$, so that the mean of the distribution is $\mu_x = nP = 3.5$.

Using the Poisson distribution to approximate the probability of at least 3 bankruptcies, we find the following:

$$P(X \geq 3) = 1 - P(X \leq 2)$$

$$P(0) = \frac{e^{-3.5}(3.5)^0}{0!} = e^{-3.5} = 0.030197$$

$$P(1) = \frac{e^{-3.5}(3.5)^1}{1!} = (3.5)(0.030197) = 0.1056895$$

$$P(2) = \frac{e^{-3.5}(3.5)^2}{2!} = (6.125)(0.030197) = 0.1849566$$

Thus,

$$P(X \leq 2) = P(0) + P(1) + P(2) = 0.030197 + 0.1056895 + 0.1849566 = 0.3208431$$
$$P(X \geq 3) = 1 - 0.3208431 = 0.6791569$$

Using the binomial distribution we compute the probability of $X \geq 3$ as:

$$P(X \geq 3) = 0.684093$$

Thus the Poisson probability is a close estimate of the actual binomial probability.

Comparison of the Poisson and Binomial Distributions

We should indicate at this point that confusion may exist about the choice of the binomial or the Poisson distribution for particular applications. The choice in many cases can be made easier by carefully reviewing the assumptions for the two distributions. For example, if the problem uses a small sample of observations, then it is not possible to find a limiting probability with n large, and, thus, the binomial is the correct probability distribution. Further, if we have a small sample and the probability of a success for a single trial is between 0.05 and 0.95, then there is further support for choosing the binomial. If we knew or could assume that each of 10 randomly selected customers in an automobile showroom had the same probability of purchase (assume $0.05 \leq P \leq 0.95$), then the number of purchases from this group would follow a binomial distribution. However, if the set of cases that could be affected is very large—say, several thousand—and the mean number of "successes" over that large set of cases is small—say, fewer than 30—then there is strong support for choosing the Poisson distribution. If we wanted to compute the probability of a certain number of defective parts in a set of 100,000 parts when the mean number of 15 defectives per 100,000 parts represented a typical production cycle, then we would use the Poisson distribution.

In the previous discussion we noted that, when P is less than 0.05 and n is large, we can approximate the binomial distribution by using the Poisson distribution. It can also be shown that when $n \geq 20$, $P \leq 0.05$, and the population mean is the same, we will find that both the binomial and the Poisson distributions generate approximately the same probability values. This result is shown in Exercise 4.63.

EXERCISES

Basic Exercises

4.50 Determine the probability of exactly four successes for a random variable with a Poisson distribution with parameter $\lambda = 2.4$.

4.51 Determine the probability of more than 7 successes for a random variable with a Poisson distribution with parameter . $\lambda = 4.2$.

4.52 Determine the probability of fewer than five successes for a random variable with a Poisson distribution with parameter $\lambda = 9.0$.

4.53 Determine the probability of fewer than or equal to five successes for a random variable with a Poisson distribution with parameter $\lambda = 9.0$.

Application Exercises

4.54 People arrive at an ATM vestibule to withdraw cash at an average rate of two people per minute. If the distribution of arrivals is Poisson, find the probability that in any given minute there will be three or fewer arrivals.

4.55 The number of accidents in a production facility has a Poisson distribution with a mean of 2.6 per month.
  a. For a given month what is the probability there will be fewer than 2 accidents?
  b. For a given month what is the probability there will be more than 3 accidents?

4.56 A customer service center in India receives, on average, 2.5 telephone calls per minute. If the distribution of calls is Poisson, what is the probability of receiving at least 3 calls during a particular minute?

4.57 Records indicate that, on average, 3.2 breakdowns per day occur on an urban highway during the morning rush hour. Assume that the distribution is Poisson.
  a. Find the probability that on any given day there will be fewer than 2 breakdowns on this highway during the morning rush hour.
  b. Find the probability that on any given day there will be more than 4 breakdowns on this highway during the morning rush hour.

4.58 Blue Cross Health Insurance reported that 4.5% of claims forms submitted for payment after a complex surgical procedure contain errors. If 100 of these forms are chosen at random, what is the probability that fewer than 3 of them contain errors? Use the Poisson approximation to the binomial distribution.

4.59 A corporation has 280 personal computers. The probability that any 1 of them will require repair in a given week is 0.01. Find the probability that fewer than 3 of the personal computers will require repair in a particular week. Use the Poisson approximation to the binomial distribution.

4.60 An insurance company holds fraud insurance policies on 6,000 firms. In any given year the probability that any single policy will result in a claim is 0.001. Find the probability that at least 3 claims are made in a given year. Use the Poisson approximation to the binomial distribution.

4.61 A state has a law requiring motorists to carry insurance. It was estimated that, despite this law, 6.0% of all motorists in the state are uninsured. A random sample of 100 motorists was taken. Use the Poisson approximation to the binomial distribution to estimate the probability that at least 3 of the motorists in this sample are uninsured. Also indicate what calculations would be needed to find this probability exactly if the Poisson approximation was not used.

4.62 A new warehouse is being designed and a decision concerning the number of loading docks is required. There are two models based on truck-arrival assumptions for the use of this warehouse, given that loading a truck requires 1 hour. Using the first model, we assume that the warehouse could be serviced by one of the many thousands of independent truckers who arrive randomly to obtain a load for delivery. It is known that, on average, 1 of these trucks would arrive each hour. For the second model, assume that the company hires a fleet of 10 trucks that are assigned full time to shipments from this warehouse. Under that assumption the trucks would arrive randomly, but the probability of any truck arriving during a given hour is 0.1. Obtain the appropriate probability distribution for each of these assumptions and compare the results.

4.6 HYPERGEOMETRIC DISTRIBUTION

The binomial distribution presented in Section 4.4 assumes that the items are drawn independently, with the probability of selecting an item being constant. In many applied problems these assumptions can be met if a small sample is drawn from a large population. But here we consider, for example, a situation where it is necessary to select 5 employees from a group of 15 equally qualified applicants—a small population. In the group of 15 there are 9 women and 6 men. Suppose that, in the group of 5 selected employees, 3 are men and 2 are women. What is the probability of selecting that particular group if the selections are made randomly without bias. In the initial group of 15, the probability of selecting a woman is 9/15. If a woman is not selected in the first drawing, then the probability of selecting a woman in the second drawing is 9/14. Thus, the probabilities change with each selection. Because the assumptions for the binomial are not met, a different probability must be selected. This probability distribution is the *hypergeometric distribution*. The hypergeometric probability distribution is given in Equation 4.23.

The preceding example describes a situation of sampling without replacement since an item drawn from the small population is not replaced before the second item is selected. Thus the probability of selection changes after each succeeding selection. This change is particularly important when the population is small relative to the size of the sample.

We can use the binomial distribution in situations that are defined as sampling with replacement. If the selected item is replaced in the population, then the probability of selecting that type of item remains the same and the binomial assumptions are met. In contrast, if the items are not replaced—sampling without replacement—the probabilities change with each selection, and, thus, the appropriate probability model is the hypergeometric distribution. If the population is large $(N > 10,000)$ and the sample size is small $(< 1\%)$, then the change in probability after each draw is very small. In those situations the binomial is a very good approximation and is typically used.

Hypergeometric Distribution

Suppose that a random sample of n objects is chosen from a group of N objects, S of which are successes. The distribution of the number of successes, X, in the sample is called the **hypergeometric distribution**. Its probability distribution is

$$P(x) = \frac{C_x^s C_{n-x}^{N-s}}{C_n^N} = \frac{\dfrac{S!}{x!(S-x)!} \times \dfrac{(N-S)!}{(n-x)!(N-S-n+x)!}}{\dfrac{N!}{n!(N-n)!}} \tag{4.23}$$

where x can take integer values ranging from the larger of 0 and $[n - (N - S)]$ to the smaller of n and S.

The logic for the hypergeometric distribution was developed in Section 3.2 using the classic definition of probability and the counting formulas for combinations. In Equation 4.23 the individual components are as follows:

1. The number of possible ways that x successes can be selected for the sample out of S successes contained in the population:

$$C_x^s = \frac{S!}{x!(S-x)!}$$

2. The number of possible ways that $n - x$ nonsuccesses can be selected from the population that contains $N - S$ nonsuccesses:

$$C_{n-x}^{N-S} = \frac{(N-S)!}{(n-x)!(N-S-n+x)!}$$

3. And, finally, the total number of different samples of size n that can be obtained from a population of size N:

$$C_n^N = \frac{N!}{n!(N-n)!}$$

When these components are combined using the classical definition of probability, the hypergeometric distribution is obtained.

The hypergeometric distribution is used for situations similar to the binomial with the important exception that sample observations are not replaced in the population when sampling from a "small population." Therefore, the probability, P, of a success is not constant from one observation to the next.

Example 4.14 Shipment of Items (Compute Hypergeometric Probability)

A company receives a shipment of 20 items. Because inspection of each individual item is expensive, it has a policy of checking a random sample of 6 items from such a shipment, and if no more than 1 sampled item is defective, the remainder will not be checked. What is the probability that a shipment of 5 defective items will not be subjected to additional checking?

Solution If "defective" is identified with "success" in this example, the shipment contains $N = 20$ items and $S = 5$ of the 20 that are successes. A sample of $n = 6$ items is selected. Then the number of successes, X, in the sample has a hypergeometric distribution with the probability distribution

$$P(x) = \frac{C_x^S C_{n-x}^{N-S}}{C_n^N} = \frac{C_x^5 C_{6-x}^{15}}{C_6^{20}} = \frac{\dfrac{5!}{x!(5-x)!} \times \dfrac{15!}{(6-x)!(9+x)!}}{\dfrac{20!}{6!14!}}$$

The shipment is not checked further if the sample contains either 0 or 1 success (defective), so that the probability of its acceptance is as follows:

$$P(\text{shipment accepted}) = P(0) + P(1)$$

The probability of no defectives in the sample is as follows:

$$P(0) = \frac{\dfrac{5!}{0!5!} \times \dfrac{15!}{6!9!}}{\dfrac{20!}{6!14!}} = 0.129$$

The probability of 1 defective item in the sample is as follows:

$$P(1) = \frac{\dfrac{5!}{1!4!} \times \dfrac{15!}{5!10!}}{\dfrac{20!}{6!14!}} = 0.387$$

Therefore, we find that the probability that the shipment of 20 items containing 5 defectives is not checked further is $P(\text{shipment accepted}) = P(0) + P(1) = 0.129 + 0.387 = 0.516$. This is a high error rate, which indicates a need for a new acceptance rule that requires total inspection if one or more defectives are found. With this new rule, only 12.9% of these shipments would be missed.

Hypergeometric probabilities can also be computed using computer packages following a procedure similar to the procedure in Example 4.9 for the binomial. We would strongly recommend that you use computer computation for hypergeometric probabilities because using the equations is very time consuming and easily subject to errors.

EXERCISES

Basic Exercises

4.63 Compute the probability of 10 successes in a random sample of size $n = 16$ obtained from a population of size $N = 70$ that contains 24 successes.

4.64 Compute the probability of 9 successes in a random sample of size $n = 25$ obtained from a population of size $N = 90$ that contains 32 successes.

4.65 Compute the probability of 4 successes in a random sample of size $n = 6$ obtained from a population of size $N = 30$ that contains 20 successes.

4.66 Compute the probability of 5 successes in a random sample of size $n = 12$ obtained from a population of size $N = 111$ that contains 60 successes.

Application Exercises

4.67 A company receives a shipment of 16 items. A random sample of 4 items is selected, and the shipment is rejected if any of these items proves to be defective.

    a. What is the probability of accepting a shipment containing 4 defective items?

    b. What is the probability of accepting a shipment containing 1 defective item?

    c. What is the probability of rejecting a shipment containing 1 defective item?

4.68 A committee of 8 members is to be formed from a group of 8 men and 8 women. If the choice of committee members is made randomly, what is the probability that precisely half of these members will be women?

4.69 A bond analyst was given a list of 13 corporate bonds. From that list she selected 3 whose ratings she felt were in danger of being downgraded in the next year. In actuality, a total of 5 of the 13 bonds on the list had their ratings downgraded in the next year. Suppose that the analyst had simply chosen 3 bonds randomly from this list. What is the probability that at least 2 of the chosen bonds would be among those whose ratings were to be downgraded in the next year?

4.70 A bank executive is presented with loan applications from 10 people. The profiles of the applicants are similar, except that 5 are minorities and 5 are not minorities. In the end the executive approves 6 of the applications. If these 6 approvals are chosen at random from the 10 applications, what is the probability that fewer than half the approvals will be of applications involving minorities?

4.7 JOINTLY DISTRIBUTED DISCRETE RANDOM VARIABLES

Business and economic applications of statistics are often concerned about the relationships between variables. Products at different quality levels have different prices. Age groups have different preferences for clothing, for automobiles, and for music. The percent returns on two different stocks may tend to be related, and the returns for both may increase when the market is growing. Alternatively, when the return on one stock is growing, the return on the other might be decreasing. When we work with probability models for problems involving relationships between variables, it is important that the effect of these relationships is included in the probability model. For example, assume that a car dealer is selling the following automobiles: (1) a red two-door compact, (2) a blue minivan, and (3) a silver full-size sedan; the probability distribution for purchasing would not be the same for women in their 20s, 30s, and 50s. Thus, it is important that probability models reflect the joint effect of variables on probabilities.

In Section 3.4 we discussed bivariate probabilities. We now consider the case where two or more, possibly related, discrete random variables are examined. With a single random variable, the probabilities for all possible outcomes can be summarized in a probability distribution. Now we need to define the probabilities that several random variables of interest simultaneously take specific values. At this point we will concentrate on two random variables, but the concepts apply to more than two. Consider the following example involving the use of two jointly distributed discrete random variables.

Example 4.15 Market Research (Joint Probabilities)

Sally Peterson, a marketing analyst, has been asked to develop a probability model for the relationship between the sale of luxury cookware and age group. This model will be important for developing a marketing campaign for a new line of chef-grade cookware. She believes that purchasing patterns for luxury cookware are different for different age groups.

Solution To represent the market, Sally proposes to use three age groups—16 to 25, 26 to 45, and 46 to 65—and two purchasing patterns—buy and not buy. Next, she collects a random sample of persons for the age range 16 to 65 and records their age group and desire to purchase. The result of this data collection is the joint probability distribution contained in Table 4.6. Table 4.6, therefore, provides a summary of the probability of purchase and age group that will be a valuable resource for marketing analysis.

Table 4.6 Joint Probability Distribution of Age Group (X) versus Purchase Decision (Y)

PURCHASE DECISION (Y)	AGE GROUP (X)			
	1 (16 TO 25)	2 (26 TO 45)	3 (46 TO 65)	$P(y)$
1 (buy)	0.10	0.20	0.10	0.40
2 (not buy)	0.25	0.25	0.10	0.60
$P(x)$	0.35	0.45	0.20	1.00

Joint Probability Distribution

Let X and Y be a pair of discrete random variables. Their **joint probability distribution** expresses the probability that simultaneously X takes the specific value x, and Y takes the value y, as a function of x and y. We note that the discussion here is a direct extension of the material in Section 3.4, where we presented the probability of the intersection of bivariate events, $P(A_i \cap B_j)$ Here, we use random variables. The notation used is $P(x, y)$, so

$$P(x, y) = P(X = x \cap Y = y)$$

The probability distributions for the individual random variables are frequently desired when dealing with jointly distributed random variables.

Derivation of the Marginal Probability Distribution

Let X and Y be a pair of jointly distributed random variables. In this context the probability distribution of the random variable X is called its **marginal probability distribution** and is obtained by summing the joint probabilities over all possible values—that is,

$$P(x) = \sum_y P(x, y) \tag{4.24}$$

Similarly, the marginal probability distribution of the random variable Y is as follows:

$$P(y) = \sum_x P(x, y) \tag{4.25}$$

An example of these marginal probability distributions is shown in the lower row and the right column in Table 4.6.

Joint probability distributions must have the following properties.

Properties of Joint Probability Distributions of Discrete Random Variables

Let X and Y be discrete random variables with joint probability distribution $P(x, y)$. Then,

    1. $0 \leq P(x, y) \leq 1$ for any pair of values x and y; and
    2. the sum of the joint probabilities $P(x, y)$ over all possible pairs of values must be 1.

The *conditional probability distribution* of one random variable, given specified values of another, is the collection of conditional probabilities.

Conditional Probability Distribution

Let X and Y be a pair of jointly distributed discrete random variables. The **conditional probability distribution** of the random variable Y, given that the random variable X takes the value x, expresses the probability that Y takes the value y, as a function of y, when the value x is fixed for X. This is denoted $P(y|x)$, and so, by the definition of conditional probability, is as follows:

$$P(y|x) = \frac{P(x, y)}{P(x)} \tag{4.26}$$

Similarly, the conditional probability distribution of X, given $Y = y$, is as follows:

$$P(x|y) = \frac{P(x, y)}{P(y)} \tag{4.27}$$

For example, using the probabilities in Table 4.6, we can compute the conditional probability of purchase $(y = 1)$, given age group 26 to 45 $(x = 2)$, as

$$P(1|2) = \frac{P(2, 1)}{P(2)} = \frac{0.20}{0.45} = 0.44$$

In Chapter 3 we discussed independence of events. This concept extends directly to random variables.

Independence of Jointly Distributed Random Variables

The jointly distributed random variables X and Y are said to be **independent** if and only if their joint probability distribution is the product of their marginal probability distributions—that is, if and only if

$$P(x, y) = P(x)P(y)$$

for all possible pairs of values x and y. And k random variables are independent if and only if

$$P(x_1, x_2, \ldots, x_K) = P(x_1) P(x_2) \cdots P(x_K) \tag{4.28}$$

From the definition of conditional probability distributions it follows that, if the random variables X and Y are independent, then the conditional probability distribution of Y, given X, is the same as the marginal probability distribution of Y—that is,

$$P(y|x) = P(y)$$

Similarly, it follows that

$$P(x|y) = P(x)$$

Example 4.16 considers the possible percent returns for two stocks, A and B, illustrates the computation of marginal probabilities and tests for independence, and finds the means and variances of two jointly distributed random variables.

Example 4.16 Stock Returns, Marginal Probability, Mean, and Variance (Joint Probabilities)

Suppose that Charlotte King has two stocks, A and B. Let X and Y be random variables of possible percent returns (0%, 5%, 10%, and 15%) for each of these two stocks, with the joint probability distribution given in Table 4.7.

   a. Find the marginal probabilities.
   b. Determine if X and Y are independent.
   c. Find the means and variances of both X and Y.

Table 4.7 Joint Probability Distribution for Random Variables X and Y

	Y RETURN			
X RETURN	0%	5%	10%	15%
0%	0.0625	0.0625	0.0625	0.0625
5%	0.0625	0.0625	0.0625	0.0625
10%	0.0625	0.0625	0.0625	0.0625
15%	0.0625	0.0625	0.0625	0.0625

Solution

   a. This problem is solved using the definitions developed in this chapter. Note that for every combination of values for X and Y, $P(x, y) = 0.0625$. That is, there is a 6.25% probability for each possible combination of x and y returns. To find the marginal probability that X has a 0% return, consider the following:

$$P(X = 0) = \sum_y P(0, y) = 0.0625 + 0.0625 + 0.0625 + 0.0625 = 0.25$$

   Here all the marginal probabilities of X are 25%. Notice that the sum of the marginal probabilities is 1. Similar results can be found for the marginal probabilities of Y.
   b. To test for independence, we need to check if $P(x, y) = P(x)P(y)$ for all possible pairs of values x and y.

$P(x, y) = 0.0625$ for all possible pairs of values x and y
$P(x) = 0.25$ and $P(y) = 0.25$ for all possible pairs of values x and y
$P(x, y) = 0.0625 = (0.25)(0.25) = P(x) P(y)$

   Therefore, X and Y are independent.
   c. The mean of X is as follows:

$$\mu_X = E[X] = \sum_x xP(x) = 0(0.25) + 0.05(0.25) + 0.10(0.25) + 0.15(0.25)$$

$$= 0.075$$

Similarly, the mean of Y is $\mu_Y = E[Y] = 0.075$.

The variance of X is

$$\sigma_X^2 = \sum_x (x - \mu_X)^2 P(x) = \sum_x (x - \mu_X)^2 P(x) = \sum_x (x - \mu_X)^2 (0.25)$$

$$= (0.25)[(0 - 0.075)^2 + (0.05 - 0.075)^2 + (0.10 - 0.075)^2 + (0.15 - 0.075)^2]$$

$$= 0.003125$$

and the standard deviation of X is

$$\sigma_X = \sqrt{0.003125} = 0.0559016, \text{ or } 5.59\%.$$

Follow similar steps to find the variance and standard deviation of Y.

Conditional Mean and Variance

The conditional mean is computed using the following:

$$\mu_{Y|X} = E[Y|X] = \sum_y (y|x)P(y|x)$$

Using the joint probability distribution in Table 4.6, we can compute the expected value of Y given that $x = 2$:

$$E[Y|x = 2] = \sum_y (y|x = 2)P(y|x = 2) = (1)\frac{0.20}{0.45} + (2)\frac{0.25}{0.45} = \frac{0.7}{0.45} = 1.56$$

Similarly the conditional variance is computed using the following:

$$\sigma_{Y|X}^2 = E[(Y - \mu_{Y|X})^2|X] = \sum_y ((y - \mu_{Y|X})^2|x)P(y|x)$$

Using the joint probability distribution in Table 4.6, we can compute the variance of Y given that $x = 2$:

$$\sigma^2(Y|x = 2) = \sum_y ((y - 1.56)^2)|x = 2)P(y|x = 2)$$

$$= (1 - 1.56)^2\frac{0.20}{0.45} + (2 - 1.56)^2\frac{0.25}{0.45} = \frac{0.111}{0.45} = 0.247$$

Computer Applications

Computation of marginal probabilities, means, and variances for jointly distributed random variables can be developed in Excel or other computer packages. For example, we can compute marginal probabilities, means, and variances for the jointly distributed random variables X and Y, from Table 4.7, using an Excel worksheet in the format shown in Figure 4.4.

Figure 4.4
Marginal
Probabilities,
Means, and
Variances for
X and Y Computed
Using Excel

X Return	Y Return 0%	5%	10%	15%	P(x)	Mean of	Var of X	StDev of
0%	0.0625	0.0625	0.0625	0.0625	0.25	0	0.0014063	
5%	0.0625	0.0625	0.0625	0.0625	0.25	0.0125	0.0001563	
10%	0.0625	0.0625	0.0625	0.0625	0.25	0.025	0.0001563	
15%	0.0625	0.0625	0.0625	0.0625	0.25	0.0375	0.0014063	
P(y)	0.25	0.25	0.25	0.25		0.075	0.003125	0.055902
Mean of Y	0	0.0125	0.025	0.0375	0.075			
Var of Y	0.00140625	0.00015625	0.00015625	0.00140625	0.003125			
StDev of Y					0.055902			

Linear Functions of Random Variables

Previously, the expectation of a function of a single random variable was defined. This definition can now be extended to functions of several random variables.

Expected Values of Functions of Jointly Distributed Random Variables

Let X and Y be a pair of discrete random variables with joint probability distribution $P(x, y)$. The expectation of any function $g(X, Y)$ of these random variables is defined as follows:

$$E[g(X, Y)] = \sum_x \sum_y g(x, y) P(x, y) \qquad (4.29)$$

Of particular interest are numerous applications involving linear combinations of random variables that have the general form

$$W = aX + bY$$

An important application is the total revenue random variable, W, resulting from monthly sales of two products where X and Y are random variables representing the sales of each product with the selling prices fixed as a and b. The mean and variance, as developed in the chapter appendix, are as follows:

$$\mu_W = E[W] = a\mu_X + b\mu_Y \qquad (4.30)$$

$$\sigma_W^2 = a^2\sigma_X^2 + b^2\sigma_Y^2 + 2ab\,Cov(X, Y) \qquad (4.31)$$

These results can be extended to the linear combination of many random variables

$$W = a_1X_1 + a_2X_2 + \cdots + a_KX_K = \sum a_iX_i$$

$$\mu_W = E[W] = \sum_{i=1}^{K} a_i\mu_i$$

$$\sigma_w^2 = \sum_{i=1}^{K} a_i^2\sigma_i^2 + 2\sum_{i=1}^{K-1}\sum_{j>i}^{K} a_ia_j\,Cov(X_i, Y_j) \qquad (4.32)$$

The term $Cov(X, Y)$ is the covariance between the two random variables, which is developed next.

Covariance

The covariance is a measure of linear association between two random variables. The covariance represents the joint variability of two random variables and is used with the variances of each random variable to compute the variance of the linear combination, as shown in Equations 4.31 and 4.32. In addition, the covariance is used to compute a standardized measure of joint variability called the correlation. We first develop the definition of the covariance in Equation 4.33 and then present some important applications.

Suppose that X and Y are a pair of random variables that are not statistically independent. We would like some measure of the nature and strength of the relationship between them. This is rather difficult to achieve, since the random variables could conceivably be related in any number of ways. To simplify matters, attention is restricted to the possibility of linear association. For example, a high value of X might be associated, on average, with a high value of Y, and a low value of X, with a low value of Y, in such a way that, to a good approximation, a straight line might be drawn through the associated values when plotted on a graph.

Suppose that the random variable X has mean μ_X and Y has mean μ_Y, and consider the product $(X - \mu_X)(Y - \mu_Y)$. If high values of X tend to be associated with high values of Y and low values of X, with low values of Y, we would expect this product to be positive, and the stronger the association, the larger the expectation of $(X - \mu_X)(Y - \mu_Y)$, to be defined as $E[(X - \mu_X)(Y - \mu_Y)]$. By contrast, if high values of X are associated with low values of Y and low X, with high Y, the expected value for this product, $E[(X - \mu_X)(Y - \mu_Y)]$, would be negative. An expectation that $E[(X - \mu_X)(Y - \mu_Y)]$ equals 0 would imply an absence of linear association between X and Y. Thus, the expected value, $E[(X - \mu_X)(Y - \mu_Y)]$, will be used as a measure of linear association in the population.

Covariance

Let X be a random variable with mean μ_X, and let Y be a random variable with mean μ_Y. The expected value of $(X - \mu_X)(Y - \mu_Y)$ is called the **covariance** between X and Y, denoted as $Cov(X, Y)$. For discrete random variables

$$Cov(X, Y) = E[(X - \mu_X)(Y - \mu_Y)] = \sum_x \sum_y (x - \mu_X)(y - \mu_Y)P(x, y) \qquad (4.33)$$

An equivalent expression is as follows:

$$Cov(X, Y) = E[XY] - \mu_X\mu_Y = \sum_x \sum_y xyP(x, y) - \mu_X\mu_Y$$

Correlation

Although the covariance provides an indication of the direction of the relationship between random variables, the covariance does not have an upper or lower bound, and its size is greatly influenced by the scaling of the numbers. A strong linear relationship is defined as a condition where the individual observation points are close to a straight line. It is difficult to use the covariance to provide a measure of the strength of a linear relationship because it is unbounded. A related measure, the correlation coefficient, provides a measure of the strength of the linear relationship between two random variables, with the measure being limited to the range from -1 to $+1$.

Correlation

Let X and Y be jointly distributed random variables. The **correlation** between X and Y is as follows:

$$\rho = Corr(X, Y) = \frac{Cov(X, Y)}{\sigma_X\sigma_Y} \qquad (4.34)$$

The correlation is the covariance divided by the standard deviations of the two random variables. This results in a standardized measure of relationship that varies from -1 to $+1$. The following interpretations are important:

1. A correlation of 0 indicates that there is no linear relationship between the two random variables. If the two random variables are independent, the correlation is equal to 0.
2. A positive correlation indicates that if one random variable is high (low), then the other random variable has a higher probability of being high (low), and we say that the variables are positively dependent. Perfect positive linear dependency is indicated by a correlation of $+1.0$.
3. A negative correlation indicates that if one random variable is high (low), then the other random variable has a higher probability of being low (high), and we say that the variables are negatively dependent. Perfect negative linear dependency is indicated by a correlation of -1.0.

The correlation is more useful for describing relationships than the covariance. With a correlation of $+1$ the two random variables have a perfect positive linear relationship, and, therefore, a specific value of one variable, X, predicts the other variable, Y, exactly. A correlation of -1 indicates a perfect negative linear relationship between two variables, with one variable, X, predicting the negative of the other variable, Y. A correlation of 0 indicates no linear relationship between the two variables. Intermediate values indicate that variables tend to be related, with stronger relationships occurring as the absolute value of the correlation approaches 1.

We also know that correlation is a term that has moved into common usage. In many cases correlation is used to indicate that a relationship exists. However, variables that have nonlinear relationships will not have a correlation coefficient close to 1.0. This distinction is important for us in order to avoid confusion between correlated random variables and those with nonlinear relationships.

Example 4.17 Joint Distribution of Stock Prices (Compute Covariance and Correlation)

Find the covariance and correlation for the stocks A and B from Example 4.16 with the joint probability distribution in Table 4.7.

Solution The computation of covariance is tedious for even a problem such as this, which is simplified so that all of the joint probabilities, $P(x, y)$, are 0.0625 for all pairs of values x and y. By definition, you need to find the following:

$$Cov(X, Y) = \sum_x \sum_y xyP(x, y) - \mu_X\mu_Y$$

$$\begin{aligned}
= \ & 0[(0)(0.0625) + (0.05)(0.0625) + (0.10)(0.0625) + (0.15)(0.0625)] \\
& + 0.05[(0)(0.0625) + (0.05)(0.0625) + (0.10)(0.0625) + (0.15)(0.0625)] \\
& + 0.10[(0)(0.0625) + (0.05)(0.0625) + (0.10)(0.0625) + (0.15)(0.0625)] \\
& + 0.15[(0)(0.0625) + (0.05)(0.0625) + (0.10)(0.0625) + (0.15)(0.0625)] \\
& - (0.075)(0.075) \\
= \ & 0.005625 - 0.005625 = 0
\end{aligned}$$

Thus,

$$\rho = Corr(X, Y) = \frac{Cov(X, Y)}{\sigma_X\sigma_Y} = 0$$

Microsoft Excel can be used for these computations by carefully following the example in Figure 4.5.

Figure 4.5 Covariance Calculation Using Microsoft Excel

Joint Probability Distribution of X and Y						
			Y Return %			
X Return %	0	0.05	0.1	0.15	$P(x)$	E(X)
0	0.0625	0.0625	0.0625	0.0625	0.25	
0.05	0.0625	0.0625	0.0625	0.0625	0.25	
0.1	0.0625	0.0625	0.0625	0.0625	0.25	
0.15	0.0625	0.0625	0.0625	0.0625	0.25	
	0.25	0.25	0.25	0.25		0.075
E(Y)					0.075	
Calculation of Covariance						
	$xy\,P(x,y)$	$xy\,P(x,y)$	$xy\,P(x,y)$	$xy\,P(x,y)$		
$xy\,P(x,y)$	0	0	0	0		
$xy\,P(x,y)$	0	0.000156	0.000313	0.000469		
$xy\,P(x,y)$	0	0.000313	0.000625	0.000938		
$xy\,P(x,y)$	0	0.000469	0.000938	0.001406		
Sum $xy\,P(x,y)$	0	0.000938	0.001875	0.002813		0.005625
						Covariance
Sum $xy\,P(x,y)$ − E(X)E(Y)			= 0.005625 − 0.005625			0

Covariance and Statistical Independence

If two random variables are **statistically independent**, the covariance between them is 0. However, the converse is not necessarily true.

The reason a covariance of 0 does not necessarily imply statistical independence is that covariance is designed to measure linear association, and it is possible that this quantity may not detect other types of dependency, as we see in the following illustration.

Suppose that the random variable X has probability distribution

$$P(-1) = 1/4 \quad P(0) = 1/2 \quad P(1) = 1/4$$

Let the random variable Y be defined as follows:

$$Y = X^2$$

Thus, knowledge of the value taken by X implies knowledge of the value taken by Y, and, therefore, these two random variables are certainly not independent. Whenever $X = 0$, then $Y = 0$, and if X is either -1 or 1, then $Y = 1$. The joint probability distribution of X and Y is

$$P(-1,1) = 1/4 \quad P(0,0) = 1/2 \quad P(1,1) = 1/4$$

with the probability of any other combination of values being equal to 0. It is then straightforward to verify that

$$E[X] = 0 \quad E[Y] = 1/2 \quad E[XY] = 0$$

The covariance between X and Y is 0. Thus we see that random variables that are not independent can have a covariance equal to 0.

To conclude the discussion of joint distributions, consider the mean and variance of a random variable that can be written as the sum or difference of other random variables. These results are summarized below and can be derived using Equations 4.30, 4.31, and 4.32.

Summary Results for Linear Sums and Differences of Random Variables

Let X and Y be a pair of random variables with means μ_X and μ_Y and variances σ_X^2 and σ_Y^2. The following properties hold:

1. The **expected value of their sum** is the sum of their expected values:

$$E[X + Y] = \mu_X + \mu_Y \tag{4.35}$$

2. The **expected value of their difference** is the difference between their expected values:

$$E[X - Y] = \mu_X - \mu_Y \tag{4.36}$$

3. If the covariance between X and Y is 0, the **variance of their sum** is the sum of their variances:

$$Var(X + Y) = \sigma_X^2 + \sigma_Y^2 \tag{4.37}$$

But if the covariance is not 0, then

$$Var(X + Y) = \sigma_X^2 + \sigma_Y^2 + 2\,Cov(X, Y)$$

4. If the covariance between X and Y is 0, the **variance of their difference** is the *sum* of their variances:

$$Var(X - Y) = \sigma_X^2 + \sigma_Y^2 \tag{4.38}$$

But if the covariance is not 0, then

$$Var(X - Y) = \sigma_X^2 + \sigma_Y^2 - 2\,Cov(X, Y)$$

Let $X_1, X_2, \ldots, X_K$ be K random variables with means $\mu_1, \mu_2, \ldots, \mu_K$ and variances $\sigma_1^2, \sigma_2^2, \ldots, \sigma_K^2$. The following properties hold:

5. The expected value of their sum is as follows:

$$E[X_1 + X_2 + \cdots + X_K] = \mu_1 + \mu_2 + \cdots + \mu_K \tag{4.39}$$

6. If the covariance between every pair of these random variables is 0, the variance of their sum is as follows:

$$Var(X_1 + X_2 + \cdots + X_K) = \sigma_1^2 + \sigma_2^2 + \cdots + \sigma_K^2 \tag{4.40}$$

7. If the covariance between every pair of these random variables is not 0, the variance of their sum is as follows:

$$Var(X_1 + X_2 + \cdots + X_K) = \sum_{i=1}^{K}\sigma_i^2 + 2\sum_{i=1}^{K-1}\sum_{j>i}^{K} Cov(X_i, Y_j) \tag{4.41}$$

Example 4.18 Simple Investment Portfolio (Means and Variances, Functions of Random Variables)

An investor has \$1,000 to invest and two investment opportunities, each requiring a minimum of \$500. The profit per \$100 from the first can be represented by a random variable X, having the following probability distributions:

$$P(X = -5) = 0.4 \quad \text{and} \quad P(X = 20) = 0.6$$

The profit per \$100 from the second is given by the random variable Y, whose probability distributions are as follows:

$$P(Y = 0) = 0.6 \quad \text{and} \quad P(Y = 25) = 0.4$$

Random variables X and Y are independent. The investor has the following possible strategies:

a. \$1,000 in the first investment
b. \$1,000 in the second investment
c. \$500 in each investment

Find the mean and variance of the profit from each strategy.

Solution Random variable X has mean

$$\mu_X = E[X] = \sum_x xP(x) = (-5)(0.4) + (20)(0.6) = \$10$$

and variance

$$\sigma_X^2 = E[(X - \mu_x)^2] = \sum_x (x - \mu_x)^2 P(x) = (-5 - 10)^2(0.4) + (20 - 10)^2(0.6) = 150$$

Random variable Y has mean

$$\mu_Y = E[Y] = \sum_y yP(y) = (0)(0.6) + (25)(0.4) = \$10$$

and variance

$$\sigma_Y^2 = E[(Y - \mu_Y)^2] = \sum_y (y - \mu_Y)^2 P(y) = (0 - 10)^2(0.6) + (25 - 10)^2(0.4) = 150$$

Strategy (a) has mean profit of $E[10X] = 10E[X] = \$100$ and variance of

$$Var(10X) = 100Var(X) = 15,000$$

Strategy (b) has mean profit $E[10Y] = 10E[Y] = \$100$ and variance of

$$Var(10Y) = 100Var(Y) = 15,000$$

Now consider strategy (c): \$500 in each investment. The return from strategy (c) is $5X + 5Y$, which has mean

$$E[5X + 5Y] = E[5X] + E[5Y] = 5E[X] + 5E[Y] = \$100$$

Thus, all three strategies have the same expected profit. However, since X and Y are independent and the covariance is 0, the variance of the return from strategy (c) is as follows:

$$Var(5X + 5Y) = Var(5X) + Var(5Y) = 25Var(X) + 25Var(Y) = 7,500$$

This is smaller than the variances of the other strategies, reflecting the decrease in risk that follows from diversification in an investment portfolio. Most investors would prefer strategy (c), since it yields the same expected return as the other two, but with lower risk.

Portfolio Analysis

Investment managers spend considerable effort developing investment portfolios that consist of a set of financial instruments that each have returns defined by a probability distribution. Portfolios are used to obtain a combined investment that has a given expected return and risk. Stock portfolios with a high risk can be constructed by combining several individual stocks whose values tend to increase or decrease together. With such a portfolio an investor will have either large gains or large losses. Stocks whose values move in opposite directions could be combined to create a portfolio with a more stable value, implying less risk. Decreases in one stock price would be balanced by increases in another stock price.

This process of **portfolio analysis** and construction is conducted using probability distributions. The mean value of the portfolio is the linear combination of the mean values of the stocks in the portfolio. The variance of the portfolio value is computed using the sum of the variances and the covariance of the joint distribution of the stock values. We will develop the method using an example with a portfolio consisting of two stocks.

Consider a portfolio that consists of a shares of stock A and b shares of stock B. We want to use the mean and variance for the market value, W, of a portfolio, where W is the linear function $W = aX + bY$. The mean and variance are derived in the chapter appendix.

The Mean and Variance for the Market Value of a Portfolio

The random variable X is the price for stock A, and the random variable Y is the price for stock B. The **portfolio market value**, W, is given by the linear function

$$W = aX + bY$$

where a is the number of shares of stock A, and b is the number of shares of stock B.

The **mean value for** W is as follows:

$$\mu_W = E[W] = E[aX + bY] = a\mu_X + b\mu_Y \tag{4.42}$$

The **variance for** W is

$$\sigma_W^2 = a^2\sigma_X^2 + b^2\sigma_Y^2 + 2abCov(X, Y) \qquad (4.43)$$

or, using the correlation, is

$$\sigma_W^2 = a^2\sigma_X^2 + b^2\sigma_Y^2 + 2abCorr(X, Y)\sigma_X\sigma_Y$$

Portfolio analysis developed using discrete random variables is expanded in Chapter 5 using continuous random variables. The development here using discrete random variables is more intuitive compared to using continuous random variables. However, the results for means, variances, covariances, and linear combinations of random variables also apply directly to continuous random variables. Since portfolios involve prices that are continuous random variables, the development in Chapter 5 is more realistic. In addition, the normal distribution developed in Chapter 5 provides important analysis tools.

Example 4.19 Analysis of Stock Portfolios (Means and Variances, Functions of Random Variables)

George Tiao has 5 shares of stock A and 10 shares of stock B, whose price variations are modeled by the probability distribution in Table 4.8. Find the mean and variance of the portfolio.

Table 4.8 Joint Probability Distribution for Stock A and Stock B Prices

STOCK A PRICE	STOCK B PRICE			
	$40	$50	$60	$70
$45	0.24	0.003333	0.003333	0.003333
$50	0.003333	0.24	0.003333	0.003333
$55	0.003333	0.003333	0.24	0.003333
$60	0.003333	0.003333	0.003333	0.24

Solution The value, W, of the portfolio can be represented by the linear combination

$$W = 5X + 10Y$$

Using the probability distribution in Table 4.8 we can compute the means, variances, and covariances for the two stock prices. The mean and variance for stock A are $53 and 31.3, respectively, while for stock B they are $55 and 125. The covariance is 59.17 and the correlation is 0.947.

The mean value for the portfolio is as follows:

$$\mu_W = E[W] = E[5X + 10Y] = 5(53) + (10)(55) = \$815$$

The variance for the portfolio value is as follows:

$$\sigma_W^2 = 5^2\sigma_X^2 + 10^2\sigma_Y^2 + 2 \times 5 \times 10 \times Cov(X, Y)$$
$$= 5^2 \times 31.3 + 10^2 \times 125 + 2 \times 5 \times 10 \times 59.17 = 19,199.5$$

George knows that high variance implies high risk. He believes that the risk for this portfolio is too high. Thus, he asks you to prepare a portfolio that has lower risk. After some investigation you discover a different pair of stocks whose prices follow the probability distribution in Table 4.9. By comparing Tables 4.8 and 4.9 we note that the stock prices tend to change directly with each other in Table 4.8, while they move in opposite directions in Table 4.9.

Table 4.9 Probability Distribution for New Portfolio of Stock C and Stock D

STOCK C PRICE	STOCK D PRICE			
	$40	$50	$60	$70
$45	0.003333	0.003333	0.003333	0.24
$50	0.003333	0.003333	0.24	0.003333
$55	0.003333	0.24	0.003333	0.003333
$60	0.24	0.003333	0.003333	0.003333

Using the probability distribution in Table 4.9 we computed the means, variances, and covariance for the new stock portfolio. The mean for stock C is $53, the same as for stock A. Similarly, the mean for stock D is $55, the same as for stock B. Thus, the mean value of the portfolio is not changed. The variance for each stock is also the same, but the covariance is now –59.17. Thus, the variance for the new portfolio includes a *negative covariance* term and is as follows:

$$\sigma_W^2 = 5^2\sigma_X^2 + 10^2\sigma_Y^2 + 2 \times 5 \times 10 \times Cov(X, Y)$$
$$= 5^2 \times 31.3 + 10^2 \times 125 + 2 \times 5 \times 10 \times (-59.17) = 7{,}365.5$$

We see that the effect of the negative covariance is to reduce the variance and, hence, to reduce the risk of the portfolio.

Figure 4.6 shows how portfolio variance—and, hence, risk—changes with different correlations between stock prices. Note that the portfolio variance is linearly related to the correlation. To help control risk, designers of stock portfolios select stocks based on the correlation between prices.

Figure 4.6 Portfolio Variance Versus Correlation of Stock Prices

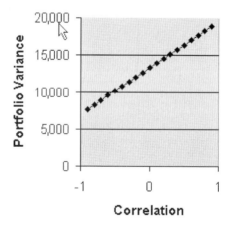

As we saw in Example 4.19, the correlation between stock prices, or between any two random variables, has important effects on the portfolio value random variable. A positive correlation indicates that both prices, X and Y, increase or decrease together. Thus, large or small values of the portfolio are magnified, resulting in greater range and variance compared to a zero correlation. Conversely, a negative correlation leads to price increases for X matched by price decreases for Y. As a result, the range and variance of the portfolio are decreased compared to a zero correlation. By selecting stocks with particular combinations of correlations, fund managers can control the variance and the risk for portfolios.

Basic Exercises

4.71 The average amount of money a person spends on lottery tickets each month is €9. By looking at the data, a Poisson discrete distribution is assumed for this variable. Calculate each of the following.

    a. The probability of buying no lottery ticket.
    b. The probability of buying 1 lottery ticket.
    c. The probability of buying 3 lottery tickets.
    d. The probability of buying fewer than or equal 3 tickets.

4.72 Consider the joint probability distribution:

		X	
		1	2
Y	0	0.15	0.35
	1	0.30	0.20

    a. Compute the marginal probability distributions for X and Y.
    b. Compute the covariance and correlation for X and Y.
    c. Compute the mean and variance for the linear function $W = X + Y$.

4.73 Consider the following probability distribution:

		X	
		1	2
Y	0	0.25	0.35
	1	0.10	0.30

    a. Compute the marginal probability distributions for X and Y.
    b. Compute the covariance and correlation for X and Y.
    c. Compute the mean and variance for the linear function $W = 2X + Y$.

4.74 Consider the joint probability distribution:

		X	
		1	2
Y	0	0.80	0.00
	1	0.00	0.20

    a. Compute the marginal probability distributions for X and Y.
    b. Compute the covariance and correlation for X and Y.
    c. Compute the mean and variance for the linear function $W = 4X + 3Y$.

4.75 Consider the joint probability distribution:

		X	
		1	2
Y	0	0.0	0.60
	1	0.40	0.0

    a. Compute the marginal probability distributions for X and Y.
    b. Compute the covariance and correlation for X and Y.
    c. Compute the mean and variance for the linear function $W = 2X - 4Y$.

4.76 Consider the joint probability distribution:

		X	
		1	2
Y	0	0.65	0.00
	1	0.00	0.35

    a. Compute the marginal probability distributions for X and Y.
    b. Compute the covariance and correlation for X and Y.
    c. Compute the mean and variance for the linear function $W = 10X - 8Y$.

Application Exercises

4.77 A researcher suspected that the number of between-meal snacks eaten by students in a day during final examinations might depend on the number of tests a student had to take on that day. The accompanying table shows joint probabilities, estimated from a survey.

Number of Snacks (Y)	Number of Tests (X)			
	0	1	2	3
0	0.07	0.09	0.06	0.01
1	0.07	0.06	0.07	0.01
2	0.06	0.07	0.14	0.03
3	0.02	0.04	0.16	0.04

    a. Find the probability distribution of X and compute the mean number of tests taken by students on that day.
    b. Find the probability distribution of Y and, hence, the mean number of snacks eaten by students on that day.
    c. Find and interpret the conditional probability distribution of Y, given that $X = 3$.
    d. Find the covariance between X and Y.
    e. Are number of snacks and number of tests independent of each other?

4.78 A real estate agent is interested in the relationship between the number of lines in a newspaper advertisement for an apartment and the volume of inquiries from potential renters. Let volume of inquiries be denoted by the random variable X, with the value 0 for little interest, 1 for moderate interest, and 2 for strong interest. The real estate agent used historical records to compute the joint probability distribution shown in the accompanying table.

Number of Lines (Y)	Number of Inquiries (X)		
	0	1	2
3	0.09	0.14	0.07
4	0.07	0.23	0.16
5	0.03	0.10	0.11

a. Find the joint cumulative probability at
   $X = 1, Y = 4$, and interpret your result.
b. Find and interpret the conditional probability
   distribution for Y, given $X = 0$.
c. Find and interpret the conditional probability
   distribution for X, given $Y = 4$.
d. Find and interpret the covariance between X and Y.
e. Are number of lines in the advertisement and
   volume of inquiries independent of one another?

4.79 The accompanying table shows, for credit-card holders with one to three cards, the joint probabilities for
number of cards owned (X) and number of credit purchases made in a week (Y).

Number of Cards (X)	Number of Purchases in a Week (Y)				
	0	1	2	3	4
1	0.06	0.13	0.09	0.07	0.03
2	0.02	0.07	0.09	0.09	0.07
3	0.01	0.02	0.05	0.08	0.12

a. For a randomly chosen person from this group,
   what is the probability distribution for number of
   purchases made in a week?
b. For a person in this group who has three cards,
   what is the probability distribution for number of
   purchases made in a week?
c. Are number of cards owned and number of purchases made statistically independent?

4.80 A market researcher wants to determine whether a
new model of a personal computer that had been advertised on a late-night talk show had achieved more
brand-name recognition among people who watched
the show regularly than among people who did not.
After conducting a survey, it was found that 13% of
all people both watched the show regularly and could
correctly identify the product. Also, 15% of all people
regularly watched the show and 46% of all people
could correctly identify the product. Define a pair of
random variables as follows:

$X = 1$	If the show is watched regularly	$X = 0$	otherwise
$Y = 1$	If product is identified correctly	$Y = 0$	otherwise

a. Find the joint probability distribution of X and Y.
b. Find the conditional probability distribution of Y,
   given $X = 1$.
c. Find and interpret the covariance between X and Y.

4.81 A college bookseller makes calls at the offices of professors and forms the impression that professors are more
likely to be away from their offices on Friday than any
other working day. A review of the records of calls,
1/5 of which are on Fridays, indicates that for 16%
of Friday calls, the professor is away from the office,
while this occurs for only 12% of calls on every other
working day. Define the random variables as follows:

$X = 1$	if call is made on a Friday	$X = 0$	otherwise
$Y = 1$	if professor is away from the office	$Y = 0$	otherwise

a. Find the joint probability distribution of
   X and Y.
b. Find the conditional probability distribution
   of Y, given $X = 0$.
c. Find the marginal probability distributions of
   X and Y.
d. Find and interpret the covariance between
   X and Y.

4.82 A restaurant manager receives occasional complaints
about the quality of both the food and the service. The
marginal probability distributions for the number of
weekly complaints in each category are shown in the
accompanying table. If complaints about food and service are independent of each other, find the joint probability distribution.

Number of Food Complaints	Probability	Number of Service Complaints	Probability
0	0.12	0	0.18
1	0.29	1	0.38
2	0.42	2	0.34
3	0.17	3	0.10

4.83 Refer to the information in the previous exercise.
Find the mean and standard deviation of the total number of complaints received in a week. Having reached this point, you are concerned that the
numbers of food and service complaints may not be
independent of each other. However, you have no
information about the nature of their dependence.
What can you now say about the mean and standard
deviation of the total number of complaints received
in a week?

4.84 A company has 5 representatives covering large territories and 10 representatives covering smaller territories. The probability distributions for the numbers
of orders received by each of these types of representatives in a day are shown in the accompanying table.
Assuming that the number of orders received by any
representative is independent of the number received
by any other, find the mean and standard deviation
of the total number of orders received by the company in a day.

Numbers of Orders (Large Territories)	Probability	Numbers of Orders (Smaller Territories)	Probability
0	0.08	0	0.18
1	0.16	1	0.26
2	0.28	2	0.36
3	0.32	3	0.13
4	0.10	4	0.07
5	0.06		

KEY WORDS

- Bernoulli random variable, 164
- binomial distribution, 166
- conditional probability distribution, 182
- continuous random variable, 151
- correlation, 186
- covariance, 186
- cumulative probability distribution, 154
- differences of random variable, 188
- discrete random variable, 151
- expected value, 156
- expected value of functions of random variables, 159

- hypergeometric distribution, 178
- independence of jointly distributed random variables, 182
- joint probability distribution, 181
- marginal probability distribution, 181
- mean, 156
- mean and variance of a binomial, 166
- Poisson approximation to the binomial distribution, 175
- Poisson probability distribution, 190
- portfolio analysis, 190
- portfolio market value, 190
- probability distribution function, 153

- properties of cumulative probability distributions, 157
- properties of joint probability distributions, 182
- random variable, 151
- relationship between probability distribution and cumulative probability distribution, 155
- variance of a discrete random variable, 157
- properties for linear functions of a random variable, 159

CHAPTER EXERCISES AND APPLICATIONS

4.85 As an investment advisor, you tell a client that an investment in a mutual fund has (over the next year) a higher expected return than an investment in the money market. The client then asks the following questions:

    a. Does that imply that the mutual fund will certainly yield a higher return than the money market?

    b. Does it follow that I should invest in the mutual fund rather than in the money market? How would you reply?

4.86 A contractor estimates the probabilities for the number of days required to complete a certain type of construction project as follows:

Time (days)	1	2	3	4	5
Probability	0.05	0.20	0.35	0.30	0.10

    a. What is the probability that a randomly chosen project will take less than 3 days to complete?

    b. Find the expected time to complete a project.

    c. Find the standard deviation of time required to complete a project.

    d. The contractor's project cost is made up of two parts—a fixed cost of $20,000, plus $2,000 for each day taken to complete the project. Find the mean and standard deviation of total project cost.

    e. If three projects are undertaken, what is the probability that at least two of them will take at least 4 days to complete, assuming independence of individual project completion times?

4.87 A car salesperson estimates the following probabilities for the number of cars that she will sell in the next week:

Number of cars	0	1	2	3	4	5
Probability	0.10	0.20	0.35	0.16	0.12	0.07

    a. Find the expected number of cars that will be sold in the week.

    b. Find the standard deviation of the number of cars that will be sold in the week.

    c. The salesperson receives a salary of $250 for the week, plus an additional $300 for each car sold. Find the mean and standard deviation of her total salary for the week.

    d. What is the probability that the salesperson's salary for the week will be more than $1,000?

4.88 A multiple-choice test has nine questions. For each question there are four possible answers from which to select. One point is awarded for each correct answer, and points are not subtracted for incorrect answers. The instructor awards a bonus point if the students spell their name correctly. A student who has not studied for this test decides to choose an answer for each question at random.

    a. Find the expected number of correct answers for the student on these nine questions.

    b. Find the standard deviation of the number of correct answers for the student on these nine questions.

    c. The student spells his name correctly:

       i Find the expected total score on the test for this student.

       ii Find the standard deviation of his total score on the test.

4.89 Develop realistic examples of pairs of random variables for which you would expect to find the following:

    a. Positive covariance

    b. Negative covariance

    c. Zero covariance

4.90 A long-distance taxi service owns four vehicles. These are of different ages and have different repair records. The probabilities that, on any given day, each vehicle will be available for use are 0.95, 0.90, 0.90, and 0.80. Whether one vehicle is available is independent of whether any other vehicle is available.

a. Find the probability distribution for the number of vehicles available for use on a given day.
b. Find the expected number of vehicles available for use on a given day.
c. Find the standard deviation of the number of vehicles available for use on a given day.

4.91 Suppose the students at the University of Amsterdam, the Netherlands, are classified according their school grades (X), and the number of daily hours spent watching shows on Netflix ($Y = 0$ for no hours, 1 for one hour, 2 for more than one hour). The joint probabilities in the accompanying table were estimated for these random variables.

Hours Spent on Netflix (Y)	Students' Grades (X)			
	1	2	3	4
0	0.06	0.04	0.02	0.00
1	0.14	0.12	0.18	0.20
2	0.04	0.04	0.09	0.10

a. Find the probability that a randomly chosen student does not watch Netflix.
b. Find the means of the random variables X and Y.
c. Find and interpret the covariance between the random variables X and Y.

4.92 A basketball team's star 3-point shooter takes six 3-point shots in a game. Historically, she makes 40% of all 3-point shots taken in a game. State at the outset what assumptions you have made.

a. Find the probability that she will make at least two shots.
b. Find the probability that she will make exactly three shots.
c. Find the mean and standard deviation of the number of shots she made.
d. Find the mean and standard deviation of the total number of points she scored as a result of these shots.

4.93 It is estimated that 55% of the freshmen entering a particular college will graduate from that college in four years.

a. For a random sample of 5 entering freshmen, what is the probability that exactly 3 will graduate in four years?
b. For a random sample of 5 entering freshmen, what is the probability that a majority will graduate in four years?
c. 80 entering freshmen are chosen at random. Find the mean and standard deviation of the proportion of these 80 that will graduate in four years.

4.94 The World Series of baseball is to be played by team A and team B. The first team to win four games wins the series. Suppose that team A is the better team, in the sense that the probability is 0.6 that team A will win any specific game. Assume also that the result of any game is independent of that of any other.

a. What is the probability that team A will win the series?
b. What is the probability that a seventh game will be needed to determine the winner?
c. Suppose that, in fact, each team wins two of the first four games.
   i What is the probability that team A will win the series?
   ii What is the probability that a seventh game will be needed to determine the winner?

4.95 Using data from different insurance companies and their income in the member countries of the European Union (EU), a researcher claims to be able to estimate candidates faced with impending financial crisis. He selects six insurance companies from a group of 16 as candidates for failure. In fact, four of the six companies selected by the researcher were among those that failed. Evaluate this test of his ability to detect failed insurance companies.

4.96 A team of 5 analysts is about to examine the earnings prospects of 20 corporations. Each of the 5 analysts will study 4 of the corporations. These analysts are not equally competent. In fact, one of them is a star, having an excellent record of anticipating changing trends. Ideally, management would like to allocate the 4 corporations whose earnings will deviate most from past trends to this analyst. However, lacking this information, management allocates corporations to analysts randomly. What is the probability that at least 2 of the 4 corporations whose earnings will deviate most from past trends are allocated to the star analyst?

4.97 On average, 2.4 customers per minute arrive at an airline check-in desk during the peak period. Assume that the distribution of arrivals is Poisson.

a. What is the probability that there will be no arrivals in a minute?
b. What is the probability that there will be more than three arrivals in a minute?

4.98 A recent study suggested that, of all current credit users of €100,000, 6.5% either paid no penalty interest rate or paid an effective rate of less than 12%. A random sample of 100 of those reporting credit in excess of €100,000 was taken. What is the probability that more than two of the sample credit users either paid no penalty interest or paid penalty interest of less than 10%?

4.99 A company has two assembly lines, each of which stalls an average of 2.4 times per week according to a Poisson distribution. Assume that the performances of these assembly lines are independent of one another. What is the probability that at least one line stalls at least once in any given week?

4.100 George Allen has asked you to analyze his stock portfolio, which contains 10 shares of stock D and 5 shares of stock C. The joint probability distribution of the stock prices is shown in Table 4.10. Compute the mean and variance for the total value of his stock portfolio.

Table 4.10 Joint Probability Distribution for Stock Prices

Stock C Price	Stock D Price			
	$40	$50	$60	$70
$45	0.00	0.00	0.05	0.20
$50	0.05	0.00	0.05	0.10
$55	0.10	0.05	0.00	0.05
$60	0.20	0.10	0.05	0.00

4.101 Consider a country that imports coal and exports furniture. The value per unit of furniture exported is measured in units of thousands of euros per furniture by the random variable X. The value per unit of coal imported is measured in units of thousands of euros per ton of coal by the random variable Y. Suppose that the country annually exports 10 pieces of furniture and imports 5 tons of coal. Compute the mean and variance of the trade balance. The joint probability distribution for the prices of furniture and coal is:

Table 4.11 Joint Distribution of Furniture and Coal Prices

Price of Coal (Y)	Price of Furniture (X)		
	€3	€4	€5
€2	0.20	0.00	0.10
€3	0.10	0.15	0.10
€7	0.10	0.20	0.05

4.102 Delta International delivers approximately one million packages a day between East Asia and the United States. A random sample of the daily number of package delivery failures over the past six months provided the following results: 15, 10, 8, 16, 12, 11, 9, 8, 12, 9, 10, 8, 7, 16, 14, 12, 10, 9, 8, 11. There was nothing unusual about the operations during these days and, thus, the results can be considered typical. Using these data and your understanding of the delivery process answer the following:

  a. What probability model should be used and why?
  b. What is the probability of 10 or more failed deliveries on a typical future day?
  c. What is the probability of less than 6 failed deliveries?
  d. Find the number of failures such that the probability of exceeding this number is 10% or less.

4.103 Bright Star Financial Advisers receives a mean of 19.5 applications per week for a personal financial review. Each review requires one day of an analyst's time to prepare a review. Assume that requests received during any week are assigned to an analyst for completion during the following week. If the analysis is not

completed during the second week the customer will cancel.

  a. How many analysts should be hired so that the company can claim that 90% of the reviews will be completed during the second week?
  b. What is the probability that two of the analysts hired for part a would have no clients for an entire week?
  c. Suppose that they decided to hire one less analyst than determined in part (a). What is the probability that customers would cancel given this staffing level?
  d. Given the number of analysts hired in part c, what is the probability that two analysts would be idle for an entire week?

4.104 Federated South Insurance Company has developed a new screening program for selecting new sales agents. Their past experience indicates that 20% of the new agents hired fail to produce the minimum sales in their first year and are dismissed. Their expectation is that this new screening program will reduce the percentage of failed new agents to 15% or less. If that occurs, they would save $1,000,000 in recruiting and training costs each year. At the end of the first year they want to develop an evaluation to determine if the new program is successful. The following questions are an important part of their research design.

A total of 20 new agents were selected.

  a. If this group performs at the same level as past groups, what is the probability 17 or more successfully meet their minimum sales goals in the first year?
  b. What is the probability 19 or more reach their minimum sales goals given performance at the same level?
  c. If the program has actually increased the probability of success to 0.85 for each new agent, what is the probability that 17 or more meet their minimum sales goals?
  d. Given the expected improvement, what is the probability that 19 or more reach their minimum sales goals?

4.105 Yoshida Toimi is a candidate for the mayor of a medium-sized Midwestern city. If he receives more than 50% of the votes, he will win the election. Prior to the election, his campaign staff is planning to ask 100 randomly selected voters if they support Yoshida.

  a. How many positive responses from this sample of 100 is required so that the probability of 50% or more voters supporting him is 0.95 or more?
  b. Carefully state the assumptions required for your answer in part (a).
  c. Suppose the campaign is able to ask 400 randomly selected voters. Now what is your answer to the question in part (a)?

4.106 Faschip, Ltd., is a new African manufacturer of notebook computers. Their quality target is that 99.999% of the computers they produce will perform exactly as promised in the descriptive literature. In order to monitor their quality performance they include with each computer a large piece of paper that includes a direct—toll free—phone number to the Senior Vice President of Manufacturing that can be used if the computer does not perform as promised. In the first year Faschip sells 1,000,000 computers.

a. If they are achieving their quality target, what is the probability that they will receive fewer than 5 calls? If this occurs what would be a reasonable conclusion about their quality program?
b. If they are achieving their quality target, what is the probability that they will receive more than 15 calls? If this occurs, what would be a reasonable conclusion about their quality program?

Appendix: Verifications

1 VERIFICATION OF AN ALTERNATIVE FORMULA FOR THE VARIANCE OF A DISCRETE RANDOM VARIABLE (EQUATION 4.6)

Begin with the original definition of variance:

$$\sigma_X^2 = \sum_x (x - \mu_X)^2 P(x) = \sum_x (x^2 - 2\mu_X x + \mu_X^2) P(x)$$

$$= \sum_x x^2 P(x) - 2\mu_X \sum_x x P(x) + \mu_X^2 \sum_x P(x)$$

But we have seen that

$$\sum_x x P(x) = \mu_X \quad \text{and} \quad \sum_x P(x) = 1$$

Thus,

$$\sigma_X^2 = \sum_x x^2 P(x) - 2\mu_X^2 + \mu_X^2$$

and, finally,

$$\sigma_X^2 = \sum_x x^2 P(x) - \mu_X^2$$

2 VERIFICATION OF THE MEAN AND VARIANCE OF A LINEAR FUNCTION OF A RANDOM VARIABLE (EQUATIONS 4.9 AND 4.10)

It follows from the definition of expectation that if Y takes the values $a + bx$ with probabilities $P_X(x)$, its mean is as follows:

$$E[Y] = \mu_Y = \sum_x (a + bx) P(x) = a \sum_x P(x) + b \sum_x x P(x)$$

Then, since the first summation on the right-hand side of this equation is 1 and the second summation is the mean of X, we have

$$E[Y] = a + b\mu_X \text{ as in Equation 4.9.}$$

Further, the variance of Y is, by definition,

$$\sigma_Y^2 = E[(Y - \mu_Y)^2] = \sum_X [(a + bx) - \mu_Y]^2 P(x)$$

Substituting $a + b\mu_X$ for μ_Y then gives

$$\sigma_Y^2 = \sum_x (bx - b\mu_X)^2 P(x) = b^2 \sum_x (x - \mu_X)^2 P(x)$$

Since the summation on the right-hand side of this equation is, by definition, the variance of X, the result in Equation 4.10 follows:

$$\sigma_W^2 = Var(a + bX) = b^2 \sigma_X^2$$

3   EXAMPLE TO DEMONSTRATE EQUATION 4.8

Show that in general

$$E[g(x)] \neq g(\mu_x)$$

Using the results in Table 4.12, we show this result for the nonlinear function

$$g(x) = bx^2$$

Where b is a constant and we see that

$$E[bX^2] = 1.2b \neq b(E[X])^2 = b(0.8)^2 = 0.64b$$

when

$$E[g(x)] \neq g(\mu_x)$$

Table 4.12

x	bx^2	$P(x)$	$E[X]$	$E[bX^2]$
0	0	0.40	0	0
1	b	0.40	0.40	$0.4b$
2	$4b$	0.20	0.40	$0.8b$
			0.80	$1.2b$

4   VERIFICATION OF THE MEAN AND VARIANCE OF THE BINOMIAL DISTRIBUTION (EQUATIONS 4.19 AND 4.20)

To find the mean and variance of the binomial distribution, it is convenient to return to the Bernoulli distribution. Consider n independent trials, each with probability of success P, and let $X_i = 1$ if the ith trial results in success and 0 otherwise. The random variables X_1, $X_2, \ldots, X_n$ are, therefore, n independent Bernoulli variables, each with probability of success P. Moreover, the total number of successes X is as follows:

$$X = X_1 + X_2 + \cdots + X_n$$

Thus, the binomial random variable can be expressed as the sum of independent Bernoulli random variables.

The mean and the variance for Bernoulli random variables can be used to find the mean and variance of the binomial distribution. Using Equations 4.15 and 4.16, we know that

$$E[X_i] = P \quad \text{and} \quad \sigma_{X_i}^2 = P(1 - P) \text{ for all } i = 1, 2, \ldots, n$$

Then, for the binomial distribution

$$E[X] = E[X_1 + X_2 + \cdots + X_n] = E[X_1] + E[X_2] + \cdots + E[X_n] = np$$

Since the Bernoulli random variables are independent, the covariance between any pair of them is zero, and

$$\sigma_X^2 = \sigma^2(X_1 + X_2 + \cdots X_n)$$
$$\sigma_X^2 = \sigma_{X_1}^2 + \sigma_{X_2}^2 + \cdots + \sigma_{X_n}^2$$
$$\sigma_X^2 = nP(1 - P)$$

5   VERIFICATION OF THE MEAN AND VARIANCE OF THE MARKET VALUE, W, OF JOINTLY DISTRIBUTED RANDOM VARIABLES AND OF A PORTFOLIO (EQUATIONS 4.30 AND 4.31)

You are given a linear combination, W, of random variables X and Y, where $W = aX + bY$ and a and b are constants. The mean of W is

$$\mu_W = E[W] = E[aX + bY] = a\mu_X + b\mu_Y$$

and the variance of W is

$$
\begin{aligned}
\sigma_W^2 &= E[(W - \mu_W)^2] \\
&= E[(aX + bY - (a\mu_X + b\mu_Y))^2] \\
&= E[(a(X - \mu_X) + b(Y - \mu_Y))^2] \\
&= E[a^2(X - \mu_X)^2 + b^2(Y - \mu_Y)^2 + 2ab(X - \mu_X)(Y - \mu_Y)] \\
&= a^2 E[(X - \mu_X)^2] + b^2 E[(Y - \mu_Y)^2] + 2ab E[(X - \mu_X)(Y - \mu_Y)] \\
&= a^2 \sigma_x^2 + b^2 \sigma_Y^2 + 2ab\,\text{Cov}(X, Y)
\end{aligned}
$$

REFERENCE

1. Hogg, R., and Craig, A. 1995. *Mathematical Statistics*, 5th ed. Englewood Cliffs, NJ: Prentice Hall.

5

Continuous Random Variables and Probability Distributions

Introduction

In Chapter 4 we developed discrete random variables and probability distributions. Here, we extend the probability concepts to continuous random variables and probability distributions. The concepts and insights for discrete random variables also apply to continuous random variables, so we are building directly on the previous chapter. Many economic and business measures such as sales, investment, consumption, costs, and revenues can be represented by continuous random variables. In addition, measures of time, distance, temperature, and weight fit into this category. Probability statements for continuous random variables are specified over ranges. The probability that sales are between 140 and 190 or greater than 200 is a typical example.

Mathematical theory leads us to conclude that, in reality, random variables for all applied problems are discrete because measurements are rounded to some value. But, for us, the important idea is that continuous random variables and probability distributions provide good approximations for many applied problems. Thus, these models are very important and provide excellent tools for business and economic applications.

We define X as a random variable and x as a specific value of the random variable. Our first step is to define the *cumulative distribution function*. Then we will define the probability density function, which is analogous to the probability distribution function used for discrete random variables.

Cumulative Distribution Function

The **cumulative distribution function**, $F(x)$, for a continuous random variable X expresses the probability that X does not exceed the value of x, as a function of x:

$$F(x) = P(X \leq x) \qquad (5.1)$$

The cumulative distribution function can be illustrated by using a simple probability structure. Consider a gasoline station that has a 1,000-gallon storage tank that is filled each morning at the start of the business day. Analysis of past history indicates that it is not possible to predict the amount of gasoline sold on any particular day, but the lower limit is 0 and the upper limit is, of course, 1,000 gallons, the size of the tank. In addition, past history indicates that any demand in the interval from 1 to 1,000 gallons is equally likely. The random variable X indicates the gasoline sales in gallons for a particular day. We are concerned with the probability of various levels of daily gasoline sales, where the probability of a specific number of gallons sold is the same over the range from 0 to 1,000 gallons. The distribution of X is said to follow a **uniform probability distribution**, and the cumulative distribution is as follows:

$$F(x) = \begin{cases} 0 & \text{if } x < 0 \\ 0.001x & \text{if } 0 \leq x \leq 1{,}000 \\ 1 & \text{if } x > 1{,}000 \end{cases}$$

This function is graphed as a straight line between 0 and 1,000, as shown in Figure 5.1. From this we see that the probability of sales between 0 and 400 gallons is as follows:

$$P(X \leq 400) = F(400) = (0.001)(400) = 0.40$$

Figure 5.1
Cumulative Distribution Function for a Random Variable Over 0 to 1,000

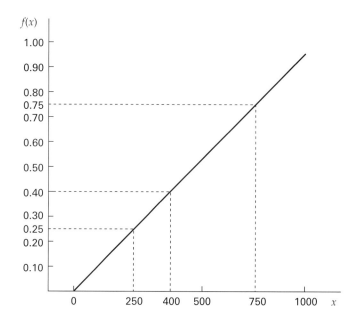

To obtain the probability that a continuous random variable X falls in a specified range, we find the difference between the cumulative probability at the upper end of the range and the cumulative probability at the lower end of the range.

Probability of a Range Using a Cumulative Distribution Function

Let X be a continuous random variable with a cumulative distribution function $F(x)$, and let a and b be two possible values of X, with $a < b$. The probability that X lies between a and b is as follows:

$$P(a < X < b) = F(b) - F(a) \qquad (5.2)$$

For continuous random variables, it does not matter whether we write "less than" or "less than or equal to" because the probability that X is precisely equal to b is 0.

For the random variable that is distributed uniformly in the range 0 to 1,000, the cumulative distribution function in that range is $F(x) = 0.001x$. Therefore, if a and b are two numbers between 0 and 1,000 with $a < b$,

$$P(a < X < b) = F(b) - F(a) = 0.001(b - a)$$

For example, the probability of sales between 250 and 750 gallons is

$$P(250 < X < 750) = (0.001)(750) - (0.001)(250) = 0.75 - 0.25 = 0.50$$

as shown in Figure 5.1.

We have seen that the probability that a continuous random variable lies between any two values can be expressed in terms of its cumulative distribution function. This function, therefore, contains all the information about the probability structure of the random variable. However, for many purposes a different function is more useful. In Chapter 4 we discussed the probability distribution for discrete random variables, which expresses the probability that a discrete random variable takes any specific value. Since the probability of a specific value is 0 for continuous random variables, that concept is not directly relevant here. However, a related function, called the *probability density function*, can be constructed for continuous random variables, allowing for graphical interpretation of their probability structure.

Probability Density Function

Let X be a continuous random variable, and let x be any number lying in the range of values for the random variable. The **probability density function**, $f(x)$, of the random variable is a function with the following properties:

1. $f(x) > 0$ for all values of x.
2. The area under the probability density function, $f(x)$, over all values of the random variable, X *within its range*, is equal to 1.0.
3. Suppose that this density function is graphed. Let a and b be two possible values of random variable X, with $a < b$. Then, the probability that X lies between a and b is the area under the probability density function between these points.

$$P(a \le X \le b) = \int_a^b f(x)dx$$

4. The cumulative distribution function, $F(x_0)$, is the area under the probability density function, $f(x)$, up to x_0,

$$F(x_0) = \int_{x_m}^{x_0} f(x)dx$$

where x_m is the minimum value of the random variable X.

The probability density function can be approximated by a discrete probability distribution with many discrete values close together, as seen in Figure 5.2.

Figure 5.2
Approximation of a
Probability Density
Function by a
Discrete Probability
Distribution

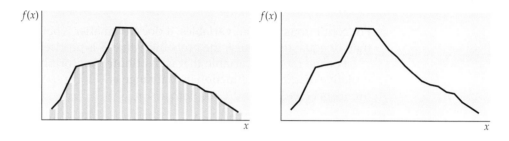

Figure 5.3 shows the plot of a probability density function for a continuous random variable. Two possible values, a and b, are shown, and the shaded area under the curve between these points is the probability that the random variable lies in the interval between them, as shown in the chapter appendix.

Figure 5.3
Shaded Area Is the
Probability That X is
Between a and b

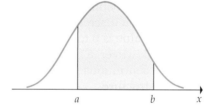

Areas Under Continuous Probability Density Functions
Let X be a continuous random variable with probability density function $f(x)$ and cumulative distribution function $F(x)$. Then, consider the following properties:

1. The total area under the curve $f(x)$ is 1.
2. The area under the curve $f(x)$ to the left of x_0 is $F(x_0)$, where x_0 is any value that the random variable can take.

These results are shown in Figure 5.4, with Figure 5.4(a) showing that the entire area under the probability density function is equal to 1 and Figure 5.4(b) indicating the area to the left of x_0.

Figure 5.4
Properties of the
Probability Density
Function

(a)   (b)

The Uniform Distribution

Now, we consider a probability density function that represents a probability distribution over the range of 0 to 1. Figure 5.5 is a graph of the uniform probability density function over the range from 0 to 1. The probability density function for the gasoline sales example is shown in Figure 5.6. Since the probability is the same for any interval of the sales range from 0 to 1,000, the probability density function is the uniform probability density function, which can be written as follows:

$$f(x) = \begin{cases} 0.001 & 0 \leq x \leq 1,000 \\ 0 & \text{otherwise} \end{cases}$$

Figure 5.5 Probability Density Function for a Uniform 0 to 1 Random Variable

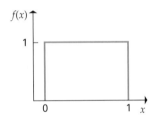

Figure 5.6 Density Function Showing the Probability That X is Between 250 and 750

For any uniform random variable defined over the range from a to b, the probability density function is as follows:

$$f(x) = \begin{cases} \dfrac{1}{b-a} & a \leq x \leq b \\ 0 & \text{otherwise} \end{cases}$$

This probability density function can be used to find the probability that the random variable falls within a specific range. For example, the probability that sales are between 250 gallons and 750 gallons is shown in Figure 5.6. Since the height of the density function is $f(x) = 0.001$, the area under the curve between 250 and 750 is equal to 0.50, which is the required probability. Note that this is the same result obtained previously using the cumulative probability function.

We have seen that the probability that a random variable lies between a pair of values is the area under the probability density function between these two values. There are two important results worth noting. The area under the entire probability density function is 1, and the cumulative probability, $F(x_0)$, is the area under the density function to the left of x_0.

Example 5.1 Probability of Pipeline Failure (Cumulative Distribution Function)

A repair team is responsible for a stretch of oil pipeline 2 miles long. The distance (in miles) at which any fracture occurs can be represented by a uniformly distributed random variable, with probability density function

$$f(x) = 0.5$$

Find the cumulative distribution function and the probability that any given fracture occurs between 0.5 mile and 1.5 miles along this stretch of pipeline.

Solution Figure 5.7 shows a plot of the probability density function, with the shaded area indicating $F(x_0)$, the cumulative distribution function evaluated at x_0. Thus, we see that

$$F(x_0) = 0.5x_0 \quad \text{for } 0 < x_0 \leq 2$$

Figure 5.7 Probability Density Function for Example 5.1

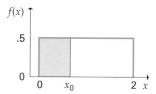

The probability that a fracture occurs between 0.5 mile and 1.5 miles along the pipe is as follows:

$$P(0.5 < X < 1.5) = F(1.5) - F(0.5) = (0.5)(1.5) - (0.5)(0.5) = 0.5$$

This is the area under the probability density function from $x = 0.5$ to $x = 1.5$.

EXERCISES

Basic Exercises

5.1 Using the uniform probability density function shown in Figure 5.7, find the probability that the random variable X is between 1.4 and 1.8.

5.2 Using the uniform probability density function shown in Figure 5.7, find the probability that the random variable X is between 0.5 and 1.6.

5.3 Using the uniform probability density function shown in Figure 5.7, find the probability that the random variable X is less than 0.8.

5.4 Using the uniform probability density function shown in Figure 5.7, find the probability that the random variable X is greater than 1.3.

Application Exercises

5.5 An analyst has available two forecasts, F_1 and F_2, of earnings per share of a corporation next year. He intends to form a compromise forecast as a weighted average of the two individual forecasts. In forming the compromise forecast, weight X will be given to the first forecast and weight $(1 - X)$, to the second,

so that the compromise forecast is $XF_1 + (1 - X)F_2$. The analyst wants to choose a value between 0 and 1 for the weight X, but he is quite uncertain of what will be the best choice. Suppose that what eventually emerges as the best possible choice of the weight X can be viewed as a random variable uniformly distributed between 0 and 1, having the probability density function

$$f(x) = \begin{cases} 1 & \text{for } 0 \leq x \leq 1 \\ 0 & \text{for all other } x \end{cases}$$

a. Graph the probability density function.
b. Find and graph the cumulative distribution function.
c. Find the probability that the best choice of the weight X is less than 0.25.
d. Find the probability that the best choice of the weight X is more than 0.75.
e. Find the probability that the best choice of the weight X is between 0.2 and 0.8.

5.6 The jurisdiction of a rescue team includes emergencies occurring on a stretch of river that is 4 miles long. Experience has shown that the distance along this stretch, measured in miles from its northernmost point, at which an emergency occurs can be represented by a uniformly distributed random variable over the range 0 to 4 miles. Then, if X denotes the distance (in miles) of an emergency from the northernmost point of this stretch of river, its probability density function is as follows:

$$f(x) = \begin{cases} 0.25 & \text{for } 0 < x < 4 \\ 0 & \text{for all other } x \end{cases}$$

a. Graph the probability density function.
b. Find and graph the cumulative distribution function.
c. Find the probability that a given emergency arises within 1 mile of the northernmost point of this stretch of river.
d. The rescue team's base is at the midpoint of this stretch of river. Find the probability that a given emergency arises more than 1.5 miles from this base.

5.7 The incomes of all families in a particular suburb can be represented by a continuous random variable. It is known that the median income for all families in this suburb is £55,000 and that 40% of all families in the suburb have incomes above £66,000.

a. For a randomly chosen family, what is the probability that its income will be between £50,000 and £66,000?
b. Given no further information, what can be said about the probability that a randomly chosen family has an income below £60,000?

5.8 At the beginning of winter, a homeowner estimates that the probability is 0.4 that his total heating bill for the three winter months will be less than $380. He also estimates that the probability is 0.6 that the total bill will be less than $460.

a. What is the probability that the total bill will be between $380 and $460?
b. Given no further information, what can be said about the probability that the total bill will be less than $400?

5.2 EXPECTATIONS FOR CONTINUOUS RANDOM VARIABLES

In Section 4.2 we presented the concepts of expected value of a discrete random variable and the expected value of a function of that random variable. Here, we extend those ideas to continuous random variables. Because the probability of any specific value is 0 for a continuous random variable, the expected values for continuous random variables are computed using integral calculus, as shown in Equation 5.3.

Rationale for Expectations of Continuous Random Variables

Suppose that a random experiment leads to an outcome that can be represented by a continuous random variable. If N independent replications of this experiment are carried out, then the **expected value** of the random variable is the average of the values taken as the number of replications becomes infinitely large. The expected value of a random variable is denoted by $E[X]$.

Similarly, if $g(X)$ is any function of the random variable X, then the expected value of this function is the average value taken by the function over repeated independent trials as the number of trials becomes infinitely large. This expectation is denoted $E[g(X)]$.

By using calculus we can define expected values for continuous random variables similar to those used for discrete random variables:

$$E[g(x)] = \int_x g(x)f(x)dx \tag{5.3}$$

These concepts can be clearly presented if one understands integral calculus, as shown in the chapter appendix. Using Equation 5.3, we can obtain the mean and variance for continuous random variables. Equations 5.4 and 5.5 present the mean and variance for continuous random variables (Hogg & Craig, 1995). If you do not understand integral calculus, then merely extend your understanding from discrete random variables as developed in Chapter 4.

Mean, Variance, and Standard Deviation for Continuous Random Variables

Let X be a continuous random variable. There are two important expected values that are used routinely to define continuous probability distributions.

1. The **mean of** X, denoted by μ_X, is defined as the expected value of X:

$$\mu_X = E[X] \tag{5.4}$$

2. The **variance of** X, denoted by σ_X^2 is defined as the expectation of the squared deviation, $(X - \mu_X)^2$, of the random variable from its mean:

$$\sigma_X^2 = E[(X - \mu_X)^2] \tag{5.5}$$

An alternative expression can be derived:

$$\sigma_X^2 = E[X^2] - \mu_X^2 \tag{5.6}$$

The **standard deviation of** X, σ_X, is the square root of the variance.

The mean and variance provide two important pieces of summary information about a probability distribution. The mean provides a measure of the center of the distribution. Consider a physical interpretation as follows: Cut out the graph of a probability density function. The point along the x-axis at which the figure exactly balances on one's finger is the mean of the distribution. For example, in Figure 5.4 the uniform distribution will balance at $x = 0.5$, and, thus, $\mu_X = 0.5$ is the mean of the random variable.

The variance—or its square root, the standard deviation—provides a measure of the dispersion or spread of a distribution. Thus, if we compare two uniform distributions with the same mean, $\mu_X = 1$—one over the range 0.5 to 1.5 and the other over the range 0 to 2—we will find that the latter has a larger variance because it is spread over a greater range.

For a *uniform distribution* defined over the range from a to b, we have the following results:

$$f(x) = \frac{1}{b - a} \quad a \leq X \leq b$$

$$\mu_X = E[X] = \frac{a + b}{2}$$

$$\sigma_X^2 = E[(X - \mu_X)^2] = \frac{(b - a)^2}{12}$$

The mean and the variance are also called the first and second moments.

In Section 4.3 we showed how to obtain the means and variances for linear functions of discrete random variables. The results are the same for continuous random variables because the derivations make use of the expected value operator. The summary results from Chapter 4 are repeated here.

Linear Functions of Random Variables

Let X be a continuous random variable with mean μ_X and variance σ_X^2 and let a and b be any constant fixed numbers. Define the random variable W as follows:

$$W = a + bX$$

Then the mean and variance of W are

$$\mu_W = E[a + bX] = a + b\mu_X \tag{5.7}$$

and

$$\sigma_W^2 = Var[a + bX] = b^2\sigma_X^2 \tag{5.8}$$

and the standard deviation of W is

$$\sigma_W = |b|\sigma_X \tag{5.9}$$

An important special case of these results is the standardized random variable

$$Z = \frac{X - \mu_X}{\sigma_X} \tag{5.10}$$

which has mean 0 and variance 1.

Linear functions of random variables have many applications in business and economics. Suppose that the number of units sold during a week is a random variable and the selling price is fixed. Thus, the total revenue is a random variable that is a function of the random variable units sold. Quantity demanded is a linear function of price that can be a random variable. Thus, quantity demanded is a random variable. The total number of cars sold per month in a dealership is a linear function of the random variable number of cars sold per sales person multiplied by the number of sales persons. Thus, total sales is a random variable.

Example 5.2 Home Heating Costs (Mean and Standard Deviation)

A homeowner estimates that within the range of likely temperatures his January heating bill, Y, in dollars, will be

$$Y = 290 - 5T$$

where T is the average temperature for the month, in degrees Fahrenheit. If the average January temperature can be represented by a random variable with a mean of 24 and a standard deviation of 4, find the mean and standard deviation of this homeowner's January heating bill.

Solution The random variable T has mean $\mu_T = 24$ and standard deviation $\sigma_T = 4$. Therefore, the expected heating bill is

$$\mu_Y = 290 - 5\mu_T$$
$$= 290 - (5)(24) = \$170$$

and the standard deviation is

$$\sigma_Y = |-5|\,\sigma_T = (5)(4) = \$20$$

Basic Exercises

5.9 The total cost for a production process is equal to €500 plus two times the number of units produced. The mean and variance for the number of units produced are 700 and 600, respectively. Find the mean and variance of the total cost.

5.10 The profit for a production process is equal to $1,000 minus two times the number of units produced. The mean and variance for the number of units produced are 50 and 90, respectively. Find the mean and variance of the profit.

5.11 The profit for a production process is equal to $2,000 minus two times the number of units produced. The mean and variance for the number of units produced are 500 and 900, respectively. Find the mean and variance of the profit.

5.12 The profit for a production process is equal to $6,000 minus three times the number of units produced. The mean and variance for the number of units produced are 1,000 and 900, respectively. Find the mean and variance of the profit.

Application Exercises

5.13 A fashion house in London offers a designer a contract, according to which she is to be paid a fixed sum of £10,000 plus £1.75 for each unit of her design sold. Her uncertainty about total sales of the design can be represented by a random variable with a mean of 25,000 and a standard deviation of 8,500. Find the mean and standard deviation of the total payments she will receive.

5.14 A contractor submits a bid on a project for which more research and development work needs to be done. It is estimated that the total cost of satisfying the project specifications will be $20 million plus the cost of the further research and development work. The contractor views the cost of this additional work as a random variable with a mean of $4 million and a standard deviation of $1 million. The contractor wishes to submit a bid such that his expected profit will be 10% of his expected costs. What should be the bid? If this bid is accepted, what will be the standard deviation of the profit made by the project?

5.15 A charitable organization solicits donations by telephone. Employees are paid $60 plus 20% of the money their calls generate each week. The amount of money generated in a week can be viewed as a random variable with a mean of $700 and a standard deviation of $130. Find the mean and standard deviation of an employee's total pay in a week.

5.16 A salesperson receives an annual salary of $6,000 plus 8% of the value of the orders she takes. The annual value of these orders can be represented by a random variable with a mean of $600,000 and a standard deviation of $180,000. Find the mean and standard deviation of the salesperson's annual income.

5.3 THE NORMAL DISTRIBUTION

In this section we present the normal probability distribution, which is the continuous probability distribution used most often for economics and business applications. An example of the normal probability density function is shown in Figure 5.8.

Figure 5.8
Probability Density Function for a Normal Distribution

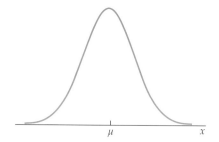

There are many reasons for its wide application.

1. The normal distribution closely approximates the probability distributions of a wide range of random variables. For example, the dimensions of parts and the weights of food packages often follow a normal distribution. This leads to quality-control applications. Total sales or production often follows a normal distribution, which leads us to a large family of applications in marketing and

in production management. The patterns of stock and bond prices are often modeled using the normal distribution in large computer-based financial trading models. Economic models use the normal distribution for a number of economic measures.

2. Distributions of sample means approach a normal distribution, given a "large" sample size, as is shown in Section 6.2.
3. Computation of probabilities is direct and elegant.
4. The most important reason is that the normal probability distribution has led to good business decisions for a number of applications.

A formal definition of the normal probability density function is given by Equation 5.11.

Probability Density Function of the Normal Distribution

The **probability density function for a normally distributed random variable** X is

$$f(x) = \frac{1}{\sqrt{2\pi\sigma^2}} e^{-(x-\mu)^2/2\sigma^2} \quad \text{for } -\infty < x < \infty \tag{5.11}$$

where μ and σ^2 are any numbers such that $-\infty < \mu < \infty$ and $0 < \sigma^2 < \infty$ and where e and π are physical constants, $e = 2.71828\ldots$, and $\pi = 3.14159.\ldots$

The normal probability distribution represents a large family of distributions, each with a unique specification for the parameters μ and σ^2. These parameters have a very convenient interpretation.

Properties of the Normal Distribution

Suppose that the random variable X follows a normal distribution with parameters μ and σ^2. Then, consider the following properties:

1. The mean of the random variable is μ:

$$E[X] = \mu$$

2. The variance of the random variable is σ^2:

$$Var(X) = E[(X - \mu)^2] = \sigma^2$$

3. The shape of the probability density function is a symmetric bell-shaped curve centered on the mean, μ, as shown in Figure 5.8.
4. If we know the mean and variance, we can define the normal distribution by using the following notation:

$$X \sim N(\mu, \sigma^2)$$

For our applied statistical analyses, the normal distribution has a number of important characteristics. It is symmetric. Central tendencies are indicated by μ. In contrast, σ^2 indicates the distribution width. By selecting values for μ and σ^2, we can define a large family of normal probability density functions.

The parameters μ and σ^2 have different effects on the probability density function of a normal random variable. Figure 5.9(a) shows probability density functions for two normal distributions with a common variance and different means. We see that increases in the mean shift the distribution without changing its shape. In Figure 5.9(b) the two density functions have the same mean but different variances. Each is symmetric about the common mean, but the larger variance results in a wider distribution.

Figure 5.9 Effects of μ and σ^2 on the Probability Density Function of a Normal Random Variable

a. Two Normal Distributions with Same Variance but Different Means
b. Two Normal Distributions with Different Variances and Mean $= 5$

Our next task is to learn how to obtain probabilities for a specified normal distribution. First, we introduce the *cumulative distribution function*.

Cumulative Distribution Function of the Normal Distribution

Suppose that X is a normal random variable with mean μ and variance σ^2—that is, $X \sim N(\mu, \sigma^2)$. Then the **cumulative distribution function of the normal distribution** is as follows:

$$F(x_0) = P(X \le x_0)$$

This is the area under the normal probability density function to the left of x_0, as illustrated in Figure 5.10. As for any proper density function, the total area under the curve is 1—that is,

$$F(\infty) = 1$$

Figure 5.10 The Shaded Area Is the Probability That X Does Not Exceed x_0 for a Normal Random Variable

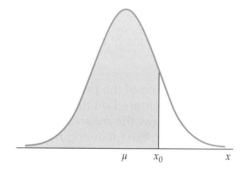

We do not have a simple algebraic expression for calculating the cumulative distribution function for a normally distributed random variable (see the chapter appendix). The general shape of the cumulative distribution function is shown in Figure 5.11.

Figure 5.11 Cumulative Distribution for a Normal Random Variable

Range Probabilities for Normal Random Variables

Let X be a normal random variable with cumulative distribution function $F(x)$, and let a and b be two possible values of X, with $a < b$. Then,

$$P(a < X < b) = F(b) - F(a) \tag{5.12}$$

The probability is the area under the corresponding probability density function between a and b, as shown in Figure 5.12.

Figure 5.12 Normal Density Function with the Shaded Area Indicating the Probability That X Is Between a and b

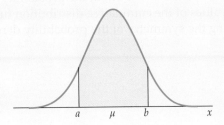

Any probability can be obtained from the cumulative distribution function. However, we do not have a convenient way to directly compute the probability for any normal distribution with a specific mean and variance. We could use numerical integration procedures with a computer, but that approach would be tedious and cumbersome. Fortunately, we can convert any normal distribution to a *standard normal distribution* with mean 0 and variance 1. Tables that indicate the probability for various intervals under the standard normal distribution have been computed and are shown inside the front cover and in Appendix Table 1.

The Standard Normal Distribution

Let Z be a normal random variable with mean 0 and variance 1—that is,

$$Z \sim N(0, 1)$$

We say that Z follows the **standard normal distribution**.

Denote the cumulative distribution function as $F(x)$ and a and b as two possible values of Z with $a < b$; then,

$$P(a < Z < b) = F(b) - F(a) \tag{5.13}$$

We can obtain probabilities for any normally distributed random variable by first converting the random variable to the standard normally distributed random variable, Z. There is always a direct relationship between any normally distributed random variable and Z. That relationship uses the transformation

$$Z = \frac{X - \mu}{\sigma}$$

where X is a normally distributed random variable:

$$X \sim N(\mu, \sigma^2)$$

This important result allows us to use the standard normal table to compute probabilities associated with any normally distributed random variable. Now let us see how probabilities can be computed for the standard normal Z.

The cumulative distribution function of the standard normal distribution is tabulated in Appendix Table 1 (also inside the front cover). This table gives values of

$$F(z) = P(Z \leq z)$$

for nonnegative values of z. For example, the cumulative probability for a Z value of 1.25 from Appendix Table 1 is as follows:

$$F(1.25) = 0.8944$$

This is the area, designated in Figure 5.13, for Z less than 1.25. Because of the symmetry of the normal distribution, the probability that $Z > -1.25$ is also equal to 0.8944. In general, values of the cumulative distribution function for negative values of Z can be inferred using the symmetry of the probability density function.

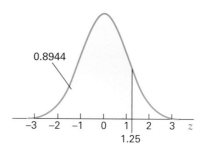

Figure 5.13
Standard Normal Distribution with Probability for $Z < 1.25$

To find the cumulative probability for a negative Z (for example, $Z = -1.0$), defined as

$$F(-Z_0) = P(Z \leq -z_0) = F(-1.0)$$

we use the complement of the probability for $Z = +1$, as shown in Figure 5.14.

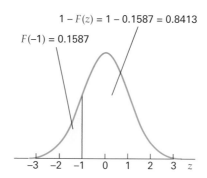

Figure 5.14
Standard Normal Distribution for Negative Z Equal to -1

From the symmetry we can state that

$$F(-z) = 1 - P(Z \leq +z) = 1 - F(z)$$
$$F(-1) = 1 - P(Z \leq +1) = 1 - F(1)$$

Figure 5.15 indicates the symmetry for the corresponding positive values of Z.

Figure 5.15
Normal Distribution for Positive

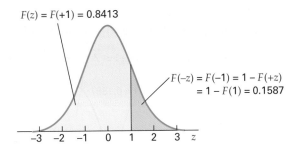

$F(z) = F(+1) = 0.8413$

$F(-z) = F(-1) = 1 - F(+z)$
$= 1 - F(1) = 0.1587$

In Figure 5.16 we can see that the area under the curve to the left of $Z = -1$ is equal to the area to the right of $Z = +1$ because of the symmetry of the normal distribution. The area substantially below $-Z$ is often called the lower tail, and the area substantially above $+Z$ is called the upper tail.

Figure 5.16
Normal Density Function with Symmetric Upper and Lower Values

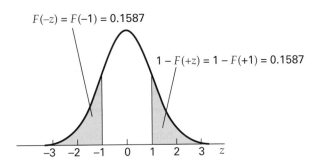

$F(-z) = F(-1) = 0.1587$

$1 - F(+z) = 1 - F(+1) = 0.1587$

We can also use normal tables that provide probabilities for just the upper-half, or positive Z, values from the normal distribution. An example of this type of table is shown inside the front cover of this textbook. This form of the normal table is used to find probabilities, the same as those previously shown. With positive Z values we add 0.50 to the values given in the table inside the front cover of the textbook. With negative values of Z we utilize the symmetry of the normal to obtain the desired probabilities.

Example 5.3 Investment Portfolio Value Probabilities (Normal Probabilities)

A client has an investment portfolio whose mean value is equal to $1,000,000 with a standard deviation of $30,000. He has asked you to determine the probability that the value of his portfolio is between $970,000 and $1,060,000.

Solution The problem is illustrated in Figure 5.17. To solve the problem, we must first determine the corresponding Z values for the portfolio limits. For $970,000 the corresponding Z value is as follows:

$$z_{970,000} = \frac{970,000 - 1,000,000}{30,000} = -1.0$$

And for the upper value, $1,060,000, the Z value is as follows:

$$z_{1,060,000} = \frac{1,060,000 - 1,000,000}{30,000} = +2.0$$

Figure 5.17 Normal Distribution for Example 5.3

$P(-1 \le Z \le +2) = 1 - 0.1587 - 0.0228 = 0.8185$

$F(-1) = 0.1587$

$P(Z \ge +2) = 1 - F(+2) = 1 - 0.9772 = 0.0228$

As shown in Figure 5.17, the probability that the portfolio value, X, is between $970,000 and $1,060,000, is equal to the probability that Z is between -1 and $+2$. To obtain the probability, we first compute the probabilities for the lower and the upper tails and subtract these probabilities from 1. Algebraically, the result is as follows:

$$P(970,000 \le X \le 1,060,000) = P(-1 \le Z \le +2) = 1 - P(Z \le -1) - P(Z \ge +2)$$
$$= 1 - 0.1587 - 0.0228 = 0.8185$$

The probability for the indicated range is, thus, 0.8185.

Recall from Chapter 2 that we presented the empirical rule, which states as a rough guide that $\mu \pm \sigma$ covers about 68% of the range, while $\mu \pm 2\sigma$ covers about 95% of the range. For all practical purposes, almost none of the range is outside $\mu \pm 3\sigma$. This useful approximation tool for interpretations based on descriptive statistics is based on the normal distribution.

Probabilities can also be computed by using Equation 5.14.

Finding Probabilities for Normally Distributed Random Variables

Let X be a normally distributed random variable with mean μ and variance σ^2. Then random variable $Z = (X - \mu)/\sigma$ has a standard normal distribution of $Z \sim N(0, 1)$.

It follows that, if a and b are any possible values of X with $a < b$, then,

$$P(a < X < b) = P\left(\frac{a - \mu}{\sigma} < Z < \frac{b - \mu}{\sigma}\right)$$
$$= F\left(\frac{b - \mu}{\sigma}\right) - F\left(\frac{a - \mu}{\sigma}\right) \tag{5.14}$$

where Z is the standard normal random variable and F denotes its cumulative distribution function.

Example 5.4 Analysis of Turkey Weights (Normal Probabilities)

Whole Life Organic, Inc., produces high-quality organic frozen turkeys for distribution in organic food markets in the upper Midwest. The company has developed a range feeding program with organic grain supplements to produce their product. The mean weight of its frozen turkeys is 15 pounds with a variance of 4. Historical experience indicates that weights can be approximated by the normal probability distribution. Market research indicates that sales for frozen turkeys over 18 pounds are limited. What percentage of the company's turkey units will be over 18 pounds?

Solution In this case the turkey weights can be represented by a random variable, X, and, thus, $X \sim N(15, 4)$, and we need to find the probability that X is larger than 18. This probability can be computed as follows:

$$
\begin{aligned}
P(X > 18) &= P\left(Z > \frac{18 - \mu}{\sigma}\right) \\
&= P\left(Z > \frac{18 - 15}{2}\right) \\
&= P(Z > 1.5) \\
&= 1 - P(Z < 1.5) \\
&= 1 - F(1.5)
\end{aligned}
$$

From Appendix Table 1, $F(1.5)$ is 0.9332, and, therefore,

$$
P(X > 18) = 1 - 0.9332 = 0.0668
$$

Thus, Whole Life can expect that 6.68% of its turkeys will weigh more than 18 pounds.

Example 5.5 Lightbulb Life (Normal Probabilities)

A company produces lightbulbs whose life follows a normal distribution, with a mean of 1,200 hours and a standard deviation of 250 hours. If we choose a lightbulb at random, what is the probability that its lifetime will be between 900 and 1,300 hours?

Solution Let X represent lifetime in hours. Then,

$$
\begin{aligned}
P(900 < X < 1,300) &= P\left(\frac{900 - 1,200}{250} < Z < \frac{1,300 - 1,200}{250}\right) \\
&= P(-1.2 < Z < 0.4) \\
&= F(0.4) - F(-1.2) \\
&= 0.6554 - (1 - 0.8849) = 0.5403
\end{aligned}
$$

Hence, the probability is approximately 0.54 that a lightbulb will last between 900 and 1,300 hours.

Example 5.6 Sales of Cell Phones (Normal Probabilities)

Silver Star, Inc., has a number of stores in major metropolitan shopping centers. The company's sales experience indicates that daily cell phone sales in its stores follow a normal distribution with a mean of 60 and a standard deviation of 15. The marketing department conducts a number of routine analyses of sales data to monitor sales performance. What proportion of store sales days will have sales between 85 and 95 given that sales are following the historical experience?

Solution Let X denote the daily cell phone sales. Then, the probability can be computed as follows:

$$P(85 < X < 95) = P\left(\frac{85 - 60}{15} < Z < \frac{95 - 60}{15}\right)$$
$$= P(1.67 < Z < 2.33)$$
$$= F(2.33) - F(1.67)$$
$$= 0.9901 - 0.9525 = 0.0376$$

That is, 3.76% of the daily sales will be in the range 85 to 95 based on historical sales patterns. Note that if actual reported sales in this range for a group of stores were above 10%, we would have evidence for higher than historical sales.

Example 5.7 Cutoff Points for Daily Cell Phone Sales (Normal Random Variables)

For the daily cell phone sales of Example 5.6, find the cutoff point for the top 10% of all daily sales.

Solution Define b as the cutoff point. To determine the numerical value of the cutoff point, we first note that the probability of exceeding b is 0.10, and, thus, the probability of being less than b is 0.90. The upper tail value of 0.10 is shown in Figure 5.18. We can now state the probability from the cumulative distribution as follows:

$$0.90 = P\left(Z < \frac{b - 60}{15}\right)$$
$$= F\left(\frac{b - 60}{15}\right)$$

Figure 5.18 Normal Distribution with Mean 60 and Standard Deviation 15 Showing Upper Tail Probability Equal to 0.10

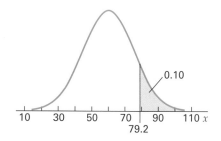

From Appendix Table 1, we find that $Z = 1.28$ when $F(Z) = 0.90$. Therefore, solving for b, we have the following:

$$\frac{b - 60}{15} = 1.28$$
$$b = 79.2$$

Thus, we conclude that 10% of the daily cell phone sales will be above 79.2, as shown in Figure 5.18.

We note that daily sales, such as those in Examples 5.6 and 5.7, are typically given as integer values, and, thus, their distribution is discrete. However, because of the large number of possible outcomes, the normal distribution provides a very good approximation for the discrete distribution. In most applied business and economic problems, we are, in fact, using the normal distribution to approximate a discrete distribution that has many different outcomes.

Normal Probability Plots

The normal probability model is the most-used probability model for the reasons previously noted. In applied problems we would like to know if the data have come from a distribution that approximates a normal distribution closely enough to ensure a valid result. Thus, we are seeking evidence to support the assumption that the normal distribution is a close approximation to the actual unknown distribution that supplied the data we are analyzing. Normal probability plots provide a good way to test this assumption and determine if the normal model can be used. Usage is simple. If the data follow a normal distribution, the plot will be a straight line. More rigorous tests are also possible, as shown in Chapter 14.

Figure 5.19 is a normal probability plot for a random sample of $n = 1,000$ observations from a normal distribution with $\mu = 100$ and $\sigma = 25$. The plot was generated using Minitab. The horizontal axis indicates the data points ranked in order from the smallest to the largest. The vertical axis indicates the cumulative normal probabilities of the ranked data values if the sample data were obtained from a population whose random variables follow a normal distribution. We see that the vertical axis has a transformed cumulative normal scale. The data plots in Figure 5.19 are close to a straight line even at the upper and lower limits, and that result provides solid evidence that the data have a normal distribution. The dotted lines provide an interval within which data points from a normally distributed random variable would occur in most cases. Thus, if the plotted points are within the boundaries established by the dotted lines, we can conclude that the data points represent a normally distributed random variable.

Figure 5.19
Normal Probability
Plot for a Normal
Distribution (Minitab
Output)

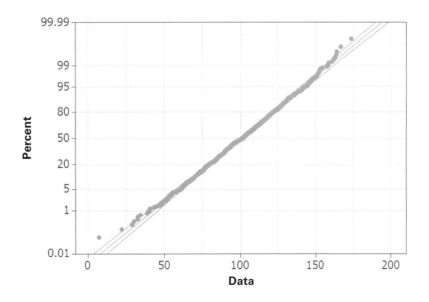

Next, consider a random sample of $n = 1,000$ observations drawn from a *uniform distribution* with limits 25 to 175. Figure 5.20 shows the normal probability plot. In this case the data plot has an S shape that clearly deviates from a straight line, and the sample data do not follow a normal distribution. Large deviations at the extreme high and low values are a major concern because statistical inference is often based on small probabilities of extreme values.

Figure 5.20
Normal Probability Plot for a Uniform Distribution (Minitab Output)

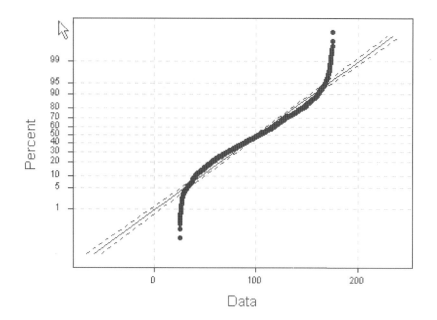

Next, let us consider a highly skewed discrete distribution, as shown in Figure 5.21. In Figure 5.22 we see the normal probability plot for this highly skewed distribution. Again, we see that the data plot is not a straight line but has considerable deviation at the extreme high and low values. This plot clearly indicates that the data do not come from a normal distribution.

Figure 5.21
Skewed Discrete Probability Distribution Function

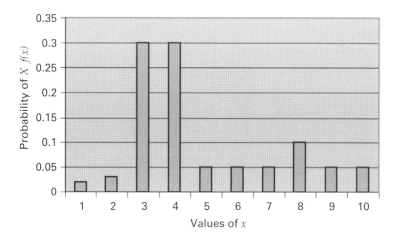

The previous examples provide us with an indication of possible results from a normal probability plot. If the plot from your problem is similar to Figure 5.19, then you are safe in assuming that the normal model is a good approximation. Note, however, that if your plot deviates from a straight line, as do those in Figures 5.20 and 5.22, then the sample data do not have a normal distribution.

Figure 5.22
Normal Probability Plot for a Highly Skewed Distribution (Minitab Output)

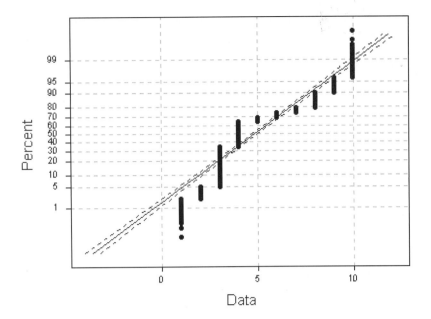

EXERCISES

Basic Exercises

5.17 Let the random variable Z follow a standard normal distribution.

  a. Find $P(Z < 1.16)$.
  b. Find $P(Z > 1.73)$.
  c. Find $P(Z > -2.29)$.
  d. Find $P(Z > -1.35)$.
  e. Find $P(1.16 < Z < 1.73)$.
  f. Find $P(-2.29 < Z < 1.16)$.
  g. Find $P(-2.29 < Z < -1.35)$.

5.18 Let the random variable Z follow a standard normal distribution.

  a. The probability is 0.70 that Z is less than what number?
  b. The probability is 0.25 that Z is less than what number?
  c. The probability is 0.2 that Z is greater than what number?
  d. The probability is 0.6 that Z is greater than what number?

5.19 Let the random variable X follow a normal distribution with $\mu = 30$ and $\sigma^2 = 81$.

  a. Find the probability that X is greater than 40.
  b. Find the probability that X is greater than 15 and less than 43.
  c. Find the probability that X is less than 35.
  d. The probability is 0.3 that X is greater than what number?
  e. The probability is 0.05 that X is in the symmetric interval about the mean between which two numbers?

5.20 Let the random variable X follow a normal distribution with $\mu = 80$ and $\sigma^2 = 100$.

  a. Find the probability that X is greater than 60.
  b. Find the probability that X is greater than 72 and less than 82.
  c. Find the probability that X is less than 55.
  d. The probability is 0.1 that X is greater than what number?
  e. The probability is 0.6826 that X is in the symmetric interval about the mean between which two numbers?

5.21 Let the random variable X follow a normal distribution with $\mu = 0.2$ and $\sigma^2 = 0.0025$.

  a. Find the probability that X is greater than 0.4.
  b. Find the probability that X is greater than 0.15 and less than 0.28.
  c. Find the probability that X is less than 0.10.
  d. The probability is 0.2 that X is greater than what number?
  e. The probability is 0.05 that X is in the symmetric interval about the mean between which two numbers?

Application Exercises

5.22 It is known that amounts of money spent on clothing in a year by students on a particular campus follow a normal distribution with a mean of $380 and a standard deviation of $50.

  a. What is the probability that a randomly chosen student will spend less than $400 on clothing in a year?

b. What is the probability that a randomly chosen student will spend more than $360 on clothing in a year?

c. Draw a graph to illustrate why the answers to parts (a) and (b) are the same.

d. What is the probability that a randomly chosen student will spend between $300 and $400 on clothing in a year?

e. Compute a range of yearly clothing expenditures—measured in dollars—that includes 80% of all students on this campus? Explain why any number of such ranges could be found, and find the shortest one.

5.23 Anticipated consumer demand at a restaurant for free-range steaks next month can be modeled by a normal random variable with mean 1,500 pounds and standard deviation 110 pounds.

a. What is the probability that demand will exceed 1,300 pounds?

b. What is the probability that demand will be between 1,400 and 1,600 pounds?

c. The probability is 0.15 that demand will be more than how many pounds?

5.24 The tread life of Road Stone tires has a normal distribution with a mean of 35,000 miles and a standard deviation of 4,000 miles.

a. What proportion of these tires has a tread life of more than 38,000 miles?

b. What proportion of these tires has a tread life of less than 32,000 miles?

c. What proportion of these tires has a tread life of between 32,000 and 38,000 miles?

d. Draw a graph of the probability density function of tread lives, illustrating why the answers to parts (a) and (b) are the same and why the answers to parts (a), (b), and (c) sum to 1.

5.25 An investment portfolio contains stocks of a large number of corporations. Over the last year the rates of return on these corporate stocks followed a normal distribution with mean 13.5% and standard deviation 7.4%.

a. For what proportion of these corporations was the rate of return higher than 19%?

b. For what proportion of these corporations was the rate of return negative?

c. For what proportion of these corporations was the rate of return between 10% and 20%?

5.26 Southwest Co-op produces bags of fertilizer, and it is concerned about impurity content. It is believed that the weights of impurities per bag are normally distributed with a mean of 12.2 grams and a standard deviation of 2.8 grams. A bag is chosen at random.

a. What is the probability that it contains less than 10 grams of impurities?

b. What is the probability that it contains more than 15 grams of impurities?

c. What is the probability that it contains between 12 and 15 grams of impurities?

d. It is possible, without doing the detailed calculations, to deduce which of the answers to parts (a) and (b) will be the larger. How would you do this?

5.27 A contractor has concluded from his experience that the cost of building a luxury home is a normally distributed random variable with a mean of $500,000 and a standard deviation of $50,000.

a. What is the probability that the cost of building a home will be between $460,000 and $540,000?

b. The probability is 0.2 that the cost of building will be less than what amount?

c. Find the shortest range such that the probability is 0.95 that the cost of a luxury home will fall in this range.

5.28 Scores on an economics test follow a normal distribution. What is the probability that a randomly selected student will achieve a score that exceeds the mean score by more than 1.5 standard deviations?

5.29 A new television series is to be shown. A broadcasting executive feels that his uncertainty about the rating that the show will receive in its first month can be represented by a normal distribution with a mean of 18.2 and a standard deviation of 1.5. According to this executive, the probability is 0.1 that the rating will be less than what number?

5.30 A broadcasting executive is reviewing the prospects for a new television series. According to his judgment, the probability is 0.25 that the show will achieve a rating higher than 17.8, and the probability is 0.15 that it will achieve a rating higher than 19.2. If the executive's uncertainty about the rating can be represented by a normal distribution, what are the mean and variance of that distribution?

5.31 The number of hits per day on the Web site of E-CommEx, Inc., is normally distributed with a mean of 510 and a standard deviation of 140.

a. What proportion of days has more than 620 hits per day?

b. What proportion of days has between 520 and 620 hits?

c. Find the number of hits such that only 10% of the days will have the number of hits below this number.

5.32 Luca Alberti, a Hungarian florist, is considering two alternative investments. In both cases she is unsure about the percentage return but believes that her uncertainty can be represented by normal distributions with the means and standard deviations shown in the accompanying table. Luca wants to make the investment that is more likely to produce a return of at least 9%. Which investment should she choose?

	Mean	Standard Deviation
Investment A	11.2	4.0
Investment B	10.0	2.5

5.33 Volvo Cars, a Swedish luxury vehicles company, purchases computer process chips from two suppliers, and the company is concerned about the percentage of defective chips. A review of the records for each supplier indicates that the percentage defectives in consignments of chips follow normal distributions with the means and standard deviations given in the following table. The company is particularly anxious that the percentage of defectives in a consignment not exceed 4% and wants to purchase from the supplier that's more likely to meet that specification. Which supplier should be chosen?

	Mean	Standard Deviation
Investment A	3.4	0.3
Investment B	3.2	0.5

5.34 A furniture manufacturer has found that the time spent by workers assembling a particular table follows a normal distribution with a mean of 150 minutes and a standard deviation of 40 minutes.

a. The probability is 0.9 that a randomly chosen table requires more than how many minutes to assemble?

b. The probability is 0.8 that a randomly chosen table can be assembled in fewer than how many minutes?

c. Two tables are chosen at random. What is the probability that at least one of them requires at least 2 hours to assemble?

5.35 A company services copiers. A review of its records shows that the time taken for a service call can be represented by a normal random variable with a mean of 75 minutes and a standard deviation of 20 minutes.

a. What proportion of service calls takes less than 1 hour?

b. What proportion of service calls takes more than 90 minutes?

c. Sketch a graph to show why the answers to parts (a) and (b) are the same.

d. The probability is 0.1 that a service call takes more than how many minutes?

5.36 Scores on an achievement test are known to be normally distributed with a mean of 420 and a standard deviation of 80.

a. For a randomly chosen person taking this test, what is the probability of a score between 400 and 480?

b. What is the minimum test score needed in order to be in the top 10% of all people taking the test?

c. For a randomly chosen individual, state, without doing the calculations, in which of the following ranges his score is most likely to be: 400–439, 440–479, 480–519, or 520–559.

d. In which of the ranges listed in part (c) is the individual's score least likely to be?

e. Two people taking the test are chosen at random. What is the probability that at least one of them scores more than 500 points?

5.37 It is estimated that the time that a well-known rock band, the Living Ingrates, spends on stage at its concerts follows a normal distribution with a mean of 200 minutes and a standard deviation of 20 minutes.

a. What proportion of concerts played by this band lasts between 180 and 200 minutes?

b. An audience member smuggles a tape recorder into a Living Ingrates concert. The reel-to-reel tapes have a capacity of 245 minutes. What is the probability that this capacity will be insufficient to record the entire concert?

c. If the standard deviation of concert time was only 15 minutes, state, without doing the calculations, whether the probability that a concert would last more than 245 minutes would be larger than, smaller than, or the same as that found in part (b). Sketch a graph to illustrate your answer.

d. The probability is 0.1 that a Living Ingrates concert will last less than how many minutes? (Assume, as originally, that the population standard deviation is 20 minutes.)

5.38 The daily selling price per 100 pounds of buffalo meat is normally distributed with a mean of $70, and the probability that the daily price is less than $85 is 0.9332. Four days are chosen at random. What is the probability that at least one of the days has a price that exceeds $80?

5.4 NORMAL DISTRIBUTION APPROXIMATION FOR BINOMIAL DISTRIBUTION

In this section we show how the normal distribution can be used to approximate the discrete binomial and proportion random variables for larger sample sizes when tables are not readily available. The normal distribution approximation of the binomial distribution also provides a benefit for applied problem solving. We learn that procedures based on the normal distribution can also be applied in problems involving binomial and proportion random variables. Thus, you can reduce the number of different statistical procedures that you need to know to solve business problems.

Let us consider a problem with n independent trials, each with the probability of success $P = 4$. The binomial random variable X can be written as the sum of n independent Bernoulli random variables,

$$X = X_1 + X_2 + \cdots + X_n$$

where the random variable X_i takes the value 1 if the outcome of the ith trial is "success" and 0 otherwise, with respective probabilities P and $1 - P$. The number X of successes that result have a binomial distribution with a mean and variance:

$$E[X] = \mu = nP$$
$$Var(X) = \sigma^2 = nP(1 - P)$$

The plot of a binomial distribution with $P = 0.5$ and $n = 100$, in Figure 5.23, shows us that this binomial distribution has the same shape as the normal distribution. This visual evidence that the binomial can be approximated by a normal distribution with the same mean and variance is also established in work done by mathematical statisticians. This close approximation of the binomial distribution by the normal distribution is an example of the central limit theorem that is developed in Chapter 6. A good rule for us is that the normal distribution provides a good approximation for the binomial distribution when $nP(1 - P) > 5$. If this value is less than 5, then use the binomial distribution to determine the probabilities.

Figure 5.23
Binomial Distribution with $n = 100$ and $P = 0.50$

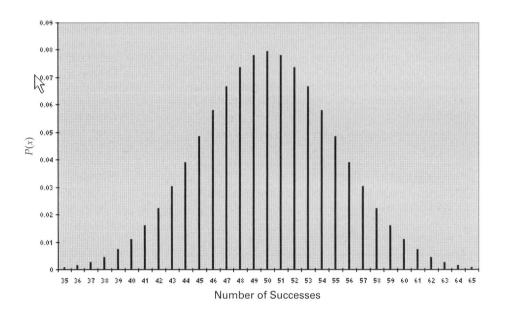

In order to better understand the normal distribution approximation for the binomial distribution, consider Figure 5.24(a) and (b). In both (a) and (b), we have shown points from a normal probability density function compared to the corresponding probabilities from a binomial distribution using graphs prepared using Minitab. In part (a) we note that the approximation rule value is

$$nP(1 - P) = 100(0.5)(1 - 0.5) = 25 > 5$$

and that the normal distribution provides a very close approximation to the binomial distribution. In contrast, the example in part (b) has an approximation rule value of

$$nP(1 - P) = 25(0.2)(1 - 0.2) = 4 < 5$$

Figure 5.24
Comparison of
Binomial and Normal
Approximation

(a)

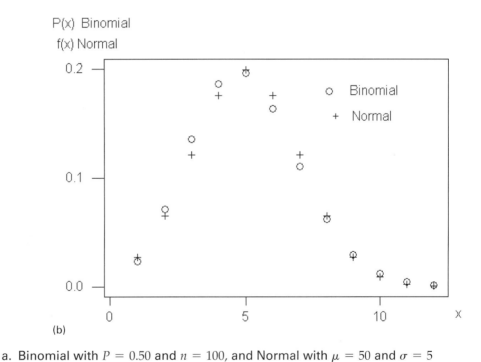

(b)

a. Binomial with $P = 0.50$ and $n = 100$, and Normal with $\mu = 50$ and $\sigma = 5$
b. Binomial with $P = 0.20$ and $n = 25$, and Normal with $\mu = 5$ and $\sigma = 2$

and the normal distribution does not provide a good approximation for the binomial distribution. Evidence such as that contained in Figure 5.24 has provided the rationale for widespread application of the normal approximation for the binomial. We will now proceed to develop the procedure for its application.

By using the mean and the variance from the binomial distribution, we find that, if the number of trials n is large—such that $nP(1 - P) > 5$—then the distribution of the random variable

$$Z = \frac{X - E[X]}{\sqrt{Var(X)}} = \frac{X - nP}{\sqrt{nP(1 - P)}}$$

is approximately a standard normal distribution.

This result is very important because it allows us to find, for large n, the probability that the number of successes lies in a given range. If we want to determine the probability that the number of successes will be between a and b, inclusive, we have

$$P(a \leq X \leq b) = P\left(\frac{a - nP}{\sqrt{nP(1 - P)}} \leq \frac{X - nP}{\sqrt{nP(1 - P)}} \leq \frac{b - nP}{\sqrt{nP(1 - P)}}\right)$$

$$= P\left(\frac{a - nP}{\sqrt{nP(1 - P)}} \leq Z \leq \frac{b - nP}{\sqrt{nP(1 - P)}}\right)$$

With n large, Z is well approximated by the standard normal, and we can find the probability using the methods from Section 5.3.

Example 5.8 Customer Visits Generated From Web Page Contacts (Normal Probabilities)

Mary David makes the initial telephone contact with customers who have responded to an advertisement on her company's Web page in an effort to assess whether a follow-up visit to their homes is likely to be worthwhile. Her experience suggests that 40% of the initial contacts lead to follow-up visits. If she has 100 Web page contacts, what is the probability that between 45 and 50 home visits will result?

Solution Let X be the number of follow-up visits. Then X has a binomial distribution with $n = 100$ and $P = 0.40$. Approximating the required probability gives the following:

$$P(45 \leq X \leq 50) \cong P\left(\frac{45 - (100)(0.4)}{\sqrt{(100)(0.4)(0.6)}} \leq Z \leq \frac{50 - (100)(0.4)}{\sqrt{(100)(0.4)(0.6)}}\right)$$

$$= P(1.02 \leq Z \leq 2.04)$$

$$= F(2.04) - F(1.02)$$

$$= 0.9793 - 0.8461 = 0.1332$$

This probability is shown as an area under the standard normal curve in Figure 5.25.

Figure 5.25 Probability of 45 to 50 Successes for a Binomial Distribution with $n = 100$ and $P = 0.4$

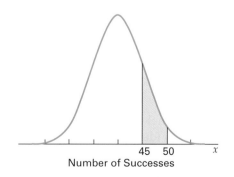

45 50
Number of Successes

Proportion Random Variable

In a number of applied problems we need to compute probabilities for proportion or percentage intervals. We can do this by using a direct extension of the normal distribution approximation for the binomial distribution. A proportion random variable, P, can be computed by dividing the number of successes, X, by the sample size, n:

$$P = \frac{X}{n}$$

Then, using the linear transformation of random variables, as shown in the chapter appendix, the mean and the variance of P can be computed as follows:

$$\mu = P$$

$$\sigma^2 = \frac{P(1-P)}{n}$$

The resulting mean and variance can be used with the normal distribution to compute the desired probability.

Example 5.9 Election Forecasting (Proportion Probabilities)

We have often observed the success of television networks in forecasting elections. This is a good example of the successful use of probability methods in applied problems. Consider how elections can be predicted by using relatively small samples in a simplified example. An election forecaster has obtained a random sample of 900 voters, in which 500 indicate that they will vote for Susan Chung. Should Susan anticipate winning the election?

Solution In this problem we assume only two candidates, and, thus, if more than 50% of the population supports Susan, she will win the election. We compute the probability that 500 or more voters out of a sample of 900 support Susan under the assumption that exactly 50%, $P = 0.50$, of the entire population supports Susan.

$$P(X \geq 500)|n = 900, P = 0.50) \approx P(X \geq 500|\mu = 450, \sigma^2 = 225)$$

$$= P\left(Z \geq \frac{500 - 450}{\sqrt{225}}\right)$$

$$= P(Z \geq 3.33)$$

$$= 0.0004$$

The probability of 500 successes out of 900 trials if $P = 0.50$ is very small, and, therefore, we conclude that P must be greater than 0.50. Hence, we predict that Susan Chung will win the election.

We could also compute the probability that more than 55.6% (500/900) of the sample indicates support for Susan if the population proportion is $P = 0.50$. Using the mean and variance for proportion random variables,

$$\mu = P = 0.50$$

$$\sigma^2 = \frac{P(1-P)}{n} = \frac{0.50(1 - 0.50)}{900}$$

$$\sigma = 0.0167$$

$$P(P \geq 0.556 \,|\, n = 900, P = 0.50) \approx P(P \geq 0.556 \,|\, \mu = 0.50, \sigma = 0.0167)$$

$$= P\left(Z \geq \frac{0.556 - 0.50}{0.0167}\right)$$

$$= P(Z \geq 3.33)$$

$$= 0.0004$$

Note that the probability is exactly the same as that for the corresponding binomial random variable. This is always the case because each proportion or percentage value is directly related to a specific number of successes. Because percent is a more common term than proportion in business and economic language, we will tend to use percent more often than proportion in exercises and discussion in this textbook.

EXERCISES

Basic Exercises

5.39 Given a random sample size of $n = 4,900$ from a binomial probability distribution with $P = 0.50$ do the following:

a. Find the probability that the number of successes is greater than 2,545.
b. Find the probability that the number of successes is fewer than 2,385.
c. Find the probability that the number of successes is between 2,430 and 2,485.
d. With probability 0.30, the number of successes is fewer than how many?
e. With probability 0.07, the number of successes is greater than how many?

5.40 Given a random sample size of $n = 1,600$ from a binomial probability distribution with $P = 0.40$, do the following:

a. Find the probability that the number of successes is greater than 1,650.
b. Find the probability that the number of successes is fewer than 1,530.
c. Find the probability that the number of successes is between 1,550 and 1,650.
d. With probability 0.09, the number of successes is fewer than how many?
e. With probability 0.20, the number of successes is greater than how many?

5.41 Given a random sample size of $n = 900$ from a binomial probability distribution with $P = 0.30$ do the following:

a. Find the probability that the number of successes is greater than 305.
b. Find the probability that the number of successes is fewer than 245.
c. Find the probability that the number of successes is between 260 and 297.
d. With probability 0.40, the number of successes is fewer than how many?
e. With probability 0.06, the number of successes is greater than how many?

5.42 Given a random sample size of $n = 1,600$ from a binomial probability distribution with $P = 0.40$ do the following:

a. Find the probability that the percentage of successes is greater than 0.45.
b. Find the probability that the percentage of successes is less than 0.35.
c. Find the probability that the percentage of successes is between 0.37 and 0.44.
d. With probability 0.20, the percentage of successes is less than what percent?
e. With probability 0.09, the percentage of successes is greater than what percent?

5.43 Given a random sample size of $n = 400$ from a binomial probability distribution with $P = 0.20$ do the following:

a. Find the probability that the percentage of successes is greater than 0.25.
b. Find the probability that the percentage of successes is less than 0.15.
c. Find the probability that the percentage of successes is between 0.17 and 0.24.
d. With probability 0.15, the percentage of successes is less than what percent?
e. With probability 0.11, the percentage of successes is greater than what percent?

Application Exercises

5.44 Avis Rent, a South African car-rental company, has determined that the probability a car will need service work in any given month is 0.15. Avis Rent has 1200 cars.

a. What is the probability that more than 200 cars will require service work in a particular month?
b. What is the probability that fewer than 170 cars will need service work in a given month?

5.45 It is known that 10% of all the items produced by a particular manufacturing process are defective. From the very large output of a single day, 100 items are selected at random.

a. What is the probability that at least 8 of the selected items are defective?

b. What is the probability that between 10 and 14 of the selected items are defective?

c. What is the probability that between 7 and 15 of the selected items are defective?

d. Without doing the calculations, state which of the following ranges of defectives has the highest probability: 15–16, 8–9, 13–14, 4–5, or 9–10.

5.46 A random sample of 200 blue-collar employees at Ricci S.p.A, an Italian construction company, is surveyed to assess their attitudes toward a proposed new work schedule. If 65% of all blue-collar employees at Ricci S.p.A favor the new schedule, what is the probability that fewer than 120 in the random sample will be in favor?

5.47 Suppose St. Vincent's Hospital Melbourne, Australia, finds that 30% of its accounts are at least 1 month in arrears. A random sample of 500 accounts was taken.

a. What is the probability that fewer than 130 accounts in the sample were at least 1 month in arrears?

b. What is the probability that the number of accounts in the sample at least 1 month in arrears was between 160 and 180 (inclusive)?

5.48 The tread life of tires from Nokian Tyres, a Finnish automobile company, can be modeled by a normal distribution with a mean of 35,000 miles and a standard deviation of 5,000 miles. A sample of 200 of these tires is taken. What is the probability that more than 40 of them have tread lives of more than 40,000 miles?

5.49 Bags of a chemical produced by a company have impurity weights that can be represented by a normal distribution with a mean of 12.2 grams and a standard deviation of 2.8 grams. A random sample of 400 of these bags is taken. What is the probability that at least 100 of them contain fewer than 10 grams of impurities?

5.5 THE EXPONENTIAL DISTRIBUTION

The *exponential distribution* has been found to be particularly useful for waiting-line, or queuing, problems. In many service-time problems, the service times can be modeled using the exponential distribution. We should note that the exponential distribution differs from the normal in two important ways: It is restricted to random variables with positive values, and its distribution is not symmetric.

The Exponential Distribution

The exponential random variable $T(t > 0)$ has a probability density function

$$f(t) = \lambda e^{-\lambda t} \quad \text{for } t > 0 \tag{5.15}$$

where λ is the mean number of independent arrivals per time unit, t is the number of time units until the next arrival, and $e = 2.71828. \ldots$ Then T is said to follow an **exponential probability distribution**. Arrivals are independent if an arrival does not affect the probability of waiting time, t, until the next arrival. It can be shown that λ is the same parameter used for the Poisson distribution in Section 4.5 and that the mean time between occurrences is $1/\lambda$.

The cumulative distribution function is as follows:

$$F(t) = 1 - e^{-\lambda t} \quad \text{for } t > 0 \tag{5.16}$$

The distribution has a mean of $1/\lambda$ and a variance of $1/\lambda^2$.

The probability that the time between arrivals is t_a or less is as follows:

$$P(T \le t_a) = (1 - e^{-\lambda t_a})$$

The probability that the time between arrivals is between t_b and t_a is as follows:

$$P(t_b \le T \le t_a) = (1 - e^{-\lambda t_a}) - (1 - e^{-\lambda t_b})$$
$$= e^{-\lambda t_b} - e^{-\lambda t_a}$$

The random variable T can be used to represent the length of time until the end of a service time or until the next arrival to a queuing process, beginning at an arbitrary time 0. The model assumptions are the same as those for the Poisson distribution. Note that the Poisson distribution provides the probability of X successes or arrivals during a time unit. In contrast, the exponential distribution provides the probability that a success or arrival will occur during an interval of time t. Figure 5.26 shows the probability density function for an exponential distribution with $\lambda = 0.2$. The area to the left of 10 gives the probability that a task will be completed before time 10. This area can be obtained by evaluating the function $1 - e^{-\lambda t}$ for the given value of $t = 10$. The function can be computed by using your electronic calculator. The probability that an arrival occurs between time 10 and 20 can be computed as follows:

$$P(t_{10} \leq T \leq t_{20}) = (1 - e^{-0.2t_{20}}) - (1 - e^{-0.2t_{10}})$$
$$= e^{-0.2t_{10}} - e^{-0.2t_{20}}$$
$$= 0.1353 - 0.0183$$
$$= 0.1170$$

Now let us consider an example problem to demonstrate the application of the exponential distribution.

Figure 5.26
Probability Density Function for an Exponential Distribution with $\lambda = 0.2$

Example 5.10 Service Time at Library Information Desk (Exponential Probabilities)

Service times for customers at a library information desk can be modeled by an exponential distribution with a mean service time of 5 minutes. What is the probability that a customer service time will take longer than 10 minutes?

Solution Let t denote the service time in minutes. The service rate is $\lambda = 1/5 = 0.2$ per minute, and the probability density function is

$$f(t) = \lambda e^{-\lambda t}$$

which is shown in Figure 5.26. The required probability can be computed as follows:

$$P(T > 10) = 1 - P(T < 10)$$
$$= 1 - F(10)$$
$$= 1 - (1 - e^{-(0.20)(10)})$$
$$= e^{-2.0} = 0.1353$$

Thus, the probability that a service time exceeds 10 minutes is 0.1353.

Example 5.11 Time Between Accidents in Typical British Industrial Plants (Exponential Probabilities)

An industrial plant in Britain with 2,000 employees has a mean number of lost-time accidents per week equal to $\lambda = 0.4$, and the number of accidents follows a Poisson distribution. What is the probability that the time between accidents is less than 2 weeks?

Solution In this problem we note that the time interval is measured in weeks and our rate is $\lambda = 0.4$ per week, giving a mean time between accidents of $\mu = 1/(0.4) = 2.5$ weeks. Then the probability that the time between accidents is less than 2 weeks is as follows:

$$P(T < 2) = F(2) = 1 - e^{-(0.4)(2)}$$
$$= 1 - e^{-0.8}$$
$$= 1 - 0.4493$$
$$= 0.5507$$

Thus, the probability of less than 2 weeks between accidents is about 55%.

Example 5.12 Time Between Boat Arrivals at a Grain Shipping Dock

In Example 4.12 we showed how to compute the probability of the number of boats arriving at a grain shipping dock in Churchill Manitoba using the Poisson probability distribution. In this example we compute the probability of a particular time interval between boat arrivals using the exponential probability distribution. In the previous problem we found that the mean number of arrivals was $\lambda = 2.5$ per 6-hour period. Now we want to compute the probability that a boat will arrive within 3 hours of the last boat arrival and also to compute the probability that a boat will arrive between 2 and 4 hours after the last arrival.

Solution To compute both of these probabilities, we need to adjust the time scale to the same form as the arrival rate. The arrival rate is given as 2.5 arrivals per 6-hour period. Thus in terms of a 6-hour time unit, 3 hours is 3/6 time units, 2 hours is 2/6 time units, and 4 hours is 4/6 time units. Thus, the probability of an arrival within 3 hours is computed as follows:

$$P\left(T \leq \frac{3}{6} | \lambda = 2.5\right) = \left(1 - e^{(-2.5)(0.5)}\right)$$

$$= 0.7135$$

And the probability that an arrival will occur between 2 and 4 hours is computed as follows:

$$P\left(\frac{2}{6} \leq T \leq \frac{4}{6}\right) = \left(1 - e^{(-2.5)(0.67)}\right) - \left(1 - e^{(-2.5)(0.33)}\right)$$

$$= e^{(-2.5)(0.33)} - e^{(-2.5)(0.67)}$$

$$= 0.4382 - 0.1873$$

$$= 0.2509$$

Basic Exercises

5.50 Given an arrival process with $\lambda = 1.0$, what is the probability that an arrival occurs in the first $t = 2$ time units?

5.51 Given an arrival process with $\lambda = 0.6$, what is the probability that an arrival occurs in the first $t = 8$ time units?

5.52 Given an arrival process with $\lambda = 5.0$, what is the probability that an arrival occurs after $t = 7$ time units?

5.53 Given an arrival process with $\lambda = 5.0$, what is the probability that an arrival occurs after $t = 5$ time units?

5.54 Given an arrival process with $\lambda = 3.0$, what is the probability that an arrival occurs in the first $t = 2$ time units?

Application Exercises

5.55 A professor sees students during regular office hours. Time spent with students follows an exponential distribution with a mean of 10 minutes.

   a. Find the probability that a given student spends fewer than 20 minutes with the professor.

   b. Find the probability that a given student spends more than 5 minutes with the professor.

   c. Find the probability that a given student spends between 10 and 15 minutes with the professor.

5.56 Times to gather preliminary information from arrivals at an outpatient clinic follow an exponential distribution with mean 15 minutes. Find the probability, for a randomly chosen arrival, that more than 18 minutes will be required.

5.57 It is known that for a laboratory computing system the number of system failures during a month has a Poisson distribution with a mean of 0.8. The system has just failed. Find the probability that at least 2 months will elapse before a further failure.

5.58 Suppose that the time between successive occurrences of an event follows an exponential distribution with a mean of $1/\lambda$ minutes. Assume that an event occurs.

   a. Show that the probability that more than 3 minutes elapses before the occurrence of the next event is $e^{-3\lambda}$.

   b. Show that the probability that more than 6 minutes elapses before the occurrence of the next event is $e^{-6\lambda}$.

   c. Using the results of parts (a) and (b), show that if 3 minutes have already elapsed, the probability that a further 3 minutes will elapse before the next occurrence is $e^{-3\lambda}$. Explain your answer in words.

5.59 Swapna David is a customer assistant consultant for Acme Information Systems, who provides assistance for computer users. The mean number of calls per hour is 30 from across Europe and calls are independent. She has just finished a call and is scheduled to take the next call. What is the probability that she will have at least 9 minutes to obtain her cup of tea?

5.60 Delivery trucks arrive independently at the Floorstore Regional distribution center with various consumer items from the company's suppliers. The mean number of trucks arriving per hour is 20. Given that a truck has just arrived answer the following:

   a. What is the probability that the next truck will not arrive for at least 5 minutes?

   b. What is the probability that the next truck will arrive within the next 2 minutes?

   c. What is the probability that the next truck will arrive between 4 and 10 minutes?

5.6 JOINTLY DISTRIBUTED CONTINUOUS RANDOM VARIABLES

In Section 4.7 we introduced jointly distributed discrete random variables. Here, we show that many of the concepts and results from discrete random variables also apply for continuous random variables. Many continuous random variables can be modeled using jointly distributed random variables. The market values of various stock prices are regularly modeled as joint random variables. Studies of the production and sales patterns for various companies and industries use jointly distributed continuous random variables. The number of units sold by a large retail store during a particular week and the price per unit can be modeled by joint random variables. Studies of import and export behavior for various countries regularly use joint random variables as part of the analysis.

After we have developed some basic concepts, we will present a number of application examples to show the importance of the procedures and how to analyze jointly distributed continuous random variables.

Joint Cumulative Distribution Function

Let $X_1, X_2, \ldots, X_K$ be continuous random variables.

1. Their **joint cumulative distribution**, $F(x_1, x_2, \ldots, x_K)$, defines the probability that simultaneously X_1 is less than x_1, X_2 is less than x_2, and so on—that is,

$$F(x_1, x_2, \ldots, x_K) = P(X_1 < x_1 \cap X_2 < x_2 \cap \ldots \cap X_K < x_K) \tag{5.17}$$

2. The cumulative distribution functions—$F(x_1), F(x_2), \ldots, F(x_K)$—of the individual random variables are called their **marginal distributions**. For any i, $F(x_i)$ is the probability that the random variable X_i does not exceed the specific value x_i.

3. The random variables are *independent* if and only if

$$F(x_1, x_2, \ldots, x_K) = F(x_1)F(x_2) \cdots F(x_K) \tag{5.18}$$

We note that the notion of independence here is precisely the same as in the discrete case. Independence of a set of random variables implies that the probability distribution of any one of them is unaffected by the values taken by the others. Thus, for example, the assertion that consecutive daily changes in the price of a share of common stock are independent of one another implies that information about the past price changes is of no value in assessing what is likely to happen tomorrow.

The notion of expectation extends to functions of jointly distributed continuous random variables. As in the case of discrete random variables, we have the concept of *covariance*, which is used in assessing linear relationships between pairs of random variables.

Covariance

Let X and Y be a pair of continuous random variables with respective means μ_X and μ_Y. The expected value of $(X - \mu_X)(Y - \mu_Y)$, is called the **covariance** (*Cov*), between X and Y,

$$Cov(X, Y) = E[(X - \mu_X)(Y - \mu_Y)] \tag{5.19}$$

An alternative, but equivalent, expression can be derived as

$$Cov(X, Y) = E[XY] - \mu_X \mu_Y \tag{5.20}$$

If the random variables X and Y are independent, then the covariance between them is 0. However, the converse is not necessarily true.

In Section 4.7 we also presented the *correlation* as a standardized measure of the relationship between two discrete random variables. The same results hold for continuous random variables.

Correlation

Let X and Y be jointly distributed random variables. The **correlation** (*Corr*) between X and Y is as follows:

$$\rho = Corr(X, Y) = \frac{Cov(X, Y)}{\sigma_X \sigma_Y} \tag{5.21}$$

In Section 4.7 we presented the means and variances for sums and differences of discrete random variables. The same results apply for continuous random variables because the results are established using expectations and, thus, are not affected by the condition of discrete or continuous random variables.

Sums of Random Variables

Let $X_1, X_2, \ldots, X_K$ be K random variables with means $\mu_1, \mu_2, \ldots, \mu_K$ and variances $\sigma_1^2, \sigma_2^2, \ldots, \sigma_K^2$. Consider the following properties:

1. The mean of their sum is the sum of their means—that is,

$$E[(X_1 + X_2 + \cdots + X_K)] = \mu_1 + \mu_2 + \cdots + \mu_K \tag{5.22}$$

2. If the covariance between every pair of these random variables is 0, then the variance of their sum is the sum of their variances—that is,

$$Var(X_1 + X_2 + \cdots + X_K) = \sigma_1^2 + \sigma_2^2 + \cdots + \sigma_K^2 \tag{5.23}$$

However, if the covariances between pairs of random variables are not 0, the variance of their sum is as follows:

$$Var(X_1 + X_2 + \cdots + X_K) = \sigma_1^2 + \sigma_2^2 + \cdots + \sigma_K^2 + 2\sum_{i=1}^{K-1}\sum_{j=i+1}^{K} Cov(X_i, X_j) \tag{5.24}$$

Differences Between a Pair of Random Variables

Let X and Y be a pair of random variables with means μ_X and μ_Y and variances σ_X^2 and σ_Y^2. Consider the following properties:

1. The mean of their difference is the difference of their means—that is,

$$E[X - Y] = \mu_X - \mu_Y \tag{5.25}$$

2. If the covariance between X and Y is 0, then the variance of their difference is as follows:

$$Var(X - Y) = \sigma_X^2 + \sigma_Y^2 \tag{5.26}$$

3. If the covariance between X and Y is not 0, then the variance of their difference is as follows:

$$Var(X - Y) = \sigma_X^2 + \sigma_Y^2 - 2\,Cov(X, Y) \tag{5.27}$$

Example 5.13 Total Project Costs (Mean and Standard Deviation)

A contractor is uncertain of the precise total costs for either materials or labor for a project. In addition, the total line of credit for financing the project is $260,000, and the contractor wants to know the probability that total costs exceed $260,000. It is believed that material costs can be represented by a normally distributed random variable with mean $100,000 and standard deviation $10,000. Labor costs are $1,500 a day, and the number of days needed to complete the project can be represented by a normally distributed random variable with mean 80 and standard deviation 12. Assuming that material and labor costs are independent, what are the mean and standard deviation of the total project cost (materials plus labor)? In addition, what is the probability that the total project cost is greater than $260,000?

Solution Let the random variables X_1 and X_2 denote, respectively, materials and labor costs. Then,

For X_1: $\qquad\qquad\qquad \mu_1 = 100{,}000$ and $\sigma_1 = 10{,}000$

For X_2: $\qquad \mu_2 = (1{,}500)(80) = 120{,}000$ and $\sigma_2 = (1{,}500)(12) = 18{,}000$

The total project cost is $W = X_1 + X_2$, and we have mean cost

$$\mu_W = \mu_1 + \mu_2 = 100{,}000 + 120{,}000 = \$220{,}000$$

Because X_1 and X_2 are independent, the variance of their sum is as follows:

$$\sigma_W^2 = \sigma_1^2 + \sigma_2^2 = (10{,}000)^2 + (18{,}000)^2 = 424{,}000{,}000$$

Taking the square root, we find that the standard deviation is \$20,591.

Since X_1 and X_2 are normally distributed, it can be shown that their sum, W, is also normally distributed. The probability that W is greater than \$260,000 can be determined by computing a standard normal random variable Z, using the mean and variance of W as follows:

$$Z = \frac{(260{,}000 - 220{,}000)}{20{,}591} = 1.94$$

Using the cumulative normal probability table, we find that the probability that the total cost exceeds \$260,000 is 0.0262. Since this probability is small, the contractor has some confidence that the project can be completed within the available line of credit.

Example 5.14 Investment Portfolio Risk (Linear Function Mean and Variance)

Henry Chang has asked for your assistance in establishing a portfolio containing two stocks. Henry has \$1,000, which can be allocated in any proportion to two alternative stocks. The returns per dollar from these investments will be designated as random variables X and Y. Both of these random variables are independent and have the same mean and variance. Henry wishes to know the risk for various allocation options. You point out that risk is directly related to variance and, thus, that his question would be answered if he knew the variance of various allocation options.

Solution The amount of money allocated to the first investment will be designated as α, and, hence, the remaining $1{,}000 - \alpha$ will be allocated to the second investment. The total return on the investment is as follows:

$$R = \alpha X + (1{,}000 - \alpha)Y$$

This random variable has the expected value

$$E[R] = \alpha E[X] + (1{,}000 - \alpha)E[Y] = \alpha\mu + (1{,}000 - \alpha)\mu = \$1{,}000\mu$$

Thus, we see that the expected return is the same for any allocation.
However, the risk or variance is a different story.

$$Var(R) = \alpha^2 Var(X) + (1{,}000 - \alpha)^2 Var(Y)$$
$$= \alpha^2\sigma^2 + (1{,}000 - \alpha)^2\sigma^2$$
$$= (2\alpha^2 - 2{,}000\,\alpha + 1{,}000{,}000)\sigma^2$$

If α is equal to either 0 or 1,000, so that the entire portfolio is allocated to just one of the stocks, the variance of the total return is $1{,}000{,}000\sigma^2$. However, if \$500 is allocated to each investment, the variance of the total return is $500{,}000\sigma^2$, which is the smallest possible variance. By spreading his investment over two stocks, Henry is able to mitigate the effect of either high or low returns from one of the shares. Thus, it is possible to obtain the same expected return with a variety of risk levels.

Linear Combinations of Random Variables

In Chapter 4 we developed the mean and variance for linear combinations of discrete random variables. These results also apply for continuous random variables because their development is based on operations with expected values and does not depend on the particular probability distributions. Equations 5.28 through 5.31 indicate the important properties of linear combinations.

Linear Combinations of Random Variables

The linear combination of two random variables, X and Y, is

$$W = aX + bY \tag{5.28}$$

where a and b are constant numbers.

The mean value for W is

$$\mu_W = E[W] = E[aX + bY] = a\mu_X + b\mu_Y \tag{5.29}$$

The variance for W is

$$\sigma_W^2 = a^2\sigma_X^2 + b^2\sigma_Y^2 + 2ab\, Cov(X, Y) \tag{5.30}$$

or, using the correlation,

$$\sigma_W^2 = a^2\sigma_X^2 + b^2\sigma_Y^2 + 2ab\, \rho(X, Y)\sigma_X\sigma_Y \tag{5.31}$$

If the linear combination in Equation 5.28 is a difference,

$$W = aX - bY \tag{5.32}$$

then the mean and the variance are

$$\mu_W = E[W] = E[aX - bY] = a\mu_X - b\mu_Y \tag{5.33}$$
$$\sigma_W^2 = a^2\sigma_X^2 + b^2\sigma_Y^2 - 2ab\, Cov(X, Y) \tag{5.34}$$

or using the correlation.

$$\sigma_W^2 = a^2\sigma_X^2 + b^2\sigma_Y^2 - 2ab\, \rho(X, Y)\sigma_X\sigma_Y \tag{5.35}$$

These results come directly from Equations 5.28 through 5.31 by merely substituting a negative value for the coefficient b in the equations.

If both X and Y are joint normally distributed random variables, then the resulting random variable, W, is also normally distributed with mean and variance derived as shown. This result enables us to determine the probability that the linear combination, W, is within a specific interval.

Financial Investment Portfolios

Example 5.15 Portfolio Analysis (Probability of a Portfolio)

Judy Chang, the account manager for Northern Securities, has a portfolio that includes 20 shares of Allied Information Systems and 30 shares of Bangalore Analytics. Both firms provide Web-access devices that compete in the consumer market. The price of Allied stock is normally distributed with mean $\mu_X = 25$ and variance $\sigma_X^2 = 81$. The price of Bangalore stock is also normally distributed with the mean $\mu_Y = 40$ and the variance $\sigma_Y^2 = 121$. The stock prices have a negative correlation, $\rho_{XY} = -0.40$. Judy has asked you to determine the probability that the portfolio value exceeds 2,000.

Solution The value of Judy's portfolio, W, is defined by the linear combination

$$W = 20X + 30Y$$

and W is normally distributed. The mean value for her stock portfolio is as follows:

$$\begin{aligned}
\mu_W &= 20\mu_X + 30\mu_Y \\
&= 20 \times 25 + 30 \times 40 \\
&= 1{,}700
\end{aligned}$$

The variance for the portfolio value is

$$\begin{aligned}
\sigma_W^2 &= 20^2\sigma_X^2 + 30^2\sigma_Y^2 + 2 \times 20 \times 30\, \rho_{XY}\sigma_X\sigma_Y \\
&= 20^2 \times 81 + 30^2 \times 121 + 2 \times 20 \times 30 \times (-0.40) \times 9 \times 11 = 93{,}780
\end{aligned}$$

and the standard deviation of the portfolio value is

$$\sigma_W = 306.24$$

The standard normal Z for 2,000 is as follows:

$$Z_W = \frac{2{,}000 - 1{,}700}{306.24} = 0.980$$

The probability that the portfolio value exceeds 2,000 is 0.1635. From the symmetry of the normal distribution, it follows that the probability that the portfolio value is less than 1,400 is also 0.1635.

If the two stock prices had a positive correlation, $\rho = +0.40$, the mean would be the same, but the variance and standard deviation are follows:

$$\begin{aligned}
\sigma_W^2 &= 20^2\sigma_X^2 + 30^2\sigma_Y^2 + 2 \times 20 \times 30\, \rho(X,Y)\sigma_X\sigma_Y \\
&= 20^2 \times 81 + 30^2 \times 121 + 2 \times 20 \times 30 \times (+0.40) \times 9 \times 11 = 188{,}820
\end{aligned}$$

$$\sigma_W = 434.53$$

The standard normal Z for 2,000 is as follows:

$$Z_{2{,}000} = \frac{2{,}000 - 1{,}700}{434.53} = 0.690$$

The probability that her portfolio value exceeds 2,000 is 0.2451, and the probability that it is less than 1,400 is also 0.2451.

Thus, we see that a positive correlation between stock prices leads to a higher variance and higher risk. The risk in this example increases the probability that the portfolio exceeds 2,000, from 0.1635 to 0.2451. This also implies a similar change in the probability that the portfolio value is less than 1,400. The higher risk implies that there is a higher probability that the portfolio has higher or lower values compared to the lower risk option.

The previous example illustrates a very important fundamental principle in the design of investment portfolios. Recall that the risk of an investment is directly related to the variance of the investment value. In the previous example we showed that if the values of the two stock prices are positively correlated, then the resulting portfolio will have a larger variance and hence a higher risk. And if the two stock prices are negatively correlated, then the resulting portfolio will have a smaller variance and hence a lower risk. The term *hedging* is often used by fund managers to describe this phenomenon. This important principle for a two-stock portfolio extends directly to a portfolio with a large number of different stocks, but in that case the algebra is more complex and is typically computed using a sophisticated computer program.

The use of linear combinations of random variables also applies directly to the estimation of portfolio return given the returns on individual stocks.

$$
\begin{pmatrix} \text{return} \\ \text{on} \\ \text{portfolio} \end{pmatrix} = \begin{pmatrix} \text{proportion} \\ \text{of portfolio} \\ \text{value,} \\ \text{stock 1} \end{pmatrix} \times \begin{pmatrix} \text{stock 1} \\ \text{return} \end{pmatrix} + \begin{pmatrix} \text{proportion} \\ \text{of portfolio} \\ \text{value,} \\ \text{stock 2} \end{pmatrix} \times \begin{pmatrix} \text{stock 2} \\ \text{return} \end{pmatrix} + \cdots
$$

$$
+ \begin{pmatrix} \text{proportion} \\ \text{of portfolio} \\ \text{value,} \\ \text{stock } K \end{pmatrix} \times \begin{pmatrix} \text{stock } K \\ \text{return} \end{pmatrix}
$$

Investment fund managers use this principle to select combinations of many different stocks in order to obtain the desired portfolio return with the risk characteristics that are the objectives for a particular investment fund. Example 5.16 develops the computations for determining portfolio return and risk.

Example 5.16 General Portfolio Analysis

In actual practice, portfolios such as mutual funds may have 100 to 300 or more different stocks. This leads to extensive computations that could not be reasonably done without powerful computers and large databases. In this discussion we will indicate how the computations can be made and illustrate this with a reduced example. A large portfolio can be modeled with the *return on stock price* for each of k stock prices represented as k random variables, X_i, with means, μ_i, with variances, σ_i^2, and with covariances between stock prices, $Cov(X_i, Y_i)$. The dollar-value proportion of the portfolio for each stock is a_i. The total value of the portfolio can be expressed as follows:

$$
W = \sum_{i=1}^{K} a_i X_i
$$

The mean value for W is as follows:

$$
\mu_W = E[W] = E\left[\sum_{i=1}^{K} a_i X_i \right]
$$

$$
= \sum_{i=1}^{K} a_i \mu_i \tag{5.36}
$$

The variance for W is as follows:

$$
\sigma_W^2 = \sum_{i=1}^{K} a_i^2 \sigma_i^2 + 2 \sum_{i=1}^{K-1} \sum_{j=i+1}^{K} a_i a_j \, Cov(X_i, X_j) \tag{5.37}
$$

These equations can be utilized to develop computer-based computations that can be used with a large data base of stock prices or other measures of performance.

Example 5.17 Returns on Financial Portfolios

Susan Chang, fund manager at Northlake Financial Growth, has asked you to analyze a portfolio consisting of Infosys Technologies, Alcoa, Inc., and Pearson PLC as part of a larger project to develop a new growth fund. In particular she wishes to know the monthly return on stock price and the variance of this return.

Solution You decide to use the monthly *return on stock price* over the 5-year period from May 2003 through April 2008. The stock-price data was obtained from Stock Investor Professional (Stock Investor Pro, 2007). The return on stock price was computed by dividing the change in month-end closing by the most recent month-end closing. Figure 5.27 contains the mean, variance, and covariance of the return on stock price for three firms—Infosys Technologies, Alcoa. Inc., Pearson PLC—for the 60 months from May 2003 through April 2008. Return on stock price is expressed as a proportion change for one month. This data are contained in the file **Return on Stock Price 60 month**. After a discussion with Susan, you decide to consider a portfolio whose dollar value includes 40% of Infosys, 30% of Alcoa, and 30% of Pearson. The mean value is computed using Equation 5.36 as follows:

$$\mu_W = E[W] = (0.40)(0.0196) + (0.30)(0.00439) + (0.30)(0.00621)$$
$$= 0.01101$$

Figure 5.27 Portfolio Statistics for Example 5.17 (Minitab Output)

Descriptive Statistics: Infosys Tech, Alcoa Inc., Pearson PLC (ADR)

Variable	N	Mean	StDev	Variance	Min	Median	Max
Infosys Tech	60	0.0196	0.0926	0.0086	−0.2456	0.0254	0.1945
Alcoa Inc.	60	0.00439	0.07113	0.00506	−0.12813	0.01134	0.17137
Pearson PLC	60	0.00621	0.04655	0.00217	−0.09474	0.00391	0.10108

Covariances: Infosys Tech, Alcoa Inc., Pearson DLC (ADR)

	Infosys Tech	Alcoa Inc.	Pearson PLC
Infosys Tech	0.00857204		
Alcoa Inc.	0.00168845	0.00505950	
Pearson PLC	0.00086330	0.00150291	0.00216704

Descriptive Statistics: Portfolio 1

Variable	N	Mean	StDev	Variance	Min	Median	Max
Portfolio 1	60	0.01101	0.05390	0.00290	−0.13783	0.01950	0.15579

Descriptive Statistics: S & P 500

Variable	N	Mean	StDev	Variance	Min	Median	Max
SP 500	60	0.00655	0.02512	0.00063	−0.06515	0.01157	0.05210

Note that this portfolio mean is 1.101% per month, or 13.2% growth per year. The variance is computed using Equation 5.37 as follows:

$$\sigma_W^2 = (0.40^2)(0.0086) + (0.30^2)(0.00506) + (0.30^2)(0.00217)$$
$$+ 2[(0.40)(0.30)(0.00168845) + (0.40)(0.30)(0.00086330)$$
$$+ (0.30)(0.30)(0.00150291)]$$
$$= 0.00290$$

The standard deviation for the portfolio value is as follows:

$$\sigma_W = 0.05390$$

These computations can also be made by computing the value of the portfolio each month and then computing the mean and variance of the monthly portfolio values. The results are, of course, the same as shown for the variable, portfolio 1, in Figure 5.27. We have also included the mean and variance for the Standard and Poors (S & P) index for the same time period for perspective. Note that the mean growth ratio is higher for portfolio 1 compared to the S & P.

Assuming that stock price growth is normally distributed, we can also compute the probabilities that the total value of the portfolio is above or below particular values.

For example, the probability that the portfolio value is above 0.10 for one month can be determined by computing the standard normal Z:

$$Z_{0.10} = \frac{(0.10 - 0.01101)}{0.0539} = 1.651$$

The probability that the portfolio exceeds 0.10 is 0.049. We can also compute the probability that the portfolio value is less than 0.0 by first computing the standard normal Z:

$$Z_{0.0} = \frac{(0.0 - 0.01101)}{0.0539} = -0.204$$

The probability that the portfolio value is less than 0.0 is 0.081.

Cautions Concerning Finance Models

The previous section introduced you to the basic understanding of the statistical modeling that is used in complex trading models. By using the means and variances computed for portfolios by these methods and the assumption of a normal distribution, analysts can determine the probability of various outcomes. This makes possible the determination of possible gains and losses adjusted by the probability of their occurrence. In addition, a number of very complex models have been developed—by extending the methods here—that use nonnormal probability distribution models and rigorous mathematical adjustments. These models have been developed by persons with strong mathematical skills, who may not have their basic education in business and economics. Computerized models are used successfully to assist very successful fund managers in their allocation of capital to the most appropriate uses.

There are, however, major examples where these models have failed with disastrous outcomes—such as the market collapse in September 2008. In some cases the models have been used to initiate trades with minimal human review. In the worst cases the models used are not well understood by the traders responsible for the funds, since the model developers may have departed from the company. The models work very well if the underlying probability distributions continue to be well approximated by the models. However, just because these approximations have occurred in the past, they are not guaranteed to occur in the future. Quoting again from Nassim Tabeb, ". . . history teaches us that things that never happened before do happen." Again, we encourage you to read his book, *Fooled by Randomness* (Taleb 2005). As noted in Chapter 3, Black Swans do occur with unknown probability. We cannot know the probability that the Chinese government will change the value of the yuan relative to the U.S. dollar, or that the U.S. dollar will lose its central role in world finance, or that some crazy people will destroy the World Trade Center. These and similar unknowns will have major and unpredictable effects on market outcomes.

Thus the wise analyst needs to constantly consider at least the following two ideas. First, under continuing stable conditions, the methods just developed will, if they are clearly understood, lead to better decisions. However, the unexpected can occur. Knowledge of probability can help one to understand that important fact. Second, one must also appreciate the fact that the unexpected could occur and lead to unexpected outcomes. If you have a broad understanding of world events you might be able to identify some possible unexpected events, but usually not their probabilities. We anticipate that patterns of events in the past will be followed by future similar patterns of events. But there is no guarantee. So, caution and continuous clear observation and thinking cannot be replaced by models developed from past events but must be used in combination with the models—which contain necessary, but not sufficient, analyses.

Basic Exercises

5.61 A random variable X is normally distributed with a mean of 144 and a variance of 144, and a random variable Y is normally distributed with a mean of 150 and a variance of 225. The random variables have a correlation coefficient equal to 0.5. Find the mean and variance of the random variable:

$$W = 6X + 4Y$$

5.62 A random variable X is normally distributed with a mean of 100 and a variance of 100, and a random variable Y is normally distributed with a mean of 200 and a variance of 400. The random variables have a correlation coefficient equal to -0.5. Find the mean and variance of the random variable:

$$W = 5X + 4Y$$

5.63 A random variable X is normally distributed with a mean of 64 and a variance of 64, and a random variable Y is normally distributed with a mean of 160 and a variance of 256. The random variables have a correlation coefficient equal to -0.5. Find the mean and variance of the random variable:

$$W = 5X - 7Y$$

5.64 A random variable X is normally distributed with a mean of 500 and a variance of 100, and a random variable Y is normally distributed with a mean of 200 and a variance of 400. The random variables have a correlation coefficient equal to 0.5. Find the mean and variance of the random variable:

$$W = 5X - 4Y$$

5.65 A random variable X is normally distributed with a mean of 100 and a variance of 500, and a random variable Y is normally distributed with a mean of 200 and a variance of 400. The random variables have a correlation coefficient equal to -0.5. Find the mean and variance of the random variable:

$$W = 5X - 4Y$$

Application Exercises

5.66 An investor plans to divide $200,000 between two investments. The first yields a certain profit of 10%, whereas the second yields a profit with expected value 18% and standard deviation 6%. If the investor divides the money equally between these two investments, find the mean and standard deviation of the total profit.

5.67 A homeowner has installed a new energy-efficient furnace. It is estimated that over a year the new furnace will reduce energy costs by an amount that can be regarded as a random variable with a mean of $200 and a standard deviation of $60. Stating any assumptions you need to make, find the mean and standard deviation of the total energy cost reductions over a period of 5 years.

5.68 A consultant is beginning work on three projects. The expected profits from these projects are €65,000, €83,000, and €57,000. The associated standard deviations are €12,500, €17,200, and €11,300. By assuming independence of the outcomes, find the mean and standard deviation of the consultant's total profit from these three projects.

5.69 A consultant has three sources of income—from teaching short courses, from selling computer software, and from advising on projects. His expected annual incomes from these sources are $40,000, $25,000, and $18,000, and the respective standard deviations are $2,000, $5,000, and $4,000. Assuming independence, find the mean and standard deviation of his total annual income.

5.70 Ten inspectors are employed by Norway's Kitron Group to check the quality of components produced on an assembly line. For each inspector the number of components that can be checked in a shift can be represented by a random variable with mean 150 and standard deviation 20. Let X represent the number of components checked by an inspector in a shift. Then the total number checked is $10X$, which has a mean of 1,500 and a standard deviation of 200. What is wrong with this argument? Assuming that inspectors' performances are independent of one another, find the mean and standard deviation of the total number of components checked in a shift.

5.71 It is estimated that in normal highway driving, the number of miles that can be covered by automobiles of a particular model on 1 gallon of gasoline can be represented by a random variable with mean 27 and standard deviation 2.5. Twenty-five of these cars, each with 1 gallon of gasoline, are driven independently under highway conditions. Find the mean and standard deviation of the average number of miles that will be achieved by these cars.

5.72 Shirley Johnson, portfolio manager, has asked you to analyze a newly acquired portfolio to determine its mean value and variability. The portfolio consists of 50 shares of Xylophone Music and 40 shares of Yankee Workshop. Analysis of past history indicates that the share price of Xylophone Music has a mean of 25 and a variance of 121. A similar analysis indicates that Yankee has a mean share price of 40 with a variance of 225. Your best evidence indicates that the share prices have a correlation of $+0.5$.

   a. Compute the mean and variance of the portfolio.
   b. Suppose that the correlation between share prices was actually -0.5. Now what are the mean and variance of the portfolio?

5.73 Prairie Flower Cereal has annual sales revenue of $400,000,000. George Severn, a 58-year-old senior vice president, is responsible for production and sales of Nougy 93 Fruity cereal. Daily production in cases is normally distributed, with a mean of 100 and a variance of 625. Daily sales in cases are also normally distributed, with a mean of 100 and a standard deviation of 8. Sales and production have a correlation of 0.60. The selling price per case is $10. The variable production cost per case is $7. The fixed production costs per day are $250.

    a. What is the probability that total revenue is greater than total costs on any day?

    b. Construct a 95% acceptance interval for total sales revenue minus total costs.

5.74 The nation of Olecarl, located in the South Pacific, has asked you to analyze international trade patterns. You first discover that each year it exports 10 units and imports 10 units of wonderful stuff. The price of exports is a random variable with a mean of 100 and a variance of 100. The price of imports is a random variable with a mean of 90 and a variance of 400. In addition, you discover that the prices of imports and exports have a correlation of $\rho = -0.40$. The prices of both exports and imports follow a normal probability density function. Define the balance of trade as the difference between the total revenue from exports and the total cost of imports.

    a. What are the mean and variance of the balance of trade?

    b. What is the probability that the balance of trade is negative?

5.75 You have been asked to determine the probability that the contribution margin for a particular product line

exceeds the fixed cost of $1420. The total number of units sold is a normally distributed random variable with a mean of 400 and a variance of 900, $X \mid N$ (400, 900). The selling price per unit is $9. The total number of units produced is a normally distributed random variable with a mean of 300 and a variance of 900 $Y \sim N(300, 900)$. The variable production cost is $6 per unit. Production and sales have a positive correlation of 0.50.

5.76 The nation of Waipo has recently created an economic development plan that includes expanded exports and imports. It has completed a series of extensive studies of the world economy and Waipo's economic capability, following Waipo's extensive 10-year educational-enhancement program. The resulting model indicates that in the next year exports will be normally distributed with a mean of 100 and a variance of 900 (in billions of Waipo yuan). In addition, imports are expected to be normally distributed with a mean of 105 and a variance of 625 in the same units. The correlation between exports and imports is expected to be +0.70. Define the trade balance as exports minus imports.

    a. Determine the mean and variance of the trade balance (exports minus imports) if the model parameters given above are true.

    b. What is the probability that the trade balance will be positive?

KEY WORDS

- correlation, 233
- covariance, 233
- cumulative distribution function, 202
- cumulative distribution function of the normal distribution, 212
- differences between pairs of random variables, 234
- expected value, 207
- exponential probability distribution, 229

- joint cumulative distribution function, 232
- linear combinations of random variables, 236
- marginal distribution, 233
- mean of X, 208
- probability density function, 203
- probability density function of the normal distribution, 211
- properties of the normal distribution, 211

- range probabilities for normal random variables, 213
- standard deviation, 208
- standard normal distribution, 213
- sums of random variables, 233
- uniform probability distribution, 202
- variance, 208

DATA FILES

- Return on Stock Price 60 month, 239, 246
- Stock Price File, 245, 246

CHAPTER EXERCISES AND APPLICATIONS

5.77 A consultant knows that it will cost him $10,000 to fulfill a particular contract. The contract is to be put out for bids, and he believes that the lowest bid, excluding his own, can be represented by a distribution that is uniform between $8,000 and $20,000. Therefore, if the random variable X denotes the lowest of all other bids

(in thousands of dollars), its probability density function is as follows:

$$f(x) = \begin{cases} 1/12 & \text{for } 8 < x < 20 \\ 0 & \text{for all other values of } x \end{cases}$$

a. What is the probability that the lowest of the other bids will be less than the consultant's cost estimate of $10,000?

b. If the consultant submits a bid of $12,000, what is the probability that he will secure the contract?

c. The consultant decides to submit a bid of $12,000. What is his expected profit from this strategy?

d. If the consultant wants to submit a bid so that his expected profit is as high as possible, discuss how he should go about making this choice.

5.78 The ages of a group of executives attending a convention are uniformly distributed between 35 and 65 years. If the random variable X denotes ages in years, the probability density function is as follows:

$$f(x) = \begin{cases} 1/30 & \text{for } 35 < x < 65 \\ 0 & \text{for all other values of } x \end{cases}$$

a. Graph the probability density function for X.

b. Find and graph the cumulative distribution function for X.

c. Find the probability that the age of a randomly chosen executive in this group is between 40 and 50 years.

d. Find the mean age of the executives in the group.

5.79 The random variable X has probability density function as follows:

$$f(x) = \begin{cases} x & \text{for } 0 < x < 1 \\ 2 - x & \text{for } 1 < x < 2 \\ 0 & \text{for all other values of } x \end{cases}$$

a. Graph the probability density function for X.

b. Show that the density has the properties of a proper probability density function.

c. Find the probability that X takes a value between 0.5 and 1.5.

5.80 An investor puts $2,000 into a deposit account with a fixed rate of return of 10% per year. A second sum of $1,000 is invested in a fund with an expected rate of return of 16% and a standard deviation of 8% per year.

a. Find the expected value of the total amount of money this investor will have after a year.

b. Find the standard deviation of the total amount after a year.

5.81 A hamburger stand sells hamburgers for $1.45 each. Daily sales have a distribution with a mean of 530 and a standard deviation of 69.

a. Find the mean daily total revenues from the sale of hamburgers.

b. Find the standard deviation of total revenues from the sale of hamburgers.

c. Daily costs (in dollars) are given by

$$C = 100 + 0.95X$$

where X is the number of hamburgers sold. Find the mean and standard deviation of daily profits from sales.

5.82 An analyst forecasts corporate earnings, and her record is evaluated by comparing actual earnings with predicted earnings. Define the following:

actual earnings = predicted earnings + forecast error

If the predicted earnings and forecast error are independent of each other, show that the variance of predicted earnings is less than the variance of actual earnings.

5.83 Let X_1 and X_2 be a pair of random variables. Show that the covariance between the random variables $Y_1 = (X_1 + X_2)$ and $Y_2 = (X_1 - X_2)$ is 0 if and only if X_1 and X_2 have the same variance.

5.84 Grade point averages of students on a large campus follow a normal distribution with a mean of 2.6 and a standard deviation of 0.5.

a. One student is chosen at random from this campus. What is the probability that this student has a grade point average higher than 3.0?

b. One student is chosen at random from this campus. What is the probability that this student has a grade point average between 2.25 and 2.75?

c. What is the minimum grade point average needed for a student's grade point average to be among the highest 10% on this campus?

d. A random sample of 400 students is chosen from this campus. What is the probability that at least 80 of these students have grade point averages higher than 3.0?

e. Two students are chosen at random from this campus. What is the probability that at least one of them has a grade point average higher than 3.0?

5.85 Aircon, a South African company, services home air conditioners. It is known that times for service calls follow a normal distribution with mean of 50 minutes and a standard deviation of 12 minutes.

a. What is the probability that a single service call takes more than 56 minutes?

b. What is the probability that a single service call takes between 40 and 60 minutes?

c. The probability is 0.05 that a single service call takes more than how many minutes?

d. Find the shortest range of times that includes 40% of all service calls.

e. A random sample of five service calls is taken. What is the probability that exactly three of them take more than 56 minutes?

5.86 It has been found that times taken by people to complete a particular tax form follow a normal distribution with a mean of 120 minutes and a standard deviation of 40 minutes.

a. What is the probability that a randomly chosen person takes less than 100 minutes to complete this form?

b. What is the probability that a randomly chosen person takes between 80 and 160 minutes to complete this form?

c. One percent of all people take more than how many minutes to complete this form?

d. Two people are chosen at random. What is the probability that at least one of them takes more than 90 minutes to complete this form?

e. Five people are chosen at random. What is the probability that exactly three of them take longer than 90 minutes to complete this form?

f. For the randomly chosen person, state in which of the following ranges (expressed in minutes) the time taken to complete the form is most likely to lie.

100–120,   110–130,   120–140,   130–150

g. For a randomly chosen person, state in which of the following ranges (expressed in minutes) the time to complete the form is least likely to lie.

100–120,   110–130,   120–140,   130–150

5.87 Pizza EATaliano, a pizzeria in Budapest, delivers to residents of Vécsey street, Budapest. Delivery times follow a normal distribution with a mean of 30 minutes and a standard deviation of 6 minutes.

a. What is the probability that a delivery will take between 25 and 35 minutes?

b. The service does not charge for the pizza if delivery takes more than 45 minutes. What is the probability of getting a free pizza from a single order?

c. During a national football tournament, a resident plans to order pizza six consecutive evenings. Assume that these delivery times are independent of each other. What is the probability that the resident will get at least one free pizza?

d. Find the shortest range of times that includes 80% of all deliveries from this service.

e. For a single delivery, state in which of the following ranges (expressed in minutes) the delivery time is most likely to lie.

28–30,   29–31,   30–32,   31–33

f. For a single delivery, state in which of the following ranges (expressed in minutes) the delivery time is least likely to lie.

28–30,   29–31,   30–32,   31–33

5.88 A online video store in the United Kingdom estimates that annual expenditures of members on rentals follow a normal distribution with a mean of £150. It was also found that 20% of all members spend more than £200 in a year. What percentage of members spends more than £220?

5.89 It is estimated that amounts of money spent on gasoline by customers at a gas station in Bristol, England, follow a normal distribution with a standard deviation £3.4. It is also found that 5% of all customers spent more than £30. What percentage of customers spent less than £25?

5.90 A market research organization has found that 45% of all supermarket shoppers refuse to cooperate when questioned by its pollsters. If 1,500 shoppers are approached, what is the probability that fewer than 700 will refuse to cooperate?

5.91 An organization that gives regular seminars on sales motivation methods determines that 55% of its clients have attended previous seminars. From a sample of 500 clients what is the probability that more than half attended previous seminars?

5.92 Helicopteros Sanitarios, an ambulance service in Fuengirola, Spain, receives an average of 20 calls per day during the time period 6 p.m. to 6 a.m. for assistance. For any given day what is the probability that fewer than 15 calls will be received during the 12-hour period? What is the probability that more than 25 calls during the 12-hour period will be received?

5.93 In a large department store a customer-complaints office handles an average of 12 complaints per hour about the quality of service. The distribution is Poisson.

a. What is the probability that in any hour exactly six complaints will be received?

b. What is the probability that more than 20 minutes will elapse between successive complaints?

c. What is the probability that fewer than 5 minutes will elapse between successive complaints?

d. The store manager observes the complaints office for a 30-minute period, during which no complaints are received. He concludes that a talk he gave to his staff on the theme "the customer is always right" has obviously had a beneficial effect. Suppose that, in fact, the talk had no effect. What is the probability of the manager observing the office for a period of 30 minutes or longer with no complaints?

5.94 A fish market in Phnom Penh, Cambodia, offers a large variety of fresh fish on its stands. You want to prepare the popular Khmer dish called amok and found that the average chunk of catfish, one of the main ingredients, on sale has a weight of 3.4 grams, with a standard deviation of 0.7 gram. Assuming the weights of catfish are normally distributed, what is the probability that a randomly selected Khmer dish with a piece of fish weighed more than 4 grams?

5.95 A Godiva Chocolate Shop in Germany offers different sizes and weights of boxes of truffles.

a. Find the probability that a box of truffles weighs between 300 and 305 grams. The mean weight of a box is 300 grams and the standard deviation is 2.4 grams.

b. After a more careful check, the standard deviation was found to be 2.5 grams. Find the new probability.

5.96 A management consultant found that the amount of time per day spent by executives performing tasks that could be done equally well by subordinates followed a normal distribution with a mean of 2.4 hours. It was also found that 10% of executives spent over 3.5 hours per day on tasks of this type. For a random sample of 400 executives, find the probability that more than 80 spend more than 3 hours per day on tasks of this type.

5.97 Guardian Wealth Management, a financial planning company in Geneva, Switzerland, buys and sells a large number of stocks routinely for the various accounts that it manages. Portfolio manager Anne Grace has asked for your assistance in the analysis of the Elias Fund. A portion of this portfolio consists of 12 shares of stock A and 8 shares of stock B. The price of A has a mean of 100 and a variance of 25, while the price of B has a mean of 130 and a variance of 16. The correlation between prices is 0.4.

a. What are the mean and variance of the portfolio value?
b. Anne has been asked to reduce the variance (risk) of the portfolio. She offers to trade the 12 shares of stock A and receives two offers, from which she can select one: 12 shares of stock 1 with a mean price of 100, a variance of 36, and a correlation with the price of stock B equal to −0.4; or 12 shares of stock 2 with a mean price of 100, a variance of 25, uncorrelated with the price of stock B. Which offer should Anne select?

5.98 BNP Paribas, France, buys and sells a large number of stocks routinely for the various accounts that it manages. Portfolio manager Louise Abou has asked for your assistance in the analysis of the Tissandier Fund. A portion of this portfolio consists of 12 shares of stock A and 8 shares of stock B. The price of A has a mean of 100 and a variance of 18, while the price of B has a mean of 130 and a variance of 20. The correlation between prices is 0.3.

a. What are the mean and variance of the portfolio value?
b. Louise has been asked to reduce the variance (risk) of the portfolio. She offers to trade the 12 shares of stock A and receives two offers, from which she can select one: 12 shares of stock 1 with a

mean price of 100, a variance of 20, and a correlation with the price of stock B equal to −0.15; or 12 shares of stock 2 with a mean price of 100, a variance of 10, and a correlation with the price of stock B, equal to 0.45. Which offer should she select?

5.99 PowerChina, a Chinese construction company, is building a large, new retail center at the Chengdu Industrial Development Zone, Sichuan. Yao Minhao, one of the project managers, requests that a pile of sand weighing between 140,000 and 142,000 pounds be placed on the newly constructed driveway. You have been asked to determine the probability that the delivered sand satisfies Yao Minhao's request. You have ordered that one big truck and one small truck be used to deliver the sand. Sand loads in the big truck are normally distributed with a mean of 90,000 and a variance of 1,200,000, and sand loads in the small truck are also normally distributed with a mean weight of 50,000 pounds and a variance of 600,000. From past experience with the sand-loading facility, you know that the weight of sand in the two trucks has a correlation of 0.20. What is the probability that the resulting pile of sand has a weight that is between 140,000 and 142,000 pounds?

5.100 An investment portfolio in Finland specializes in pulp and paper stocks and includes two of them. One is Valmet (mean 0.1; standard deviation .025), and it accounts for 40% of the portfolio shares. The other Finnish pulp and paper manufacturer present in the portfolio is Stora Enso (mean 0.22; standard deviation 0.3), a higher-risk, higher-return investment.

a. What is the expected value and the standard deviation of the portfolio if the coefficient of correlation of the two stocks is 0.7?
b. What will they be if the correlation is 0.4 instead?

PORTFOLIO MINI CASE STUDIES

 Visit www.MyStatLab.com or www.pearson globaleditions.com to access the data files.

The following exercises, or case studies, provide the opportunity to prepare small stock portfolios and to analyze their characteristics in terms of growth and risk. These require considerably more work than other exercises, but they do provide important insights into portfolio computations and analysis. We have deliberately selected stock performance data from before the 2008 crash to avoid the major additional complexities that occur in a major financial collapse. So you will be working with real data on real stocks, but avoiding the situation where it is very difficult if not impossible to predict long term performance from the data.

5.101 Shirley Johnson is developing a new mutual fund portfolio and in the process has asked you to develop the mean and variance for the stock price

that consists of 10 shares of stocks from each of the following firms: Alcoa Inc., Reliant Energy, and Sea Container. Using the data file **Stock Price File,** compute the mean and variance for this portfolio. Prepare the analysis by using means, variances, and covariances for individual stocks following the methods used in Examples 5.16 and 5.17 then confirm your results by obtaining the portfolio price for each year using the computer. Assuming that the portfolio price is normally distributed, determine the narrowest interval that contains 95% of the distribution of portfolio value.

5.102 Zafer Toprak is a developing a new mutual fund portfolio and in the process has asked you to develop the mean and variance for the stock price that consists of 10 shares of stocks from Alcoa Inc., 20 shares from AB Volvo, 10 shares from TCF Financial, and 20 shares from Pentair Inc. Using the data file **Stock Price File,** compute the mean and variance for this portfolio. Prepare the analysis by using means, variances, and covariances for individual stocks following the methods used in Examples 5.16 and 5.17, and then confirm your results by obtaining the portfolio price for each year using the computer. Assuming that the portfolio price is normally distributed, determine the narrowest interval that contains 95% of the distribution of portfolio value.

5.103 Charles Thorson has asked you to determine the mean and variance for a portfolio that consists of 100 shares of stock from each of the following firms: 3M Company, Alcoa, Inc., Intel Corporation, Potlatch Corp., General Motors, and Sea Containers. Using the data file **Stock Price File,** compute the mean and variance for this portfolio. Assuming that the portfolio price is normally distributed determine the narrowest interval that contains 95% of the distribution of portfolio value.

5.104 You have been asked to evaluate the monthly stock price growth for a portfolio which contains the following firms: 3M Company, Alcoa, Inc., Intel Corporation, Potlatch Corp., General Motors, and Sea Containers. The fraction of the portfolio dollar value for each firm will be the same. Using the data file **Return on Stock Price 60 month**, compute the mean and variance for the stock price growth and the covariance between them. Then determine the mean and variance for the entire portfolio.

5.105 Deep Water Financial of Duluth, Minnesota, has asked you to evaluate the stock price growth for a portfolio containing the following firms: General Motors, International Business Machines, Potlatch, Inc., Sea Containers, Ltd., and Tata Communications. Compute the means, variances, and covariances for the stocks. Using the data file **Stock Price File**, compute the mean and variance for a portfolio that represents the five stocks equally. Second, modify the portfolio by removing Potlatch and Sea Containers and including in the portfolio 40% General Motors, 30% International Business Machines, and 30% Tata Communications. Determine the mean and variance for the second portfolio and compare it with the first.

5.106 Consider a portfolio that contains stocks from the following firms: AB Volvo, Pentair, Inc., Reliant Energy, Inc., TCF Financial, 3M Company, and Restoration Hardware. Data for these stocks for a 60-month period (May 2003–April 2008) are contained in the data file **Return on Stock Price 60 month**. Compute the means, variances, and covariances for the monthly stock price growth rate. Determine the mean and variance for a portfolio that contains equal fractions of the six stocks. Construct a second portfolio by removing TCF Financial and Restoration Hardware. Determine the mean and variance of this second portfolio that includes 20% AB Volvo, 30% Pentair, 30% Reliant Energy, and 20% 3M Company. Compare this portfolio with the first and recommend a choice between them.

Appendix: Mathematical Definition of Important Results

1. Readers with knowledge of calculus will recognize that the probability that a random variable lies in a given range is the integral of the probability density function between the endpoints of the range—that is,

$$P(a < X < b) = \int_a^b f(x)\, dx$$

2. Formally, in integral calculus notation,

$$\int_{-\infty}^{\infty} f(x)\, dx = 1$$

The cumulative distribution function is thus the integral

$$F(x_0) = \int_{-\infty}^{x_0} f(x)\, dx$$

It therefore follows that the probability density function is the derivative of the cumulative distribution function—that is,

$$f(x) = \frac{dF(x)}{dx}$$

3. Formally using integral calculus, we express the expected value of the random variable X by

$$E[X] = \int_{-\infty}^{\infty} xf(x)dx$$

and the expected value of the function $g(X)$ by

$$E[g(X)] = \int_{-\infty}^{\infty} g(x)f(x)dx$$

As was shown for discrete random variables,

$$E[g(X)] \neq g(E[X])$$

unless $g(X)$ is a linear function of X, as developed in Section 5.6.

Notice that in forming these expectations, the integral plays the same role as the summation operator in the discrete case.

4. The integral

$$F(x_0) = \int_{-\infty}^{x_0} \frac{1}{\sqrt{2\pi\sigma^2}} e^{-(x-\mu)^2/2\sigma^2} dx$$

does not have a simple algebraic form.

5. Using integral calculus we see that the cumulative exponential distribution is

$$P(t \leq T) = \int_0^T \lambda e^{-\lambda t} dt$$

$$= 1 - e^{-\lambda T}$$

6. Mean and Variance for the Proportion Random Variable

In Chapter 4 we derived the mean and variance for the Bernoulli random variable as

$$E[X] = P$$
$$\sigma_X^2 = P(1 - P)$$

The proportion random variable is the sum of n Bernoulli random variables divided by n and thus

$$\mu = E\left[\frac{\sum_{i=1}^{n} X_i}{n}\right] = E\left[\frac{1}{n}X_1 + \frac{1}{n}X_2 + \cdots + \frac{1}{n}X_n\right] = P$$

$$\sigma^2 = E\left[\frac{\sum_{i=1}^{n} \sigma_i^2}{n^2}\right] = \frac{\sigma_X^2}{n} = \frac{P(1 - P)}{n}$$

REFERENCES

1. Hogg, R., and Craig, A. 1995. *Mathematical Statistics*, 5th ed. Englewood Cliffs, NJ: Prentice Hall.
2. Stock Investor Pro, American Association of Individual Investors, 2007.
3. Taleb, N. N. 2005. *Fooled by Randomness*. New York: Random House.

6

Sampling and Sampling Distributions

Introduction

The remainder of this book will develop various procedures for using statistical sample data to make inferences about statistical populations. This is the core of statistical analysis. Important questions include the following:

   a. How can we use a sample of voters to predict election outcomes?
   b. How can we use a sample of cereal box weights to estimate the mean weight of all cereal boxes produced in a particular week and the probability that a particular box weighs less than some minimum weight?
   c. How can we use a sample of sales receivable for a company to estimate the mean dollar value of all sales receivables held by the company?
   d. How can we use a sample of daily stock market prices to estimate the mean value and the risk for a stock over a 1-year interval?
   e. How can we use a sample of selling prices for homes to estimate the mean selling price for all homes sold in a large city?

These examples indicate some of the vast array of important business and economic questions that can be studied using statistical procedures.

Statistical analysis requires that we obtain a proper sample from a population of items of interest that have measured characteristics. If we do not have a proper sample, then our statistical methods do not work correctly. Thus we must first learn how to obtain a proper sample. Sample observations can be shown to be random variables—if properly chosen. And, statistics such as the sample mean or proportion computed from sample observations are also random variables. Using our understanding of random variables from Chapters 4 and 5, we can make probability statements about the sample statistics computed from sample data and make inferences about the populations from which the samples were obtained. All this leads to some important and amazing results.

But first we need to have probability distributions for the sample statistics—for example, the sampling distribution of the sample mean. That is our task in this chapter, so let us get on with it!

6.1 SAMPLING FROM A POPULATION

A population is generated by a process that can be modeled as a series of random experiments, as presented in Chapter 3. Thus, consider a population of 500,000 cereal boxes, each having a specific weight—which can be treated as an infinite population in terms of our sampling procedures. The weight of each box is determined by the amount of cereal and the cereal density for each box filled. This weight results from a complex process that we will treat as the random experiment noted in Section 3.1, and the weight of each box is treated as a random variable. Similarly, the diameter of engine pistons produced by a set of high production machines in a factory will have small variations. We can treat the production process as a random experiment and the piston diameters as random variables. Similarly, stock prices, daily store sales, and voting choices result from complex processes that can be treated as a random experiment, and the outcomes can be treated as random variables. Populations for various statistical studies are modeled as random variables whose probability distributions have a mean and variance, which are generally not known as we conduct our statistical sampling and analysis.

We will select a sample of observations—realizations of a random variable—from our population and compute sample statistics that will be used to obtain inferences about the population, such as the population mean and variance. To make inferences we need to know the sampling distribution of the observations and the computed sample statistics. The process of determining the sampling distribution uses observations that are obtained as a simple random sample.

Simple Random Sample

A **simple random sample** is chosen by a process that selects a sample of n objects from a population in such a way that each member of the population has the same probability of being selected, the selection of one member is independent of the selection of any other member, and every possible sample of a given size, n, has the same probability of selection. This method is so common that the adjective *simple* is generally dropped, and the resulting sample is called a **random sample**.

Random samples are the ideal. It is important that a sample represent the population as a whole. Random sampling is our insurance policy against allowing personal biases to influence the selection. In a number of real-world sampling studies, analysts develop alternative sampling procedures to lower the costs of sampling. But the basis for determining if these alternative sampling strategies are acceptable is how closely the results approximate those of a simple random sample.

In general, we achieve greater accuracy by carefully obtaining a random sample of the population instead of spending the resources to measure every item. There are three important reasons for this result. First, it is often very difficult to obtain and measure every item in a population, and, even if possible, the cost would be very high for a large population. For example, it is well known among statistical professionals that the census conducted every 10 years produces an undercount, in which certain groups are seriously underrepresented (Hogan 1992). Second, as we learn in this chapter, properly selected samples can be used to obtain measured estimates of population characteristics that are quite close to the actual population values. Third, by using the probability distribution of sample statistics we can determine the error associated with our estimates of population characteristics.

Random sampling can be implemented in many ways. To provide a reference metaphor for our thinking, we could consider placing N population items—for example, the numbered balls used in a bingo or lottery event—in a large barrel and mix them thoroughly. Then, from this well-mixed barrel, we select individual balls from different parts of the barrel. In practice, we often use random numbers to select objects that can be assigned some numerical value. For example, market-research groups may use random numbers to select telephone numbers to call and ask about preferences for a product. Various statistical computer packages and spreadsheets have routines for obtaining random numbers, and these are used for sampling studies. These computer-generated random numbers have the required properties to develop random samples. Organizations that require random samples from large human populations—for example, political candidates seeking to determine voter preference—will use professional sampling firms, which are organized to select and manage the sampling process. Sampling that accurately represents the population requires considerable work by experienced professionals and has a high cost.

We use sample information to make inferences about the parent population. The distribution of all values in this population can be represented by a random variable. It would be too ambitious to attempt to describe the entire population distribution based on a small random sample of observations. However, we can make quite firm inferences about important characteristics of the population distribution, such as the population mean and variance. For example, given a random sample of the fuel consumption for 25 cars of a particular model, we can use the sample mean and variance to make inferential statements about the population mean and variance of fuel consumption. This inference is based on the sample information. We can also ask and answer questions such as this: If the fuel consumption, in miles per gallon, of the population of all cars of a particular model has a mean of 30 and a standard deviation of 2, what is the probability that for a random sample of 25 such cars the sample mean fuel consumption will be less than 29 miles per gallon? We need to distinguish between the population attributes and the random sample attributes. The population mean μ, is a fixed (but unknown) number. We make inferences about this attribute by drawing a random sample from the population and computing the sample mean. For each sample we draw, there will be a different sample mean, and the sample mean can be regarded as a random variable with a probability distribution. The distribution of possible sample means provides a basis for inferential statements about the sample. In this chapter we examine the properties of *sampling distributions*.

Sampling Distributions

Consider a random sample selected from a population that is used to make an inference about some population characteristic, such as the population mean, μ, using a sample statistic, such as the sample mean, $\bar{x}$. We realize that every sample has different observed values and, hence, different sample means. The **sampling distribution** of the sample mean is the probability distribution of the sample means obtained from all possible samples of the same number of observations drawn from the population. Using the sampling distribution we can make an inference about the population mean.

Development of a Sampling Distribution

We illustrate—using a simple example—the concept of a sampling distribution by considering the position of a supervisor with six employees, whose years of experience are

2   4   6   6   7   8

The mean of the years of experience for this population of six employees is

$$\mu = \frac{2 + 4 + 6 + 6 + 7 + 8}{6} = 5.5$$

Two of these employees are to be chosen randomly for a particular work group. In this example we are sampling without replacement in a small population, and thus the first observation has a probability of $1/6$ of being selected, while the second observation has a probability of $1/5$ of being selected. For most applied problems, when sampling from large populations this is not an issue to worry about. If we were selecting from a population of several thousand or more employees, then the change in probability from the first to the second observation would be trivial and is ignored. Thus, we assume that we are sampling with replacement of the first observation in essentially all real-world sampling studies.

Now, let us consider the mean number of years of experience of the two employees chosen randomly from the population of six. Fifteen possible different random samples could be selected. Table 6.1 shows all the possible samples and associated sample means. Note that some samples (such as 2, 6) occur twice because there are two employees with 6 years of experience in the population.

Table 6.1 Samples and Sample Means from the Worker Population Sample Size $n = 2$

SAMPLE	SAMPLE MEAN	SAMPLE	SAMPLE MEAN
2, 4	3.0	4, 8	6.0
2, 6	4.0	6, 6	6.0
2, 6	4.0	6, 7	6.5
2, 7	4.5	6, 8	7.0
2, 8	5.0	6, 7	6.5
4, 6	5.0	6, 8	7.0
4, 6	5.0	7, 8	7.5
4, 7	5.5		

Each of the 15 samples in Table 6.1 has the same probability, $1/15$, of being selected. Note that there are several occurrences of the same sample mean. For example, the sample mean 5.0 occurs three times, and, thus, the probability of obtaining a sample mean of 5.0 is $3/15$. Table 6.2 presents the sampling distribution for the various sample means from the population, and the probability function is graphed in Figure 6.1.

Table 6.2 Sampling Distribution of the Sample Means from the Worker Population Sample Size $n = 2$

SAMPLE MEAN $\bar{x}$	PROBABILITY OF $\bar{x}$
3.0	1/15
4.0	2/15
4.5	1/15
5.0	3/15
5.5	1/15
6.0	2/15
6.5	2/15
7.0	2/15
7.5	1/15

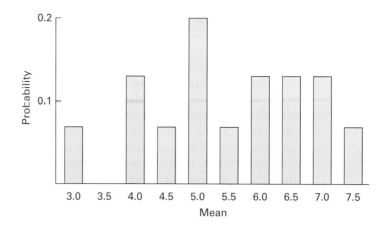

Figure 6.1
Probability Function for the Sampling Distribution of Sample Means: Sample Size $n = 2$

We see that, although the number of years of experience for the six workers ranges from 2 to 8, the possible values of the sample mean have a range from only 3.0 to 7.5. In addition, more of the values lie in the central portion of the range.

Table 6.3 presents similar results for a sample size of $n = 5$, and Figure 6.2 presents the graph for the sampling distribution. Notice that the means are concentrated over a narrower range. These sample means are all closer to the population mean, $\mu = 5.5$. We will always find this to be true—the sampling distribution becomes concentrated closer to the population mean as the sample size increases. This important result provides an important foundation for statistical inference. In the following sections and chapters, we build a set of rigorous analysis tools on this foundation.

Table 6.3 Sampling Distribution of the Sample Means from the Worker Population Sample Size $n = 5$

SAMPLE	$\bar{x}$	PROBABILITY
2, 4, 6, 6, 7	5.0	1/6
2, 4, 6, 6, 8	5.2	1/6
2, 4, 6, 7, 8	5.4	1/3
2, 6, 6, 7, 8	5.8	1/6
4, 6, 6, 7, 8	6.2	1/6

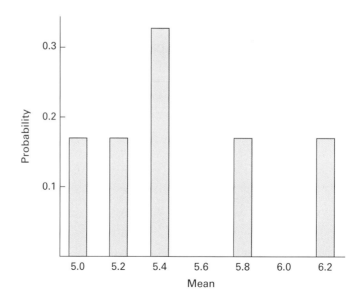

Figure 6.2
Probability Function for the Sampling Distribution of Sample Means: Sample Size $n = 5$

In this section we have developed the basic concept of sampling distributions. Here, the examples have come from a simple discrete distribution where it is possible to define all possible samples of a given sample size. From each possible sample, the sample mean was computed, and the probability distribution of all possible sample means was constructed. From this simple process we discovered that as the sample size increases, the distribution of the sample means—the sampling distribution—becomes more concentrated around the population mean. In most applied statistical work, the populations are very large, and it is not practical or rational to construct the distribution of all possible samples of a given sample size. But by using what we have learned about random variables, we can show that the sampling distributions for samples from all populations have characteristics similar to those shown for our simple discrete population. That result provides the basis for the many useful applications that will be developed in subsequent chapters.

EXERCISES

Basic Exercises

6.1 Suppose you have a traditional die with 6 faces numbered from 1 to 6.

    a. What is the population distribution of numbers on the die?

    b. Determine the sampling distribution of the sample mean of the numbers by rolling the die twice.

6.2 Suppose you are given a die and are asked to roll the die two times and write down the numerical value that results from each roll. You are also told that you can keep rolling as long as you get a different number from what your got on your first roll. Without actually rolling the die, write down the sampling distribution of the sample means.

Application Exercises

6.3 A population contains two million 0s and nine million 1s. What is the approximate sampling distribution of the sample mean in each of the following cases?

    a. The sample size is $n = 4$

    b. The sample size is $n = 50$

    Note: There is a hard way and an easy way to answer this question. We recommend the latter.

6.4 Suppose that a mathematician said that it is impossible to obtain a simple random sample from a real-world population. Therefore, the whole basis for applying statistical procedures to real problems is useless. How would you respond?

6.2 SAMPLING DISTRIBUTIONS OF SAMPLE MEANS

We now develop important properties of the sampling distribution of the sample means. Our analysis begins with a random sample of n observations from a very large population with mean μ and variance σ^2; the sample observations are random variables $X_1, X_2, \ldots, X_n$. Before the sample is observed, there is uncertainty about the outcomes. This uncertainty is modeled by viewing the individual observations as random variables from a population with mean μ and variance σ^2. Our primary interest is in making inferences about the population mean μ. An obvious starting point is the *sample mean*.

Sample Mean

Let the random variables $X_1, X_2, \ldots, X_n$ denote a random sample from a population. The **sample mean** value of these random variables is defined as follows:

$$\overline{X} = \frac{1}{n} \sum_{i=1}^{n} X_i$$

Consider the sampling distribution of the random variable $\overline{X}$. At this point we cannot determine the shape of the sampling distribution, but we can determine the mean and variance of the sampling distribution from basic definitions we learned in Chapters 4 and 5. First, determine the mean of the distribution. In Chapters 4 and 5 we saw that the expectation of a linear combination of random variables is the linear combination of the expectations:

$$E[\overline{X}] = E\left[\frac{1}{n}(X_1 + X_2 + \cdots + X_n)\right] = \frac{n\mu}{n} = \mu$$

Thus, the mean of **the sampling distribution of the sample means** is the population mean. If samples of n random and independent observations are repeatedly and independently drawn from a population, then as the number of samples becomes very large, the mean of the sample means approaches the true population mean. This is an important result of random sampling and indicates the protection that random samples provide against unrepresentative samples. A single sample mean could be larger or smaller than the population mean. However, on average, there is no reason for us to expect a sample mean that is either higher or lower than the population mean. Later in this section this result is demonstrated using computer-generated random samples.

Example 6.1 Expected Value of the Sample Mean (Expected Value)

Compute the expected value of the sample mean for the employee group example previously discussed.

Solution The sampling distribution of the sample means is shown in Table 6.2 and Figure 6.1. From this distribution we can compute the expected value of the sample mean as

$$E[\overline{X}] = \sum \overline{x}P(\overline{x}) = (3.0)\left(\frac{1}{15}\right) + (4.0)\left(\frac{2}{15}\right) + \cdots + (7.5)\left(\frac{1}{15}\right) = 5.5$$

which is the population mean, μ. A similar calculation can be made to obtain the same result using the sampling distribution in Table 6.3.

Now that we have established that the distribution of sample means is centered about the population mean, we wish to determine the variance of the distribution of sample means. Suppose that a random sample of 25 cars yields a mean fuel consumption of $\overline{x} = 31$ miles per gallon. But we also wish to know how good an approximation $\overline{x} = 31$ is of the population mean. We use the variance of the sampling distribution of the sample means to provide the answer.

If the population is very large compared to the sample size, then the distributions of the individual independent random sample observations are the same. In Chapters 4 and 5 we saw that the variance of a linear combination of independent random variables is the sum of the linear coefficients squared times the variance of the random variables. It follows that

$$Var(\overline{X}) = Var\left(\frac{1}{n}X_1 + \frac{1}{n}X_2 + \cdots + \frac{1}{n}X_n\right) = \sum_{i=1}^{n}\left(\frac{1}{n}\right)^2 \sigma_i^2 = \frac{n\sigma^2}{n^2} = \frac{\sigma^2}{n}$$

The variance of the sampling distribution of $\overline{X}$ decreases as the sample size n increases. In effect, this says that larger sample sizes result in more concentrated sampling distributions. The simple example in the previous section demonstrated this result. Thus, larger samples result in greater certainty about our inference of the population mean. This is to be expected. The variance of the sample mean is denoted as $\sigma_{\overline{x}}^2$ and the corresponding standard deviation, called the standard error of $\overline{X}$, is given by the following:

$$\sigma_{\overline{x}} = \frac{\sigma}{\sqrt{n}}$$

If the sample size, n, is not a small fraction of the population size, N, then the individual sample members are not distributed independently of one another, as noted in

Section 6.1. Thus, the observations are not selected independently. It can be shown in this case that the variance of the sample mean is as follows:

$$Var(\overline{X}) = \frac{\sigma^2}{n} \cdot \frac{N - n}{N - 1}$$

The term $(N - n)/(N - 1)$ is often called a **finite population correction factor**. This result is included for completeness since almost all the real sampling studies use large populations. However, there are some examples in business applications, such as auditing, that involve finite populations. We will see examples using the finite population correction factor in Chapters 7 and 9. Careful evaluation of this expression would also dispel the notion that it is important that the sample be a substantial fraction of the population in order to provide useful information. It is the sample size—not the fraction of the population in the sample—that determines the precision—measured by the variance of the sample mean—of results from a random sample.

We have now developed expressions for the mean and variance of the sampling distribution of $\overline{X}$. For most applications the mean and variance define the sampling distribution. Fortunately, we will see that with some additional analysis these results can become very powerful for many practical applications. First, we examine these results under the assumption that the underlying population has a normal probability distribution. Next, we explore the sampling distributions of the sample mean when the underlying population does not have a normal distribution. This second case will provide some very powerful results for many practical applications in business and economics.

First, we consider the results if the parent population—from which the random sample is obtained—has a normal distribution. If the parent population has a normal distribution, then the sampling distribution of the sample means also has a normal distribution. This intuitive conclusion comes from the well-established result that linear functions of normally distributed random variables are also normally distributed. We saw applications of this in the portfolio problems in Chapter 5. With the sampling distribution as a normal probability distribution, we can compute the standard normal Z for the sample mean. In Chapter 5 we saw that we can use the standard normal Z to compute probabilities for any normally distributed random variable. That result also applies for the sample mean.

Standard Normal Distribution for the Sample Means

Whenever the sampling distribution of the sample means is a normal distribution, we can compute a **standardized normal random variable**, Z, that has a mean of 0 and a variance of 1:

$$Z = \frac{\overline{X} - \mu}{\sigma_{\overline{X}}} = \frac{\overline{X} - \mu}{\dfrac{\sigma}{\sqrt{n}}} \tag{6.1}$$

Finally, the results of this section are summarized in the following section.

Results for the Sampling Distribution of the Sample Means

Let $\overline{X}$ denote the sample mean of a random sample of n observations from a population with mean μ_X and variance σ^2.

1. The sampling distribution of $\overline{X}$ has mean

$$E[\overline{X}] = \mu \tag{6.2}$$

2. The sampling distribution of $\overline{X}$ has standard deviation

$$\sigma_{\overline{X}} = \frac{\sigma}{\sqrt{n}} \tag{6.3}$$

This is called the standard error of $\overline{X}$.

3. If the sample size, n, is not small compared to the population size, N, then the standard error of $\overline{X}$ is as follows:

$$\sigma_{\overline{X}} = \frac{\sigma}{\sqrt{n}} \cdot \sqrt{\frac{N-n}{N-1}} \tag{6.4}$$

4. If the parent population distribution is normal and, thus, the sampling distribution of the sample means is normal, then the random variable

$$Z = \frac{X - \mu}{\sigma_{\overline{X}}} \tag{6.5}$$

has a standard normal distribution with a mean of 0 and a variance of 1.

Figure 6.3 shows the sampling distribution of the sample means for sample sizes $n = 25$ and $n = 100$ from a normal distribution. Each distribution is centered on the mean, but as the sample size increases, the distribution becomes concentrated more closely around the population mean because the standard error of the sample mean decreases as the sample size increases. Thus, the probability that a sample mean is a fixed distance from the population mean decreases with increased sample size.

Figure 6.3
Probability Density
Functions for
Sample Means from
a Population with
$\mu = 100$ and $\sigma = 5$

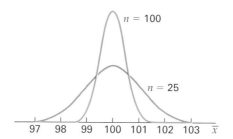

Example 6.2 Executive Salary Distributions (Normal Probability)

Suppose that, based on historical data, we believe that the annual percentage salary increases for the chief executive officers of all midsize corporations are normally distributed with a mean of 12.2% and a standard deviation of 3.6%. A random sample of nine observations is obtained from this population, and the sample mean is computed. What is the probability that the sample mean will be greater than 14.4%?

Solution We know that

$$\mu = 12.2 \quad \sigma = 3.6 \quad n = 9$$

Let $\overline{x}$ denote the sample mean, and compute the standard error of the sample mean:

$$\sigma_{\overline{x}} = \frac{\sigma}{\sqrt{n}} = \frac{3.6}{\sqrt{9}} = 1.2$$

Then we can compute

$$P(\overline{x} > 14.4) = P\left(\frac{\overline{x} - \mu}{\sigma_{\overline{x}}} > \frac{14.4 - 12.2}{1.2}\right) = P(z > 1.83) = 0.0336$$

where Z has a standard normal distribution and the resulting probability is obtained from Appendix Table 1 using the procedures developed in Chapter 5.

From this analysis we conclude that the probability that the sample mean will be greater than 14.4% is only 0.0336. If a sample mean greater than 14.4% actually occurred, we might begin to suspect that the population mean is greater than 12.2% or that we do not have a random sample that properly represents the population probability distribution.

Example 6.3 Spark Plug Life (Normal Probability)

A spark plug manufacturer claims that the lives of its plugs are normally distributed with a mean of 60,000 miles and a standard deviation of 4,000 miles. A random sample of 16 plugs had an average life of 58,500 miles. If the manufacturer's claim is correct, what is the probability of finding a sample mean of 58,500 or less?

Solution To compute the probability, we first need to obtain the standard error of the sample mean:

$$\sigma_{\bar{x}} = \frac{\sigma}{\sqrt{n}} = \frac{4,000}{\sqrt{16}} = 1,000$$

The desired probability is as follows:

$$P(\bar{x} < 58,500) = P\left(\frac{\bar{x} - \mu}{\sigma_{\bar{x}}} < \frac{58,500 - 60,000}{1,000}\right) = P(z < -1.50) = 0.0668$$

Figure 6.4(a) shows the probability density function of $\overline{X}$, with the shaded portion indicating the probability that the sample mean is less than 58,500. In Figure 6.4(b) we see the standard normal density function, and the shaded area indicates the probability that Z is less than -1.5. Note that in comparing these figures, we see that every value of $\overline{X}$ has a corresponding value of Z and that the comparable probability statements provide the same result.

Figure 6.4 (a) Probability That Sample Mean Is Less than 58,500 (b) Probability That a Standard Normal Random Variable Is Less than -1.5

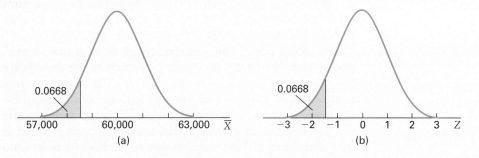

Using the standard normal Z, the normal probability values from Appendix Table 1 and the procedures from Chapter 5, we find that the probability that $\overline{X}$ is less than 58,500 is 0.0668. This probability suggests that if the manufacturer's claims— $\mu = 60,000$ and $\sigma = 4,000$—are true, then a sample mean of 58,500 or less has a small probability. As a result, if we obtained a sample mean less than 58,500 we would be skeptical about the manufacturer's claims. This important concept—using the probability of sample statistics to question the original assumption—is developed more fully in Chapter 9.

Central Limit Theorem

In the previous section we learned that the sample mean $\bar{x}$ for a random sample of size n drawn from a population with a normal distribution with mean μ and variance σ^2, is also normally distributed with mean μ and variance σ^2/n. In this section we present the *central limit theorem*, which shows that the mean of a random sample, drawn from a population with any probability distribution, will be approximately normally distributed with mean μ and variance σ^2/n, given a large-enough sample size. The central limit theorem shows that the sum of n random variables from any probability distribution will be approximately normally distributed if n is large, as noted in the chapter appendix. Since the mean is the sum divided by n, the mean is also approximately normally distributed and that is the result that is important for our statistical applications in business and economics.

This important result enables us to use the normal distribution to compute probabilities for sample means obtained from many different populations. In applied statistics the probability distribution for the population being sampled is often not known, and in particular there is no way to be certain that the underlying distribution is normal.

Statement of the Central Limit Theorem

Let $X_1, X_2, \ldots, X_n$ be a set of n independent random variables having identical distributions with mean μ, variance σ^2, and $\overline{X}$ as the mean of these random variables. As n becomes large, the **central limit theorem** states that the distribution of

$$Z = \frac{\overline{X} - \mu_X}{\sigma_{\overline{X}}}$$

(6.6)

approaches the standard normal distribution.

The central limit theorem provides the basis for considerable work in applied statistical analysis. Many random variables can be modeled as sums or means of independent random variables, and the normal distribution very often provides a good approximation of the true distribution. Thus, the standard normal distribution can be used to obtain probability values for many observed sample means.

The central limit theorem can be applied to both discrete and continuous random variables. In Section 6.3 we use this theorem with discrete random variables to develop probabilities for proportion random variables by treating proportions as a special case of sample means.

A related and important result is the **law of large numbers**, which concludes that given a random sample of size n from a population, the sample mean will approach the population mean as the sample size n becomes large, regardless of the underlying probability distribution. One obvious result is, of course, a sample that contains the entire population. However, we can also see that as the sample size n becomes large, the variance becomes small, until eventually the distribution approaches a constant, which is the sample mean. This result combined with the central limit theorem provides the basis for statistical inference about populations by using random samples.

The central limit theorem has a formal mathematical proof (Hogg and Craig 1995, 246) that is beyond the scope of this book. Results from random sample simulations can also be used to demonstrate the central limit theorem. In addition, there are homework problems that enable you to conduct further experimental analysis.

Monte Carlo Simulations: Central Limit Theorem

We now present some results using Monte Carlo sample simulations to obtain sampling distributions. To obtain each of these results, we selected 1,000 random samples of size n generated from computer simulations produced using Minitab 16 and displayed the sampling distributions of the sample means in histograms. This process constructs empirical sampling distributions of the sample means. Histograms showing the results of these simulations are shown in Figures 6.5, 6.6, and 6.7. The chapter appendix presents the pro-

Figure 6.5

Sampling Distributions from a Distribution of 100 Normally Distributed Random Values with Various Sample Sizes: Demonstration of Central Limit Theorem

Distribution of Random Variable

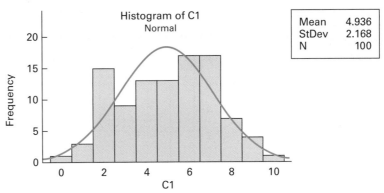

Mean	4.936
StDev	2.168
N	100

Sample Size $n = 10$

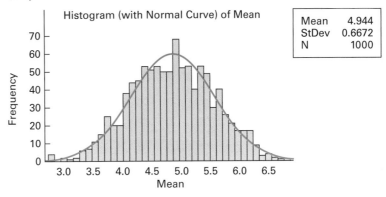

Mean	4.944
StDev	0.6672
N	1000

Sample Size $n = 25$

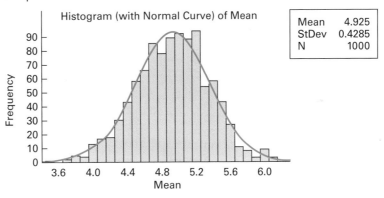

Mean	4.925
StDev	0.4285
N	1000

Sample Size $n = 50$

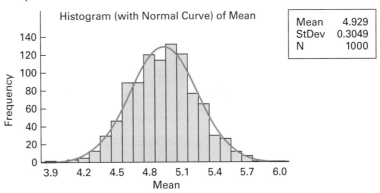

Mean	4.929
StDev	0.3049
N	1000

Figure 6.6
Sampling
Distributions from a
Uniform Distribution
with Various Sample
Sizes; Demonstration
of Central Limit
Theorem

Distribution of Random Variable

Sample Size $n = 10$

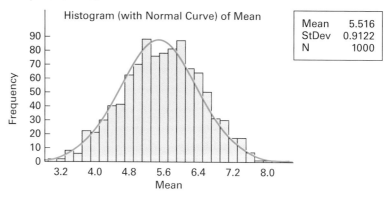

Sample Size $n = 25$

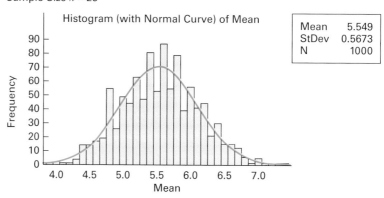

Sample Size $n = 50$

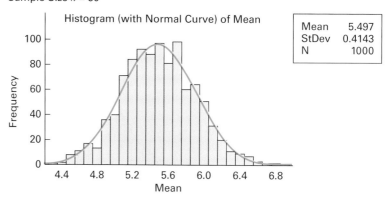

Figure 6.7
Sampling Distributions from a Skewed Distribution with Various Sample Sizes: Demonstration of Central Limit Theorem

Distribution of Random Variable

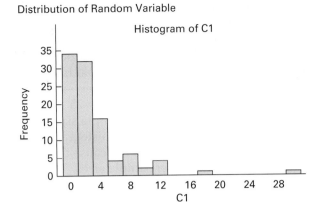

Distribution of Sample means with $n = 10$

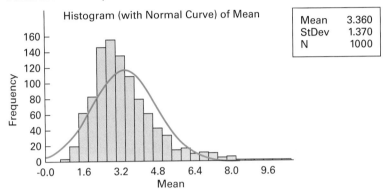

Distribution of Sample Means with $n = 25$

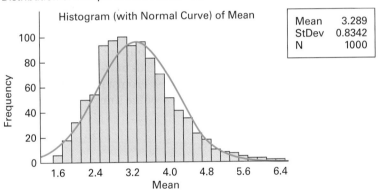

Distribution of Sample Means with $n = 50$

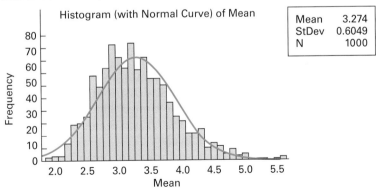

cedure for obtaining sampling distributions for the sample means from any probability distribution. In this appendix and in the data directory, we include a Minitab Computer Macro for you to use in easily obtaining your own sampling distributions.

First, for Figure 6.5 we constructed a population of 100 randomly selected values using the normal distribution. The actual histogram of the population used is shown. Next, we obtained 1,000 random samples—sampling with replacement—from this distribution using sample sizes $n = 10, n = 25$, and $n = 50$. In this example the histograms of the sample means for all three sample sizes follow a normal distribution, as shown by the normal curve drawn over the histogram. Note also that the distributions are narrower with increasing sample size because the standard deviation of the sample means becomes smaller with larger sample sizes. The normal distribution used to obtain the observations had a mean of 5 and a standard deviation of 2. Thus, about 95% of the observations for the histogram should be between 5 ± 2 standard deviations, or between 1 and 9. For the histogram with sample size 50, the interval for 95% of the sample means would be as follows:

$$5 \pm (1.96)\frac{2}{\sqrt{50}}$$

$$5 \pm 0.55$$

$$4.45 \rightarrow 5.55$$

When random samples of various sizes are obtained from a population with known mean and variance, we see that the ranges for various percentages of the sample means follow the results obtained using the normal distribution.

Next we considered a uniform probability distribution over the range 1 to 10. The probability distribution is shown in Figure 6.6. Clearly, the values of the random variable are not normally distributed, since the values are uniform over the range 1 to 10. The distributions of sample means for sample sizes 10, 25, and 50 are shown in Figure 6.6. A normal probability density function with the same mean and variance is sketched over each histogram to provide a comparison. Generally, the distribution of sample means from uniform or symmetric distributions can be closely approximated by the normal distribution, with samples of size 25 or more. The mean for the uniform distribution is 5.5, and the standard deviation is 2.886. From a normal distribution of sample means, with $n = 50$, we would expect to find 95% of the sample means in the following interval:

$$5.5 \pm (1.96)\frac{2.887}{\sqrt{50}}$$

$$5.5 \pm 0.80$$

$$4.70 \rightarrow 6.30$$

An examination of Figure 6.6 indicates that the normal interval applies here.

Next, let us consider a population with a probability distribution that is skewed to the right, as shown in Figure 6.7. Distributions of observations for many business and economic processes are skewed. For example, family incomes and housing prices in a city, state, or country are often skewed to the right. There is typically a small percentage of families with very high incomes, and these families tend to live in expensive houses. Consider the skewed probability distribution shown in Figure 6.7. This could be a distribution of family incomes for the United States of America. Suppose that you wanted to compare the mean income for the United States with the means for a larger set of countries with similar educational levels.

The sampling distributions of mean incomes are compared using random samples of size 10, 25, and 50 from the probability distribution. If you use a random sample of size $n = 10$ and assume that the sample mean is normally distributed, the chances for estimating incorrect probabilities are great. These mistakes in probability estimates are particularly large for sample means in the upper tail of the distribution. Note that the histogram is different from one that would be obtained from a normal distribution. But if you use a random sample of size $n = 25$, your results are much better. Note that the second histogram with $n = 25$ is much closer to a normal distribution. The results are even better when the sample size is 50. Thus, even when the distribution of individual observations is highly skewed, the sampling distribution of sample means closely approximates a normal distribution when $n \geq 50$. The mean and standard deviation for the skewed distribution are 3.3 and 4.247. Thus, the interval from the normal distribution for 95% of the sample means of size $n = 50$ is as follows:

$$3.3 \pm (1.96)\frac{4.247}{\sqrt{50}}$$

$$3.3 \pm 1.18$$

$$2.12 \rightarrow 4.48$$

The distribution of sample means for $n = 50$ appears to fit this interval.

From the random sampling studies in this chapter and our previous study of the binomial distribution, we have additional evidence to demonstrate the central limit theorem. Similar demonstrations have been produced numerous times by many statisticians. As a result, a large body of empirical evidence supports the application of the central limit theorem to realistic statistical applications, in addition to theoretical results. In Chapter 5 we learned that the binomial random variable has an approximate normal distribution as the sample size becomes large.

The question for applied analysis concerns the sample size required to ensure that sample means have a normal distribution. Based on considerable research and experience, we know that, if the distributions are symmetric, then the means from samples of $n = 20$ to 25 are well approximated by the normal distribution. For skewed distributions the required sample sizes are generally somewhat larger. But note that in the previous examples using a skewed distribution a sample size of $n = 50$ produced a sampling distribution of sample means that closely followed a normal distribution.

In this chapter we have begun our discussion of the important statistical problem of making inferences about a population based on results from a sample. The sample mean or sample proportion is often computed to make inferences about population means or proportions. By using the central limit theorem, we have a rationale for applying the techniques we develop in future chapters to a wide range of problems. The following examples show important applications of the central limit theorem.

Example 6.4 Marketing Study for Antelope Coffee (Normal Probability)

Antelope Coffee, Inc., is considering the possibility of opening a gourmet coffee shop in Big Rock, Montana. Previous research has indicated that its shops will be successful in cities of this size if the mean annual family income is above $70,000. It is also assumed that the standard deviation of income is $5,000 in Big Rock, Montana.

A random sample of 36 people was obtained, and the mean income was $72,300. Does this sample provide evidence to conclude that a shop should be opened?

Solution The distribution of incomes is known to be skewed, but the central limit theorem enables us to conclude that the sample mean is approximately normally distributed. To answer the question, we need to determine the probability of obtaining a sample mean of $\bar{x} = 72,300$ or larger if the population mean is $\mu = 70,000$.

First, compute the value for the standardized normal Z statistic:

$$z = \frac{\bar{x} - \mu}{\sigma/\sqrt{n}} = \frac{72,300 - 70,000}{5,000/\sqrt{36}} = 2.76$$

From the standard normal table we find that the probability of obtaining a Z value of 2.76 or larger is 0.0029. Because this probability is very small, we can conclude that it is likely that the population mean income is not $70,000 but is a larger value. This result provides strong evidence that the population mean income is higher than $70,000 and that the coffee shop is likely to be a success. In this example we can see the importance of sampling distributions and the central limit theorem for problem solving.

Acceptance Intervals

In many statistical applications we would like to determine the range within which sample means are likely to occur. Determining such ranges is a direct application of the sampling distribution concepts we have developed. An **acceptance interval** is an interval within which a sample mean has a high probability of occurring, given that we know the population mean and variance. If the sample mean is within that interval, then we can accept the conclusion that the random sample came from the population with the known population mean and variance. Thus acceptance intervals provide an operating rule for process-monitoring applications. The probability that the sample mean is within a particular interval can be computed if the sample means have a distribution that is close to normal. Acceptance intervals can also be computed for nonnormal probability distributions.

Acceptance intervals find wide application for monitoring manufacturing processes to determine if product standards continue to be achieved. For example, in a manufacturing process the manufacturing engineer carefully sets and tests a new process so that it will produce products that all meet the guaranteed specifications for size, weight, or other measured properties. Thus, the mean and standard deviation for the units produced are specified so that the desired product quality will be obtained. In addition, these intervals are also used for monitoring various business activities that involve customer service. Acceptance standards are established that meet stated marketing goals and customer service-level capability. These standards, in turn, are used to develop means, variances, and acceptance intervals to be used for process monitoring (Deming, 1986).

However, it is possible that the process could come out of adjustment and produce defective product items. Changes in either the mean or variance of the critical measurement result from a process that is out of adjustment. Therefore, the process is monitored regularly by obtaining random samples and measuring the important properties, such as the sample mean and variance. If the measured values are within the acceptance interval, then the process is allowed to continue. If the values are not, then the process is stopped and necessary adjustments are made.

Acceptance intervals based on the normal distribution are defined by the distribution mean and variance. From the central limit theorem we know that the sampling distribution of sample means is often approximately normal, and, thus, acceptance intervals based on the normal distribution have wide applications. Assuming that we know the population mean μ and variance σ^2, then we can construct a symmetric acceptance interval

$$\mu \pm z_{\alpha/2}\sigma_{\bar{x}}$$

provided that $\bar{x}$ has a normal distribution and $z_{\alpha/2}$ is the standard normal when the upper tail probability is $\alpha/2$. The probability that the sample mean $\bar{x}$ is included in the interval is $1 - \alpha$.

As noted, acceptance intervals are widely used for quality-control monitoring of various production and service processes. The interval

$$\mu \pm z_{\alpha/2}\sigma_{\bar{x}}$$

is plotted over time (the result is called an X-bar chart) and provides limits for the sample mean $\bar{x}$, given that the population mean is μ. Typically, α is very small ($\alpha < .01$), and standard practice in U.S. industries is to use $z = 3$. This is the source for the term *Six Sigma* used for various quality-assurance programs (Hiam, 1992). If the sample mean is outside the acceptance interval, then we suspect that the population mean is not μ. In a typical project engineers will take various steps to achieve a small variance for important product measurements that are directly related to product quality. Once the process has been adjusted so that the variance is small, an acceptance interval for a sample mean—called a *control interval*—is established in the form of a control chart (Montgomery, 1997). Then periodic random samples are obtained and compared to the control interval. If the sample mean is within the control interval, it is concluded that the process is operating properly and no action is taken. But if the sample mean is outside the control interval, it is concluded that the process is not operating properly and steps are taken to correct the process.

Example 6.5 Monitoring Health Insurance Claims (Acceptance Interval)

Charlotte King, vice president of financial underwriting for a large health insurance company, wishes to monitor daily insurance claim payments to determine if the average dollar value of subscriber claims is stable, increasing, or decreasing. The value of individual claims varies up and down from one day to the next, and it would be naive to draw conclusions or change operations based on these daily variations. But at some point the changes become substantial and should be noted. She has asked you to develop a procedure for monitoring the dollar value of individual claims.

Solution Your initial investigation indicates that health insurance claims are highly skewed, with a small number of very large claims for major medical procedures. To develop a monitoring process, you first need to determine the historical mean and variance for individual claims. After some investigation you also find that the mean for random samples of $n = 100$ claims is normally distributed. Based on past history the mean, μ, level for individual claims is $6,000 with a standard deviation of $\sigma = 2,000$.

Using this information you proceed to develop a claims-monitoring system that obtains a random sample of 100 claims each day and computes the sample mean. The company has established a 95% acceptance interval for monitoring claims. An interval defined for the standard normal using $Z = \pm 1.96$ includes 95% of the values. From this you compute the 95% acceptance interval for insurance claims as follows:

$$6,000 \pm 1.96 \frac{2,000}{\sqrt{100}}$$

$$6,000 \pm 392$$

Each day the sample mean for 100 randomly selected claims is computed and compared to the acceptance interval. If the sample mean is inside the interval 5,608 to 6,392, Ms. King can conclude that claims are not deviating from the historical standard. You explain to her that if the claims are following the historical standard then 95% of the time the sample mean will be within the interval. The sample mean could be outside the interval even if the population mean is 6,000 with probability 0.05. In those cases Ms. King's conclusion that the mean claim level has changed from the historical standard would be wrong and this error would occur 5% of the time. Therefore if the sample mean is outside the interval there is strong evidence to conclude that the claims are no longer following the historical standard. To simplify the analysis, you instruct the analysts to plot the daily claims mean on a control chart, shown in Figure 6.8. Using this control chart Charlotte King and her staff can study the patterns of the sample means and determine if there are trends and if means are outside of the boundaries that indicate standard claims' behavior.

Figure 6.8 Ninety-Five Percent Acceptance Interval for Health Insurance Claims

Example 6.6 Prairie View Cereal Package Weights (Acceptance Intervals)

Prairie View Cereals. Inc., is concerned about maintaining correct package weights at its cereal-packaging facility. The package label weight is 440 grams, and company officials are interested in monitoring the process to ensure that package weights are stable.

Solution A random sample of five packages is collected every 30 minutes, and each package is weighed electronically. The mean weight is then plotted on an X-bar control chart such as the one in Figure 6.9. When an X-bar chart is used for monitoring limits on product quality—this usage is practiced by numerous highly successful firms—the central limit theorem provides the rationale for using the normal distribution to establish limits for the small sample means. Thus, a fundamentally important statistical theory drives a key management process.

Figure 6.9 X-Bar Chart For Cereal-Package Weight

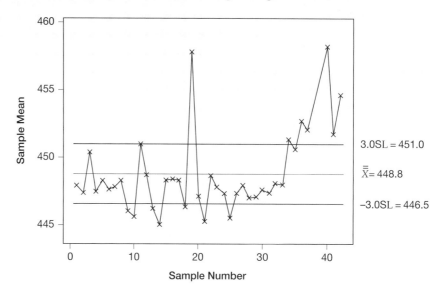

In this chart SL is the standard deviation for the sample mean. The upper and lower limits are set at $\pm 3\sigma_{\bar{X}}$ instead of $\pm 1.96\sigma_{\bar{X}}$, or 95%, the acceptance interval used in the previous example. The interval $\bar{X} \pm 3\sigma_{\bar{X}}$ (Minitab labels the mean for the entire population as $\bar{\bar{X}}$) includes almost all the sample means under the normal distribution, given a stable mean and variance. Thus, a sample mean outside the control limits indicates that something has changed and that adjustments should be made. Given the number of points outside the acceptance interval, we recommend that the process be stopped and adjusted.

EXERCISES

Basic Exercises

6.5 Given a population with a mean of $\mu = 105$ and a variance of $\sigma^2 = 16$, the central limit theorem applies when the sample size is $n \geq 25$. A random sample of size $n = 25$ is obtained.

a. What are the mean and variance of the sampling distribution for the sample means?

b. What is the probability that $\bar{x} > 106$?

c. What is the probability that $104 \leq \bar{x} \leq 106$?

d. What is the probability that $\bar{x} \leq 105.5$?

6.6 Given a population with a mean of $\mu = 150$ and a variance of $\sigma^2 = 1,600$, the central limit theorem applies when the sample size is $n \geq 25$. A random sample of size $n = 36$ is obtained.

a. What are the mean and variance of the sampling distribution for the sample means?

b. What is the probability that $\bar{x} > 155$?
c. What is the probability that $145 \le \bar{x} \le 160$?
d. What is the probability that $\bar{x} \le 165$?

6.7 Given a population with a mean of $\mu = 104$ and a variance of $\sigma^2 = 81$, the central limit theorem applies when the sample size is $n \ge 25$. A random sample of size $n = 25$ is obtained.

a. What are the mean and variance of the sampling distribution for the sample means?
b. What is the probability that $\bar{x} > 106$?
c. What is the probability that $102 \le \bar{x} \le 105$?
d. What is the probability that $\bar{x} \le 104.5$?

6.8 Given a population with mean $\mu = 400$ and variance $\sigma^2 = 1,600$, the central limit theorem applies when the sample size is $n \ge 25$. A random sample of size $n = 35$ is obtained.

a. What are the mean and variance of the sampling distribution for the sample means?
b. What is the probability that $\bar{x} > 412$?
c. What is the probability that $393 \le \bar{x} \le 407$?
d. What is the probability that $\bar{x} \le 389$?

6.9 When a production process is operating correctly, the number of units produced per hour has a normal distribution with a mean of 105 and a standard deviation of 20. A random sample of 25 different hours was taken.

a. Find the mean of the sampling distribution of the sample means.
b. Find the variance of the sampling distribution of the sample mean.
c. Find the standard error of the sampling distribution of the sample mean.
d. What is the probability that the sample mean exceeds 106 units?

Application Exercises

6.10 The lifetimes of lightbulbs produced by a particular manufacturer have a mean of 1,200 hours and a standard deviation of 400 hours. The population distribution is normal. Suppose that you purchase nine bulbs, which can be regarded as a random sample from the manufacturer's output.

a. What is the mean of the sample mean lifetime?
b. What is the variance of the sample mean?
c. What is the standard error of the sample mean?
d. What is the probability that, on average, those nine lightbulbs have lives of fewer than 1,050 hours?

6.11 The fuel consumption, in miles per gallon, of all cars of a particular model has a mean of 21 and a standard deviation of 5. The population distribution can be assumed to be normal. A random sample of these cars is taken.

a. Find the probability that sample mean fuel consumption will be fewer than 20 miles per gallon if
  i. a sample of 1 observation is taken.
  ii. a sample of 4 observations is taken.
  iii. a sample of 9 observations is taken.
b. Explain why the three answers in part (a) differ in the way they do. Draw a graph to illustrate your reasoning.

6.12 The mean selling price of senior condominiums in Green Valley over a year was $215,000. The population standard deviation was $25,000. A random sample of 100 new unit sales was obtained.

a. What is the probability that the sample mean selling price was more than $210,000?
b. What is the probability that the sample mean selling price was between $213,000 and $217,000?
c. What is the probability that the sample mean selling price was between $214,000 and $216,000?
d. Without doing the calculations, state in which of the following ranges the sample mean selling price is most likely to lie:
$213,000 to $215,000; $214,000 to $216,000; $215,000 to $217,000; $216,000 to $218,000
e. Suppose that, after you had done these calculations, a friend asserted that the population distribution of selling prices of senior condominiums in Green Valley was almost certainly not normal. How would you respond?

6.13 Candidates for employment at a city fire department are required to take a written aptitude test. Scores on this test are normally distributed with a mean of 280 and a standard deviation of 60. A random sample of nine test scores was taken.

a. What is the standard error of the sample mean score?
b. What is the probability that the sample mean score is less than 270?
c. What is the probability that the sample mean score is more than 250?
d. Suppose that the population standard deviation is, in fact, 40, rather than 60. Without doing the calculations, state how this would change your answers to parts (a), (b), and (c). Illustrate your conclusions with the appropriate graphs.

6.14 A random sample of 16 junior managers in the offices of corporations in a large city center was taken to estimate average daily commuting time for all such managers. Suppose that the population times have a normal distribution with a mean of 87 minutes and a standard deviation of 22 minutes.

a. What is the standard error of the sample mean commuting time?
b. What is the probability that the sample mean is fewer than 100 minutes?
c. What is the probability that the sample mean is more than 80 minutes?
d. What is the probability that the sample mean is outside the range 85 to 95 minutes?
e. Suppose that a second (independent) random sample of 50 junior managers is taken. Without doing the calculations, state whether the probabilities in parts (b), (c), and (d) would be higher, lower, or the same for the second sample. Sketch graphs to illustrate your answers.

6.15 A company produces breakfast cereal. The true mean weight of the contents of its cereal packages is 20 ounces, and the standard deviation is 0.6 ounce. The population distribution of weights is normal. Suppose that you purchase four packages, which can be regarded as a random sample of all those produced.

   a. What is the standard error of the sample mean weight?

   b. What is the probability that, on average, the contents of these four packages will weigh fewer than 19.7 ounces?

   c. What is the probability that, on average, the contents of these four packages will weigh more than 20.6 ounces?

   d. What is the probability that, on average, the contents of these four packages will weigh between 19.5 and 20.5 ounces?

   e. Two of the four boxes are chosen at random. What is the probability that the average contents of these two packages will weigh between 19.5 and 20.5 ounces?

6.16 Assume that the standard deviation of monthly rents paid by students in a particular town is $40. A random sample of 100 students was taken to estimate the mean monthly rent paid by the whole student population.

   a. What is the standard error of the sample mean monthly rent?

   b. What is the probability that the sample mean exceeds the population mean by more than $5?

   c. What is the probability that the sample mean is more than $4 below the population mean?

   d. What is the probability that the sample mean differs from the population mean by more than $3?

6.17 The times spent studying by students in the week before final exams follows a normal distribution with standard deviation 8 hours. A random sample of four students was taken in order to estimate the mean study time for the population of all students.

   a. What is the probability that the sample mean exceeds the population mean by more than 2 hours?

   b. What is the probability that the sample mean is more than 3 hours below the population mean?

   c. What is the probability that the sample mean differs from the population mean by more than 4 hours?

   d. Suppose that a second (independent) random sample of 10 students was taken. Without doing the calculations, state whether the probabilities in parts (a), (b), and (c) would be higher, lower, or the same for the second sample.

6.18 An industrial process produces batches of a chemical whose impurity levels follow a normal distribution with standard deviation 1.6 grams per 100 grams of chemical. A random sample of 100 batches is selected in order to estimate the population mean impurity level.

   a. The probability is 0.05 that the sample mean impurity level exceeds the population mean by how much?

   b. The probability is 0.10 that the sample mean impurity level is below the population mean by how much?

   c. The probability is 0.15 that the sample mean impurity level differs from the population mean by how much?

6.19 The price-earnings ratios for all companies whose shares are traded on the Tokyo Stock Exchange follow a normal distribution with a standard deviation of 3.5. A random sample of these companies is selected in order to estimate the population mean price-earnings ratio.

   a. How large a sample is necessary in order to ensure that the probability that the sample mean differs from the population mean by more than 0.8 is less than 0.05?

   b. Without doing the calculations, state whether a larger or smaller sample size compared to the sample size in part (a) would be required to guarantee that the probability of the sample mean differing from the population mean by more than 0.8 is less than 0.10.

   c. Without doing the calculations, state whether a larger or smaller sample size compared to the sample size in part a would be required to guarantee that the probability of the sample mean differing from the population mean by more than 0.4 hours is less than 0.05.

6.20 The number of hours spent studying by students on a large campus in the week before final exams follows a normal distribution with a standard deviation of 8.4 hours. A random sample of these students is taken to estimate the population mean number of hours studying.

   a. How large a sample is needed to ensure that the probability that the sample mean differs from the population mean by more than 2.0 hours is less than 0.05?

   b. Without doing the calculations, state whether a larger or smaller sample size compared to the sample size in part (a) would be required to guarantee that the probability of the sample mean differing from the population mean by more than 2.0 hours is less than 0.10.

   c. Without doing the calculations, state whether a larger or smaller sample size compared to the sample size in part (a) would be required to guarantee that the probability of the sample mean differing from the population mean by more than 1.5 hours is less than 0.05.

6.21 A chain of coffee shops, BeanBoy, is experiencing financial pressures due to increased competition for its numerous urban coffee shops. Total sales revenue has dropped by 15% and BeanBoy wishes to establish a sales monitoring process to identify shops that are underperforming. Historically, the daily mean sales for a shop have been €13,000 with a variance of 1,000,000. BeanBoy's monitoring plan will take a random sample of 8 days' sales per month and use the sample mean sales to identify shops that are underperforming. Establish the lower limit sales such that only 5% of the shops would have sample sales mean below this value.

6.22 In taking a sample of n observations from a population of N members, the variance of the sampling distribution of the sample means is as follows:

$$\sigma_{\bar{x}}^2 = \frac{\sigma_x^2}{n} \cdot \frac{N-n}{N-1}$$

The quantity $\dfrac{(N-n)}{(N-1)}$ is called the *finite population correction factor*.

a. To get some feeling for possible magnitudes of the finite population correction factor, calculate it for samples of $n = 20$ observations from populations of members: 20, 40, 100, 1,000, 10,000.
b. Explain why the result found in part a, is precisely what one should expect on intuitive grounds.
c. Given the results in part a, discuss the practical significance of using the finite-population correction factor for samples of 20 observations from populations of different sizes.

6.23 Suppose Incheon, a city in South Korea, has 500 real estate agents. The mean value of the properties sold in a year by these agents is $550,000, and the standard deviation is $200,000. A random sample of 100 agents is selected, and the value of the properties they sold in a year is recorded.

a. What is the standard error of the sample mean?
b. What is the probability that the sample mean exceeds $557,000?
c. What is the probability that the sample mean exceeds $534,000?
d. What is the probability that the sample mean is between $541,000 and $559,000?

6.24 An English literature course was taken by 250 students. Each member of a random sample of 50 of these students was asked to estimate the amount of time he or she spent on the previous week's assignment. Suppose that the population standard deviation is 30 minutes.

a. What is the probability that the sample mean exceeds the population mean by more than 2.5 minutes?
b. What is the probability that the sample mean is more than 5 minutes below the population mean?
c. What is the probability that the sample mean differs from the population mean by more than 10 minutes?

6.25 For an audience of 600 people attending a concert, the average time on the journey to the concert was 32 minutes, and the standard deviation was 10 minutes. A random sample of 150 audience members was taken.

a. What is the probability that the sample mean journey time was more than 31 minutes?
b. What is the probability that the sample mean journey time was less than 33 minutes?
c. Construct a graph to illustrate why the answers to parts (a) and (b) are the same.
d. What is the probability that the sample mean journey time was not between 31 and 33 minutes?

6.3 SAMPLING DISTRIBUTIONS OF SAMPLE PROPORTIONS

In Section 4.4 we developed the binomial distribution as the sum of n independent Bernoulli random variables, each with probability of success P. To characterize the distribution, we need a value for P. Here, we indicate how we can use the sample proportion to obtain inferences about the population proportion. The proportion random variable has many applications, including percent market share, percent successful business investments, and outcomes of elections.

Sample Proportion
Let X be the number of successes in a binomial sample of n observations with the parameter P. The parameter is the proportion of the population members that have a characteristic of interest. We define the **sample proportion** as follows:

$$\hat{p} = \frac{X}{n} \tag{6.7}$$

X is the sum of a set of n independent Bernoulli random variables, each with probability of success P. As a result, $\hat{p}$ is the mean of a set of independent random variables, and the results we developed in the previous sections for sample means apply. In addition, the central limit theorem can be used to argue that the probability distribution for $\hat{p}$ can be modeled as a normally distributed random variable.

There is also a variation of the law of large numbers that applies when sampling to determine the percent of successes in a large population that has a known proportion P of success. If random samples are obtained from the population and the success or failure is determined for each observation, then the sample proportion of success approaches P as the sample size increases. Thus, we can make inferences about the population proportion using the sample proportion and the sample proportion will get closer as our sample size increases. However, the difference between the expected number of sample successes—the sample size multiplied by P—and the number of successes in the sample might actually increase.

In Section 5.4 it was shown that the number of successes in a binomial distribution and the proportion of successes have a distribution that is closely approximated by a normal distribution (see Figures 5.23 and 5.24). This provides a very close approximation when $nP(1 - P) > 5$.

The mean and variance of the sampling distribution of the sample proportion $\hat{p}$ can be obtained from the mean and variance of the number of successes, X:

$$E[X] = nP \quad Var(X) = nP(1 - P)$$

Thus,

$$E[\hat{p}] = E\left[\frac{X}{n}\right] = \frac{1}{n}E[X] = P$$

We see that the mean of the distribution of $\hat{p}$ is the population proportion, P.

The variance of $\hat{p}$ is the variance of the population distribution of the Bernoulli random variables divided by n:

$$\sigma_{\hat{p}}^2 = Var\left(\frac{X}{n}\right) = \frac{1}{n^2} Var(X) = \frac{P(1 - P)}{n}$$

The standard deviation of $\hat{p}$, which is the square root of the variance, is called its standard error.

Since the distribution of the sample proportion is approximately normal for large sample sizes, we can obtain a standard normal random variable by subtracting P from $\hat{p}$ and dividing by the standard error.

Sampling Distribution of the Sample Proportion

Let $\hat{p}$ be the sample proportion of successes in a random sample from a population with proportion of success P. Then,

1. the sampling distribution of $\hat{p}$ has mean P:

$$E[\hat{p}] = P \tag{6.8}$$

2. the sampling distribution of $\hat{p}$ has standard deviation

$$\sigma_{\hat{p}} = \sqrt{\frac{P(1 - P)}{n}} \tag{6.9}$$

3. and, if the sample size is large, the random variable

$$Z = \frac{\hat{p} - P}{\sigma_{\hat{p}}} \tag{6.10}$$

is approximately distributed as a standard normal. This approximation is good if

$$nP(1 - P) > 5$$

Similar to the results from the previous section, we see that the standard error of the sample proportion, $\hat{p}$, decreases as the sample size increases and the distribution becomes more concentrated, as seen in Figure 6.10, using samples from a population with 80% success rate. This is expected because the sample proportion is a sample mean. With larger sample sizes our inferences about the population proportion improve. From the central limit theorem we know that the binomial distribution can be approximated by the normal distribution with corresponding mean and variance. We see this result in the following examples.

Figure 6.10
Probability Density Functions for the Sample Proportions with $P = 0.80$

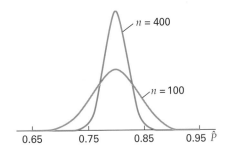

Example 6.7 Evaluation of Home Electric Wiring (Probability of Sample Proportion)

A random sample of 270 homes was taken from a large population of older homes to estimate the proportion of homes with unsafe wiring. If, in fact, 20% of the homes have unsafe wiring, what is the probability that the sample proportion will be between 16% and 24%?

Solution For this problem we have the following:

$$P = 0.20 \quad n = 270$$

We can compute the standard deviation of the sample proportion, $\hat{p}$, as follows:

$$\sigma_{\hat{p}} = \sqrt{\frac{P(1 - P)}{n}} = \sqrt{\frac{0.20(1 - 0.20)}{270}} = 0.024$$

The required probability is

$$P(0.16 < \hat{p} < 0.24) = P\left(\frac{0.16 - P}{\sigma_{\hat{p}}} < \frac{\hat{p} - P}{\sigma_{\hat{p}}} < \frac{0.24 - P}{\sigma_{\hat{p}}}\right)$$

$$= P\left(\frac{0.16 - 0.20}{0.024} < Z < \frac{0.24 - 0.20}{0.024}\right)$$

$$= P(-1.67 < Z < 1.67)$$

$$= 0.9050$$

where the probability for the Z interval is obtained using Appendix Table 1.

Thus, we see that the probability is 0.9050 that the sample proportion is within the interval 0.16 to 0.24, given $P = 0.20$, and a sample size of $n = 270$. This interval can be called a 90.50% acceptance interval. We can also note that if the sample proportion was actually outside this interval, we might begin to suspect that the population proportion, P, is not 0.20.

Example 6.8 Business Course Selection (Probability of Sample Proportion)

It has been estimated that 43% of business graduates believe that a course in business ethics is very important for imparting ethical values to students (David, Anderson, and Lawrimore 1990). Find the probability that more than one-half of a random sample of 80 business graduates have this belief.

Solution We are given that

$$P = 0.43 \quad n = 80$$

We first compute the standard deviation of the sample proportion:

$$\sigma_{\hat{p}} = \sqrt{\frac{P(1 - P)}{n}} = \sqrt{\frac{0.43(1 - 0.43)}{80}} = 0.055$$

Then the required probability can be computed as follows:

$$P(\hat{p} > 0.50) = P\left(\frac{\hat{p} - P}{\sigma_{\hat{p}}} > \frac{0.50 - P}{\sigma_{\hat{p}}}\right)$$

$$= P\left(Z > \frac{0.50 - 0.43}{0.055}\right)$$

$$= P(Z > 1.27)$$

$$= 0.1020$$

This probability, as shown in Figure 6.11, was obtained from Appendix Table 1. The probability of having more than one-half of the sample believing in the value of business ethics courses is approximately 0.1.

Figure 6.11 The Probability that a Standard Normal Random Variable Exceeds 1.27

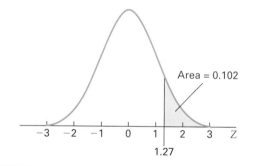

EXERCISES

Basic Exercises

6.26 Suppose that we have a population with proportion $P = 0.30$ and a random sample of size $n = 200$ drawn from the population.

a. What is the probability that the sample proportion is greater than 0.28?

b. What is the probability that the sample proportion is less than 0.25?

c. What is the probability that the sample proportion is between 0.22 and 0.40?

6.27 Suppose that we have a population with proportion $P = 0.20$ and a random sample of size $n = 100$ drawn from the population.

a. What is the probability that the sample proportion is greater than 0.18?

b. What is the probability that the sample proportion is less than 0.15?

c. What is the probability that the sample proportion is between 0.17 and 0.32?

6.28 Suppose that we have a population with proportion $P = 0.55$, and a random sample of size $n = 150$ drawn from the population.

a. What is the probability that the sample proportion is more than 0.60?

b. What is the probability that the sample proportion is less than 0.52?

c. What is the probability that the sample proportion is between 0.51 and 0.59?

6.29 Suppose that we have a population with proportion $P = 0.30$, and a random sample of size $n = 900$ drawn from the population.

a. What is the probability that the sample proportion is more than 0.32?

b. What is the probability that the sample proportion is less than 0.29?

c. What is the probability that the sample proportion is between 0.28 and 0.33?

Application Exercises

6.30 In 1992, Canadians voted in a referendum on a new constitution. In the province of Quebec, 42.4% of those who voted were in favor of the new constitution. A random sample of 100 voters from the province was taken.

a. What is the mean of the distribution of the sample proportion in favor of a new constitution?

b. What is the variance of the sample proportion?

c. What is the standard error of the sample proportion?

d. What is the probability that the sample proportion is more than 0.5?

6.31 Suppose that 80% of all tax returns in your country lead to a refund. A random sample of 100 tax returns is taken.

a. What is the mean of the distribution of the sample proportion of returns leading to refunds?

b. What is the variance of the sample proportion?

c. What is the standard error of the sample proportion?

d. What is the probability that the sample proportion exceeds 0.90?

6.32 A record store owner finds that 20% of customers entering her store make a purchase. One morning 180 people, who can be regarded as a random sample of all customers, enter the store.

a. What is the mean of the distribution of the sample proportion of customers making a purchase?

b. What is the variance of the sample proportion?

c. What is the standard error of the sample proportion?

d. What is the probability that the sample proportion is less than 0.15?

6.33 An administrator for a large group of hospitals believes that of all patients 30% will generate bills that become at least 2 months overdue. A random sample of 200 patients is taken.

a. What is the standard error of the sample proportion that will generate bills that become at least 2 months overdue?

b. What is the probability that the sample proportion is less than 0.25?

c. What is the probability that the sample proportion is more than 0.33?

d. What is the probability that the sample proportion is between 0.27 and 0.33?

6.34 A corporation receives 120 applications for positions from recent college graduates in business. Assuming that these applicants can be viewed as a random sample of all such graduates, what is the probability that between 35% and 45% of them are women if 40% of all recent college graduates in business are women?

6.35 A charity has found that 42% of all donors from last year will donate again this year. A random sample of 300 donors from last year was taken.

a. What is the standard error of the sample proportion who will donate again this year?

b. What is the probability that more than half of these sample members will donate again this year?

c. What is the probability that the sample proportion is between 0.40 and 0.45?

d. Without doing the calculations, state in which of the following ranges the sample proportion is more likely to lie: 0.39 to 0.41, 0.41 to 0.43, 0.43 to 0.45, or 0.45 to 0.46.

6.36 A corporation is considering a new issue of convertible bonds. Management believes that the offer terms will be found attractive by 20% of all its current stockholders. Suppose that this belief is correct. A random sample of 130 current stockholders is taken.

a. What is the standard error of the sample proportion who find this offer attractive?

b. What is the probability that the sample proportion is more than 0.15?

c. What is the probability that the sample proportion is between 0.18 and 0.22?

d. Suppose that a sample of 500 current stockholders had been taken. Without doing the calculations, state whether the probabilities in parts (b) and (c) would have been higher, lower, or the same as those found.

6.37 A store has determined that 30% of all lawn mower purchasers will also purchase a service agreement. In 1 month 280 lawn mowers are sold to customers, who can be regarded as a random sample of all purchasers.

a. What is the standard error of the sample proportion of those who will purchase a service agreement?

b. What is the probability that the sample proportion will be less than 0.32?

c. Without doing the calculations, state in which of the following ranges the sample proportion is most likely to be: 0.29 to 0.31, 0.30 to 0.32, 0.31 to 0.33, or 0.32 to 0.34.

6.38 A random sample of 100 voters is taken to estimate the proportion of a state's electorate in favor of increasing the gasoline tax to provide additional revenue for highway repairs. What is the largest value that the standard error of the sample proportion in favor of this measure can take?

6.39 Ahead of the 2019 Indian general election, a random sample of 100 voters is taken to estimate the proportion of a state's electorate in favor of increasing the fuel tax to provide additional revenue for highway repairs. Suppose that it is decided that a sample of 100 voters is too small to provide a sufficiently reliable estimate of the population proportion. It is required instead that the probability that the sample proportion differs from the population proportion (whatever its value) by more than 0.07 should not exceed 0.075. How large a sample is needed to guarantee that this requirement is met?

6.40 A company wants to estimate the proportion of people who are likely to purchase electric shavers from those who watch the FIFA World Cup. A random sample obtained information from 150 people who were identified as persons who watch football telecasts. Suppose that the proportion of those likely to purchase electric shavers in the population who watch the telecast is 0.30.

    a. The probability is 0.15 that the sample proportion watching the telecast exceeds the population proportion by how much?

    b. The probability is 0.01 that the sample proportion is lower than the population proportion by how much?

    c. The probability is 0.20 that the sample proportion differs from the population proportion by how much?

6.41 Suppose that in Europe, 55% of all adults believe that a major overhaul of the economy's health care delivery system is essential. What is the probability that more than 65% of a random sample of 150 adult Europeans would hold this belief?

6.42 Suppose that 50% of all adult Americans believe that federal budget deficits at recent levels cause long-term harm to the nation's economy. What is the probability that more than 58% of a random sample of 250 adult Americans would hold this belief?

6.43 A journalist wanted to learn the views of the chief executive officers of the 500 largest U.S. corporations on program trading of stocks. In the time available, it was possible to contact only a random sample of 81 of these chief executive officers. If 55% of all the population members believe that program trading should be banned, what is the probability that less than half the sample members hold this view?

6.44 Forty percent of students at small colleges have brought their own personal computers to campus. A random sample of 120 entering freshmen was taken.

    a. What is the standard error of the sample proportion bringing their own personal computers to campus?

    b. What is the probability that the sample proportion is less than 0.33?

    c. What is the probability that the sample proportion is between 0.38 and 0.46?

6.45 Seong-Un is a local fishery in Busan, the second most-populous city in South Korea. In 2017, an employee survey conducted by Seong-Un found that 55% of its employees were concerned about future health care benefits. A random sample of 90 of these employees were asked if they were now concerned about future health care benefits. Answer the following, assuming that there has been no change in the level of concern about health care benefits compared to the survey in 2017.

    a. What is the standard error of the sample proportion who are concerned?

    b. What is the probability that the sample proportion is less than 0.50?

    c. What is the upper limit of the sample proportion such that only 3% of the time the sample proportion would exceed this value?

6.46 The annual percentage salary increases for the chief executive officers of all midsize corporations are normally distributed with mean 12.2% and standard deviation 3.6%. A random sample of 81 of these chief executive officers was taken. What is the probability that more than half the sample members had salary increases of less than 10%?

6.4 Sampling Distributions of Sample Variances

Now that sampling distributions for sample means and proportions have been developed, we consider sampling distributions of sample variances. As business and industry increase their emphasis on producing products that satisfy customer quality standards, there is an increased need to measure and reduce population variance. High variance for a process implies a wider range of possible values for important product characteristics. This wider range of outcomes will result in more individual products that perform below an acceptable standard. After all, a customer does not care if a product performs well "on average." She is concerned that the particular item that she purchased works. High-quality products can be obtained from a manufacturing process if the process has a low population variance, so that fewer units are below the desired quality standard. By understanding the sampling distribution of sample variances, we can make inferences about the population variance. Thus, processes that have high variance can be identified and improved. In addition, a smaller population variance improves our ability to make inferences about population means using sample means.

We begin by considering a random sample of n observations drawn from a population with unknown mean μ and unknown variance σ^2. Denote the sample members as x_1, $x_2, \ldots, x_n$. The population variance is the expectation

$$\sigma^2 = E[(X - \mu)^2]$$

which suggests that we consider the mean of $(x_i - \bar{x})^2$ over n observations. Since μ is unknown, we use the sample mean $\bar{x}$ to compute a sample variance.

Sample Variance

Let $x_1, x_2, \ldots, x_n$ be a random sample of observations from a population. The quantity

$$s^2 = \frac{1}{n-1} \sum_{i=1}^{n} (x_i - \bar{x})^2$$

is called the **sample variance**, and its square root, s, is called the *sample standard deviation*. Given a specific random sample, we could compute the sample variance, and the sample variance would be different for each random sample because of differences in sample observations.

We might be initially surprised by the use of $(n - 1)$ as the divisor in the preceding definition. One simple explanation is that in a random sample of n observations, we have n different independent values or degrees of freedom. But after we know the computed sample mean, there are only $n - 1$ different values that can be uniquely defined. In addition, it can be shown that the expected value of the sample variance computed in this way is the population variance. This result is established in the chapter appendix and holds when the actual sample size, n, is a small proportion of the population size N:

$$E[s^2] = \sigma^2$$

The conclusion that the expected value of the sample variance is the population variance is quite general. But for statistical inference we would like to know more about the sampling distribution. If we can assume that the underlying population distribution is normal, then it can be shown that the sample variance and the population variance are related through a probability distribution known as the *chi-square distribution*.

Chi-Square Distribution of Sample and Population Variances

Given a random sample of n observations from a normally distributed population whose population variance is σ^2 and whose resulting sample variance is s^2, it can be shown that

$$\chi^2_{(n-1)} = \frac{(n-1)s^2}{\sigma^2} = \frac{\sum_{i=1}^{n} (x_i - \bar{x})^2}{\sigma^2}$$

has a distribution known as the **chi-square (χ^2) distribution** with $n - 1$ degrees of freedom.

The chi-square family of distributions is used in applied statistical analysis because it provides a link between the sample and the population variances. The chi-square distribution with $n - 1$ degrees of freedom is the distribution of the sum of squares of $n - 1$ independent standard normal random variables. The preceding chi-square distribution and the resulting computed probabilities for various values of s^2 require that the population distribution be normal. Thus, the assumption of an underlying normal distribution is more important for determining probabilities of sample variances than it is for determining probabilities of sample means.

The distribution is defined for only positive values, since variances are all positive values. An example of the probability density function is shown in Figure 6.12. The density function is asymmetric with a long positive tail. We can characterize a particular member of the family of chi-square distributions by a single parameter referred to as the degrees of freedom, denoted as v. A chi-square distribution with v degrees of freedom is denoted as χ_v^2. The mean and variance of this distribution are equal to the number of degrees of freedom and twice the number of degrees of freedom:

$$E[\chi_v^2] = v \quad \text{and} \quad Var(\chi_v^2) = 2v$$

Figure 6.12
Probability Density Functions for the Chi-Square Distribution 4, 6, and 8 Degrees of Freedom

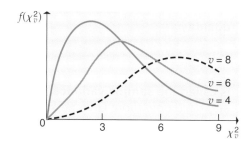

Using these results for the mean and variance of the chi-square distribution, we find that

$$E\left[\frac{(n-1)s^2}{\sigma^2}\right] = (n-1)$$

$$\frac{(n-1)}{\sigma^2}E[s^2] = (n-1)$$

$$E[s^2] = \sigma^2$$

To obtain the variance of s^2, we have

$$Var\left(\frac{(n-1)s^2}{\sigma^2}\right) = 2(n-1)$$

$$\frac{(n-1)^2}{\sigma^4}Var(s^2) = 2(n-1)$$

$$Var(s^2) = \frac{2\sigma^4}{(n-1)}$$

The parameter v of the χ^2 distribution is called the *degrees of freedom*. To help understand the degrees of freedom concept, consider first that the sample variance is the sum of squares for n values of the form $(x_i - \bar{x})$. These n values are not independent because their sum is zero (as we can show using the definition of the mean). Thus, if we know any $n-1$ of the values $(x_i - \bar{x})$,

$$\sum_{i=1}^{n}(x_i - \bar{x}) = 0$$

$$-1 \times (x_n - \bar{x}) = \sum_{i=1}^{n-1}(x_i - \bar{x})$$

Since we can determine the nth quantity if we know the remaining $n-1$ quantities, we say that there are $n-1$ degrees of freedom—independent values—for computing s^2. In contrast, if μ were known, we could compute an estimate of σ^2 by using the quantities

$$(x_1 - \mu), (x_2 - \mu), \ldots, (x_n - \mu)$$

each of which is independent. In that case we would have n degrees of freedom from the n independent sample observations, x_i. However, because μ is not known, we use its estimate $\bar{x}$ to compute the estimate of σ^2. As a result, one degree of freedom is lost in computing the sample mean, and we have $n-1$ degrees of freedom for s^2.

For many applications involving the population variance, we need to find values for the cumulative distribution of χ^2, especially the upper and lower tails of the distribution—for example,

$$P(\chi^2_{10} < K) = 0.05$$
$$P(\chi^2_{10} > K) = 0.05$$

For this purpose we have the distribution of the chi-square random variable tabulated in Appendix Table 7. In Table 7 the degrees of freedom are noted in the left column and the critical values of K for various probability levels are indicated in the other columns. Thus, for 10 degrees of freedom the value of K for the lower interval is 3.940. This result is found by going to the row with 10 degrees of freedom in the left column and then reading over to the column headed by the probability 0.950 to the right of these column entries. The chi-square value is 3.940. Similarly, for the upper 0.05 interval the value of K is 18.307. This result is found by going to the row with 10 degrees of freedom in the left column and then reading over to the column headed by the upper-tail probability 0.050 to the right of these column entries. The chi-square value is 18.307. These probabilities are shown schematically in Figure 6.13.

$$P(\chi^2_{10} < 3.940) = 0.05$$
$$P(\chi^2_{10} > 18.307) = 0.05$$

Figure 6.13
Upper and Lower χ^2_{10} Probabilities with 10 Degrees of Freedom

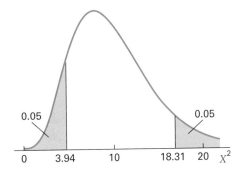

The sampling distribution results are summarized next.

Sampling Distribution of the Sample Variances

Let s^2 denote the sample variance for a random sample of n observations from a population with a variance σ^2.

1. The sampling distribution of s^2 has mean σ^2:

$$E[s^2] = \sigma^2 \qquad (6.11)$$

2. The variance of the sampling distribution of s^2 depends on the underlying population distribution. If that distribution is normal, then

$$Var(s^2) = \frac{2\sigma^4}{n-1} \qquad (6.12)$$

3. If the population distribution is normal, then $\chi^2_{(n-1)} = \dfrac{(n-1)s^2}{\sigma^2}$ is distributed as the chi-squared distribution with $n-1$ degrees of freedom, $(\chi^2_{(n-1)})$.

Thus, if we have a random sample from a population with a normal distribution, we can make inferences about the sample variance σ^2 by using s^2 and the chi-square distribution. This process is illustrated in the following examples.

Example 6.9 Process Monitoring for Integrated Electronics (Probability of Sample Variance)

George Samson is responsible for quality assurance at Integrated Electronics. Integrated Electronics has just signed a contract with a company in China to manufacture a control device that is a component of its manufacturing robotics products. Integrated Electronics wants to be sure that these new, lower-cost components meet its high-quality standards. George has asked you to establish a quality-monitoring process for checking shipments of control device A. The variability of the electrical resistance, measured in ohms, is critical for this device. Manufacturing standards specify a standard deviation of 3.6, and the population distribution of resistance measurements is normal when the components meet the quality specification. The monitoring process requires that a random sample of $n = 6$ observations be obtained from each shipment of devices and the sample variance be computed. Determine an upper limit for the sample variance such that the probability of exceeding this limit, given a population standard deviation of 3.6, is less than 0.05.

Solution For this problem we have $n = 6$ and $\sigma^2 = (3.6)^2 = 12.96$. Using the chi-square distribution, we can state that

$$P(s^2 > K) = P\left(\frac{(n-1)s^2}{12.96} > 11.070\right) = 0.05$$

where K is the desired upper limit and $\chi_5^2 = 11.070$ is the upper 0.05 critical value of the chi-square distribution with 5 degrees of freedom, from row 5 of the chi-square distribution from Appendix Table 7. The required upper limit for s^2—labeled as K—can be obtained by solving

$$\frac{(n-1)K}{12.96} = 11.070$$

$$K = \frac{(11.070)(12.96)}{(6-1)} = 28.69$$

If the sample variance, s^2, from a random sample of size $n = 6$ exceeds 28.69, there is strong evidence to suspect that the population variance exceeds 12.96 and that the supplier should be contacted and appropriate action taken. This action could include returning the entire shipment or checking each item in the shipment at the suppliers expense.

Example 6.10 Process Analysis for Green Valley Foods (Probability of Sample Variance)

Shirley Mendez is the manager of quality assurance for Green Valley Foods, Inc., a packer of frozen-vegetable products. Shirley wants to be sure that the variation of package weights is small so that the company does not produce a large proportion of packages that are under the stated package weight. She has asked you to obtain upper limits for the ratio of the sample variance divided by the population variance for a random sample of $n = 20$ observations. The limits are such that the probability that the ratio is above the upper limit is 0.025. Thus, 97.5% of the ratios will be below this limit. The population distribution can be assumed to be normal.

Solution We are asked to obtain a value K_U such that

$$P\left(\frac{s^2}{\sigma^2} < K_U\right) = 0.975$$

given that a random sample of size $n = 20$ is used to compute the sample variance.
For the upper limit we can state the following:

$$0.025 = P\left[\frac{(n-1)s^2}{\sigma^2} > (n-1)K_U\right] = P\left[\chi^2_{19,\,0.025} > (n-1)K_U\right]$$

This upper limit of chi-square defines an interval such that, if the sample computed chi-square is within that interval, we accept the assumption that the process variance is at the assumed value. This interval is defined as an *acceptance interval*.

Using the upper bound for the chi-square acceptance interval, we can compute the acceptance interval limit, K_U, for the ratio of sample variance to population variance. The upper value for the chi-square distribution can be found in Table 7 as

$$\chi^2_{19,\,0.025U} = 32.852$$

For the upper limit we have

$$0.025 = P\left[\chi^2_{19,\,0.025U} > (n-1)K_U\right] = P[32.852 > (19)K_U]$$

and, thus,

$$K_U = \left(\frac{32.852}{19}\right) = 1.729$$

The 97.5% acceptance interval for the ratio of sample variance divided by population variance is as follows:

$$P\left(\frac{s^2}{\sigma^2} \leq 1.729\right) = 0.975$$

Thus, the sample variance is less than 1.729 times the population variance with probability 0.975.

At this point it is important that we emphasize that the procedures used to make inferences about the population variance are substantially influenced by the assumption of a normal population distribution. Inferences concerning the population mean based on the sample mean are not substantially affected by departures from a normal distribution. In addition, inferences based on the sample mean can make use of the central limit theorem, which states that sample means will typically be normally distributed if the sample size is reasonably large. Thus, we state that inferences based on the sample mean are robust with respect to the assumption of normality. Unfortunately, inferences based on sample variances are not robust with respect to the assumption of normality.

We know that in many applications the population variance is of direct interest to an investigator. But when using the procedures we have demonstrated, we must keep in mind that if only a moderate number of sample observations are available, serious departures from normality in the parent population can severely invalidate the conclusions of analyses. The cautious analyst will therefore be rather tentative in making inferences in these circumstances.

EXERCISES

Basic Exercises

6.47 Consider a normally distributed population with a population mean of $\mu = 100$ and a variance of $\sigma^2 = 40$.

a. What is the probability that the sample variance is greater than 70 when $n = 17$?

b. What is the probability that the sample variance is greater than 85 when $n = 18$?

c. Find the probability that the sample variance is greater than 75 when $n = 17$?

6.48 A random sample of size $n = 25$ is obtained from a normally distributed population with a population mean of $\mu = 198$ and a variance of $\sigma^2 = 100$.

a. What is the probability that the sample mean is greater than 200?

b. What is the value of the sample variance such that 5% of the sample variances would be less than this value?

c. What is the value of the sample variance such that 5% of the sample variances would be greater than this value?

6.49 A random sample of size $n = 18$ is obtained from a normally distributed population with a population mean of $\mu = 46$ and a variance of $\sigma^2 = 50$.

a. What is the probability that the sample mean is greater than 50?

b. What is the value of the sample variance such that 5% of the sample variances would be less than this value?

c. What is the value of the sample variance such that 5% of the sample variances would be greater than this value?

6.50 A process produces batches of a chemical whose impurity concentrations follow a normal distribution with a variance of 1.75. A random sample of 20 of these batches is chosen. Find the probability that the sample variance exceeds 3.10.

6.51 Monthly rates of return on the shares of a particular common stock are independent of one another and normally distributed with a standard deviation of 2.2. A sample of 12 months is taken.

a. Find the probability that the sample standard deviation is less than 2.7.

b. Find the probability that the sample standard deviation is more than 1.3.

6.52 It is believed that first-year salaries for newly qualified accountants follow a normal distribution with a standard deviation of $2,500. A random sample of 16 observations was taken.

a. Find the probability that the sample standard deviation is more than $3,000.

b. Find the probability that the sample standard deviation is less than $1,500.

Application Exercises

6.53 A mathematics test of 100 multiple-choice questions is to be given to all freshmen entering a large university. Initially, in a pilot study the test was given to a random sample of 20 freshmen. Suppose that, for the population of all entering freshmen, the distribution of the number of correct answers would be normal with a variance of 250.

a. What is the probability that the sample variance would be less than 100?

b. What is the probability that the sample variance would be more than 500?

6.54 In a large city it was found that summer electricity bills for single-family homes followed a normal distribution with a standard deviation of $100. A random sample of 25 bills was taken.

a. Find the probability that the sample standard deviation is less than $75.

b. Find the probability that the sample standard deviation is more than $150.

6.55 The number of hours spent watching Netflix by students in the week before their final exams has a normal distribution with a standard deviation of 5 hours. A random sample of 41 students was taken.

a. Is the probability more than 0.975 that the sample standard deviation exceeds 4 hours?

b. Is the probability more than 0.99 that the sample standard deviation is less than 6.5 hours?

6.56 In Table 6.1 we considered the 15 possible samples of two observations from a population of $N = 6$ values of years on the job for employees. The population variance for these six values is as follows:

$$\sigma = \frac{47}{12}$$

For each of the 15 possible samples, calculate the sample variance. Find the average of these 15 sample variances, thus confirming that the expected value of the sample variance is not equal to the population variance when the number of sample members is not a small proportion of the number of population members. In fact, as you can verify here,

$$E[s^2] = N\sigma^2/(N-1)$$

6.57 A production process manufactures electronic components with timing signals whose duration follows a normal distribution. A random sample of nine components was taken, and the durations of their timing signals were measured.

a. The probability is 0.05 that the sample variance is greater than what percentage of the population variance?

b. The probability is 0.10 that the sample variance is less than what percentage of the population variance?

6.58 A random sample of 10 stock market mutual funds was taken. Suppose that rates of returns on the population of all stock market mutual funds follow a normal distribution.

a. The probability is 0.10 that sample variance is greater than what percentage of the population variance?

b. Find any pair of numbers, a and b, to complete the following sentence: The probability is 0.95 that the sample variance is between a% and b% of the population variance.

c. Suppose that a sample of 20 mutual funds had been taken. Without doing the calculations, indicate how this would change your answer to part (b).

6.59 Each member of a random sample of 16 business economists was asked to predict the rate of inflation for the coming year. Assume that the predictions for the whole population of business economists follow a normal distribution with standard deviation 1.7%.

a. The probability is 0.01 that the sample standard deviation is bigger than what number?

b. The probability is 0.025 that the sample standard deviation is less than what number?

c. Find any pair of numbers such that the probability that the sample standard deviation that lies between these numbers is 0.95.

6.60 A precision instrument is checked by making 12 readings on the same quantity. The population distribution of readings is normal.

a. The probability is 0.95 that the sample variance is more than what percentage of the population variance?

b. The probability is 0.90 that the sample variance is more than what percentage of the population variance?

c. Determine any pair of appropriate numbers, a and b, to complete the following sentence: The probability is 0.95 that the sample variance is between a% and b% of the population variance.

6.61 A drug company produces pills containing an active ingredient. The company is concerned about the mean weight of this ingredient per pill, but it also requires that the variance (in squared milligrams) be no more than 1.5. A random sample of 20 pills is selected, and the sample variance is found to be 2.05. How likely is it that a sample variance this high or higher would be found if the population variance is, in fact, 1.5? Assume that the population distribution is normal.

6.62 A manufacturer has been purchasing raw materials from a supplier whose consignments have a variance of 15.4 (in squared pounds) in impurity levels. A rival supplier claims that she can supply consignments of this raw material with the same mean impurity level but with lower variance. For a random sample of 25 consignments from the second supplier, the variance in impurity levels was found to be 12.2. What is the probability of observing a value this low or lower for the sample variance if, in fact, the true population variance is 15.4? Assume that the population distribution is normal.

KEY WORDS

- acceptance intervals, 264
- central limit theorem, 258
- chi-square distribution, 275
- finite population correction factor, 255
- law of large numbers, 258
- sample mean, 253
- sample proportion, 269
- random sample, 249
- sample variance, 275
- sampling distributions of sample means, 254
- sampling distributions of sample proportions, 269
- sampling distribution of the sample variances, 277
- sampling distributions, 250
- simple random sample, 249
- standard normal distribution for the sample means, 255
- standardized normal random variable, 255

DATA FILES

- Bottles, 283
- Granola, 283
- Sugar Coated Wheat, 283

CHAPTER EXERCISES AND APPLICATIONS

 Visit www.MyStatLab.com or www.pearsonglobal editions.com to access the data files.

6.63 What is meant by the statement that the sample mean and the sample proportion have a sampling distribution? What other statistical examples can you provide?

6.64 There are six white-collar workers at a university department with the following ages:

56, 38, 29, 58, 43, 47

Two of the workers are to be chosen at random.

a. How many possible samples of two workers are there?

b. List all possible samples.

c. Find the probability function of the sampling distribution of the sample means.

d. Verify directly that the mean of the sampling distribution of the sample means is equal to the population mean.

6.65 Of what relevance is the central limit theorem to the sampling distribution of the sample means?

6.66 The scores of all applicants taking an aptitude test required by a law school have a normal distribution with a mean of 420 and a standard deviation of 100. A random sample of 25 scores is taken.

a. Find the probability that the sample mean score is higher than 450.

b. Find the probability that the sample mean score is between 400 and 450.

c. The probability is 0.10 that the sample mean score is higher than what number?

d. The probability is 0.10 that the sample mean score is lower than what number?

e. The probability is 0.05 that the sample standard deviation of the scores is higher than what number?

f. The probability is 0.05 that the sample standard deviation of the scores is lower than what number?

g. If a sample of 50 test scores had been taken, would the probability of a sample mean score higher than

450 be smaller than, larger than, or the same as the correct answer to part (a)? It is not necessary to do the detailed calculations here. Sketch a graph to illustrate your reasoning.

6.67 A company services home air conditioners. It has been found that times for service calls follow a Normal distribution with a mean of 60 minutes and a standard deviation of 10 minutes. A random sample of four service calls was taken.

   a. What is the probability that the sample mean service time is more than 65 minutes?

   b. The probability is 0.10 that the sample mean service time is less than how many minutes?

   c. The probability is 0.10 that the sample standard deviation of service times is more than how many minutes?

   d. The probability is 0.10 that the sample standard deviation of service times is less than how many minutes?

   e. What is the probability that more than two of these calls take more than 65 minutes?

6.68 In a particular year, the percentage rates of return of U.S. common stock mutual funds had a normal distribution with a mean of 14.8 and a standard deviation of 6.3. A random sample of nine of these mutual funds was taken.

   a. What is the probability that the sample mean percentage rate of return is more than 19.0?

   b. What is the probability that the sample mean percentage rate of return is between 10.6 and 19.0?

   c. The probability is 0.25 that the sample mean percentage return is less than what number?

   d. The probability is 0.10 that the sample standard deviation of percentage return is more than what number?

   e. If a sample of 20 of these funds was taken, state whether the probability of a sample mean percentage rate of return of more than 19.0 would be smaller than, larger than, or the same as the correct answer to part (a). Sketch a graph to illustrate your reasoning.

6.69 The lifetimes of a certain electronic component are known to be normally distributed with a mean of 1,600 hours and a standard deviation of 400 hours.

   a. For a random sample of 16 components, find the probability that the sample mean is more than 1,500 hours.

   b. For a random sample of 16 components, the probability is 0.15 that the sample mean lifetime is more than how many hours?

   c. For a random sample of 16 components, the probability is 0.10 that the sample standard deviation lifetime is more than how many hours?

6.70 Refer to the chapter appendix in order to derive the mean of the sampling distribution of the sample variances for a sample of n observations from a population of N members when the population variance is σ^2. By appropriately modifying the argument

regarding variances in the chapter appendix, show that

$$E[s^2] = N\sigma^2/(N-1)$$

Note the intuitive plausibility of this result when $n = N$.

6.71 It has been found that times taken by people to complete a particular tax form follow a normal distribution with a mean of 100 minutes and a standard deviation of 30 minutes. A random sample of nine people who have completed this tax form was taken.

   a. What is the probability that the sample mean time taken is more than 120 minutes?

   b. The probability is 0.20 that the sample mean time taken is less than how many minutes?

   c. The probability is 0.05 that the sample standard deviation of time taken is less than how many minutes?

6.72 It was found that 80% of seniors at a particular college had accepted a job offer before graduation. For those accepting offers, salary distribution was normal with a mean of $37,000 and a standard deviation of $4,000.

   a. For a random sample of 60 seniors what is the probability that less than 70% have accepted job offers?

   b. For a random sample of 6 seniors, what is the probability that less than 70% have accepted job offers?

   c. For a random sample of 6 seniors who have accepted job offers, what is the probability that the average salary is more than $38,000?

   d. A senior is chosen at random. What is the probability that she has accepted a job offer with a salary of more than $38,000?

6.73 Plastic bags used for packaging produce are manufactured so that the breaking strengths of the bags are normally distributed with a standard deviation of 1.8 pounds per square inch. A random sample of 16 bags is selected.

   a. The probability is 0.01 that the sample standard deviation of breaking strengths exceeds what number?

   b. The probability is 0.15 that the sample mean exceeds the population mean by how much?

   c. The probability is 0.05 that the sample mean differs from the population mean by how much?

6.74 A quality-control manager was concerned about variability in the amount of an active ingredient in diarrhea pills produced by a particular process. A random sample of 26 pills was taken. What is the probability that the sample variance of the amount of an active ingredient was more than 1.5 times the population variance? What is the probability of an active ingredient being more than 1.5 times the population variance with a sample size of 41?

6.75 A sample of 200 students is to be taken to determine which of two brands of fruit juice (A and B) is preferred in a blind taste test. Suppose that, in the whole population of students, 60% would prefer brand A.

   a. What is the probability that more than two third of the sample members prefer brand A?

b. What is the probability that between 55% and 65% of the sample members prefer brand A?

c. Suppose that a sample of only 50 students was available. Indicate how the method of calculation of probabilities would differ, compared with your solutions to parts (a) and (b)?

6.76 Scores on a particular test, taken by a large group of students, follow a normal distribution with a variance of 2500. A random sample of 25 scores was taken to estimate the population's mean score. Let the random variable $\bar{x}$ denote the sample mean. What is the probability that the interval $(\bar{x} - 10)$ to $(\bar{x} + 10)$ contains the true population mean?

6.77 A manufacturer of liquid detergent claims that the mean weight of liquid in containers sold is at least 50 ounces. It is known that the population distribution of weights is normal with a standard deviation of 1.1 ounces. In order to check the manufacturer's claim, a random sample of 30 containers of detergent is examined. The claim will be questioned if the sample mean weight is less than 49.8 ounces. What is the probability that the claim will be questioned if, in fact, the population mean weight is 50 ounces?

6.78 In a particular year 1/3 of home sales were partially financed by the seller. A random sample of 300 sales is examined.

a. The probability is 0.9 that the sample proportion is more than what amount?

b. The probability is 0.6 that the sample proportion is less than what amount?

c. The probability is 0.7 that the sample proportion differs from the population proportion by how much?

6.79 A candidate for office intends to campaign in a state if her initial support level exceeds 30% of the voters. A random sample of 500 voters is taken, and it is decided to campaign if the sample proportion supporting the candidate exceeds 0.275.

a. What is the probability of a decision not to campaign if, in fact, the initial support level is 23%?

b. What is the probability of a decision not to campaign if, in fact, the initial support level is 35%?

6.80 It is known that the incomes of subscribers to a particular British magazine have a normal distribution with a variance of 49,000,000. A random sample of 41 subscribers is taken.

a. What is the probability that the sample standard deviation of their incomes is more than £5,000?

b. What is the probability that the sample standard deviation of their incomes is less than £9,000?

6.81 Batches of chemical are manufactured by a production process. Samples of 30 batches from a production run are selected for testing. If the standard deviation of the percentage of impurity contents in the sample batches exceeds 3.5%, the production process is thoroughly checked. Assume that the population distribution of percentage impurity concentrations is normal. What is the probability that the production process will be thoroughly checked if the population standard deviation of percentage impurity concentrations is 3%?

6.82 A consumer product that has flourished in the last few years is bottled natural spring water. Jon Thorne is the CEO of a company that sells natural spring water. He has requested a report of the filling process of the 24-ounce (710-milliliter) bottles to be sure that they are being properly filled. To check if the process needs to be adjusted, Emma Astrom, who monitors the process, randomly samples and weighs five bottles every 15 minutes for a 5-hour period. The data are contained in the data file **Bottles**.

a. Compute the sample mean, sample standard deviations for individual bottles, and the standard deviation of the sample mean for each sample.

b. Determine the probability that the sample means are below 685 milliliters if the population mean is 710.

c. Determine the probability that the sample means are above 720 milliliters.

6.83 Prairie Flower Cereal, Inc., is a small but growing producer of hot and ready-to-eat breakfast cereals. The company was started in 1910 by Gordon Thorson, a successful grain farmer. You have been asked to test the cereal-packing process of 18-ounce (510-gram) boxes of sugar-coated wheat cereal. Two machines are used for the packaging process. Twenty samples of five packages each are randomly sampled and weighed. The data are contained in the file **Sugar Coated Wheat**.

a. Compute the overall sample mean, sample variance, and variance of the sample means for each machine.

b. Determine the probability that a single sample mean is below 500 if the process is operating properly for each machine.

c. Determine the probability that a single sample mean is above 508 if the process is operating properly for each machine.

d. Using your statistical computer package, obtain 20 random samples of size $n = 5$ packages for each machine and compute the sample mean for each sample. Count the number of sample means that are below 500 and the number that are above 508.

6.84 Another product packaged by Prairie Flower Cereal, Inc., is an apple-cinnamon cereal. To test the packaging process of 40-ounce (1,134-gram) packages of this cereal, 23 samples of six packages each are randomly sampled and weighed. The lower and upper acceptance limits have been set at 1,120 grams and 1,150 grams, respectively. The data are contained in the data file **Granola**.

a. Compute the overall sample mean, sample variance, and variance of the sample means for each sample.

b. Compute the probability that the sample means will be within the acceptance limits.

c. Using your statistical computer package, obtain 23 random samples of size $n = 6$ and compute the sample mean for each sample. Count the number of sample means that are outside the acceptance limits.

Appendix: Mathematical and Simulation Results

1   CENTRAL LIMIT THEOREM FROM LINEAR SUM OF RANDOM VARIABLES

In applied statistical analysis many of the random variables used can be characterized as the sum or mean of a large number of random variables. For example, total daily sales in a store are the result of a number of sales to individual customers—each of whom can be modeled as a random variable. Total national investment spending in a month is the sum of many individual investment decisions by specific firms. Thus, if $X_1, X_2, \ldots, X_n$ represents the result of individual random events, the observed random variable

$$X = X_1 + X_2 + \cdots + X_n$$

and from Chapter 5

$$E[X] = n\mu \quad Var(X) = n\sigma^2$$

The central limit theorem states that the resulting sum, X, is normally distributed and can be used to compute a random variable, Z, with a mean of 0 and a variance of 1:

$$Z = \frac{X - E[X]}{\sqrt{Var(X)}} = \frac{X - n\mu}{\sqrt{n\sigma^2}}$$

In addition, if X is divided by n to obtain a mean of $\overline{X}$, then a corresponding Z with a mean of 0 and a variance of 1 can also be computed:

$$Z = \frac{X - \mu_X}{\sigma_{\overline{X}}} = \frac{X - \mu_X}{\dfrac{\sigma}{\sqrt{n}}}$$

Using these results, we have the central limit theorem.

2   MONTE CARLO SAMPLE SIMULATIONS USING MINITAB

In Section 6.2 we presented results from Monte Carlo sampling simulations to demonstrate the central limit theorem. In this appendix we indicate how you can construct similar simulations for a probability distribution. The simulation can be performed using a Minitab macro named **Centlimit.mac**, which is contained in the data directory for the textbook.

 Visit **www.MyStatLab.com** or **www.pearsonglobaleditions.com** to access the macro and data files.

To use this macro, copy it to the directory located with your Minitab program

    MTBWIN\MACROS\

using Windows Explorer. This macro will then be stored with other macros supplied with the Minitab package. When the macro is stored in this directory, it can be run directly in Minitab. Alternatively, the macro can be stored in another directory, and the entire path is supplied to run the macro. To run the sampling simulation, use the following steps:

1. In column one store a set of values that have the frequency indicated by the probability distribution that you are interested in simulating. Typically, we store 100 values, but any number could be stored. For example, to store a binomial distribution with $P = 0.40$, you would store 40 1s and 60 0s in column one. You could also store an empirical distribution of numbers from a population being studied. Another procedure for obtaining the sample values is to use the following command:

`CALC<RANDOM DATA>"SELECT PROBABILITY DISTRIBUTION"`

This would provide you with a random sample from one of a number of common probability distributions.

2. In the Minitab Session Window, type the command

`MTB>%CENTLIMIT N1 N2 C1-C3`

where N1 is the sample size for the individual samples being simulated and N2 is the number of samples whose means are to be obtained from the simulation. Generally, 500 to 1,000 samples will provide a good sampling distribution, but you can select any reasonable value. Recognize that the greater the number of samples, the longer it will take to run the simulation. C1 to C3 are the columns used by Minitab for the simulation with your probability distribution of interest in column one. You could use any columns as long as your probability distribution is in column one. Figure 6.14 shows an example of the setup for the sampling simulation.

Figure 6.14
Monte Carlo
Sampling Simulation
Setup in Minitab

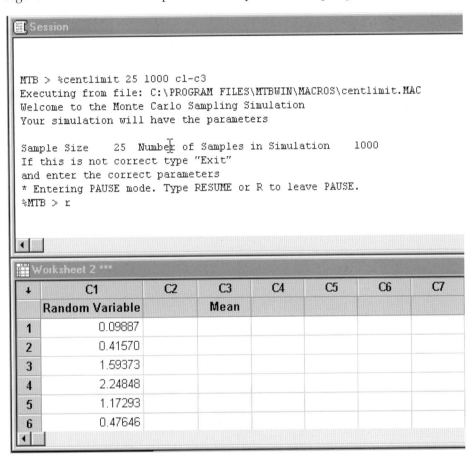

The simulation will generate samples in column two and compute the sample mean. The mean for each sample will be stored in column three, titled "Mean." Descriptive statistics and histograms will be computed for the random variable values in column one and for the sample means in column three. By clicking on the menu command

`WINDOWS>TILE`

you can obtain the screen in Figure 6.15, which is useful for comparing the original distribution and the sampling distribution with a comparable normal.

In Figure 6.15 we see that the distribution of the random variable in the lower left corner is definitely not normal; rather, it is highly skewed to the right. In contrast, the sampling distribution of the means in the upper left corner closely approximates a normal distribution. Figure 6.16 presents a copy of the **Centlimit.mac** Minitab macro, which is

Figure 6.15
Results of the Monte
Carlo Sampling
Simulation

Figure 6.16 Copy
of the Minitab Macro
Centlimit.Mac

```
Macro
Centlimit n1,n2,Dist,Samp,Xbar
#  Dr.William L. Carlson
#  Professor of Economics
#  St Olaf College
#  Northfield MN   55057
#  Carlson@Stolaf.edu
#  To Execute this Macro in Minitab  Type
#  %Centlimit "sample size"  "Number of Samples"  C1 C2 C3
#
#The output includes a histogram and a normal probability plot for the
original #distribution and a histogram and normal probability plot for the
sampling #distribution of sample means
#Macro is Stored as a text file in C:\program
files\mtbwin\macros\centlimit.mac
#
#Definition of Variables
#
# n1  Sample size obtained from probability distribution
# n2  Number of samples of size n1 obtained in this simulation
# Dist      Column that contains an empirical distribution from which the
random #          sample is obtained.
# Xbar      Column that contains the sample means from each of the n2 samples
#           obtained in the simulation
# Samp      Column that will be used to generate each of the samples.
#
#
Mconstant  n1 n2 k1 k2
Mcolumn Dist Xbar Samp c11 c12 c13 c14
Name Dist 'Random Variable' Xbar 'Mean'
Let c11="Sample Size"
Let c12= n1
Let c13="Number of Samples in Simulation"
Let c14=n2
Note Welcome to the Monte Carlo Sampling Simulation
Note Your simulation will have the parameters
Write 'Terminal' c11-c14
Note If this is not correct type "exit"
Note and enter the correct parameters
Pause
Brief 0
Do k1=1:n2
Sample n1 Dist Samp;
Replace.
Mean Samp k2
Let xbar(k1)=k2
Enddo
Brief
Describe Dist Xbar;
GNHist.
Endmacro
```

stored in the data directory for the textbook. Users familiar with Minitab macros could modify this macro to obtain different outputs.

3 MEAN OF THE SAMPLING DISTRIBUTION OF THE SAMPLE VARIANCES

In this appendix, we show that the mean of the sampling distribution of the sample variances is the population variance. We begin by finding the expectation of the sum of squares of the sample members about their mean—that is, the expectation of

$$\sum_{i=1}^{n}(x_i - \bar{x})^2 = \sum_{i=1}^{n}[(x_i - \mu) - (\bar{x} - \mu)]^2$$

$$= \sum_{i=1}^{n}[(x_i - \mu)^2 - 2(\bar{x} - \mu)(x_i - \mu) + (\bar{x} - \mu)^2]$$

$$= \sum_{i=1}^{n}(x_i - \mu)^2 - 2(\bar{x} - \mu)\sum_{i=1}^{n}(x_i - \mu) + \sum_{i=1}^{n}(\bar{x} - \mu)^2$$

$$= \sum_{i=1}^{n}(x_i - \mu)^2 - 2n(\bar{x} - \mu)^2 + n(\bar{x} - \mu)^2$$

$$= \sum_{i=1}^{n}(x_i - \mu)^2 - n(\bar{x} - \mu)^2$$

Taking expectations then gives

$$E\left[\sum_{i=1}^{n}(x_i - \bar{x})^2\right] = E\left[\sum_{i=1}^{n}(x_i - \mu)^2\right] - nE[(\bar{x} - \mu)^2]$$

$$= \sum_{i=1}^{n}E[(x_i - \mu)^2] - nE[(\bar{x} - \mu)^2]$$

Now, the expectation of each $(x_i - \mu)^2$ is the population variance, σ^2, and the expectation of $(\bar{x} - \mu)^2$ is the variance of the sample mean, σ^2/n. Hence, we have the following:

$$E\left[\sum_{i=1}^{n}(x_i - \bar{x})^2\right] = n\sigma^2 - \frac{n\sigma^2}{n} = (n - 1)\sigma^2$$

Finally, for the expected value of the sample variance we have the following:

$$E[s^2] = E\left[\frac{1}{n - 1}\sum_{i=1}^{n}(x_i - \bar{x})^2\right]$$

$$= \frac{1}{n - 1}E\left[\sum_{i=1}^{n}(x_i - \bar{x})^2\right]$$

$$= \frac{1}{n - 1}(n - 1)\sigma^2 = \sigma^2$$

This is the result we set out to establish.

REFERENCES

1. David, F. R., L. M. Anderson, and K. W. Lawrimore. 1990. "Perspectives on Business Ethics in Management Education." *S. A. M. Advanced Management Journal* 55 (4): 26–32.
2. Deming, W. E. 1986. *Out of the Crisis*, M. I. T. Center for Advanced Engineering Study
3. Hiam, A., 1992. *Closing the Quality Gap.*, Englewood Cliffs, NJ: Prentice Hall.
4. Hogan, H. 1992. "The 1990 Post-enumeration Survey: An Overview." *American Statistician* 46: 261–269.
5. Hogg, R., and Craig, A. 1995. *Mathematical Statistics*, 5th ed. Englewood Cliffs, NJ: Prentice Hall.
6. Montgomery D. C., 1997. *Introduction to Statistical Quality Control*, 3rd. ed. New York: Wiley.

7

Estimation: Single Population

Introduction

What is the average number of gallons of orange juice sold weekly by a local grocery store? Management of this grocery store could use an estimate of the average weekly demand for orange juice (milk, bread, or fresh fruit) to improve the ordering process, reduce waste (such as spoiled fruit), reduce costs, and increase profits. How satisfied are customers who use an online pharmaceutical company with the company's actual delivery time? The online company may begin with obtaining an estimate of the average time (in days) to ship an order once the order is received. What proportion of customers is satisfied with a new product? An estimate of this proportion, along with other data, might be used by the company to enhance its quality efforts. Who will win an upcoming election for the presidency of the university's student government association, the mayor of a city, the senator of a state, or the president of a nation? Political campaign managers estimate the proportion of registered voters in various districts (precincts, counties, states, etc.) who intend to vote for a particular candidate if the election were to be held that day. This type of estimate can provide guidance to campaign managers in their preparation of campaign strategies.

In this chapter we address these and other types of situations that require an estimate of some population parameter. Inferential statements concerning estimates of a single population parameter, based on information contained in a random sample are presented. More specifically, we discuss procedures to estimate the mean of a population, a proportion of population members that possess some specific characteristic, and the variance of a population.

We present two estimation procedures in this chapter. First, we estimate an unknown population parameter by a single number called a point estimate. Properties of this point estimate are considered in Section 7.1. For most practical problems, a point estimate alone is not adequate. A more complete understanding of the process that generated the population also requires a measure of variability. Next we discuss a procedure that takes into account this variation by establishing an interval of values, known as a confidence interval, which is likely to include the quantity.

Initially we consider populations that are infinite (or very large compared to the sample size) and where sampling is with replacement. As mentioned in Chapter 6, most sampling studies use large populations, but there are some business applications, such as auditing, that involve finite populations. For completeness, in Section 7.6 we discuss estimation procedures when the sample size is considered to be relatively large compared to the population size. This situation occurs when the sample size, n, is more than 5% of the population size, N, and thus the finite-population correction factor introduced in Chapter 6 is required. We conclude this chapter with a discussion of sample-size determination for selected parameters from large populations (Section 7.7) and for selected parameters from finite populations (Section 7.8).

7.1 PROPERTIES OF POINT ESTIMATORS

Any inference drawn about the population will be based on sample statistics. The choice of appropriate statistics will depend on which population parameter is of interest. The value of the population parameter will be unknown, and one objective of sampling is to estimate its value. A distinction must be made between the terms *estimator* and *estimate*.

Estimator and Estimate
An **estimator** of a population parameter is a random variable that depends on the sample information; its value provides approximations of this unknown parameter. A specific value of that random variable is called an **estimate**.

We point out that there is "a technical distinction between an *estimator* as a function of random variables and an *estimate* as a single number. It is the distinction between a process (the *estimator*) and the result of that process (the *estimate*)" (Hildebrand and Ott 1998). To clarify this distinction between estimator and estimate, consider the estimation of the mean weekly sales of a particular brand of orange juice. One possible *estimator* of the population mean is the sample mean. If the mean of a random sample of weekly sales is found to be 3,280 gallons, then 3,280 is an *estimate* of the population mean weekly sales. Another possible *estimator* of the mean weekly sales could be the sample median.

In Chapter 2 we studied other descriptive statistics, such as sample variance, s^2, and sample correlation coefficient, r. If the value of the sample variance, s^2, for the weekly demand of orange juice is 300 gallons, then s^2 is the estimator and 300 is the estimate.

In discussing the estimation of an unknown parameter, two possibilities must be considered. First, a *single number* could be computed from the sample as most representative of the unknown population parameter. This is called a *point estimate*. The estimate of 3,280 gallons of orange juice is an example of a point estimate. Alternatively, it might be possible to find an interval or range that most likely contains the value of the population parameter. For example, the mean weekly demand in this store for this particular brand of orange juice is, with some specified degree of confidence, between 2,500 and 3,500 gallons. This interval estimate is an example of one type of *confidence interval* that we discuss in this chapter.

Point Estimator and Point Estimate

Consider a population parameter such as the population mean μ or the population proportion P. A **point estimator** of a population parameter is a function of the sample information that produces a single number called a **point estimate**. For example, the sample mean $\overline{X}$ is a point estimator of the population mean, μ, and the value that $\overline{X}$ assumes for a given set of data is called the point estimate, $\overline{x}$.

At the outset we must point out that no single mechanism exists for the determination of a uniquely "best" point estimator in all circumstances. What is available instead is a set of criteria under which particular estimators can be evaluated. The sample median also gives a point estimate of the population mean, μ. However, we show later in this chapter that the median is not the best estimator for the population mean of some distributions.

We evaluate estimators based on two important properties: unbiasedness and efficiency. (See the chapter appendix for the property of consistency.)

Unbiased

In searching for an estimator of a population parameter, the first property an estimator should possess is *unbiasedness*.

Unbiased Estimator

A point estimator $\hat{\theta}$ is said to be an **unbiased estimator** of a population parameter θ if its expected value is equal to that parameter; that is, if

$$E(\hat{\theta}) = \theta$$

then $\hat{\theta}$ is an unbiased estimator of θ.

Notice that unbiasedness does not mean that a *particular* value of $\hat{\theta}$ must be exactly the correct value of θ. Rather, an unbiased estimator has "the capability of estimating the population parameter correctly on the average. . . . An unbiased estimator is correct on the average. We can think of the expected value of $\hat{\theta}$ as the average of $\hat{\theta}$ values for all possible samples, or alternatively, as the long-run average of $\hat{\theta}$ values for repeated samples. The condition that the estimator $\hat{\theta}$ should be unbiased says that the *average* $\hat{\theta}$ value is exactly correct. It does not state that a particular $\hat{\theta}$ value is exactly correct" (Hildebrand and Ott 1998).

Sometimes $\hat{\theta}$ will overestimate and other times underestimate the parameter, but it follows from the notion of expectation that, if the sampling procedure is repeated many times, then, on the average, the value obtained for an unbiased estimator will be equal to the population parameter. It seems reasonable to assert that, all other things being equal, unbiasedness is a desirable property in a point estimator. Figure 7.1 illustrates the probability density functions for two estimators, $\hat{\theta}_1$ and $\hat{\theta}_2$, of the parameter θ. It should be obvious that $\hat{\theta}_1$ is an unbiased estimator of θ and $\hat{\theta}_2$ is not an unbiased estimator of θ.

Figure 7.1
Probability Density Functions for Estimators $\hat{\theta}_1$ (Unbiased) and $\hat{\theta}_2$ (Biased)

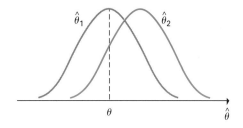

In Chapter 6 we showed the following:

1. The sample mean is an unbiased estimator of μ; $E(\overline{X}) = \mu$.
2. The sample variance is an unbiased estimator of σ^2; $E(s^2) = \sigma^2$.
3. The sample proportion is an unbiased estimator of P; $E(\hat{p}) = P$.

It follows, then, that the sample mean, sample variance, and sample proportion are unbiased estimators of their corresponding population parameters.

An estimator that is not unbiased is *biased*. The extent of the bias is the difference between the mean of the estimator and the true parameter.

Bias
Let $\hat{\theta}$ be an estimator of θ. The **bias** in $\hat{\theta}$ is defined as the difference between its mean and θ:

$$\text{bias}(\hat{\theta}) = E(\hat{\theta}) - \theta$$

It follows that the bias of an unbiased estimator is 0.

Unbiasedness alone is not the only desirable characteristic of an estimator. There may be several unbiased estimators for a population parameter. For example, if the population is normally distributed, both the sample mean and the median are unbiased estimators of the population mean.

Most Efficient

In many practical problems, different unbiased estimators can be obtained, and some method of choosing among them needs to be found. In this situation it is natural to prefer the estimator whose distribution is most closely concentrated about the population parameter being estimated. Values of such an estimator are less likely to differ, by any fixed amount, from the parameter being estimated than are those of its competitors. Using variance as a measure of concentration, the *efficiency* of an estimator as a criterion for preferring one estimator to another estimator is introduced.

Most Efficient Estimator and Relative Efficiency

If there are several unbiased estimators of a parameter, then the unbiased estimator with the smallest variance is called the **most efficient estimator,** or the **minimum variance unbiased estimator.** Let $\hat{\theta}_1$ and $\hat{\theta}_2$ be two unbiased estimators of θ, based on the same number of sample observations. Then,

1. $\hat{\theta}_1$ is said to be more efficient than $\hat{\theta}_2$ if $Var(\hat{\theta}_1) < Var(\hat{\theta}_2)$, and

2. the **relative efficiency** of $\hat{\theta}_1$ with respect to $\hat{\theta}_2$ is the ratio of their variances.

$$relative\ efficiency = \frac{Var(\hat{\theta}_2)}{Var(\hat{\theta}_1)}$$

Example 7.1 Selection from Competing Unbiased Estimators (Relative Efficiency)

Let $x_1, x_2, \ldots, x_n$ be a random sample from a normally distributed population with mean μ and variance σ^2. Should the sample mean or the sample median be used to estimate the population mean?

Solution Assuming a population that is normally distributed with a very large population size compared to the sample size, the sample mean, $\overline{X}$, is an unbiased estimator of the population mean, μ, with variance (Chapter 6):

$$Var(\overline{X}) = \frac{\sigma^2}{n}$$

As an alternative estimator, we could use the median of the sample observations. It can be shown that this estimator is also unbiased for μ and that when n is large, its variance is as follows:

$$Var(median) = \frac{\pi}{2} \times \frac{\sigma^2}{n} = \frac{1.57\sigma^2}{n}$$

The sample mean is more efficient than the median, the relative efficiency of the mean with respect to the median being as follows:

$$relative\ efficiency = \frac{Var(median)}{Var(\overline{X})} = 1.57$$

The variance of the sample median is 57% higher than that of the sample mean. One advantage of the median over the mean is that it gives less weight to extreme observations. A potential disadvantage of using the sample median as a measure of central location lies in its relative efficiency.

We emphasize the importance of using a normal probability plot to determine if there is any evidence of nonnormality. If the population is not normally distributed, the sample mean may not be the most efficient estimator of the population mean. In particular, if outliers heavily affect the population distribution, the sample mean is less efficient than other estimators (such as the median). Table 7.1 is a summary of some properties for selected point estimators. It is neither an exhaustive list of estimators nor an exhaustive list of properties that an estimator possesses.

Table 7.1 Properties of Selected Point Estimators

POPULATION PARAMETER	POINT ESTIMATOR	PROPERTIES
Mean, μ	$\overline{X}$	Unbiased, most efficient (assuming normality)
Mean, μ	Median	Unbiased (assuming normality), but not most efficient
Proportion, P	$\hat{p}$	Unbiased, most efficient
Variance, σ^2	s^2	Unbiased, most efficient (assuming normality)

Example 7.2 Price-Earnings Ratios (Estimators)

Suppose that we randomly sampled stocks traded on the New York Stock Exchange on a particular day and found the price-earnings ratios of these stocks to be as follows:

$$10 \quad 16 \quad 13 \quad 11 \quad 12 \quad 14 \quad 12$$
$$15 \quad 14 \quad 14 \quad 13 \quad 13 \quad 13$$

Does the normal probability plot suggest non-normality? Find point estimates of the mean and variance. Discuss the properties of these estimators.

Solution From the normal probability plot in Figure 7.2, there appears to be no evidence of nonnormality. Assuming a normal distribution, an estimate of the mean price-earnings ratios is the sample mean, 13.1, and an estimate of the variance is $s^2 = 2.58$. Both $\overline{X}$ and s^2 are unbiased and efficient point estimators of μ and σ^2, respectively.

Figure 7.2 Price-Earnings Ratios (Normality)

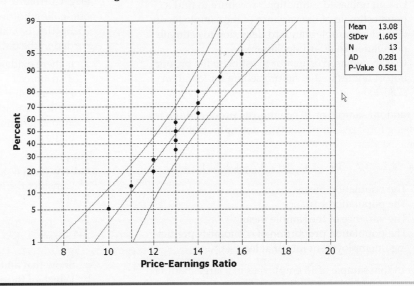

A problem that often arises in practice is how to choose an appropriate point estimator for a population parameter. An attractive possibility is to choose the most efficient of all unbiased estimators. However, sometimes there are estimation problems for which no unbiased estimator is very satisfactory, or there may be situations in which it is not always possible to find a minimum variance unbiased estimator. It is also possible that data may not be normally distributed. In these situations selecting the best point estimator is not straightforward and involves considerable mathematical intricacy beyond the scope of this book.

Visit www.MyStatLab.com or www.pearsonglobal editions.com to access the data files.

Basic Exercises

7.1 There is concern about the speed of automobiles traveling over a particular stretch of highway. For a random sample of 28 automobiles, radar indicated the following speeds, in miles per hour:

58 63 68 57 56 72 58

69 53 55 61 66 51 59

54 64 58 57 66 61 65

70 63 65 57 56 61 59

a. Check for evidence of nonnormality.
b. Find a point estimate of the population mean that is unbiased and efficient.
c. Use an unbiased estimation procedure to find a point estimate of the variance of the sample mean.

7.2 A random sample of 10 homes in a particular suburb had the following selling prices (in thousands of pounds):

209 256 257 272 275 277 278 285 306 327

a. Check for evidence of nonnormality.
b. Find a point estimate of the population mean that is unbiased and efficient.
c. Use an unbiased estimation procedure to find a point estimate of the variance of the sample mean. (*Hint*: Use sample standard deviation to estimate population standard deviation).
d. Use an unbiased estimator to estimate the proportion of homes in this suburb selling for less than £280,000.

7.3 A random sample of 10 economists produced the following forecasts for percentage unemployment rate in the next year:

4.4 4.2 3.7 3.9 4.4 3.9 3.7 4.0 4.1 4.0

a. The population mean
b. The population variance
c. The variance of the sample mean
d. The population proportion of economists predicting unemployment rate of at least 4.0%

7.4 A random sample of 15 employees in a large manufacturing plant found the following figures for number of hours of overtime worked in the last month:

24 16 17 18 21 17 16 19 19 24 15 19 18 21 24

Use unbiased estimation procedures to find point estimates for the following:

a. The population mean
b. The population variance
c. The variance of the sample mean
d. The population proportion of employees working more than 20 hours of overtime in this plant in the last month

Application Exercises

7.5 The Mendez Mortgage Company case study was introduced in Chapter 2. A random sample of $n = 350$ accounts of the company's total portfolio is stored in the data file **Mendez Mortgage**. Consider the variable "Original Purchase Price." Use unbiased estimation procedures to find point estimates of the following:

a. The population mean
b. The population variance
c. The variance of the sample mean
d. The population proportion of all mortgages with original purchase price of less than $10,000

7.6 The demand for bottled water increases during the hurricane season in Florida. The operations manager at a plant that bottles drinking water wants to be sure that the filling process for 1-gallon bottles (1 gallon is approximately 3.785 liters) is operating properly. Currently, the company is testing the volumes of one-gallon bottles. Suppose that a random sample of 75 bottles is tested, and the measurements are recorded in the data file **Water**.

a. Is there evidence that the data are not normally distributed?
b. Find a minimum variance unbiased point estimate of the population mean.
c. Find a minimum variance unbiased point estimate of the population variance.

7.7 Suppose that x_1 and x_2 are random samples of observations from a population with mean μ and variance s^2. Consider the following three point estimators, X, Y, Z, of μ:

$$X = \frac{1}{2}x_1 + \frac{1}{2}x_2 \quad Y = \frac{1}{4}x_1 + \frac{3}{4}x_2 \quad Z = \frac{1}{3}x_1 + \frac{2}{3}x_2$$

a. Show that all three estimators are unbiased.
b. Which of the estimators is the most efficient?
c. Find the relative efficiency of X with respect to each of the other two estimators.

We first assume that a random sample is taken from a population that is normally distributed with an unknown mean and a *known* variance. The chief virtue in beginning with this problem is that it allows a fairly straightforward exposition of the procedures involved in finding confidence intervals. Our objective is to find a range of values, rather than a single number, to estimate a population mean. *This problem may seem to be unrealistic, since rarely will a population variance be precisely known and yet the mean be unknown.* However, it does sometimes happen that similar populations have been sampled so often in the past that the variance of the population of interest can be assumed known to a very close approximation on the basis of past experience. Also, when the sample size n is large enough, the procedures developed for the case with the population variance known can be used even if that population variance has to be estimated from the sample. We consider the more practical situation with population variance *unknown* in Section 7.3.

The average number of bottles of suntan lotion filled per day by Hawaiian Tropic or Panama Jack or the mean number of days for an online order to be shipped by online companies such as Amazon or Zappos are important measures. Wide variation above and below the mean might result in excessive inventory costs, lost sales, or changes in customer satisfaction. We need an estimator and an estimate that take into account this variation, giving a range of values in which the quantity to be estimated appears likely to lie. In this section we establish the general format for such estimators.

In sampling from a population, with all other things being equal, a more secure *knowledge* about that population is obtained with a relatively large sample than would be obtained from a smaller sample. However, this factor is not reflected in point estimates. For example, a point estimate of the proportion of defective parts in a shipment would be the same if one defective part in a sample of 10 parts is observed or if 100 defective parts in a sample of 1,000 parts are observed. Increased precision in our information about population parameters is reflected in *confidence interval estimates*; specifically, all other things being equal, the larger the sample size, the narrower the interval estimates that reflect our uncertainty about a parameter's true value.

Confidence Interval Estimator

A **confidence interval estimator** for a population parameter is a rule for determining (based on sample information) an interval that is likely to include the parameter. The corresponding estimate is called a **confidence interval estimate**.

So far, interval estimators have been described as being "likely" or "very likely" to include the true, but unknown, value of the population parameter. To make our discussion more precise, it is necessary to phrase such terms as probability statements. Suppose that a random sample has been taken and that, based on the sample information, it is possible to find two random variables, A and B, with A less than B. If the specific sample values of the random variables A and B are a and b, then the interval extending from a to b either includes the parameter or it doesn't. We really don't know for sure.

However, suppose that random samples are repeatedly taken from the population and, in the same fashion, similar intervals are found. In the long run a certain percentage of these intervals (say, 95% or 98%) will contain the unknown value. According to the relative frequency concept of probability, an interpretation of such intervals follows: *If the population is repeatedly sampled and intervals are calculated in this fashion, then in the long run 95% (or some other percentage) of the intervals would contain the true value of the unknown parameter.* The interval from A to B is then said to be a 95% confidence interval estimator for the population proportion. The general case follows.

Confidence Interval and Confidence Level

Let θ be an unknown parameter. Suppose that on the basis of sample information, random variables A and B are found such that $P(A < \theta < B) = 1 - \alpha$, where α is any number between 0 and 1. If the specific sample values of A and B are a and b, then the interval from a to b is called a $100(1 - \alpha)\%$ **confidence interval** of θ. The quantity $100(1 - \alpha)\%$ is called the **confidence level** of the interval.

If the population is repeatedly sampled a very large number of times, the true value of the parameter θ will be covered by $100(1 - \alpha)\%$ of intervals calculated this way. The confidence interval calculated in this manner is written as $a < \theta < b$, with $100(1 - \alpha)\%$ confidence.

Keep in mind that any time sampling occurs, one expects the possibility of a difference between the particular value of an estimator and the parameter's true value. The true value of an unknown parameter θ might be somewhat greater or somewhat less than the value determined by even the best point estimator $\hat{\theta}$. It is not surprising that for many estimation problems, a confidence interval estimate of the unknown parameter takes on the general form

$$\hat{\theta} \pm ME$$

where ME, the margin of error, is the error factor.

Intervals Based on the Normal Distribution

Let $x_1, x_2, \ldots, x_n$ be a random sample of n observations from a normally distributed population with unknown mean μ and known variance σ^2. Suppose that we want a $100(1 - \alpha)\%$ confidence interval of the population mean. In Chapter 6 we saw that

$$Z = \frac{\bar{x} - \mu}{\sigma/\sqrt{n}}$$

has a standard normal distribution and $z_{\alpha/2}$ is the value from the standard normal distribution such that the upper tail probability is $\alpha/2$. We use basic algebra to find the following:

$$
\begin{aligned}
1 - \alpha &= P(-z_{\alpha/2} < Z < z_{\alpha/2}) \\
&= P\left(-z_{\alpha/2} < \frac{\bar{x} - \mu}{\sigma/\sqrt{n}} < z_{\alpha/2}\right) \\
&= P\left(-z_{\alpha/2}\frac{\sigma}{\sqrt{n}} < \bar{x} - \mu < z_{\alpha/2}\frac{\sigma}{\sqrt{n}}\right) \\
&= P\left(\bar{x} - z_{\alpha/2}\frac{\sigma}{\sqrt{n}} < \mu < \bar{x} + z_{\alpha/2}\frac{\sigma}{\sqrt{n}}\right)
\end{aligned}
$$

For a 95% confidence level it follows that

$$P\left(\bar{x} - 1.96\frac{\sigma}{\sqrt{n}} < \mu < \bar{x} + 1.96\frac{\sigma}{\sqrt{n}}\right) = 0.95$$

Figure 7.3 shows that the probability is 0.95 and that a standard normal random variable falls between the numbers -1.96 and 1.96.

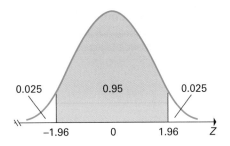

Figure 7.3
$P(-1.96 < Z < 1.96) =$
0.95, Where Z Is a
Standard Normal
Random Variable

Confidence Interval Estimation for the Mean of a Population That Is Normally Distributed: Population Variance Known

Consider a random sample of n observations from a normal distribution with mean μ and variance σ^2. If the sample mean is $\bar{x}$, then a $100(1 - \alpha)\%$ **confidence interval for the population mean with known variance** is given by

$$\bar{x} \pm z_{\alpha/2}\frac{\sigma}{\sqrt{n}} \tag{7.1}$$

or, equivalently,

$$\bar{x} \pm ME$$

where ME, the **margin of error** (also called the **sampling error**), is given by

$$ME = z_{\alpha/2}\frac{\sigma}{\sqrt{n}} \tag{7.2}$$

The **width**, w, is equal to twice the margin of error:

$$w = 2(ME) \tag{7.3}$$

The **upper confidence limit (UCL)** is given by

$$UCL = \bar{x} + z_{\alpha/2}\frac{\sigma}{\sqrt{n}} \tag{7.4}$$

The **lower confidence limit (LCL)** is given by

$$LCL = \bar{x} - z_{\alpha/2}\frac{\sigma}{\sqrt{n}} \tag{7.5}$$

We need to interpret accurately confidence intervals. If random samples of n observations are drawn repeatedly and independently from the population and $100(1 - \alpha)\%$ confidence intervals are calculated by Equation 7.1, then over a very large number of repeated trials, $100(1 - \alpha)\%$ of these intervals will contain the true value of the population mean.

For selected confidence levels, Table 7.2 lists corresponding values of $z_{\alpha/2}$, sometimes called the **reliability factor**. For a 90% confidence interval, Equation 7.1 becomes the following:

$$\bar{x} \pm 1.645\frac{\sigma}{\sqrt{n}}$$

Table 7.2 Selected Confidence Levels and Corresponding Values of $z_{\alpha/2}$

CONFIDENCE LEVEL	90%	95%	98%	99%
α	0.100	0.05	0.02	0.01
$z_{\alpha/2}$	1.645	1.96	2.33	2.58

For a 95% confidence interval, Equation 7.1 becomes the following:

$$\bar{x} \pm 1.96\frac{\sigma}{\sqrt{n}}$$

Example 7.3 Time at the Grocery Store (Confidence Interval)

Suppose that shopping times for customers at a local mall are normally distributed with known population standard deviation of 20 minutes. A random sample of 64 shoppers in the local grocery store had a mean time of 75 minutes. Find the standard error, margin of error, and the upper and lower confidence limits of a 95% confidence interval for the population mean, μ.

Solution The standard error and the margin of error are as follows:

$$\text{standard error} = \frac{\sigma}{\sqrt{n}} = \frac{20}{\sqrt{64}} = 2.5$$

$$ME = z_{\alpha/2}\frac{\sigma}{\sqrt{n}} = 1.96(2.5) = 4.9$$

It follows from Equations 7.4 and 7.5 that the upper and lower confidence limits for a 95% confidence interval are as follows:

$$UCL = \bar{x} + z_{\alpha/2}\frac{\sigma}{\sqrt{n}} = 75 + 4.9 = 79.9$$

$$LCL = \bar{x} - z_{\alpha/2}\frac{\sigma}{\sqrt{n}} = 75 - 4.9 = 70.1$$

How should such a confidence interval be interpreted? Based on a sample of 64 observations, a 95% confidence interval for the unknown population mean extends from approximately 70 minutes to approximately 80 minutes. Now, this particular sample is just one of many that might have been drawn from the population. If we start over again and take a second sample of 64 shoppers, it is virtually certain that the mean of the second sample will differ from that of the first. Accordingly, if a 95% confidence interval is calculated from the results of the second sample, it probably will differ from the interval just found. Imagine taking a very large number of independent random samples of 64 observations from this population and, from each sample result, calculating a 95% confidence interval. *The confidence level of the interval implies that in the long run, 95% of intervals found in this manner contain the true value of the population mean.* It is in this sense reported that there is 95% confidence in our interval estimate. However, it is not known whether our interval is one of the good 95% or bad 5% without knowing μ.

Figure 7.4 shows the sampling distribution of the sample mean of n observations from a population that is normally distributed with mean μ and standard deviation σ. This sampling distribution is normally distributed with mean μ and standard deviation $\sigma/\sqrt{n}$. A confidence interval for the population mean will be based on the observed value of the sample mean—that is, on an observation drawn from our sampling distribution.

Figure 7.5 shows a schematic description of a sequence of 95% confidence intervals, obtained from independent samples taken from the population. The centers of these intervals, which are just the observed sample means, will often be quite close to the population mean, μ. However, some may differ quite substantially from μ. It follows that 95% of a large number of these intervals will contain the population mean.

Figure 7.4

Sampling Distribution of Sample Mean of n Observations from a Normal Distribution with Mean μ, Variance σ^2, and 95% Confidence Level

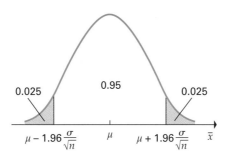

Figure 7.5

Schematic Description of 95% Confidence Intervals

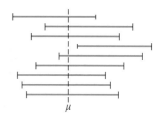

Reducing Margin of Error

Can the margin of error (and, consequently, the width) of a confidence interval be reduced? Consider the factors that affect the margin of error: the population standard deviation, the sample size n, and the confidence level.

Keeping all other factors constant, the more that the population standard deviation, σ, can be reduced, the smaller the margin of error. Corporations strive to reduce variability in product measurements. When possible, this should be the first step to decrease width. However, sometimes the population standard deviation cannot be reduced.

Another way to reduce the margin of error is to increase the sample size. This will reduce the standard deviation of the sampling distribution of the sample mean and, hence, the margin of error. That is, keeping all other factors constant, an increase in the sample size n will decrease the margin of error. The more information obtained from a population, the more precise our inference about its mean. When looking at Equation 7.2 for the margin of error, notice that the interval width is directly proportional to $1/\sqrt{n}$. For example, if the sample size is increased by a factor of 4, the interval width is reduced by half. If the original sample size were 100, an increase to a sample size of 400 would lead to an interval half the width of the original confidence interval (keeping all other factors constant). The disadvantage to an increased sample size is increased costs.

Finally, keeping all other factors constant, if the confidence level $(1 - \alpha)$ is decreased, the margin of error is also reduced. For example, a 95% confidence interval is shorter than a 99% confidence interval based on the same information. *Caution:* The reduction of the confidence level reduces the probability that the interval includes the value of the true population parameter. Figure 7.6 illustrates some of the effects of sample size n, population standard deviation σ, and confidence level $(1 - \alpha)$ on confidence intervals for the mean of a population that has a normal distribution; in each case the sample mean is 19.80.

Figure 7.6
Effects of Sample Size, Population Standard Deviation, and Confidence Level on Confidence Intervals

EXERCISES

Basic Exercises

7.8 Find the reliability factor, $Z_{\alpha\backslash 2}$, to estimate the mean, μ, of a normally distributed population with known population variance for the following.

 a. 81% confidence level
 b. 86% confidence level
 c. 80% confidence level

7.9 Find the reliability factor, $z_{\alpha\backslash 2}$, to estimate the mean, μ, of a normally distributed population with known population variance for the following.

 a. $\alpha = 0.09$
 b. $\alpha\backslash 2 = 0.01$

7.10 Assume a normal distribution with known population variance. Calculate the margin of error to estimate the population mean for the following.

 a. 99% confidence level; $n = 81; \sigma^2 = 169$
 b. 90% confidence level; $n = 200; \sigma = 120$

7.11 Assume a normal distribution with known population variance. Calculate the width to estimate the population mean, μ, for the following.

 a. 90% confidence level; $n = 100; \sigma^2 = 169$
 b. 95% confidence level; $n = 120; \sigma = 25$

7.12 Assume a normal distribution with known population variance. Calculate the LCL and UCL for each of the following.

 a. $\bar{x} = 255; n = 304; \sigma = 30; \alpha = 0.01$
 b. $\bar{x} = 395; n = 105; \sigma^2 = 100; \alpha = 0.05$
 c. $\bar{x} = 510; n = 485; \sigma = 50; \alpha = 0.10$

Application Exercises

7.13 A personnel manager has found that historically the scores on aptitude tests given to applicants for entry-level positions follow a normal distribution with a standard deviation of 32.4 points. A random sample of nine test scores from the current group of applicants had a mean score of 187.9 points.

 a. Find an 80% confidence interval for the population mean score of the current group of applicants.
 b. Based on these sample results, a statistician found for the population mean a confidence interval extending from 165.8 to 210.0 points. Find the confidence level of this interval.

7.14 It is known that the standard deviation in the volumes of 20-ounce (591-millliliter) bottles of natural spring water bottled by a particular company is 5 millliliters. One hundred bottles are randomly sampled and measured.

 a. Calculate the standard error of the mean.
 b. Find the margin of error of a 90% confidence interval estimate for the population mean volume.
 c. Calculate the width for a 98% confidence interval for the population mean volume.

7.15 A college admissions officer for an MBA program has determined that historically applicants have undergraduate grade point averages that are normally distributed with standard deviation 0.45. From a random sample of 25 applications from the current year, the sample mean grade point average is 2.90.

 a. Find a 95% confidence interval for the population mean.
 b. Based on these sample results, a statistician computes for the population mean a confidence interval extending from 2.81 to 2.99. Find the confidence level associated with this interval.

7.16 A process produces bags of refined sugar. The weights of the contents of these bags are normally distributed with standard deviation 1.2 ounces. The contents of a random sample of 25 bags had a mean weight of 19.8 ounces. Find the upper and lower confidence limits of a 99% confidence interval for the true mean weight for all bags of sugar produced by the process.

7.3 CONFIDENCE INTERVAL ESTIMATION FOR THE MEAN OF A NORMAL DISTRIBUTION: POPULATION VARIANCE UNKNOWN

In the preceding section confidence intervals for the mean of a normal population when the population variance was known were derived. Now, we study the case of considerable practical importance where the value of the population variance is unknown. For example, consider the following:

1. Corporate executives employed by retail distributors may want to estimate mean daily sales for their retail stores.
2. Manufacturers may want to estimate the average productivity, in units per hour, for workers using a particular manufacturing process.
3. Automobile/truck manufacturers may want to estimate the average fuel consumption, measured in miles per gallon, for a particular vehicle model.

In these types of situations, there is probably no historical information concerning either the population mean or the population variance. To proceed further, it is necessary to introduce a new class of probability distributions that were developed by William Sealy Gosset, an Irish statistician, who was employed by the Guinness Brewery in Dublin in the early 1900s (Pearson and Plackett 1990; Salsburg 2002).

Student's *t* Distribution

Gosset sought to develop a probability distribution, when the population variance σ^2 is not known, for a normally distributed random variable. At this time laboratory tests and the scientific method were beginning to be applied to the brewing industry. Gosset, whose works appeared under the pseudonym "Student," was influential in the development of modern statistical thinking and process variation: "The circumstances of brewing work, with its variable materials and susceptibility to temperature change . . . emphasize the necessity for a correct method of treating small samples. It was thus no accident, but the circumstances of his work that directed Student's attention to this problem, and led to his discovery of the distribution of the sample standard deviation . . ." (Pearson and Wishart 1958). Gosset showed the connection between statistical research and practical problems. The distribution is still known as the Student's *t* distribution. The Student's *t* distribution developed by Gosset is the ratio of the standard normal distribution to the square root of the chi-square distribution divided by its degrees of freedom, v (see the chapter appendix).

The development of Section 7.2 was based on the fact that the random variable Z, given by

$$Z = \frac{\overline{X} - \mu}{\sigma/\sqrt{n}}$$

has a standard normal distribution. In the case where the population standard deviation is unknown, this result cannot be used directly. It is natural in such circumstances to consider the random variable obtained by replacing the unknown σ by the sample standard deviation, *s*, giving

$$t = \frac{\overline{x} - \mu}{s/\sqrt{n}}$$

This random variable does not follow a standard normal distribution. However, its distribution is known and is, in fact, a member of a family of distributions called Student's *t*.

Student's t Distribution

Given a random sample of n observations, with mean $\bar{x}$ and standard deviation s, from a normally distributed population with mean μ, the random variable t follows the **Student's t distribution** with $(n - 1)$ degrees of freedom and is given by

$$t = \frac{\bar{x} - \mu}{s/\sqrt{n}}$$

A specific member of the family of Student's t distributions is characterized by the number of degrees of freedom associated with the computation of the standard error. We will use the parameter v to represent the degrees of freedom and a Student's t random variable with v degrees of freedom will be denoted t_v. The shape of the Student's t distribution is rather similar to that of the standard normal distribution. Both distributions have mean 0, and the probability density functions of both are symmetric about their means. However, the density function of the Student's t distribution has a wider dispersion (reflected in a larger variance) than the standard normal distribution. This can be seen in Figure 7.7, which shows density functions for the standard normal distribution and the Student's t distribution with 3 degrees of freedom.

Figure 7.7
Probability Density Functions of the Standard Normal and the Student's t Distribution with 3 Degrees of Freedom

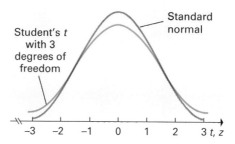

The additional dispersion in the Student's t distribution arises as a result of the extra uncertainty caused by replacing the known population standard deviation with its sample estimator. As the number of degrees of freedom increases, the Student's t distribution becomes increasingly similar to the standard normal distribution. For large degrees of freedom, the two distributions are virtually identical. That is, the Student's t distribution converges to $N(0, 1)$, which is quite close to the t as long as n is large. This is intuitively reasonable and follows from the fact that for a large sample, the sample standard deviation is a very precise estimator of the population standard deviation.

In order to base inferences about a population mean on the Student's t distribution, critical values analogous to $z_{\alpha/2}$ are needed. Just as $z_{\alpha/2}$ is the value from the standard normal distribution such that the upper tail probability is $\alpha/2$, so $t_{v,\alpha/2}$ is the value from the Student's t distribution for v (degrees of freedom) such that the upper tail probability is $\alpha/2$, as shown in Figure 7.8.

Figure 7.8
$P(t_v > t_{v,\alpha/2}) = \alpha/2$, Where t_v is a Student's t Random Variable with v Degrees of Freedom

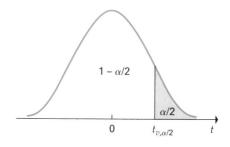

Suppose that the number that is exceeded with probability 0.05 by a Student's t random variable with 15 degrees of freedom is required:

$$P(t_{15} > t_{15,0.05}) = 0.05$$

Reading directly from the Student's t distribution table,

$$t_{15,0.05} = 1.753$$

Many computer programs can be used to obtain these values as well.

Intervals Based on the Student's t Distribution

We will encounter many situations in which the population variance is not known. Finding the $100(1 - \alpha)\%$ confidence interval for this type of problem follows precisely the same line of reasoning as in Section 7.2. Terminology is analogous.

Assume that a random sample of n observations is available from a normal population with mean μ and unknown variance and that confidence intervals for the population mean are required. This type of situation occurs in applications to business, government, and medical or other research. First, we stress the importance of checking to see if the data indicate nonnormality. Although we assume normality throughout this chapter, we demonstrate one method to check this assumption in Example 7.4 by using the normal probability plot introduced in Chapter 5. The normal probability plot tests whether the data are not normally distributed. Confidence interval terminology for a population mean with unknown variance is similar to the situation with variance known.

Example 7.4 Trucks: Gasoline Consumption (Confidence Interval)

Recently gasoline prices rose drastically. Suppose that a study was conducted using truck drivers with equivalent years of experience to test run 24 trucks of a particular model over the same highway. Estimate the population mean fuel consumption for this truck model with 90% confidence if the fuel consumption, in miles per gallon, for these 24 trucks was as follows:

15.5	21.0	18.5	19.3	19.7	16.9	20.2	14.5
16.5	19.2	18.7	18.2	18.0	17.5	18.5	20.5
18.6	19.1	19.8	18.0	19.8	18.2	20.3	21.8

The data are stored in the data file **Trucks**.

Solution We check the normality assumption by constructing the normal probability plot. Figure 7.9 does not provide evidence of nonnormality.

Figure 7.9 Normal Probability Plot

Next, calculating the mean and standard deviation, we find the following:

$$\bar{x} = 18.68 \quad s = 1.69526 \quad t_{n-1,\alpha/2} = t_{23,0.05} = 1.714$$

By Equation 7.6 the 90% confidence interval is as follows:

$$\bar{x} \pm t_{n-1,\alpha/2}\frac{s}{\sqrt{n}} = 18.68 \pm t_{23,0.05}\frac{1.69526}{\sqrt{24}} = 18.68 \pm (1.714) \times (0.3460)$$

$$= 18.68 \pm 0.5930$$

The lower confidence limit is approximately equal to 18.1, and the upper confidence limit is approximately equal to 19.3. Figure 7.10 is the Excel output of descriptive statistics generated for the data file **Trucks**.

The interpretation of the confidence interval is important. If independent random samples of 24 trucks are repeatedly selected from the population and confidence intervals for each of these samples are determined, then over a very large number of repeated trials, 90% of these intervals will contain the value of the true mean fuel consumption for this model truck. In practice, however, one does not repeatedly draw such independent samples.

Figure 7.10 Output for
Data File **Trucks** (Excel)

Mean	**18.67917**
Standard Error	0.346043
Median	18.65
Mode	18.5
Standard Deviation	1.605257
Sample Variance	2.873895
Kurtosis	0.624798
Skewness	−0.60902
Range	7.3
Minimum	14.5
Maximum	21.8
Sum	448.3
Count	24
Confidence Level (90.0%)	**0.593072**

The question may arise about how to handle confidence interval estimation of a population mean when the sample size is large and the population variance is unknown. Recall that in Example 2.7, the sample size for the Healthy Eating Index–2005 data was $n = 4,460$ individuals. Clearly, the population variance is unknown and the sample size is quite large. A confidence interval estimate for the population mean HEI score is presented in Example 7.5.

Example 7.5 Healthy Eating Index–2005 (Confidence Interval Estimate of the Population Mean, for Normal Distribution, Large Sample Size)

The HEI measures on a 100-point scale, the adequacy of consumption of vegetables, fruits, grains, milk, meat and beans, and liquid oils. This scale is called HEI2005 (Guenther et al. 2007). There are two observations for each person in the study. The first observation, identified by daycode = 1, contains data from the first interview and the second observation, daycode = 2, contains data from the second interview. This data, for a random sample of $n = 4,460$ participants are stored in the data file **HEI Cost Data Variable Subset.** Find a 95% confidence interval for the mean HEI–2005 score for participants at the time of their first interview.

Solution With a large sample size of $n = 4,460$ observations, we find the sample mean and the sample standard deviation for the HEI–2005 scores using Excel, Minitab, SPSS, or some other software. Figure 7.11 provides the Excel output giving these descriptive measures.

Figure 7.11 HEI–2005
Scores: First Interview
Descriptive Measures
(Excel)

HEI2005	
Mean	**52.01003**
Standard Error	**0.212601**
Median	51.53633
Mode	#N/A
Standard Deviation	14.19817
Sample Variance	201.588
Kurtosis	−0.57356
Skewness	0.186753
Range	88.28539
Minimum	11.17156
Maximum	99.45695
Sum	2,319,64.7
Count	4,460

Clearly from the central limit theorem (Chapter 6) and the large sample size, it follows that the reliability factor is approximately 1.96; that is,

$$t_{4459,0.025} \cong 1.96$$

Using Equation 7.6, we find the 95% confidence interval for the population mean HEI–2005 score of participants at the first interview as follows:

$$\bar{x} \pm t_{n-1,\alpha/2}\frac{s}{\sqrt{n}} = 52.0 \pm t_{4459,0.025}\frac{14.19817}{\sqrt{4,460}}$$

The 95% confidence interval estimate of the population mean HEI–2005 score is found to be

$$52.01 \pm 1.96(0.2126) = 52.01 \pm 0.4167$$

EXERCISES

 Visit www.MyStatLab.com or www.pearsonglobal editions.com to access the data files.

Basic Exercises

7.17 Find the standard error to estimate the population mean for each of the following.

   a. $n = 17$; 95% confidence level; $s = 16$
   b. $n = 25$; 90% confidence level; $s^2 = 43$

7.18 Calculate the margin of error to estimate the population mean for each of the following.

   a. 99% confidence level;
      $x_1 = 25; x_2 = 30; x_3 = 33; x_4 = 21$
   b. 90% confidence level;
      $x_1 = 15; x_2 = 17; x_3 = 13; x_4 = 11; x_5 = 14$

7.19 Twenty people in one large metropolitan area were asked to record the time (in minutes) that it takes them to drive to work. These times were as follows:

   30 42 35 40 45 22 32 15 41 45

   28 32 45 27 47 50 30 25 46 25

   a. Calculate the standard error.
   b. Find $t_{v,\alpha/2}$ for a 95% confidence interval for the true population mean.
   c. Calculate the width for a 95% confidence interval for the population mean time spent driving to work.

7.20 Find the LCL and UCL for each of the following.

   a. $\alpha = 0.05; n = 25; \bar{x} = 560; s = 45$
   b. $\alpha/2 = 0.05; n = 9; \bar{x} = 160; s^2 = 36$
   c. $1 - \alpha = 0.98; n = 22; \bar{x} = 58; s = 15$

7.21 A random sample of 16 tires was tested to estimate the average life of this type of tire under normal driving conditions. The sample mean and sample standard deviation were found to be 47,500 miles and 4,200 miles, respectively.

   a. Calculate the margin of error for a 95% confidence interval estimate of the mean lifetime of this type of tire if driven under normal driving conditions.
   b. Find the UCL and the LCL of a 90% confidence interval estimate of the mean lifetime of this type of tire if driven under normal driving conditions.

7.22 Calculate the width for each of the following.

   a. $n = 6; s = 40; \alpha = 0.05$
   b. $n = 22; s^2 = 400; \alpha = 0.01$
   c. $n = 25; s = 50; \alpha = 0.10$

Application Exercises

7.23 In Example 7.5 we calculated a 95% confidence interval estimate of the Healthy Eating Index–2005 score for a random sample of participants at the time of their first interview. Recall that there are two observations for each person in the study. The first observation, identified by daycode = 1, contains data from the first interview and the second observation, daycode = 2, contains data from the second interview. Find a 95% confidence interval for the mean HEI–2005 score for participants at the time of their second interview. The data are stored in the data file **HEI Cost Data Variable Subset.**

7.24 A machine that packages 18-ounce (510-gram) boxes of sugar-coated wheat cereal is being studied. The weights for a random sample of 100 boxes of cereal packaged by this machine are contained in the data file **Sugar**.

   a. Find a 90% confidence interval for the population mean cereal weight.
   b. Without doing the calculations, state whether an 80% confidence interval for the population mean would be wider than, narrower than, or the same as the answer to part a.

7.25 How much do students pay, on an average, for textbooks during the first semester of college? From a random sample of 250 students from the Corvinus University of Budapest, Hungary, the mean cost was found to be 361.75 Hungarian Forint (Ft), and the sample standard deviation was 37.54 Ft. Assuming that the population is normally distributed, find the margin of error of a 90% confidence interval for the population mean.

7.26 There is concern about the speed of automobiles traveling over a particular stretch of highway. For a random sample of 28 automobiles, radar indicated the following speeds, in miles per hour:

   59 63 68 57 56 71 59

   69 53 58 60 66 51 59

   54 64 58 57 66 61 65

   70 63 65 57 56 61 59

Assuming a normal population distribution (See Exercise 7.1), find the margin of error of a 95% confidence interval for the mean speed of all automobiles traveling over this stretch of highway.

7.27 Weight Medics, a clinic in the United Kingdom, offers a weight-loss program for its clients. A review of its records found the following amounts of weight loss, in pounds, for a random sample of 20 clients at the end of a 4-month program:

24	19	5	12	16	10	18	15	8	17
11	6	14	8	19	22	13	20	11	30

a. Find a 95% confidence interval for the population mean.

b. Without doing the calculations, explain whether a 90% confidence interval for the population mean would be wider than, narrower than, or the same as that found in part a.

7.28 A business school placement director wants to estimate the mean annual salaries 5 years after students graduate. A random sample of 25 such graduates found a sample mean of $42,740 and a sample standard deviation of $4,780. Find a 90% confidence interval for the population mean, assuming that the population distribution is normal.

7.29 Build Rental is a plant hire company in the United Kingdom that provides machinery, equipment, and tools for a limited period to construction contractors. It is interested in the amount of time its equipment are out of operation for repair work. State all assumptions and find a 90% confidence interval for the mean number of days in a year that all Build Rental's equipment are out of operation if a random sample of nine pieces of equipment showed the following number of days that each had been inoperative:

16   15   11   26   18   23   8   8   24   14

7.4 CONFIDENCE INTERVAL ESTIMATION FOR POPULATION PROPORTION (LARGE SAMPLES)

What percent of European students expect to pursue doctoral degrees? What percent of college admission personnel think that SAT scores are a good indicator of academic success in college? What proportion of the students at a particular university would like classes to be offered on Saturdays? What proportion of registered voters will vote for a particular candidate in the upcoming election? In each of these scenarios the proportion of population members possessing some specific characteristic is of interest. If a random sample is taken from the population, the sample proportion provides a natural point estimator of the population proportion. In this section confidence intervals for the population proportion are established.

Using the binomial setup, we let $\hat{p}$ denote the proportion of "successes" in n independent trials, each with probability of success P. We saw in Chapter 6 that if the number n of sample members is large, then the random variable

$$Z = \frac{\hat{p} - P}{\sqrt{\dfrac{P(1 - P)}{n}}}$$

has, to a close approximation, a standard normal distribution. If the sample size is large enough that $nP(1 - P) > 5$, then a good approximation is obtained if P is replaced by the point estimator $\hat{p}$ in the denominator:

$$\sqrt{\frac{P(1 - P)}{n}} \approx \sqrt{\frac{\hat{p}(1 - \hat{p})}{n}}$$

Hence, for large sample sizes, the distribution of the random variable

$$Z = \frac{\hat{p} - P}{\sqrt{\hat{p}(1 - \hat{p})/n}}$$

is approximately standard normal. This result can now be used to obtain confidence intervals for the population proportion. The derivation is similar to the preceding examples.

$$1 - \alpha = P(-z_{\alpha/2} < Z < z_{\alpha/2})$$

$$= P\left(-z_{\alpha/2} < \frac{\hat{p} - P}{\sqrt{\dfrac{\hat{p}(1 - \hat{p})}{n}}} < z_{\alpha/2}\right)$$

$$= P\left(-z_{\alpha/2}\sqrt{\frac{\hat{p}(1 - \hat{p})}{n}} < \hat{p} - P < z_{\alpha/2}\sqrt{\frac{\hat{p}(1 - \hat{p})}{n}}\right)$$

$$= P\left(\hat{p} - z_{\alpha/2}\sqrt{\frac{\hat{p}(1 - \hat{p})}{n}} < P < \hat{p} + z_{\alpha/2}\sqrt{\frac{\hat{p}(1 - \hat{p})}{n}}\right)$$

Therefore, if the observed sample proportion is $\hat{p}$ an approximate $100(1 - \alpha)\%$ confidence interval for the population proportion is given, as seen in Equation 7.8, which follows.

Confidence Intervals for Population Proportion (Large Samples)

Let $\hat{p}$ denote the observed proportion of "successes" in a random sample of n observations from a population with a proportion of successes P. Then, if $nP(1 - P) > 5$, a $100(1 - \alpha)\%$ **confidence interval for the population proportion** is given by

$$\hat{p} \pm z_{\alpha/2}\sqrt{\frac{\hat{p}(1 - \hat{p})}{n}} \tag{7.8}$$

or, equivalently,

$$\hat{p} \pm ME$$

where ME, the margin of error, is given by

$$ME = z_{\alpha/2}\sqrt{\frac{\hat{p}(1 - \hat{p})}{n}} \tag{7.9}$$

Confidence intervals for the population proportion are centered on the sample proportion. Also, it can be seen that, all other things being equal, the larger the sample size, n, the narrower the confidence interval. This reflects the increasing precision of the information about the population proportion obtained as the sample size becomes larger.

Example 7.6 Modified Bonus Plan (Confidence Interval)

Management wants an estimate of the proportion of the corporation's employees who favor a modified bonus plan. From a random sample of 344 employees, it was found that 261 were in favor of this particular plan. Find a 90% confidence interval estimate of the true population proportion that favors this modified bonus plan.

Solution The sample proportion, $\hat{p}$, and the reliability factor for a 90% confidence interval estimate $(\alpha = 0.10)$ of the true population proportion, P, are found to be

$$\hat{p} = 261/344 = 0.759$$
$$z_{\alpha/2} = z_{0.05} = 1.645$$

Therefore, from Equation 7.8, a 90% confidence interval for the population proportion is

$$0.759 \pm 1.645\sqrt{\frac{(0.759)(0.241)}{344}}$$

$$0.759 \pm 0.038$$

Strictly speaking, what does this interval [0.721, 0.797] imply? Imagine taking a very large number of independent random samples of 344 observations from this population and, from each sample result, calculating a 90% confidence interval. *The confidence level of the interval implies that in the long run 90% of intervals found in this manner contain the true value of the population proportion.* It is in this sense, we report that there is 90%

confidence in our interval estimate. However, it is not known whether our interval is one of the good 90% or bad 10% without knowing P.

Let's compare the 90% and the 99% confidence intervals. That is, what is the effect on the margin of error (and consequently the width) if the confidence level is increased and all other factors remain constant? From Equation 7.9, the margin of error for the 99% confidence is found to be

$$ME = 2.58\sqrt{\frac{(0.759)(0.241)}{344}} \cong 0.059$$

We see that by increasing the confidence level from 90% to 99%, the margin of error increased from approximately 3.8% to approximately 5.9%. Wide intervals for a given α reflect imprecision in our knowledge about the population proportion. Narrower confidence intervals can be obtained by reducing the confidence level or by taking larger sample sizes.

EXERCISES

 Visit www.MyStatLab.com or www.pearsonglobal editions.com to access the data files.

Basic Exercises

7.30 Find the margin of error to estimate the population proportion for each of the following.

  a. $n = 350$; $\hat{p} = 0.30$; $\alpha = 0.01$
  b. $n = 275$; $\hat{p} = 0.45$; $\alpha = 0.05$
  c. $n = 500$; $\hat{p} = 0.05$; $\alpha = 0.10$

7.31 Calculate the confidence interval to estimate the population proportion for each of the following.

  a. 90% confidence level; $n = 700$; $\hat{p} = 0.20$
  b. 99% confidence level; $n = 140$; $\hat{p} = 0.01$
  c. $\alpha = 0.03$; $n = 345$; $\hat{p} = 0.90$

7.32 A small private university is planning to start a volunteer football program. A random sample of alumni is surveyed. It was found that 250 were in favor of this program, 75 were opposed, and 25 had no opinion.

  a. Estimate the percent of alumni in favor of this program. Let $\alpha = 0.05$.
  b. Estimate the percent of alumni opposed to this volunteer football program with a 90% confidence level.

Application Exercises

7.33 Suppose that a random sample of 126 graduate-admissions personnel from Finland was asked what role scores on standardized tests (such as the GMAT or GRE) play in the consideration of a candidate for graduate school. Of these sample members, 69 answered "very important." Find a 95% confidence interval for the population proportion of graduate admissions personnel with this view.

7.34 In a random sample of 95 manufacturing firms, 67 indicated that their company attained ISO certification within the last two years. Find a 99% confidence interval for the population proportion of companies that have been certified within the last 2 years.

7.35 The Mendez Mortgage Company case study was given in Chapter 2. A random sample of $n = 350$ accounts of the company's total portfolio was selected. Estimate the proportion of all the company's accounts with an original purchase price of less than

$10,000. The data is stored in the data file **Mendez Mortgage**. Use $\alpha = 0.02$.

7.36 Consider again the Mendez Mortgage Company case study in Chapter 2. From a random sample of $n = 350$ accounts of the company's total portfolio, estimate with 95% confidence the proportion of all the company's accounts in which the purchaser's latest FICO score was at least 750. The data is stored in the data file **Mendez Mortgage.**

7.37 From a random sample of 400 registered voters in one city, 320 indicated that they would vote in favor of a proposed policy in an upcoming election.

  a. Calculate the LCL for a 98% confidence interval estimate for the population proportion in favor of this policy.
  b. Calculate the width of a 90% confidence interval estimate for the population proportion in favor of this policy.

7.38 A statistician at the Nagoya University, Japan, was assessing the number of students' résumés with false or misleading information. Suppose the students of the university were asked if such a practice is ethical. Of a random sample of 196 students, 96 said résumé inflation is unethical. Based on this, the statistician computed a confidence interval extending from 0.443 to 0.537 for the population proportion. What is the confidence level of this interval?

7.39 In a presidential election year, candidates want to know how voters in various parts of the country will vote. Suppose that 1 month before the election a random sample of 540 registered voters from one geographic region is surveyed. From this sample 320 indicate that they plan to vote for this particular candidate. Based on this survey data, find the 95% confidence interval estimate of this candidate's current support in this geographic area.

7.40 Do you think that the government should bail out the automobile industry? Suppose that this question was asked in a recent survey of 460 Americans. Respondents were also asked to select the category corresponding to their age (younger than 30; 30 to 50; or older than 50). It was found that 140 respondents were younger than 30;

and 120 respondents were over 50 years old. From the respondents who were younger than 30 years of age, 60 were in favor of the bailout and 30 were undecided. From the respondents who were older than 50 years of age, two-thirds of these respondents were opposed to the bailout; the remaining were in favor; from the age group of 30 to 50, 60% of the respondents were opposed; 25% in favor; and the remainder were undecided.

a. Estimate the proportion of all Americans who are opposed to the bailout using a 95% confidence level.
b. Estimate the proportion of all Americans who are in favor of the bailout using a 90% confidence level.

7.41 It is important for airlines to follow the published scheduled departure times of flights. Suppose that one airline that recently sampled the records of 246 flights originating in Orlando found that 10 flights were delayed for severe weather, 4 flights were delayed for maintenance concerns, and all the other flights were on time.

a. Estimate the percentage of on-time departures using a 98% confidence level.
b. Estimate the percentage of flights delayed for severe weather using a 98% confidence level.

7.5 CONFIDENCE INTERVAL ESTIMATION FOR THE VARIANCE OF A NORMAL DISTRIBUTION

On occasion, interval estimates are required for the variance of a population. As might be expected, such estimates are based on the sample variance. We emphasize here that the population must be normally distributed, and that this normality assumption must be verified.

Suppose a random sample of n observations from a normally distributed population with variance σ^2 and sample variance s^2 is taken. The random variable

$$\chi^2_{n-1} = \frac{(n-1)s^2}{\sigma^2}$$

follows a chi-square distribution with $(n-1)$ degrees of freedom. This result forms the basis for the derivation of confidence intervals for the population variance when sampling from a normal distribution.

In order to develop the formula for calculating confidence intervals for the variance, an additional notation is needed.

Notation

A random variable having the chi-square distribution with $v = n - 1$ degrees of freedom will be denoted by χ^2_v or simply χ^2_{n-1}. Define as $\chi^2_{n-1,\alpha}$ the number for which

$$P(\chi^2_{n-1} > \chi^2_{n-1,\alpha}) = \alpha$$

For a specified probability α, a chi-square number for $n - 1$ degrees of freedom is needed—that is, $\chi^2_{n-1,\alpha}$. This number can be found from values of the cumulative distribution function of a chi-square random variable. We illustrate this notation in Figure 7.12.

Figure 7.12
Chi-Square
Distribution

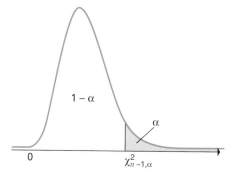

For instance, suppose the number that is exceeded with probability 0.05 by a chi-square random variable with 6 degrees of freedom is needed:

$$P(\chi^2_6 > \chi^2_{6,0.05}) = 0.05$$

From Appendix Table 7, $\chi^2_{6,0.05} = 12.592$. Similarly,

$$P(\chi^2_{n-1} > \chi^2_{n-1,\alpha/2}) = \frac{\alpha}{2}$$

It follows that $\chi^2_{n-1,1-\alpha/2}$ is given by

$$P(\chi^2_{n-1} > \chi^2_{n-1,1-\alpha/2}) = 1 - \frac{\alpha}{2}$$

and hence

$$P(\chi^2_{n-1} < \chi^2_{n-1,1-\alpha/2}) = \frac{\alpha}{2}$$

Finally,

$$P(\chi^2_{n-1,1-\alpha/2} < \chi^2_{n-1} < \chi^2_{n-1,\alpha/2}) = 1 - \frac{\alpha}{2} - \frac{\alpha}{2} = 1 - \alpha$$

This probability is illustrated in Figure 7.13.

Figure 7.13
Chi-Square Distribution for $n-1$ and $(1-\alpha)\%$ Confidence Level

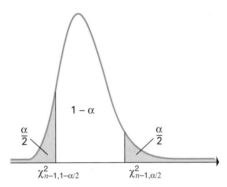

Suppose a pair of numbers is needed such that the probability that a chi-square random variable with 6 degrees of freedom lying between these numbers is 0.90. Then $\alpha = 0.10$ and

$$P(\chi^2_{6,0.95} < \chi^2_6 < \chi^2_{6,0.05}) = 0.90$$

Previously, we found that $\chi^2_{6,0.05} = 12.592$. From Appendix Table 7, we find that $\chi^2_{6,0.95} = 1.635$.

The probability is 0.90 that this chi-square random variable falls between 1.635 and 12.592. To find confidence intervals for the population variance,

$$1 - \alpha = P(\chi^2_{n-1,1-\alpha/2} < \chi^2_{n-1} < \chi^2_{n-1,\alpha/2})$$

$$= P\left(\chi^2_{n-1,1-\alpha/2} < \frac{(n-1)s^2}{\sigma^2} < \chi^2_{n-1,\alpha/2}\right)$$

$$= P\left(\frac{(n-1)s^2}{\chi^2_{n-1,\alpha/2}} < \sigma^2 < \frac{(n-1)s^2}{\chi^2_{n-1,1-\alpha/2}}\right)$$

Confidence Intervals for the Variance of a Normal Population

Suppose that there is a random sample of n observations from a normally distributed population with variance σ^2. If the observed sample variance is s^2, then the lower and upper confidence limits of a $100(1-\alpha)\%$ **confidence interval for the population variance** is given by

$$LCL = \frac{(n-1)s^2}{\chi^2_{n-1,\alpha/2}} \quad \text{and} \quad UCL = \frac{(n-1)s^2}{\chi^2_{n-1,1-\alpha/2}} \tag{7.10}$$

where $\chi^2_{n-1,\alpha/2}$ is the number for which

$$P(\chi^2_{n-1} > \chi^2_{n-1,\alpha/2}) = \frac{\alpha}{2}$$

and $\chi^2_{n-1,1-\alpha/2}$ is the number for which

$$P(\chi^2_{n-1} < \chi^2_{n-1,1-\alpha/2}) = \frac{\alpha}{2}$$

and the random variable χ^2_{n-1} follows a chi-square distribution with $(n-1)$ degrees of freedom.

Although it is assumed throughout this section that the population is normally distributed, we should always check for any evidence that this assumption fails. Notice that the confidence interval in Equation 7.10 is not the usual form, sample point estimator $\pm$ margin of error.

Example 7.7 Comparing Temperature Variances (Confidence Interval)

The manager of Northern Steel, Inc., wants to assess the temperature variation in the firm's new electric furnace. It is known that temperatures are normally distributed. A random sample of 25 temperatures over a 1-week period is obtained, and the sample variance is found to be $s^2 = 100$. Find a 95% confidence interval for the population variance temperature.

Solution Here, $n = 25$ and $s^2 = 100$, and for a 95% confidence interval, $\alpha = 0.05$. It follows from the chi-square distribution in Appendix Table 7 (see Figure 7. 14) that

$$\chi^2_{n-1,1-\alpha/2} = \chi^2_{24,0.975} = 12.401 \quad \text{and} \quad \chi^2_{n-1,\alpha/2} = \chi^2_{24,0.025} = 39.364$$

From Equation 7.10, the lower confidence limit for a 95% confidence interval for the population variance is given by

$$\text{LCL} = \frac{(n-1)s^2}{\chi^2_{n-1,\alpha/2}} = \frac{(24)(100)}{39.364} = 60.97$$

and from Equation 7.10, the upper confidence limit is found as follows:

$$\text{UCL} = \frac{(n-1)s^2}{\chi^2_{n-1,1-\alpha/2}} = \frac{(24)(100)}{12.401} = 193.53.$$

Figure 7.14 Chi-Square Distribution for $n = 25$ and 95% Confidence Level

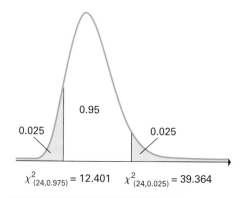

0.95

0.025

0.025

$\chi^2_{(24,0.975)} = 12.401 \qquad \chi^2_{(24,0.025)} = 39.364$

It is dangerous to follow the procedure just demonstrated when the population distribution is not normal. The validity of the interval estimator for the population variance depends far more critically on the assumption of normality than does that of the interval estimator for the population mean.

EXERCISES

 Visit www.MyStatLab.com or www.pearsonglobal editions.com to access the data files.

Basic Exercises

7.42 Find the lower confidence limit for the population variance for each of the following normal populations.

a. $n = 21; \alpha = 0.05; s^2 = 16$
b. $n = 16; \alpha = 0.05; s = 8$
c. $n = 28; \alpha = 0.01; s = 15$

7.43 Find the upper confidence limit for parts a–c of Exercise 7.42.

7.44 Consider the following random sample from a normal population:

11 17 8 7 9

a. Find the 90% confidence interval for population variance.
b. Find the 95% confidence interval for the population variance.

Application Exercises

7.45 LDS wants to be sure that the leak rate (in cubic centimeters per second) of transmission oil coolers (TOCs) meets the established specification limits. A random sample 50 TOCs is tested, and the leak rates are recorded in the data file **TOC**. Estimate the variance in leak rate with a 95% confidence level (check normality).

7.46 A clinic offers a weight-loss program. A review of its records found the following amounts of weight loss, in pounds, for a random sample of 10 clients at the conclusion of the program:

18.2 25.9 6.3 11.8 15.4 20.3 16.8 18.5 12.3 17.2

Find a 90% confidence interval for the population variance of weight loss for clients of this weight-loss program.

7.47 The quality-control manager of a chemical company randomly sampled twenty 100-pound bags of fertilizer to estimate the variance in the pounds of impurities. The sample variance was found to be 6.62. Find a 95% confidence interval for the population variance in the pounds of impurities.

7.48 A psychologist wants to estimate the variance of employee test scores. A random sample of 18 scores had a sample standard deviation of 10.4. Find a 90% confidence interval for the population variance. What are the assumptions, if any, to calculate this interval estimate?

7.49 Pegatron Corporation, a Taiwanese electronics manufacturing company, is concerned about the variability of the levels of impurity contained in consignments of raw material from a supplier. A random sample of 25 consignments showed a standard deviation of 3.45 in the concentration of impurity levels. Assume normality.

a. Find a 95% confidence interval for the population variance.
b. Would a 99% confidence interval for this variance be wider or narrower than that found in part a?

7.50 A watch manufacturer in Switzerland uses sputtered titanium coating for some models it creates. A random sample of nine observations on the thickness of this coating is taken from a week's output, and the recorded thicknesses (in millimeters) are as follows:

19.5 21.4 18.7 20.3 21.7 19.1 19.5 20.8 20.1

Assuming normality, find a 90% confidence interval for the population variance.

7.6 CONFIDENCE INTERVAL ESTIMATION: FINITE POPULATIONS

In this section we consider confidence intervals where the number of sample members is not a negligible proportion of the number of population members. Generally, the sample size is considered to be relatively large compared to the population size if it is more than 5% of the population size, that is, if $n > 0.05N$. We assume that the sample is sufficiently large and that recourse to the central limit theorem is appropriate. As a result, the **finite population correction (fpc) factor**, $(N - n)/(N - 1)$, which was introduced in Chapter 6, will be used. In these situations the individual members are not distributed independently of one another and sampling is without replacement.

Population Mean and Population Total

Here, we consider problems where a sample of n individuals or objects is to be drawn from a population containing N members. We develop confidence intervals for the population mean and the population total when the sample size is more than 5% of the population size.

Estimation of the Population Mean, Simple Random Sample, Finite Population

Let $x_1, x_2, \ldots, x_n$ denote the values observed from a simple random sample of size n, taken from a population of N members with mean μ.

1. The sample mean is an unbiased estimator of the population mean, μ. The point estimate is

$$\bar{x} = \frac{1}{n}\sum_{i=1}^{n} x_i$$

2. An unbiased estimation procedure for the variance of the sample mean yields the point estimate

$$\hat{\sigma}_{\bar{x}}^2 = \frac{s^2}{n}\left(\frac{N-n}{N-1}\right) \tag{7.11}$$

3. A $100(1-\alpha)\%$ confidence interval for the population mean is given by

$$\bar{x} \pm t_{n-1,\alpha/2}\hat{\sigma}_{\bar{x}} \tag{7.12}$$

where ME, the margin of error, is given by

$$ME = t_{n-1,\alpha/2}\hat{\sigma}_{\bar{x}} \tag{7.13}$$

Example 7.8 Mortgages (Confidence Interval)

In a particular city 1,118 mortgages were financed last year. A random sample of 60 of these had a mean amount \$87,300 and standard deviation \$19,200. Estimate the mean amount of all mortgages financed in this city last year, and find a 95% confidence interval.

Solution Denote the population mean by μ. We know that

$$N = 1{,}118 \quad n = 60 \quad \bar{x} = \$87{,}300 \quad s = 19{,}200$$

To obtain interval estimates, use Equation 7.11,

$$\hat{\sigma}_{\bar{x}}^2 = \frac{s^2}{n}\left(\frac{N-n}{N-1}\right) = \frac{(19{,}200)^2}{60}\left(\frac{1{,}058}{1{,}117}\right) = 5{,}819{,}474$$

and take the square root to obtain the estimated standard error,

$$\hat{\sigma}_{\bar{x}} = 2{,}412$$

With $t_{59,0.025} \cong 2.00$ (Appendix Table 8) the margin of error of a 95% confidence interval for the mean amount of all mortgages financed in this city last year is calculated from Equation 7.13 as follows:

$$ME = t_{n-1,\alpha/2}\hat{\sigma}_{\bar{x}} = 2(2{,}412) = \$4{,}824$$

The resulting 95% confidence interval estimate for the mean amount of all mortgages financed in this city last year is

$$\$87{,}300 \pm \$4{,}824$$

That is, the interval runs from \$82,476 to \$92,124.

In Example 7.9, we illustrate a situation when auditors are asked to conduct a sampling audit of a firm's accounts receivable to estimate the mean value of the accounts receivable.

Example 7.9 Confirmation Audit of Receivables (Confidence Interval)

Toivo Steendahl Associates, a major auditing firm, has been engaged to audit Big Woods Furniture, an upper-Midwest furniture retailer, in order to determine the value of the firm's assets preceding a take over by National Distributor. As part of this audit we have been asked to conduct a sampling audit of the accounts receivable to estimate mean value of the accounts receivable. The company presently has 1,420 accounts receivable on the ledger.

Solution Based on our experience from past audits, we decide to conduct a customer confirmation audit by contacting a random sample of 100 accounts receivable customers and asking them to either verify the value of the receivable in the company transaction file or to indicate the correct value of the receivable. From this sample of 100 customers we have a value for the receivable. From the data, the mean and variance are as follows:

$$\bar{x} = 784$$
$$s^2 = 2,300$$

Thus, we can report that the point estimate for the mean value of the receivables is $784. However, in addition we wish to report a confidence interval for our estimate. Since we are working with a finite population it is necessary to obtain an estimate for the population variance as

$$\hat{\sigma}_{\bar{x}}^2 = \frac{s^2}{n}\left(\frac{N-n}{N-1}\right) = \frac{2,300}{100}\left(\frac{1,320}{1,419}\right) = 21.395$$

and take the square root to obtain the estimated standard error,

$$\hat{\sigma}_{\bar{x}} = 4.626$$

Using Equation 7.12 and $t_{99,0.025} \cong 1.96$, a 95% confidence interval estimation of the mean accounts receivable is

$$\bar{x} \pm t_{n-1,\alpha/2}\hat{\sigma}_{\bar{x}} = 784 \pm 1.96(4.626)$$

The margin of error is approximately $9, giving a 95% confidence interval estimate for the accounts receivable as $775 to $793.

Frequently, interest centers on the population total rather than the mean. For example, the publisher of a business statistics text will want an estimate of the total number of students taking business statistics courses in all U.S. colleges. Inference about the population total is straightforward. The relevant results follow from the fact that, in our notation, population total $= N\mu$.

Estimation of the Population Total, Simple Random Sample, Finite Population

Suppose a simple random sample of size n from a population of size N is selected and that the quantity to be estimated is the **population total** $N\mu$.

1. An unbiased estimation procedure for the population total $N\mu$ yields the point estimate $N\bar{x}$.
2. An unbiased estimation procedure for the variance of our estimator of the population total yields the point estimate

$$N^2\hat{\sigma}_{\bar{x}}^2 = N^2\frac{s^2}{n}\left(\frac{N-n}{N-1}\right) \tag{7.14}$$

It follows that

$$N\hat{\sigma}_{\bar{x}} = \frac{Ns}{\sqrt{n}}\sqrt{\left(\frac{N-n}{N-1}\right)} \qquad (7.15)$$

3. A $100(1-\alpha)\%$ **confidence interval for the population total,** $N\mu$, is obtained from

$$N\bar{x} \pm t_{n-1,\alpha/2}N\hat{\sigma}_{\bar{x}} \qquad (7.16)$$

where ME, the margin of error, is given by

$$ME = t_{n-1,\alpha/2}N\hat{\sigma}_{\bar{x}} \qquad (7.17)$$

Example 7.10 Enrollment in Business Statistics Courses (Confidence Interval)

Suppose that there are 1,395 colleges in the United States. From a simple random sample of 400 of these schools, it was found that the sample mean enrollment during the past year in business statistics courses was 320.8 students, and the sample standard deviation was found to be 149.7 students. Estimate the total number of students enrolled in business statistics courses in the previous year, and find a 99% confidence interval.

Solution If the population mean is μ, an estimate of $N\mu$ includes the following:

$$N = 1,395 \quad n = 400 \quad \bar{x} = 320.8 \quad s = 149.7$$

Our point estimate for the total is

$$N\bar{x} = (1,395)(320.8) = 447,516$$

We estimate that a total of 447,516 students are enrolled in business statistics courses. To obtain interval estimates, Equation 7.15 is used to obtain

$$N\hat{\sigma}_{\bar{x}} = \frac{Ns}{\sqrt{n}}\sqrt{\frac{N-n}{N-1}} = \frac{(1,395)(149.7)}{\sqrt{400}}\sqrt{\frac{995}{1,394}} = 8,821.6$$

Since the sample size is large, the 99% confidence interval for the population total, $N\mu$, is found by Equation 7.16 and the central limit theorem with $z_{\alpha/2} = 2.58$:

$$N\bar{x} \pm z_{\alpha/2}N\hat{\sigma}_{\bar{x}}$$
$$447,516 \pm 2.58(8,821.6)$$
$$447,516 \pm 22,760$$

Thus, our interval runs from 424,756 to 470,276 students.

Population Proportion

Finally, consider the case where it is required to estimate the proportion P of individuals in the population possessing some specific characteristic. Inference about this proportion should be based on the hypergeometric distribution when the number of sample members is not very small compared to the number of population members. Again, assume that the sample size is large enough to allow the central limit theorem to be invoked.

Estimation of the Population Proportion, Simple Random Sample, Finite Population

Let $\hat{p}$ be the proportion possessing a particular characteristic in a random sample of n observations from a population with a proportion, P, of whose members possess that characteristic.

1. The sample proportion, $\hat{p}$, is an unbiased estimator of the population proportion, P.
2. An unbiased estimation procedure for the variance of our estimator of the population proportion yields the point estimate

$$\hat{\sigma}_{\hat{p}}^2 = \frac{\hat{p}(1 - \hat{p})}{n - 1}\left(\frac{N - n}{N - 1}\right)$$

(7.18)

3. Provided the sample size is large, $100(1 - \alpha)\%$ confidence intervals for the population proportion are given by

$$\hat{p} \pm z_{\alpha/2}\hat{\sigma}_{\hat{p}}$$

(7.19)

where ME, the margin of error, is given by

$$ME = z_{\alpha/2}\hat{\sigma}_{\hat{p}}$$

(7.20)

Example 7.11 Two Semesters of Business Statistics (Confidence Interval)

From a simple random sample of 400 of the 1,395 colleges in our population, it was found that business statistics was a two-semester course in 141 of the sampled colleges. Estimate the proportion of all colleges for which the course is two semesters long, and find a 90% confidence interval.

Solution Given

$$N = 1{,}395 \quad n = 400 \quad \hat{p} = \frac{141}{400} = 0.3525$$

our point estimate of the population proportion, P, is simply $\hat{p} = 0.3525$. That is, the course is two semesters long in approximately 35.25% of all colleges. To calculate interval estimates, the variance of our estimate is found by Equation 7.18:

$$\hat{\sigma}_{\hat{p}}^2 = \frac{\hat{p}(1 - \hat{p})}{n}\left(\frac{N - n}{N - 1}\right) = \frac{(0.3525)(0.6475)}{400}\left(\frac{995}{1{,}394}\right) = 0.0004073$$

so

$$\hat{\sigma}_{\hat{p}} = 0.0202$$

For a 90% confidence interval, $z_{\alpha/2} = z_{0.05} = 1.645$. The margin of error of a 90% confidence interval is found by Equation 7.20 as follows:

$$ME = z_{\alpha/2}\hat{\sigma}_{\hat{p}} = 1.645(0.0202) \cong 0.0332$$

Finally, from Equation 7.19, the 90% confidence interval is $\hat{p} \pm z_{\alpha/2}\hat{\sigma}_{\hat{p}} = 0.3525 \pm 0.0332$.

Thus, the 90% confidence interval for the percentage of all colleges in which business statistics is a two-semester course runs from 31.93% to 38.57%.

Basic Exercises

7.51 Assume simple random sampling. Calculate the variance of the sample mean, $\sigma_{\bar{x}}^2$, for each of the following.

   a. $N = 1,300; n = 100; s = 15$
   b. $N = 1,500; n = 200; s^2 = 91$
   c. $N = 3,000; n = 220; s^2 = 150$

7.52 Assume simple random sampling. Calculate the 95% confidence interval estimate for the population mean for each of the following.

   a. $N = 1600; n = 80; s = 10; \bar{x} = 144$
   b. $N = 1575; n = 70; s^2 = 64; \bar{x} = 234.2$
   c. $N = 6200; n = 200; s^2 = 120; \bar{x} = 57.6$

7.53 Assume simple random sampling. Calculate the confidence interval for the population total for each of the following.

   a. $N = 1,500; n = 200; s = 25; \bar{x} = 100$; 90% confidence level
   b. $N = 2,000; n = 250; s = 100; \bar{x} = 3,250$; 98% confidence level

7.54 Assume simple random sampling. Calculate the confidence interval for the population proportion, P, for each of the following.

   a. $N = 1,675; n = 400; x = 120$; 99% confidence level
   b. $N = 955; n = 100; x = 30$; 95% confidence level

Application Exercises

7.55 Take a random sample of 80 pages from this book and estimate the proportion of all pages that contain mathematical formulas.

7.56 Axion Revisionsbyrå, a Swedish accounting firm, employs 268 junior accountants. In a random sample of 49 of these, the mean number of hours overtime billed in a particular week was 7.6, and the sample standard deviation was 4.7 hours.

   a. Find a 90% confidence interval for the mean number of hours overtime billed per junior accountant at Axion that week.
   b. Find a 95% confidence interval for the total number of hours overtime billed by junior accountants at Axion during the week of interest.

7.57 An auditor, examining a total of 830 accounts receivable of a corporation, took a random sample of 80 of them. The sample mean was €129.19, and the sample standard deviation was €43.11.

   a. Using an unbiased estimation procedure, find an estimate of the population mean.
   b. Using an unbiased estimation procedure, find an estimate of the variance of the sample mean.
   c. Find a 90% confidence interval for the population mean.
   d. A statistician found, for the population mean, a confidence interval running from €117.43 to €137.43. What is the probability content of this interval?
   e. Find a 95% confidence interval for the total amount of these 830 accounts.

7.58 On a particular day Citizens Advice, a consumer-advice bureau in London, received 215 calls. For a random sample of 49 of these calls, it was found that the mean time taken in providing the requested advice was 8.42 minutes, and the sample standard deviation was 5.86 minutes.

   a. Find a 90% confidence interval the mean time taken per call.
   b. Find a 99% confidence interval for the total amount of time taken in answering these 215 calls.

7.59 For each of the following statements, add the word wider or narrower so that they are true.

   a. For a given number of population members and a given sample variance, the larger the number of sample members, the _____ the 95% confidence interval for the population mean.
   b. For a given number of population members and a given number of sample members, the larger the sample variance, the _____ the 95% confidence interval for the population mean.
   c. For a given number of sample members and a given sample variance, the larger the number of population members, the _____ the 95% confidence interval for the population mean. Justify your answer.
   d. For a given number of population members, a given number of sample members, and a given sample variance, a 95% confidence interval for the population mean is _____ than a 99% confidence interval for the population mean.

7.60 A senior manager, responsible for a group of 150 junior executives, is interested in the total amount of time per week spent by these people in internal meetings. A random sample of 36 of these executives was asked to keep diary records during the next week. When the results were analyzed, it was found that these sample members spent a total of 178 hours in internal meetings. The sample standard deviation was 4.6 hours. Find a 90% confidence interval for the total number of hours spent in internal meetings by all 150 junior executives in the week.

7.61 A simple random sample of 200 from a total 1,380 colleges in a country maintained that 18 colleges use the text *Statistics Made Difficult and Boring*. Find a 95% confidence interval for the proportion of all colleges using this text.

7.62 The dean of The Business School of Auckland University, New Zealand, is contemplating proposing a change in the requirements for graduation. At present, business majors are required to take one science course, chosen from a list of possible courses. The proposal is that this be replaced by the requirement that a course in ecology be taken. The business school has 520 students. In a random sample of 125 of these students, 72 expressed opposition to this proposal. Find a 90% confidence interval for the proportion of all the school's students opposed to the proposed change in requirements.

7.63 An accounting firm has 1,200 clients. From a random sample of 121 clients, 110 indicated very high satisfaction with the firm's service. Find a 95% confidence interval for the proportion of all clients who are very highly satisfied with this firm.

7.64 A class has 270 students. The final examination is optional – taking it can raise, but cannot lower, a student's grade. Of a random sample of 45 students, 27 indicated that they would take the final examination. Find a 95% confidence interval for the total number of students in this class intending to take the final examination.

7.7 SAMPLE-SIZE DETERMINATION: LARGE POPULATIONS

We have developed confidence intervals for population parameters on the basis of the information contained in a given sample. Following such a process, we may believe that the resulting confidence interval is too wide, reflecting an undesirable amount of uncertainty about the parameter being estimated. Typically, one way to obtain a narrower interval with a given confidence level is to take a larger sample.

In some circumstances we may be able to fix in advance the width of the confidence interval, choosing a sample size big enough to guarantee that width. In this section we consider how sample size can be chosen in this way for two interval estimation problems. Similar procedures can be employed to solve other problems. We concentrate on populations that are not necessarily large in Section 7.8.

Mean of a Normally Distributed Population, Known Population Variance

If a random sample of n observations is taken from a normally distributed population with mean μ and known variance σ^2, we saw in Section 7.2 that a $100(1 - \alpha)\%$ confidence interval for the population mean is provided by

$$\bar{x} \pm z_{\alpha/2}\frac{\sigma}{\sqrt{n}}$$

where $\bar{x}$ is the observed sample mean and $z_{\alpha/2}$ is the appropriate cutoff point of the standard normal distribution. Recall that this interval is centered on the sample mean and extends a distance called the margin of error,

$$ME = \frac{z_{\alpha/2}\sigma}{\sqrt{n}}$$

on each side of the sample mean, so that ME is half the width of the interval. Suppose, now, that the investigator wants to fix the margin of error, ME, in advance. From basic algebra it follows that

$$\sqrt{n} = \frac{z_{\alpha/2}\sigma}{ME}$$

and by squaring both sides of the equation, the sample size n is as follows:

$$n = \frac{z_{\alpha/2}^2\sigma^2}{ME^2}$$

This choice of the sample size guarantees that the confidence interval extends a distance ME on each side of the sample mean.

Sample Size for the Mean of a Normally Distributed Population with Known Population Variance
Suppose that a random sample from a normally distributed population with known variance σ^2 is selected. Then a $100(1 - \alpha)\%$ confidence interval for the population mean extends a distance ME (sometimes called the

sampling error) on each side of the sample mean if the sample size, n, is as follows:

$$n = \frac{z_{\alpha/2}^2 \sigma^2}{ME^2} \tag{7.21}$$

Of course, the number of sample observations must necessarily be an integer. If the number n resulting from the sample-size formula is not an integer, then *round up* to the next whole number in order to guarantee that our confidence interval does not exceed the required width.

Example 7.12 Length of Metal Rods (Sample Size)

The lengths of metal rods produced by an industrial process are normally distributed with a standard deviation of 1.8 millimeters. Based on a random sample of nine observations from this population, the 99% confidence interval was found for the population mean length to extend from 194.65 to 197.75. Suppose that a production manager believes that the interval is too wide for practical use and, instead, requires a 99% confidence interval extending no further than 0.50 mm on each side of the sample mean. How large a sample is needed to achieve such an interval?

Solution Since

$$ME = 0.50, \quad \sigma = 1.8, \quad \text{and} \quad z_{\alpha/2} = z_{0.005} = 2.576$$

the required sample size is as follows:

$$\begin{aligned}
n &= \frac{z_{\alpha/2}^2 \sigma^2}{ME^2} \\
&= \frac{(2.576)^2 (1.8)^2}{(0.5)^2} \approx 86
\end{aligned}$$

Therefore, to satisfy the manager's requirement, a sample of at least 86 observations is needed. This large increase in the sample size represents the additional cost of achieving the higher precision in the estimate of the true value of the population mean, reflected in a narrower confidence interval. The value 2.576, rather than 2.58, was used to determine the sample size needed. Figure 7.15 is the Excel (PHStat) output for determining sample size for Example 7.12.

Figure 7.15 Metal Rods (Sample Size)

Sample Size Determination	
Data	
Population Standard Deviation	1.8
Sampling Error	0.5
Confidence Level	99%
Intermediate Calculations	
Z Value	-2.5758293
Calculated Sample Size	85.98825995
Result	
Sample Size Needed	86

Population Proportion

Earlier in this chapter (Section 7.4) we saw that for a random sample of n observations, a $100(1 - \alpha)\%$ confidence interval for the population proportion P is

$$\hat{p} \pm z_{\alpha/2}\sqrt{\frac{\hat{p}(1 - \hat{p})}{n}}$$

where $\hat{p}$ is the observed sample proportion. This interval is centered on the sample proportion and extends a distance (margin of error)

$$ME = z_{\alpha/2}\sqrt{\frac{\hat{p}(1 - \hat{p})}{n}}$$

on each side of the sample proportion. Now, this result *cannot* be used directly to determine the sample size necessary to obtain a confidence interval of some specific width since it involves the sample proportion, which will not be known at the outset. However, whatever the outcome, $\hat{p}(1 - \hat{p})$ cannot be bigger than 0.25, its value when the sample proportion is 0.5. Thus, the *largest* possible value for the margin of error, ME, is given by the following:

$$ME = z_{\alpha/2}\sqrt{\frac{0.25}{n}} = \frac{(0.5)z_{\alpha/2}}{\sqrt{n}}$$

Suppose, then, that a sufficiently large sample size is chosen to *guarantee* that the confidence interval extends no more than ME on each side of the sample proportion. Again using basic algebra,

$$\sqrt{n} = \frac{0.5z_{\alpha/2}}{ME}$$

and squaring yields the following:

$$n = \frac{0.25(z_{\alpha/2})^2}{(ME)^2}$$

Sample Size for Population Proportion

Suppose that a random sample is selected from a population. Then, a $100(1 - \alpha)\%$ confidence interval for the population proportion, extending a distance of at most ME on each side of the sample proportion, can be guaranteed if the sample size is as follows:

$$n = \frac{0.25(z_{\alpha/2})^2}{(ME)^2} \tag{7.22}$$

Example 7.13 Graduate Admissions Personnel (Sample Size)

In Exercise 7.33 we calculated a 95% confidence interval for the proportion of graduate-admissions personnel who viewed scores on standardized exams as very important in the consideration of a candidate. Based on 142 observations, the interval obtained extended from 0.533 to 0.693. Suppose, instead, that it must be ensured that a 95% confidence interval for the population proportion extends no further than 0.06 on each side of the sample proportion. How large of a sample must be taken?

Solution It is given that

$$ME = 0.06 \quad \text{and} \quad z_{\alpha/2} = z_{0.025} = 1.96$$

Thus, the number of sample observations needed is as follows:

$$n = \frac{0.25z_{\alpha/2}^2}{(ME)^2} = \frac{0.25(1.96)^2}{(0.06)^2} = 266.78 \Rightarrow n = 267$$

To achieve this narrower confidence interval, a minimum of 267 sample observations is required (a significant increase over the original 142 observations). The Excel (PHStat) printout is displayed in Figure 7.16.

Figure 7.16 Graduate Admissions Personnel (Sample Size)

Sample Size Determination	
Data	
Estimate of True Proportion	0.5
Sampling Error	0.06
Confidence Level	95%
Intermediate Calculations	
Z Value	-1.95996398
Calculated Sample Size	266.7679737
Result	
Sample Size Needed	267

The media frequently report the results of opinion surveys concerning issues of current interest, such as the president's rating on domestic issues or foreign policy or people's views on some new tax proposal. These surveys generally represent the opinions of some subset of the population. Typically, these reports give estimates of the percentage of population members holding particular views. These reports often end with a statement such as, There is $\pm 3\%$ sampling error or The poll has a 3% margin of error. Specifically, these intervals are the sample percentage, plus or minus the advertised sampling error or margin of error. However, we stress that the margin of error does not include any errors due to biased or otherwise inadequate samples.

Example 7.14 Electoral College (Sample Size)

Suppose that an opinion survey following a presidential election reported the views of a sample of U.S. citizens of voting age concerning changing the Electoral College process. The poll was said to have a 3% margin of error. The implication is that a 95% confidence interval for the population proportion holding a particular opinion is the sample proportion plus or minus at most 3%. How many citizens of voting age need to be sampled to obtain this 3% margin of error?

Solution Using Equation 7.22,

$$n = \frac{0.25z_{\alpha/2}^2}{(ME)^2} = \frac{(0.25)(1.96)^2}{(0.03)^2} = 1067.111 \Rightarrow n = 1,068$$

Therefore, 1,068 U.S. citizens of voting age need to be sampled to achieve the desired result. Figure 7.17 is the Excel (PHStat) output for Example 7.14.

Figure 7.17 Electoral College (Sample Size)

Sample Size Determination	
Data	
Estimate of True Proportion	0.5
Sampling Error	0.03
Confidence Level	95%
Intermediate Calculations	
Z Value	-1.95996398
Calculated Sample Size	1067.071895
Result	
Sample Size Needed	1068

EXERCISES

Basic Exercises

7.65 How large of a sample is needed to estimate the mean of a normally distributed population for each of the following?
  a. $ME = 2; \sigma = 39; \alpha = 0.05$
  b. $ME = 4; \sigma = 39; \alpha = 0.05$
  c. Compare and comment on your answers to parts a and b.

7.66 How large a sample is needed to estimate the population proportion for each of the following?
  a. $ME = 0.03; \alpha = 0.05$
  b. $ME = 0.05; \alpha = 0.05$
  c. Compare and comment on your answers to parts a and b.

7.67 How large a sample is needed to estimate the population proportion for each of the following?
  a. $ME = 0.05; \alpha = 0.01$
  b. $ME = 0.05; \alpha = 0.10$
  c. Compare and comment on your answers to parts a and b.

Application Exercises

7.68 A research group wants to estimate the proportion of consumers who plan to buy a scanner for their PC during the next 3 months.

  a. How many people should be sampled so that the sampling error is at most 0.04 with a 90% confidence interval?
  b. What is the sample size required if the confidence is increased to 95%, keeping the sampling error the same?
  c. What is the required sample size if the research group extends the sampling error to 0.05 and wants a 98% confidence level?

7.69 A politician wants to estimate the proportion of constituents favoring a controversial piece of proposed legislation. Suppose that a 99% confidence interval that extends at most 0.05 on each side of the sample proportion is required. How many sample observations are needed?

7.70 The student council at a university wants to estimate the percentage of the student body that supports a change being considered in the academic calendar of the university for the next academic year. How many students should be surveyed if a 99% confidence interval is desired and the margin of error is to be only 1%?

7.8 SAMPLE-SIZE DETERMINATION: FINITE POPULATIONS

An important aspect of the planning of any survey involves the determination of an appropriate number of sample members. Several factors may be relevant. If the procedure for contacting sample members is thought likely to lead to a high rate of nonresponse, this eventuality should be taken into account. In many instances the resources available to the investigator, in terms of time and money, will place constraints on what can be achieved. In this section, however, we abstract from such considerations and relate sample size to the variances of the estimators of population parameters and consequently to the widths of resulting confidence intervals. To compensate for nonresponse or missing data, practitioners may add a certain percent (like 10%) to the sample size, n, determined by the equations in this section.

Sample Sizes for Simple Random Sampling: Estimation of the Population Mean or Total

Consider the problem of estimating the population mean from a simple random sample of n observations. If the random variable $\overline{X}$ denotes the sample mean, it is known from Chapter 6 that the variance of this random variable is as follows:

$$Var(\overline{X}) = \sigma_{\overline{X}}^2 = \frac{\sigma^2}{n}\left(\frac{N-n}{N-1}\right)$$

If the population variance σ^2 is known, by solving the equation $Var(\overline{X})$ you can determine the sample size n that is needed to achieve any specified value of $s_{\overline{x}}^2$ for the variance of the sample mean. Similar procedures are available if the quantity of interest is the population total.

Sample Size: Population Mean or Total, Simple Random Sampling

Consider estimating the mean of a population of N members, which has variance σ^2. If the desired variance, $\sigma_{\overline{X}}^2$, of the sample mean is specified, the *required sample size to estimate the population mean through simple random sampling* is

$$n = \frac{N\sigma^2}{(N-1)\sigma_{\overline{x}}^2 + \sigma^2} \tag{7.23}$$

or, equivalently,

$$n = \frac{n_0 N}{n_0 + (N-1)} \tag{7.24}$$

where $n_0 = n$ in Equation 7.21,

$$n_0 = \frac{z_{\alpha/2}^2 \sigma^2}{ME^2}$$

1. Often it is more convenient to specify directly the width of confidence intervals for the population mean rather than $\sigma_{\overline{X}}^2$. This is easily accomplished, since, for example, a 95% confidence interval for the population mean will extend approximately $1.96\sigma_{\overline{X}}$ on each side of the sample mean.
2. If the object of interest is the population total, the variance of the sample estimator of this quantity is $N^2\sigma_{\overline{X}}^2$, and a 95% confidence interval for it extends approximately $1.96N\sigma_{\overline{X}}$ on each side of $N\overline{x}$.

An obvious difficulty with the practical use of Equation 7.23 is that it involves the population variance, σ^2, which typically will be unknown. However, often an investigator will have a rough idea of the value of this quantity. Sometimes the population variance can be estimated from a preliminary sample of the population or approximated from historical data.

Example 7.15 Mortgages (Sample Size)

As in Example 7.8, suppose that in a city last year, 1,118 mortgages were taken out and that a simple random sample is to be taken in order to estimate the mean amount of these mortgages. From previous experience of such populations it is estimated that the population standard deviation is approximately $20,000. A 95% confidence interval for the population mean must extend $4,000 on each side of the sample mean. How many sample observations are needed to achieve this objective?

Solution First,

$$N = 1{,}118 \quad \sigma = 20{,}000 \quad 1.96\sigma_{\bar{X}} = 4{,}000$$

The required sample size by using Equation 7.23 is then

$$n = \frac{N\sigma^2}{(N-1)\sigma_{\bar{x}}^2 + \sigma^2} = \frac{(1{,}118)(20{,}000)^2}{(1{,}117)(2{,}041)^2 + (20{,}000)^2} = 88.5 \Rightarrow n = 89$$

By calculating the sample size using Equation 7.21 and Equation 7.24, we find the following:

$$n_0 = \frac{z_{\alpha/2}^2 \sigma^2}{ME^2} = \frac{(1.96)^2(20{,}000)^2}{(4{,}000)^2} = (1.96)^2(25) = (3.8416)(25) = 96.04$$

$$n = \frac{n_0 N}{n_0 + (N-1)} = \frac{(96.04)(1118)}{96.04 + 1117} = 88.5 \Rightarrow n = 89$$

Thus, a simple random sample of 89 observations is the minimum needed to meet our objective. Figure 7.18 is the Excel (PHStat) output giving the sample size for Example 7.15 when the finite population correction factor is used and when it is not used.

Figure 7.18 Mortgages (Sample Size)

Sample Size Determination	
Data	
Population Standard Deviation	20000
Sampling Error	4000
Confidence Level	95%
Intermediate Calculations	
Z Value	-1.95996398
Calculated Sample Size	96.03647052
Result	
Sample Size Needed	97
Finite Populations	
Population Size	1118
Sample Size with FPC	88.51240391
Sample Size Needed	89

Sample Sizes for Simple Random Sampling: Estimation of Population Proportion

Consider simple random sampling for the estimation of a population proportion P. Recall from earlier in the text that

$$Var(\hat{p}) = \sigma_{\hat{p}}^2 = \frac{P(1-P)}{n}\left(\frac{N-n}{N-1}\right)$$

Solving for n leads to the sample size given in Equations 7.24 and 7.25.

Sample Size: Population Proportion, Simple Random Sampling

Consider estimation of the proportion P of individuals in a population size of N who possess a certain attribute. If the desired variance, $\sigma_{\hat{p}}^2$, of the sample proportion is specified, the required sample size to estimate the population proportion through simple random sampling is as follows:

$$n = \frac{NP(1 - P)}{(N - 1)\sigma_{\hat{p}}^2 + P(1 - P)} \tag{7.25}$$

The largest possible value for this expression, whatever the value of P, is

$$n_{max} = \frac{0.25N}{(N - 1)\sigma_{\hat{p}}^2 + 0.25} \tag{7.26}$$

A 95% confidence interval for the population proportion will extend approximately $1.96\sigma_{\hat{p}}$ on each side of the sample proportion.

Example 7.16 Campus Survey (Sample Size)

As in Example 7.10, suppose that a simple random sample of the 1,395 U.S. colleges is taken to estimate the proportion for which the business statistics course is two semesters long. Whatever the true proportion, a 95% confidence interval must extend no further than 0.04 on each side of the sample proportion. How many sample observations should be taken?

Solution From the problem

$$1.96\sigma_{\hat{p}} = 0.04$$

$$\sigma_{\hat{p}} = 0.020408$$

the sample size needed is then

$$n_{max} = \frac{0.25N}{(N - 1)\sigma_{\hat{p}}^2 + 0.25} = \frac{(0.25)(1{,}395)}{(1{,}394)(0.020408)^2 + 0.25} = 419.88 \Rightarrow n = 420$$

Hence, a sample of 420 observations is needed. The sample size determination using Excel (PHStat) is illustrated in Figure 7.19.

Figure 7.19 Campus Survey (Sample Size)

Sample Size Determination	
Data	
Estimate of True Proportion	0.5
Sampling Error	0.04
Confidence Level	95%
Intermediate Calculations	
Z Value	-1.95996398
Calculated Sample Size	600.2279407
Result	
Sample Size Needed	601
Finite Populations	
Population Size	1,395
Calculated Sample Size	419.8707481
Sample Size Needed	420

Basic Exercises

7.71 Determine the sample size needed for each of the following situations.

   a. $N = 1,950$; $\sigma = 600$; $1.96\sigma_{\bar{x}} = 75$
   b. $N = 1,950$; $\sigma = 600$; $1.96\sigma_{\bar{x}} = 150$
   c. $N = 1,950$; $\sigma = 600$; $1.96\sigma_{\bar{x}} = 225$
   d. Compare and comment on your answers to parts a through c.

7.72 Determine the sample size needed for each of the following situations.

   a. $N = 1,000$; $\sigma = 450$; $1.96\sigma_{\bar{x}} = 50$
   b. $N = 3,000$; $\sigma = 450$; $1.96\sigma_{\bar{x}} = 50$
   c. $N = 1,000,000$; $\sigma = 450$; $1.96\sigma_{\bar{x}} = 50$
   d. Compare and comment on your answers to parts a through c.

7.73 Determine the sample size needed for each of the following situations.

   a. $N = 5,000$; $\hat{p} = 0.5$; $1.96\sigma_{\hat{p}} = 0.10$
   b. $N = 5,000$; $\hat{p} = 0.5$; $1.96\sigma_{\hat{p}} = 0.05$

Application Exercises

7.74 The mean amount of the 1,560 mortgages taken out in Vienna, Austria, in the past year must be estimated. Based on previous experience, a real estate broker knows that the population standard deviation is likely to be about €25,000. If a 95% confidence interval for the population mean is to extend €2,500 on each side of the sample mean, how many sample observations are needed if a simple random sample is taken?

7.75 An automobile dealer has an inventory of 500 used cars. To estimate the mean mileage of this inventory, she intends to take a simple random sample of used cars. Previous studies suggest that the population standard deviation is 9,000 miles. A 90% confidence interval for the population mean must extend 1,500 miles on each side of its sample estimate. How large of a sample size is necessary to satisfy this requirement?

7.76 The Vikla Golf and country club, Cyprus, wants to poll a random sample of its 560 members to estimate the proportion likely to attend an early-season function. The number of sample observations should be sufficiently large to ensure that a 99% confidence interval for the population extends at most 0.04 on each side of the sample proportion. How large of a sample is necessary?

7.77 An instructor in a class of 417 students is considering the possibility of a take-home final examination. She wants to take a random sample of class members to estimate the proportion who prefer this form of examination. If a 90% confidence interval for the population proportion must extend at most 0.04 on each side of the sample proportion, how large a sample is needed?

KEY WORDS

DATA FILES

Visit www.MyStatLab.com or www.pearsonglobal editions.com to access the data files.

7.78 Several drugs are used to treat diabetes. A sales specialist for a leading pharmaceutical company needs an estimate of the number of new prescriptions that were written during a particular month for his company's new diabetes drug. The numbers of new prescriptions in a random sample of 25 sales districts are as follows:

210 240 190 275 290 185 223 190 185 192

265 312 284 261 243 168 240 170 187 190

215 240 210 235 290

a. Find a 90% confidence interval for the average number of new prescriptions written for this new drug among all the sales districts. State the assumptions.

b. Calculate the widths for 95% and 98% confidence intervals.

7.79 Suppose that Brent Matthews, manager of a Sam's Club in Chattanooga, Tennessee, wants to estimate the mean number of gallons of milk that are sold during a typical weekday. Brent checks the sales records for a random sample of 16 days and finds the mean number of gallons sold is 150 gallons per day; the sample standard deviation is 12 gallons. With 95% confidence, estimate the mean number of gallons that Brent should stock daily.

7.80 Everyone knows that exercise is important. Recently, employees of one large international corporation were surveyed and asked, How many minutes do you spend daily on some form of rigorous exercise? From a random sample of 25 employees, the mean time spent on vigorous daily exercise was 28.5 minutes. The standard deviation was found to be 6.8 minutes. Find a 90% interval estimate of the mean daily time spent on rigorous exercise by all employees.

7.81 The following data represent the number of passengers per flight for a random sample of 50 flights from Jacksonville, Florida, to Baltimore, Maryland, on one particular airline:

163 165 094 137 123 095 170 096 117 129

152 138 147 119 166 125 148 180 152 149

167 120 129 159 150 119 113 147 169 151

116 150 110 110 143 090 134 145 156 165

174 133 128 100 086 148 139 150 145 100

Estimate the average number of passengers per flight with a 95% interval estimate.

7.82 The manager of a local fitness center wants an estimate of the number of times members use the weight room per month. From a random sample of 25 members the average number of visits to the weight room over the course of a month was 12.5 visits with a standard deviation of 3.8 visits. Assuming that the monthly number of visits is normally distributed, determine a 95% confidence interval for the average monthly usage of all members of this fitness center.

7.83 Eight randomly selected batches of a chemical were tested for impurity concentration. The percentage impurity levels found in this sample were as follows:

3.2 4.3 2.1 2.8 3.2 3.6 4.0 3.8

a. Find the most efficient estimates of the population mean and variance.

b. Estimate the proportion of batches with impurity levels greater than 3.75%.

7.84 A marketing research assistant for a veterinary hospital surveyed a random sample of 457 pet owners. Respondents were asked to indicate the number of times that they visit their veterinarian each year. The sample mean response was 3.59 and the sample standard deviation was 1.045. Based on these results, a confidence interval from 3.49 to 3.69 was calculated for the population mean. Find the probability content for this interval.

7.85 A random sample of 174 college students was asked to indicate the number of hours per week that they surf the Internet for either personal information or material for a class assignment. The sample mean response was 6.06 hours and the sample standard deviation was 1.43 hours. Based on these results, a confidence interval extending from 5.96 to 6.16 was calculated for the population mean. Find the confidence level of this interval.

7.86 A sample of 33 accounting students recorded the number of hours that they spent studying for a final exam. The data are stored in the data file **Study**.

a. Give an example of an unbiased, consistent, and efficient estimator of the population mean.

b. Find the sampling error for a 95% confidence interval estimate of the mean number of hours students studied for this exam.

7.87 Dr. Mihaela Sabou wants to estimate the average length of a hospital stay (number of days) for patients with a certain infectious disease. From a random sample of 25 patient records, she finds that the average number of days in the hospital for such patients is 6 days, with a standard deviation of 1.8 days.

a. Find the reliability factor for a 95% confidence interval estimate of the population mean length of stay.

b. Find the LCL for a 99% confidence interval estimate of the population mean length of stay.

7.88 Suppose that a survey of race fans at this week's Daytona 500 NASCAR race were asked, Is this your first time attending the Daytona 500? From a random sample of 250 race fans, 100 answered in the affirmative.

a. Find the standard error to estimate the population proportion of first timers.

b. Find the sampling error to estimate the population proportion of first timers with 95% confidence level.

c. Estimate the proportion of repeat fans with 92% confidence level.

7.89 The following data represent the number of passengers per flight in a random sample of 20 flights from Vienna, Austria, to Cluj-Napoca, Romania, with a new airline:

63 65 94 37 83 95 70 96 47 29

52 38 47 79 66 25 48 80 52 49

a. What is the reliability factor for a 90% confidence interval estimate of the mean number of passengers per flight?
b. Find the LCL for a 99% confidence interval estimate of the mean number of passengers per flight.

7.90 What is the most common method to renew vehicle registration? In checking a random sample of 1,250 motor vehicle renewal registrations in one county, the finance department found that 200 were mailed, 300 were paid in person at the county finance department office, and the remainder was paid online at the county's Web site. Phone registration renewals were not available.

a. Estimate the population proportion to pay for vehicle registration renewals in person at the county finance department office. Use a 90% confidence level.
b. Estimate the population proportion of online renewals. Use a 95% confidence level.

7.91 Consider the data in Exercise 7.90. Suppose that we computed for the population proportion who pay for vehicle registration by mail a confidence interval extending from 0.15 to 0.17. What is the confidence level of this interval?

7.92 Consider the data in Exercise 7.90. It was reported in the local paper that almost two-thirds (from 57% to 63%) of the population prefers the online renewal process. What is the confidence level of this interval estimate?

7.93 The county finance department in Exercise 7.90 also wants information about renewals of disabled parking placards. Suppose that in a sample of 430 transactions for disabled parking placards, it was found that 360 were paid electronically.

a. What is the margin of error for a 95% confidence interval estimate of the population proportion of disabled renewal transactions paid electronically?
b. Without calculating, is the margin of error for a 90% confidence interval estimate of the population proportion of disabled renewal transactions paid electronically larger, smaller, or the same as that found in part a for a 95% confidence interval?

7.94 What is the typical age of a person who renews his or her driver's license online? From a random sample of 460 driver's license renewal transactions, the mean age was 42.6 and the standard deviation was 5.4. Compute the 98% confidence interval estimate of the mean age of online renewal users in this county.

7.95 A test was taken by 90 students. A random sample of 10 scores found the following results:

93 71 62 75 81 63 87 59 84 72

a. Find a 90% confidence interval for the population's mean score.
b. Without doing the calculations, state whether a 95% confidence interval for the population mean would be wider or narrower than the interval found in part a.

7.96 A corporation has 272 accounts receivable in a particular category. A random sample of 50 of them was taken. The sample mean was $492.36, and the sample standard deviation was $149.92.

a. Find a 99% confidence interval for the population mean value of these accounts receivable.
b. Find a 95% confidence interval for the total value of these accounts receivable.
c. Without doing the calculations, state whether a 90% confidence interval for the population total would be wider or narrower than the interval found in part b.

7.97 A corporation employs 148 sales representatives. A random sample of 60 of them was taken, and it was found that, for 36 of the sample members, the volume of orders taken this month was higher than for the same month last year. Find a 95% confidence interval for the population proportion of sales representatives with a higher volume of orders.

7.98 Several drugs are used to treat high blood pressure. A sales specialist for a leading pharmaceutical company randomly sampled the records of 10 sales districts to estimate the number of new prescriptions that had been written during a particular month for the company's new blood pressure medication. The numbers of new prescriptions were as follows:

210, 240, 190, 275, 290, 265, 312, 284, 261, 243

a. Find a 90% confidence interval for the average number of new prescriptions written for this new drug among all the sales districts. What are the assumptions?
b. Assuming that the confidence level remains constant, what sample size is needed to reduce by half the margin of error of the confidence interval in part a?

7.99 The president's policy on domestic affairs received a 45% approval rating in a recent poll. The margin of error was given as 0.035. What sample size was used for this poll if we assume a 95% confidence level?

7.100 An automobile dealer has an inventory of 328 used cars. The mean mileage of these vehicles is to be estimated. Previous experience suggests that the population standard deviation is likely to be about 12,000 miles. If a 90% confidence interval for the population mean is to extend 2,000 miles on each side of the sample mean, how large of a sample is required if simple random sampling is employed?

7.101 A simple random sample is to be taken of 527 business majors in a college to estimate the proportion favoring greater emphasis on business ethics in the curriculum. How many observations are necessary to ensure that a 95% confidence interval for the population proportion extends at most 0.06 on each side of the sample proportion?

7.102 Show algebraically that Equation 7.23 is equal to Equation 7.24. That is,

$$\frac{N\sigma^2}{(N-1)\sigma_{\bar{X}}^2 + \sigma^2} = \frac{n_0 N}{n_0 + (N-1)}$$

7.103 The demand for bottled water increases during the hurricane season in Florida. The operations manager at a plant that bottles drinking water wants to be sure that the filling process for 1-gallon bottles (1 gallon is approximately 3.785 liters) is operating properly. Currently, the company is testing the volumes of 1-gallon bottles. Suppose that a random sample of 75 one-gallon bottles is tested. Find the 95% confidence interval estimate of the population mean volume. The measurements are recorded in the data file **Water**.

Appendix

CONSISTENT ESTIMATOR

Consistency is another property that some estimators possess.

Consistent Estimator

A point estimator $\hat{\theta}$ is said to be a **consistent estimator** of the parameter θ if the difference between the expected value of the estimator and the parameter decreases as the sample size increases. In other words, the bias becomes smaller with increased sample size.

Consistent estimators are used in cases where it is difficult or impossible to obtain unbiased estimators, which occurs in some advanced econometric work. Not all unbiased estimators are consistent, and by no means are all consistent estimators unbiased. If the sample variance were calculated as

$$s^2 = \frac{\sum_{i=1}^{n}(x_i - \bar{x})^2}{n}$$

then it would be a biased estimator of the population variance. However, it is consistent, since it approaches the unbiased estimator

$$s^2 = \frac{\sum_{i=1}^{n}(x_i - \bar{x})^2}{n-1}$$

as the sample size increases.

Loosely speaking, the use of a consistent estimator with an infinite amount of sample information gives the correct result. Conversely, the use of an inconsistent estimator does not yield the correct result even with an infinite amount of sample information. For this reason, inconsistency in a point estimator is regarded as undesirable.

STUDENT'S *t* DISTRIBUTION

Gosset sought to develop a probability distribution for normally distributed random variables that did not include the population variance σ^2. As a result, he took the ratio of Z, a standard normal random variable, and the square root of χ^2 divided by its degrees of freedom, v. In mathematical notation

$$t = \frac{Z}{\sqrt{\chi^2/v}}$$

$$t = \frac{(x-\mu)/\sigma}{\sqrt{s^2(n-1)/\sigma^2(n-1)}} = \frac{(x-\mu)}{s}$$

The resulting t statistic has $n - 1$ degrees of freedom. Notice that the t probability distribution is based on normally distributed random variables. For applications, the normal Z is used when the population variance σ^2 is available, and the Student's t is used when only the sample variance s^2 is available. Statistical research using computer-generated random samples has shown that t can be used to study the distribution of sample means even if the distribution of the individual random variables is not normal.

REFERENCES

1. Guenther, P. M., J. Reedy, S. M. Krebs-Smith, B. B. Reeve, and P. P. Basiotis. November 2007. Development and Evaluation of the Healthy Eating Index–2005: Technical Report. *Center for Nutrition Policy and Promotion, U.S. Department of Agriculture, Available at http://www.cnpp.usda.gov/ HealthyEatingIndex.htm.*

2. Hildebrand, David, and A. L. Ott. 1998. *Statistical Thinking for Managers*. New York: Brooks/ Cole.

3. Pearson, Egon Sharpe, and R. L. Plackett, eds. 1990. *Student: A Statistical Biography of William Sealy Gosset*. Oxford, England: Clarendon Press.

4. Pearson, Egon Sharpe, and John Wishart, eds. 1958. *Development of Statistics: Student's Collected Papers*. Cambridge: Foreword by Launce McMullen. Materials provided to the authors by Teresa O'Donnell, Guinness (GIG) Archivist, September 13, 2000.

5. Salsburg, David. 2002. *The Lady Tasting Tea: How Statistics Revolutionized Science in the Twentieth Century*. New York: Holt.

CHAPTER

8

Estimation: Additional Topics

Introduction

Confidence interval procedures to estimate certain parameters of a *single* population were presented in Chapter 7. In this chapter we consider confidence interval procedures to estimate certain parameters of *two* populations. An important problem in statistical inference deals with the comparison of the difference between *two means* from normally distributed populations or the comparison of the difference between *two proportions* from large populations. For example, consider the following:

1. Corporate executives employed by retail distributors may want to estimate the difference between the mean daily sales of two retail stores.
2. Manufacturers may want to compare the average productivity, in units per hour, of day-shift workers and night-shift workers in a plant.
3. The campaign manager for a presidential candidate may want to compare the popularity rating of this candidate in two different regions of the country.
4. A clinical trial may be designed to compare the effectiveness of a new drug compared to a standard drug for cancer patients. Data for both drugs are collected on factors such as carcinoma recurrence rates, side effects, and survival rates.
5. A chemical company receives shipments from two suppliers. Independent random samples of batches from each supplier are selected, and a comparison of impurity levels of the two batches is made.

The confidence interval procedures discussed in this chapter are extensions of the procedures developed in Chapter 7 and follow the same general form:

$$\text{best point estimate} \pm ME$$

where ME, the margin of error, is the error term. More specifically, we will see that confidence interval estimates of the difference between the means of normally distributed populations X and Y will be as follows:

$$(\bar{x} - \bar{y}) \pm ME$$

Similarly, confidence interval estimates of the difference between two population proportions (large samples) will be of the general form

$$(\hat{p}_x - \hat{p}_y) \pm ME$$

8.1 CONFIDENCE INTERVAL ESTIMATION OF THE DIFFERENCE BETWEEN TWO NORMAL POPULATION MEANS: DEPENDENT SAMPLES

To compare population means, random samples are drawn from the two populations. The procedure that we use to select the samples determines the appropriate method that we use to analyze inferences based on the sample results. In this section we present a sampling scheme for *dependent* samples. In Section 8.2 we focus our attention on sampling schemes for *independent* samples.

We consider samples to be *dependent* if the values in one sample are influenced by the values in the other sample. Dependent samples are either *matched pairs* or the same individual or objects tested twice. The idea of matched pairs is that, apart from the factor under study, the members of these pairs should resemble one another as closely as possible so that the comparison of interest can be made directly. In clinical trials to compare the effectiveness of two medications, dependent samples will be selected and the members will be matched on various factors such as the patients' age or weight.

Dependent sampling also refers to two measurements taken on the same person or object. Suppose that the effectiveness of a speed-reading course is to be measured. One possible approach would be to record the number of words per minute read by a sample of students *before* taking the course and compare the data to the results for the same students *after* completing the course. In this case each pair of observations consists of "before" and "after" measurements on a single student. This type of dependent sampling is sometimes referred to as *repeated measurements*.

An interval estimate for the general case of n matched pairs of observations, denoted by $(x_1, y_1), (x_2, y_2), \ldots, (x_n, y_n)$, selected from populations with means μ_X and μ_Y follows.

Confidence Intervals of Two Means: Dependent Samples (Matched Pairs)

Suppose that there is a random sample of n matched pairs of observations from normal distributions with means μ_x and μ_y. That is, let $x_1, x_2, \ldots, x_n$ denote the values of the observations from the population with mean μ_x and let $y_1, y_2, \ldots, y_n$ denote the matched sampled values from the population with the mean μ_y. Let $\bar{d}$ and s_d denote the observed sample mean and standard deviation for the n differences $d_i = x_i - y_i$. If the population distribution of the differences is assumed to be normal, then a $100(1 - \alpha)\%$ **confidence interval for the difference between two means, dependent samples** $(\mu_d = \mu_x - \mu_y)$ is given by

$$\bar{d} \pm t_{n-1,\alpha/2} \frac{s_d}{\sqrt{n}} \tag{8.1}$$

or, equivalently,

$$\bar{d} \pm ME$$

The standard deviation of the differences, s_d, and the margin of error, ME, are

$$s_d = \sqrt{\frac{\Sigma (d_i - \bar{d})^2}{n - 1}}$$

$$ME = t_{n-1,\alpha/2}\frac{s_d}{\sqrt{n}} \tag{8.2}$$

where $t_{n-1,\alpha/2}$ is the number for which

$$P(t_{n-1} > t_{n-1,\alpha/2}) = \frac{\alpha}{2}$$

The random variable, t_{n-1}, has a Student's t distribution with $(n - 1)$ degrees of freedom.

Example 8.1 Cholesterol Reduction Study (Confidence Interval)

Clinical trials are conducted to compare the difference in effectiveness of drugs in lowering cholesterol levels, blood pressure, cancer recurrence, and numerous other medical conditions. Suppose that one research team is studying the effectiveness of two drugs to reduce cholesterol levels. In order to control variation in reduction that might be due to factors other than the drug itself, a matched pair sample design is selected. Each member of a pair is matched by age, weight, lifestyle, and other pertinent factors. Drug X is tested by one person randomly selected from each pair, and drug Y is tested by the other individual in the pair. After a specified amount of time, each person's cholesterol level is measured again. Although clinical studies may involve many hundreds or even thousands of participants, we simply illustrate the matched-pair statistical procedure for dependent samples in Example 8.1 with a very small random sample of pairs of participants with known cholesterol problems. Table 8.1 gives the number of points by which each person's cholesterol level was reduced as well as the differences, $d_i = x_i - y_i$, for each pair. Notice the missing value in pair 5. Estimate with a 99% confidence level the mean difference in the effectiveness of the two drugs, X and Y, to lower cholesterol.

Table 8.1 Cholesterol Reduction

PAIR	DRUG X	DRUG Y	DIFFERENCE $(d_i = x_i - y_i)$
1	29	26	3
2	32	27	5
3	31	28	3
4	32	27	5
5	30		
6	32	30	2
7	29	26	3
8	31	33	−2
9	30	36	−6

Solution Missing values are common in survey responses, clinical trials, and other research. For some reason (perhaps the individual simply chose to withdraw from the clinical trial) the participant in pair 5 who was to test drug Y did not complete the clinical trial. In a study of dependent samples, first delete all observations from your sample that contain missing values. It follows that our sample size is reduced from nine matched pairs to eight matched pairs. From Table 8.1 we compute the sample mean, $\bar{d}$, and the observed sample standard deviation, s_d, of the differences in cholesterol reduction as follows:

$$\bar{d} = 1.625 \quad \text{and} \quad s_d = 3.777$$

From the Student's t distribution table, $t_{n-1,\alpha/2} = t_{7,0.005} = 3.499$. From Equation 8.1 we find the 99% confidence interval estimate for the difference between the effectiveness of drug X and drug Y as follows:

$$\bar{d} \pm t_{n-1,\alpha/2}\frac{s_d}{\sqrt{n}}$$

$$1.625 \pm 3.499\frac{3.777}{\sqrt{8}}$$

The lower confidence limit is a negative number (−3.05), whereas the upper confidence limit is a positive number (6.30).

Since the confidence interval contains the value of zero, one of the following three possibilities exist: (1) $\mu_x - \mu_y$ could be positive, suggesting that drug X is more effective; (2) $\mu_x - \mu_y$ could be negative, suggesting that drug Y is more effective; or (3) $\mu_x - \mu_y$ could be zero, suggesting that drug X and drug Y are equally effective. Thus, it is not possible, based on this data, to determine if either drug is more effective in reducing one's cholesterol level.

In addition to matched pairs, another type of situation that involves dependent samples is sometimes known as *repeated measurements* since two scores are obtained for each individual. For example, sales representatives may attend a motivational course on sales techniques. For each sales representative attending the course, data on the value of sales (in thousands of dollars) is obtained for a 3-month period prior to the course and for a 3-month period following the completion of the course. Example 8.2 illustrates dependent samples with repeated measurements.

Example 8.2 Improve SAT Scores (Confidence Interval)

Countless Web sites, study guides, software, online interactive courses, books, and classes promise to increase students' vocabulary, to refresh students' math skills, and to teach test-taking strategies in order to improve SAT scores, which should help to enhance chances of college acceptance or increase the possibilities of receiving certain scholarships. Similarly, the same types of offerings exist to improve GMAT scores, LSAT scores, MCAT scores, and other such standardized tests. One company randomly sampled 140 of its clients and collected data on each person's SAT score before taking the online course and the person's score after taking the course. The data are stored in the data file **Improve Your Score**. Estimate with a 95% confidence level the difference in the mean SAT scores before and after taking this course.

Solution Let $x_1, x_2, \ldots, x_n$ denote the SAT scores after each person completed the course, and let $y_1, y_2, \ldots, y_n$ denote the SAT scores before each person took the course. The difference, $d_i = x_i - y_i$, is the "after score−before score" for each person.

Using Excel, Minitab, SPSS, or some other software package, we obtain the following information:

$$\bar{d} = 77.7 \quad \text{and} \quad s_d = 43.68901$$

Using the normal approximation we have $t_{n-1,\alpha/2} = t_{139,0.025} \cong 1.96$. From Equation 8.1 we find the 95% confidence interval estimate for the difference between the mean SAT scores before and the mean SAT scores after completing the online course as follows:

$$\bar{d} \pm t_{n-1,\alpha/2}\frac{s_d}{\sqrt{n}}$$

$$77.7 \pm 1.96\frac{43.68901}{\sqrt{140}}$$

$$77.7 \pm 7.2$$

The result is a 95% confidence interval estimate that extends from 70.5 to 84.9. Table 8.2 shows the Excel printout for this problem. Notice that the value of the margin of error appears on the line Confidence Level (95.0%). The slight difference in the value of the margin of error between our calculation of 7.2 and the value in Excel's output of 7.3 is due to our using the normal approximation to the Student's t distribution.

Table 8.2 Improvement in SAT Scores

DEPENDENT SAMPLES	
DIFFERENCE = AFTER SCORE − BEFORE SCORE	
Mean	77.7
Standard Error	3.692395
Median	80
Mode	80
Standard Deviation	43.68901
Sample Variance	1908.729
Range	260
Minimum	−50
Maximum	210
Sum	10878
Count	140
Confidence Level (95.0%)	7.300521

EXERCISES

Basic Exercises

8.1 A dependent random sample from two normally distributed populations gives the following results:

$$n = 11 \quad \bar{d} = 28.5 \quad s_d = 3.3$$

a. Find the 98% confidence interval for the difference between the means of the two populations.

b. Find the margin of error for a 98% confidence interval for the difference between the means of the two populations.

8.2 A confidence interval for the difference between the means of two normally distributed populations based on the following dependent samples is desired:

Before	After
6	8
12	14
8	9
10	13
6	7

a. Find the margin of error for a 90% confidence level.
b. Find the UCL and the LCL for a 90% confidence level.
c. Find the width of a 95% confidence interval.

8.3 An educational study was designed to investigate the effectiveness of a reading program of elementary age children. Each child was given a pretest and posttest. Higher posttest scores would indicate reading improvement. From a very large population, a random sample of scores for the pretest and posttest are as follows:

Child	Pretest Score	Posttest Score
1	40	48
2	36	42
3	32	
4	38	36
5		43
6	33	38
7	35	45

Child 3 moved from the school district and did not take the posttest. Child 5 moved into the district after the start of the study and did not take the pretest. Find a 95% confidence interval estimate of the mean improvement in the reading scores.

Application Exercises

8.4 A random sample of 10 pairs of identical houses was chosen in a large Midwestern city, and a passive solar heating system was installed in one house from each pair. The total fuel bills (in dollars) for three winter months for these homes were then determined, as shown in the accompanying table. Assuming normal population distributions, find a 90% confidence interval for the difference between the two population means.

Pair	Without Passive Solar	With Passive Solar	Pair	Without Passive Solar	With Passive Solar
1	485	452	6	386	380
2	423	386	7	426	395
3	515	502	8	473	411
4	425	376	9	454	415
5	653	605	10	496	441

8.5 A random sample of six salespeople who attended a motivational course on sales techniques was monitored 3 months before and 3 months after the course. The table shows the values of sales (in thousands of euros) generated by these six salespeople in the two periods. Assume that the population distributions are normal. Find an 80% confidence interval for the difference between the two population means.

Salesperson	Before the Course	After the Course
1	210	235
2	289	301
3	212	196
4	327	340
5	163	191
6	205	194

8.2 CONFIDENCE INTERVAL ESTIMATION OF THE DIFFERENCE BETWEEN TWO NORMAL POPULATION MEANS: INDEPENDENT SAMPLES

In this section we develop confidence interval estimation when two samples are drawn *independently* from two normally distributed populations. We consider three situations: (1) both population variances are known; (2) both population variances are not known but can be considered to be equal; and (3) both population variances are not known but are not considered to be equal.

Two Means, Independent Samples, and Known Population Variances

In this scheme, samples are drawn *independently* from the two normally distributed populations so that the membership of one sample is not influenced by the membership of the other sample. Also we know the *population variances of both populations.*

Consider the case where independent samples, not necessarily of equal size, are taken from the two populations of interest. Suppose that there is a random sample of n_x observations from a population with mean μ_x and variance σ_x^2 and an independent random sample of n_y observations from a population with mean μ_y and variance σ_y^2. Let the respective sample means be $\bar{x}$ and $\bar{y}$.

As a first step, examine the situation when the two population distributions are normal with known variances. Since the object of interest is the difference between the two population means, it is natural to base an inference on the difference between the corresponding sample means. This random variable has mean

$$E(\overline{X} - \overline{Y}) = E(\overline{X}) - E(\overline{Y}) = \mu_x - \mu_y$$

and, since the samples are independent,

$$Var(\overline{X} - \overline{Y}) = Var(\overline{X}) + Var(\overline{Y}) = \frac{\sigma_x^2}{n_x} + \frac{\sigma_y^2}{n_y}$$

Furthermore, it can be shown that its distribution is normal. It therefore follows that the random variable

$$Z = \frac{(\overline{x} - \overline{y}) - (\mu_x - \mu_y)}{\sqrt{\dfrac{\sigma_x^2}{n_x} + \dfrac{\sigma_y^2}{n_y}}}$$

has a standard normal distribution. An argument parallel to that in Chapter 7 can then be used to obtain the confidence interval for the difference between the population means.

Confidence Intervals of the Difference Between Means: Independent Samples (Normal Distributions and Known Population Variances)

Suppose that there are two independent random samples of n_x and n_y observations from normally distributed populations with means μ_x and μ_y and variances σ_x^2 and σ_y^2. If the observed sample means are $\overline{x}$ and $\overline{y}$, then a $100(1 - \alpha)\%$ **confidence interval for the difference between two means, independent samples, and known population variances** is given by

$$(\overline{x} - \overline{y}) \pm z_{\alpha/2} \sqrt{\frac{\sigma_x^2}{n_x} + \frac{\sigma_y^2}{n_y}} \tag{8.3}$$

or, equivalently,

$$(\overline{x} - \overline{y}) \pm ME$$

where the margin of error, ME, is given by the following:

$$ME = z_{\alpha/2} \sqrt{\frac{\sigma_x^2}{n_x} + \frac{\sigma_y^2}{n_y}} \tag{8.4}$$

In some applications, historical variances from similar studies can be used as the true population variances.

Example 8.3 Comparison of GPAs (Confidence Interval)

From a very large university, independent random samples of 120 students majoring in marketing and 90 students majoring in finance were selected. The mean GPA for the random sample of marketing majors was found to be 3.08, and the mean GPA for the random sample of finance majors was 2.88. From similar past studies the population standard deviation for the marketing majors is assumed to be 0.42; similarly, the population standard deviation for the finance majors is 0.64. Denoting the population mean for marketing majors by μ_x and the population mean for finance majors by μ_y, find a 95% confidence interval for $(\mu_x - \mu_y)$.

Solution We use Equation 8.3,

$$(\bar{x} - \bar{y}) \pm z_{\alpha/2}\sqrt{\frac{\sigma_x^2}{n_x} + \frac{\sigma_y^2}{n_y}}$$

with

$$n_x = 120 \quad \bar{x} = 3.08 \quad \sigma_x = 0.42$$
$$n_y = 90 \quad \bar{y} = 2.88 \quad \sigma_y = 0.64$$

And for a 95% confidence interval,

$$z_{\alpha/2} = z_{0.025} = 1.96$$

The confidence interval is then

$$(3.08 - 2.88) \pm 1.96\sqrt{\frac{(0.42)^2}{120} + \frac{(0.64)^2}{90}}$$

or

$$0.20 \pm 0.1521$$

This interval extends from 0.0479 to 0.3521.

Two Means, Independent Samples, and Unknown Population Variances Assumed to Be Equal

It seems reasonable that if we do not know the population means, we most likely do not know the population variances either. Two possibilities arise: Either the unknown population variances are assumed to be equal, or they are *not* assumed to be equal. We turn our attention first to the situation where the unknown population variances are assumed to be equal. We present both of the situations but defer discussion of how to determine whether population variances are equal to Chapter 10.

Suppose again that there are two independent random samples of n_x and n_y observations from normally distributed populations with means μ_x and μ_y, and assume that the populations have a common (unknown) variance σ^2—that is, $\sigma_x^2 = \sigma_y^2 = \sigma^2$. Inference about the population means is based on the difference $(\bar{x} - \bar{y})$ between the two sample means. This random variable has a normal distribution with mean $(\mu_x - \mu_y)$ and variance

$$Var(\overline{X} - \overline{Y}) = Var(\overline{X}) + Var(\overline{Y}) = \frac{\sigma^2}{n_x} + \frac{\sigma^2}{n_y}$$

It therefore follows that the random variable,

$$Z = \frac{(\bar{x} - \bar{y}) - (\mu_x - \mu_y)}{\sqrt{\frac{\sigma^2}{n_x} + \frac{\sigma^2}{n_y}}}$$

has a standard normal distribution. However, this result cannot be used as it stands because the unknown population variance is involved.

Since $\sigma_x^2 = \sigma_y^2 = \sigma^2$, then both s_x^2 and s_y^2 are estimators of the common population variance σ^2. To use only s_x^2 or only s_y^2 to estimate the common variance would ignore information from the other sample. If the sample sizes are the same ($n_x = n_y$), then the average of s_x^2 and s_y^2 could be used to estimate the common variance. However, in the more general situation of unequal sample sizes, an estimate is needed that acknowledges the fact that more information about the common variance is obtained from the sample with the larger sample size. Thus, a weighted average of s_x^2 and s_y^2 is used. This estimator s_p^2, pools the two sets of sample information and is given in Equation 8.7.

Confidence Intervals of Two Means: Unknown Population Variances That Are Assumed to Be Equal

Suppose that there are two independent random samples with n_x and n_y observations from normally distributed populations with means μ_x and μ_y, and a common, but unknown, population variance. If the observed sample means are $\bar{x}$ and $\bar{y}$, and the observed sample variances are s_x^2 and s_y^2, then a $100(1 - \alpha)\%$ **confidence interval for the difference between two means, independent samples, and unknown population variances assumed to be equal** is given by

$$(\bar{x} - \bar{y}) \pm t_{n_x+n_y-2,\alpha/2}\sqrt{\frac{s_p^2}{n_x} + \frac{s_p^2}{n_y}} \tag{8.5}$$

or, equivalently,

$$(\bar{x} - \bar{y}) \pm ME$$

where the margin of error, ME, is

$$ME = t_{n_x+n_y-2,\alpha/2}\sqrt{\frac{s_p^2}{n_x} + \frac{s_p^2}{n_y}} \tag{8.6}$$

and the **pooled sample variance**, s_p^2, is given by

$$s_p^2 = \frac{(n_x - 1)s_x^2 + (n_y - 1)s_y^2}{n_x + n_y - 2} \tag{8.7}$$

$t_{n_x+n_y-2,\alpha/2}$ is the number for which

$$P\left(t_{n_x+n_y-2} > t_{n_x+n_y-2,\alpha/2}\right) = \frac{\alpha}{2}$$

Example 8.4 Traffic Fines (Confidence Interval)

The residents of St. Paul, Minnesota, complain that traffic speeding fines given in their city are higher than the traffic speeding fines that are given in nearby Minneapolis. Independent random samples of the amounts paid by residents for speeding tickets in each of the two cities over the last 3 months were obtained. These amounts were as follows:

St. Paul	100	125	135	128	140	142	128	137	156	142
Minneapolis	95	87	100	75	110	105	85	95		

Assuming equal population variances, find a 95% confidence interval for the difference in the mean costs of speeding tickets in these two cities.

Solution Let the X population be all speeding tickets given in St. Paul and the Y population be all speeding tickets given in Minneapolis. First, we use a statistical package such as Minitab and conclude that normal probability plots for both samples do not indicate evidence of nonnormality. Next we calculate the mean and variance of both samples and obtain results as follows:

$$n_x = 10 \quad \bar{x} = \$133.30 \quad s_x^2 = 218.0111$$
$$n_y = 8 \quad \bar{y} = \$94.00 \quad s_y^2 = 129.4286$$

The pooled sample variance is found by Equation 8.7 to be

$$s_p^2 = \frac{(n_x - 1)s_x^2 + (n_y - 1)s_y^2}{n_x + n_y - 2} = \frac{(10 - 1)(218.0111) + (8 - 1)(129.4286)}{10 + 8 - 2} = 179.2563$$

and

$$(\bar{x} - \bar{y}) = (133.30 - 94.00) = \$39.30$$

The degrees of freedom result is $n_x + n_y - 2 = 16$ and $t_{16,0.025} = 2.12$.
We obtain the confidence interval by Equation 8.5 as follows:

$$(\bar{x} - \bar{y}) \pm t_{n_x+n_y-2,\alpha/2}\sqrt{\frac{s_p^2}{n_x} + \frac{s_p^2}{n_y}}$$

$$39.3 \pm (2.12)\sqrt{\frac{179.2563}{10} + \frac{179.2563}{8}}$$

$$\$39.30 \pm \$13.46$$

Figure 8.1 is the Minitab output for this example.

Figure 8.1 Traffic Fines (Confidence Interval)

	N	Mean	StDev	SE Mean
St. Paul	10	133.3	14.8	4.7
Minneapolis	8	94.0	11.4	4.0

Difference = mu (St. Paul) − mu (Minneapolis)
Estimate for difference: 39.30
95% CI for difference: (25.84, 52.76)

Two Means, Independent Samples, and Unknown Population Variances Not Assumed to Be Equal

In many applications it is not reasonable to assume equality of population variances. In that case we do not have need for a pooled sample variance. When the population variances are unknown and not assumed to be equal, the approximate value of the degrees of freedom is given in Equation 8.10 and is known as Satterthwaite's approximation (Satterthwaite 1946). Most statistical packages provide both procedures (with and without equal variances) for finding confidence intervals for differences in means of independent samples.

Confidence Intervals of Two Means: Unknown Population Variances, Not Assumed to Be Equal

Suppose that there are two independent random samples of n_x and n_y observations from *normally* distributed populations with means μ_x and μ_y, and it is assumed that the population variances are not equal. If the observed sample means and variances are $\bar{x}, \bar{y}$, and s_x^2, s_y^2, then a $100(1 - \alpha)\%$ **confidence interval for the difference between two means, independent samples, and unknown population variances not assumed to be equal** is given by

$$(\bar{x} - \bar{y}) - t_{v,\alpha/2}\sqrt{\frac{s_x^2}{n_x} + \frac{s_y^2}{n_y}} \tag{8.8}$$

where the margin of error, *ME*, is

$$ME = t_{v,\alpha/2}\sqrt{\frac{s_x^2}{n_x} + \frac{s_y^2}{n_y}} \tag{8.9}$$

and the degrees of freedom, v, is given by

$$v = \frac{\left[\left(\dfrac{s_x^2}{n_x}\right) + \left(\dfrac{s_y^2}{n_y}\right)\right]^2}{\left(\dfrac{s_x^2}{n_x}\right)^2 / (n_x - 1) + \left(\dfrac{s_y^2}{n_y}\right)^2 / (n_y - 1)} \tag{8.10}$$

If the sample sizes are equal, $n_x = n_y = n$, then the degrees of freedom reduces to the following:

$$v = \left(1 + \frac{2}{\dfrac{s_x^2}{s_y^2} + \dfrac{s_y^2}{s_x^2}}\right) \times (n - 1) \tag{8.11}$$

Example 8.5 Auditors (Confidence Interval)

An accounting firm conducts a random sample of the accounts payable for the east and the west offices of one of its clients. From these two independent samples, the company wants to estimate the difference between the population mean values of the payables. The sample statistics obtained are as follows:

	EAST OFFICE (POPULATION X)	WEST OFFICE (POPULATION Y)
Sample mean	$290	$250
Sample size	16	11
Sample standard deviation	15	50

We do not assume that the unknown population variances are equal. Estimate the difference between the mean values of the payables for the two offices. Use a 95% confidence level.

Solution First, we calculate the degrees of freedom by using Equation 8.10:

$$v = \frac{\left[\left(\dfrac{s_x^2}{n_x}\right) + \left(\dfrac{s_y^2}{n_y}\right)\right]^2}{\left(\dfrac{s_x^2}{n_x}\right)^2 / (n_x - 1) + \left(\dfrac{s_y^2}{n_y}\right)^2 / (n_y - 1)} = \frac{[(225/16 + 2500/11)]^2}{\left(\dfrac{225}{16}\right)^2 / 15 + \left(\dfrac{2500}{11}\right)^2 / 10} \approx 11$$

The margin of error is now found by using Equation 8.9:

$$ME = t_{v, \alpha/2}\sqrt{\frac{s_x^2}{n_x} + \frac{s_y^2}{n_y}} = t_{11, 0.025}\sqrt{\frac{225}{16} + \frac{2500}{11}} = 2.201(15.53497) = 34.19$$

Using Equation 8.8, the 95% confidence interval is as follows:

$$(290 - 250) \pm 34.19$$

The 95% confidence interval estimate for the difference between the mean values of the payables in these two offices extends from $5.81 to $74.19. Figure 8.2 is the Minitab output for these data.

Figure 8.2 Accounts Payable (Confidence Interval)

Two-Sample T-Test and CI

Sample	N	Mean	StDev	SE Mean
1	16	290.0	15.0	3.8
2	11	250.0	50.0	15.0

Difference = mu (1) − mu (2)
Estimate for difference: 40.0000
95% CI for difference: (5.8078, 74.1922)
T-Test of difference = 0 (vs not =): T-Value = 2.57 P-Value = 0.026 **DF = 11**

EXERCISES

Visit **www.MyStatLab.com** or **www.pearsonglobal editions.com** to access the data files.

Basic Exercises

8.6 Independent random sampling from two normally distributed populations gives the following results:

$$n_x = 87; \bar{x} = 115; \sigma_x = 25$$

$$n_y = 88; \bar{y} = 109; \sigma_y = 15$$

Find a 99% confidence interval estimate of the difference in the means of the two populations.

8.7 Independent random sampling from two normally distributed populations gives the following results:

$$n_x = 81; \bar{x} = 140; \sigma_x^2 = 25$$

$$n_y = 100; \bar{y} = 120; \sigma_y^2 = 14$$

Find a 95% confidence interval estimate of the difference between the means of the two populations.

8.8 Assuming equal population variances, determine the number of degrees of freedom for each of the following:

a. $n_x = 16$ $s_x^2 = 30$
   $n_y = 9$ $s_y^2 = 36$

b. $n_x = 12$ $s_x^2 = 30$
   $n_y = 14$ $s_y^2 = 36$

c. $n_x = 20$ $s_x^2 = 16$
   $n_y = 8$ $s_y^2 = 25$

8.9 Assuming equal population variances, compute the pooled sample variance s_p^2 for part a through part c of Exercise 8.8.

8.10 Assuming unequal population variances, determine the number of degrees of freedom for each of the following:

a. $n_x = 16$ $s_x^2 = 5$
   $n_y = 4$ $s_y^2 = 36$

b. $n_x = 9$ $s_x^2 = 30$
   $n_y = 16$ $s_y^2 = 4$

8.11 Determine the margin of error for a 95% confidence interval for the difference between population means for each of the following (assume equal population variances):

a. $n_x = 100$ $s_x^2 = 36$ $\bar{x} = 300$
   $n_y = 64$ $s_y^2 = 49$ $\bar{y} = 320$

b. $n_x = 25$ $s_x^2 = 36$ $\bar{x} = 300$
   $n_y = 16$ $s_y^2 = 49$ $\bar{y} = 320$

c. The sample sizes in part a are 4 times larger than the sample sizes in part b. Comment on your answers to part a compared to your answers to part b.

Application Exercises

8.12 A manufacturer knows that the number of items produced per hour by machine A and by machine B are normally distributed with a standard deviation of 4.6 items for machine A and a standard deviation of 6.8 items for machine B. The mean hourly amount produced by machine A for a random sample of 50 hours was 230 units; the mean hourly amount produced by machine B for a random sample of 45 hours was 215 units. Find a 90% confidence interval for the difference in mean parts produced per hour by these two machines.

8.13 In January 2019, the Lufthansa Innovation Hub (LIH) enetered its first collaboration with INSEAD, Singapore. Collaborative learning is a good driver of growth in the current global market. Suppose from a random sample of six employees at one division of the LIH that uses collaborative learning, the mean output was found to be 76.02 and the sample standard deviation was 2.3. For an independent random sample of eight employees in another LIH division that does not use collaborative learning, the sample mean and standard deviation were 71.86 and 8.5, respectively. Estimate with 99% confidence the difference between the two population mean output; do not assume equal population variances.

8.14 Happy Heart, Inc., a Norwegian company, offers health care and nutritional services for parents. It uses Birth Season to define when a baby is born (1 = spring/summer; 2 = autumn/winter) and Walking to define age (in months) at which the baby started walking. One specialist states that babies born in spring or summer tend to walk sooner. Estimate whether the specialist's statement is true. Use a 95% confidence interval and the data file **Baby Walking**. Explain your findings.

8.15 Recent business graduates currently employed in full-time positions were surveyed. Family backgrounds were self-classified as relatively high or low socioeconomic status. For a random sample of

16 high-socioeconomic-status recent business graduates, the mean total compensation was \$34,500 and the sample standard deviation was \$8,520. For an independent random sample of 9 low-socioeconomic-status recent business graduates, the mean total compensation was \$31,499 and the sample standard deviation was \$7,521. Find a 90% confidence interval for the difference between the two population means.

8.16 Suppose that for a random sample of 250 firms that revalued their fixed assets, the mean ratio of debt to tangible assets was 0.625 and the sample standard deviation was 0.176. For an independent random sample of 450 firms that did not revalue their fixed assets, the mean ratio of debt to tangible assets was 0.598 and the sample standard deviation was 0.164. Find a 95% confidence interval for the difference between the two population means.

8.17 A researcher intends to estimate the effect of a drug on the scores of human subjects performing a task of psychomotor coordination. The members of a random sample of 9 subjects were given the drug prior to testing. The mean score in this group was 9.29, and the sample variance was 17.43. An independent random sample of 10 subjects was used as a control group and given a placebo prior to testing. The mean score in this control group was 15.72, and the sample variance was 27.03. Assuming that the population distributions are normal with equal variances, find a 99% confidence interval for the difference between the population mean scores.

8.3 CONFIDENCE INTERVAL ESTIMATION OF THE DIFFERENCE BETWEEN TWO POPULATION PROPORTIONS (LARGE SAMPLES)

We derived confidence intervals for a single population proportion in Chapter 7. Often a comparison of two population proportions is of interest. For instance, one might want to compare the proportion of residents in one city who indicate that they will vote for a particular presidential candidate with the proportion of residents in another city who indicate the same candidate preference. In this section, we consider confidence intervals for the difference between two population proportions with independent large samples taken from these two populations.

Suppose that a random sample of n_x observations from a population with proportion P_x of "successes" yields sample proportion $\hat{p}_x$ and that an independent random sample of n_y observations from a population with proportion P_y of "successes" produces sample proportion $\hat{p}_y$. Since our concern is with the population difference $(P_x - P_y)$, it is natural to examine the random variable $(\hat{p}_x - \hat{p}_y)$. This has mean

$$E(\hat{p}_x - \hat{p}_y) = E(\hat{p}_x) - E(\hat{p}_y) = P_x - P_y$$

and, since the samples are taken independently, it has the variance

$$Var(\hat{p}_x - \hat{p}_y) = Var(\hat{p}_x) + Var(\hat{p}_y) = \frac{P_x(1 - P_x)}{n_x} + \frac{P_y(1 - P_y)}{n_y}$$

Furthermore, if the sample sizes are large, the distribution of this random variable is approximately normal, so subtracting its mean and dividing by its standard deviation gives a standard normally distributed random variable. Moreover, for large sample sizes this approximation remains valid when the unknown population proportions P_x and P_y are replaced by the corresponding sample quantities. Thus, to a good approximation, the random variable

$$Z = \frac{(\hat{p}_x - \hat{p}_y) - (P_x - P_y)}{\sqrt{\dfrac{\hat{p}_x(1 - \hat{p}_x)}{n_x} + \dfrac{\hat{p}_y(1 - \hat{p}_y)}{n_y}}}$$

has a standard normal distribution. This result allows the derivation of confidence intervals for the difference between the two population proportions when the same sample sizes are large.

Confidence Intervals of the Difference Between Population Proportions (Large Samples)

Let P_x denote the observed proportion of successes in a random sample of n_x observations from a population with proportion P_x of successes, and let $\hat{p}_y$ denote the proportion of successes observed in an independent random sample of n_y observations from a population with proportion P_y of successes. Then, if the sample sizes are large (generally at least 40 observations in each sample), a $100(1 - \alpha)\%$ **confidence interval for the difference between population proportions (large samples)**, $(P_x - P_y)$, is given by

$$(\hat{p}_x - \hat{p}_y) \pm ME \tag{8.12}$$

where the margin of error, ME, is as follows:

$$ME = z_{\alpha/2}\sqrt{\frac{\hat{p}_x(1 - \hat{p}_x)}{n_x} + \frac{\hat{p}_y(1 - \hat{p}_y)}{n_y}} \tag{8.13}$$

Example 8.6 Precinct Preference (Confidence Interval)

During a presidential election year, many forecasts are made to determine how voters perceive a particular candidate. In a random sample of 120 registered voters in precinct X, 107 indicated that they supported the candidate in question. In an independent random sample of 141 registered voters in precinct Y, only 73 indicated support for the same candidate. The respective population proportions are denoted P_x and P_y. Find a 95% confidence interval for the population difference, $(P_x - P_y)$.

Solution   From the sample information it follows that

$$n_x = 120 \quad \text{and} \quad \hat{p}_x = 107/120 = 0.892$$
$$n_y = 141 \quad \text{and} \quad \hat{p}_y = 73/141 = 0.518$$

For a 95% confidence interval, $\alpha = 0.05$, and so

$$z_{\alpha/2} = z_{0.025} = 1.96$$

The required interval is, therefore,

$$(0.892 - 0.518) \pm 1.96\sqrt{\frac{(0.892)(0.108)}{120} + \frac{(0.518)(0.482)}{141}}$$

It follows that the 95% confidence interval estimate of the difference for the population proportion of registered voters in precinct X and precinct Y extends from 0.274 to 0.473.

Figure 8.3 is the Minitab output for Example 8.6.

Figure 8.3 Precinct Preference (Confidence Interval)

Sample	X	N	Sample p
1	107	120	0.891667
2	73	141	0.517730

Estimate for p (1) − p (2): 0.373936
95% CI for p (1) − p (2): (0.274463, 0.473409)

Basic Exercises

8.18 Calculate the margin of error for each of the following:

    a. $n_x = 300$ $\hat{p}_x = 0.62$
       $n_y = 350$ $\hat{p}_y = 0.72$
    b. $n_x = 100$ $\hat{p}_x = 0.44$
       $n_y = 120$ $\hat{p}_y = 0.55$

8.19 Calculate the 95% confidence interval for the difference in population proportions for each of the following:

    a. $n_x = 260$ $\hat{p}_x = 0.35$
       $n_y = 240$ $\hat{p}_y = 0.30$
    b. $n_x = 145$ $\hat{p}_x = 0.20$
       $n_y = 120$ $\hat{p}_y = 0.25$

Application Exercises

8.20 In randomized, double-blind clinical trials of a new medical supplement, test subjects were randomly divided into two groups. The people in Group X received the new supplement while those in Group Y received a control supplement. After the first dose, 107 of 715 subjects in Group A experienced showed an improvement in health. After the first dose, 59 of 630 subjects in Group B experienced showed an improvement in health. Construct a 95% confidence interval for the difference between the two population proportions.

8.21 Regulatory agencies and the U.S. Congress recognize both the values and emerging issues for small firms as the Sarbanes-Oxley Act of 2002 (SOX) is implemented. On April 23, 2006, the Advisory Committee on Smaller Public Companies issued a final report to the Security and Exchange Commission assessing the impact of Sarbanes-Oxley Act of 2002 on smaller public companies (Final Report of the Advisory Committee on Smaller Public Companies to the U.S. Securities and Exchange Commission, April 23, 2006). Suppose that one study collected data from a random sample of 150 CEOs, CFOs, and board members of small firms (those firms with annual revenue less than or equal to $250 million) and a random sample of 200 similar executives from large firms (those firms with annual revenues exceeding $750 million). From the small firms, 60 respondents indicated that the implementation of SOX had a major overall impact on their firm. From the large firms, 164 respondents believed that the implementation of SOX had a major overall impact on their firm. Estimate with 98% confidence the difference in the population proportion between all small and large firms concerning the impact of SOX.

8.22 Would you use your school library more if the hours were extended? From a random sample of 121 freshmen, 75 indicated that they would use the school's library more if the hours were extended. In an independent random sample of 105 sophomores, 87 responded that they would use the library more if the hours were extended. Estimate the difference in proportion of first-year and second-year students responding affirmatively to this question. Use a 95% confidence level.

8.23 A random sample of 100 men contained 61 in favor of a state constitutional amendment to retard the rate of growth of property taxes. An independent random sample of 100 women contained 54 in favor of this amendment. A confidence interval extending from 0.04 to 0.10 was calculated for the difference between the population proportions. Determine the confidence level of this interval.

8.24 Supermarket shoppers were observed and questioned immediately after putting an item in their cart. Of a random sample of 220 choosing a product at the regular price, 137 claimed to check the price before putting the item in their cart. Of an independent random sample of 280 choosing a product at a special price, 206 made this claim. Find a 90% confidence interval for the difference between the two population proportions.

KEY WORDS

DATA FILES

Visit www.MyStatLab.com or www.pearsonglobal editions.com to access the data files.

8.25 Independent random samples from two normally distributed populations give the following results:

$$n_x = 15 \quad \bar{x} = 400 \quad s_x = 20$$
$$n_y = 13 \quad \bar{y} = 360 \quad s_y = 25$$

Assume that the unknown population variances are equal and find a 90% confidence interval for the difference between population means.

8.26 Independent random samples from two normally distributed populations give the following results:

$$n_x = 22 \quad \bar{x} = 2500 \quad s_x = 250$$
$$n_y = 20 \quad \bar{y} = 2100 \quad s_y = 100$$

If we do not assume that the unknown population variances are equal, what is the 99% confidence interval for the difference between the population means?

8.27 Independent random samples from two normally distributed populations give the following results:

$$n_x = 10 \quad \bar{x} = 480 \quad s_x = 30$$
$$n_y = 12 \quad \bar{y} = 520 \quad s_y = 25$$

a. If we assume that the unknown population variances are equal, find the 90% confidence interval for the difference of population means.

b. If we do not assume that the unknown population variances are equal, find the 90% confidence interval for the difference between population means.

8.28 A company sends a random sample of 16 of its salespeople to a course designed to increase their motivation and, hence, presumably their effectiveness. In the following year these people generated sales with an average value of $625,000 and a sample standard deviation of $80,000. During the same period, an independently chosen random sample of 10 salespeople who had not attended the course obtained sales with an average value of $608,000 and a sample standard deviation of $73,000. Assume that the two population distributions are normal and have the same variance. Find a 90% confidence interval estimate for the difference between the population mean sales for salespeople who attended the motivational course and for those salespeople who did not attend the course.

8.29 A proposal for a new 1-cent tax increase to support cancer research is to appear on the ballot in one county's next election. The residents in Hangzhou and Chengdu, two cities in China, were questioned as to their level of support. In Hangzhou a recent survey of 450 residents showed that 352 people supported the proposal, 18 were undecided, and the remainder were opposed to the new proposal. In Chengdu, the results of a random sample of 400 residents found that 326 people supported the tax, 32 were opposed, and the remainder

were undecided. Estimate the difference in the percentages of residents from these two cities who support this proposal. Use a 95% confidence level.

8.30 Is the average amount spent on textbooks per semester by accounting majors significantly different from the average amount spent on textbooks per semester by management majors? Answer this question with a 90% confidence interval using the following data from random samples of students majoring in accounting or management. Discuss the assumptions.

	Accounting Majors	Management Majors
Mean	$340	$285
Standard deviation	20	30
Sample size	40	50

8.31 Brämhults Juice, based in Sweden, produces chilled fruit and vegetable juices. A manager at Brämhults is considering purchasing a new machine to bottle 16-fluid-ounce (473-milliliter) bottles of 100% pure carrot juice and wants an estimate of the difference in the mean filling weights between the new machine and the old machine. Random samples of bottles of carrot juice that had been filled by both machines were obtained. Estimate the difference in the mean filling weights between the new and the old machines? Discuss the assumptions. Use $\alpha = 0.10$.

	New Machine	Old Machine
Mean	472 milliliters	468 milliliters
Standard deviation	5.5 milliliters	6.5 milliliters
Sample size	22	20

8.32 The **Baby Walking** data file contains information concerning the birth, first steps, age, and so on for 98 babies. The variable "siblings" refers to the number of siblings the baby has, and the variable "walking" refers to the age, in months, in which the baby started walking.

Some specialists say that babies with siblings start walking sooner than babies without siblings. Use an appropriate 95% confidence interval to confirm or reject this theory.

8.33 A newspaper article reported that 350 people in one state were surveyed and 60% were opposed to a recent court decision. The same article reported that a similar survey of 550 people in another state indicated opposition by only 20%. Construct a 95% confidence interval of the difference in population proportions based on the data.

8.34 The **Taiwan Real Estate** data file contains information on several variables related to houses sold in Taiwan in 2012 and 2013. Build an appropriate 90% confidence interval to check if there has been a significant increase in the price (USD/m²) from 2012 to 2013.

8.35 The **Taiwan Real Estate** data file contains information on several variables related to houses sold in Taiwan in 2012 and 2013. Build an appropriate 95% confidence interval to compare the age of the houses sold in 2012 and in 2013.

Appendix

STUDENT'S t DISTRIBUTION FOR THE DIFFERENCE IN THE MEANS OF TWO NORMALLY DISTRIBUTED POPULATIONS WITH UNKNOWN POPULATION VARIANCES NOT ASSUMED TO BE EQUAL

We saw in the Chapter 7 appendix that Gosset developed a probability distribution for normally distributed random variables that did not include the population variance σ^2. He took the ratio of Z, a standard normal random variable, to the square root of χ^2 divided by its degrees of freedom, v. In mathematical notation

$$t = \frac{Z}{\sqrt{\chi^2/v}}$$

Now, for the difference between the means of two normally distributed populations, the random variable Z is

$$Z = \frac{(\bar{x} - \bar{y}) - (\mu_x - \mu_y)}{\sqrt{\dfrac{\sigma_x^2}{n_x} + \dfrac{\sigma_y^2}{n_y}}}$$

and the random variable χ^2 is

$$\chi^2 = \chi_x^2 + \chi_y^2$$

That is, the random variable χ^2 is the sum of two independent chi-square random variables, χ_X^2 and χ_Y^2, based on the two independent random samples, X and Y. We saw in Section 7.5 that χ_X^2 and χ_Y^2 are defined as

$$\chi_x^2 = \frac{(n_x - 1)s_x^2}{\sigma_x^2}$$

$$\chi_y^2 = \frac{(n_y - 1)s_y^2}{\sigma_y^2}$$

with $(n_x - 1)$ and $(n_y - 1)$ degrees of freedom, respectively. The degrees of freedom for χ^2 is the sum of the component degrees of freedom, $v = (n_x - 1) + (n_y - 1) = n_x + n_y - 2$.

Bringing these pieces together,

$$t = \frac{[(\bar{x} - \bar{y}) - (\mu_x - \mu_y)]/\sqrt{\sigma_x^2/n_x + \sigma_y^2/n_y}}{\sqrt{[(n_x - 1)s_x^2/\sigma_x^2 + (n_y - 1)s_y^2/\sigma_y^2]/(n_x + n_y - 2)}}$$

If $\sigma_x^2 = \sigma_y^2$, then this reduces to the following:

$$t = \frac{(\bar{x} - \bar{y}) - (\mu_x - \mu_y)}{\sqrt{\dfrac{s_p^2}{n_x} + \dfrac{s_p^2}{n_y}}}$$

REFERENCES

1. Carlson, William L. 1997. *Cases in Managerial Data Analysis.* Belmont, CA: Wadsworth Publishing Company.
2. Final Report of the Advisory Committee on Smaller Public Companies to the U.S. Securities and Exchange Commission. April 23, 2006. http://www.sec.gov/info/smallbus/acspc/acspc-finalreport.pdf (accessed August 8, 2011).
3. Guenther, P. M., J. Reedy, S. M. Krebs-Smith, B. B. Reeve, and P. P. Basiotis. November 2007. Development and Evaluation of the Healthy Eating Index–2005: Technical Report. *Center for Nutrition Policy and Promotion, U.S. Department of Agriculture, Available at http://www.cnpp.usda.gov/HealthyEatingIndex.htm.*
4. Satterthwaite, F. E. 1946. An approximate distribution of estimates of variance components. *Biometrics Bulletin*, 2, 110–114.

CHAPTER

9

Hypothesis Testing: Single Population

Introduction

In this chapter we develop hypothesis-testing procedures that enable us to test the validity of some conjecture or claim by using sample data. This form of inference contrasts and complements the estimation procedures developed in Chapters 7 and 8. The process begins with an investigator forming a hypothesis about the nature of some population. We clearly state this hypothesis as involving two options, and then we select one option based on the results of a statistic computed from a random sample of data. Following are examples of typical problems:

1. Malt-O-Meal, Inc., a producer of ready-to-eat cereal, claims that, on average, its cereal packages weigh at least 16 ounces, and thus do not weigh less than 16 ounces. The company can test this claim by collecting a random sample of cereal packages, determining the weight of each one, and computing the sample mean package weight from the data.
2. An automobile-parts factory wishes to monitor its manufacturing process to ensure that the diameter of pistons meets engineering tolerance specifications. It could obtain random samples every 2 hours from the production line and use them to determine if standards are being maintained.

These examples indicate a standard procedure. We state a hypothesis about some population parameter and then collect sample data to test the validity of our hypothesis.

9.1 CONCEPTS OF HYPOTHESIS TESTING

Here we introduce a general framework to test hypotheses. First, as noted earlier, we need to define two alternatives that cover all possible outcomes. Then, by using statistics computed from random samples, we select one of the two alternatives. Since these statistics have a sampling distribution, our decision is made in the face of random variation. Thus, clear decision rules are needed for choosing between the two alternatives. The sample statistics cannot in general be used to absolutely "prove" that one of the two alternatives is correct. However, we can find that one of the alternatives has a very small probability of being correct. Thus as a result we would select the other alternative. This approach is the fundamental decision-making process used in scientific research. The term "counterfactual" testing is commonly used to define this decision process.

The process that we develop here has a direct analogy to a criminal jury trial. A person charged with a crime is either innocent or guilty. In a jury trial we initially assume that the accused is innocent, and the jury will decide that a person is guilty only if there is very strong evidence against the presumption of innocence. That is, the jury would reject the initial assumption of innocence. The criminal jury trial process for choosing between guilt and innocence has the following characteristics:

1. Rigorous procedures or rules for presenting and evaluating evidence
2. A judge to enforce the rules
3. A decision process that assumes innocence unless there is evidence to prove guilt beyond a reasonable doubt

Note that this process will fail to convict some people who are, in fact, guilty. But if a person's innocence is rejected and the person is found guilty, we have strong evidence that the person is guilty.

We begin the hypothesis-testing procedure by considering a value for a population probability distribution parameter such as the mean, μ, the variance, σ^2, or the proportion, P. Our approach starts with a hypothesis about the parameter—called the **null hypothesis**—that will be maintained unless there is strong evidence against this null hypothesis. If we reject the null hypothesis, then the second hypothesis, named the **alternative hypothesis**, will be accepted. However, if we fail to reject the null hypothesis, we cannot necessarily conclude that the null hypothesis is correct. If we fail to reject, then either the null hypothesis is correct or the alternative hypothesis is correct, but our test procedure is not strong enough to reject the null hypothesis.

Using our Malt-O-Meal example, we could begin by assuming that the mean package weight is just equal to 16 ounces, so our null hypothesis is defined as follows:

$$H_0 : \mu = 16$$

A hypothesis, whether null or alternative, might specify a single value—in this case, $\mu = 16$—for the population parameter μ. We define this hypothesis as a **simple hypothesis**, which is read as follows: The null hypothesis is that the population parameter μ is equal to a specific value of 16. For this cereal example, a possible alternative hypothesis is that the population mean package weight falls in a range of values greater than 16 ounces:

$$H_1 : \mu > 16$$

We define this alternative hypothesis as a **one-sided composite alternative hypothesis**. Another possibility would be to test the null hypothesis against the general **two-sided composite alternative hypothesis**:

$$H_1 : \mu \neq 16$$

We choose these hypotheses so that one or the other must be true. In this book we denote the null hypothesis as H_0 and the alternative hypothesis as H_1.

Similar to a jury trial, our decision to choose one hypothesis or the other follows a rigorous procedure. The decision process uses a decision statistic computed from a random sample, such as a sample mean, $\bar{x}$, a sample variance, s^2, or a sample proportion, $\hat{p}$. The decision statistic will have a known sampling distribution based on the sampling procedure and the parameter value specified by the null hypothesis. From this sampling distribution we determine values of the decision statistic that have a small probability of occurring if the null hypothesis is true. If the decision statistic has a value that has a small probability of occurring when the null hypothesis is true, we reject the null hypothesis and accept the alternative hypothesis. However, if the decision statistic does not have a small probability of occurring when the null hypothesis is true, then we do not reject the null hypothesis. The specification of null and alternative hypotheses depends on the problem, as indicated in the following examples.

1. Malt-O-Meal would like to have its mean package weight above the label weight. Let μ denote the population mean weight (in ounces) of cereal per box. The composite null hypothesis is that this mean is at most 16 ounces:

$$H_0 : \mu \leq 16$$

And the obvious alternative is that the mean weight is greater than 16 ounces:

$$H_1 : \mu > 16$$

For this problem we would seek strong evidence that the mean weight of packages is not less than or equal to 16 ounces and thus is greater than 16 ounces. The company wishes to avoid legal action and/or customer dissatisfaction because of low package weights. The company would have confidence in its conclusion—that mean package weight exceeds 16 ounces—if it had strong evidence that resulted in rejecting H_0.

2. An automobile-parts factory has proposed a process to monitor the diameter of pistons on a regular schedule. Every 2 hours a random sample of $n = 6$ pistons would be selected from the production process and their diameters measured. The mean diameter for the 6 pistons would be computed and used to test the simple null hypothesis,

$$H_0 : \mu = 3.800$$

versus the alternative hypothesis,

$$H_1 : \mu \neq 3.800$$

In this example a piston that is either too big or too small cannot be used.

The company would continue to operate unless the null hypothesis was rejected in favor of the alternative hypothesis. Rejection would occur if the sample mean had a small value or a large value, either of which had a small probability of occurring if the null hypothesis—the piston diameter is equal to 3.800—was true. Strong evidence that the pistons were not meeting the tolerance standards would result in an interruption of the production process.

Once we have specified the null and the alternative hypotheses and collected sample data, we must make a decision concerning the null hypothesis. We can either reject the null hypothesis and accept the alternative, or fail to reject the null hypothesis. For good reasons many statisticians prefer not to say, "accept the null hypothesis"; instead, they say, "fail to reject the null hypothesis." When we fail to reject the null hypothesis, then either the null hypothesis is true or our test procedure was not strong enough to reject it and we have committed an error. To select the hypothesis—null or alternative—we develop a decision rule based on sample evidence. Later in this chapter we present specific decision rules for various problems. In many cases the form of the rule is fairly obvious. To test the null hypothesis that the mean weight of cereal boxes is at most 16 ounces, we obtain a random sample of boxes and compute the sample mean. If the sample mean is substantially above 16 ounces, we can reject the null hypothesis and accept the alternative hypothesis. In general, the greater the sample mean is above 16, the greater the chance is of rejecting the null hypothesis. We develop specific decision rules next.

From our discussion of sampling distributions in Chapter 6, we know that the sample mean is different from the population mean. With only one sample mean, we cannot be certain of the value of the population mean. Thus, we know that the adopted decision rule will have some chance of reaching an erroneous conclusion. Table 9.1 summarizes the possible types of error. We define **Type I error** as the probability of rejecting the null hypothesis when the null hypothesis is true. Our decision rule will be defined so that the probability of rejecting a true null hypothesis, denoted as α, is "small." We define α to be the **significance level** of the test. The probability of failing to reject the null hypothesis when it is true is $(1 - \alpha)$. We also have another possible error, called a **Type II error**, that arises when we fail to reject a false null hypothesis. For a particular decision rule, the probability of making such an error when the null hypothesis is false will be denoted as β. Then the probability of rejecting a false null hypothesis is $(1 - \beta)$, which is called the *power* of the test.

Table 9.1 States of Nature and Decisions on the Null Hypothesis, with Probabilities of Making the Decisions, Given the States of Nature

DECISIONS ON NULL HYPOTHESIS	STATES OF NATURE	
	NULL HYPOTHESIS IS TRUE	NULL HYPOTHESIS IS FALSE
Fail to reject H_0	Correct decision	Type II error
	Probability $= 1 - \alpha$	Probability $= \beta$
Reject H_0	Type I error Probability $= \alpha$ (α is called the significance level)	Correct decision Probability $= 1 - \beta$ ($1 - \beta$ is called the power of the test)

We illustrate these ideas by reference to an earlier example. A factory manager is trying to determine if the population mean package weight is greater than the package label weight. The null hypothesis is that in the population, the mean package weight is less than or equal to the label weight of 16 ounces. This null hypothesis is tested against the alternative hypothesis that the mean package weight is greater than 16 ounces. To test the hypothesis, we obtain an independent random sample of cereal packages and compute the sample mean. If the sample mean is substantially larger than 16 ounces, the null hypothesis is rejected. Otherwise, we will not reject the null hypothesis. Let $\bar{x}$ denote the sample mean. Then, a possible decision rule is as follows:

$$\text{reject } H_0 \text{ if } \bar{x} > 16.13$$

Now, suppose that the null hypothesis is true. We could still find that the sample mean is greater than 16.13, and, according to our decision rule, the null hypothesis would be rejected. In that case we would have committed a Type I error. The probability of rejection when the null hypothesis is true is the significance level α. By contrast, suppose that the null hypothesis is false and that the population mean package weight is greater than 16. We could still find that the sample mean was less than 16.13, and, according to our decision rule, the null hypothesis would not be rejected. Thus, a Type II error would have occurred. The probability of making such an error will depend on just how much the population mean exceeds 16. We will find that it is more likely that the null hypothesis would be rejected for a given sample size if the population mean was 16.5 compared to the case where the population mean was 16.1.

Ideally, we would like to have the probabilities of both types of errors be as small as possible. However, there is a trade-off between the probabilities of the two types of errors. Given a particular sample, any reduction in the probability of Type I error, α, will result in an increase in the probability of Type II error, β, and vice versa. We need to emphasize here that there is not a direct linear substitution (e.g., a reduction of 0.02 in α does not usually result in an increase of 0.02 in β). Thus, in the previous example the probability of Type I error, α, could be reduced by changing the decision rule to the following:

$$\text{reject } H_0 \text{ if } \bar{x} > 16.23$$

But failure to reject the null hypothesis is more likely even if the null hypothesis is false. As a result, the probability of Type II error, β, would be increased. In practice, we select a small (e.g., less than 0.10) probability of Type I error, and that probability is used to set the decision rule. The probability of Type II error is then determined, as shown in Figure 9.1.

Figure 9.1 Consequences of Fixing the Significance Level of a Test

Suppose that a plant manager wishes to test whether the true mean weight of cereal boxes is greater than 16 ounces. He would begin the analysis by first fixing the probability of Type I error. In a sense this is like deciding the rules for a baseball or soccer game before the game starts instead of making up the rules as the game is played. After analyzing the nature of the decision process, he might decide that the decision rule should have a probability of $\alpha = 0.05$ or less of rejecting the null hypothesis when it is true. He would do this by selecting an appropriate number, $\bar{x}_c$, according to the following decision rule: Reject the null hypothesis if the sample mean is greater than $\bar{x}_c$ ounces. In the following sections we indicate the procedure for choosing $\bar{x}_c$. Once the number $\bar{x}_c$ has been chosen, the probability of Type II error can be computed—for a particular value of μ included in H_1—using the procedures to be developed in Section 9.5.

Another concept used in hypothesis testing is the **power** of the test, defined as the probability of rejecting H_0 when H_1 is true. The power is computed for particular values of μ that satisfy the null hypothesis. The power is typically different for every different value of μ. Consider the cereal problem with

$$H_0 : \mu = 16$$
$$H_1 : \mu > 16$$

Thus, for any value of μ contained in the alternative hypothesis, H_1

$$\text{Power} = P \left(\text{reject } H_0 \,|\, \mu, \, (\mu \subset H_1) \right)$$

Since the decision rule is determined by the significance level chosen for the test, the concept of power does not directly affect the decision to reject or fail to reject a null hypothesis. However, by computing the power of the test for particular significance levels and values of μ included in H_1, we will have valuable information about the properties of the decision rule. For example, we will see that, by taking a larger sample size, the power of the test will be increased for a given significance level, α. Thus, we will balance the increased costs of a larger sample size against the benefits of increasing the power of the test. Another important use of power calculations occurs when, for a given sample size, we have a choice between two or more possible tests with the same significance levels. Then it would be appropriate to choose the test that has the smallest probability of Type II error—that is, the test with the highest power.

In Sections 9.2 through 9.4, we show how, for given significance levels, decision rules can be formulated for some important classes of hypothesis-testing problems. In Section 9.5 we show how the power of a test can be computed. A summary of the important terms and ideas that have been developed thus far is as follows.

Summary of Hypothesis-Testing Terminology

Null hypothesis, H_0: A maintained hypothesis that is considered to be true unless sufficient evidence to the contrary is obtained.

Alternative hypothesis, H_1: A hypothesis against which the null hypothesis is tested and which will be held to be true if the null is declared to be false.

Simple hypothesis: A hypothesis that specifies a single value for a population parameter of interest.

Composite hypothesis: A hypothesis that specifies a range of values for a population parameter.

One-sided alternative: An alternative hypothesis involving all possible values of a population parameter on either one side or the other of the value specified by a simple null hypothesis—that is, either greater than or less than.

Two-sided alternative: An alternative hypothesis involving all possible values of a population parameter other than the value specified by a simple null hypothesis—that is, both greater than or less than.

Hypothesis test decisions: A decision rule is formulated, leading the investigator to either reject or fail to reject the null hypothesis on the basis of sample evidence.

Type I error: The rejection of a true null hypothesis.

Type II error: The failure to reject a false null hypothesis.

Significance level: The probability α of rejecting a null hypothesis that is true. This probability is sometimes expressed as a percentage, so a test of significance level α is referred to as a (100α)%-level test (e.g., when $\alpha = 0.05$, we have a 5% level test).

Power: The probability of rejecting a null hypothesis that is false.

We use the terms *reject* and *failure to reject* for possible decisions about a null hypothesis in formal summaries of the outcomes of tests. We will see that these terms do not adequately reflect the asymmetry of the status of null and alternative hypotheses or the consequences of a procedure in which the significance level is fixed and the probability of a Type II error is not controlled. The null hypothesis has the status of a maintained hypothesis—one held to be true—unless the data contain strong evidence to reject the hypothesis. By setting the significance level, α at a low level, we have a small probability of rejecting a true null hypothesis. When we reject a true null hypothesis, the probability of error is the significance level, α. But if there is only a small sample, then we will reject the null hypothesis only when it is wildly in error. As we increase the sample size, the probability of rejecting a false null hypothesis is increased. But failure to reject a null hypothesis leads to much greater uncertainty because we do not know the probability of Type II error. Thus, if we fail to reject, then either the null hypothesis is true or our procedure for detecting a false null hypothesis does not have sufficient power—for example, the sample size is too small. When we reject the null hypothesis, we have strong evidence that the null hypothesis is not true and, therefore, that the alternative hypothesis is true. If we seek strong evidence in favor of a particular outcome, we define that outcome as the alternative hypothesis, H_1, and the other outcome as the null hypothesis, H_0. This is called a **counterfactual argument**. When we reject H_0, there is strong evidence in favor of H_1, and we are confident that our decision is correct. But failing to reject H_0 leads to great uncertainty. We see many applications of this idea in the following sections.

The analogy to a criminal trial is apparent. An accused defendant is presumed innocent (the null hypothesis) unless sufficient strong evidence is produced to indicate guilt beyond a reasonable doubt (rejection of the null hypothesis). The defendant may be found not guilty either because he or she is innocent or because the evidence was not strong enough to convict. The burden of proof rests on the sample data.

Basic Exercises

9.1 Mary Arnold wants to use the results of a random sample market survey to seek strong evidence that her brand of breakfast cereal has more than 20% of the total market. Formulate the null and alternative hypotheses, using P as the population proportion.

9.2 The board of a national central bank is meeting to decide if it should reduce interest rates in order to prevent deflation. State the null and alternative hypotheses regarding deflation that the board would formulate to guide its decision.

9.3 John Stull, senior vice president of manufacturing, is seeking strong evidence to support his hope that new operating procedures have reduced the percentage of underfilled cereal packages from the Ames production line. State his null and alternative hypotheses and indicate the results that would provide strong evidence.

Application Exercises

9.4 Many people in Europe object to purchasing genetically modified food that is produced by farmers in the United States. The U.S. farmers argue that there is no scientific evidence to conclude that these products are not healthy. The Europeans argue that there still might be a problem with the food.

  a. State the null and alternative hypotheses from the perspective of the Europeans.

  b. State the null and alternative hypotheses from the perspective of the U.S. farmers.

9.5 The 2000 presidential election in the United States was very close, and the decision came down to the results of the presidential voting in the state of Florida. The election was finally decided in favor of George W. Bush over Al Gore by a U.S. Supreme Court decision that stated that it was not appropriate to hand count ballots that had been rejected by the voting machines in various counties. At that time Bush had a small lead based on the ballots that had been counted. Imagine that you were a lawyer for George W. Bush. State your null and alternative hypotheses concerning the population vote totals for each candidate. Given your hypotheses, what would you argue about the results of the proposed recount—if it had actually occurred?

9.6 Here we have the complement of Exercise 9.5. The 2000 presidential election in the United States was very close, and the decision came down to the results of the presidential voting in the state of Florida. The election was finally decided in favor of George W. Bush over Al Gore by a U.S. Supreme Court decision that stated that it was not appropriate to hand count ballots that had been rejected by the voting machines in various counties. At that time Bush had a small lead based on the ballots that had been counted. Imagine that you were a lawyer for Al Gore. State your null and alternative hypotheses concerning the population vote totals for each candidate. Given your hypotheses, what would you argue about the results of the proposed recount—if it had actually occurred?

9.2 TESTS OF THE MEAN OF A NORMAL DISTRIBUTION: POPULATION VARIANCE KNOWN

In this section we present hypothesis **tests of the mean of a normal distribution (population variance known)** that have applications to business and economic problems. These procedures use a random sample of n normally distributed observations $x_1, x_2, \ldots, x_n$ that were obtained from a population with mean μ and known variance σ^2. We will test a hypothesis concerning the unknown population mean. Later, our assumption of normality will be relaxed in many cases because of the central limit theorem.

In the discussion of hypothesis testing in Section 9.1, we noted that if a null hypothesis is rejected using a test with significance level α, then the probability of error is known. In this case either the decision is correct or we have committed a Type I error. But if we fail to reject a null hypothesis, we do not know the probability of error. Thus, we have strong evidence to support a specific position if the null and alternative hypotheses are chosen such that rejecting the null hypothesis and accepting the alternative hypothesis lead to the support of our specific position. Consider our previous example concerning the filling of cereal boxes. Suppose that industry regulations state that if the population mean package weight is 16.1 ounces or less for a population of packages with label weight 16 ounces, then the manufacturer will pay a substantial fine. Thus, our objective is to obtain strong evidence that the mean package weight, μ, is greater than 16.1 ounces. In this case we would state our null hypothesis as

$$H_0: \mu = \mu_0 = 16.1$$

and the alternative hypothesis would be

$$H_1: \mu > \mu_0 = 16.1$$

By designing our testing rule with significance level α, we know that rejecting the null hypothesis provides strong evidence that the mean weight is greater than 16.1 ounces, because the probability of error is a small value, α.

Our test of the population mean uses the sample mean $\bar{x}$. If the sample mean is substantially greater than $\mu_0 = 16.1$, then we reject the null hypothesis. In order to obtain the appropriate decision value we use the fact that the standardized random variable

$$Z = \frac{\overline{X} - \mu_0}{\sigma/\sqrt{n}}$$

has a standard normal distribution with a mean of 0 and a variance of 1, given that H_0 is true. If α is the probability of Type I error and Z is large such that

$$P(Z > z_\alpha) = \alpha$$

then to test the null hypothesis, we can use the following decision rule:

$$\text{reject } H_0 \text{ if } \frac{\bar{x} - \mu_0}{\sigma/\sqrt{n}} > z_\alpha$$

It follows that the probability of rejecting the null hypothesis, H_0, when it is true is the significance level α.

Note that by simple algebraic manipulation, we could also state the decision rule as follows:

$$\text{reject } H_0 \text{ if } \bar{x} > \bar{x}_c = \mu_0 + z_\alpha \sigma/\sqrt{n}$$

The value $\bar{x}_c$ is often called the **critical value** for the decision. Note that for every value z_α obtained from the standard normal distribution, there is also a value $\bar{x}_c$, and either of the previous decision rules provide exactly the same result.

Suppose that for this problem the population standard deviation is $\sigma = 0.4$ and we obtain a random sample of size 25. For a one-sided hypothesis test with significance level $\alpha = 0.05$, the value of z_α is 1.645 from the standard normal table. In this case our decision rule is as follows:

$$\text{reject } H_0 \text{ if } \frac{\bar{x} - \mu_0}{\sigma/\sqrt{n}} = \frac{\bar{x} - 16.1}{0.4/\sqrt{25}} > 1.645$$

Equivalently, the rule is as follows:

$$\text{reject } H_0 \text{ if } \bar{x} > \bar{x}_c = \mu_0 + z_\alpha \sigma/\sqrt{n} = 16.1 + 1.645 \times (0.4/\sqrt{25}) = 16.232$$

If we reject H_0 using this rule, then we accept the alternative hypothesis that the mean weight is greater than 16.1 ounces with the probability of Type I error 0.05 or less. This provides strong evidence to support our conclusion. But, failure to reject the null hypothesis leads us to conclude that either H_0 is true or the selected testing procedure was not sensitive enough to reject H_0. The decision rules are illustrated in Figure 9.2.

Figure 9.2
Normal Probability Density Function Showing Both Z and $\bar{x}$ Values for the Decision Rule to Test the Null Hypothesis $H_0: \mu = 16.1$ versus $H_1: \mu > 16.1$

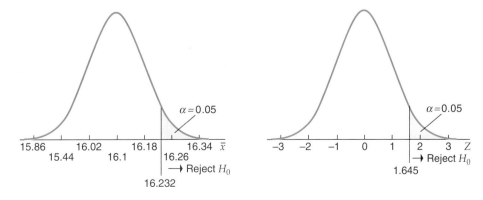

We summarize the hypothesis test for a simple null hypothesis concerning the population mean as follows.

A Test of the Mean of a Normal Population: Population Variance Known

A random sample of n observations is obtained from a normally distributed population with mean μ and known variance σ^2. Compute the sample mean $\bar{x}$. Then, a test with significance level α of the null hypothesis

$$H_0 : \mu = \mu_0$$

against the alternative

$$H_1 : \mu > \mu_0$$

is obtained by using the following decision rule:

$$\text{Reject } H_0 \text{ if } \frac{\bar{x} - \mu_0}{\sigma / \sqrt{n}} > z_\alpha \tag{9.1}$$

Or, equivalently,

$$\text{reject } H_0 \text{ if } \bar{x} > \bar{x}_c = \mu_0 + z_\alpha \sigma / \sqrt{n}$$

where z_α is the number for which

$$P(Z > z_\alpha) = \alpha$$

and Z is the standard normal random variable.

Let us pause to consider what is meant by the rejection of a null hypothesis. In the cereal-package problem, the hypothesis that the population mean is 16.1 would be rejected with significance level 0.05 if $\bar{x} > 16.232$. This certainly does not mean that we would have proof that the population mean weight exceeds 16.1 units. Given only sample information, we can never be certain about a population parameter. Rather, we conclude that the data have cast strong doubt on the truth of the null hypothesis. If the null hypothesis were true, then we see that an observed value of the sample mean $\bar{x} = 16.25$ (e.g., $16.25 > 16.232$) would represent a single unlikely observation drawn from a normal distribution with mean 16.1 and standard error

$$\frac{\sigma}{\sqrt{n}} = \frac{0.4}{\sqrt{25}} = 0.08$$

We are really asking how likely it would be to observe such an extreme value if the null hypothesis were, in fact, true. We saw that the probability of observing a mean value greater than 16.232 is 0.05. Hence, in rejecting the null hypothesis, either the null hypothesis is false or we have observed an unlikely event—one that would occur only with a probability of less than that specified by the significance level. This is the sense in which the sample information has aroused doubt about the null hypothesis.

p-Value

There is another popular procedure for considering the test of the null hypothesis. Notice that in our cereal problem, the null hypothesis was rejected at significance level 0.05 but would not have been rejected at the lower 0.01 level. If we use a lower significance level, we would reduce the probability of rejecting a true null hypothesis. This would modify our decision rule to make it less likely that the null hypothesis would be rejected whether or not it is true. Obviously, the lower the significance level at which we reject a null hypothesis, the greater the doubt cast on its truth when the null hypothesis is rejected. Rather than testing hypotheses at preassigned levels of significance, investigators can also determine the smallest level of significance at which a null hypothesis can be rejected given the single observed sample mean.

The **p-value** is the probability of obtaining a value of the test statistic as extreme as or more extreme than the actual value obtained when the null hypothesis is true. Thus, the p-value is the smallest significance level at which a null hypothesis can be rejected, given the observed sample statistic. For example, suppose that in the cereal-package problem with the population mean equal to 16.1, $\sigma = 0.4$, and $n = 25$ and that under the null hypothesis, we had obtained a sample mean of 16.3 ounces. Then the p-value would be as follows:

$$P(\bar{x} > 16.3 \,|\, H_0 : \mu = 16.1) = P\left(Z > \frac{16.3 - 16.1}{0.08} = 2.5\right) = 0.0062$$

From the normal probability table we find that the probability of obtaining a sample mean of 16.3 or greater from a normal distribution with a population mean of 16.1 and a standard deviation of the sample mean of 0.08 is equal to 0.0062. Thus, the p-value for this test is 0.0062. Now, the p-value (0.0062) represents the smallest significance level, α, that would lead to rejection of the null hypothesis. When the p-value is calculated, we can test the null hypothesis by using the following rule:

$$\text{reject } H_0 \text{ if } p\text{-value} < \alpha$$

This rule will result in the same conclusion obtained using Equation 9.1.

There is another, more important reason for the popularity of the p-value. The p-value provides more precise information about the strength of the rejection of the null hypothesis that results from one observed sample mean. Suppose that in the test of the cereal-package weight we had set the significance level at $\alpha = 0.05$—a popular choice. Then with a sample mean equal to 16.3, we would state that the null hypothesis was rejected at significance level 0.05. However, in fact, that sample result points to a much stronger conclusion. We could have rejected the null hypothesis at a significance level of $\alpha = 0.0063$. Alternatively, suppose that the computed p-value based on a different sample mean had been 0.07. In that case we could not reject the null hypothesis, but we would know that we were quite close to rejecting the null hypothesis. In contrast, a p-value of 0.30 would tell us that we were quite far from rejecting the null hypothesis. The popularity of the p-value is that it provides more information than merely stating that the null hypothesis was accepted or rejected at a particular significance level. The p-value is summarized as follows.

Interpretation of the Probability Value, or p-Value

The probability value, or p-value, is the smallest significance level at which the null hypothesis can be rejected given the single observed sample mean. Consider a random sample of n observations from a population that has a normal distribution with mean μ and standard deviation σ, and the resulting computed sample mean, $\bar{x}$. The null hypothesis

$$H_0 : \mu = \mu_0$$

is tested against the alternative hypothesis

$$H_1 : \mu > \mu_0$$

The p-value for the test is

$$p\text{-value} = P\left(\frac{\bar{x} - \mu_0}{\sigma/\sqrt{n}} \geq z_p \,\Big|\, H_0 : \mu = \mu_0\right) \tag{9.2}$$

where z_p is the standard normal value associated with the smallest significance level at which the null hypothesis can be rejected. The p-value is regularly computed by most statistical computer programs based on the computed single sample mean and provides more information about the test, based on the observed sample mean. Thus, it is a popular tool for many statistical applications.

It is important to note that the *p*-value is an observed random variable that will be different for each random sample obtained for a statistical test. Thus, two different analysts could obtain their own random samples and sample means from a process population, and, thus, each would compute a different *p*-value.

Example 9.1 Evaluating a New Production Process (Hypothesis Test)

The production manager of Northern Windows, Inc., has asked you to evaluate a proposed new procedure for producing its Regal line of double-hung windows. The present process has a mean production of 80 units per hour with a population standard deviation of $\sigma = 8$. The manager does not want to change to a new procedure unless there is strong evidence that the mean production level is higher with the new process.

Solution The manager will change to the new process only if there is strong evidence in its favor. Therefore, we will define the null hypothesis as

$$H_0: \mu \leq 80$$

and the alternative hypothesis as

$$H_1: \mu > 80$$

We see that if we define the significance level $\alpha = 0.05$ and conclude that the new process has higher productivity, then our probability of error is 0.05 or less. This would imply strong evidence in favor of our recommendation.

We obtain a random sample of $n = 25$ production hours using the proposed new process and compute the sample mean, $\bar{x}$, often using a computer. With a significance level of $\alpha = 0.05$ the decision rule is

$$\text{reject } H_0 \text{ if } \frac{\bar{x} - 80}{8/\sqrt{25}} > 1.645$$

where $z_{0.05} = 1.645$ is obtained from the standard normal table. Alternatively, we could use the following rule:

$$\text{reject } H_0 \text{ if } \bar{x} > \bar{x}_c = \mu_0 + z_\alpha \sigma/\sqrt{n} = 80 + 1.645 \times (8/\sqrt{25}) = 82.63$$

Suppose that the resulting sample mean was $\bar{x} = 83$. Based on that result

$$z = \frac{83 - 80}{8/\sqrt{25}} = 1.875 > 1.645$$

we would reject the null hypothesis and conclude that we have strong evidence to support the conclusion that the new process resulted in higher productivity. Given this sample mean, we could also compute the *p*-value as follows:

$$p\text{-value} = P(Z > 1.875) = 0.03$$

Thus we could recommend the new process to the production manager.

A Test of the Mean of a Normal Distribution (Variance Known): Composite Null and Alternative Hypotheses

The appropriate procedure for testing, at significance level α, the null hypothesis

$$H_0: \mu \leq \mu_0$$

against the alternative hypothesis

$$H_1 : \mu > \mu_0$$

is precisely the same as when the null hypothesis is $H_0 : \mu = \mu_0$. In addition, the p-values are also computed in exactly the same way.

Consider our previous example concerning the filling of cereal packages. Suppose that industry regulations state that if the mean package weight is not 16 ounces or more for a population of packages with label weight 16 ounces, then the company will be prosecuted. In this situation we, as the regulators, could prosecute only if we found strong evidence that the mean package weight was less than 16 ounces. Thus, our objective is to prove that the mean package weight, μ, is not 16.0 ounces or more. In this case we would state the simple null hypothesis as

$$H_0 : \mu = \mu_0 = 16.0$$

or, using the composite hypothesis, as

$$H_0 : \mu \geq \mu_0 = 16.0$$

And the alternative hypothesis would be

$$H_1 : \mu < \mu_0 = 16.0$$

for either the simple or the composite hypothesis. By designing our testing rule with significance level α, we know that if we reject the null hypothesis, then we have strong evidence that the mean weight is less than 16.0 ounces because the probability of a Type I error is a small value, α.

Our test of the population mean uses the sample mean, $\bar{x}$. If the sample mean is substantially less than $\mu_0 = 16.0$, then we reject the null hypothesis. In order to obtain the appropriate decision value, we use the fact that the standard random variable

$$Z = \frac{\bar{X} - \mu_u}{\sigma / \sqrt{n}}$$

has a standard normal distribution with mean of 0 and variance of 1 when the population mean is μ_0. If z has a large negative value such that

$$P(Z < -z_\alpha) = \alpha$$

then to test the null hypothesis, we can use the following decision rule:

$$\text{reject } H_0 \text{ if } \frac{\bar{x} - \mu_0}{\sigma / \sqrt{n}} < -z_\alpha$$

It follows that the probability of rejecting a true null hypothesis, H_0, is the significance level α.

Note that by simple algebraic manipulation we could also state the decision rule as follows:

$$\text{reject } H_0 \text{ if } \bar{x} < \bar{x}_c = \mu_0 - z_\alpha \sigma / \sqrt{n}$$

The value $\bar{x}_c$ is the "critical value" for the decision. Note that for every value $-z_\alpha$ obtained from the standard normal distribution, there is also a value $\bar{x}_c$ and either of the preceding decision rules provides exactly the same result.

Suppose that for this problem the population standard deviation is $\sigma = 0.4$ and we obtain a random sample of 25. From the standard normal table with a significance level of $\alpha = 0.05, z_\alpha = 1.645$. In this case our decision rule is

$$\text{reject } H_0 \text{ if } \frac{\bar{x} - \mu_0}{\sigma / \sqrt{n}} = \frac{\bar{x} - 16.0}{0.4 / \sqrt{25}} < -1.645$$

or we could use the following decision rule:

$$\text{reject } H_0 \text{ if } \bar{x} < \bar{x}_c = \mu_0 - z_\alpha \sigma / \sqrt{n} = 16.0 - 1.645 \times (0.4 / \sqrt{25}) = 15.868$$

If we reject H_0 using this rule, then we accept the alternative hypothesis that the mean weight is less than 16.0 ounces with the probability of Type I error 0.05 or less. This provides strong evidence to support our conclusion. This decision rule is illustrated in Figure 9.3.

Figure 9.3
Normal Probability Density Function Showing $\bar{x}$ Values for the Decision Rule to Test the Null Hypothesis $H_0 : \mu \geq 16.0$ versus $H_1 : \mu < 16.0$

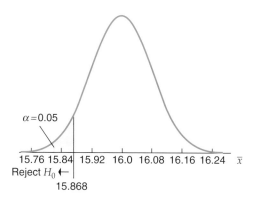

Note that this hypothesis test is the complement of the first example. The hypothesis-testing rules for alternative hypotheses dealing with the lower tail are mirror images of those dealing with the upper tail of the distribution. This result is summarized in Equation 9.3. Computation of p-values also follows, using the lower-tail instead of the upper-tail probabilities.

The cereal examples presented two different objectives. In the first case we wanted strong evidence that the mean weight was greater than 16.1 ounces, and, thus, we defined the null hypothesis as follows:

$$H_0 : \mu \leq 16.1$$

In the second case we wanted strong evidence that the mean was less than 16 ounces; therefore, we defined the null hypothesis as follows:

$$H_0 : \mu \geq 16$$

Possibilities of this type are present in many decision situations, and the decision maker is required to determine which option should be used in the particular problem being considered.

A Test of the Mean of a Normal Distribution (Variance Known): Composite or Simple Null and Alternative Hypotheses

The appropriate procedure for testing, at significance level α, the null hypothesis

$$H_0 : \mu = \mu_0 \quad \text{or} \quad \mu \geq \mu_0$$

against the alternative hypothesis

$$H_1 : \mu < \mu_0$$

uses the following decision rule:

$$\text{reject } H_0 \text{ if } \frac{\bar{x} - \mu_0}{\sigma / \sqrt{n}} < -z_\alpha$$

Equivalently,

$$\text{reject } H_0 \text{ if } \bar{x} < \bar{x}_c = \mu_0 - z_\alpha \sigma/\sqrt{n} \qquad (9.3)$$

where $-z_\alpha$ is the number for which

$$P(Z < -z_\alpha) = \alpha$$

and Z is the standard normal random variable.

In addition, the p-values can be computed by using the lower-tail probabilities.

Example 9.2 Ball Bearing Production (Hypothesis Test)

The production manager of Twin Forks Ball Bearing, Inc., has asked your assistance in evaluating a modified ball bearing production process. When the process is operating properly, the process produces ball bearings whose weights are normally distributed with a population mean of 5 ounces and a population standard deviation of 0.1 ounce. A new raw-material supplier was used for a recent production run, and the manager wants to know if that change has resulted in a lowering of the mean weight of the ball bearings. There is no reason to suspect a problem with the new supplier, and the manager will continue to use the new supplier unless there is strong evidence that underweight ball bearings are being produced.

Solution In this case we are interested in knowing if there is strong evidence to conclude that lower-weight bearings are being produced. Therefore, we will test the null hypothesis

$$H_0: \mu = \mu_0 = 5$$

against the alternative hypothesis

$$H_1: \mu < 5$$

Note how the notion of strong evidence leads us to choose the null and alternative hypotheses. We take action only if the null hypothesis is rejected and the alternative accepted. The significance level is specified as $\alpha = 0.05$, and, thus, the corresponding lower-tail value for the standard normal random variable is $z_\alpha = -1.645$ from the normal distribution table. For this problem we obtained a random sample of $n = 16$ observations, and the sample mean was 4.962. Our decision rule for this problem is

$$\text{reject } H_0 \text{ if } \frac{\bar{x} - \mu_0}{\sigma/\sqrt{n}} < -1.645$$

or

$$\text{reject } H_0 \text{ if } \bar{x} < \bar{x}_c = \mu_0 - z_\alpha \sigma/\sqrt{n} = 5 - 1.645(0.1/\sqrt{16}) = 4.959$$

We see that we cannot reject the null hypothesis, H, since $\dfrac{4.962 - 5}{0.1/\sqrt{16}} = -1.52$ and $\bar{x} = 4.962 > \bar{x}_c = 4.959$. Thus, we conclude that we do not have strong evidence that the production process is producing underweight ball bearings.

We could also compute the p-value for this sample result by noting that for the standard normal distribution,

$$p\text{-value} = P(z_p < -1.52) = 0.0643$$

Two-Sided Alternative Hypothesis

There are some problems where deviations either too high or too low are of equal importance. For example, the diameter of an automobile engine piston cannot be too large or too small. In those situations we consider the test of the null hypothesis

$$H_0: \mu = \mu_0$$

against the alternative hypothesis

$$H_1: \mu \neq \mu_0$$

Here, we have no strong reason for suspecting departures either above or below the hypothesized population mean, μ_0. The null hypothesis would be doubted if the sample mean were much greater or much smaller than μ_0. Again, if the random variable has a normal distribution with known variance σ, we obtain a test with significance level α by using the result that under the null hypothesis,

$$P(Z > z_{\alpha/2}) = \frac{\alpha}{2} \quad \text{and} \quad P(Z < -z_{\alpha/2}) = \frac{\alpha}{2}$$

In this case we have divided the significance level α equally between the two tails of the normal distribution. Hence, the probability that Z either exceeds $z_{\alpha/2}$ or is less than $-z_{\alpha/2}$ is α. The decision rule for a test with significance level α is

$$\text{reject } H_0 \text{ if } \frac{\bar{x} - \mu_0}{\sigma/\sqrt{n}}$$

is either greater than $z_{\alpha/2}$ or less than $-z_{\alpha/2}$. These results are summarized in Equation 9.4.

A Test of the Mean of a Normal Distribution Against Two-Sided Alternative (Variance Known)

The appropriate procedure for testing, at significance level α, the null hypothesis

$$H_0: \mu = \mu_0$$

against the alternative hypothesis

$$H_1: \mu \neq \mu_0$$

is obtained from the decision rule

$$\text{reject } H_0 \text{ if } \frac{\bar{x} - \mu_0}{\sigma/\sqrt{n}} < -z_{\alpha/2} \quad \text{or} \quad \text{reject } H_0 \text{ if } \frac{\bar{x} - \mu_0}{\sigma/\sqrt{n}} > z_{\alpha/2} \tag{9.4}$$

Equivalently,

$$\text{reject } H_0 \text{ if } \bar{x} < \mu_0 - z_{\alpha/2}\sigma/\sqrt{n} \quad \text{or} \quad \text{reject } H_0 \text{ if } \bar{x} > \mu_0 + z_{\alpha/2}\sigma/\sqrt{n}$$

In addition, the p-values can be computed by noting that the corresponding tail probability would be doubled to reflect a p-value that refers to the sum of the upper- and lower-tail probabilities for the positive and negative values of Z. The p-value for the two-tailed test is

$$p\text{-value} = 2P\left(\left|\frac{\bar{x} - \mu_0}{\sigma/\sqrt{n}}\right| > z_{p/2} \mid H_0: \mu = \mu_0\right) \tag{9.5}$$

where $z_{p/2}$ is the standard normal value associated with the smallest probability of rejecting the null hypothesis at either tail of the probability distribution.

Example 9.3 Analysis of Drill Hole Diameters (Hypothesis Test)

The production manager of Circuits Unlimited has asked for your assistance in analyzing a production process. This process involves drilling holes whose diameters are normally distributed with a population mean of 2 inches and a population standard deviation of 0.06 inch. A random sample of nine measurements had a sample mean of 1.95 inches. Use a significance level of $\alpha = 0.05$ to determine if the observed sample mean is unusual and, therefore, that the drilling machine should be adjusted.

Solution In this case the diameter could be either too large or too small. Therefore, we perform a two-tailed hypothesis test with the null hypothesis

$$H_0: \mu = 2.0$$

and the alternative hypothesis

$$H_1: \mu \neq 2.0$$

The decision rule is to reject H_0 in favor of H_1 if

$$\frac{\bar{x} - \mu_0}{\sigma/\sqrt{n}} < -z_{\alpha/2} \quad \text{or} \quad \frac{\bar{x} - \mu_0}{\sigma/\sqrt{n}} > z_{\alpha/2}$$

and, for this problem,

$$\frac{\bar{x} - \mu_0}{\sigma/\sqrt{n}} = \frac{1.95 - 2.0}{0.06/\sqrt{9}} = -2.50$$

for a 5%-level test $\alpha = 0.05$ and $z_{\alpha/2} = z_{0.05/2} = 1.96$. Thus, since -2.50 is less than -1.96, we reject the null hypothesis and conclude that the drilling machine requires adjustment.

To compute the p-value, we first find that the probability of obtaining Z less than -2.50 from the normal table is 0.0062. Here, we want the p-value for a two-tailed test, and we must double the one-tail value. Thus, the p-value for this test is $2 \times 0.0062 = 0.0124$, and the null hypothesis would have been rejected for a significance level above 1.24%.

We have summarized the various hypothesis-testing alternatives discussed in this section in Figure 9.11, located in the chapter appendix.

EXERCISES

Basic Exercises

9.7 A random sample is obtained from a population with variance $\sigma^2 = 625$, and the sample mean is computed. Test the null hypothesis $H_0: \mu = 100$ versus the alternative hypothesis $H_1: \mu > 100$ with $\alpha = 0.05$. Compute the critical value $\bar{x}_c$ and state your decision rule for the following options.

a. Sample size $n = 25$
b. Sample size $n = 16$
c. Sample size $n = 44$
d. Sample size $n = 32$

9.8 A random sample of $n = 25$ is obtained from a population with variance σ^2, and the sample mean is computed. Test the null hypothesis $H_0: \mu = 120$ versus the alternative hypothesis $H_1: \mu > 120$ with $\alpha = 0.10$.

Compute the critical value $\bar{x}_c$ and state your decision rule for the following options.

a. The population variance is $\sigma^2 = 196$.
b. The population variance is $\sigma^2 = 625$.
c. The population variance is $\sigma^2 = 900$.
d. The population variance is $\sigma^2 = 500$.

9.9 A random sample is obtained from a population with a variance of $\sigma^2 = 400$, and the sample mean is computed to be $\bar{x}_c = 70$. Consider the null hypothesis $H_0: \mu = 80$ versus the alternative hypothesis $H_1: \mu < 80$. Compute the p-value for the following options.

a. Sample size $n = 25$
b. Sample size $n = 16$
c. Sample size $n = 44$
d. Sample size $n = 32$

9.10 A random sample of $n = 25$ is obtained from a population with variance σ^2, and the sample mean is computed to be $\bar{x} = 70$. Consider the null hypothesis $H_0: \mu = 80$ versus the alternative hypothesis $H_1: \mu < 80$. Compute the p-value for the following options.

    a. The population variance is $\sigma^2 = 225$.
    b. The population variance is $\sigma^2 = 900$.
    c. The population variance is $\sigma^2 = 400$.
    d. The population variance is $\sigma^2 = 600$.

Application Exercises

9.11 A manufacturer of cereals claims that the contents of boxes sold weigh on average at least 20 ounces. The distribution of weight is known to be normal, with a standard deviation of 0.5 ounce. A random sample of 25 boxes yielded a sample mean weight of 19.96 ounces. Test at the 10% significance level the null hypothesis that the population mean weight is at least 20 ounces.

9.12 Kongsberg Maritime, a Norwegian technology enterprise, receives a shipment of batteries from Grenland Energy, a battery manufacturer in Skien, Norway, and tests a random sample of nine before agreeing to take it. Kongsberg is concerned that the true mean lifetime for all batteries in the shipment should be at least 50 hours. From past experience it is safe to conclude that the population distribution of lifetimes is normal with a standard deviation of 3.6 hours. For one particular shipment the mean lifetime for a sample on 16 batteries was 48.8 hours. Test at the 10% level the null hypothesis that the population mean lifetime is at least 50 hours.

9.13 A pharmaceutical manufacturer is concerned that the impurity concentration in pills should not exceed 3%. It is known that from a particular production run impurity concentrations follow a normal distribution with a standard deviation of 0.5%. A random sample of 81 pills from a production run was checked, and the sample mean impurity concentration was found to be 3.08%.

    a. Test at the 5% level the null hypothesis that the population mean impurity concentration is 3% against the alternative that it is more than 3%.
    b. Find the p-value for this test.
    c. Suppose that the alternative hypothesis had been two-sided, rather than one-sided, with the null hypothesis $H_0: \mu = 3$. State, without doing the calculations, whether the p-value of the test would be higher than, lower than, or the same as that found in part (b). Sketch a graph to illustrate your reasoning.
    d. In the context of this problem, explain why a one-sided alternative hypothesis is more appropriate than a two-sided alternative.

9.3 TESTS OF THE MEAN OF A NORMAL DISTRIBUTION: POPULATION VARIANCE UNKNOWN

In this section we consider the same form of hypothesis tests discussed in Section 9.2. The only difference is that the population variance is unknown; thus, we must use tests based on the Student's t distribution. We introduced the Student's t distribution in Section 7.3 and showed its application for developing confidence intervals. Recall that the Student's t distribution depends on the degrees of freedom for computing the sample variance, $n - 1$. In addition, the Student's t distribution becomes close to the normal distribution as the sample size increases. Thus, for sample sizes greater than 100 the normal probability distribution can be used to approximate the Student's t distribution. Using the sample mean and variance, we know that the random variable

$$t_{n-1} = \frac{\bar{x} - \mu}{s/\sqrt{n}}$$

follows a Student's t distribution, with $n - 1$ degrees of freedom. The procedures for performing hypothesis **tests of the mean of a normal distribution (with population variance unknown)** are defined in Equations 9.6, 9.7, and 9.8.

Tests of the Mean of a Normal Distribution: Population Variance Unknown

We are given a random sample of n observations from a normal population with mean μ. Using the sample mean and sample standard deviation, $\bar{x}$ and s, respectively, we can use the following tests with significance level α.

1. To test either null hypothesis

$$H_0: \mu = \mu_0 \quad \text{or} \quad H_0: \mu \leq \mu_0$$

against the alternative

$$H_1: \mu > \mu_0$$

the decision rule is

$$\text{reject } H_0 \text{ if } t = \frac{\bar{x} - \mu_0}{s/\sqrt{n}} > t_{n-1,\alpha}$$

or, equivalently,

$$\text{reject } H_0 \text{ if } \bar{x} > \bar{x}_c = \mu_0 + t_{n-1,\alpha}s/\sqrt{n} \tag{9.6}$$

2. To test either null hypothesis

$$H_0: \mu = \mu_0 \quad \text{or} \quad H_0: \mu \geq \mu_0$$

against the alternative

$$H_1: \mu < \mu_0$$

the decision rule is

$$\text{reject } H_0 \text{ if } t = \frac{\bar{x} - \mu_0}{s/\sqrt{n}} < -t_{n-1,\alpha} \tag{9.7}$$

or, equivalently,

$$\text{reject } H_0 \text{ if } \bar{x} < \bar{x}_c = \mu_0 - t_{n-1,\alpha}s/\sqrt{n}$$

3. To test the null hypothesis

$$H_0: \mu = \mu_0$$

against the alternative hypothesis

$$H_1: \mu \neq \mu_0$$

the decision rule is

$$\text{reject } H_0 \text{ if } \frac{\bar{x} - \mu_0}{s/\sqrt{n}} < -t_{n-1,\alpha/2} \quad \text{or} \quad \text{reject } H_0 \text{ if } \frac{\bar{x} - \mu_0}{s/\sqrt{n}} > t_{n-1,\alpha/2} \tag{9.8}$$

or, equivalently,

$$\text{reject } H_0 \text{ if } \bar{x} < \mu_0 - t_{n-1,\alpha/2}s/\sqrt{n} \quad \text{or} \quad \text{reject } H_0 \text{ if } \bar{x} > \mu_0 + t_{n-1,\alpha/2}s/\sqrt{n}$$

where $t_{n-1,\alpha/2}$ is the Student's t value for $n - 1$ degrees of freedom and the tail probability is $\alpha/2$.

The p-values for these tests are computed in the same way as we did for tests with known variance except that the Student's t value is substituted for the normal Z value. To obtain the p-value we often need to interpolate in the t table or use a computer package.

Example 9.4 Analysis of Weekly Sales of Frozen Broccoli (Hypothesis Test)

Grand Junction Vegetables is a producer of a wide variety of frozen vegetables. The company president has asked you to determine if the weekly sales of 16-ounce packages of frozen broccoli has increased. The mean weekly number of sales per store has been 2,400 packages over the past 6 months. You have obtained a random sample of sales data from 134 stores for your study. The data are contained in the data file **Broccoli**.

Solution Given the project objectives, you decide that the null hypothesis test is that population mean sales are 2,400 versus the alternative that sales have increased using a significance level $\alpha = 0.05$. The null hypothesis is

$$H_0 : \mu = 2,400$$

versus the alternative hypothesis

$$H_1 : \mu > 2,400$$

Figure 9.4 shows the Minitab output containing the sample mean and variance. From the Minitab output we see that the sample mean is much larger than the median and that the the distance between the third quartile and the maximum sales is quite large. Thus, it is clear that the distribution of the individual observations is not a normal distribution. But the sample size is large, and, thus, by applying the central limit theorem from Chapter 6, we can assume that the sampling distribution for the sample mean is normal. Therefore, a Student's t test would be appropriate for the hypothesis test. We see that the sample mean is 3,593 and the sample standard deviation is 4,919. The test statistic is as follows:

$$t = \frac{3,593 - 2,400}{4,919/\sqrt{134}} = \frac{3,593 - 2,400}{425} = 2.81$$

Figure 9.4 Broccoli Sales (Descriptive Statistics)

Descriptive Statistics: Broccoli

Variable	N	N*	Mean	SE Mean	StDev	Minimum	Q1	Median	Q3	Maximum
Broccoli	134	0	3593	425	4919	156	707	2181	2300	27254

The value of t for $n - 1 = 133$ degrees of freedom and $\alpha = 0.05$ for the upper tail is approximately 1.645. Based on this result, we reject the null hypothesis and conclude that mean sales have increased.

Minitab and most good statistical packages have options for computing the critical values and performing the hypothesis test following the previous procedure. However, to properly use the option, you must understand how to formulate the hypothesis following the discussion in Section 9.2. You will have a better understanding if you initially follow the computation details in the preceding examples. Then, after you are comfortable with the procedure, you can use the computational options to carry out the computational details.

The tests presented in this section are summarized in Figure 9.10, located in the chapter appendix.

EXERCISES

Basic Exercises

9.14 Test the hypotheses

$$H_0 : \mu \leq 100$$
$$H_1 : \mu > 100$$

using a random sample of $n = 36$, a probability of Type I error equal to 0.05, and the following sample statistics.

a. $\bar{x} = 108;\ s = 20$
b. $\bar{x} = 104;\ s = 10$
c. $\bar{x} = 96;\ \ s = 10$
d. $\bar{x} = 95;\ \ s = 8$

9.15 Test the hypotheses

$$H_0 : \mu \leq 100$$
$$H_1 : \mu > 100$$

using a random sample of $n = 49$, a probability of Type I error equal to 0.05, and the following sample statistics.

a. $\bar{x} = 108;\ s = 20$
b. $\bar{x} = 104;\ s = 10$
c. $\bar{x} = 96;\ \ s = 10$
d. $\bar{x} = 95;\ \ s = 8$

Application Exercises

9.16 An engineering research center claims that through the use of a new computer control system, automobiles should achieve, on average, an additional 3 miles per gallon of gas. A random sample of 100 automobiles was used to evaluate this product. The sample mean increase in miles per gallon achieved was 2.4, and the sample standard deviation was 1.8 miles per gallon. Test the hypothesis that the population mean is at least 3 miles per gallon. Find the p-value of this test, and interpret your findings.

9.17 A random sample of 1,556 employees at Boris&Boris, Inc., Russia, has been asked to attend an ethics workshop. The employees were asked to rate the following statement from a scale from 1 (strongly disagree) to 7 (strongly agree): Only senior executives play a crucial role in environment sustainability. The sample mean response was 4.04, and the sample standard deviation was 1.22. Test at the 1% significance level, against a two-sided alternative, the null hypothesis that the population mean is 4.

9.18 You have been asked to evaluate single-employer plans after the establishment of the Health Benefit Guarantee Corporation. A random sample of 76 percentage changes in promised health benefits was observed. The sample mean percentage change was 0.078, and the sample standard deviation was 0.201. Find and interpret the p-value of a test of the null hypothesis that the population mean percentage change is 0 against a two-sided alternative.

9.19 A random sample of 171 employees was asked to rate, on a scale from 1 (not important) to 5 (extremely important), health benefits as a job characteristic. The sample mean rating was 2.07, and the sample standard deviation was 0.80. Test at the 10% significance level the null hypothesis that the population mean rating is at most 2 against the alternative that it is larger than 2.0.

9.20 A random sample of 170 people was provided with a forecasting problem. Each sample member was given, in two ways, the task of forecasting the next value of a retail sales variable. The previous 20 values were presented both as numbers and as points on a graph. Subjects were asked to predict the next value. The absolute forecasting errors were measured. The sample then consisted of 170 differences in absolute forecast errors (numerical minus graphical). The sample mean of these differences was –2.91, and the sample standard deviation was 11.33. Find and interpret the p-value of a test of the null hypothesis that the population mean difference is 0 against the alternative that it is negative. (The alternative can be viewed as the hypothesis that, in the aggregate, people make better forecasts when they use graphs of past history compared to using numerical values from past history.)

9.21 The accounts of a corporation show that, on average, accounts payable are $125.32. An auditor checked a random sample of 16 of these accounts. The sample mean was $131.78 and the sample standard deviation was $25.41. Assume that the population distribution is normal. Test at the 5% significance level against a two-sided alternative the null hypothesis that the population mean is $125.32.

9.22 On the basis of a random sample the null hypothesis

$$H_0 : \mu = \mu_0$$

is tested against the alternative

$$H_1 : \mu > \mu_0$$

and the null hypothesis is not rejected at the 5% significance level.

a. Does this necessarily imply that μ_0 is contained in the 95% confidence interval for μ?

b. Does this necessarily imply that μ_0 is contained in the 90% confidence interval for μ if the observed sample mean is larger than μ_0?

9.23 A company selling licenses for new e-commerce computer software advertises that firms using this software obtain, on average during the first year, a yield of 10% on their initial investments. A random sample of 10 of these franchises produced the following yields for the first year of operation:

6.6 9.2 11.4 8.4 12.6 5.6 8.9 10.6 9.5 8.79

Assuming that population yields are normally distributed, test the company's claim at the 1% significance level.

9.24 A process that produces bottles of shampoo, when operating correctly, produces bottles whose contents weigh, on average, 20 ounces. A random sample of nine bottles from a single production run yielded the following content weights (in ounces):

21.4 19.7 19.7 20.6 20.8 20.1 19.7 20.3 20.9

Assuming that the population distribution is normal, test at the 5% level against a two-sided alternative the null hypothesis that the process is operating correctly.

9.25 A statistics instructor is interested in the ability of students to assess the difficulty of a test they have taken. This test was taken by a large group of students, and the average score was 80.3. A random sample of eight students was asked to predict this average score. Their predictions were as follows:

77 88 73 61 62 79 97 75

Assuming a normal distribution, test the null hypothesis that the population mean prediction would be 80.3. Use a two-sided alternative and a 10% significance level.

9.26 A beer distributor claims that a new display featuring a life-size picture of a well-known rock singer will increase product sales in supermarkets by an average of 50 cases in a week. For a random sample of 20 high-volume liquor outlets, the average sales increase was 41.3 cases, and the sample standard deviation was 12.2 cases. Test at the 5% level the null hypothesis that the population mean sales increase is at least 50 cases, stating any assumptions you make.

9.27 In contract negotiations a company claims that a new incentive scheme has resulted in average weekly earnings of at least $400 for all customer service workers. A union representative takes a random sample of

15 workers and finds that their weekly earnings have an average of $381.35 and a standard deviation of $48.60. Assume a normal distribution.

a. Test the company's claim.

b. If the same sample results had been obtained from a random sample of 50 employees, could the company's claim be rejected at a lower significance level than that used in part a?

9.4 TESIS OF THE POPULATION PROPORTION (LARGE SAMPLES)

Another important set of business and economics problems involves population proportions. Business executives are interested in the percent market share for their products, and government officials are interested in the percentage of people that support a proposed new program. Inference about the population proportion based on sample proportions is an important application of hypothesis testing.

From our work in Chapters 5 and 6, we know that the distribution of the sample proportion can be approximated quite accurately by using the normal distribution. In this approximation we denote P as the population proportion and $\hat{p}$ as the sample proportion. Thus, the sample proportion $\hat{p}$ estimated from a random sample of size n has an approximate normal distribution with mean P and variance $P(1-P)/n$. Then the standard normal statistic is as follows:

$$Z = \frac{\hat{p} - P}{\sqrt{P(1-P)/n}}$$

If the null hypothesis is that the population proportion is

$$H_0 : P = P_0$$

it follows that, when this hypothesis is true, the random variable

$$Z = \frac{\hat{p} - P_0}{\sqrt{P_0(1-P_0)/n}}$$

approximately follows a standard normal distribution. The procedures for **tests of a population proportion (large sample sizes)** are defined in Equations 9.9, 9.10 and 9.11.

Tests of the Population Proportion (Large Sample Sizes)

We begin by assuming a random sample of n observations from a population that has a proportion P whose members possess a particular attribute. If $nP(1-P) > 5$ and the sample proportion is $\hat{p}$, then the following tests have significance level α.

1. To test either the hypothesis

$$H_0 : P = P_0 \quad \text{or} \quad H_0 : P \leq P_0$$

against the alternative

$$H_1 : P > P_0$$

the decision rule is as follows:

$$\text{reject } H_0 \text{ if } \frac{\hat{p} - P_0}{\sqrt{P_0(1-P_0)/n}} > z_\alpha \tag{9.9}$$

2. To test either null hypothesis

$$H_0 : P = P_0 \quad \text{or} \quad H_0 : P \geq P_0$$

against the alternative

$$H_1 : P < P_0$$

10.1 Tests of the Difference Between Two Normal Population Means: Dependent Samples

There are a number of applications where we wish to draw conclusions about the differences between population means instead of conclusions about the absolute levels of the means. For example, we might want to compare the output of two different production processes for which neither population mean is known. Similarly, we might want to know if one marketing strategy results in higher sales than another without knowing the population mean sales for either. These questions can be handled effectively by various different hypothesis-testing procedures.

As we saw in Section 8.1, several different assumptions can be made when confidence intervals are computed for the differences between two population means. These assumptions generally lead to specific methods for computing the population variance for the difference between sample means. There are parallel hypothesis tests that involve similar methods for obtaining the variance. We organize our discussion of the various hypothesis-testing procedures in parallel with the confidence interval estimates in Section 8.1. In Section 10.1 we treat situations where the two samples can be assumed to be dependent. In these cases the best design, if we have control over data collection, is using two matched pairs as shown below. Then in Section 10.2 we treat a variety of situations where the samples are independent.

Two Means, Matched Pairs

Here, we assume that a random sample of n matched pairs of observations is obtained from populations with means μ_x and μ_y. The observations are denoted $(x_1, y_1), (x_2, y_2), \ldots,$ (x_n, y_n). When we have matched pairs and the pairs are positively correlated, the variance of the difference between the sample means,

$$\bar{d} = \bar{x} - \bar{y}$$

will be reduced compared to using independent samples. This results because some of the characteristics of the pairs are similar, and, thus, that portion of the variability is removed from the total variability of the differences between the means. For example, when we consider measures of human behavior, differences between twins will usually be less than the differences between two randomly selected people. In general, the dimensions for two parts produced on the same specific machine will be closer than the dimensions for parts produced on two different, independently selected machines. Thus, whenever possible, we would prefer to use matched pairs of observations when comparing measurements from two populations because the variance of the difference will be smaller. With a smaller variance, there is a greater probability that we will reject H_0 when the null hypothesis is not true. This principle was developed in Section 9.5 in the discussion of the power of a test. The specific decision rules for different forms of the hypothesis test are summarized in Equations 10.1, 10.2, and 10.3.

> ## Tests of the Difference Between Population Means: Matched Pairs
>
> Suppose that we have a random sample of n matched pairs of observations from distributions with means μ_x and μ_y. Let $\bar{d}$ and s_d denote the observed sample mean and standard deviation for the n differences $(x_i - y_i)$. If the population distribution of the differences is a normal distribution, then the following tests have significance level α:
>
> **1.** To test either null hypothesis
>
> $$H_0: \mu_x - \mu_y = 0 \quad \text{or} \quad H_0: \mu_x - \mu_y \leq 0$$

against the alternative

$$H_1 : \mu_x - \mu_y > 0$$

the decision rule is as follows:

$$\text{reject } H_0 \text{ if } \frac{\bar{d}}{s_d / \sqrt{n}} > t_{n-1,\alpha} \qquad (10.1)$$

2. To test either null hypothesis

$$H_0 : \mu_x - \mu_y = 0 \quad \text{or} \quad H_0 : \mu_x - \mu_y \geq 0$$

against the alternative

$$H_1 : \mu_x - \mu_y < 0$$

the decision rule is as follows:

$$\text{reject } H_0 \text{ if } \frac{\bar{d}}{s_d / \sqrt{n}} < -t_{n-1,\alpha} \qquad (10.2)$$

3. To test the null hypothesis

$$H_0 : \mu_x - \mu_y = 0$$

against the two-sided alternative

$$H_1 : \mu_x - \mu_y \neq 0$$

the decision rule is as follows:

$$\text{reject } H_0 \text{ if } \frac{\bar{d}}{s_d / \sqrt{n}} < -t_{n-1,\alpha/2} \quad \text{or} \quad \frac{\bar{d}}{s_d / \sqrt{n}} > t_{n-1,\alpha/2} \qquad (10.3)$$

Here, $t_{n-1,\alpha}$ is the number for which

$$P(t_{n-1} > t_{n-1,\alpha}) = \alpha$$

where the random variable t_{n-1} follows a Student's t distribution with $(n-1)$ degrees of freedom.

For all these tests, p-values are interpreted as the probability of getting a value at least as extreme as the one obtained, given the null hypothesis.

Example 10.1 Analysis of Alternative Turkey-Feeding Programs (Hypothesis Test for Differences Between Means)

Marian Anderson, production manager of Turkeys Unlimited, has been conducting a study to determine if a new feeding process produces a significant increase in mean weight of turkeys produced in the facilities of Turkeys Unlimited LLC. In the process she obtains a random set of matched turkey chicks hatched from the same hen. One group of chicks is from the hens fed using the old feeding method and the second group of chicks is from the same hens fed using the new method. The weights for each of the turkeys and the differences between the matched pairs are shown in Table 10.1. These data are contained in the data file **Turkey Feeding**. Perform the necessary analysis to determine if the new feeding process produces a significant ($\alpha = 0.025$) increase in turkey weight.

Table 10.1 Finish Weight of Turkeys for Old and New Feeding Programs

OLD	NEW	DIFFERENCE	HEN
17.76	18.15	0.38	1
18.66	19.92	1.26	2
21.84	23.60	1.76	3
16.64	17.96	1.33	4
17.37	16.25	−1.12	5
16.75	17.50	0.74	6
18.01	20.79	2.77	7
22.00	22.89	0.89	8
17.68	20.25	2.57	9
18.23	20.95	2.72	10
20.63	22.76	2.13	11
20.03	20.64	0.61	12
15.90	14.67	−1.23	13
15.89	16.15	0.25	14
18.53	22.56	4.03	15
13.92	15.46	1.54	16
18.60	16.33	−2.26	17
20.09	21.03	0.94	18
18.04	18.51	0.47	19
19.87	22.32	2.45	20
19.00	24.53	5.53	21
18.59	21.15	2.56	22
21.02	26.36	5.35	23
15.62	18.56	2.94	24
15.41	14.02	−1.39	25

Solution In this study we are attempting to determine if the new feeding process results in a significantly greater weight compared to the old feeding process. Define the weights from the new feeding process by the random variable X and the weights from the old feeding process by the random variable Y. The null and alternative processes for this study are, thus,

$$H_0: \mu_x - \mu_y \leq 0$$
$$H_1: \mu_x - \mu_y > 0$$

The null hypothesis states that there was no increase in weight for the new process over the old. The alternative hypothesis states that there was an increase. If we reject the null hypothesis, then we can conclude that the new feeding process does result in higher turkey weights. We perform the test using the Student's t test for matched pairs with a critical value $\alpha = 0.025$. Figure 10.1 provides the Minitab computation for the mean difference (1.489), the standard deviation of the mean differences (0.385), and the Student's t. The Student's t statistic for the test can be computed as

$$t = \frac{\bar{d}}{s_d/\sqrt{n}} = \frac{1.489}{1.926/\sqrt{25}} = \frac{1.489}{0.385} = 3.86$$

Figure 10.1 Hypothesis Testing for Differences Between New and Old Turkey Weights

Paired T-Test and CI: New, Old

Paired T for New – old

	N	Mean	StDev	SE Mean
New	25	19.732	3.226	0.645
old	25	18.244	2.057	0.411
Difference	25	1.489	1.926	0.385

95% lower bound for mean difference: 0.829
T-Test of mean difference = 0 (vs > 0): T-Value = 3.86 P-Value = 0.000

The computed value of Student's t is greater than the critical value with $\alpha = 0.025$ and 24 degrees of freedom, equal to 2.064 from the Student's t table (Appendix Table 8).

From this analysis we see that there is strong evidence to conclude that the new feeding method increases the weight of turkeys more than the old method.

Note also that the variance of the difference between the matched pairs could be computed as follows (the correlation between the pairs is 0.823) using Equation 5.27:

$$S_d^2 = (0.411)^2 + (0.645)^2 - 2 \times (0.823)(0.411)(0.645) = 0.146$$
$$S_d = 0.385$$

This is the standard deviation of the differences as computed in the computer output.

EXERCISES

 Visit www.MyStatLab.com or www.pearsonglobal editions.com to access the data files.

Basic Exercises

10.1 You have been asked to determine if two different production processes have different mean numbers of units produced per hour. Process 1 has a mean defined as μ_1 and process 2 has a mean defined as μ_2. The null and alternative hypotheses are as follows:

$$H_0: \mu_1 - \mu_2 = 0$$
$$H_1: \mu_1 - \mu_2 > 0$$

Using a random sample of 25 paired observations, the sample means are 50 and 60 for populations 1 and 2, respectively. Can you reject the null hypothesis using a probability of Type I error $\alpha = 0.05$ in each case?

a. The sample standard deviation of the difference is 20
b. The sample standard deviation of the difference is 30
c. The sample standard deviation of the difference is 15
d. The sample standard deviation of the difference is 40

10.2 You have been asked to determine if two different production processes have different mean numbers of units produced per hour. Process 1 has a mean defined

as μ_1 and process 2 has a mean defined as μ_2. The null and alternative hypotheses are as follows:

$$H_0: \mu_1 - \mu_2 \geq 0$$
$$H_1: \mu_1 - \mu_2 < 0$$

Using a random sample of 25 paired observations, the standard deviation of the difference between sample means is 25. Can you reject the null hypothesis using a probability of Type I error $\alpha = 0.05$ in each case?

a. The sample means are 56 and 50
b. The sample means are 59 and 50
c. The sample means are 56 and 48
d. The sample means are 54 and 50

Application Exercises

10.3 In a study comparing banks in two countries, a sample of 148 matched pairs of banks was formed. Each pair contained one bank from the Netherlands and one from Croatia. The pairings were made in such a way that the two members were as similar as possible in regard to such factors as size and age. The ratio of total loans outstanding to total assets was calculated for each of the banks. For this ratio, the sample mean difference (The Netherlands–Croatia) was 0.0504, and the sample standard deviation of the differences was 0.3053.

10.4 ⊕ You have been asked to conduct a national study of urban home selling prices to determine if there has been an increase in selling prices over time. There has been some concern that housing prices in major urban areas have not kept up with inflation over time. Your study will use data collected from Atlanta, Chicago, Dallas, and Oakland, which is contained in the data file **House Selling Price**. Formulate an appropriate hypothesis test and use your statistical computer package to compute the appropriate statistics for analysis. Perform the hypothesis test and indicate your conclusion.

Repeat the analysis using data from only the city of Atlanta.

10.5 ⊕ An agency in Belgium offers preparation courses for a graduate school admissions test to students. As part of an experiment to evaluate the merits of the course, 40 students were chosen and divided into 20 pairs in such a way that the members of any pair had similar academic records. Before taking the test, one member of each pair was assigned at random to take the preparation course, while the other member did not take a course. The achievement test scores are contained in the **Achievement Test Scores** data file. Assuming that the differences in scores follow a normal distribution, test, at the 1% level, the null hypothesis that the two population means are equal against the alternative that the true mean is higher for students taking the preparation course.

10.2 TESTS OF THE DIFFERENCE BETWEEN TWO NORMAL POPULATION MEANS: INDEPENDENT SAMPLES

Two Means, Independent Samples, Known Population Variances

Now we consider the case where we have independent random samples from two normally distributed populations. The first population has a mean of μ_x and a variance of σ_x^2 and we obtain a random sample of size n_x. The second population has a mean of μ_y and a variance of σ_y^2 and we obtain a random sample of size n_y.

In Section 8.2, we showed that if the sample means are denoted by $\bar{x}$ and $\bar{y}$, then the random variable

$$Z = \frac{(\bar{x} - \bar{y}) - (\mu_x - \mu_y)}{\sqrt{\dfrac{\sigma_x^2}{n_x} + \dfrac{\sigma_y^2}{n_y}}}$$

has a standard normal distribution. If the two population variances are known, tests of the difference between the population means can be based on this result, using the same arguments as before. Generally, we are comfortable using known population variances if the process being studied has been stable over some time and we have obtained similar variance measurements over this time. And because of the central limit theorem, the results presented here hold for large sample sizes even if the populations are not normal. For large sample sizes, the approximation is quite satisfactory when sample variances are used for population variances. The appropriate tests are summarized in Equations 10.4, 10.5, and 10.6.

Tests of the Difference Between Population Means: Independent Samples (Known Variances)

Suppose that we have independent random samples of n_x and n_y observations from normal distributions with means μ_x and μ_y and variances σ_x^2 and σ_y^2, respectively. If the observed sample means are $\bar{x}$ and $\bar{y}$, then the following tests have significance level α:

1. To test either null hypothesis

$$H_0: \mu_x - \mu_y = 0 \quad \text{or} \quad H_0: \mu_x - \mu_y \leq 0$$

against the alternative

$$H_1: \mu_x - \mu_y > 0$$

the decision rule is as follows:

$$\text{reject } H_0 \text{ if } \frac{\bar{x} - \bar{y}}{\sqrt{\dfrac{\sigma_x^2}{n_x} + \dfrac{\sigma_y^2}{n_y}}} > z_\alpha \qquad (10.4)$$

2. To test either null hypothesis

$$H_0 : \mu_x - \mu_y = 0 \quad \text{or} \quad H_0 : \mu_x - \mu_y \geq 0$$

against the alternative

$$H_1 : \mu_x - \mu_y < 0$$

the decision rule is as follows:

$$\text{reject } H_0 \text{ if } \frac{\bar{x} - \bar{y}}{\sqrt{\dfrac{\sigma_x^2}{n_x} + \dfrac{\sigma_y^2}{n_y}}} < -z_\alpha \qquad (10.5)$$

3. To test the null hypothesis

$$H_0 : \mu_x - \mu_y = 0$$

against the two-sided alternative

$$H_1 : \mu_x - \mu_y \neq 0$$

the decision rule is as follows:

$$\text{reject } H_0 \text{ if } \frac{\bar{x} - \bar{y}}{\sqrt{\dfrac{\sigma_x^2}{n_x} + \dfrac{\sigma_y^2}{n_y}}} < -z_{\alpha/2} \quad \text{or} \quad \frac{\bar{x} - \bar{y}}{\sqrt{\dfrac{\sigma_x^2}{n_x} + \dfrac{\sigma_y^2}{n_y}}} > z_{\alpha/2} \qquad (10.6)$$

If the sample sizes are large ($n > 100$), then a good approximation at significance level α can be made if we replace the population variances with the sample variances. In addition, the central limit theorem leads to good approximations even if the populations are not normally distributed. The p-values for all these tests are interpreted as the probability of getting a value at least as extreme as the one obtained, given the null hypothesis.

Example 10.2 Comparison of Alternative Fertilizers (Hypothesis Test for Differences Between Means)

Shirley Brown, an agricultural economist, wants to compare cow manure and turkey dung as fertilizers. Historically, farmers had used cow manure on their cornfields. Recently, a major turkey farmer offered to sell composted turkey dung at a favorable price. The farmers decided that they would use this new fertilizer only if there was strong evidence that productivity increased over the productivity that occurred with cow manure. Shirley was asked to conduct the research and statistical analysis in order to develop a recommendation to the farmers.

Solution To begin the study, Shirley specified a hypothesis test with

$$H_0 : \mu_x - \mu_y \leq 0$$

versus the alternative that

$$H_1 : \mu_x - \mu_y > 0$$

where μ_x is the population mean productivity using turkey dung and μ_y is the population mean productivity using cow manure. H_1 indicates that turkey dung results in higher productivity. The farmers will not change their fertilizer unless there is strong evidence in favor of increased productivity. She decided before collecting the data that a significance level of $\alpha = 0.05$ would be used for this test.

Using this design, Shirley implemented an experiment to test the hypothesis. Cow manure was applied to one set of $n_y = 25$ randomly selected fields. The sample mean productivity was $\bar{y} = 100$. From past experience the variance in productivity for these fields was assumed to be $\sigma_y^2 = 400$. Turkey dung was applied to a second random sample of $n_x = 25$ fields, and the sample mean productivity was $\bar{x} = 115$. Based on published research reports, the variance for these fields was assumed to be $\sigma_x^2 = 625$. The two sets of random samples were independent. The decision rule is to reject H_0 in favor of H_1 if

$$\frac{\bar{x} - \bar{y}}{\sqrt{\dfrac{\sigma_x^2}{n_x} + \dfrac{\sigma_y^2}{n_y}}} > z_\alpha$$

The computed statistics for this problem are as follows:

$$n_x = 25 \quad \bar{x} = 115 \quad \sigma_x^2 = 625$$
$$n_y = 25 \quad \bar{y} = 100 \quad \sigma_y^2 = 400$$

$$z = \frac{115 - 100}{\sqrt{\dfrac{625}{25} + \dfrac{400}{25}}} = 2.34$$

Comparing the computed value of $z = 2.34$ with $z_{0.05} = 1.645$, Shirley concluded that the null hypothesis is clearly rejected. In fact, we found that the p-value for this test is 0.0096. As a result, there is overwhelming evidence that turkey dung results in higher productivity than cow manure.

Two Means, Independent Samples, Unknown Population Variances Assumed to Be Equal

In those cases where the population variances are not known and the sample sizes are under 100, we need to use the Student's t distribution. There are some theoretical problems when we use the Student's t distribution for differences between sample means. However, these problems can be solved using the procedure that follows if we can assume that the population variances are equal. This assumption is realistic in many cases where we are comparing groups. In Section 10.4 we present a procedure for testing the equality of variances from two normal populations.

The major difference is that this procedure uses a commonly pooled estimator of the equal population variance. This estimator is as follows:

$$s_p^2 = \frac{(n_x - 1)s_x^2 + (n_y - 1)s_y^2}{(n_x + n_y - 2)}$$

The degrees of freedom for s_p^2 and for the Student's t statistic below is $n_x + n_y - 2$. The hypothesis test is performed using the Student's t statistic for the difference between two means:

$$t = \frac{(\bar{x} - \bar{y}) - (\mu_x - \mu_y)}{\sqrt{\dfrac{s_p^2}{n_x} + \dfrac{s_p^2}{n_y}}}$$

Note that the form for the test statistic is similar to that of the Z statistic, which is used when the population variances are known. The various tests using this procedure are summarized next.

Tests of the Difference Between Population Means: Population Variances Unknown and Equal

In these tests it is assumed that we have an independent random sample of size n_x and n_y observations drawn from normally distributed populations with means μ_x and μ_y and a common variance. The sample variances s_x^2 and s_y^2 are used to compute a pooled variance estimator:

$$s_p^2 = \frac{(n_x - 1)s_x^2 + (n_y - 1)s_y^2}{(n_x + n_y - 2)} \qquad (10.7)$$

We emphasize here that s_p^2 is the weighted average of the two sample variances, s_x^2 and s_y^2.

Then, using the observed sample means $\bar{x}$ and $\bar{y}$, the following tests have significance level α:

1. To test either null hypothesis

$$H_0 : \mu_x - \mu_y = 0 \quad \text{or} \quad H_0 : \mu_x - \mu_y \leq 0$$

against the alternative

$$H_1 : \mu_x - \mu_y > 0$$

the decision rule is as follows:

$$\text{reject } H_0 \text{ if } \frac{\bar{x} - \bar{y}}{\sqrt{\dfrac{s_p^2}{n_x} + \dfrac{s_p^2}{n_y}}} > t_{n_x + n_y - 2, \alpha} \qquad (10.8)$$

2. To test either null hypothesis

$$H_0 : \mu_x - \mu_y = 0 \quad \text{or} \quad H_0 : \mu_x - \mu_y \geq 0$$

against the alternative

$$H_1 : \mu_x - \mu_y < 0$$

the decision rule is as follows:

$$\text{reject } H_0 \text{ if } \frac{\bar{x} - \bar{y}}{\sqrt{\dfrac{s_p^2}{n_x} + \dfrac{s_p^2}{n_y}}} < -t_{n_x + n_y - 2, \alpha} \qquad (10.9)$$

3. To test the null hypothesis

$$H_0 : \mu_x - \mu_y$$

against the two-sided alternative

$$H_1 : \mu_x - \mu_y \neq 0$$

the decision rule is as follows:

$$\text{reject } H_0 \text{ if } \frac{\bar{x} - \bar{y}}{\sqrt{\dfrac{s_p^2}{n_x} + \dfrac{s_p^2}{n_y}}} < -t_{n_x + n_y - 2, \alpha/2} \quad \text{or} \quad \frac{\bar{x} - \bar{y}}{\sqrt{\dfrac{s_p^2}{n_x} + \dfrac{s_p^2}{n_y}}} > t_{n_x + n_y - 2, \alpha/2} \qquad (10.10)$$

Here, $t_{n_x+n_y-2,\alpha}$ is the number for which

$$P\left(t_{n_x+n_y-2} > t_{n_x+n_y-2,\alpha}\right) = \alpha$$

Note that the degrees of freedom for the Student's t is $n_x + n_y - 2$ for all of these tests.

We interpret p-values for all these tests as the probability of getting a value as extreme as the one obtained, given the null hypothesis.

Example 10.3 Retail Sales Patterns (Hypothesis Test for Differences Between Means)

A sporting goods store operates in a medium-sized shopping mall. In order to plan staffing levels, the manager has asked for your assistance to determine if there is strong evidence that Monday sales are higher than Saturday sales.

Solution To answer the question, you decide to gather random samples of 25 Saturdays and 25 Mondays from a population of several years of data. The samples are drawn independently. You decide to test the null hypothesis

$$H_0 : \mu_M - \mu_S \leq 0$$

against the alternative hypothesis

$$H_1 : \mu_M - \mu_S > 0$$

where the subscripts M and S refer to Monday and Saturday sales. The sample statistics are as follows:

$$\bar{x}_M = 1078 \quad s_M = 633 \quad n_M = 25$$
$$\bar{y}_S = 908.2 \quad s_S = 469.8 \quad n_S = 25$$

The pooled variance estimate is as follows:

$$s_p^2 = \frac{(25-1)(633)^2 + (25-1)(469.8)^2}{25 + 25 - 2} = 310{,}700$$

The test statistic is then computed as follows:

$$t = \frac{\bar{x}_M - \bar{y}_s}{\sqrt{\dfrac{s_p^2}{n_x} + \dfrac{s_p^2}{n_y}}} = \frac{1078 - 908.2}{\sqrt{\dfrac{310{,}700}{25} + \dfrac{310{,}700}{25}}} = 1.08$$

Using a significance level of $\alpha = 0.05$ and 48 degrees of freedom, we find that the critical value of t is 1.677. Therefore, we conclude that there is not sufficient evidence to reject the null hypothesis, and, thus, there is no reason to conclude that mean sales on Mondays are higher.

Example 10.4 Analysis of Alternative Turkey-Feeding Programs (Hypothesis Test for Differences Between Means)

In this example we revisit the turkey-feeding problem from Example 10.1. In that example we used a matched-pairs test and concluded that the new feeding program did result in greater weight gain than the old program, using $\alpha = 0.025$. In this example we solve the same problem. The hypothesis test from Example 10.1 is exactly the same in this example. However, here we assume that the two samples are independent and we do not have matched pairs. We use the same data file, **Turkey Feeding**, which contains the sample of weights for the old and new feeding programs.

Solution This solution follows the same general approach as seen in Example 10.1. However, we assume that we have independent random samples from populations with equal variances. Figure 10.2 contains the computer computation of the statistics needed to test the hypothesis. Note that the difference in sample means is still 1.489, but the pooled standard deviation for the difference is substantially larger at 2.7052:

$$s_d^2 = \left(\frac{2.7052}{\sqrt{25}}\right)^2 + \left(\frac{2.7052}{\sqrt{25}}\right)^2 = 0.585$$

$$s_d = 0.765$$

and the resulting computed Student's t is

$$t = \frac{1.489}{0.765} = 1.946$$

Figure 10.2 Turkey Weight Study: Independent Samples, Population Variances Equal (Minitab Output)

Two-Sample T-Test and CI: New, Old

Two-sample T for New vs old

	N	Mean	StDev	SE Mean
New	25	19.73	3.23	0.65
old	25	18.24	2.06	0.41

Difference = mu (New) − mu (Old)
Estimate for difference: 1.489
95% lower bound for difference: 0.205
T-Test of difference = 0 (vs >): T-Value = 1.95 P-Value = 0.029 DF = 48
Both use Pooled StDev = 2.7052

Since the degrees of freedom with the independent samples assumption is 48, the critical value of the Student's t is 2.01, with $\alpha = 0.025$. The computed value is smaller, and we cannot reject the null hypothesis; thus we cannot conclude that the new feeding process results in a greater weight gain. Note that since the variance and standard deviation are larger, the resulting test does not have the same power. In Example 10.1 the p-value for the hypothesis test with paired observations was 0.00, whereas in Example 10.4, assuming independent samples, the p-value was 0.029.

Two Means, Independent Samples, Unknown Population Variances Not Assumed to Be Equal

Hypothesis tests of differences between population means when the individual variances are unknown and not equal require modification of the variance computation and the degrees of freedom. The computation of sample variance for the difference between sample means is changed. There are substantial complexities in the determination of degrees of freedom for the critical value of the Student's t statistic. The specific computational forms were presented in Section 8.2. Equations 10.11–10.14 summarize the procedures.

Tests of the Difference Between Population Means: Population Variances Unknown and Not Equal

These tests assume that we have independent random samples of size n_x and n_y observations from normal populations with means μ_x and μ_y and unequal variances. The sample variances s_x^2 and s_y^2 are used. The number of degrees of freedom v for the Student's t statistic is given by the following:

$$v = \frac{\left[\left(\frac{s_x^2}{n_x}\right) + \left(\frac{s_y^2}{n_y}\right)\right]^2}{\left(\frac{s_x^2}{n_x}\right)^2/(n_x - 1) + \left(\frac{s_y^2}{n_y}\right)^2/(n_y - 1)} \tag{10.11}$$

Then, using the observed sample means $\bar{x}$ and $\bar{y}$, the following tests have significance level α:

1. To test either null hypothesis

$$H_0:\mu_x - \mu_y = 0 \quad \text{or} \quad H_0:\mu_x - \mu_y \leq 0$$

against the alternative

$$H_1:\mu_x - \mu_y > 0$$

the decision rule is as follows:

$$\text{reject } H_0 \text{ if } \frac{\bar{x} - \bar{y}}{\sqrt{\frac{s_x^2}{n_x} + \frac{s_y^2}{n_y}}} > t_{v,\alpha} \tag{10.12}$$

2. To test either null hypothesis

$$H_0:\mu_x - \mu_y = 0 \quad \text{or} \quad H_0:\mu_x - \mu_y \geq 0$$

against the alternative

$$H_1:\mu_x - \mu_y < 0$$

the decision rule is as follows:

$$\text{reject } H_0 \text{ if } \frac{\bar{x} - \bar{y}}{\sqrt{\frac{s_x^2}{n_x} + \frac{s_y^2}{n_y}}} < -t_{v,\alpha} \tag{10.13}$$

3. To test the null hypothesis

$$H_0:\mu_x - \mu_y = 0$$

against the two-sided alternative

$$H_1:\mu_x - \mu_y \neq 0$$

the decision rule is as follows:

$$\text{reject } H_0 \text{ if } \frac{\bar{x} - \bar{y}}{\sqrt{\frac{s_x^2}{n_x} + \frac{s_y^2}{n_y}}} < -t_{v,\alpha/2} \quad \text{or} \quad \frac{\bar{x} - \bar{y}}{\sqrt{\frac{s_x^2}{n_x} + \frac{s_y^2}{n_y}}} > t_{v,\alpha/2} \tag{10.14}$$

Here, $t_{v,\alpha}$ is the number for which

$$P(t_v > t_{v,\alpha}) = \alpha$$

The analysis for Example 10.4 was run again without assuming equal population variances. The computer output is shown in Figure 10.3. The computational results are all the same except that the degrees of freedom are now 40 instead of 48 when we assumed that the variances were equal in Example 10.4. The change in critical value of the Student's t is so small that the p-value did not change. And we still do not have evidence to reject the null hypothesis and cannot conclude that the new program results in greater weight gain.

Figure 10.3
Turkey Weight
Study: Independent
Samples, Population
Variances not
Assumed Equal

Two-Sample T-Test and CI: New, Old

Two-sample T for New vs old

	N	Mean	StDev	SE Mean
New	25	19.73	3.23	0.65
old	25	18.24	2.06	0.41

Difference = mu (New) − mu (Old)
Estimate for difference: 1.489
95% lower bound for difference: 0.200
T-Test of difference = 0 (vs >): T-Value = 1.95 P-Value = 0.029 DF = 40

EXERCISES

Basic Exercises

10.6 You have been asked to determine if two different production processes have different mean numbers of units produced per hour. Process 1 has a mean defined as μ_1 and process 2 has a mean defined as μ_2. The null and alternative hypotheses are as follows:

$$H_0 : \mu_1 - \mu_2 = 0$$
$$H_1 : \mu_1 - \mu_2 > 0$$

Use a random sample of 25 observations from process 1 and 28 observations from process 2 and the known variance for process 1 equal to 900 and the known variance for process 2 equal to 1,600. Can you reject the null hypothesis using a probability of Type I error $\alpha = 0.05$ in each case?

a. The process means are 50 and 60.
b. The difference in process means is 20.
c. The process means are 45 and 50.
d. The difference in process means is 15.

10.7 You have been asked to determine if two different production processes have different mean numbers of units produced per hour. Process 1 has a mean defined as μ_1 and process 2 has a mean defined as μ_2. The null and alternative hypotheses are as follows:

$$H_0 : \mu_1 - \mu_2 \leq 0$$
$$H_1 : \mu_1 - \mu_2 > 0$$

The process variances are unknown but assumed to be equal. Using random samples of 49 observations from Process 1 and 25 observations from Process 2, the sample means are 55 and 46 for populations 1 and 2, respectively. Can you reject the null hypothesis using a probability of Type I error $\alpha = 0.05$ in each case?

a. The sample standard deviation from Process 1 is 28 and from Process 2 is 25.

b. The sample standard deviation from Process 1 is 20 and from Process 2 is 31.
c. The sample standard deviation from Process 1 is 28 and from Process 2 is 34.
d. The sample standard deviation from Process 1 is 17 and from Process 2 is 40.

Application Exercises

10.8 A screening procedure was designed to measure attitudes toward minorities as managers. High scores indicate negative attitudes and low scores indicate positive attitudes. Independent random samples were taken of 151 male financial analysts and 108 female financial analysts. For the former group the sample mean and standard deviation scores were 85.8 and 19.13, whereas the corresponding statistics for the latter group were 71.5 and 12.2. Test the null hypothesis that the two population means are equal against the alternative that the true mean score is higher for male than for female financial analysts.

10.9 For a random sample of 125 British entrepreneurs, the mean number of job changes was 1.91 and the sample standard deviation was 1.32. For an independent random sample of 86 British corporate managers, the mean number of job changes was 0.21 and the sample standard deviation was 0.53. Test the null hypothesis that the population means are equal against the alternative that the mean number of job changes is higher for British entrepreneurs than for British corporate managers.

10.10 A political science professor is interested in comparing the characteristics of students who do and do not vote in national elections. For a random sample of 114 students who claimed to have voted in the last presidential election, she found a mean grade point average of 2.71 and a standard deviation of 0.64. For an independent random sample of 123 students who did not vote, the mean grade point average was 2.79 and the standard deviation was 0.56. Test, against a two-sided alternative, the null hypothesis that the population means are equal.

10.11 Auditors might be helped in determining the chances of fraud if they carefully measure cash flow. To evaluate if auditors might be helped in determining the chances of fraud if they carefully measure cash flow, samples of midlevel auditors from CPA firms were asked to indicate the chance of material fraud on a scale from 0 to 100 for a case. A random sample of 36 auditors used the cash-flow information. Their mean assessment was 38.92, and the sample standard deviation was 23.96. For an independent random sample of 36 auditors not using the cash-flow information, the sample mean and standard deviation were, respectively, 54.75 and 28.04. Assuming that the two population distributions are normal with equal variances, test against a two-sided alternative the null hypothesis that the population means are equal. (Use $\alpha = 0.05$.)

10.12 The recent financial collapse has led to considerable concern about the information provided to potential investors. The government and many researchers have pointed out the need for increased regulation of financial offerings. The study in this exercise concerns the effect of sales forecasts on initial public offerings.

Initial public offerings' prospectuses were examined. In a random sample of 70 prospectuses in which sales forecasts were disclosed, the mean debt-to-equity ratio prior to the offering issue was 3.97, and the sample standard deviation was 6.14. For an independent random sample of 51 prospectuses in which sales earnings forecasts were not disclosed, the mean debt-to-equity ratio was 2.86, and the sample standard deviation was 4.29. Test, against a two-sided alternative, the null hypothesis that population mean debt-to-equity ratios are the same for disclosers and nondisclosers of earnings forecasts.

10.13 A publisher is interested in the effects on sales of college texts that include more than 100 data files. The publisher plans to produce 20 texts in the business area and randomly chooses 10 to have more than 100 data files. The remaining 10 are produced with at most 100 data files. For those with more than 100, first-year sales averaged 9,254, and the sample standard deviation was 2,107. For the books with at most 100, average first-year sales were 8,167, and the sample standard deviation was 1,681. Assuming that the two population distributions are normal with the same variance, test the null hypothesis that the population means are equal against the alternative that the true mean is higher for books with more than 100 data files.

10.3 TESTS OF THE DIFFERENCE BETWEEN TWO POPULATION PROPORTIONS (LARGE SAMPLES)

Next, we develop procedures for comparing two population proportions. We consider a standard model with a random sample of n_x observations from a population with a proportion P_x of successes and a second independent random sample of n_y observations from a population with a proportion P_y of successes.

In Chapter 5 we saw that, for large samples, proportions can be approximated as normally distributed random variables, and, as a result,

$$Z = \frac{(\hat{p}_x - \hat{p}_y) - (P_x - P_y)}{\sqrt{\dfrac{P_x(1 - P_x)}{n_x} + \dfrac{P_y(1 - P_y)}{n_y}}}$$

has a standard normal distribution.

We want to test the hypothesis that the population proportions P_x and P_y are equal.

$$H_0: P_x - P_y = 0 \quad \text{or} \quad H_0: P_x = P_y$$

Denote their common value by P_0. Then under this hypothesis

$$Z = \frac{(\hat{p}_x - \hat{p}_y)}{\sqrt{\dfrac{P_0(1 - P_0)}{n_x} + \dfrac{P_0(1 - P_0)}{n_y}}}$$

follows to a close approximation a standard normal distribution.

Finally, the unknown proportion P_0 can be estimated by a pooled estimator defined as follows:

$$\hat{p}_0 = \frac{n_x \hat{p}_x + n_y \hat{p}_y}{n_x + n_y}$$

The null hypothesis in these tests assumes that the population proportions are equal. If the null hypothesis is true, then an unbiased and efficient estimator for P_0 can be obtained by combining the two random samples, and, as a result, $\hat{p}_0$ is computed using this equation. Then, we can replace the unknown P_0 by $\hat{p}_0$ to obtain a random variable that has a distribution close to the standard normal for large sample sizes.

The tests are summarized as follows.

Testing the Equality of Two Population Proportions (Large Samples)

We are given independent random samples of size n_x and n_y with proportion of successes $\hat{p}_x$ and $\hat{p}_y$. When we assume that the population proportions are equal, an estimate of the common proportion is as follows:

$$\hat{p}_0 = \frac{n_x \hat{p}_x + n_y \hat{p}_y}{n_x + n_y}$$

For large sample sizes—$nP_0(1 - P_0) > 5$—the following tests have significance level α:

1. To test either null hypothesis

$$H_0 : P_x - P_y = 0 \quad \text{or} \quad H_0 : P_x - P_y \leq 0$$

against the alternative

$$H_1 : P_x - P_y > 0$$

the decision rule is as follows:

$$\text{reject } H_0 \text{ if } \frac{(\hat{p}_x - \hat{p}_y)}{\sqrt{\dfrac{\hat{p}_0(1 - \hat{p}_0)}{n_x} + \dfrac{\hat{p}_0(1 - \hat{p}_0)}{n_y}}} > z_\alpha \tag{10.15}$$

2. To test either null hypothesis

$$H_0 : P_x - P_y = 0 \quad \text{or} \quad H_0 : P_x - P_y \geq 0$$

against the alternative

$$H_1 : P_x - P_y < 0$$

the decision rule is as follows:

$$\text{reject } H_0 \text{ if } \frac{(\hat{p}_x - \hat{p}_y)}{\sqrt{\dfrac{\hat{p}_0(1 - \hat{p}_0)}{n_x} + \dfrac{\hat{p}_0(1 - \hat{p}_0)}{n_y}}} < -z_\alpha \tag{10.16}$$

3. To test the null hypothesis

$$H_0 : P_x - P_y = 0$$

against the two-sided alternative

$$H_1 : P_x - P_y \neq 0$$

the decision rule is as follows:

$$\text{reject } H_0 \text{ if } \frac{(\hat{p}_x - \hat{p}_y)}{\sqrt{\dfrac{\hat{p}_0(1 - \hat{p}_0)}{n_x} + \dfrac{\hat{p}_0(1 - \hat{p}_0)}{n_y}}} < -z_{\alpha/2} \quad \text{or}$$

$$\frac{(\hat{p}_x - \hat{p}_y)}{\sqrt{\dfrac{\hat{p}_0(1 - \hat{p}_0)}{n_x} + \dfrac{\hat{p}_0(1 - \hat{p}_0)}{n_y}}} > z_{\alpha/2} \qquad (10.17)$$

It is also possible to compute and interpret p-values as the probability of getting a value at least as extreme as the one obtained, given the null hypothesis.

Example 10.5 Change in Customer Recognition of New Products After an Advertising Campaign (Hypothesis Tests of Differences Between Proportions)

Northern States Marketing Research has been asked to determine if an advertising campaign for a new cell phone increased customer recognition of the new World A phone. A random sample of 270 residents of a major city were asked if they knew about the World A phone before the advertising campaign. In this survey 50 respondents had heard of World A. After the advertising campaign, a second random sample of 203 residents were asked exactly the same question using the same protocol. In this case 81 respondents had heard of the World A phone. Do these results provide evidence that customer recognition increased after the advertising campaign?

Solution Define P_x and P_y as the population proportions that recognized the World A phone before and after the advertising campaign, respectively. The null hypothesis is

$$H_0 : P_x - P_y \geq 0$$

and the alternative hypothesis is

$$H_1 : P_x - P_y < 0$$

The null hypothesis states that there was no increase in the proportion that recognized the new phone after the advertising campaign and the alternative hypothesis states that there was an increase.

The decision rule is to reject H_0 in favor of H_1 if

$$\frac{(\hat{p}_x - \hat{p}_y)}{\sqrt{\dfrac{\hat{p}_0(1 - \hat{p}_0)}{n_x} + \dfrac{\hat{p}_0(1 - \hat{p}_0)}{n_y}}} < -z_{\alpha}$$

The data for this problem are as follows:

$$n_x = 270 \quad \hat{p}_x = 50/270 = 0.185 \quad n_y = 203 \quad \hat{p}_y = 81/203 = 0.399$$

The estimate of the common variance P_0 under the null hypothesis is as follows:

$$\hat{p}_0 = \frac{n_x \hat{p}_x + n_y \hat{p}_y}{n_x + n_y} = \frac{(270)(0.185) + (203)(0.399)}{270 + 203} = 0.277$$

The test statistic is as follows:

$$\frac{(\hat{p}_x - \hat{p}_y)}{\sqrt{\frac{\hat{p}_0(1 - \hat{p}_0)}{n_x} + \frac{\hat{p}_0(1 - \hat{p}_0)}{n_y}}} = \frac{0.185 - 0.399}{\sqrt{\frac{(0.277)(1 - 0.277)}{270} + \frac{(0.277)(1 - 0.277)}{203}}} = -5.15$$

For a one-tailed test with $\alpha = 0.05$, the $-z_{0.05}$ value is -1.645. Thus, since $-5.15 < -1.645$, we reject the null hypothesis and conclude that customer recognition did increase after the advertising campaign.

EXERCISES

Basic Exercise

10.14 Test the hypotheses

$$H_0: P_x - P_y = 0$$
$$H_1: P_x - P_y < 0$$

using the following statistics from random samples.

a. $\hat{p}_x = 0.42, n_x = 500$;
$\hat{p}_y = 0.50, n_y = 600$
b. $\hat{p}_x = 0.60, n_x = 500$;
$\hat{p}_y = 0.64, n_y = 600$
c. $\hat{p}_x = 0.42, n_x = 500$;
$\hat{p}_y = 0.49, n_y = 600$
d. $\hat{p}_x = 0.25, n_x = 500$;
$\hat{p}_y = 0.34, n_y = 600$
e. $\hat{p}_x = 0.39, n_x = 500$;
$\hat{p}_y = 0.42, n_y = 600$

Application Exercises

10.15 Random samples of 900 people in the United States and in Great Britain indicated that 60% of the people in the United States were positive about the future economy, whereas 66% of the people in Great Britain were positive about the future economy. Does this provide strong evidence that the people in Great Britain are more optimistic about the economy?

10.16 A random sample of 1,556 people in country A were asked to respond to this statement: *Increased world trade can increase our per capita prosperity.* Of these sample members, 38.4% agreed with the statement. When the same statement was presented to a random sample of 1,108 people in country B, 52.0% agreed. Test the null hypothesis that the population proportions agreeing with this statement were the same in the two countries against the alternative that a higher proportion agreed in country B.

10.17 Small-business telephone users were surveyed 6 months after access to carriers other than Carrier A became available for wide-area telephone service. Of a random sample of 240 Carrier A users, 133 said they were attempting to learn more about their options, as did 201 of an independent random sample of 260 users of alternate carriers. Test, at the 1%

significance level against a two-sided alternative, the null hypothesis that the two population proportions are the same.

10.18 Employees of a building materials chain in Monaco who were facing a shutdown were surveyed on a prospective employee ownership plan. Some employees pledged €10,000 to this plan, putting up €1,000 immediately, while others indicated that they did not intend to pledge. Of a random sample of 254 people who had pledged, 108 had already been laid off, whereas 226 of a random sample of 680 people who had not pledged had already been laid off. Test, at the 5% level against a two-sided alternative, the null hypothesis that the population proportions already laid off were the same for people who pledged as for those who did not.

10.19 Of a random sample of 455 high-quality investment equity options, 203 had less than 30% debt. Of an independent random sample of 205 high-risk investment equity options, 183 had less than 30% debt. Test, against a two-sided alternative, the null hypothesis that the two population proportions are equal.

10.20 Two different independent random samples of consumers were asked about satisfaction with their computer system each in a slightly different way. The options available for answer were slightly different in the two cases. When asked how *satisfied* they were with their computer system, 138 of the first group of 240 sample members opted for "very satisfied." When the second group was asked how *dissatisfied* they were with their computer system, 128 of 240 sample members opted for very satisfied. Test, at the 5% significance level against the obvious one-sided alternative, the null hypothesis that the two population proportions are equal.

10.21 Of a random sample of 1,000 people in Denmark, 500 had a positive attitude toward TV salespeople. Of an independent random sample of 1,600 people in France, 730 had a positive attitude toward TV salespeople. Test, at the 10% level, the null hypothesis that the population proportions are equal, against the alternative that a higher proportion of French have a positive attitude toward TV salespeople.

10.4 TESTS OF THE EQUALITY OF THE VARIANCES BETWEEN TWO NORMALLY DISTRIBUTED POPULATIONS

There are a number of situations in which we are interested in comparing the variances from two normally distributed populations. For example, the Student's t test in Section 10.2 assumed equal variances and used the two sample variances to compute a pooled estimator for the common variances. Quality-control studies are often concerned with the question of which process has the smaller variance.

In this section we develop a procedure for testing the assumption that population variances from independent samples are equal. To perform such tests, we introduce the F probability distribution. We begin by letting s_x^2 be the sample variance for a random sample of n_x observations from a normally distributed population with population variance σ_x^2. A second independent random sample of size n_y provides a sample variance of s_y^2 from a normal population with population variance σ_y^2. Then the random variable

$$F = \frac{s_x^2/\sigma_x^2}{s_y^2/\sigma_y^2}$$

follows a distribution known as the F distribution. This family of distributions, which is widely used in statistical analysis, is identified by the degrees of freedom for the numerator and the degrees of freedom for the denominator. The number of degrees of freedom for the numerator is associated with the sample variance s_x^2 and equal to $(n_x - 1)$. Similarly, the number of degrees of freedom for the denominator is associated with the sample variance s_y^2 and equal to $(n_y - 1)$.

The F distribution is constructed as the ratio of two chi-square random variables, each divided by its degrees of freedom. The chi-square distribution relates the sample and population variances for a normally distributed population. Hypothesis tests that use the F distribution depend on the assumption of a normal distribution. The characteristics of the F distribution are summarized next.

The F Distribution

We have two independent random samples with n_x and n_y observations from two normal populations with variances σ_x^2 and σ_y^2. If the sample variances are s_x^2 and s_y^2, then the random variable

$$F = \frac{s_x^2/\sigma_x^2}{s_y^2/\sigma_y^2} \tag{10.18}$$

has an **F distribution** with numerator degrees of freedom $(n_x - 1)$ and denominator degrees of freedom $(n_y - 1)$.

An F distribution with numerator degrees of freedom v_1 and denominator degrees of freedom v_2 is denoted F_{v_1, v_2}. We denote as $F_{v_1, v_2, \alpha}$ the number for which

$$P\left(F_{v_1, v_2} > F_{v_1, v_2, \alpha}\right) = \alpha$$

We need to emphasize that this test is quite sensitive to the assumption of normality.

The cutoff points for $F_{v_1, v_2, \alpha}$, for α equal to 0.05 and 0.01, are provided in Appendix Table 9. For example, for 10 numerator degrees of freedom and 20 denominator degrees of freedom, we see from the table that

$$F_{10,20,0.05} = 2.348 \quad \text{and} \quad F_{10,20,0.01} = 3.368$$

Hence,

$$P(F_{10,20} > 2.348) = 0.05 \quad \text{and} \quad P(F_{10,20} > 3.368) = 0.01$$

Figure 10.4 presents a schematic description of the F distribution for this example.

Figure 10.4
F Probability Density
Function with 10
Numerator Degrees
of Freedom and
20 Denominator
Degrees of Freedom

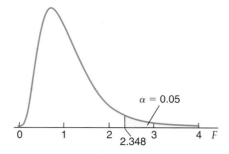

In practical applications we usually arrange the *F* ratio so that the larger sample variance is in the numerator and the smaller is in the denominator. Thus, we need to use only the upper cutoff points to test the hypothesis of equality of variances. When the population variances are equal, the *F* random variable becomes

$$F = \frac{s_x^2}{s_y^2}$$

and this ratio of sample variances becomes the test statistic. The intuition for this test is quite simple: If one of the sample variances greatly exceeds the other, then we must conclude that the population variances are not equal. The hypothesis tests of equality of variances are summarized as follows.

Tests of Equality of Variances from Two Normal Populations

Let s_x^2 and s_y^2 be observed sample variances from independent random samples of size n_x and n_y from normally distributed populations with variances σ_x^2 and σ_y^2. Use s_x^2 to denote the larger variance. Then the following tests have significance level α:

1. To test either null hypothesis

$$H_0: \sigma_x^2 = \sigma_y^2 \quad \text{or} \quad H_0: \sigma_x^2 \le \sigma_y^2$$

against the alternative

$$H_1: \sigma_x^2 > \sigma_y^2$$

the decision rule is as follows:

$$\text{reject } H_0 \text{ if } F = \frac{s_x^2}{s_y^2} > F_{n_x-1, n_y-1, \alpha} \tag{10.19}$$

2. To test the null hypothesis

$$H_0: \sigma_x^2 = \sigma_y^2$$

against the two-sided alternative

$$H_1: \sigma_x^2 \ne \sigma_y^2$$

the decision rule is as follows:

$$\text{reject } H_0 \text{ if } F = \frac{s_x^2}{s_y^2} > F_{n_x-1, n_y-1, \alpha/2} \tag{10.20}$$

where s_x^2 is the larger of the two sample variances. Since either sample variance could be larger, this rule is actually based on a two-tailed test, and, hence, we use $\alpha/2$ as the upper-tail probability.

Here, F_{n_x-1, n_y-1} is the number for which

$$P\left(F_{n_x-1, n_y-1} > F_{n_x-1, n_y-1, \alpha}\right) = \alpha$$

where F_{n_x-1, n_y-1} has an *F* distribution with $(n_x - 1)$ numerator degrees of freedom and $(n_y - 1)$ denominator degrees of freedom.

For all these tests a p-value is the probability of getting a value at least as extreme as the one obtained, given the null hypothesis. Because of the complexity of the F distribution, critical values are computed for only a few special cases. Thus, p-values will be typically computed using a statistical package such as Minitab.

Example 10.6 Study of Maturity Variances (Hypothesis Tests for the Equality of Two Variances)

The research staff of Investors Now, an online financial trading firm, was interested in determining if there is a difference in the variance of the maturities of AAA-rated industrial bonds compared to CCC-rated industrial bonds.

Solution This question requires that we design a study that compares the population variances of maturities for the two different bonds. We will test the null hypothesis

$$H_0 : \sigma_x^2 = \sigma_y^2$$

against the alternative hypothesis

$$H_1 : \sigma_x^2 \neq \sigma_y^2$$

where σ_x^2 is the variance in maturities for AAA-rated bonds and σ_y^2 is the variance in maturities for CCC-rated bonds. The significance level of the test was chosen as $\alpha = 0.02$.

The decision rule is to reject H_0 in favor of H_1 if

$$\frac{s_x^2}{s_y^2} > F_{n_x-1,n_y-1,\alpha/2}$$

Note here that either sample variance could be larger, and we place the larger sample variance in the numerator. Hence, the probability for this upper tail is $\alpha/2$. A random sample of 17 AAA-rated bonds resulted in a sample variance $s_x^2 = 123.35$, and an independent random sample of 11 CCC-rated bonds resulted in a sample variance $s_y^2 = 8.02$. The test statistic is as follows:

$$\frac{s_x^2}{s_y^2} = \frac{123.35}{8.02} = 15.380$$

Given a significance level of $\alpha = 0.02$, we find that the critical value of F, from interpolation in Appendix Table 9, is as follows:

$$F_{16,10,0.01} = 4.520$$

Clearly, the computed value of F (15.380) exceeds the critical value (4.520), and we reject H_0 in favor of H_1. Thus, there is strong evidence that variances in maturities are different for these two types of bonds.

EXERCISES

Basic Exercise

10.22 Test the hypothesis

$$H_0 : \sigma_x^2 = \sigma_y^2$$
$$H_1 : \sigma_x^2 > \sigma_y^2$$

using the following data.

a. $s_x^2 = 125, n_y = 45; s_y^2 = 51, n_y = 41$

b. $s_x^2 = 125, n_y = 45; s_y^2 = 235, n_y = 44$

c. $s_x^2 = 134, n_y = 48; s_y^2 = 51, n_y = 41$

d. $s_x^2 = 88, n_y = 39; s_y^2 = 167, n_y = 25$

Application Exercises

10.23 A professor claims that exam scores for non-accounting majors are more variable than for accounting majors. Random samples of 30 non-accounting majors and 30 accounting majors are taken from a final exam. Test at the 1% level the null hypothesis that the two population variances are equal against the alternative that the true variance is higher for the non-accounting majors. Assume the populations are normally distributed. For the non-accounting group, the sample variance was 1654.008, whereas for the accounting group, it was 409.002. Test the null hypothesis that the two population variances are equal against the alternative that the true variance is higher for the high-expertise group.

10.24 It is hypothesized that the total sales of a corporation should vary more in an industry with active price competition than in one with duopoly and tacit collusion. In a study of the merchant ship production industry it was found that in 4 years of active price competition, the variance of company A's total sales was 114.09. In the following 7 years, during which there was duopoly and tacit collusion, this variance was 16.08. Assume that the data can be regarded as an independent random sample from two normal distributions. Test, at the 5% level, the null hypothesis that the two population variances are equal against the alternative that the variance of total sales is higher in years of active price competition.

10.25 To evaluate if auditors might be helped in determining the chances of fraud if they carefully measure cash flow, samples of midlevel auditors from CPA firms were asked to indicate the chance of material fraud on a scale from 0 to 100 for a case. A random sample of 32 auditors used the cash-flow information. Their mean assessment was 35.44, and the sample standard deviation was 28.54. For an independent random sample of 32 auditors not using the cash-flow information, the sample mean and standard deviation were respectively 45.07 and 32.73.

Test at the 10% level the assumption that the population variances were the same for auditors using cash-flow information as for auditors not using cash-flow information against a two-sided hypothesis. Assume the populations are normally distributed.

10.26 A publisher is interested in the effects on sales of college texts that include more than 100 data files. The publisher plans to produce 20 texts in the business area and randomly chooses 10 to have more than 100 data files. The remaining 10 are produced with at most 100 data files. For those with more than 100, first-year sales averaged 9,254, and the sample standard deviation was 2,107. For the books with at most 100, average first-year sales were 8,167, and the sample standard deviation was 1,681. Assuming that the two population distributions are normal, test the null hypothesis that the population variances are equal against the alternative that the population variance is higher for books with more than 100 data files.

10.27 A university research team was studying the relationship between idea generation by groups with and without a moderator. For a random sample of four groups with a moderator, the mean number of ideas generated per group was 78.0, and the standard deviation was 24.4. For a random sample of four groups without a moderator, the mean number of ideas generated was 63.5, and the standard deviation was 20.2. Test the assumption that the two population variances were equal against the alternative that the population variance is higher for groups with a moderator.

10.5 SOME COMMENTS ON HYPOTHESIS TESTING

In this chapter we have presented several important applications of hypothesis-testing methodology. In an important sense, this methodology is fundamental to decision making and analysis in the face of random variability. As a result, the procedures have great applicability to a number of research and management decisions. The procedures are relatively easy to use, and various computer processes minimize the computational effort. Thus, we have a tool that is appealing and quite easy to use. However, there are some subtle problems and areas of concern that we need to consider to avoid serious mistakes.

The null hypothesis plays a crucial role in the hypothesis-testing framework. In a typical investigation we set the significance level, α, at a small probability value. Then, we obtain a random sample and use the data to compute a test statistic. If the test statistic is outside the acceptance region (depending on the direction of the test), the null hypothesis is rejected and the alternative hypothesis is accepted. When we do reject the null hypothesis, we have strong evidence—a small probability of error—in favor of the alternative hypothesis. In some cases we may fail to reject a drastically false null hypothesis simply because we have only limited sample information or because the test has low power. A test with low power usually results from a small sample size, poor measurement procedures, a large variance in the underlying population, or some combination of these factors. There may be important cases where this outcome is appropriate. For example, we would not change an existing process that is working effectively unless we had strong evidence that a new process clearly would be better. In other cases, however, the special status of the null hypothesis is neither warranted nor appropriate. In those cases we might consider the costs of making both Type I and Type II errors in a decision process. We might also consider a different specification of the null hypothesis—noting that rejection of the null provides strong evidence in favor of the alternative. When we have two alternatives, we could initially choose either as the null hypothesis. In the cereal-package-weight example at the beginning of Chapter 9, the null hypothesis could be either that

$$H_0 : \mu \geq 16$$

or that

$$H_0 : \mu \leq 16$$

In the first case rejection would provide strong evidence that the population mean weight is less than 16. In the latter case rejection would provide strong evidence that the population mean weight is greater than 16. As we have indicated, failure to reject either of these null hypotheses would not provide strong evidence. There are also procedures for controlling both Type I and Type II errors simultaneously (see, for example, Carlson and Thorne 1997).

Our work in Chapter 10 considers null hypotheses for the differences between population means of the form

$$H_0 : \mu_1 - \mu_2 \geq 16$$

or

$$H_0 : \mu_1 - \mu_2 \leq 16$$

The entire discussion here applies similarly to hypothesis tests on the difference between population means.

On some occasions very large amounts of sample information are available, and we reject the null hypothesis even when differences are not practically important. Thus, we need to contrast statistical significance with a broader definition of significance. Suppose that very large samples are used to compare annual mean family incomes in two cities. One result might be that the sample means differ by $2.67, and that difference might lead us to reject a null hypothesis and thus conclude that one city has a higher mean family income than the other. Although that result might be statistically significant, it clearly has no practical significance with respect to consumption or quality of life.

In specifying a null hypothesis and a testing rule, we are defining the test conditions before we look at the sample data that were generated by a process that includes a random component. Thus, if we look at the data before defining the null and alternative hypotheses, we no longer have the stated probability of error, and the concept of "strong evidence" resulting from rejecting the null hypothesis is not valid. For example, if we decide on the significance level of our test after we have seen the p-values, then we cannot interpret our results in probability terms. Suppose that an economist compares each of five different income-enhancing programs against a standard minimal level using a hypothesis test. After collecting the data and computing p-values, she determines that the null hypothesis—income not above the standard minimal level—can be rejected for one of the five programs with a significance level of $\alpha = 0.20$. Clearly, this result violates the proper use of hypothesis testing. But we have seen this done by supposedly research professionals.

As statistical computing tools have become more powerful, there are a number of new ways to violate the principle of specifying the null hypothesis before seeing the data. The recent popularity of data mining—using a computer program to search for relationships between variables in a very large data set—introduces new possibilities for abuse. Data mining provides *a description of subsets and differences* in a particularly large sample of data. However, after seeing the results from a data-mining operation, analysts may be tempted to define hypothesis tests that will use random samples from the same data set. This clearly violates the principle of defining the hypothesis test before seeing the data. A drug company may screen large numbers of medical treatment cases and discover that 5 out of 100 drugs have significant effects for the treatment of diseases that were not specified for treatment based on initial tests for these drugs. Such a result might legitimately be used to identify potential research questions for a new research study with new random samples. However, if the original data are then used to test a hypothesis concerning the treatment benefits of the five drugs, we have a serious violation of the proper application of hypothesis testing, and none of the probabilities of error are correct.

Defining the null and alternative hypotheses requires careful consideration of the objectives of the analysis. For example, we might be faced with a proposal to introduce a specific new production process. In one case the present process might include considerable new equipment, well-trained workers, and a belief that the process performs very well. In that case we would define the productivity for the present process as the null hypothesis and the new process as the alternative. Then, we would adopt the new process only if there is strong evidence—rejecting the null hypothesis with a small α—that the new process has higher productivity. Alternatively, the present process might be old and include equipment that needs to be replaced and a number of workers that require supplementary training. In that case we might choose to define the new process productivity as the null hypothesis. Thus, we would continue with the old process only if there is strong evidence that the old process's productivity is higher.

When we establish control charts for monitoring process quality using acceptance intervals as in Chapter 6, we set the desired process level as the null hypothesis and we also set a very small significance level—$\alpha < 0.01$. Thus, we reject only when there is very strong evidence that the process is no longer performing properly. However, these control-chart hypothesis tests are established only after there has been considerable work to bring the process under control and minimize its variability. Therefore, we are quite confident that the process is working properly, and we do not wish to change in response to small variations in the sample data. But, if we do find a test statistic from sample data outside the acceptance interval and hence reject the null hypothesis, we can be quite confident that something has gone wrong and we need to carefully investigate the process immediately to determine what has changed in the original process.

The tests developed in this chapter are based on the assumption that the underlying distribution is normal or that the central limit theorem applies for the distribution of sample means or proportions. When the normality assumption no longer holds, those probabilities of error may not be valid. Since we cannot be sure that most populations are precisely normal, we might have some serious concerns about the validity of our tests. Considerable research has shown that tests involving means do not strongly depend on the normality assumption. These tests are said to be "robust" with respect to normality. However, tests involving variances are not robust. Thus, greater caution is required when using hypothesis tests based on variances. In Chapter 5 we showed how we can use normal probability plots to quickly check to determine if a sample is likely to have come from a normally distributed population. This should be part of good practice in any statistical study of the types discussed in this textbook.

KEY WORDS

- alternative hypothesis, 390
- F distribution, 407
- null hypothesis, 390
- tests of equality of variances from two normal populations, 408

DATA FILES

- Achievement Test Scores, 395
- Food Nutrition Atlas, 413, 414, 415
- HEI Cost Data Variable Subset, 416
- House Selling Price, 395
- Ole, 415
- Storet, 415
- Turkey Feeding, 392, 400

CHAPTER EXERCISES AND APPLICATIONS

 Visit www.MyStatLab.com or www.pearsonglobal editions.com to access the data files.

Note: If the probability of Type I error is not indicated, select a level that is appropriate for the situation described.

10.28 A statistician tests the null hypothesis that the proportion of men favoring a tax reform proposal is the same as the proportion of women. Based on sample data, the null hypothesis is rejected at the 5% significance level. Does this imply that the probability is at least 0.95 that the null hypothesis is false? If not, provide a valid probability statement.

10.29 In a study of performance ratings of ex-smokers, a random sample of 34 ex-smokers had a mean rating of 2.21 and a sample standard deviation of 2.21. For an independent random sample of 86 long-term ex-smokers, the mean rating was 1.47 and the sample standard deviation was 1.69. Find the lowest level of significance at which the null hypothesis of equality of the two population means can be rejected against a two-sided alternative.

10.30 Independent random samples of business managers and college economics faculty were asked to respond on a scale from 1 (strongly disagree) to 7 (strongly agree) to this statement: Grades in advanced economics are good indicators of students' analytical skills. For a sample of 70 business managers, the mean response was 4.4 and the sample standard deviation was 1.3. For a sample of 106 economics faculty the mean response was 5.3 and the sample standard deviation was 1.4.

   a. Test, at the 5% level, the null hypothesis that the population mean response for business managers would be at most 4.0.

   b. Test, at the 5% level, the null hypothesis that the population means are equal against the alternative that the population mean response is higher for economics faculty than for business managers.

10.31 Independent random samples of bachelor's and master's degree holders in statistics, whose initial job was with a major actuarial firm and who subsequently moved to an insurance company, were questioned. For a sample of 56 bachelor's degree holders, the mean number of months before the first job change was 34.68 and the sample standard deviation was 20.53. For a sample of 72 master's degree holders, the mean number of months before the first job change was 35.64 and the sample standard deviation was 20.79. Test, at the 10% level against a two-sided alternative, the null hypothesis that the population mean numbers of months before the first job change are the same for the two groups.

10.32 A study was aimed at assessing the effects of group size and group characteristics on the generation of advertising concepts. To assess the influence of group size, groups of four and eight members were compared. For a random sample of four-member groups, the mean number of advertising concepts generated per group was 78.0 and the sample standard deviation was 24.4. For an independent random sample of eight-member groups, the mean number of advertising concepts generated per group was 114.7 and the sample standard deviation was 14.6. (In each case, the groups had a moderator.) Stating any assumptions that you need to make, test, at the 1% level, the null hypothesis that the population means are the same against the alternative that the mean is higher for eight-member groups.

10.33 You have been hired by the National Nutrition Council to study nutrition practices in the United States. In particular they want to know if their nutrition guidelines are being met by people in the United States. These guidelines indicate that per capita consumption of fruits and vegetables should be above 170 pounds per year, per capita consumption of snack foods should be less than 114 pounds, per capita consumption of soft drinks should be less than 65 gallons, and per capita consumption of meat should be more than 70 pounds. In this project you are to determine if the consumption of these food groups are greater in the metro compared to the non-metro counties. As part of your research you have developed the data file **Food Nutrition Atlas**—described in the Chapter 9 appendix—which contains a number of nutrition and population variables collected by county over all states. It is true that some counties do not report all of the variables. Perform an analysis using the available data and prepare a short report indicating how well the nutrition guidelines are being met. Your conclusions should be supported by rigorous statistical analysis.

10.34 A recent report from a health concerns study indicated that there is strong evidence of a nation's overall health decay if the percent of obese adults exceeds 28%. In addition, if the low-income preschool obesity rate exceeds 13%, there is great concern about long-term health. You are asked to conduct an analysis to determine if there is a difference in these two obesity rates in metro versus nonmetro counties. Use the data file **Food Nutrition Atlas**—described in the Chapter 9 appendix—as the basis for your statistical analysis. Prepare a rigorous analysis and a short statement that reports your statistical results and your conclusions.

10.35 Independent random samples of business and economics faculty were asked to respond on a scale from 1 (strongly disagree) to 4 (strongly agree) to this statement: *The threat and actuality of takeovers of publicly held companies provide discipline for boards and managers to maximize the value of the company to shareholders.* For a sample of 202 business faculty, the mean response was 2.83 and the sample standard deviation was 0.89. For a sample of 291 economics faculty, the mean response was 3.00 and the sample standard deviation was 0.67. Test the null hypothesis that the population means are equal against the alternative that the mean is higher for economics faculty.

10.36 Independent random samples of patients who had received knee and hip replacement were asked to assess the quality of service on a scale from 1 (low) to 7 (high). For a sample of 83 knee patients, the mean rating was 6.543 and the sample standard deviation was 0.649. For a sample of 54 hip patients, the mean rating was 6.733 and the sample standard deviation was 0.425. Test, against a two-sided alternative, the null hypothesis that the population mean ratings for these two types of patients are the same.

10.37 Of a random sample of 148 accounting majors, 75 rated a sense of humor as a very important trait to their career performance. This same view was held by 81 of an independent random sample of 178 finance majors.

    a. Test, at the 5% level, the null hypothesis that at least one-half of all finance majors rate a sense of humor as very important.

    b. Test, at the 5% level against a two-sided alternative, the null hypothesis that the population proportions of accounting and finance majors who rate a sense of humor as very important are the same.

10.38 Aimed at finding substantial earnings decreases, a random sample of 23 firms with substantial earnings decreases showed that the mean return on assets 3 years previously was 0.058 and the sample standard deviation was 0.055. An independent random sample of 23 firms without substantial earnings decreases showed a mean return of 0.146 and a standard deviation 0.058 for the same period. Assume that the two population distributions are normal with equal standard deviations. Test, at the 5% level, the null hypothesis that the population mean returns on assets are the same against the alternative that the true mean is higher for firms without substantial earnings decreases.

10.39 Random samples of employees were drawn in fast-food restaurants where the employer provides a training program. Of a sample of 67 employees who had not completed high school, 11 had participated in a training program provided by their current employer. Of an independent random sample of 113 employees who had completed high school but had not attended college, 27 had participated. Test, at the 1% level, the null hypothesis that the participation rates are the same for the two groups against the alternative that the rate is lower for those who have not completed high school.

10.40 Of a random sample of 80 health insurance firms in Europe, 63 did public relations in-house, as did 52 of an independent random sample of 80 casualty insurance firms. Find and interpret the p-value of a test of equality of the population proportions against a two-sided alternative.

10.41 Independent random samples were taken of male and female clients of University Entrepreneurship Centers. These clients were considering starting a business. Of 94 male clients, 53 actually started a business venture, as did 47 of 68 female clients. Find and interpret the p-value of a test of equality of the population proportions against the alternative that the proportion of female clients actually starting a business is higher than the proportion of male clients.

10.42 A recent report from a health concerns study indicated that there is strong evidence of a nation's overall health decay if the percent of obese adults exceeds 28%. In addition, if the low-income preschool obesity rate exceeds 13%, there is great concern about long-term health. You are asked to conduct an analysis to determine if there is a difference in these two obesity rates in metro versus nonmetro counties. Your analysis is restricted to counties in the following states; California, Michigan, Minnesota, and Florida. Conduct your analysis for each state. Use the data file **Food Nutrition Atlas**—described in the Chapter 9 appendix—as the basis for your statistical analysis. You will first need to obtain a subset of the data file using the capabilities of your statistical analysis computer program.

Prepare a rigorous analysis and a short statement that reports your statistical results and your conclusions.

10.43 National education officials are concerned that there may be a large number of low-income students who are eligible for free lunches in their schools. They also believe that the percentage of students eligible for free lunches is larger in rural areas.

    As part of a larger research study, you have been asked to determine if rural counties have a greater percentage of students eligible for free lunches compared to urban residents. As your study begins you obtain the data file **Food Nutrition Atlas**—described in the Chapter 9 appendix—which contains a number of health and nutrition variables measured over counties in the United States. Perform an analysis to determine if there is strong evidence to conclude that rural residents have higher rates of free-lunch eligibility and prepare a short report on your results.

10.44 You are in charge of rural economic development in a rapidly developing country that is using its newfound oil wealth to develop the entire country. As part of your responsibility you have been asked to determine if there is evidence that the new rice-growing procedures have increased output per hectare. A random sample of 27 fields was planted using the old procedure, and the sample mean output was 60 per hectare with a sample variance of 100. During the second year the new procedure was applied to the same fields and the sample mean output was 64 per hectare, with a sample variance of 150. The sample correlation between the two fields was 0.38. The population variances are assumed to be equal, and that assumption should be used for the problem analysis.

    a. Use a hypothesis test with a probability of Type I error = 0.05 to determine if there is strong evidence to support the conclusion that the new process leads to higher output per hectare, and interpret the results.

    b. Under the assumption that the population variances are equal, construct a 95% acceptance interval for the ratio of the sample variances. Do the observed sample variances lead us to conclude that the population variances are the same? Please explain.

10.45 The president of Amalgamated Retailers International, Samiha Peterson, has asked for your assistance in studying the market penetration for the company's new cell phone. You are asked to study two markets and determine if the difference in market share remains the same. Historically, in market 1 in western Poland, Amalgamated has had a 30% market share. Similarly, in market 2 in southern Austria, Amalgamated has had a 35% market share. You obtain a random sample of potential customers from each area. From market 1, 258 out of a total sample of 800 indicate they will purchase from Amalgamated. From market 2, 260 out of 700 indicate they will purchase from Amalgamated.

    a. Using a probability of error $\alpha = 0.03$, test the hypothesis that the market shares are equal versus the hypothesis that they are not equal (market 2 – market 1).

    b. Using a probability of error $\alpha = 0.03$, test the hypothesis that the market shares are equal versus the hypothesis that the share in market 2 is larger.

10.46 National education officials are concerned that there may be a large number of low-income students who are eligible for free lunches in their schools. They also believe that the percentage of students eligible for free lunches is larger in rural areas.

As part of a larger research study you have been asked to determine if rural counties have a greater percentage of students eligible for free lunches compared to urban residents. In this part of the study you are to answer the free-lunch-eligibility question for each of the three states, California, Texas, and Florida. For this study you will have to learn how to create subsets from large data files using your local statistical package. Assistance for that effort can be obtained from your professor, teaching assistant, the Help option in your statistical package, or similar sources. As your study begins, you obtain the data file **Food Nutrition Atlas**—described in the Chapter 9 appendix—which contains a number of health and nutrition variables measured over counties in the United States. Perform an analysis to determine if there is strong evidence to conclude that rural residents have higher rates of eligibility for free lunches and prepare a short report on your results.

10.47   You are the product manager for brand 4 in a large food company. The company president has complained that a competing brand, called brand 2, has higher average sales. The data services group has stored the latest product sales (saleb2 and saleb4) and price data (apriceb2 and apriceb4) in a file named **Storet** described in Chapter 10 appendix.

a. Based on a statistical hypothesis test, does the president have strong evidence to support her complaint? Show all statistical work and reasoning.

b. After analyzing the data, you note that a large outlier of value 971 is contained in the sample for brand 2. Repeat part a with this extreme observation removed. What do you now conclude about the president's complaint?

10.48   Joe Ortega is the product manager for Ole ice cream. You have been asked to determine if Ole ice cream has greater sales than Carl's ice cream, which is a strong competitor. The data file **Ole** contains weekly sales and price data for the competing brands over the year in three different supermarket chains. These sample data represent a random sample of all ice cream sales for the two brands. The variable names clearly identify the variables.

a. Design and implement an analysis to determine if there is strong evidence to conclude that Ole ice cream has higher mean sales than Carl's ice cream ($\alpha = 0.05$). Explain your procedure and show all computations. You may include Minitab output if appropriate to support your analysis. Explain your conclusions.

b. Design and implement an analysis to determine if the prices charged for the two brands are different ($\alpha = 0.05$). Carefully explain your analysis, show all computations, and interpret your results.

10.49   Mary Peterson is in charge of preparing blended flour for exotic bread making. The process is to take two different types of flour and mix them together in order to achieve high-quality breads. For one of the products, flour A and flour B are mixed together. The package of flour A comes from a packing process that has a population mean weight of 8 ounces with a population variance of 0.04. The package of flour B has a population mean weight of 8 ounces and a population variance of 0.06. The package weights have a correlation of 0.40. The A and B packages are mixed together to obtain a 16-ounce package of special exotic flour. Every 60 minutes a random sample of four packages of exotic flour is selected from the process, and the mean weight for the four packages is computed. Prepare a 99% acceptance interval for a quality-control chart for the sample means from the sample of four packages. Show all your work and explain your reasoning. Explain how this acceptance chart would be used to ensure that the package weights continue to meet the standard.

10.50   A study was conducted to determine if there was a difference in humor content in British and American trade magazine advertisements. In an independent random sample of 300 American trade magazine advertisements, 64 were humorous. An independent random sample of 200 British trade magazine advertisements contained 51 humorous ads. Do these data provide evidence that there is a difference in the proportion of humorous ads in British versus American trade magazines?

Nutrition Research–Based Exercises

A large research study conducted by the Economic Research Service (ERS), a prestige think tank research center in the U.S. Department of Agriculture is conducting a series of research studies to determine the nutrition characteristics of people in the United States. This research is used for both nutrition education and government policy designed to improve personal health.

The U.S. Department of Agriculture (USDA) developed the Healthy Eating Index (HEI) to monitor the diet quality of the U.S. population, particularly how well it conforms to dietary guidance. The HEI–2005 measures how well the population follows the recommendations of the 2005 Dietary Guidelines for Americans. In particular, it measures, on a 100-point scale, the adequacy of consumption of vegetables, fruits, grains, milk, meat and beans, and liquid oils. Full credit for these groups is given only when the consumer consumes some whole fruit, vegetables from the dark green, orange, and legume subgroup, and whole grains. In addition the HEI–2005 measures how well the U.S. population limits consumption of saturated fat, sodium, and extra calories from solid fats, added sugars, and alcoholic beverages. You will use the Total HEI–2005 score as the measure of the quality of a diet. Further background on the HEI and important research on nutrition can be found at the government Web sites indicated at the end of this case-study document.

A healthy diet results from a combination of appropriate food choices, which are strongly influenced by a number of behavioral, cultural, societal, and health conditions. We cannot simply tell people to drink orange juice, purchase all food from organic farms, or take some new miracle drug. Research and experience have developed considerable knowledge, and if we, for example, follow the diet guidelines associated with the food pyramid, we will be healthier. It is also important that we know more about the characteristics that lead to healthier diets so that better recommendations and policies can be developed. And, of course, better diets will lead to a higher quality of life and lowered medical-care costs. In the following exercises you will apply your understanding of statistical analysis to perform analysis similar to that done by professional researchers.

The data file **HEI Cost Data Variable Subset** contains considerable information on randomly selected individuals who participated in an extended interview and medical examination. There are two observations for each person in the study. The first observation, identified by daycode = 1, contains data from the first interview, and the second observation, daycode = 2, contains data from the second interview. This data file contains the data for the following exercises. The variables are described in the data dictionary in the Chapter 10 appendix.

10.51 Individuals have their HEI measured on two different days with the first and second day indicated by the variable daycode. A number of researchers argue that individuals will have a higher-quality diet for the second interview because they will adjust their diet after the first interview. You are asked to perform an appropriate hypothesis test to determine if there is strong evidence to conclude that individuals have a higher HEI on the second day compared to the first day.

10.52 Previous research has suggested that immigrants in the United States have a stronger interest in good diet compared to the rest of the population. If true, this behavior could result from a desire for overall life improvement, historical experience from their previous country, or some other complex rationale. You have been asked to determine if immigrants (variable immigrant = 1) have healthier diets compared to non-immigrants (= 0). Perform an appropriate statistical test to determine if there is strong evidence to conclude that immigrants have better diets compared to natives.

You will do the analysis based first on the data from the first interview, create subsets of the data file using daycode = 1; then a second time, using data from the second interview, create subsets of the data file using daycode = 2. Note differences in the results between the first and second interviews.

10.53 There is an increasing interest in healthier lifestyles, especially among the younger population. This is exhibited in the increased interest in exercise and a variety of emphases on eating foods that contribute to a higher-quality diet. You have been asked to determine if people who are physically active (variable activity level = 2 or 3) have healthier diets compared to those who are not (variable activity level = 1). Determine if there is strong evidence for your conclusion. You will do the analysis based first on the data from the first interview and create subsets of the data file using daycode = 1, and then a second time using data from the second interview, creating subsets of the data file using daycode = 2. Note differences in the results between the first and second interviews.

10.54 Various research studies and personal lifestyle advisers argue that increased social interaction is important for a higher quality of life. You have been asked to determine if people who are single (variable single = 1) have a healthier diet than those who are married or living with a partner. Determine if there is strong evidence for your conclusion. You will do the analysis based first on the data from the first interview, creating subsets of the

data file using daycode = 1, and a second time using data from the second interview, creating subsets of the data file using daycode = 2. Note differences in the results between the first and second interviews.

10.55 Throughout society there are various claims of behavioral differences between men and women on many different characteristics. You have been asked to conduct a comparative study of diet quality between men and women. The variable female is coded 1 for females and 0 for males. Perform an appropriate analysis to determine if men and women have different diet-quality levels. You will do the analysis based first on the data from the first interview by creating subsets of the data file using daycode = 1 and then a second time using data from the second interview, creating subsets of the data file using daycode = 2. Note differences in the results between the first and second interviews.

10.56 A recent radio commentator argued that his experience indicated that women believed that purchasing higher-cost food would improve their lifestyle. Is there evidence to conclude that women have a lower daily food cost compared to men (daily-cost)? Use an appropriate test to determine the answer. You will do the analysis based first on the data from the first interview, creating subsets of the data file using daycode = 1, and a second time using data from the second interview, creating subsets of the data file using daycode = 2. Note differences in the results between the first and second interviews.

10.57 The food stamp program has been part of a long-term public policy to ensure that lower-income families will be provided with adequate nutrition at lower cost. Some people argue that providing food income supplements will merely encourage lower-income people to purchase more expensive food, without any improvement in their diet. Perform an analysis to determine how the nutrition level of people receiving food stamps compares with the rest of the population. Is there evidence that people who receive food stamps have a higher-quality diet compared to the rest of the population? Is there evidence that they have a lower-quality diet? Is there evidence that people who receive food stamps spend more for their food compared to the rest of the population? Is there evidence that they spend less for their food? Based on your statistical analysis, what do you conclude about the food stamp program? You will do the analysis based first on the data from the first interview, creating subsets of the data file using daycode = 1, and a second time using data from the second interview, creating subsets of the data file using daycode = 2. Note differences in the results between the first and second interviews.

10.58 Excess body weight is, of course, related to diet, but, in turn, what we eat depends on who we are in terms of culture and our entire life experience. Does the immigrant population have a lower percentage of people that are overweight compared to the remainder of the population? Provide strong evidence to support your conclusion. You will do the analysis based first on the data from the first interview, creating subsets of the data file using daycode = 1, and a second time using data from the second interview, creating subsets of the data file using daycode = 2. Note differences in the results between the first and second interviews.

Appendix

GUIDELINES FOR CHOOSING THE APPROPRIATE DECISION RULE

Figure 10.5 Flow Chart for Selecting the Appropriate Hypothesis Test When Comparing Two Population Means

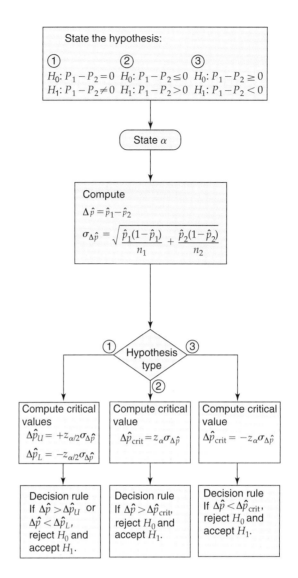

Figure 10.6 Flow Chart for Selecting the Appropriate Hypothesis Test When Comparing Two Population Proportions

Data File Descriptions

VARIABLE LIST FOR DATA FILE HEI COST DATA VARIABLE SUBSET

	VARIABLE	LABEL
1	Suppl	Take supplements
2	doc_bp	1 – Doctor diagnosed high blood pressure
3	daycode	1 – First interview day, 2 – Second interview day
4	sr_overweight	1 – Subject reported was overweight
5	try_wl	1 – Tried to lose weight
6	try_mw	1 – Trying to maintain weight, active
7	sr_did_lm_wt	1 – Subject reported did limit weight
8	daily_cost	One day_adjusted_food_cost
9	HEI2005	TOTAL HEI–2005 SCORE
10	daily_cost2	Daily food cost squared
11	Friday	1 – dietary_recall_occurred_on_Friday
12	weekend_ss	1 – Dietary_recall_occurred_on_Sat_or Sun
13	week_mth	1 – Dietary recall occurred Mon through Thur
14	keeper	1 – Data is complete for 2 days

	Variable	Label
15	WIC	1 – Someone_in_the_HH_participates_in
16	fsp	1 – Someone_in_the_HH_approved_for_food stamps (SNAP program)
17	fsec	1 – Family_has_high_food_security
18	PIR_p	Poverty_Income_Ratio_as_Percent (Family Income/Poverty Level Income)
19	PIR_grp	Poverty_Income_Ratio_group
20	nhw	1 – Non_Hispanic_White, 0 – Else
21	hisp	1 – Hispanic
22	nhb	1 – Non_Hispanic_Black
23	single	1 – Single__no_partner_in_the_home
24	female	1 – Subject is female
25	waist_cir	Waist circumference (cm) separate by male and female
26	waistper	Ratio of subject waist measure to waist cutoff for obese
27	age	Age at screening adjudicated—Recode
28	hh_size	Total number of people in the household
29	WTINT2YR	Full Sample 2 Year Interview Weight
30	WTMEC2YR	Full Sample 2 Year MEC Exam Weight
31	immigrant	1 – immigrant
32	citizen	1 – U.S citizen
33	native_born	1 – Native born
34	hh_income_est	Household income estimated by subject
35	English	1 – Primary Language spoken in Home is English
36	Spanish	1 – Primary Language spoken in Home is Spanish
37	Smoker	1 – Currently smokes
38	doc_chol	1 – Doctor diagnosis of high cholestorol that was made before interview
39	BMI	Body Mass Index (kg/m**2) 20–25 Healthy, 26–30 Overweight, >30 Obese
40	doc_dib	1 – Doctor diagnosis diabetes
41	no_days_ph_ng	no. of days physical health was not good
42	no_days_mh_ng	no. of days mental health was not good
43	doc_ow	1 – Doctor diagnosis overweight was made before interview
44	screen_hours	Number of hours in front of computer or TV screen
45	activity_level	1 = Sedentary, 2 = Active, 3 = Very Active
46	total_active_min	Active minutes per day
47	waist_large	Waist circumference > cut_off
48	Pff	Percent of calories from fast food, deli, pizza restaurant
49	Prest	Percent of Calories from table service restaurant
50	P_Ate_At_Home	Percent of Calories eaten at home
51	Hs	1 = High School Graduate
52	Col_grad	1 = College Graduate or Higher
53	Pstore	Percent of Calories purchased at store and consumer at home

DESCRIPTION OF DATA FILE STORET

Name	Count	Description
Weeknum	52	Consecutive week number
saleb1	52	Total unit sales for brand 1
apriceb1	52	Actual retail price for brand 1
rpriceb1	52	Regular or recommended price brand 1
promotb1	52	Promotion code for brand 1
		0 No promotion
		1 Newspaper advertising only
		2 In-store display only
		3 Newspaper ad and in-store display

(continued)

Name	Count	Description
saleb2	52	Total unit sales for brand 2
apriceb2	52	Actual retail price for brand 2
rpriceb2	52	Regular or recommended price for brand 2
promotb2	52	Promotion code for brand 2
saleb3	52	Total unit sales for brand 3
apriceb3	52	Actual retail price for brand 3
rpriceb3	52	Regular or recommended price for brand 3
promotb3	52	Promotion code for brand 3
saleb4	52	Total unit sales for brand 4
apriceb4	52	Actual retail price for brand 4
rpriceb4	52	Regular or recommended price for brand 4
promotb4	52	Promotion code for Brand 4
saleb5	52	Total unit sales for Brand 5
apriceb5	52	Actual retail price for Brand 5
rpriceb5	52	Regular or recommended price for Brand 5
promotb5	52	Promotion code for Brand 5

REFERENCES

1. Carlson, A., D. Dong, and M. Lino. 2010. *Are the Total Daily Cost of Food and Diet Quality Related: A Random Effects Panel Data Analysis.* Paper presented at 1st Joint EAAE/AAEA Seminar, The Economics of Food, Food Choice and Health.

2. Freising, Germany, September 15–17, 2010.

3. Carlson, W. L., and B. Thorne. 1997. *Applied Statistical Methods.* Upper Saddle River, NJ: Prentice Hall, 539–53.

4. Centers for Disease Control and Prevention (CDC). 2003–2004. National Health and Nutrition Examination Survey Data. Hyattsville, MD: U.S. Department of Health and Human Services, Centers for Disease Control and Prevention. http://www.cdc.gov/nchs/nhanes/nhanes2003-2004/nhanes03_04.htm

5. Food Nutrition Atlas, Economic Research Service, United States Department of Agriculture, 2010.

6. Guenther, P.M., J. Reedy, S. M. Krebs-Smith, B. B. Reeve, and P. P. Basiotis. November 2007. *Development and Evaluation of the Healthy Eating Index–2005: Technical Report.* Center for Nutrition Policy and Promotion, U.S. Department of Agriculture. Available at http://www.cnpp.usda.gov/HealthyEatingIndex.htm.

7. Hogg, R. V., and A. T. Craig. 1995. *Introduction to Mathematical Statistics*, 5th ed. Englewood Cliffs, N.J: Prentice-Hall.

CHAPTER

11

Simple Regression

Introduction

Our study to this point has focused on analysis and inference related to a single variable. In this chapter we extend our analysis to relationships between variables. Our analysis builds on the descriptive relationships using scatter plots and covariance/correlation coefficients developed in Chapter 2. We assume that the reader is familiar with that material.

The analysis of business and economic processes makes extensive use of relationships between variables. These relationships are expressed mathematically as

$$Y = f(X)$$

where the function can follow linear and nonlinear forms. In many applications the form of the relationship is not precisely known. Here, we present analyses based on linear models developed using least squares regression. In many cases linear relationships provide a good model of the process. In other cases we are interested in a limited portion of a nonlinear relationship that can be approximated by a linear relationship. In Section 12.7 we show how some important nonlinear relationships can also be analyzed using regression analysis.

Thus, the regression procedures have a broad range of applications, including many in business and economics, as indicated in the following examples:

- The president of Amalgamated Materials, a manufacturer of dry wall building material, believes that the mean annual quantity of dry wall sold, Y, in his region is a linear function of the total value of building permits issued, X, during the previous year.
- A grain dealer wants to know the effect of total output on price per ton so that she can develop a prediction model using historical data.
- The marketing department analysts need to know how gasoline price, X, affects total sales of gasoline, Y. By using weekly price and sales data, they plan to develop a linear model that will tell them how much sales change as the result of price changes.

Each of these relationships can be expressed as a linear model,

$$Y = \beta_0 + \beta_1 X$$

where β_0 and β_1 are numerical coefficients for each specific model.

With the advent of many high-quality statistical packages and spreadsheets such as Excel, it is now possible for almost anyone to compute the required coefficients and other regression statistics. Unfortunately, we cannot interpret and use these computer results correctly without understanding the methodology of regression analysis. In this and the following two chapters you will learn key insights that will guide your use of regression analysis.

11.1 OVERVIEW OF LINEAR MODELS

In Chapter 2 we saw how the relationship between two variables can be described by using scatter plots to provide a picture of the relationship and correlation coefficients to provide a numerical measure. In many economic and business problems, a specific functional relationship is needed to obtain numerical results.

- A manager would like to know what mean level of sales can be expected if the price is set at $10 per unit.
- If 250 workers are employed in a factory, how many units can be produced during an average day?
- If a developing country increases its fertilizer production by 1,000,000 tons, how much increase in grain production should it expect?

In many cases we can adequately approximate the desired functional relationships by a linear equation,

$$Y = \beta_0 + \beta_1 X$$

where Y is the dependent, or endogenous, variable, X is the independent, or exogenous, variable, β_0 is the Y-intercept, and β_1 is the slope of the line, or the change in Y for every unit change in X. Figure 11.1 is an example of a typical simple regression model showing the number of tables produced, Y, using different numbers of workers, X. The assumption made in developing the least squares regression procedure is that for each value of X, there will be a corresponding mean value of Y that results because of the underlying linear relationship in the process being studied. The linear equation model computes the mean of Y for every value of X and is the basis for obtaining many economic and business relationships including demand functions, production functions, consumption functions, and sales forecasts.

Figure 11.1
Linear Function and
Data Points

The slope coefficient β_1 is extremely important for many business and economic applications because it indicates the change in an output or endogenous variable for each unit change in an input or exogenous variable. The relationship in Figure 11.1

$$\hat{y} = -13.02 + 2.545x$$

shows that each additional worker, X, increases the number of tables produced, Y, by 2.545. The intercept, -13.02, merely adjusts the regression line up or down and has no real meaning for this application result. This equation is valid only over the range of X, from 11 to 30. Under certain specific situations the management might have good reasons—other than just the estimated regression model—to believe that the linear relationship will hold above or below the range of X (11–30). In those cases they might extend the model beyond the range of X based on their additional management knowledge.

By using the regression model, management can determine if the value of the increased output is greater than the cost of an additional worker.

We use regression to determine the best linear relationship between Y and X for a particular application. This requires us to find the best values for the coefficients β_0 and β_1. We use the data available from the process to compute "estimates" or numerical values for the coefficients, β_0, and β_1. These estimates—defined as b_0 and b_1—are computed by using *least squares regression,* a technique widely implemented in statistical packages such as Minitab, SPSS, SAS, and STATA and in spreadsheets such as Excel. Coefficients are computed for the best-fit line given a set of data points, such as shown in Figure 11.1.

Least Squares Regression
The **least squares regression line** based on sample data is

$$\hat{y} = b_0 + b_1 x \tag{11.1}$$

b_1 is the **slope** of the line, or change in y for every unit change in x, and calculated as

$$b_1 = \frac{Cov(x, y)}{s_x^2} = r \frac{s_y}{s_x} \tag{11.2}$$

and b_0 is the **y-intercept** calculated as

$$b_0 = \bar{y} - b_1 \bar{x} \tag{11.3}$$

Using the following results from Chapter 2,

$$s_x^2 = \frac{\sum (x_i - \bar{x})^2}{n-1}$$

$$s_y^2 = \frac{\sum (y_i - \bar{y})^2}{n-1}$$

$$Cov(x, y) = \frac{\sum (x_i - \bar{x})(y_i - \bar{y})}{n-1}$$

$$r = \frac{Cov(x, y)}{s_x s_y}$$

Example 11.1 Manufacturing Plant (Regression Line)

The Rising Hills Manufacturing Company in Redwood Falls regularly collects data to monitor its operations. These data are stored in the data file **Rising Hills**. The number of workers, X, and the number of tables, Y, produced per hour for a sample of 10 workers is shown in Figure 11.1. If management decides to employ 25 workers, estimate the expected number of tables that are likely to be produced.

Solution Using the data, we computed the descriptive statistics:

$$Cov(x, y) = 106.93, \quad s_x^2 = 42.01, \quad \bar{y} = 41.2, \quad \bar{x} = 21.3$$

From the covariance we see that the direction of the relationship is *positive*.

Using the descriptive statistics, we compute the sample regression coefficients:

$$b_1 = \frac{Cov(x, y)}{s_x^2} = \frac{106.93}{42.01} = 2.545$$

$$b_0 = \bar{y} - b_1 \bar{x} = 41.2 - 2.545(21.3) = -13.02$$

From this, the sample regression line is as follows:

$$\hat{y} = b_0 + b_1 x = -13.02 + 2.545x$$

For 25 employees we would expect to produce

$$\hat{y} = -13.02 + 2.545(25) = 50.605$$

or approximately 51 tables. In most situations we use a statistical software package such as Minitab or a spreadsheet such as Excel to obtain the regression coefficients to reduce the work load and improve computational accuracy.

Because the number of workers in the Rising Hill Manufacturing Plant ranged from 11 to 30, we cannot predict the number of tables produced per hour if 100 workers were employed.

EXERCISES

Basic Exercises

11.1 Complete the following for the (x, y) pairs of data points (3,1), (4,5), (5,4), (7, 6), and (9, 8).

    a. Prepare a scatter plot of these data points.
    b. Compute b_1.

    c. Compute b_0.
    d. What is the equation of the regression line?

11.2 The following data give X, the price charged per piece of plywood, and Y, the quantity sold (in thousands).

Price per Piece, X	Thousands of Pieces Sold, Y
$6	80
7	60
8	70
9	40
10	0

a. Prepare a scatter plot of these data points.
b. Compute the covariance.
c. Compute and interpret b_1.
d. Compute b_0.
e. What quantity of plywood would you expect to sell if the price were $7 per piece?

11.3 A random sample of data for 7 days of operation produced the following (price, quantity) data values:

Price per Gallon of Paint, X	Quantity Sold, Y
10	100
8	120
5	200
4	200
10	90
7	110
6	150

a. Prepare a scatter plot of the data.
b. Compute and interpret b_1.
c. Compute and interpret b_0.
d. How many gallons of paint would you expect to sell if the price is $7 per gallon?

Application Exercises

11.4 A large consumer goods company has been studying the effect of advertising on total profits. As part of this study, data on advertising expenditures and total sales were collected for a five-month period and are as follows:

$(10, 100)\ (15, 200)\ (7, 80)(12, 120)\ (14, 150)$

The first number is advertising expenditures and the second is total sales.

a. Plot the data.
b. Does the plot provide evidence that advertising has a positive effect on sales?
c. Compute the regression coefficients, b_0 and b_1.

11.5 Simoné Berk, president of Food Unlimited, has asked you to study the relationship between market price (euros) and the amount of rice (kg) supplied by her competitor, Good Food, Inc. Simoné supplies you with the following observations, of price per kg and number of kgs, obtained from the company's database:

Price (x)	3	5	4	7	4	6	7	3
Quantity (y)	5	10	8	16	6	15	20	4

a. Prepare a scatter plot.
b. Determine the regression coefficients, b_0 and b_1.
c. Write a short explanation of the regression equation that tells Simoné how the equation can be used to describe her competition. Include an indication of the range over which the equation can be applied.

11.6 A random sample of 12 college baseball players participated in a special weight-training program in an attempt to improve their batting averages. The program lasted for 20 weeks immediately prior to the start of the baseball season. The average number of hours per week and the change in their batting averages from the preceding season are as follows:

$(8.0, 10)\ (20.0, 100)\ (5.4, -10)\ (12.4, 79)\ (9.2, 50)$
$(15.0, 89)\ (6.0, 34)\ (8.0, 30)\ (18.0, 68)\ (25.0, 110)$
$(10.0, 34)\ (5.0, 10)$

a. Plot the data. Does it appear that the weight-training program was successful?
b. Estimate the regression equation.

11.2 LINEAR REGRESSION MODEL

Using basic economics we know that the quantity of goods purchased, Y, in a specific market can be modeled as a linear function of the disposable income, X. If income is a specific level, x_i, purchasers respond by purchasing a quantity, y_i. In the real world we know there are other factors that influence the actual quantity purchased. These include identifiable factors, such as the price of the goods in question, advertising, and the prices of competing goods. In addition, there are other unknown factors that can influence the actual quantity purchased.

In a simple linear equation we model the effect of all factors, other than the X variable—in this example disposable income—are assumed to be part of the random error term, labeled as ε. This random error term is a random variable (Chapter 5) with mean 0 and a probability distribution—often modeled by a normal distribution. Thus, the model is as follows:

$$Y = \beta_0 + \beta_1 X + \varepsilon$$

Least squares regression provides us with an estimated model of the linear relationship between an independent, or exogenous, variable and a dependent, or endogenous, variable. We begin the process of regression modeling by assuming a population model that has predetermined X values, and for every X there is a mean value of Y plus a random error term. We use the estimated regression equation—as shown in Figure 11.1—to estimate the mean value of Y for every value of X. Individual points vary about this line because the random error term, ε, has a mean of 0 and a common variance for all values of X. The random error represents all the influences on Y that are not represented by the linear relationship between Y and X. Effects of these factors, which are assumed to be independent of X, behave like a random variable whose population mean is 0. The random deviations ε_i about the linear model are shown in Figure 11.2, and they are combined with the mean of Y_i for every X_i to obtain the observed value y_i.

Figure 11.2
Population Model for
Linear Regression

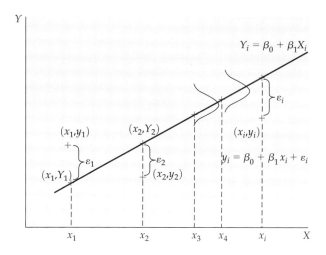

Figure 11.2 presents an example of a set of observations that were generated by an underlying linear model of a process. The mean level of Y, for every X, is represented by the population equation

$$Y = \beta_0 + \beta_1 X$$

The linear regression model provides the expected value of the random variable Y when X takes on a specific value. The assumption of linearity implies that this expectation can be written as

$$E(Y \mid X = x) = \beta_0 + \beta_1 x$$

where β_0 represents the Y intercept of the equation and β_1 is the slope. β_0 and β_1 are parameters of the model whose values are not known, but estimated values can be computed from the data. The actual observed value of Y for a given value of X is modeled as the computed value of Y plus a random error, ε, that has a mean of 0 and a variance of σ^2:

$$y_i = \beta_0 + \beta_1 x_i + \varepsilon_i$$

The random error term ε represents the variation in y that is not estimated by the linear relationship. The following assumptions are used to make inferences about the population linear model by using the estimated model coefficients.

Linear Regression Assumptions

1. The Y's are linear functions of X plus a random error term

$$y_i = \beta_0 + \beta_1 x_i + \varepsilon_i$$

2. The x values are fixed numbers, or they are realizations of random variable X that are independent of the error terms, $\varepsilon_i(i = 1, \ldots, n)$. In the latter case inference is carried out conditionally on the observed values of $x_i(i = 1, \ldots, n)$.

3. The error terms are random variables, $\varepsilon_i(i = 1, \ldots, n)$, which have a mean of 0 and variance σ^2. This property is called homoscedasticity, or uniform variance:

$$E[\varepsilon_i] = 0 \quad \text{and} \quad E[\varepsilon_i^2] = \sigma^2 \quad \text{for} \quad (i = 1, \ldots, n)$$

4. The random error terms, ε_i, are not correlated with one another, so that

$$E[\varepsilon_i \varepsilon_j] = 0 \quad \text{for all } i \neq j$$

Linear Regression Population Model

In the application of regression analysis, the process being studied is represented by a population model, and an estimated least squares regression model is computed, utilizing available data. The population model is specified as

$$y_i = \beta_0 + \beta_1 x_i + \varepsilon_i \tag{11.4}$$

where β_0 and β_1 are the population model coefficients and ε_i is a random error term. For every observed value x_i, an observed value y_i is generated by the population model. For purposes of statistical inference, which we develop in Section 11.5, ε is assumed to have a normal distribution with a mean of 0 and a variance of σ^2. Later we see that the central limit theorem can be used to relax the assumption of a normal distribution. The model of the linear relationship between Y and X is defined by the two coefficients β_0 and β_1. Figure 11.2 represents the model schematically.

The linear equation represented by the line is the best-fit linear equation. We see that individual data points are above and below the line and that the line has points with both positive and negative deviations. The distance—in the Y or vertical dimension—for each point (x_i, y_i) from the linear equation is defined as the residual, e_i. We would like to choose the equation so that the positive and negative residuals are as small as possible as we find estimates for the coefficients, β_0 and β_1, which we label as b_0 and b_1. Equations to compute these estimates are developed using the least squares regression procedure. Least squares regression chooses b_0 and b_1 such that the sum of the squared residuals is minimized. The least squares procedure is intuitively rational and provides estimators that have good statistical properties.

Figure 11.3
Estimated
Regression Model

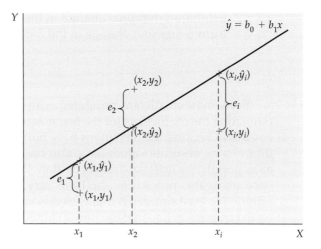

In the least squares regression model, we assume that values of the independent variable, x_i, are selected, and for each x_i there is a population mean of Y. The observed values of y_i contain the mean and the random deviation ε_i. A set of n points is observed and used to obtain estimates of the model coefficients using the least squares procedure. We extend the concepts of classical inference developed in Chapters 7–10 to make inferences about the underlying population model by using the estimated regression model. In Chapter 12 we see how several independent variables can be considered simultaneously using multiple regression.

The estimated linear regression model as shown schematically in Figure 11.3 is given by the equation

$$y_i = b_0 + b_1 x_i + e_i$$

where b_0 and b_1 are the estimated values of the coefficients and e_i is the difference between the predicted value Y on the regression line, defined as

$$\hat{y}_i = b_0 + b_1 x_i$$

and the observed value y_i. The difference between y_i and $\hat{y}_i$ for each value of X is defined as the residual

$$e_i = y_i - \hat{y}_i$$
$$= y_i - (b_0 + b_1 x_i)$$

Thus, for each observed value of X there is a predicted value of Y from the estimated model and an observed value. The difference between the observed and predicted values of Y is defined as the residual, e_i. The residual, e_i, is not the model error, ε_i, but is the combined measure of the model error and errors that result because b_0 and b_1 are sample results and, thus, subject to random variation or error; in turn, this leads to variation or error in estimating the predicted value.

We determine the estimated regression model by obtaining estimates b_0 and b_1 of the population coefficients using the process called least squares analysis, which we develop in Section 11.3. These coefficients are, in turn, used to obtain predicted values of Y for every value of X. Regression analysis produces a number of random variables such as $b_0, b_1, \hat{y}$, which are linear functions of ε, the error-term random variable in linear regression.

Linear Regression Outcomes
Linear regression provides two important results:

1. Predicted values, $\hat{y}$, of the dependent, or endogenous, variable as a function of the independent or exogenous variable
2. Estimated marginal change in the endogenous variable, b_1, that results from a one-unit change in the independent, or exogenous, variable

Early mathematicians struggled with the problem of developing a procedure for estimating the coefficients for the linear equation. Simply minimizing the deviations was not useful because the deviations have both positive and negative signs. Various procedures using absolute values have also been developed, but none has proven as useful or as popular as least squares regression. We will learn later that the coefficients developed using this procedure also have very useful statistical properties. One important caution for least squares is that extreme outlier points can have such a strong influence on the regression line that the line is shifted toward this point. Thus, you should always examine scatter plots to be sure that the regression relationship is not based on just a few extreme points.

Our discussion continues with an example that indicates a typical application of regression analysis and the kind of results that can be obtained.

Example 11.2 Sales Prediction for Northern Household Goods (Regression Model Estimation)

The president of Northern Household Goods has asked you to develop a model that will predict total sales for proposed new retail store locations. Northern is a rapidly expanding general retailer, and it needs a rational strategy for determining where new stores should be located. As part of the project you need to estimate a linear equation that predicts retail sales per household as a function of household disposable income for their customers. The company has obtained data from a sampling survey of households in each of the target sales areas for their existing stores, and the variables retail sales (Y) and income (X) per household will be used to develop the model.

Solution Figure 11.4 is a scatter plot that shows the relationship between retail sales and disposable income for families. The actual data are shown in Table 11.1 and stored in a data file named **Retail Sales**. From economic theory we know that sales should increase with increases in disposable income, and the plot strongly supports that theory. Regression analysis provides us with a linear model that can be used to predict retail sales per household for various levels of disposable income. A line drawn on the graph represents the simple regression model

$$Y = 559 + 0.3815X$$

where Y is retail sales per household and X is disposable income per household. Thus, the regression equation provides us with the best linear model for predicting sales for a given disposable income based on the data. Notice that this model tells us that every $1 increase in per capita disposable family income, X, is associated with an increase in the expected value of retail sales, Y, of $0.38. Clearly, that result is important for predicting household retail sales and, in turn, for goods sold by Northern. For example, we find that a family income of $55,000 would predict retail sales at $21,542 ($559 + $55,000 × 0.3815).

Figure 11.4 Retail Sales per Household versus Per Capita Disposable Income

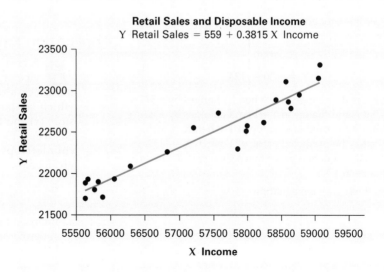

Table 11.1 Data on Disposable Income per Household (X) and Retail Sales per Household (Y)

RETAIL STORE	INCOME (X)	RETAIL SALES (Y)	RETAIL STORE	INCOME (X)	RETAIL SALES (Y)
1	$55,641	$21,886	12	$57,850	$22,301
2	$55,681	$21,934	13	$57,975	$22,518
3	$55,637	$21,699	14	$57,992	$22,580
4	$55,825	$21,901	15	$58,240	$22,618
5	$55,772	$21,812	16	$58,414	$22,890
6	$55,890	$21,714	17	$58,561	$23,112
7	$56,068	$21,932	18	$59,066	$23,315
8	$56,299	$22,086	19	$58,596	$22,865
9	$56,825	$22,265	20	$58,631	$22,788
10	$57,205	$22,551	21	$58,758	$22,949
11	$57,562	$22,736	22	$59,037	$23,149

At this point we need to emphasize that the regression results summarize the information contained in the data and do not "prove" that increased income "causes" increased sales. Economic theory suggests that there is causation, and the estimated regression model supports that theory. Scatter plots, correlations, and regression equations cannot prove causation, but they can provide supporting evidence. Thus, in order to establish conclusions, we need a combination of theory—experience in business management and economics—and good statistical analysis.

EXERCISES

Basic Exercises

11.7 Given the regression equation

$$Y = 107 + 10X$$

a. What is the change in Y when X changes by +2?
b. What is the change in Y when X changes by −4?
c. What is the predicted value of Y when $X = 15$?
d. What is the predicted value of Y when $X = 22$?
e. Does this equation prove that a change in X causes a change in Y?

11.8 Given the regression equation

$$Y = -50 + 12X$$

a. What is the change in Y when X changes by +3?
b. What is the change in Y when X changes by −4?
c. What is the predicted value of Y when $X = 12$?
d. What is the predicted value of Y when $X = 23$?
e. Does this equation prove that a change in X causes a change in Y?

11.9 Given the regression equation

$$Y = 43 + 10X$$

a. What is the change in Y when X changes by +8?
b. What is the change in Y when X changes by −6?
c. What is the predicted value of Y when $X = 11$?
d. What is the predicted value of Y when $X = 29$?
e. Does this equation prove that a change in X causes a change in Y?

11.10 Given the regression equation

$$Y = 100 + 21X$$

a. What is the change in Y when X changes by +5?
b. What is the change in Y when X changes by −7?
c. What is the predicted value of Y when $X = 14$?
d. What is the predicted value of Y when $X = 27$?
e. Does this equation prove that a change in X causes a change in Y?

Application Exercises

11.11 A critically important aspect of customer service at a supermarket is the waiting time at the checkout. Refer to the data file **Supermarket**, which contains total number of customers in the store (x) and the waiting times (y) during time periods where there were a constant number of checkout counters open. The linear regression equation is given below.

$$\hat{y}_i = -0.4142 + 0.1274x_i$$

a. Interpret the coefficient $b_1 = 0.1274$ for the supermarket.
b. What will the waiting time be on average when there are 23 customers?
c. Suppose you were asked to estimate the waiting time if only six customers are in the store. Discuss your response to this request.

11.12 As the new market manger for Blue Crunchies breakfast cereal, you are asked to estimate the demand for next month using regression analysis. Two months ago the target market had 20,000 families and sales were 3,780 boxes and, 1 month ago the target market was 40,000 families and sales were 5,349 boxes. Next month you plan to target 75,000 families. How would you respond to the request to use regression analysis and the currently available data to estimate sales next month?

11.13 An agent for a real estate company in a large European city collected data, as shown in the following table, on the sizes (x in square feet) and monthly rents (y in euros) of a sample of eight apartments in a neighborhood.

Monthly Rent (€)	900	1500	825	1600	2000	950	1750	1400
Size (square feet)	900	1250	950	1100	2000	750	1350	1100

Consider the following rent prediction model:

$$\hat{y}_i = 222.6 + 0.973x_i$$

a. Estimate the mean monthly rent for an apartment of 1,000 square feet.

b. Interpret the coefficients b_0 and b_1 for the real estate company.

c. You have been asked to estimate the mean monthly rent for an apartment of 2,500 square feet. Discuss how you would proceed and indicate your cautions.

11.14 What is the difference between a population linear model and an estimated linear regression model?

11.15 Explain the difference between the residual e_i and the model error ε_i.

11.16 Suppose that we obtained an estimated equation for the regression of weekly sales of palm pilots and the price charged during the week. Interpret the constant b_0 for the product brand manager.

11.17 A regression model of total grocery sales on disposable income was estimated using data from small, isolated towns in the western United States. Prepare a list of factors that might contribute to the random error term.

11.3 LEAST SQUARES COEFFICIENT ESTIMATORS

The population regression line is a useful theoretical construct, but for applications we need to determine an estimate of the model using available data. Suppose that we have n pairs of observations, $(x_1, y_1), (x_2, y_2), \ldots, (x_n, y_n)$. We would like to find the straight line that best fits these points. To do this, we need to find estimators of the unknown coefficients β_0 and β_1 of the population regression line.

We obtain the **least squares coefficient estimators** b_0 and b_1 with equations derived by using the least squares procedure. As shown in Figure 11.3, there is a deviation, e_i, between the observed value, y_i, and the predicted value, $\hat{y}_i$, in the estimated regression equation for each value of X, where $e_i = y_i - \hat{y}_i$. We then compute a mathematical function that represents the effect of squaring all the residuals and computing the sum of the squared residuals. This function—whose left side is labeled SSE—includes the coefficients b_0 and b_1. The quantity SSE is defined as the *error sum of squares*. The coefficient estimators b_0 and b_1 are selected as the estimators that minimize the error sum of squares.

Least Squares Procedure

The **least squares procedure** obtains estimates of the linear equation coefficients b_0 and b_1 in the model

$$\hat{y}_i = b_0 + b_1 x_i \tag{11.5}$$

by minimizing the sum of the squared residuals e_i:

$$SSE = \sum_{i=1}^{n} e_i^2$$

$$= \sum_{i=1}^{n} (y_i - \hat{y}_i)^2 \tag{11.6}$$

The coefficients b_0 and b_1 are chosen so that the quantity

$$SSE = \sum_{i=1}^{n} e_i^2$$

$$= \sum_{i=1}^{n} (y_i - (b_0 + b_1 x_i))^2 \tag{11.7}$$

is minimized. We use differential calculus to obtain the coefficient estimators that minimize *SSE*. The derivation of the estimators using calculus is presented in the chapter appendix.

The resulting coefficient estimator is as follows:

$$b_1 = \frac{\sum_{i=1}^{n}(x_i - \bar{x})(y_i - \bar{y})}{\sum_{i=1}^{n}(x_i - \bar{x})^2}$$

$$= \frac{Cov(x, y)}{s_x^2}$$

$$= r\frac{s_y}{s_x}$$

$$= \frac{\sum_{i=1}^{n}(x_i - \bar{x})}{\sum_{i=1}^{n}(x_i - \bar{x})x_i}y_i$$

Note that the numerator of the estimator is the sample covariance of X and Y and the denominator is the sample variance of X. The fourth line shows that the coefficient b_1 is a linear function of the Ys. We spend considerable time with the slope coefficient because for many applications, this is the key result. The slope coefficient b_1 is an estimate of the change in Y when X changes by one unit. For example, if Y is total output and X is number of workers, then b_1 is an estimate of the marginal increase in output for each new worker. Results such as this explain why regression has become such an important analysis tool.

In the chapter appendix we also show that the constant estimator is as follows:

$$b_0 = \bar{y} - b_1\bar{x}$$

Substituting this value for b_0 into the linear equation, we have the following:

$$y = \bar{y} - b_1\bar{x} + b_1x$$
$$y - \bar{y} = b_1(x - \bar{x})$$

From this equation we see that when $x = \bar{x}$, then $y = \bar{y}$ and that the regression equation always passes through the point $(\bar{x}, \bar{y})$. The estimated value of the dependent variable, $\hat{y}_i$, is then obtained by using

$$\hat{y}_i = b_0 + b_1x_i$$

or by using

$$\hat{y}_i = \bar{y} + b_1(x_i - \bar{x})$$

This latter form emphasizes that the regression line goes through the means of X and Y.

Least Squares Derived Coefficient Estimators
The slope coefficient estimator is

$$b_1 = \frac{\sum_{i=1}^{n}(x_i - \bar{x})(y_i - \bar{y})}{\sum_{i=1}^{n}(x_i - \bar{x})^2} = r\frac{s_Y}{s_X}$$

and the constant or intercept estimator is

$$b_0 = \bar{y} - b_1\bar{x}$$

We also note that the regression line always goes through the mean $(\bar{x}, \bar{y})$.

The least squares procedure could be used to compute coefficient estimates b_0 and b_1 using any set of paired data. However, in most applications we want to make inferences about the underlying population model that is part of our economic or business problem. In order to make inferences it is necessary that we agree on the linear regression assumptions given in Section 11.2. Given these assumptions, it can be shown that the least squares coefficient estimators are unbiased and have minimum variance.

The second of these assumptions—where x values are fixed and independent of the model error—is generally, with justification, taken to be true, although in some advanced econometric work, it is untenable. (The assumption fails to hold, for example, when the x_i cannot be measured precisely or when the regression is part of a system of interdependent equations.) Here, however, we will take this assumption as given.

Assumptions 3 and 4 concern the error terms, ε_i, in the regression equation. The expected error term is 0, and all error terms have the same variance. Thus, we do not expect the variances of the error terms to be higher for some observations than for others. Figure 11.2 shows this pattern with the errors for all X values being sampled from populations with the same variance. Finally, it is assumed that the instances of ε_i $(i = 1, \ldots, n)$ are not correlated with one another. Thus, for example, the occurrence of a large positive discrepancy at one observation point does not help us predict the values of any of the other error terms. Assumptions 3 and 4 will be satisfied if the error terms, ε_i, can be viewed as a random sample from a population with a mean of 0. In the remainder of this chapter, these assumptions will hold. With larger sample sizes we can show that the central limit theorem can be applied to the coefficient estimators and they can be treated just as we did sample means in various forms of inference in Chapters 7–10. Thus, the assumption of normality can be relaxed. The possibility for relaxing some of the other assumptions is considered in Chapter 13.

Computer Computation of Regression Coefficients

Extensive application of regression analysis has been made possible by statistical computer packages and Excel. As you might suspect, the computations to obtain the regression coefficient estimates are lengthy and thus we typically use a computer. Excel can be used to obtain the basic regression output without too much difficulty. But if you wish to use some of the advanced applied regression analysis procedures or insightful graphical analysis, then you should use a good statistical computer package. Since we are primarily interested in applications, our most important task is proper analysis of the regression computations for these applications. This analysis is guided by knowing the estimator equations and the related discussion. However, *we assign the computation to computers—our tasks are to think, analyze, and make recommendations*.

There are numerous statistical packages, and your school probably has several available. Your teacher may have a favorite package, and you are most likely best served by using that package. We cannot possibly present examples from every statistical package but will present example output from Minitab and Excel in generic form. You will recognize similar estimates from whichever package you actually use. Data sets for exercises and examples are presented in Excel spreadsheet format and can be easily used by your local computer package.

Figure 11.5 presents a portion of the Minitab output for the retail sales example. Note the location of the estimates for the constant, b_0, and the slope coefficient, b_1, in the computer output. The remaining items on each line help interpret the quality of the estimates and are developed in subsequent sections.

Figure 11.5
Regression Analysis
for Retail Sales
Using Minitab

Regression Analysis: Y Retail Sales versus X Income

```
The regression equation is
Y  Retail Sales = 559 + 0.382 X   Income                    Coefficients b₀, b₁

Predictor      Coef   SE Coef      T       P
Constant        559      1451   0.39   0.704
X  Income    0.38152   0.02529  15.08   0.000

S = 147.670    R-Sq = 91.9%    R-Sq(adj) = 91.5%

Analysis of Variance

Source          DF        SS       MS        F      P
Regression       1   4961434  4961434   227.52  0.000
Residual Error  20    436127    21806
Total           21   5397561

Unusual Observations

               Y  Retail
Obs  X  Income    Sales      Fit  SE Fit  Residual  St Resid
 12      57850   22301.0  22630.2    34.0    -329.2     -2.29R

R denotes an observation with a large standardized residual
```

In this regression the estimated constant, b_0, is 559 and the estimated slope coefficient, b_1, is 0.382. These values were computed using the coefficient estimator equations previously developed. The estimated equation can be written as

$$\hat{y} = 559 + 0.382x$$

or, using the means $\bar{x} = 57{,}342$ and $\bar{y} = 22{,}436$, as

$$\hat{y}_i = 22{,}436 + 0.382(x_i - 57{,}342)$$

Typically, regression models should be used only over the range of the observed X values where we have information about the relationship because the relationship may not be linear outside this range. The second form of the regression model is centered on the data means with a rate of change equal to b_1. By using this form, we focus on the mean location of the regression model and not on the intercept with the Y-axis. Naïve users of regression analysis will sometimes attempt interpretations of the constant b_0, claiming certain conclusions about the dependent variable when the independent variable has a value of 0. Consider the example regression of retail sales on disposable income. Would we really claim that retail sales are $559 when disposable income is 0? In fact, we simply do not have data to support any sales amount when disposable income is 0. This is another example of the importance of good analysis instead of silly interpretations. As professional analysts we must be careful not to claim results that simply do not exist.

EXERCISES

 Visit www.MyStatLab.com or www.pearson globaleditions.com to access the data files.

Basic Exercise

11.18 Compute the coefficients for a least squares regression equation and write the equation, given the following sample statistics.

a. $\bar{x} = 10, \bar{y} = 50, S_X = 80, S_Y = 75, R_{XY} = 0.4, n = 60$
b. $\bar{x} = 60, \bar{y} = 50, S_X = 80, S_Y = 65, R_{XY} = 0.7, n = 60$
c. $\bar{x} = 90, \bar{y} = 100, S_X = 60, S_Y = 70, R_{XY} = 0.4, n = 60$
d. $\bar{x} = 20, \bar{y} = 210, S_X = 100, S_Y = 65, R_{XY} = 0.4, n = 60$
e. $\bar{x} = 50, \bar{y} = 50, S_X = 25, S_Y = 70, R_{XY} = 0.6, n = 60$

Application Exercises

11.19 A company sets different prices for a particular DVD system in eight different regions of the country. The accompanying table shows the numbers of units sold and the corresponding prices (in dollars).

Sales	420	380	350	400	440	380	450	420
Price	104	195	148	204	96	256	141	109

a. Graph these data, and estimate the linear regression of sales on price.
b. What effect would you expect a $50 increase in price to have on sales?

11.20 For a sample of 20 monthly observations, a financial analyst wants to regress the percentage rate of return (Y) of the common stock of a corporation on the percentage rate of return (X) of the Standard & Poor's 500 index. The following information is available:

$$\sum_{i=1}^{20} y_i = 22.6 \quad \sum_{i=1}^{20} x_i = 25.4 \quad \sum_{i=1}^{20} x_i^2 = 145.7 \quad \sum_{i=1}^{20} x_i y_i = 150.5$$

a. Estimate the linear regression of Y on X.
b. Interpret the slope of the sample regression line.
c. Interpret the intercept of the sample regression line.

11.21 A corporation administers an aptitude test to all new sales representatives. Management is interested in the extent to which this test is able to predict sales representatives' eventual success. The accompanying table records average weekly sales (in thousands of dollars) and aptitude test scores for a random sample of eight representatives.

Weekly sales	10	12	28	24	18	16	15	12
Test score	55	60	85	75	80	85	65	60

a. Estimate the linear regression of weekly sales on aptitude test scores.
b. Interpret the estimated slope of the regression line.

11.22 It was hypothesized that the number of bottles of an imported premium beer sold per evening in the restaurants of a city depends linearly on the average costs of meals in the restaurants. The following results were obtained for a sample of $n = 17$ restaurants of approximately equal size where

y = number of bottles sold per evening

x = average cost, in dollars, of a meal

$$\bar{x} = 25.5 \quad \bar{y} = 16.0 \quad \frac{\sum_{i=1}^{n}(x_i - \bar{x})^2}{n-1} = 350$$

$$\frac{\sum_{i=1}^{n}(x_i - \bar{x})(y_i - \bar{y})}{n-1} - 180$$

a. Find the sample regression line.
b. Interpret the slope of the sample regression line.
c. Is it possible to provide a meaningful interpretation of the constant in the sample regression at the end with equation? Explain.

It is recommended that the following exercises be solved by using a computer.

11.23 Refer to the following data, which contains the percentage change (X) in a stock market index over the first five trading days of the year and percentage change (Y) in the index over the whole year.

(X)	1.4	0.3	−0.1	2.8	2.2	−1.6	−1.6	5.5	−1.2	1.4	1.5	−4.7	0.6
(Y)	14.7	−9.3	19.8	20.3	−3.6	27.8	22.6	2.3	11.8	28	−4.3	20.5	−1.1

a. Estimate the linear regression of Y on X.
b. Provide interpretations of the intercept and slope of the sample regression line.

11.24 On Friday, November 13, 1989, prices on the New York Stock Exchange fell steeply; the Standard & Poor's 500-share index was down 6.1% on that day. The data file **New York Stock Exchange Gains and Losses** shows the percentage *losses* (y) of the 25 largest mutual funds on November 13, 1989. Also shown are the percentage *gains* (x), assuming reinvested dividends and capital gains, for these same funds for 1989 through November 11.

a. Estimate the linear regression of November 13 losses on pre–November 13, 1989, gains.
b. Interpret the slope of the sample regression line.

11.4 THE EXPLANATORY POWER OF A LINEAR REGRESSION EQUATION

The estimated regression model that we have developed can be viewed as a method for explaining the changes in a dependent variable Y that results from changes in an independent variable X. If we had observations only of the dependent variable, Y, then the central tendency of Y would be represented by the mean $\bar{y}$, and the total variability about the central tendency Y would be represented by the numerator of the sample variance estimator, $\sum(y_i - \bar{y})^2$. When we also have measures of X, we have shown that the central tendency of Y can now be expressed as a function of X. We expect that the linear equation would be closer to the individual values of Y, and, thus, the variability about the linear equation would be smaller than the variability about the mean.

Now we are ready to develop measures that indicate how effectively the variable X explains the behavior of Y. In our retail sales example shown in Figure 11.4, retail sales, Y, tend to increase with disposable income, X, and, thus, disposable income explains some of the differences in retail sales. The points, however, are not all on the line, so the explanation is not perfect. Here, we develop measures based on the partitioning of variability that measure the capability of X to explain Y in a specific regression application.

The analysis of variance, ANOVA, for least squares regression is developed by partitioning the total variability of Y into an explained component and an error component. In Figure 11.6 we show that the deviation of an individual Y value from its mean can be partitioned into the deviation of the predicted value from the mean and the deviation of the observed value from the predicted value:

$$y_i - \bar{y} = (\hat{y}_i - \bar{y}) + (y_i - \hat{y}_i)$$

Figure 11.6
Partitioning of
Variability

We square each side of the equation—because the sum of deviations about the mean is equal to 0—and sum the result over all n points:

$$\sum_{i=1}^{n} (y_i - \bar{y})^2 = \sum_{i=1}^{n} (\hat{y}_i - \bar{y})^2 + \sum_{i=1}^{n} (y_i - \hat{y})^2$$

Some of you may note the squaring of the right-hand side should include the cross product of the two terms in addition to their squared quantities. It can be shown that the cross-product term goes to 0. This equation is expressed as follows:

$$SST = SSR + SSE$$

Here, we see that the total variability—SST—can be partitioned into a component—SSR—that represents variability that is explained by the slope of the regression equation. (The mean of Y is different at different levels of X.) The second component—SSE—results from the random or unexplained deviation of points from the regression line. This variability provides an indication of the uncertainty that is associated with the regression model. We define the left side as the *sum of squares total*:

$$SST = \sum_{i=1}^{n} (y_i - \bar{y})^2$$

The amount of variability explained by the regression equation is defined as the *sum of squares regression* and is computed as follows:

$$SSR = \sum_{i=1}^{n} (\hat{y}_i - \bar{y})^2 = b_1^2 \sum_{i=1}^{n} (x_i - \bar{x})^2$$

We see that the variability explained by the regression depends directly on the size of the coefficient b_1 and on the spread of the independent, X, variable data. The deviations about the regression line, e_i, that are used to compute the unexplained or *sum of squares error* can be defined using the following algebraic forms:

$$SSE = \sum_{i=1}^{n} (y_i - (b_0 + b_1 x_i))^2 = \sum_{i=1}^{n} (y_i - \hat{y}_i)^2 = \sum_{i=1}^{n} e_i^2$$

For a given set of observed values of the dependent variables, Y, the SST is fixed as the total variability of all observations from the mean. We see that in this partitioning, larger values of SSR and hence smaller values of SSE indicate a regression equation that "fits," or comes closer to, the observed data. This partitioning is shown graphically in Figure 11.6. From the equation for SSR we see that explained variability, SSR, is directly related to the deviations from the mean for the independent or X variable. Thus, as we are thinking about regression applications, we know that we should try to obtain data that have a large range for the independent variable so that the resulting regression model will have a smaller unexplained variability.

Analysis of Variance

The total variability in a regression analysis, SST, can be partitioned—**analysis of variance**—into a component explained by the regression, SSR, and a component due to unexplained error, SSE,

$$SST = SSR + SSE \tag{11.8}$$

with the components defined as follows:

Sum of squares total

$$SST = \sum_{i=1}^{n} (y_i - \bar{y})^2 \tag{11.9}$$

Sum of squares error

$$SSE = \sum_{i=1}^{n} (y_i - (b_0 + b_1 x_i))^2 = \sum_{i=1}^{n} (y_i - \hat{y}_i)^2 = \sum_{i=1}^{n} e_i^2 \tag{11.10}$$

Sum of squares regression

$$SSR = \sum_{i=1}^{n} (\hat{y}_i - \bar{y})^2 = b_1^2 \sum_{i=1}^{n} (x_i - \bar{x})^2 \tag{11.11}$$

With this background let us return to our retail sales example (Example 11.2) with data file **Retail Sales** and look at how we use the partitioned variability to determine how well our model explains the process being studied. Table 11.2 shows the detailed calculations of residuals, e_i; deviations of Y from the mean, and deviations of predicted values of Y from the mean. These provide us with the components to compute SSE, SST, and SSR. The sum of squared residuals for column 5 is $SSE = 436{,}127$. The sum of squared deviations from the mean for column 6 is $SST = 5{,}397{,}565$. Finally, the sum of squared deviations—predicted values minus the mean—for column 7 is $SSR = 4{,}961{,}438$. Figure 11.7 presents the Minitab and Excel regression outputs with the analysis of variance section included.

Coefficient of Determination, R^2

We have seen that the fit of the regression equation to the data is improved as SSR increases and SSE decreases. The ratio of the sum of squares regression, SSR, divided by the total sum of squares, SST, provides a descriptive measure of the proportion, or percent, of the total variability that is explained by the regression model. This measure is called the *coefficient of determination*—or, more generally, R^2:

$$R^2 = \frac{SSR}{SST} = 1 - \frac{SSE}{SST}$$

The coefficient of determination is often interpreted as the percent of variability in y that is explained by the regression equation. Previously, we showed that SSR increases directly with the deviations from the mean of the independent variable X:

$$SSR = \sum_{i=1}^{n} (\hat{y}_i - \bar{y})^2 = b_1^2 \sum_{i=1}^{n} (x_i - \bar{x})^2$$

Table 11.2 Actual and Predicted Values for Retail Sales per Household and Residuals from Its Linear Regression on Income per Household

RETAIL STORE	INCOME (X)	RETAIL SALES (Y)	PREDICTED RETAIL SALES	RESIDUAL	OBSERVED DEVIATION FROM THE MEAN	PREDICTED DEVIATION FROM THE MEAN
1	55,641	21,886	21,787	99	−550	−649
2	55,681	21,934	21,803	131	−502	−633
3	55,637	21,699	21,786	−87	−737	−650
4	55,825	21,901	21,858	43	−535	−578
5	55,772	21,812	21,837	−25	−624	−599
6	55,890	21,714	21,882	−168	−722	−554
7	56,068	21,932	21,950	−18	−504	−486
8	56,299	22,086	22,039	48	−350	−398
9	56,825	22,265	22,239	26	−171	−197
10	57,205	22,551	22,384	167	115	−52
11	57,562	22,736	22,520	216	300	84
12	57,850	22,301	22,630	−329	−135	194
13	57,975	22,518	22,678	−160	82	242
14	57,992	22,580	22,684	−104	144	248
15	58,240	22,618	22,779	−161	182	343
16	58,414	22,890	22,845	45	454	409
17	58,561	23,112	22,902	211	676	465
18	59,066	23,315	23,094	221	879	658
19	58,596	22,865	22,915	−50	429	479
20	58,631	22,788	22,928	−140	352	492
21	58,758	22,949	22,977	−28	513	541
22	59,037	23,149	23,083	66	713	647
		Sum of squared values		436,127	5,397,565	4,961,438

Figure 11.7
Regression Analysis for Retail Sales on Disposable Income

Regression Analysis: Y Retail Sales versus X Income

```
The regression equation is
Y  Retail Sales = 559 + 0.382 X  Income

Predictor     Coef    SE Coef      T       P
Constant       559       1451    0.39   0.704
X  Income   0.38152    0.02529   15.08   0.000
```

s_e, Standard error of the estimate

```
S = 147.670   R-Sq = 91.9%   R-Sq(adj) = 91.5%
```

R^2, Coefficient of determination

```
Analysis of Variance

Source           DF        SS        MS        F       P
Regression        1   4961434   4961434   227.52   0.000
Residual Error   20    436127     21806
Total            21   5397561
```

s_e^2, Model error variance

$SSR = 4,961,434$
$SSE = 436,127$
$SST = 5,397,561$

```
Unusual Observations

                    Y  Retail
Obs   X  Income       Sales     Fit    SE Fit   Residual   St Resid
 12      57850      22301.0  22630.2     34.0     -329.2      -2.29R

R denotes an observation with a large standardized residual.
```

Thus, we see that R^2 also increases directly with the deviations from the mean of the independent variable. When you are seeking data to estimate a regression model, it is important to choose the observations of the independent variable that provide the largest possible range in X so that we obtain a regression model with the highest R^2.

Coefficient of Determination R^2

The **coefficient of determination**, R^2, for a regression equation is defined as follows:

$$R^2 = \frac{SSR}{SST} = 1 - \frac{SSE}{SST} \tag{11.12}$$

This quantity varies from 0 to 1, and higher values indicate a better regression. Caution should be used in making general interpretations of R^2 because a high value can result from either a small *SSE*, a large *SST*, or both.

R^2 can vary from 0 to 1, since SST is fixed and $0 < SSR < SST$. A larger R^2 implies a better regression, everything else being equal. In the regression output—Figure 11.7—we see that the R^2 for the retail sales regression is 0.919, or 91.9%. One popular interpretation is that R^2 is the *percent explained variability*.

Global interpretations of R^2 that apply to all regression equations are dangerous. The second form of the equation emphasizes that R^2 depends on the ratio of SSE divided by SST. We can have a high R^2 because there is a small SSE—the desired goal—or because there is a large SST, or both Two regression models with the same set of observed y_i values can always be compared using R^2, and the model with the larger R^2 provides a better explanation of Y. But global comparisons of R^2—stating that a model is good because its R^2 is above a particular value—are misleading. Generally, experienced analysts have found that R^2 is 0.80 or above for models based on time-series data. Cross-section data models (e.g., cities, states, firms) have values in the 0.40 to 0.60 range, and models based on data from individual people often have R^2 values in the 0.10 to 0.20 range.

To illustrate the danger of global interpretations of R^2, consider two regression models—whose plots are shown in Figure 11.8—each of which is based on a total of 25 observations. Both models have SSE equal to 17.89, so the fit of the regression equation to the data points is the same. But the first model has a total sum of squares equal to 5,201.05, whereas the second has SST equal to 68.22. The R^2 values for the two models are as follows:

Model 1

$$R^2 = 1 - \frac{SSE}{SST} = 1 - \frac{17.89}{5,201.05} = 0.997$$

Model 2

$$R^2 = 1 - \frac{SSE}{SST} = 1 - \frac{17.89}{68.22} = 0.738$$

Since both models have the same SSE, and thus the same goodness of fit, one cannot claim that Model 1 fits the data better. Yet Model 1 has a substantially higher R^2 compared to Model 2. As we see here, one should be very careful about global interpretations of R^2. Note that the different values for SST result from the two different vertical axis intervals in Figure 11.8. Figure 11.8(a) has a Y-variable range from 10 to 60, whereas Figure 11.8(b) has a range from 9 to 16.

The correlation coefficient can also be linked with R^2, as shown, by noting that the correlation squared is equal to the coefficient of determination and, therefore, the percent explained variability.

Figure 11.8
Comparison of R^2
for Two Regression
Models

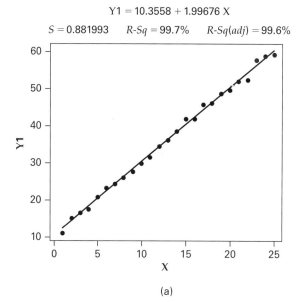

Regression Model with High R Squared

Y1 = 10.3558 + 1.99676 X

$S = 0.881993$ $R\text{-}Sq = 99.7\%$ $R\text{-}Sq(adj) = 99.6\%$

(a)

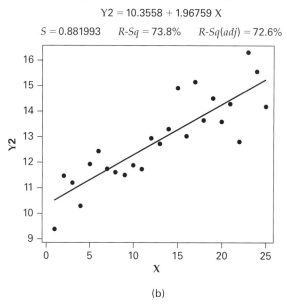

Regression Model with Low R Squared

Y2 = 10.3558 + 1.96759 X

$S = 0.881993$ $R\text{-}Sq = 73.8\%$ $R\text{-}Sq(adj) = 72.6\%$

(b)

Correlation and R^2

The coefficient of determination, R^2, for simple regression is equal to the simple correlation squared:

$$R^2 = r^2 \qquad (11.13)$$

This provides an important link between **correlation and R^2**, the regression model.

The sum-of-squares error is used to obtain an estimate of the variance of the model error ε_i, which, in turn, is used for regression-model statistical inference. Recall that we have assumed that the population error, ε_i, is a random error with a mean of 0 and a variance of σ^2. The estimator for σ^2 is computed in the following section.

Estimation of Model Error Variance

The quantity *SSE* is a measure of the total squared deviation about the estimated regression line, and e_i is the residual. **Estimation of model error variance** uses this unbiased estimator for the variance of the population model error which is:

$$\hat{\sigma}^2 = s_e^2 = \frac{\sum_{i=1}^{n} e_i^2}{n-2} = \frac{SSE}{n-2} \tag{11.14}$$

Division by $n-2$ instead of $n-1$ results because the simple regression model uses two estimated parameters, b_0 and b_1, instead of one. In the next section we see that this variance estimator is the basis for statistical inference in the regression model.

EXERCISES

 Visit www.MyStatLab.com or www.pearson globaleditions.com to access the data files.

Basic Exercises

11.25 Compute *SSR*, *SSE*, s_e^2, and the coefficient of determination, given the following statistics computed from a random sample of pairs of *X* and *Y* observations.

a. $\sum_{i=1}^{n}(y_i - \bar{y})^2 = 130{,}000; R^2 = 0.50; n = 50$

b. $\sum_{i=1}^{n}(y_i - \bar{y})^2 = 60{,}000; R^2 = 0.40; n = 33$

c. $\sum_{i=1}^{n}(y_i - \bar{y})^2 = 230{,}000; R^2 = 0.20; n = 69$

d. $\sum_{i=1}^{n}(y_i - \bar{y})^2 = 120{,}000; R^2 = 0.40; n = 51$

e. $\sum_{i=1}^{n}(y_i - \bar{y})^2 = 270{,}000; R^2 = 0.70; n = 41$

Application Exercises

11.26 Let the sample regression line be

$$y_i = b_0 + b_1 x_i + e_i = \hat{y}_i + e_i \ (i = 1, 2, \ldots, n)$$

and let $\bar{x}$ and $\bar{y}$ denote the sample means for the independent and dependent variables, respectively.

a. Show that
$$e_i = y_i - \bar{y} - b(x_i - \bar{x})$$

b. Using the result in part a, show that
$$\sum_{i=1}^{n} e_i = 0$$

c. Using the result in part a, show that
$$\sum_{i=1}^{n} e_i^2 = \sum_{i=1}^{n}(y_i - \bar{y})^2 - b^2 \sum_{i=1}^{n}(x_i - \bar{x})^2$$

d. Show that
$$\hat{y}_i - \bar{y} = b_i(x_i - \bar{x})$$

e. Using the results in parts c and d, show that
$$SST = SSR + SSE$$

f. Using the result in part a, show that
$$\sum_{i=1}^{n} e_i(x_i - \bar{x}) = 0$$

11.27 Let
$$R^2 = \frac{SSR}{SST}$$

denote the coefficient of determination for the sample regression line.

a. Using part d of the previous exercise, show that
$$R^2 = b_1^2 \frac{\sum_{i=1}^{n}(x_i - \bar{x})^2}{\sum_{i=1}^{n}(y_i - \bar{y})^2}$$

b. Using the result in part a, show that the coefficient of determination is equal to the square of the sample correlation between *X* and *Y*.

c. Let b_1 be the slope of the least squares regression of *Y* on *X*, b_1^* be the slope of the least squares regression of *X* on *Y*, and *r* be the sample correlation between *X* and *Y*. Show that $b_1 \cdot b_1^* = r^2$

11.28 Find and interpret the coefficient of determination for the regression of DVD system sales on price, using the following data.

Sales	420	380	350	400	440	380	450	420
Price	98	194	244	207	89	261	149	198

11.29 Find and interpret the coefficient of determination for the regression of the percentage change in the stock market index in a year based on the percentage change in the index over the first five trading days of the year. Compare your answer with the sample correlation found for these data. Use the data file **Stock Market**.

11.30 Find the proportion of the sample variability in mutual fund percentage losses on November 13, 1989, explained by their linear dependence on 1989 percentage gains through November 12, based on the data in the data file **New York Stock Exchange Gains and Losses**.

11.31 In a study it was shown that for a sample of 353 college faculty, the correlation was 0.11 between annual raises and teaching evaluations. What would be the coefficient of determination of a regression of annual raises on teaching evaluations for this sample? Interpret your result.

11.5 STATISTICAL INFERENCE: HYPOTHESIS TESTS AND CONFIDENCE INTERVALS

Now that we have developed the coefficient estimators and an estimator for σ^2, we are ready to make population model inferences. The basic approach follows that developed in Chapters 7–10. We develop variance estimators for the coefficient estimators, b_0 and b_1, and then use the estimated parameters and variances to test hypotheses and compute confidence intervals using the Student's t distribution. Inferences from regression analysis will help us understand the process being modeled and make decisions about the process. Initially, we assume that random model errors, ε, are normally distributed. Later, this assumption will be replaced by the central limit theorem assumption. We begin by developing variance estimators and useful test forms. Then we apply these using our retail sales data.

In Section 11.2 we defined the population model for simple regression as

$$y_i = \beta_0 + \beta_1 x_i + \varepsilon_i$$

with the x_i's being predetermined values and not random variables. From our work in Chapters 4 and 5 on linear functions of random variables, we know that, if ε_i is a normally distributed random variable with variance σ^2, then y_i is also normally distributed with the same variance. The right-hand side is a linear function of X and the random variable ε_i. If we add the fixed value $\beta_0 + \beta_1 x_i$ to a random variable, we do not change the variance.

In Section 11.3 we found that the estimator for the slope coefficient, b_1, is

$$b_1 = \frac{\sum_{i=1}^{n}(x_i - \bar{x})(y_i - \bar{y})}{\sum_{i=1}^{n}(x_i - \bar{x})^2}$$

$$= \sum \left(\frac{(x_i - \bar{x})}{\sum (x_i - \bar{x})^2} \right) y_i$$

$$= \sum a_i y_i$$

where

$$a_i = \frac{(x_i - \bar{x})}{\sum_{i=1}^{n}(x_i - \bar{x})^2}$$

In this estimator we see that b_1 is a linear function of the independent random variables y_i, whose variances are all σ^2. Thus, the variance of b_1 is a simple transformation of the variance of Y. Using the results from Chapter 5, the linear function can be written as follows:

$$b_1 = \sum_{i=1}^{n} a_i y_i$$

$$a_i = \frac{(x_i - \bar{x})}{\sum_{i=1}^{n}(x_i - \bar{x})^2}$$

$$\sigma_{b_1}^2 = \sum_{i=1}^{n} a_i^2 \sigma^2$$

$$\sigma_{b_1}^2 = \sum_{i=1}^{n} \left(\frac{(x_i - \bar{x})}{\sum_{i=1}^{n}(x_i - \bar{x})^2} \right)^2 \sigma^2$$

$$= \frac{\sum_{i=1}^{n}(x_i - \bar{x})^2}{\left(\sum_{i=1}^{n}(x_i - \bar{x})^2\right)^2} \sigma^2$$

$$= \frac{\sigma^2}{\sum_{i=1}^{n}(x_i - \bar{x})^2}$$

Since y_i is normally distributed and b_1 is a linear function of independent normal variables, this linear function implies that b_1 is also normally distributed. From this analysis we can derive the population and sample variances.

Sampling Distribution of the Least Squares Coefficient Estimator

If the standard least squares assumptions hold, then b_1 is an unbiased estimator for β_1 and has a population variance

$$\sigma_{b_1}^2 = \frac{\sigma^2}{\sum_{i=1}^{n}(x_i - \bar{x})^2} = \frac{\sigma^2}{(n-1)s_x^2} \tag{11.15}$$

and an unbiased sample variance estimator

$$s_{b_1}^2 = \frac{s_e^2}{\sum_{i=1}^{n}(x_i - \bar{x})^2} = \frac{s_e^2}{(n-1)s_x^2} \tag{11.16}$$

The regression constant estimator, b_0, is also a linear function of the random variable y_i, and, thus, it can be shown to be normally distributed, and its variance estimator can be derived as

$$s_{b_0}^2 = \left(\frac{1}{n} + \frac{\bar{x}^2}{(n-1)s_x^2} \right) s_e^2$$

It is important to observe that the variance of the slope coefficient, b_1, depends on two important quantities:

1. The distance of the points from the regression line measured by s_e^2. Higher values imply greater variance for b_1.
2. The total deviation of the X values from the mean, which is measured by $(n-1)s_x^2$. Greater deviations in the X values and larger sample sizes result in a smaller variance for the slope coefficient.

These two results are very important as we think about choices of data for a regression model. Previously, we noted that a wider spread in the independent, X, variable resulted in a higher R^2, indicating a stronger relationship. Now, we see that a wider spread in the independent variable—measured by s_x^2—results in a smaller variance for the estimated slope coefficient, b_1. It follows that smaller-variance estimators of the slope coefficient imply a better regression model. We need to also add that many research conclusions and policy decisions are based on the change in Y that results from a change in X, as estimated by b_1. Thus, we would like to have the variance of this important decision variable, b_1, be as small as possible.

The equation that computes the estimated coefficients for b_1 assumes that the variances of the error terms ε_i are uniform or equal over the range of the independent variables. This is the condition defined as homoscedasticity. However, there are a number of situations where homoscedasticity does not apply and we say that the errors are defined as heteroscedastic—that is, the variances of the ε_i's are not uniform. For example, the variation in annual household consumption generally increases with increasing levels of household disposable income, because with higher incomes, households have greater flexibility between consumption and saving. A plot of annual household consumption versus disposable income would show the data "fanning out" around a linear trend as disposable income increases. Similarly, the variance in factory output could increase as additional workers are added if the additional workers have less experience and training. When the variance of the instances of ε_i are not uniform or heteroscedastic we can show that the estimated coefficients are still unbiased. However, the estimated coefficient variances, $\sigma^2_{b_1}$, are not correct and need to be adjusted. In Section 13.6 we discuss heteroscedasticity and indicate modifications to the inference procedures when the errors fan out or the variances of the instances of ε_i are not uniform.

In applied regression analysis, we first would like to know if there is a relationship. In the regression model we see that if β_1 is 0, then there is no linear relationship between X and Y—Y would not continuously increase or decrease with increases in X. To determine if there is a linear relationship, we can test the hypothesis

$$H_0 : \beta_1 = 0$$

versus

$$H_1 : \beta_1 \neq 0$$

Given that b_1 is normally distributed, we can test this hypothesis using the Student's t statistic

$$t = \frac{b_1 - \beta_1}{s_{b_1}} = \frac{b_1 - 0}{s_{b_1}} = \frac{b_1}{s_{b_1}}$$

that is distributed as Student's t with $(n - 2)$ degrees of freedom. The hypothesis test can also be performed for values of β_1 other than 0. One rule of thumb is to conclude that a relationship exists if the absolute value of the t statistic is greater than 2. This result holds exactly for a two-tailed test with $\alpha = 0.05$ and 60 degrees of freedom and provides a close approximation when $n > 30$.

Basis for Inference about the Population Regression Slope

Let β_1 be a population regression slope and b_1 be its least squares estimate based on n pairs of sample observations. Then, if the standard regression assumptions hold and it can also be assumed that the errors, ε_i, are normally distributed, the random variable

$$t = \frac{b_1 - \beta_1}{s_{b_1}} \qquad (11.17)$$

is distributed as Student's t with $(n - 2)$ degrees of freedom. In addition, the central limit theorem enables us to conclude that this result is approximately valid for a wide range of nonnormal distributions and large-enough sample sizes, n.

The coefficient standard deviation and Student's t statistic—for $\beta_1 = 0$—are routinely computed in most regression programs. Example output from Minitab is shown in Figure 11.9.

Figure 11.9
Retail Sales Model: Coefficient Variance Estimators (Minitab Output)

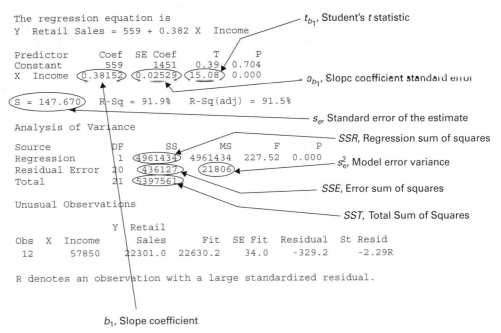

Regression Analysis: Y Retail Sales versus X Income

```
The regression equation is
Y  Retail Sales = 559 + 0.382 X  Income

Predictor      Coef   SE Coef      T       P
Constant        559      1451    0.39   0.704
X  Income    0.38152   0.02529   15.08  0.000

S = 147.670    R-Sq = 91.9%    R-Sq(adj) = 91.5%

Analysis of Variance

Source          DF        SS       MS       F       P
Regression       1   4961434   4961434   227.52   0.000
Residual Error  20    436127     21806
Total           21   5397561

Unusual Observations

              Y   Retail
Obs   X  Income    Sales      Fit   SE Fit  Residual  St Resid
 12      57850   22301.0  22630.2    34.0    -329.2    -2.29R

R denotes an observation with a large standardized residual.
```

- t_{b_1}, Student's t statistic
- s_{b_1}, Slope coefficient standard error
- s_e, Standard error of the estimate
- SSR, Regression sum of squares
- s_e^2, Model error variance
- SSE, Error sum of squares
- SST, Total Sum of Squares
- b_1, Slope coefficient

For the retail sales model, the slope coefficient is $b_1 = 0.382$ with a standard deviation of $s_{b_1} = 0.02529$. To decide if there is a relationship between retail sales, Y, and disposable income, X, we can test the hypothesis

$$H_0 : \beta_1 = 0$$

versus

$$H_1 : \beta_1 \neq 0$$

Under the null hypothesis the ratio of the coefficient estimator, b_1, to its standard deviation has a Student's t distribution. For the retail sales example we find that the computed Student's t statistic is as follows:

$$t = \frac{b_1 - \beta_1}{s_{b_1}} = \frac{b_1 - 0}{s_{b_1}} = \frac{0.38152 - 0}{0.02529} = 15.08$$

The resulting Student's t statistic, $t = 15.08$, as shown in the regression output, provides strong evidence to reject the null hypothesis and conclude that there is a strong relationship between retail sales and disposable income. We also note that the p-value for b_1 is 0.000, providing alternative evidence that β_1 is not equal to 0. Recall from Chapter 9 that the p-value is the smallest significance level at which the null hypothesis can be rejected, or the p-value is the probability that the null hypothesis is true.

Hypothesis tests could also be performed on the equation constant, b_0, using the standard deviation previously developed and shown in the Minitab output. However, because we are usually interested in rates of change—measured by b_1—tests involving the constant are generally less important.

If the sample size is large enough for the central limit theorem to apply, then we can perform such hypothesis tests even if the errors, ε_i, are not normally distributed. The key question concerns the distribution of b_1. If b_1 has an approximately normal distribution, then the hypothesis test can be performed. In most applications b_1 has an approximate normal distribution and the test procedure does apply.

Tests of the Population Regression Slope β_1

If the regression errors, ε_i, are normally distributed and the standard least squares assumptions hold (or if the distribution of b_1 is approximately normal), the following **tests of the population regression slope β_1** have significance level α.

1. To test either null hypothesis

$$H_0 : \beta_1 = \beta_1^* \quad \text{or} \quad H_0 : \beta_1 \leq \beta_1^*$$

against the alternative

$$H_1 : \beta_1 > \beta_1^*$$

the decision rule is as follows:

$$\text{Reject } H_0 \text{ if } \frac{b_1 - \beta_1^*}{s_{b_1}} \geq t_{n-2,\alpha} \tag{11.18}$$

2. To test either null hypothesis

$$H_0 : \beta_1 = \beta_1^* \quad \text{or} \quad H_0 : \beta_1 \geq \beta_1^*$$

against the alternative

$$H_1 : \beta_1 < \beta_1^*$$

the decision rule is as follows:

$$\text{Reject } H_0 \text{ if } \frac{b_1 - \beta_1^*}{s_b} \leq -t_{n-2,\alpha} \tag{11.19}$$

3. To test the null hypothesis

$$H_0 : \beta_1 = \beta_1^*$$

against the two-sided alternative

$$H_1 : \beta_1 \neq \beta_1^*$$

the decision rule is as follows:

$$\text{Reject } H_0 \text{ if } \frac{b_1 - \beta_1^*}{s_{b_1}} \geq t_{n-2,\alpha/2} \quad \text{or} \quad \frac{b_1 - \beta_1^*}{s_{b_1}} \leq -t_{n-2,\alpha/2} \tag{11.20}$$

If, in these tests, $\beta_1^* = 0$, rejection of the null hypothesis implies that there is a relationship between X and Y. Note that for a two-tailed test (Test 3) with $\alpha = 0.05$ and $n > 60$, a Student's t statistic with an absolute value greater than 2.0 indicates that there is a relationship. This provides a useful rule of thumb when screening regression analysis output.

We can derive confidence intervals for the slope β_1 of the population regression line by using the coefficient and variance estimators we have developed and the rationale presented in Chapter 7.

Confidence Interval for the Population Regression Slope β_1

If the regression errors, ε_i, are normally distributed or if the distribution of b_1 is approximately normal and the standard regression assumptions hold, a $100(1 - \alpha)\%$ **confidence interval for the population regression slope β_1** is given by

$$b_1 - t_{(n-2,\alpha/2)}s_{b_1} < \beta_1 < b_1 + t_{(n-2,\alpha/2)}s_{b_1} \tag{11.21}$$

where $t_{n-2,\,\alpha/2}$ is the number for which

$$P(t_{n-2} > t_{n-2,\alpha/2}) = \alpha/2$$

and the random variable t_{n-2} follows a Student's t distribution with $(n-2)$ degrees of freedom.

From the regression output for the retail sales on disposable income regression in Figure 11.9, we know that

$$n = 22 \quad b_1 = 0.3815 \quad s_{b_1} = 0.0253$$

For a 99% confidence interval for β_1 we have $1 - \alpha = 0.99$ and $n - 2 = 20$ degrees of freedom; thus, from Appendix Table 8

$$t_{n-2,\alpha/2} = t_{20,0.005} = 2.845$$

Therefore, we have the 99% confidence interval

$$0.3815 - (2.845)(0.0253) < \beta_1 < 0.3815 + (2.845)(0.0253)$$

or

$$0.3095 < \beta_1 < 0.4535$$

We see that the 99% confidence interval for the expected increase in retail sales per household associated with a \$1 increase in disposable income per household covers the range from \$0.3095 to \$0.4353. Figure 11.10 shows the 90%, 95%, and 99% confidence intervals for the population regression slope.

Figure 11.10
Confidence Intervals for the Retail Sales Population Regression Slope at Confidence Levels, 90%, 95%, and 99%

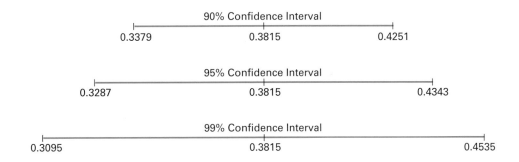

Hypothesis Test for Population Slope Coefficient Using the F Distribution

There is an alternative test for the hypothesis that the slope coefficient, β_1, is equal to 0:

$$H_0 : \beta_1 = 0$$

$$H_1 : \beta_1 \neq 0$$

This test is based on the partitioning of variability that we developed in Section 11.4. The assumption for this test is that if the null hypothesis is true, then both SSE and SSR can be used to obtain independent estimators of the model error variance σ^2. To perform this test, we obtain two sample estimates of the population standard deviation σ. These are defined as mean square terms. The regression sum of squares, SSR, has 1 degree of freedom, since it refers to the single slope coefficient, and the mean square for regression, MSR, is as follows:

$$MSR = \frac{SSR}{1} = SSR$$

If the null hypothesis—no relationship—is true, then MSR is an estimate of the overall model variance, σ^2. We also use the sum-of-squares error as before to obtain the mean square for error, MSE:

$$MSE = \frac{SSE}{n-2} = s_e^2$$

In Section 10.4 we introduced the F distribution as the ratio of independent sample estimates of variance, given equal population variances. It can be shown that MSR and MSE are independent and that under H_0 both are estimates of the population variance, σ^2. Thus, if H_0 is true, then we can show that the ratio

$$F = \frac{MSR}{MSE} = \frac{SSR}{s_e^2}$$

has an F distribution with 1 degree of freedom for the numerator and $(n-2)$ degrees of freedom for the denominator. It should also be noted that the F statistic is equal to the squared t statistic for the slope coefficient. This can be shown algebraically. From distribution theory we can show that a squared Student's t with $(n-2)$ degrees of freedom and the F with 1 degree of freedom for the numerator and $(n-2)$ degrees of freedom for the denominator are equal:

$$F_{\alpha,1,n-2} = t_{n-2,\alpha/2}^2$$

The analysis of variance for the retail sales regression from the Minitab output is shown in Figure 11.9. In our retail sales example the sum-of-squares error is divided by the 20 degrees of freedom to compute the MSE:

$$MSE = \frac{436,127}{20} = 21,806$$

Then the F ratio is computed as the ratio of the two mean squares:

$$F = \frac{MSR}{MSE} = \frac{4,961,434}{21,806} = 227.52$$

This F ratio is substantially larger than the critical value for $\alpha = 0.01$ with 1 degree of freedom for the numerator and 20 degrees of freedom for the denominator $(F_{1,20,0.01} = 8.10)$ from Table 9 in the appendix. The Minitab output—Figure 11.9—for the retail sales regression shows the p-value for this computed F as 0.000, providing alternative evidence to reject H_0. Also note that the F statistic is equal to t^2 where the Student's t statistic is computed for the slope coefficient, b_1:

$$F = t^2$$
$$227.52 = 15.08^2$$

F Test for Simple Regression Coefficient
We can test the hypothesis

$$H_0 : \beta_1 = 0$$

against the alternative

$$H_1 : \beta_1 \neq 0$$

using the F statistic

$$F = \frac{MSR}{MSE} = \frac{SSR}{s_e^2} \qquad (11.22)$$

The decision rule is as follows:

$$\text{Reject } H_0 \text{ if } F \geq F_{1,n-2,\alpha} \qquad (11.23)$$

We can also show that the F statistic is

$$F = t^2_{b_1} \tag{11.24}$$

for any simple regression analysis.

From this result we see that hypothesis tests relating to the population slope coefficient will provide exactly the same result when using either the Student's t or the F distribution. From the discussion of the hypothesis test using Student's t, we noted that a value of t greater than 2 indicates a relationship; thus, from Equation 11.24 we can also see that a value of F greater than 4 also indicates a relationship between X and Y (with $\alpha = 0.05$ and $n > 60$). We will learn in Chapter 13 that the F distribution—when used in a multiple regression analysis—also provides the opportunity for testing the hypothesis that several population slope coefficients are simultaneously equal to 0.

EXERCISES

 Visit www.MyStatLab.com or www.pearson globaleditions.com to access the data files.

Basic Exercises

11.32 Given the simple regression model

$$Y = \beta_0 + \beta_1 X$$

and the regression results that follow, test the null hypothesis that the slope coefficient is 0 versus the alternative hypothesis of greater than zero using probability of Type I error equal to 0.01, and determine the two-sided 90% and 95% confidence intervals.

a. A random sample of size $n = 35$ with $b_1 = 5, s_{b_1} = 1.9$
b. A random sample of size $n = 50$ with $b_1 = 5.2, s_{b_1} = 1.9$
c. A random sample of size $n = 35$ with $b_1 = 1.8, s_{b_1} = 1.25$
d. A random sample of size $n = 32$ with $b_1 = 8.6, s_{b_1} = 1.2$

11.33 Use a simple regression model to test the hypothesis

$$H_0 : \beta_1 = 0$$

versus

$$H_1 : \beta_1 \neq 0$$

with $\alpha = 0.05$, given the following regression statistics.

a. The sample size is 35, $SST = 100{,}000$, and the correlation between X and Y is 0.46.
b. The sample size is 61, $SST = 123{,}000$, and the correlation between X and Y is 0.65.
c. The sample size is 25, $SST = 128{,}000$, and the correlation between X and Y is 0.69.

Application Exercises

11.34 Mumbai Electronics is planning to extend its marketing region from the western United States to include the midwestern states. In order to predict its sales in this new region, the company has asked you to develop a linear regression of DVD system sales on price, using the following data supplied by the marketing department:

Sales	418	384	343	407	432	386	444	427
Price	98	194	231	207	89	255	149	195

a. Use an unbiased estimation procedure to find an estimate of the variance of the error terms in the population regression.
b. Use an unbiased estimation procedure to find an estimate of the variance of the least squares estimator of the slope of the population regression line.
c. Find a 90% confidence interval for the slope of the population regression line.

11.35 A local wholesaler is interested in assessing the effect of the price of a premium bars of on the quantity sold. The results in the accompanying table on price, in pounds, and sales, in bars, were obtained from a sample of 8 weeks of sales records.

Price	19.2	20.5	19.7	21.2	20.9	19.8	17.9	17.1
Sales	25.8	14.5	18.8	11.4	11.3	15.7	29.3	35.6

a. Estimate by least squares the linear regression of increase in sales on increase in price.

b. Find an 90% confidence interval for the slope of the population regression line.

It is recommended that a computer be used for the following exercises.

11.36 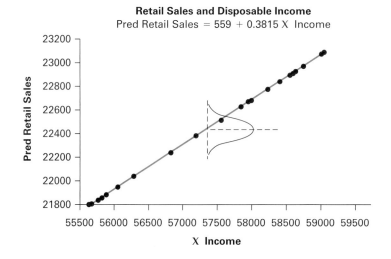 You have been asked to determine the effect of per capita disposable income on retail sales using cross-section data by state. The data are contained in the data file **Economic Activity**. Estimate the appropriate regression equation and determine the 95% confidence interval for the expected change in retail sales that would result from a $1,000 increase in per capita disposable income.

11.37 Estimate the regression equation for the percentage change in the Dow Jones index in a year on the percentage change in the index over the first five trading days of the year. Use the data file **Dow Jones**.

a. Use an unbiased estimation procedure to find a point estimate of the variance of the error terms in the population regression.

b. Use an unbiased estimation procedure to find a point estimate of the variance of the least squares estimator of the slope of the population regression line.

c. Find and interpret a 95% confidence interval for the slope of the population regression line.

d. Test at the 10% significance level, against a two-sided alternative, the null hypothesis that the slope of the population regression line is 0.

11.38 Estimate a linear regression model for mutual fund losses on November 13, 1989, using the data file **New York Stock Exchange Gains and Losses**.

a. Use an unbiased estimation procedure to obtain a point estimate of the variance of the error terms in the population regression.

b. Use an unbiased estimation procedure to obtain a point estimate of the variance of the least squares estimator of the slope of the population regression line.

c. Find 90%, 95%, and 99% confidence intervals for the slope of the population regression line.

11.6 PREDICTION

Regression models can be used to compute predictions or forecasts for the dependent variable, given an assumed future value for the independent variable. Suppose that we are interested in forecasting the value of the dependent variable, given that the independent variable is equal to a specified value, x_{n+1}, and that the linear relationship between dependent and independent variables continues to hold. The corresponding value of the dependent variable will then be

$$y_{n+1} = \beta_0 + \beta_1 x_{n+1} + \varepsilon_{n+1}$$

which, given x_{n+1}, has expectation

$$E[y_{n+1}|x_{n+1}] = \beta_0 + \beta_1 x_{n+1}$$

Two distinct options are of interest:

1. We might want to estimate or predict the actual value that will result for a single observation, y_{n+1}. This option used in forecasting or predicting the result of a single outcome is shown in Figure 11.11.

Figure 11.11
Least Squares Estimated Regression Line of Predicted Retail Sales on Disposable Income for a Single Observed Value

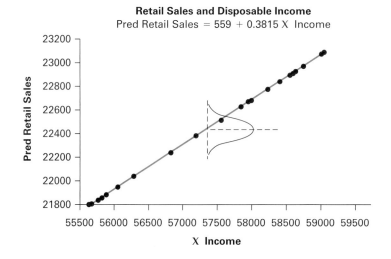

Retail Sales and Disposable Income
Pred Retail Sales = 559 + 0.3815 X Income

2. Alternatively, we might want to estimate the conditional expected value, $E[y_{n+1} \mid x_{n+1}]$ — that is, the average value of the dependent variable when the independent variable is fixed at x_{n+1}. This option is shown in Figure 11.12.

Figure 11.12
Least Squares
Estimated
Regression Line
of Predicted Retail
Sales on Disposable
Income for the
Expected Value

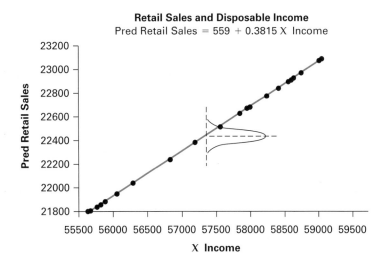

You should note that the range of errors or variance is larger when forecasting a single value, as shown in Figure 11.11, compared to forecasting the mean, as shown in Figure 11.12.

Given that the standard regression assumptions continue to hold, the same point estimate results for either option. We simply replace the unknowns β_0 and β_1 by their least squares estimates, b_0 and b_1. That is, $(\beta_0 + \beta_1 x_{n+1})$ is estimated by $(b_0 + b_1 x_{n+1})$. We know that the corresponding estimator is the best linear unbiased estimator for Y, given X. With the first option we are interested in the best forecast for a single occurrence of the process. But for the second option we are interested in the expected value, or long-term average, for the process. For both options, an appropriate point estimate under our assumptions is as follows:

$$\hat{y}_{n+1} = b_0 + b_1 x_{n+1}$$

This follows because we do not know anything useful about the random variable, ε_{n+1}, except that its mean is 0. Thus, without other information we will use 0 as its point estimate.

However, we usually want intervals in addition to point estimates, and for that purpose the two options are different. This is because the variance estimators are different for the two different quantities being estimated. The results for these different variance estimators lead to the two different intervals. The interval for the first option is generally defined as a prediction interval because we are predicting the value for a single point. The interval for the second option is referred to as a confidence interval because it is the interval for the expected value.

Forecast Prediction Intervals and Confidence Intervals for Predictions

Suppose that the population regression model is

$$y_i = \beta_0 + \beta_1 x_i + \varepsilon_i \quad (i = 1, \ldots, n)$$

the standard regression assumptions hold, and the ε_i are normally distributed. Let b_0 and b_1 be the least squares estimates of β_0 and β_1, based on $(x_1, y_1), (x_2, y_2), \ldots, (x_n, y_n)$. Then it can be shown that the following are $100(1 - \alpha)\%$ intervals.

1. For the forecast of the single outcome value resulting for Y_{n+1}, the **prediction interval** is as follows:

$$\hat{y}_{n+1} \pm t_{n-2, \alpha/2} \sqrt{\left[1 + \frac{1}{n} + \frac{(x_{n+1} - \bar{x})^2}{\sum\limits_{i=1}^{n} (x_i - \bar{x})^2} \right] s_e} \qquad (11.25)$$

2. For the forecast of the mean or conditional expectation $E(Y_{n+1} \upharpoonright X_{n+1})$, the **confidence interval for predictions** is

$$\hat{y}_{n+1} \pm t_{n-2, \alpha/2} \sqrt{\left[\frac{1}{n} + \frac{(x_{n+1} - \bar{x})^2}{\sum\limits_{i=1}^{n} (x_i - \bar{x})^2} \right] s_e} \qquad (11.26)$$

where

$$\bar{x} = \frac{\sum\limits_{i=1}^{n} x_i}{n} \quad \text{and} \quad \hat{y}_{n+1} = b_0 + b_1 x_{n+1}$$

These prediction and confidence intervals have the same interpretation indicated in Chapters 7 and 8 for confidence intervals. The probability is $1 - \alpha$ that this interval includes the true prediction of Y or the true mean of Y when X has the value x_{n+1}.

Note that in most applications the central limit theorem applies for the predicted value, $\hat{y}_{n+1}$, and the intervals are appropriate.

Example 11.3 Forecasting Retail Sales (Regression Model Forecasting)

We illustrate the interval computation using the retail sales and disposable income from Example 11.2. We have been asked to forecast retail sales per household for a proposed new store to be located in a market area with disposable income per household of $58,000. Determine both the the actual value for the first year and the expected value for the long run. In addition, we have been asked to compute prediction intervals and confidence intervals for these forecasts. Use the data file **Retail Sales**.

Solution The forecast values for the first year and for the long run are both as follows:

$$\hat{y}_{n+1} = b_0 + b_1 x_{n+1}$$
$$= 559 + (0.3815)(58,000) = 22,686$$

Thus, we find that the estimated sales are $22,686 when disposable income is $58,000. The disposable income of $58,000 is within the range of the data used to estimate the regression model and thus the prediction is appropriate. We have also found that

$$n = 22 \quad \bar{x} = 57,342 \quad \sum (x_i - \bar{x})^2 = 34,084,596 \quad s_e^2 = 21,806$$

Hence, the standard error for a predicted single observation of Y is as follows:

$$\sqrt{\left[1 + \frac{1}{n} + \frac{(x_{n+1} - \bar{x})^2}{\sum\limits_{i=1}^{n} (x_i - \bar{x})^2} \right] s_e} = \sqrt{\left[1 + \frac{1}{22} + \frac{(58,000 - 57,342)^2}{34,084,596} \right] \sqrt{21,806}} = 151.90$$

Similarly, we find that the standard error for the expected value of Y is as follows:

$$\sqrt{\left[\frac{1}{n} + \frac{(x_{n+1} - \bar{x})^2}{\sum_{i=1}^{n}(x_i - \bar{x})^2}\right]} s_e = \sqrt{\left[\frac{1}{22} + \frac{(58{,}000 - 57{,}342)^2}{34{,}084{,}596}\right]} \sqrt{21{,}806} = 35.61$$

Suppose that 95% intervals are required for the forecasts with $\alpha = 0.05$ and

$$t_{n-2, \alpha/2} = t_{20,0.025} = 2.086$$

Using these results, we find that the 95% prediction interval for the first year's retail sales when disposable income is $58,000 is computed as follows:

$$22{,}686 \pm (2.086)(151.90)$$
$$22{,}686 \pm 317$$

Thus, the 95% prediction interval for sales in the proposed new store whose market area has a per capita income of $58,000 runs from $22,369 to $23,003.

The confidence interval for the expected value of retail sales when disposable income is $58,000 is as follows:

$$22{,}686 \pm (2.086)(35.61)$$
$$22{,}686 \pm 74$$

Hence, the 95% confidence interval for the expected value runs from $22,612 to $22,760.

The distinction between these two interval estimation problems is illustrated in Figures 11.11 and 11.12. We see in each figure the estimated regression line for our retail sales—disposable income data. Also, in Figure 11.11 we see a probability density function representing our uncertainty about the value that retail sales will occur in the new store whose market area has disposable income equal to $58,000. The probability density function in Figure 11.12 represents our uncertainty about expected, or average, retail sales in years when disposable income is $58,000. Of course, we would be less certain about sales in the first year for single specific stores than about average sales, and this is reflected in the shapes of the two density functions. We see that both are centered on retail sales of $22,686, but that the density function for the prediction of a single outcome in Figure 11.11 has greater dispersion. As a result, the prediction interval for a specific value is wider than the confidence interval for expected retail sales.

We can obtain some further insights by studying the general forms of the prediction and confidence intervals. As we have seen, the wider the interval, the greater the uncertainty surrounding the point forecast. From these formulas we make four observations:

1. All other things being equal, the larger the sample size n, the narrower are both the prediction interval and the confidence interval. Thus, we see that the more sample information we have available, the more confident we will be about our prediction.
2. All other things being equal, the larger s_e^2 is, the wider are both the prediction interval and the confidence interval. Again, this is to be expected, since s_e^2 is an estimate of σ^2, the variance of the regression errors, ε_i. Since these errors

$$\varepsilon_i = y_i - \beta_0 - \beta_1 x_i$$

represent the discrepancy between the observed values of the dependent variables and their expectations, given the independent variables, the bigger the magnitude of discrepancy, the more imprecise will be our prediction.

3. Consider now the quantity $\left(\sum_{i=1}^{n}(x_i - \bar{x})^2\right)$. This is simply a multiple of the sample dispersion of the observations of the independent variable. A large dispersion implies that we have information for a wide range of values of this variable, which allows

more precise estimates of the population regression line and correspondingly narrower confidence intervals and narrower prediction intervals.

4. We also see that larger values of the quantity $(x_{n+1} - \bar{x})^2$ result in wider confidence intervals and wider prediction intervals. Thus, both intervals become wider as we move from the mean of the independent variable, X. Since our sample data are centered at the mean $\bar{x}$, we would expect to be more definitive about our inference when the independent variable is relatively close to this central value than when it is some distance away.

Extrapolation of the regression equation outside the range of the data used for estimation can lead to major errors. Suppose that you are asked to predict retail sales for a proposed store in a market area with per household disposable income of $70,000. Referring to the data in Table 11.1 and the regression line in Figure 11.12, we see that $70,000 is well outside the range of the data used to develop the regression model. An inexperienced analyst might use the procedures previously developed to estimate a prediction or a confidence interval. From the equations we can see that the resulting intervals would be very wide, and, thus, the forecast would be of limited value. However, there is a more fundamental problem with forecasts made outside the range of the original data: We simply have no evidence to indicate the nature of the relationship outside the range of the data. There is no reason in economic theory that requires absolutely that the relationship will remain linear with the same rate of change when we move outside the range of the data used to estimate the regression model coefficients. Any extrapolation of the model outside the range of the data to obtain predicted values must be based on knowledge or evidence beyond that contained in the regression analysis on the available data. Such extrapolation would be based on judgment, experience, and opinion and not on rigorous statistical analysis.

EXERCISES

 Visit www.MyStatLab.com or www.pearson globaleditions.com to access the data files.

Basic Exercises

11.39 Given a simple regression analysis, suppose that we have obtained a fitted regression model

$$\hat{y}_i = 11 + 14x_i$$

and also

$$s_e = 10.66; \quad \bar{x} = 10; \quad n = 42; \quad \sum_{i-1}^{n}(x_i - \bar{x})^2 = 400$$

Find the 90% confidence interval and 90% prediction interval for the point where $x = 12$.

11.40 Given a simple regression analysis, suppose that we have obtained a fitted regression model

$$\hat{y}_i = 14 + 7x_i$$

and also

$$s_e = 7.45 \quad \bar{x} = 8 \quad n = 25 \quad \sum_{i=1}^{n}(x_i - \bar{x})^2 = 300$$

Find the 95% confidence interval and 95% prediction interval for the point where $x = 11$.

11.41 Given a simple regression analysis, suppose that we have obtained a fitted regression model

$$\hat{y}_i = 22 + 8x_i$$

and also

$$s_e = 3.45 \quad \bar{x} = 11 \quad n = 22 \quad \sum_{i=1}^{n}(x_i - \bar{x})^2 = 400$$

Find the 95% confidence interval and 95% prediction interval for the point where $x = 17$.

11.42 Given a simple regression analysis, suppose that we have obtained a fitted regression model

$$\hat{y}_i = 8 + 10x_i$$

and also

$$s_e = 11.23 \quad \bar{x} = 8 \quad n = 44 \quad \sum_{i=1}^{n}(x_i - \bar{x})^2 = 800$$

Find the 95% confidence interval and 95% prediction interval for the point where $x = 17$.

Application Exercises

11.43 A sample of 10 blue-collar employees at a production plant was taken. Each employee was asked to assess their job satisfaction (x) on a scale of 1 to 10. In addition, the numbers of days absent (y) from work during the last year were found for these employees. The sample regression line

$$\hat{y}_i = 11.3 - 1.1x$$

was estimated by least squares for these data. Also found were

$$\bar{x} = 4.0; \quad \sum_{i=1}^{10}(x_i - \bar{x})^2 = 90; \quad SSE = 36.2$$

a. Test, at the 5% significance level against the appropriate one-sided alternative, the null hypothesis that job satisfaction has no linear effect on absenteeism.
b. A particular employee has job satisfaction level 5. Find a 95% interval for the number of days this employee would be absent from work in a year.

11.44 Doctors are interested in the relationship between the dosage of a medicine and the time required for a patient's recovery. The following table shows, for a sample of 10 patients, dosage levels (in grams) and recovery times (in hours). These patients have similar characteristics except for medicine dosages.

Dosage level	1.2	1.3	1.0	1.4	1.5	1.8	1.2	1.3	1.4	1.3
Recovery time	25	28	40	38	10	9	27	30	16	18

a. Estimate the linear regression of recovery time on dosage level.
b. Find and interpret a 90% confidence interval for the slope of the population regression line.
c. Would the sample regression derived in part a be useful in predicting recovery time for a patient given 2.5 grams of this drug? Explain your answer.

11.45 For a sample of 20 monthly observations, a financial analyst wants to regress the percentage rate of return (Y) of the common stock of a corporation on the percentage rate of return (X) of the Standard & Poor's 500 index. The following information is available:

$$\sum_{i=1}^{20} y_i = 22.6 \quad \sum_{i=1}^{20} x_i = 25.4 \quad \sum_{i=1}^{20} x_i^2 = 145.7$$

$$\sum_{i=1}^{20} x_i y_i = 150.5 \quad \sum_{i=1}^{20} y_i^2 = 196.2$$

a. Test the null hypothesis that the slope of the population regression line is 0 against the alternative that it is positive.
b. Test against the two-sided alternative the null hypothesis that the slope of the population regression line is 1.

11.46 Estimate a linear regression model for mutual fund losses on November 13, 1989, on previous gains in 1989, using the data file **New York Stock Exchange Gains and Losses**. Test, against a two-sided alternative, the null hypothesis that mutual fund losses on Friday, November 13, 1989, did not depend linearly on previous gains in 1989.

11.47 Denote by r the sample correlation between a pair of random variables.

a. Show that

$$\frac{1 - r^2}{n - 2} = \frac{s_e^2}{SST}$$

b. Using the result in part a, show that

$$\frac{r}{\sqrt{(1 - r^2)/(n - 2)}} = \frac{b}{s_e/\sqrt{\sum(x_i - \bar{x})^2}}$$

11.48 It was hypothesized that the number of bottles of craft beer sold per evening in the restaurants of a city depends linearly on the average costs of meals in the restaurants. The following results were obtained for a sample of $n = 17$ restaurants, of approximately equal size, where

y = number of bottles sold per evening
x = average cost, in dollars, of a meal

$$\bar{x} = 25.5 \quad \bar{y} = 16.0 \quad \frac{\sum_{i=1}^{n}(x_i - \bar{x})^2}{n - 1} = 350$$

$$\frac{\sum_{i=1}^{n}(x_i - \bar{x})(y_i - \bar{y})}{n - 1} = 180$$

$$\frac{\sum(y_i - \bar{y})^2}{n - 1} = 250$$

Compute a 95% prediction interval and a 95% confidence interval for the number of bottles of beer sold when the average cost of a meal is $27.

11.49 For a sample of 50 monthly observations the regression of the percentage return on an investment (y) against the percentage change in the consumer price index (x) was estimated. The sample regression line, obtained through least squares, is as follows:

$$y = -0.003 + 8.2x$$

The estimated standard deviation of the slope of the population regression line was 2.3. Test the null hypothesis that the slope of the population regression line is 0 against the alternative that the slope is positive.

11.50 A liquor wholesaler is interested in assessing the effect of the price of a premium scotch whiskey on the quantity sold. The results in the accompanying table on price, in dollars, and sales, in cases, were obtained from a sample of 8 weeks of sales records.

Price	19.2	20.5	19.7	21.3	20.8	19.9	17.8	17.2
Sales	25.4	14.7	18.6	11.4	11.1	15.7	29.2	35.2

Test, at the 5% level against the appropriate one-sided alternative, the null hypothesis that sales do not depend linearly on price for this premium scotch whiskey.

11.51 The data file **Trading Stocks** shows percentage changes (x_i) in a stock market over the first five trading days of each of 11 years and also the corresponding percentage changes (y_i) in the index over the whole year. If the stock market increases by 3.0% in the first five trading days of a year, find 95% confidence intervals for the *actual* and also the *expected* percentage changes in the index over the whole year. Discuss the distinction between these intervals.

11.52 You have been asked to study the relationship between mean health care costs and mean disposable income using the state level data contained in the data file **Economic Activity**. Estimate the regression of health and personal expenditures on disposable income. Compute the 95% prediction interval and the 95% confidence interval for health and personal expenditures when disposable income is $32,000.

11.53   An economic policy research organization has asked you to study the relationship between disposable income and unemployment level. The data for this study are contained in the data file **Economic**

Activity. As a first step you estimate the regression model for the relationship between unemployment regressed on disposable income. Determine if there is a significant relationship between unemployment and disposable income and whether the relationship is increasing or decreasing. Compute the 95% prediction interval for unemployment when disposable income is $30,000.

11.7 CORRELATION ANALYSIS

In this section we use correlation coefficients to study relationships between variables. In Chapter 2 we used the sample correlation coefficient to describe the relationship between variables indicated in the data. In Chapters 4 and 5 we learned about the population correlation. Here, we develop inference procedures that use the correlation coefficient for studying linear relationships between variables.

In principle, there are many ways in which a pair of random variables might be related to each other. As we begin our analysis, it is helpful to postulate some functional form for their relationship. It is often reasonable to conjecture, as a good approximation, that the association is linear. If the pair of linearly related random variables X and Y is being considered, a scatter plot of the joint observations on this pair will tend to be clustered around a straight line. Conversely, if a linear relationship does not exist, then the scatter plot will not follow a straight line. Not all the relationships that we study will be tightly clustered about a straight line. Many important relationships will have scatter plots that show a tendency toward a linear relationship, but with considerable deviation from a straight line. Correlations have wide applications in business and economics. In many applied economic problems we argue that there is an independent, or exogenous, variable X, whose values are determined by activities outside of the economic system being modeled, and that there is a dependent or endogenous variable Y, whose value depends on the value of X. If we ask if sales increase when prices are reduced, we are thinking about a situation in which a seller deliberately and independently adjusts prices up or down and observes changes in sales. Now suppose that prices and quantities sold result from equilibriums of supply and demand as proposed by the basic economic model. Then we could both model prices and quantities as random variables and ask if these two random variables are related to each other. The correlation coefficient can be used to determine if there is a relationship between variables in either of these situations.

Suppose that both X and Y are determined simultaneously by factors that are outside the economic system being modeled. Therefore, a model in which both X and Y are random variables is often more realistic. In Chapter 4 we developed the correlation coefficient, ρ_{xy}, as a measure of the relationship between two random variables, X and Y. In those cases we used the population correlation coefficient, ρ_{xy}, to indicate a linear relationship without implying that one variable is independent and the other is dependent. In situations where one variable is logically dependent on a second variable, we can use regression analysis to develop a linear model. Here, we develop statistical inference procedures that use sample correlations to determine characteristics of population correlations.

Hypothesis Test for Correlation

The sample correlation coefficient

$$r = \frac{s_{xy}}{s_x s_y}$$

$$s_{xy} = \frac{\sum_{i=1}^{n}(x_i - \bar{x})(y_i - \bar{y})}{n - 1}$$

is useful as a descriptive measure of the strength of linear association in a sample. We can also use the correlation to test the hypothesis that there is no linear association in the population between a pair of random variables—that is,

$$H_0 : \rho = 0$$

This particular null hypothesis of no linear relationship between a pair of random variables is of great interest in a number of applications. When we compute the sample correlation from data, the result is likely to be different from 0 even if the population correlation is 0. Thus, we would like to know how large a difference from 0 is required for a sample correlation to provide evidence that the population correlation is not 0.

We can show that, when the null hypothesis is true and the random variables have a joint normal distribution, then the random variable

$$t = \frac{r\sqrt{(n-2)}}{\sqrt{(1-r^2)}}$$

follows a Student's t distribution with $(n-2)$ degrees of freedom. The appropriate hypothesis tests are shown in Equations 11.27–11.29.

Tests for Zero Population Correlation

Let r be the sample correlation coefficient, calculated from a random sample of n pairs of observations from a joint normal distribution. The following **tests for zero population correlation** use the null hypothesis

$$H_0 : \rho = 0$$

have a significance value α. We emphasize that all the following hypothesis tests are based on the assumption that the correlation is 0.

1. To test H_0 against the alternative

$$H_1 : \rho > 0$$

the decision rule is as follows:

$$\text{reject } H_0 \text{ if } \frac{r\sqrt{(n-2)}}{\sqrt{(1-r^2)}} > t_{n-2,\alpha} \tag{11.27}$$

2. To test H_0 against the alternative

$$H_1 : \rho < 0$$

the decision rule is as follows:

$$\text{reject } H_0 \text{ if } \frac{r\sqrt{(n-2)}}{\sqrt{(1-r^2)}} < -t_{n-2,\alpha} \tag{11.28}$$

3. To test H_0 against the two-sided alternative

$$H_1 : \rho \neq 0$$

the decision rule is as follows:

$$\text{reject } H_0 \text{ if } \frac{r\sqrt{(n-2)}}{\sqrt{(1-r^2)}} < -t_{n-2,\alpha/2} \quad \text{or} \quad \frac{r\sqrt{(n-2)}}{\sqrt{(1-r^2)}} > t_{n-2,\alpha/2} \tag{11.29}$$

Here, $t_{n-2,\alpha}$ is the number for which

$$P(t_{n-2} > t_{n-2,\alpha}) = \alpha$$

where the random variable t_{n-2} follows a Student's t distribution with $(n-2)$ degrees of freedom.

4. If we set $t_{n-2,\alpha/2} = 2.0$ in Equation 11.29, an approximate rule to remember for testing the previous hypothesis that the population correlation is 0 can be shown to be

$$|r| > \frac{2}{\sqrt{n}}$$

Example 11.4 Political Risk Score (Hypothesis Test for Correlation)

A research team was attempting to determine if political risk in countries is related to inflation for these countries. In this research a survey of political risk analysts produced a mean political risk score for each of 49 countries (Mampower, Livingston, and Lee 1987).

Solution The political risk score is scaled such that the higher the score, the greater the political risk. The sample correlation between political risk score and inflation for these countries was 0.43.

We wish to determine if the population correlation, ρ, between these measures is different from 0. Specifically, we want to test

$$H_0 : \rho = 0$$

against

$$H_1 : \rho > 0$$

using the sample information

$$n = 49 \quad r = 0.43$$

The test is based on the statistic

$$t = \frac{r\sqrt{(n-2)}}{\sqrt{(1-r^2)}} = \frac{0.43\sqrt{(49-2)}}{\sqrt{1-(0.43)^2}} = 3.265$$

Since there are $(n-2) = 47$ degrees of freedom, we have from the Student's t (Appendix Table 8),

$$t_{47,0.005} < 2.704$$

Therefore, we can reject the null hypothesis at the 0.05% significance level. As a result, we have strong evidence of a positive linear relationship between inflation and experts' judgments of political riskiness of countries. Note that from this result we cannot conclude that one variable caused the other, but only that they are related.

We noted previously that the null hypothesis $H_0 : \rho = 0$ can be rejected by using the approximate rule of thumb $|r| > \dfrac{2}{\sqrt{n}}$. This result provides a quick test to determine if two variables are linearly related when one or more sample correlations are being examined. Thus, for a sample size of $n = 25$, the absolute value of the sample correlation would have to exceed $\dfrac{2}{\sqrt{25}} = 0.40$. But for a sample of size $n = 64$, the absolute value of the sample correlation would have to exceed only $\dfrac{2}{\sqrt{64}} = 0.25$. This result has been found to be useful in many statistical applications. This rule of thumb would have led us to conclude that a relationship does exist in Example 11.4.

EXERCISES

 Visit www.MyStatLab.com or www.pearson globaleditions.com to access the data files.

Basic Exercises

11.54 Given the following pairs of (x, y) observations, compute the sample correlation.

  a. $(2, 5), (5, 8), (3, 7), (1, 2), (8, 15)$
  b. $(7, 5), (10, 8), (8, 7), (6, 2), (13, 15)$
  c. $(12, 4), (15, 6), (16, 5), (21, 8), (14, 6)$
  d. $(2, 8), (5, 12), (3, 14), (1, 9), (8, 22)$

11.55 Using a 0.10 level of significance, test the null hypothesis

$$H_0 : \rho = 0$$

versus

$$H_1 : \rho \neq 0$$

given the following.

  a. A sample correlation of 0.46 for a random sample of size $n = 25$.
  b. A sample correlation of 0.52 for a random sample of size $n = 45$.
  c. A sample correlation of 0.16 for a random sample of size $n = 40$.
  d. A sample correlation of 0.19 for a random sample of size $n = 60$.

11.56 An instructor in a statistics course set a final examination and also required the students to do a data analysis project. For a random sample of 10 students, the scores obtained are shown in the table. Find the sample correlation between the examination and project scores.

Examination	81	62	74	78	93	69	72	83	90	84
Project	76	71	69	76	87	62	80	75	92	79

Application Exercises

11.57 In a study of 33 countries, the sample correlation between an index of political turmoil and the infant mortality rate was 0.28. At the 0.05 level, test the null hypothesis of no correlation between these quantities against the alternative.

11.58 For a random sample of 353 high school teachers, the correlation between annual raises and teaching evaluations was found to be 0.11. Test the null hypothesis that these quantities are uncorrelated in the population against the alternative that the population correlation is positive.

11.59 The sample correlation for 68 pairs of annual returns on common stocks in country A and country B was found to be 0.51. Test the null hypothesis that the population correlation is 0 against the alternative that it is positive.

It is recommended that the following exercises be solved by using a computer.

11.60 The accompanying table and the data file **Dow Jones** show percentage changes (x_i) in the Dow Jones index over the first five trading days of each of 13 years and also the corresponding percentage changes (y_i) in the index over the whole year.

  a. Calculate the sample correlation.
  b. Test, at the 10% significance level against a two-sided alternative, the null hypothesis that the population correlation is 0.

x	y	x	y
1.5	14.9	5.6	2.3
0.2	−9.2	−1.4	11.9
−0.1	19.6	1.4	27.0
2.8	20.3	1.5	−4.3
2.2	−3.7	4.7	20.3
−1.6	27.7	1.1	4.2
−1.3	22.6		

11.61 A college administers a student evaluation questionnaire for all its courses. For a random sample of 12 courses, the accompanying table and the data file **Student Evaluation** show both the average student ratings of the instructor (on a scale of 1 to 5), and the average expected grades of the students (on a scale of A = 4 to F = 0).

Instructor rating	2.8	3.7	4.4	3.6	4.7	3.5	4.1	3.2	4.9	4.2	3.8	3.3
Expected grade	2.6	2.9	3.3	3.2	3.1	2.8	2.7	2.4	3.5	3.0	3.4	2.5

  a. Find the sample correlation between instructor ratings and expected grades.
  b. Test, at the 10% significance level, the hypothesis that the population correlation coefficient is zero against the alternative that it is positive.

11.62 In an advertising study the researchers wanted to determine if there was a relationship between the per capita cost and the per capita revenue. The following variables were measured for a random sample of advertising programs:

x_i = Cost of Advertisement ÷ Number of Inquiries Received

y_i = Revenue from Inquiries ÷ Number of Inquiries Received

The sample data results are shown in the data file **Advertising Revenue**. Find the sample correlation and test, against a two-sided alternative, the null hypothesis that the population correlation is 0.

The financial discipline has developed a number of measures and analysis procedures to help investors measure and control financial risk in the development of investment portfolios. Risk can be identified as diversifiable risk and nondiversifiable risk. *Diversifiable risk* is that risk associated with specific firms and industries and includes labor conflicts, new competition, consumer market changes, and many other factors. This risk can be controlled by larger portfolio sizes and by including stocks whose returns have negative correlations. We developed these procedures in Chapter 5. *Nondiversifiable risk* is that risk associated with the entire economy. Shifts in the economy resulting from business cycles, international crisis, the evolving world energy demands, or others affect all firms but do not have the same effect on each firm. The overall effect is measured by the average return on stocks such as measured by the Standard & Poor's 500 stock composite index (S & P 500). The effect on individual firms is measured by the beta coefficient.

The beta coefficient for a specific firm is the slope coefficient that is obtained when the return for a particular firm is regressed on the returns for a broad index such as the S & P 500. This slope coefficient indicates how responsive the returns for a particular firm are to the overall market returns. In most cases the beta is positive, but in some limited cases a firm's returns will move in the opposite direction compared to the overall economy. If the firm's returns follow the market exactly, then the beta coefficient will be 1. If the firm's returns are more responsive to the market, then the beta would be greater than 1, and if the firm's returns are less responsive to the market, then the beta will be less than 1. Using financial analysis based on the capital asset pricing model, the required return on an investment is given by the following:

$$\begin{pmatrix} \text{required return} \\ \text{on investment} \end{pmatrix} = \begin{pmatrix} \text{risk-free} \\ \text{rate} \end{pmatrix} + \left[\begin{pmatrix} \text{beta for} \\ \text{investment} \end{pmatrix} \times \left(\begin{pmatrix} \text{market} \\ \text{return} \end{pmatrix} - \begin{pmatrix} \text{risk-free} \\ \text{rate} \end{pmatrix} \right) \right]$$

From the previous result we see that a higher value of beta results in the need for a higher required return on investment. This higher required return would adjust for the fact that the stock return is influenced more heavily by the nondiversifiable market risk. Diversification through larger portfolios cannot adjust for overall shifts in the market.

A financial manager might be concerned only about the actual value of the beta. However, a statistical analyst would also be concerned about the "quality" of the regression model that provides the estimate of beta and, thus, standard error of the coefficient, Student's t, R-squared, and other measures become appropriate. A statistical analyst would also be concerned about the time period represented by the data. We would like the period to be as long as possible to obtain an estimate with a low variance. However, we also know that major changes occur over time that may result in a sea change in the economy. In those cases we might be mixing data from two different kinds of economy, and the resulting estimated beta might not be appropriate for present decisions. Thus, it is important that the statistical analyst work closely with experienced financial analysts and fund managers who can help reflect on overall economic conditions.

Example 11.5 shows how we can estimate beta using our present knowledge of regression analysis.

Example 11.5 Estimation of Beta Coefficients

The research department of Blue Star Investments has been asked to determine the beta coefficients for the firms Pearson PLC and Infosys, and you have been assigned the project. Both firms are large multinational organizations. Pearson is a wide-range publisher and provider of various media, whereas Infosys is a large computer software and information services firm with headquarters in India.

Solution After discussions with a number of analysts, you decide that you will use monthly data going back 60 months from April 2008. The measure is month end proportion change in stock value, and the data are contained in the data file **Return on Stock Price 60 Month**. The regression analysis results and scatter plot for the Pearson analysis are shown in Figure 11.13, and the analysis for Infosys is shown in Figure 11.14.[1]

Figure 11.13 Computation of Beta for Pearson

Regression Analysis: Pearson PLC (ADR) versus SP 500

```
The regression equation is
Pearson PLC (ADR) = - 0.00098 + 1.10 SP 500

Predictor        Coef    SE Coef      T       P
Constant    -0.000982   0.005046   -0.19   0.846
SP 500         1.0991     0.1960    5.61   0.000
```

As indicated in Figure 11.13, the Pearson return has a beta of 1.10 with a coefficient Student's $t = 5.61$ and an overall R-squared of 35.2%. Thus, we see that the nondiversifiable risk for Pearson follows the market quite closely. For the 60-month period, the monthly return for Pearson was 0.6%.

The Infosys return has a beta of 1.87 with a coefficient Student's $t = 4.49$ and an overall R-squared of 25.8%. Thus, we see that the nondiversifiable risk response for Infosys is substantially above the overall market. For the 60-month period, the monthly return for Infosys was 1.96%. Recall the previous discussion from the capital asset pricing model, which indicated that a higher beta would require a higher market return to adjust for the risk. In fact, we see that the Infosys return was over three times that of Pearson.

---

[1]The authors have decided to use stock market data sets that end on April 2008 for the examples and exercises in the 8th edition even though more recent data are available. We are doing this because of the major stock market crash and recession that began in September 2008. Using more recent data would require financial and economic analysis that is beyond the level of this textbook. Our objective is to learn about statistical methodology, and that study would be complicated by the real issues associated with the stock market crash of 2008.

Figure 11.14 Computation of Beta for Infosys Technology

Regression Analysis: Infosys Tech versus SP 500

```
The regression equation is
Infosys Tech = 0.0073 + 1.87 SP 500

Predictor      Coef   SE Coef      T      P
Constant    0.00731   0.01074   0.68  0.499
SP 500       1.8729    0.4169   4.49  0.000
```

EXERCISES

 Visit www.MyStatLab.com or www.pearson globaleditions.com to access the data files.

11.63   As part of a process to build a new banking portfolio, you have been asked to determine the beta coefficients for two Dutch banking and financial services companies, ING and Rabobank. Data for this task are contained in the data file **Return on Banking Stock Price**. Compare the required return on the two stocks to compensate for the risk.

11.64   In this exercise you are asked to determine the beta coefficient for Senior Housing Properties Trust. Data for this task are contained in the data file **Return on Stock Price 60 Months**. Interpret this coefficient.

11.65   An investor is considering the possibility of including TCF Financial in her portfolio. Data for this task are contained in the data file **Return on Stock Price 60 Months**. Compare the mean and variance of the monthly return with the S & P 500 mean and variance.

Then, estimate the beta coefficient. Based on this analysis, what would you recommend to the investor?

11.66   Allied Financial is considering the possibility of adding one or more computer industry stocks to its portfolio. You are asked to consider the possibility of Seagate, Microsoft, and Tata Information systems. Data for this task are contained in the data file **Return on Stock Price 60 Months**. Compare the return on these three stocks by computing the beta coefficients and the mean and variance of the returns. What is your recommendation regarding these three stocks?

11.67   Charlie Ching has asked you to analyze the possibility of including Seneca Foods and Safeco in his portfolio. Data for this task are contained in the data file **Return on Stock Price 60 Months**. Compute the beta coefficients for the stock price growth for each stock. Then construct a portfolio that includes equal dollar value for both stocks. Compute the beta coefficient for that portfolio. Compare the mean and variance for the portfolio with the S & P 500. What is your recommendation regarding the inclusion of these two stocks in Charlie's portfolio?

11.9 GRAPHICAL ANALYSIS

We have developed the theory and analysis procedures that provide the capability to perform regression analysis and build linear models. The regression model is based on a set of assumptions. However, there are many ways that regression analysis applications can go wrong, including assumptions that are not satisfied if the data do not follow the assumed patterns.

The example of retail sales regressed on disposable income—Figure 11.4—has a scatter plot that follows the pattern assumed in regression analysis. That pattern, however, does not always occur when new data are studied. One of the best ways to detect potential problems for simple regression analysis is to prepare scatter plots and observe the pattern. Here, we will consider some analysis tools and regression examples that can help us prepare better regression analysis applications.

In this section, graphical analysis is used to show the effect on regression analysis of points that have extreme X values and points that have Y values that deviate considerably from the least squares regression equation. In later chapters we show how residuals analysis can be used to examine other deviations from standard data patterns.

Extreme points are defined as points that have X values that deviate substantially from the X values for the other points. Refer to Equation 11.26, which presents the confidence interval for the expected value of Y at a specific value of X. Central to this confidence interval is a term typically called the *leverage*, h_i, for a point, which is defined as follows:

$$h_i = \frac{1}{n} + \frac{(x_i - \bar{x})^2}{\sum_{i=1}^{n} (x_i - \bar{x})^2}$$

(11.30)

This leverage term–Equation 11.30—will increase the standard deviation of the expected value as data points are farther from the mean of X and, thus, lead to a wider confidence interval. A point i is defined as an extreme point if its value of h is substantially different from the h values for all other data points. We see in the following example that Minitab will identify points that have a high leverage with an X if $h_i > 3p/n$, where p is the number of predictors, including the constant. The same feature is available in most good statistical packages, but not in Excel. Using this capability, extreme points can be identified, as shown in Example 11.6.

Example 11.6 The Effect of Extreme X Values (Scatter Plot Analysis)

We are interested in determining the effect of extreme X values on the regression. In this example the effect of points with X values that are substantially different from the other points is investigated using two samples that differ in only two points. These comparative examples, while somewhat unusual, are used to emphasize the effect of extreme points on a regression analysis.

Solution Figure 11.15 is a scatter plot with a regression line drawn on the points, and Figure 11.16 is the output from the regression analysis computed

Figure 11.15 Scatter Plot with Two Extreme X Points: Positive Slope

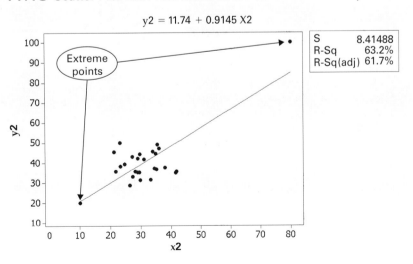

Figure 11.16 Regression Analysis with Two Extreme X Points: Positive Slope (Minitab Output)

Regression Analysis: Y2 versus x2

```
The regression equation is
Y2 = 11.74 + 0.9145 x2


S = 8.41488   R-Sq = 63.2%   R-Sq(adj) = 61.7%

Analysis of Variance

Source       DF        SS        MS       F       P
Regression    1   3034.80   3034.80   42.86   0.000
Error        25   1770.26     70.81
Total        26   4805.05
```

with the data. The regression slope is positive and $R^2 = 0.632$. But note that two extreme points seem to determine the regression relationship. Now let us consider the effect of changing the two extreme data points, as shown in Figures 11.17 and 11.18.

As a result of changing only two data points, the relationship now has a statistically significant negative slope, and the predictions would be substantially different. Without examining the scatter plots we would not know why we had either a positive or a negative slope. We might have thought that our results represented a standard regression situation such as we saw in the retail sales scatter plot. Note that in Figure 11.17 that observation 26 has been labeled as an extreme observation by the symbol X.

Figure 11.17 Scatter Plot with Extreme X Points: Negative Slope

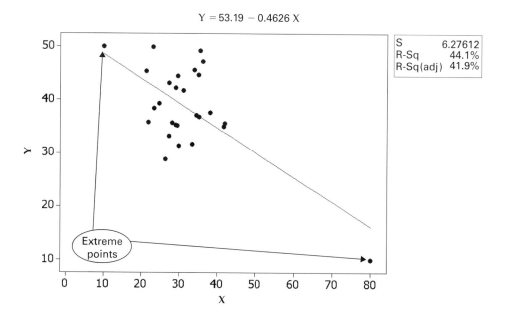

Figure 11.18 Minitab Output for Regression with Extreme X Points: Negative Slope

Regression Analysis: Y versus X

```
The regression equation is
Y1 = 53.2 - 0.463 X

Predictor        Coef    SE Coef       T       P
Constant       53.195      3.518   15.12   0.000
X1            -0.4626      0.1042   -4.44   0.000

s = 6.27612   R-Sq = 44.1%   R-Sq(adj) = 41.9%

Analysis of Variance

Source         DF        SS        MS       F       P
Regression      1    776.56    776.56   19.71   0.000
Residual Error 25    984.74     39.39
Total          26   1761.30

Unusual Observations

Obs     X      Y    Fit   Se Fit   Residual    St Resid
 7    35.5  49.14  36.78    1.27      12.37        2.01R
26    80.0  10.00  16.19    5.17      -6.19       -1.74 X

R denotes an observation with a large standardized residual.
X denotes an observation whose X value gives it large influence.
```

Observation 26 is an extreme point with large influence.

This example demonstrates a common problem when historical data are used. Suppose that X is the number of workers employed on a production shift and Y is the number of units produced on that shift. Most of the time the factory operates with a relatively stable workforce, and output depends in large part on the amount of raw materials available and the sales requirements. The operation adjusts up or down over a narrow range in response to demands and to the available workforce, X. Thus, we see that in most cases the scatter plot covers a narrow range for the X variable. But occasionally there is a very large or small workforce—or the number of workers is recorded incorrectly. On those days the production might be unusually high or low—or might be recorded incorrectly. As a result, we have extreme points that can have a major influence on the regression model. These few days determine the slope of the regression equations. Without the extreme points the regression would indicate little or no relationship. If these extreme points represent extensions of the relationship, then the estimated model is useful. But if these points result from unusual conditions or recording errors, the estimated model is misleading.

In a particular application we may find that these extreme points are correct and should be used to determine the regression line. But the analyst needs to make that decision knowing that all the other data points do not support a significant relationship. In fact, you do need to understand the system and process that generated the data to evaluate the available data.

Outlier points are defined as those that deviate substantially in the Y direction from the predicted value. Typically, these points are identified by computing the standardized residual as follows:

$$e_{is} = \frac{e_i}{s_e \sqrt{1 - h_i}} \tag{11.31}$$

That is, the standardized residual—Equation 11.31—is the residual divided by the standard error of the residual. Note that in the previous equation, points with high leverage—large h_i—will have a smaller standard error of the residual. This occurs because points with high leverage are likely to influence the location of the estimated regression line, and, hence, the observed and expected values of Y will be closer. Minitab will mark observations that have an absolute value of the standardized residual greater than 2.0 with an R to indicate that they are outliers. This capability is also available in most good statistical packages, but not in Excel. Using this capability, outlier points can be identified, as shown in Example 11.7.

Example 11.7 The Effect of Outliers in the Y Variable (Scatter Plot Analysis)

In this example we consider the effect of outliers in the y, or vertical, direction. Recall that the regression analysis model assumes that all the variation is in the Y direction. Thus, we know that outliers in the Y direction will have large residuals, and these will result in a higher estimate of the model error. In this example we see that the effects can be even more extreme.

Solution To begin, observe the scatter plot and regression analysis in Figures 11.19 and 11.20. In this example we have a strong relationship between the X and Y variables. The scatter plot clearly supports a linear relationship, with $b_1 = 11.88$. In addition, the regression model R^2 is close to 1, and the Student's t statistic is very large. Clearly, we have strong evidence to support a linear model.

Figure 11.19 Scatter Plot with Anticipated Pattern

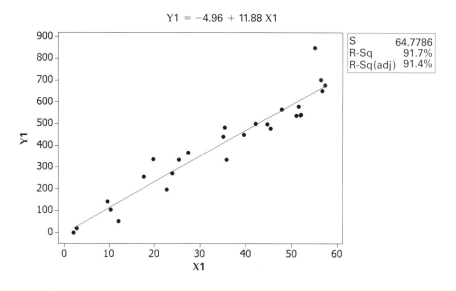

Figure 11.20 Regression with Anticipated Pattern (Minitab Output)

Regression Analysis: Y1 versus X1

```
The regression equation is
Y1 = -4.96 + 11.88 X1


s = 64.7786   R-Sq = 91.7%   R-Sq(adj) = 91.4%


Analysis of Variance

Source        DF        SS        MS       F        P
Regression     1   1160171   1160171  276.48    0.000
Error         25    104907      4196
Total         26   1265077
```

Now let us consider the effect of changing two observations to outlier data points, as shown in Figure 11.21. This could occur because of a data-recording error or because of a very unusual condition in the process being studied.

Figure 11.21 Scatter Plot with Y Outlier Points

The regression slope is still positive, but now $b_1 = 6.40$, and the slope estimate has a larger standard error, as shown in Figure 11.22. The confidence interval is much wider, and the predicted value from the regression line is not as accurate. The correct

Figure 11.22 Regression with Y Outlier Points (Minitab Output)

Regression Analysis: Y1 versus X1

```
The regression equation is
Y1 = 184 + 6.40 X1

Predictor        Coef     SE Coef        T        P
Constant       183.92       82.10     2.24    0.034
X1              6.400        2.126     3.01    0.006


S = 192.721   R-Sq = 26.6%   R-Sq(adj) = 23.7%


Analysis of Variance

Source          DF         SS         MS        F        P
Regression       1     336540     336540     9.06    0.006
Residual Error  25     928537      37141
Total           26    1265077


Unusual Observations

Obs    X1      Y1     Fit    Se Fit   Residual    St Resid
26    2.0   850.0   196.7     78.3      653.3        3.71R
27   55.0     0.0   535.9     57.3     -535.9       -2.91R


R denotes an observation with a large standardized residual.
```
Outliers marked with R

regression model is now not as clear. Minitab identifies observations 26 and 27 as outliers by printing an R next to the standardized residual. Standardized residuals whose absolute value is greater than 2 are indicated in the output. If the two outlier points actually occurred in the normal operation of the process, then you must include them in your analysis. But the fact that they deviate so strongly from the pattern indicates that you should carefully investigate the data situations that generated those points and study the process that you are modeling.

In the two preceding examples, we have shown that extreme points and outliers have a great influence on the estimated regression equation compared to other observations. In any applied analysis, either these unusual points are part of the data that represent the process being studied or they are not. In the former case they should be included in the data set, and in the latter case they should not. The analyst must decide! Typically, these decisions require a good understanding of the process and good judgment. First, the individual points should be examined carefully and their source checked. These unusual points could have resulted from measurement or recording errors and, thus, would be eliminated or corrected. Further investigation may reveal unusual circumstances that are not expected to be part of the standard process, and this would indicate exclusion of the data points. Decisions concerning what a standard process is and other related decisions require careful judgment and examination of other information about the process being studied. A good analyst uses the previously mentioned statistical computations to identify observations that should be examined more carefully but does not rely exclusively on these measures for unusual observations to make the final decision.

There are many other examples that could be generated. You might find that a nonlinear relationship is suggested by the scatter plot and, thus, would provide a better model for a particular application problem. In Chapters 12 and 13 we learn how we can use regression to model nonlinear relationships. You will see many different data patterns as you proceed with various applications of regression. The important point is that you must regularly follow analysis procedures—including the preparation of scatter plots—that can provide as much insight as possible. As a good analyst, you must "Know Thy Data!" in the next chapter we consider how residuals can also be used graphically to provide further tests of regression models.

EXERCISES

Visit www.MyStatLab.com or www.pearson globaleditions.com to access the data files.

Application Exercises

11.68 Frank Anscombe, senior research executive, has asked you to analyze the following four linear models using data contained in the data file **Anscombe**:

$$Y_1 = \beta_0 + \beta_1 X_1$$
$$Y_2 = \beta_0 + \beta_1 X_2$$
$$Y_3 = \beta_0 + \beta_1 X_3$$
$$Y_4 = \beta_0 + \beta_1 X_4$$

Use your computer package to obtain a linear regression estimate for each model. Prepare a scatter plot for the data used in each model. Write a report, including regression and graphical outputs, that compares and contrasts the four models.

11.69 Josie Foster, president of Public Research, Inc., has asked for your assistance in a study of the occurrence of crimes in different states before and after a large federal government expenditure to reduce crime. As part of this study she wants to know if the crime rate for selected crimes after the expenditure can be predicted using the crime rate before the expenditure. She has asked you to test the hypothesis that crime before predicts crime after for total crime rate and for the murder, rape, and robbery rates. The data for your analysis are contained in the data file **Crime Study**. Perform appropriate analysis and write a report that summarizes your results.

KEY WORDS

DATA FILES

CHAPTER EXERCISES AND APPLICATIONS

 Visit www.MyStatLab.com or www.pearson globaleditions.com to access the data files.

11.70 For a random sample of 53 building supply stores in a chain, the correlation between annual sales per square meter of floor space and annual rent per square meter of floor space was found to be 0.37. Test the null hypothesis that these two quantities are uncorrelated in the population against the alternative that the population correlation is positive.

11.71 For a random sample of 526 firms, the sample correlation between the proportion of a firm's officers who are directors and a risk-adjusted measure of return on the firm's stock was found to be 0.1398. Test, against a two-sided alternative, the null hypothesis that the population correlation is 0.

11.72 For a sample of 66 months, the correlation between the returns on Canadian and Singapore 10-year bonds was found to be 0.293. Test the null hypothesis that the population correlation is 0 against the alternative that it is positive.

11.73 Based on a sample on n observations, (x_1, y_1), $(x_2, y_2), \ldots, (x_n, y_n)$, the sample regression of y on x is calculated. Show that the sample regression line passes through the point $(x = \bar{x}, y = \bar{y})$, where $\bar{x}$ and $\bar{y}$ are the sample means.

11.74 An attempt was made to evaluate the inflation rate as a predictor of the spot rate in the German treasury bill market. For a sample of 79 quarterly observations, the estimated linear regression

$$\hat{y} = 0.0027 + 0.7916x$$

was obtained, where

y = actual change in the spot rate

x = change in the spot rate predicted by the inflation rate

The coefficient of determination was 0.097, and the estimated standard deviation of the estimator of the slope of the population regression line was 0.2759.

a. Interpret the slope of the estimated regression line.

b. Interpret the coefficient of determination.

c. Test the null hypothesis that the slope of the population regression line is 0 against the alternative that the true slope is positive, and interpret your result.

d. Test, against a two-sided alternative, the null hypothesis that the slope of the population regression line is 1, and interpret your result.

11.75 The following table shows, for eight vintages of select wine, purchases per buyer (y) and the wine buyer's rating in a year (x):

x	3.6	3.3	2.8	2.6	2.7	2.9	2.0	2.6
y	24	21	22	22	18	13	9	6

a. Estimate the regression of purchases per buyer on the buyer's rating.

b. Interpret the slope of the estimated regression line.

c. Find and interpret the coefficient of determination.

d. Find and interpret a 90% confidence interval for the slope of the population regression line.
e. Find a 90% confidence interval for expected purchases per buyer for a vintage for which the buyer's rating is 2.0.

11.76 For a sample of 306 students in a basic business statistics course, the sample regression line

$$y = 58.813 + 0.2875x$$

was obtained. Here,

y = final student score at the end of the course
x = score on a diagnostic statistics test given at the beginning of the course

The coefficient of determination was 0.1158, and the estimated standard deviation of the estimator of the slope of the population regression line was 0.04566.

a. Interpret the slope of the sample regression line.
b. Interpret the coefficient of determination.
c. The information given allows the null hypothesis that the slope of the population regression line is 0 to be tested in two different ways against the alternative that it is positive. Carry out these tests and show that they reach the same conclusion.

11.77 Based on a sample of 30 observations, the population regression model

$$y_i = \beta_0 + \beta_1 x_i + \varepsilon_i$$

was estimated. The least squares estimates obtained were as follows:

$$b_0 = 10.1 \quad \text{and} \quad b_1 = 8.4$$

The regression and error sums of squares were as follows:

$$SSR = 128 \quad \text{and} \quad SSE = 286$$

a. Find and interpret the coefficient of determination.
b. Test at the 10% significance level against a two-sided alternative the null hypothesis that β_1 is 0.
c. Find

$$\sum_{i=1}^{30} (x_i - \bar{x})^2$$

11.78 Based on a sample of 25 observations, the population regression model

$$y_i = \beta_0 + \beta_1 x_1 + \varepsilon_i$$

was estimated. The least squares estimates obtained were as follows:

$$b_0 = 15.6 \quad \text{and} \quad b_1 = 1.3$$

The total and error sums of squares were as follows:

$$SST = 268 \quad \text{and} \quad SSE = 204$$

a. Find and interpret the coefficient of determination.
b. Test, against a two-sided alternative at the 5% significance level, the null hypothesis that the slope of the population regression line is 0.
c. Find a 95% confidence interval for β_1.

11.79 An analyst believes that the only important determinant of banks' returns on assets (Y) is the ratio of loans to deposits (X). For a random sample of 20 banks, the sample regression line

$$y = 0.97 + 0.47x$$

was obtained with coefficient of determination 0.720.

a. Find the sample correlation between returns on assets and the ratio of loans to deposits.
b. Test against a two-sided alternative at the 5% significance level the null hypothesis of no linear association between the returns and the ratio.

11.80 If a regression of the yield per acre of corn on the quantity of fertilizer used is estimated using fertilizer quantities in the range typically used by farmers, the slope of the estimated regression line will certainly be positive. However, it is well known that, if an enormously high amount of fertilizer is used, corn yield will be very low. Discuss the benefits of applying regression analysis to a data set that includes a few cases of excessive fertilizer use combined with data from typical operations.

The following exercises require the use of a computer.

11.81 A college's economics department is attempting to determine if verbal or mathematical proficiency is more important for predicting academic success in the study of economics. The department faculty have decided to use the grade point average (GPA) in economics courses for graduates as a measure of success. Verbal proficiency is measured by the SAT verbal and the ACT English entrance examination test scores. Mathematical proficiency is measured by the SAT mathematics and the ACT mathematics entrance examination scores. The data for 112 students are available in a data file named **Student GPA**. The designation of the variable columns is presented in the Chapter 11 appendix. You should use your local statistical computer program to perform the analysis for this problem.

a. Prepare a graphical plot of the economics GPA versus each of the two verbal proficiency scores and each of the two mathematical proficiency scores. Which variable is a better predictor? Note any unusual patterns in the data.
b. Compute the linear model coefficients and the regression analysis statistics for the models that predict economics GPA as a function of each verbal and each mathematics score. Using both the SAT mathematics and verbal measures and the ACT mathematics and English measures, determine whether mathematical or verbal proficiency is the best predictor of economics GPA.
c. Compare the descriptive statistics—mean, standard deviation, upper and lower quartiles, and range—for the predictor variables. Note the differences and indicate how these differences affect the capability of the linear model to predict.

11.82 The administrator of the National Highway Traffic Safety Administration (NHTSA) wants to know if the different types of vehicles in a state have a relationship to the highway death rate in the state. She has asked you to perform several regression analyses to determine if average vehicle weight, percentage of imported cars, percentage of light trucks, or average car age is related to crash deaths in automobiles and pickups. The data for the analyses are in the data file **Vehicle Travel State**. The variable descriptions and locations are contained in the Chapter 11 appendix.

a. Prepare graphical plots of crash deaths versus each of the potential predictor variables. Note the relationship and any unusual patterns in the data points.
b. Prepare a simple regression analysis of crash deaths on the potential predictor variables. Determine which, if any, of the regressions indicate a significant relationship.
c. State the results of your analysis and rank the predictor variables in terms of their relationship to crash deaths.

11.83 The Department of Transportation wishes to know if states with a larger percentage of urban population have higher rates of automobile and pickup crash deaths. In addition, it wants to know if either the average speed on rural roads or the percentage of rural roads that are surfaced is related to crash death rates. Data for this study are included in the data file **Vehicle Travel State**.

a. Prepare graphical plots of crash deaths versus each of the potential predictor variables. Note the relationship and any unusual patterns in the data points.
b. Prepare a simple regression analysis of crash deaths on the potential predictor variables. Determine which, if any, of the regressions indicate a significant relationship.
c. State the results of your analysis and rank the predictor variables in terms of their relationship to crash deaths.

11.84 An economist wishes to predict the market value of owner-occupied homes in small midwestern cities. She has collected a set of data from 45 small cities for a 2-year period and wants you to use these as the data source for the analysis. The data are stored in the file **Citydatr**. She wants you to develop two prediction equations: one that uses the size of the house as a predictor and a second that uses the tax rate as a predictor.

a. Plot the market value of houses (hseval) versus the size of houses (sizense), and then versus the tax rates (taxrate). Note any unusual patterns in the data.
b. Prepare regression analyses for the two predictor variables. Which variable is the stronger predictor of the value of houses?
c. A business developer in a midwestern state has stated that local property tax rates in small towns

need to be lowered because if they are not, no one will purchase a house in these towns. Based on your analysis in this problem, evaluate the business developer's claim.

11.85 Stuart Wainwright, the vice president of purchasing for a large national retailer, has asked you to prepare an analysis of retail sales by state. He wants to know if either the percent of male unemployment or the per capita disposable income are related to per capita retail sales. Data for this study are stored in the data file **Economic Activity**, which is described in the data file catalog in the Chapter 11 appendix. Note that you may have to compute new variables using those variables in the data file.

a. Prepare graphical plots and regression analyses to determine the relationships between per capita retail sales and unemployment and personal income. Compute 95% confidence intervals for the slope coefficients in each regression equation.
b. What is the effect of a $1,000 decrease in per capita income on per capita sales?
c. For the per capita income regression equation what is the 95% confidence interval for retail sales at the mean per capita income and at $1,000 above the mean per capita income?

11.86 A major national supplier of building materials for residential construction is concerned about total sales for next year. It is well known that the company's sales are directly related to the total national residential investment. Several New York bankers are predicting that interest rates will rise about two percentage points next year. You have been asked to develop a regression analysis that can be used to predict the effect of interest rate changes on residential investment. The time series data for this study are contained in the data file **Macro2010**, which is described in the Chapter 13 appendix.

a. Develop two regression models to predict residential investment, using the prime interest rate for one and the federal funds interest rate for the other. Analyze the regression statistics and indicate which equation provides the best predictions.
b. Determine the 95% confidence interval for the slope coefficient in both regression equations.
c. Based on each model, predict the effect of a two-percentage-point increase in interest rates on residential investment.
d. Using both models, compute 95% confidence intervals for the change in residential investment that results from a two-percentage-point increase in interest rates.

11.87 A prestigious national news service has gathered information on a number of nationally ranked private colleges; these data are contained in the data file **Private Colleges.** You have been asked to determine if the student/faculty ratio has an influence on the quality rating. Note that the smallest number indicates the highest rank. Prepare and analyze this question using simple regression and a scatter plot. Prepare a short discussion of your conclusion.

11.88   A prestigious national news service has gathered information on a number of nationally ranked private colleges; these data are contained in the data file **Private Colleges**. You have been asked to determine if the student/faculty ratio has an influence on the total annual cost after need-based financial aid. Prepare and analyze this question using simple regression and a scatter plot. Prepare a short discussion of your conclusion.

11.89   A prestigious national news service has gathered information on a number of nationally ranked private colleges; these data are contained in the data file **Private Colleges**. You have been asked to determine if the total cost after need-based aid has an influence on average debt. Prepare and analyze this question using simple regression and a scatter plot. Prepare a short discussion of your conclusion.

11.90   A prestigious national news service has gathered information on a number of nationally ranked private colleges; these data are contained in the data file **Private Colleges**. You have been asked to determine if the percentage of students admitted has an influence on the 4-year graduation rate. Prepare and analyze this question using simple regression and a scatter plot. Prepare a short discussion of your conclusion.

11.91   A prestigious national news service has gathered information on a number of nationally ranked private colleges; these data are contained in the data file **Private Colleges**. You have been asked to determine if the student faculty ratio has an influence on the 4-year graduation rate. Prepare and analyze this question using simple regression and a scatter plot. Prepare a short discussion of your conclusion.

11.92   You have been asked to study the relationship between median income and poverty rate at the county level. After some investigation you determine that the data file **Food Nutrition Atlas** includes both these measures for county-level data. Perform an appropriate analysis and report your conclusions. Your analysis should include a regression of median income on poverty level and an appropriate scatter plot. Additional analysis would also prove helpful.

11.93   The federal nutrition guidelines prepared by the Center for Nutrition Policy and Promotion of the U.S. Department of Agriculture stress the importance of eating substantial servings of fruits and vegetables to obtain a healthy diet. You have been asked to determine if the per capita consumption of fruits and vegetables at the county level are related to the percentage of obese adults in the county. Data for this study are contained in the data file **Food Nutrition Atlas**, whose variable descriptions are found in the Chapter 9 appendix.

11.94   The federal nutrition guidelines prepared by the Center for Nutrition Policy and Promotion of the U.S. Department of Agriculture stress the importance of eating substantial servings of fruits and vegetables to obtain a healthy diet. You have been asked to determine if the per capita consumption of fruits and vegetables at the county level is related to the percentage of adults with diabetes in the county.

Data for this study are contained in the data file **Food Nutrition Atlas,** whose variable descriptions are found in the Chapter 9 appendix.

11.95   The federal nutrition guidelines prepared by the Center for Nutrition Policy and Promotion of the U.S. Department of Agriculture stress the importance of eating reduced amounts of meat to obtain a healthy diet. You have been asked to determine if the per capita consumption of meat at the county level are related to the percentage of obese adults in the county. Data for this study are contained in the data file **Food Nutrition Atlas**, whose variable descriptions are found in the Chapter 9 appendix.

11.96   The federal nutrition guidelines prepared by the Center for Nutrition Policy and Promotion of the U.S. Department of Agriculture stress the importance of eating reduced amounts of meat to obtain a healthy diet. You have been asked to determine if the per capita consumption of meat at the county level are related to the percentage of adults with diabetes in the county. Data for this study are contained in the data file **Food Nutrition Atlas**, whose variable descriptions are found in the Chapter 9 appendix.

Nutrition Research–Based Exercises

The Economic Research Service (ERS), a highly ranked think tank research center in the U.S. Department of Agriculture is conducting a series of research studies to determine the nutrition characteristics of people in the United States. This research is used for both nutrition education and government policy designed to improve personal health (Carlson, A., D. Dong, and M. Lino. 2010).

The following exercises are typical analyses that would be conducted as part of their research.

The U.S. Department of Agriculture (USDA) developed the Healthy Eating Index (HEI) to monitor the diet quality of the U.S. population, particularly how well it conforms to dietary guidance (Guenther, P.M., J. Reedy, S. M. Krebs-Smith, B. B. Reeve, and P. P. Basiotis. November 2007). The HEI–2005 measures how well the population follows the recommendations of the 2005 Dietary Guidelines for Americans. In particular, it measures, on a 100-point scale, the adequacy of consumption of vegetables, fruits, grains, milk, meat and beans, and liquid oils. Full credit for these groups is given only when the consumer consumes some whole fruit, vegetables from the dark green, orange, and legume subgroup, and whole grains. In addition, the HEI–2005 measures how well the U.S. population limits consumption of saturated fat, sodium, and extra calories from solid fats, added sugars, and alcoholic beverages. You will use the Total HEI–2005 score as the measure of the quality of a diet. Further background on the HEI and important research on nutrition can be found on the government Web sites cited at the end of this case study.

A healthy diet results from a combination of appropriate food choices, which are strongly influenced by a number of behavioral, cultural, societal, and health conditions. One cannot simply tell people to drink orange juice, purchase all food from organic farms, or take some new miracle drug. Research and experience have developed considerable knowledge, and if we, for example, follow the diet guidelines associated with the food pyramid we will be healthier. It is also important that we know more about the characteristics that lead to healthier diets so that better recommendations and policies can be developed. And, of course, better diets will lead to a higher quality of life and lowered medical care costs. In the following exercises you apply your understanding of statistical analysis to perform analysis similar to that done by professional researchers.

The data file **HEI Cost Data Variable Subset** contains considerable information on randomly selected individuals who participated in an extended interview and medical examination (Centers for Disease Control and Prevention (CDC) 2003–2004). This data file contains the data for the following exercises. The variables are described in the data dictionary in the Chapter 10 appendix.

11.97 There is a belief among many people that a healthy diet will cost more than a less healthy diet. Using research based on the available population survey data, can you conclude that a healthy diet will in fact cost more than a less healthy diet? Using the daily cost and the measure of HEI, provide evidence to either accept or reject this general belief. You will do the analysis based first on the data from the first interview, creating subsets of the data file using daycode = 1, and a second time using data from the second interview, creating subsets of the data file using daycode = 2. Note differences in the results between the first and second interviews.

11.98 A group of social workers who work with low-income people have argued that the poverty income ratio is directly related to the quality of an individual person's diet. That is, people with higher ratios will be more likely to have higher-quality diets, and those with lower ratios will have lower-quality diets. Perform an appropriate analysis to determine if their claim is supported by evidence. You will do the analysis based first on the data from the first interview, creating subsets of the data file using daycode = 1, and a second time using data from the second interview, creating subsets of the data file using daycode = 2. Note differences in the results between the first and second interviews.

11.99 A number of nutritionists have argued that fast-food restaurants have a negative effect on nutrition quality. In this exercise you are asked to determine if there is evidence to conclude that increasing the number of meals at fast-food restaurants will have a negative effect on diet quality. In addition, you are asked to determine the effect of eating in fast-food restaurants has on the daily cost of food. You will do the analysis based first on the data from the first interview, creating subsets of the data file using daycode = 1, and a second time using data from the second interview, creating subsets of the data file using daycode = 2. Note differences in the results between the first and second interviews.

11.100 In recent news commentaries, it has been argued that the quality of family life has decayed in recent years. Arguments include statements that families do not share meals together. Because of busy schedules, families just go out to eat because there is limited time for food preparation. What is the relationship between the percent of calories consumed at home and the quality of diet, based on an appropriate analysis of the survey data? In addition, what is the effect of eating at home on daily food cost? You will do the analysis based first on the data from the first interview, creating subsets of the data file using daycode = 1, and a second time using data from the second interview, creating subsets of the data file using daycode = 2. Note differences in the results between the first and second interviews.

11.101 In recent news commentaries, it has been argued that the quality of family life has decayed in recent years. Arguments include statements that families do not share meals together. Because of busy schedules, families just go out to eat because there is limited time for food preparation. In addition, it is also argued that a meal that is carefully prepared at home using purchased food ingredients will provide better nutrition. What is the relationship between the percent of calories purchased at a food store for consumption at home and the quality of diet, based on an appropriate analysis of the survey data? Also, what is the effect of percent of food purchased at a store on the daily food cost? You will do the analysis based first on the data from the first interview, creating subsets of the data file using daycode = 1, and a second time using data from the second interview, creating subsets of the data file using daycode = 2. Note differences in the results between the first and second interviews.

Appendix

DERIVATION OF LEAST SQUARES ESTIMATORS

In this appendix we derive the least squares estimators of the population regression parameters. We want to find the values b_0 and b_1 for which the sum of squared discrepancies

$$SSE = \sum_{i=1}^{n} e_i^2 = \sum_{i=1}^{n} (y_i - b_0 - b_1 x_i)^2$$

is as small as possible.

As a first step, we keep b_1 constant and differentiate with respect to b_0, giving

$$\frac{\partial SSE}{\partial b_0} = 2\sum_{i=1}^{n}(y_i - b_0 - b_1 x_i)$$

$$= -2\left(\sum y_i - nb_0 - b_1\sum x_i\right)$$

Since this derivative must be 0 for a minimum, we have the following:

$$\sum y_i - nb_0 - b_1\sum x_i = 0$$

Hence, dividing through by n yields

$$b_0 = \bar{y} - b_1\bar{x}$$

Substituting this expression for b_0 gives

$$SSE = \sum_{i=1}^{n}\left[(y_i - \bar{y}) - b_1(x_i - \bar{x})\right]^2$$

Differentiating this expression with respect to b_1 then gives

$$\frac{\partial SSE}{\partial b_1} = -2\sum_{i=1}^{n}(x_i - \bar{x})\left[(y_i - \bar{y}) - b_1(x_i - \bar{x})\right]$$

$$= 2\left(\sum(x_i - \bar{x})(y_i - \bar{y}) - b_1\sum(x_i - \bar{x})^2\right)$$

This derivative must be 0 for a minimum, so we have the following:

$$\sum(x_i - \bar{x})(y_i - \bar{y}) = b_1\sum(x_i - \bar{x})^2$$

Hence,

$$b_1 = \frac{\sum(x_i - \bar{x})(y_i - \bar{y})}{\sum(x_i - \bar{x})^2}$$

Data File Descriptions

Economic Activity

This data file contains observations for 50 states and the District of Columbia. The data for the year 1984 were obtained from the 2010 Statistical Abstract.

ECONOMIC ACTIVITY	
VARIABLE	DESCRIPTION
State	Name of State
Tot Retail	Total Retail Sales in Millions of $ 2008
Auto Parts	Total Retail Sales for Auto Parts & Dealers Millions $ 2008
Health	Total Retail Sales for Health & Personal Million $ 2008
Clothing	Total Retail Sales for Clothing Million $ 2008
Tot Employ	Percent of Civilian Noninstitutionalized Population Employed 2008
Male Employ	Total Male Percent of Civilian Work Force Employed 2008
Female Employ	Total Female Percent of Civilian Work Force Employed 2008
Tot Unemploy	Percent of Civilian Noninstitutionalized Population Unemployed 2008
Male Unemploy	Total Male Percent of Civilian Work Force Unemployed 2008
Female Unemploy	Total Female Percent of Civilian Work Force Unemployed 2008
Mfg Pay	Manufacturing Total Payroll Millions 2008
Mfg Pcap	Manufacturing Payroll per Worker 2008
Pers Income	Personal Income 1000s 2000 Dollars 2008
Percap Disp	Per Capita Disposable Income 2000 dollars 2008
Population	Population in 1000s 2008 Census

Vehicle Travel State

This data file contains observations by state. The data file will be used for various highway crash and travel analyses.

VEHICLE TRAVEL STATE	
VARIABLE	DESCRIPTION
State	Name of State
Pers Income	2007 Personal Income 1000s of 2000 Dollars
Percap Disp	2007 Per Capita Disposable Income in 2000 dollars
Population	Population in 1000s 2007 Census
P Urban	Percent of Population in Urban Areas 2007
Fatalities	Total Traffic Fatalities in 2007
Fat Rate	Traffic Fatality Rate per 100M Miles in 2007
BAC 08	Number of Fatal Crashes with Driver BAC > 0.08
Tot Regist	Total Motor Vehicle Registrations 1000s 2007
Auto Regist	Total Automobile Registrations 1000s 2007
Drivers	Total Licensed Drivers 1000s 2007
H Miles	Total Highway Mileage 2007
Inter Miles	Total Interstate Highway Miles 2007
R Miles	Total Rural Highway Miles 2007
Fuel Tax	Motor Vehicle Fuel Tax Millions $2007
Tax pgal	Motor Vehicle Fuel Tax Cents per gal
H Expend	Total Highway Expenditure in Millions $2007
Doctors	Total Doctors 2007
Nurses	Total Nurses 2007
P Ninsur	Percent Not Covered by Health Insurance 2007
Medicaid	Medicaid Enrollment in 1000s 2007

Food Nutrition Atlas

VARIABLE_CODE	VARIABLE_NAME
GROCPC	Grocery stores per 1,000 pop
SNAPStoresPerThous	SNAP-authorized stores per 1,000 pop
SNAPRedempPerStore	SNAP redemption/SNAP-authorized stores
AMB_PAR06	Average monthly SNAP $ benefits
PCT_FREE_LUNCH	% Students free-lunch eligible
PCT_REDUCED_LUNCH	% Students reduced-price-lunch eligible
PC_FRUVEG	Lbs per capita fruit&veg
PC_SNACKS	Lbs per capita pkg sweetsnacks
PC_SODA	Gals per capita soft drinks
PC_MEAT	Lbs per capita meat&poultry
PC_FATS	Lbs per capita solid fats
PC_PREPFOOD	Lbs per capita prepared foods
MILK_PRICE	Relative price of low-fat milk
SODA_PRICE	Relative price of sodas
PCT_DIABETES_ADULTS	Adult diabetes rate
PCT_OBESE_ADULTS	Adult obesity rate
PCT_Child_Obesity	Low-income preschool obesity rate
PcTNHWhite08	% White
PcTNHBlack08	% Black
PcTHisp08	% Hispanic
PcTNHAsian08	% Asian
PcTNHNA08	% Amer. Indian or Alaska Native
Median_Income	Median household income
Percent_Poverty	Poverty rate
metro	1 = Metro 0 = nonmetro counties

Student GPA Data File

This data file contains academic test score measurements

Variable Name	Description
Data File Description for File	Student GPA
sex	Male or Female
GPA	Overall Undergraduate Grade Point Average
SATverb	SAT Verbal Test Score
SATmath	SAT Mathematics Test Score
Acteng	ACT Verbal Test Score
ACTmath	ACT Mathematics Test Score
ACTss	ACT Social Science Test Score
ACTcomp	ACT Comprehensive Overall Test Score
HSPct	High School Percentile Academic Rank
EconGPA	Undergraduate Grade Point Average in Economics Courses

REFERENCES

1. Carlson, A., D. Dong, and M. Lino. 2010. "Are the Total Daily Cost of Food and Diet Quality Related: A Random Effects Panel Data Analysis". Paper presented at 1st Joint EAAE/AAEA Seminar, "The Economics of Food, Food Choice and Health." Freising, Germany, September 15–17, 2010.

2. Centers for Disease Control and Prevention (CDC). 2003–2004. National Health and Nutrition Examination Survey Data. Hyattsville, MD: U.S. Department of Health and Human Services, Centers for Disease Control and Prevention. http://www.cdc.gov/nchs/nhanes/nhanes2003-2004/nhanes03_04.htm

3. *Food Environment Atlas*, Economic Research Service, United States Department of Agriculture.

4. Guenther, P.M., J. Reedy, S. M. Krebs-Smith, B. B. Reeve, and P. P. Basiotis. November 2007. Development and Evaluation of the Healthy Eating Index–2005: Technical Report. Center for Nutrition Policy and Promotion, U.S. Department of Agriculture, http://www.cnpp.usda.gov/HealthyEatingIndex.htm

5. Mampower, J. L., S. Livingston, and T. J. Lee. 1987. Expert Judgments of Political Risk, *Journal of Forecasting* 6: 51–65.

Multiple Regression

Introduction

In Chapter 11 we developed simple regression as a procedure for obtaining a linear equation that predicts a dependent or endogenous variable as a function of a single independent or exogenous variable—for example, total number of items sold as a function of price. However, in many situations, several independent variables jointly influence a dependent variable. Multiple regression enables us to determine the simultaneous effect of several independent variables on a dependent variable using the least squares principle.

Many important applications of multiple regression occur in business and economics. These applications include the following:

1. The quantity of goods sold is a function of price, income, advertising, price of substitute goods, and other variables.
2. Capital investment occurs when a business person believes that a profit can be made. Thus, capital investment is a function of variables related to the potential for profit, including interest rate, gross domestic product, consumer expectations, disposable income, and technological level.
3. Salary is a function of experience, education, age, and job rank.
4. Large retail, hotel, and restaurant companies decide on locations for new outlets based on the anticipated sales revenue and/or profitability. Using data from previous successful and unsuccessful locations, analysts can build models that predict sales or profit for a potential new location.

Business and economic analysis has some unique characteristics compared to analysis in other disciplines. Natural scientists work in a laboratory, where many—but not all—variables can be controlled. In contrast, the economist's and manager's laboratory is the world, and conditions cannot be controlled. Thus, we need tools such as multiple regression to estimate the simultaneous effect of several variables. Multiple regression as a "lab tool" is very important for the work of managers and economists. In this chapter we will see many specific applications in discussion examples and problem exercises.

The methods for fitting multiple regression models are based on the same least squares principle presented in Chapter 11, and, thus, the insights gained there extend directly to multiple regression. However, there are complexities introduced because of the relationships between the various exogenous variables. These require additional insights that are developed in this chapter.

12.1 THE MULTIPLE REGRESSION MODEL

Our objective here is to learn how to use multiple regression for creating and analyzing models. Thus, we learn how multiple regression works and some guidelines for interpretation. A good understanding provides the capability for solving a wide range of applied problems. This study of multiple regression methods parallels the study of simple regression. The first step in model development is model specification, which includes the selection of model variables and the model form. Next, we study the least squares process, followed by an analysis of variability to identify the effects of each predictor variable. Then we study estimation, confidence intervals, and hypothesis testing. Computer applications are used extensively to indicate how the theory is applied to realistic problems. Your study of this material will be aided if you relate the ideas in this chapter to those presented in Chapter 11.

Model Specification

We begin with an application that illustrates the important task of regression model specification. Model specification includes selection of the exogenous variables and the functional form of the model.

Example 12.1 Process Manufacturing (Regression Model Specification)

The production manager for Flexible Circuits, Inc., has asked for your assistance in studying a manufacturing process. Flexible circuits are produced from a continuous roll of flexible resin material with a thin film of copper-conducting material bonded to its surface. Copper is bonded to the resin by passing the resin through a copper-based solution. The thickness of the copper is critical for high-quality circuits. Copper thickness depends, in part, on the temperature of the copper solution, speed of the production line, density of the solution, and thickness of the flexible resin material. To control the thickness of the bonded copper, the production manager needs to know the effect of each of these variables. You have been asked for assistance in developing a multiple regression model.

Solution Model development begins with a careful analysis of the problem context. The first step for this example would be an extended discussion with product design and manufacturing engineers so that you understand the process being modeled in detail. In some cases, you would study existing literature related to the process. The process must be understood and agreed to by the engineers and analysts before a useful model can be developed using multiple regression analysis. In this example the dependent variable, Y, is the copper thickness. Independent variables include temperature of the copper solution, X_1; speed of the production line, X_2; density of the solution, X_3; and thickness of the flexible resin material, X_4. These variables were identified as potential predictors of copper thickness, Y, by engineers and scientists that understand the technology of the plating process. Based on the study of the process, the resulting model specification is as follows:

$$Y = \beta_0 + \beta_1 X_1 + \beta_2 X_2 + \beta_3 X_3 + \beta_4 X_4$$

In this linear model the β_js are constant linear coefficients of the independent variables X_j that indicate the conditional effect of each independent variable on the determination of the dependent variable, Y, in the population. Thus, the coefficients β_j are parameters in the linear regression model. A series of production runs would then be made to obtain measurements of various combinations of independent and dependent variables. (See the discussion of experimental design in Section 13.2.)

Example 12.2 Store Location (Model Specification)

The director of planning for a large retailer was dissatisfied with the company's new-store development experience. In the past 4 years 25% of new stores failed to obtain their projected sales within the 2-year trial period and were closed, with substantial economic losses. The director wanted to develop better criteria for choosing store locations and decided that the historical experience of successful and unsuccessful stores should be studied.

Solution Discussion with a consultant indicated that data from stores that met and that did not meet anticipated sales could be used to develop a multiple regression model. The consultant suggested that the second year's sales should be used as the dependent variable, Y. A regression model would be used to predict second-year sales as a function of several independent variables that define the area surrounding the store. Stores would be located only where the predicted sales exceeded a minimum level. The model would also indicate the effect of various independent variables on sales.

After considerable discussion with people in the company, the consultant recommended the following independent variables:

1. X_1 = size of store
2. X_2 = traffic volume on highway in front of store
3. X_3 = stand-alone store versus shopping mall location
4. X_4 = location of competing store within 1/4 mile
5. X_5 = per capita income of population within 5 miles
6. X_6 = total number of people within 5 miles
7. X_7 = per capita income of population within 10 miles
8. X_8 = total number of people within 10 miles

Multiple regression was used to obtain estimates of the coefficients of the sales-prediction model from data collected for all stores opened during the past 8 years. The data set included both those stores that were still operating and those that were closed. A model was developed that could be used to predict second-year sales. This estimated equation included coefficient estimators, b_j, for the model parameters, β_j. To apply the estimated equation

$$\hat{y}_i = b_0 + \sum_{j=1}^{8} b_j x_{ji}$$

measurements of the independent variables were collected for each proposed new store location and the predicted sales were computed for that location. A predicted sales level was used, along with the judgment of marketing analysts and a committee of successful store managers, as input to the store location decision process.

Model Objectives

The strategy for model specification is influenced by the model objectives. One objective is prediction of a dependent or outcome variable. Applications include predicting or forecasting sales, output, total consumption, total investment, and many other business and economic performance criteria. A second objective is estimating the marginal effect of each independent variable. Economists and managers need to know how changes of independent variables, X_j, where $j = 1, \ldots, K$, change performance measures, Y. For example, consider the following:

1. How do sales change as a result of a price increase and advertising expenditures?
2. How does output change when the amounts of labor and capital are changed?
3. Does infant mortality become lower when health care expenditures and local sanitation are increased?

Regression Objectives

Multiple regression provides two important results:

1. An estimated linear equation that predicts the dependent variable, Y, as a function of K observed independent variables, X_j, where $j = 1, \ldots, K$:

$$\hat{y}_i = b_0 + b_1 x_{1i} + b_2 x_{2i} + \cdots + b_K x_{Ki}$$

where $i = 1, \ldots, n$ observations. The predicted value, $\hat{y}_i$, depends on the effect of the independent variables individually and their effect in combination with the other independent variables. Thus, we are interested in the combined effect of a particular combination of predictor variables.

2. The marginal change in the dependent variable, Y, that is related to changes in the independent variables—estimated by the coefficients, b_j. In multiple regression these coefficients depend on what other variables are included in the model. The coefficient b_j estimates the change in Y, given a unit change in X_j, while controlling for the simultaneous effect of the other independent variables.

In some problems both results are equally important. However, usually one will predominate (e.g., prediction of store sales, Y, in the store location example).

Marginal change is more difficult to estimate because the independent variables are related not only to the dependent variables but also to each other. If two or more independent variables change in a direct linear relationship with each other, it is difficult to determine the individual effect of each independent variable on the dependent variable.

Consider in detail the model in Example 12.2. The coefficient of x_5 indicates the change in sales for each unit change in the per capita income of the population within 5 miles, whereas that of x_7 indicates the sales change for change in per capita income of the population within 10 miles. It is, of course, likely that the variables x_5 and x_7 are correlated. Thus, to the extent that these variables both change at the same time, it is difficult to determine the contribution of each variable to change in store sales revenue. This correlation between independent variables introduces a complexity to the model. It is important to understand that the model predicts store sales revenue using the particular combination of variables contained in the model. The effect of a predictor variable is the effect of that variable when combined with the other variables. Thus, in general, the coefficient of a variable does not provide an indication of that variable's effect under all conditions. These complexities are explored further as we develop the multiple regression model.

Model Development

When applying multiple regression, we construct a model to explain variability in the dependent variable. In order to do this, we want to include the simultaneous and individual influences of several independent variables. For example, suppose that we wanted to develop a model that would predict the annual profit margin for savings and loan associations using data collected over a period of years. An initial model specification indicated that the annual profit margin was related to the net revenue per deposit dollar and the number of savings and loan offices. The net annual revenue is expected to increase the annual profit margin, and the number of savings and loan offices is anticipated to decrease the annual profit margin because of increased competition. This would lead us to specify a population regression model:

$$Y = \beta_0 + \beta_1 X_1 + \beta_2 X_2 + \varepsilon$$

where

Y = annual profit margin
X_1 = net annual revenue per deposit dollar
X_2 = number of savings and loan offices for that year

Table 12.1 and the data file named **Savings and Loan** contain 25 observations by year of these variables. These data will be used to develop a linear model that predicts annual profit margin as a function of revenue per deposit dollar and number of offices (Spellman 1978).

But before we can estimate the model, we need to develop and understand the multiple regression procedure. To begin, let us consider the general multiple regression

Table 12.1 Savings and Loan Associations Operating Data

Year	Revenue per Dollar	Number of Offices	Profit Margin	Year	Revenue per Dollar	Number of Offices	Profit Margin
1	3.92	7,298	0.75	14	3.78	6,672	0.84
2	3.61	6,855	0.71	15	3.82	6,890	0.79
3	3.32	6,636	0.66	16	3.97	7,115	0.7
4	3.07	6,506	0.61	17	4.07	7,327	0.68
5	3.06	6,450	0.7	18	4.25	7,546	0.72
6	3.11	6,402	0.72	19	4.41	7,931	0.55
7	3.21	6,368	0.77	20	4.49	8,097	0.63
8	3.26	6,340	0.74	21	4.70	8,468	0.56
9	3.42	6,349	0.9	22	4.58	8,717	0.41
10	3.42	6,352	0.82	23	4.69	8,991	0.51
11	3.45	6,361	0.75	24	4.71	9,179	0.47
12	3.58	6,369	0.77	25	4.78	9,318	0.32
13	3.66	6,546	0.78				

model and note the differences from the simple regression model. The multiple regression model is

$$y_i = \beta_0 + \beta_1 x_{1i} + \beta_2 x_{2i} + \cdots + \beta_K x_{Ki} + \varepsilon_i$$

where ε_i is the random error term with a mean of 0 and a variance of σ^2, and the β_j terms are the coefficients, or marginal effects, of the independent, or exogenous variables, X_j, where $j = 1, \ldots, K$, given the effects of the other independent variables. The i terms indicate the observations with $i = 1, \ldots, n$. We use lowercase letters x_{ji} to denote specific values of variable X_j at observation i. We assume that the random errors ε_i are independent of the variables X_j and of each other to ensure proper estimates of the coefficients and their variances. In Chapter 13 we indicate the effect of relaxing these assumptions.

The sample estimated model is

$$y_i = b_0 + b_1 x_{1i} + b_2 x_{2i} + \cdots + b_K x_{Ki} + e_i$$

where e_i is the residual or difference between the observed value of Y and the estimated value of Y obtained by using the estimated coefficients, b_j, where $j = 1, \ldots, K$. The regression procedure obtains simultaneous estimates, b_j, of the population model coefficients, β_j, using the least squares procedure.

In our savings and loan associations example, the population model for individual data points is as follows:

$$y_i = \beta_0 + \beta_1 x_{1i} + \beta_2 x_{2i} + \varepsilon_i$$

This reduced model with only two predictor variables provides the opportunity for developing additional insights into the regression procedure. The regression function can be depicted graphically in three dimensions, as shown in Figure 12.1. The regression function is shown as a plane whose Y values are a function of the independent variable values of X_1 and X_2. For each possible pair, x_{1i}, x_{2i}, the expected value of the dependent variable, Y, is on the plane. Figure 12.2 specifically illustrates the savings and loan example. An increase in X_1 leads to an increase in the expected value of Y, conditional on the effect of X_2. Similarly, an increase in X_2 leads to a decrease in the expected value of Y, conditional on the effect of X_1.

To complete our model, we add an error term defined as ε. This error term recognizes that no postulated relationship will hold exactly and that there are likely to be additional variables that also affect the observed value of Y. Thus, in the application setting we observe

Figure 12.1 The Plane Is the Expected Value of Y as a Function of X_1 and X_2

Figure 12.2 Comparison of the Observed and Expected Values of Y as a Function of Two Independent Variables

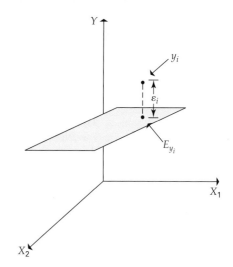

the expected value of the dependent variable, Y—as depicted by the plane in Figure 12.2—plus a random error term, ε, that represents the portion of Y not included in the expected value. As a result, the data model has the form

$$y_i = \beta_0 + \beta_1 x_{1i} + \beta_2 x_{2i} + \cdots + \beta_K x_{Ki} + \varepsilon_i$$

The Population Multiple Regression Model

The **population multiple regression model** defines the relationship between a dependent, or endogenous variable, Y, and a set of independent, or exogenous, variables, X_j, where $j = 1, \ldots, K$. The x_{ji} terms are assumed to be fixed numbers; Y is a random variable *with* y_i defined for each observation, i, where $i = 1, \ldots, n$ and n is the number of observations. The model is defined as

$$y_i = \beta_0 + \beta_1 x_{1i} + \beta_2 x_{2i} + \cdots + \beta_K x_{Ki} + \varepsilon_i \qquad (12.1)$$

where the β_j terms are constant coefficients and the instances of ε_i are random variables with a mean of 0 and a variance of σ^2.

For the savings and loan example, with two independent variables, the population regression model is as follows:

$$y_i = \beta_0 + \beta_1 x_{1i} + \beta_2 x_{2i} + \varepsilon_i$$

Given particular values of the net percentage revenue, x_{1i}, and the number of savings and loan offices, x_{2i}, the observed profit margin, y_i, is the sum of two parts: the expected value, $\beta_0 + \beta_1 x_{1i} + \beta_2 x_{2i}$, and the random error term, ε_i. The random error term can be regarded as the combination of the effects of numerous other unidentified factors that affect profit margins. Figure 12.2 illustrates the model, with the plane indicating the expected value for various combinations of the independent variables and with the ε_i, shown as the deviation between the expected value, and the observed value of Y, marked by a large dot, for a particular data point. In general, the observed values of Y will not lie on the plane but instead will be above or below the plane because of the positive or negative error terms, ε_i.

Simple regression, developed in the previous chapter, is merely a special case of multiple regression with only one predictor variable, and, hence, the plane is reduced to a line. Thus, the theory and analysis developed for simple regression also apply to multiple regression. However, there are some additional interpretations that we will develop in our study of multiple regression. One of the important interpretations is illustrated in the following discussion of three-dimensional graphing.

Three-Dimensional Graphing

Your understanding of the multiple regression procedure might be helped by considering a simplified graphical image. Look at the corner of the room in which you are sitting. The lines formed by the two walls and the floor represent the axes for two independent variables, X_1 and X_2. The corner between the two walls is the axis for the dependent variable, Y. To estimate a regression line, we collect sets of points (x_{1i}, x_{2i}, and y_i).

Now, picture these points plotted in your room using the wall and floor corners as the three axes. With these points hanging in your room, we find a plane in space that comes close to all of them. This plane is the geometric form of the least squares equation. With these points in space we now maneuver a plane up and down and rotate it in two directions; all these shifts are done simultaneously until we have a plane that is "close" to all the points. Recall that we did this with a straight line in two dimensions in Chapter 11 to obtain the equation

$$\hat{y} = b_0 + b_1 x$$

Then, we extend that idea to three dimensions to obtain the equation

$$\hat{y} = b_0 + b_1 x_1 + b_2 x_2$$

This process is, of course, more complicated compared to simple regression. But real problems are complicated, and regression provides a way to better analyze the complexity of these problems. We want to know how Y changes with changes in X_1. However, these changes are, in turn, influenced by the way X_2 changes. And if X_1 and X_2 have a fixed relationship with each other, we cannot tell how much each variable contributes to changes in Y.

Geometric interpretations of multiple regression become increasingly complex as the number of independent variables increases. However, the analogy to simple regression is extremely useful. We estimate the coefficients by minimizing the sum of squared deviations in the Y dimension about a linear function of the independent variables. In simple regression the function is a straight line on a two-dimensional graph. With two independent variables the function is a plane in three-dimensional space. Beyond two independent variables we have various complex hyperplanes that are impossible to visualize.

EXERCISES

Basic Exercises

12.1   Given the estimated linear model

$$\hat{y} = 12 + 5x_1 + 6x_2 + 2x_3$$

a. Compute $\hat{y}$ when $x_1 = 11, x_2 = 24$, and $x_3 = 27$.
b. Compute $\hat{y}$ when $x_1 = 31, x_2 = 20$, and $x_3 = 17$.
c. Compute $\hat{y}$ when $x_1 = 32, x_2 = 29$, and $x_3 = 13$.
d. Compute $\hat{y}$ when $x_1 = 30, x_2 = 26$, and $x_3 = 9$.

12.2   Given the estimated linear model

$$\hat{y} = 10 + 5x_1 + 4x_2 + 2x_3$$

a. Compute $\hat{y}$ when $x_1 = 20, x_2 = 11$, and $x_3 = 10$.
b. Compute $\hat{y}$ when $x_1 = 15, x_2 = 14$, and $x_3 = 20$.
c. Compute $\hat{y}$ when $x_1 = 35, x_2 = 19$, and $x_3 = 25$.
d. Compute $\hat{y}$ when $x_1 = 10, x_2 = 17$, and $x_3 = 30$.

12.3   Given the estimated linear model

$$\hat{y} = 10 + 2x_1 + 12x_2 + 8x_3$$

a. Compute $\hat{y}$ when $x_1 = 20, x_2 = 11, x_3 = 10$.
b. Compute $\hat{y}$ when $x_1 = 15, x_2 = 24, x_3 = 20$.
c. Compute $\hat{y}$ when $x_1 = 20, x_2 = 19, x_3 = 25$.
d. Compute $\hat{y}$ when $x_1 = 10, x_2 = 9, x_3 = 30$.

12.4   Given the following estimated linear model

$$\hat{y} = 10 + 2x_1 + 12x_2 + 8x_3$$

a. What is the change in $\hat{y}$ when x_1 increases by 4?
b. What is the change in $\hat{y}$ when x_3 increases by 1?
c. What is the change in $\hat{y}$ when x_2 increases by 2?

12.5 Given the following estimated linear model

$$\hat{y} = 10 - 2x_1 - 14x_2 + 6x_3$$

  a. What is the change in $\hat{y}$ when x_1 increases by 4?
  b. What is the change in $\hat{y}$ when x_3 decreases by 1?
  c. What is the change in $\hat{y}$ when x_2 decreases by 2?

Application Exercises

12.6 An aircraft company wanted to predict the number of worker-hours necessary to finish the design of a new plane. Relevant explanatory variables were thought to be the plane's top speed, its weight, and the number of parts it had in common with other models built by the company. A sample of 27 of the company's planes was taken, and the following model was estimated:

$$y_i = \beta_0 + \beta_1 x_{1i} + \beta_2 x_{2i} + \beta_3 x_{3i} + \varepsilon_i$$

where

  y_i = design effort, in millions of worker-hours
  x_{1i} = plane's top speed, in miles per hour
  x_{2i} = plane's weight, in tons
  x_{3i} = percentage number of parts in common with other models

The estimated regression coefficients were as follows:

$$b_0 = 2 \quad b_1 = 0.661 \quad b_2 = 0.065 \quad b_3 = -0.018$$

Interpret these estimates.

12.7 In a study of the influence of financial institutions on bond interest rates in Germany, quarterly data over a period of 12 years were analyzed. The postulated model was

$$y_i = \beta_0 + \beta_1 x_{1i} + \beta_2 x_{2i} + \varepsilon_i$$

where

  y_i = change over the quarter in the bond interest rates
  x_{1i} = change over the quarter in bond purchases by financial institutions
  x_{2i} = change over the quarter in bond sales by financial institutions

The estimated regression coefficients were as follows:

$$b_1 = 0.046 \quad b_2 = -0.073$$

Interpret these estimates.

12.8 The following model was fitted to a sample of 30 families in order to explain household milk consumption:

$$y_i = \beta_0 + \beta_1 x_{1i} + \beta_2 x_{2i} + \varepsilon_i$$

where

  y_i = milk consumption, in quarts per week
  x_{1i} = weekly income, in hundreds of dollars
  x_{2i} = family size

The least squares estimates of the regression parameters were as follows:

$$b_0 = -0.025 \quad b_1 = 0.052 \quad b_2 = 1.14$$

  a. Interpret the estimates b_1 and b_2.
  b. Is it possible to provide a meaningful interpretation of the estimate b_0?

12.9 The following model was fitted to a sample of 25 students using data obtained at the end of their freshman year in college. The aim was to explain students' weight gains:

$$y_i = \beta_0 + \beta_1 x_{1i} + \beta_2 x_{2i} + \beta_3 x_{3i} \varepsilon_i$$

where

  y_i = weight gained, in pounds, during freshman year
  x_{1i} = average number of meals eaten per week
  x_{2i} = average number of hours of exercise per week
  x_{3i} = average number of beers consumed per week

The least squares estimates of the regression parameters were as follows:

$$b_0 = 7.35 \quad b_1 = 0.653 \quad b_2 = -1.345 \quad b_3 = 0.613$$

  a. Interpret the estimates b_1, b_2, and b_3.
  b. Is it possible to provide a meaningful interpretation of the estimate b_0?

12.2 ESTIMATION OF COEFFICIENTS

Multiple regression coefficients are computed using estimators obtained by the least squares procedure. This least squares procedure is similar to that presented in Chapter 11 for simple regression. However, the estimators are complicated by the relationships between the independent X_j variables that occur simultaneously with the relationships between the independent and dependent variables. For example, if two independent variables increase or decrease linearly with each other—a positive or negative correlation—while at the same time there are increases or decreases in the dependent variable, we cannot identify the unique effect of each independent variable to the change in the dependent variable. As a result, we will find that the estimated regression coefficients are less reliable if there are high correlations between two or more independent variables. The estimates of coefficients and their variances are always obtained using a computer. However, we will spend considerable effort studying the algebra and computational forms in least squares regression. This effort will provide you with the background to understand the procedure and to determine how different data patterns influence the results. We begin with the standard assumptions for the multiple regression model.

Standard Multiple Regression Assumptions

The population multiple regression model is

$$y_i = \beta_0 + \beta_1 x_{1i} + \beta_2 x_{2i} + \cdots + \beta_K x_{Ki} + \varepsilon_i$$

and we assume that n sets of observations are available. The following standard assumptions are made for the model:

1. The x_{ji} terms are fixed numbers, or they are realizations of random variables, X_j, that are independent of the error terms, ε_i. In the latter case, inference is carried out conditionally on the observed values of the x_{ji}s.
2. The expected value of the random variable Y is a linear function of the independent X_j variables.
3. The error terms are normally distributed random variables with a mean of 0 and the same variance, σ^2. The latter is called homoscedasticity, or uniform variance.

$$E[\varepsilon_i] = 0 \quad \text{and} \quad E[\varepsilon_i^2] = \sigma^2 \quad \text{for } (i = 1, \ldots, n)$$

4. The random error terms, ε_i, are not correlated with one another, so that

$$E[\varepsilon_i \varepsilon_l] = 0 \quad \text{for all } i \neq l$$

5. It is not possible to find a set of nonzero numbers, $c_1, \ldots, c_K$, such that

$$c_1 x_{1i} + c_2 x_{2i} + \cdots + c_K x_{Ki} = 0$$

This is the property of no direct linear relationship between the X_j variables.

The first four assumptions are essentially the same as those made for simple regression. The error terms in assumption 3 are assumed to be normally distributed for statistical inference. But we will see that just as with simple regression, the central limit theorem allows us to relax that assumption if the sample size is large enough. Assumption 5 excludes certain cases in which there are linear relationships between the predictor variables. For example, suppose we are interested in explaining the variability in rates charged for shipping corn. One obvious explanatory variable would be the distance the corn is shipped. Distance could be measured in several different units, such as miles or kilometers. But it would not make sense to use both distance in miles and distance in kilometers as predictor variables. These two measures are linear functions of each other and would not satisfy assumption 5. In addition, it would be foolish to try to assess their separate effects. As we shall see, the equations that compute the coefficient estimates and the computer programs will not work if assumption 5 is violated. In most cases, proper model specification will avoid violating assumption 5.

Least Squares Procedure

The least squares procedure for multiple regression computes the estimated coefficients so as to minimize the sum of the residuals squared. Recall that the residual is defined as

$$e_i = y_i - \hat{y}_i$$

where y_i is the observed value of Y and $\hat{y}_i$ is the value of Y predicted from the regression. Formally, we minimize SSE:

$$SSE = \sum_{i=1}^{n} e_i^2$$

$$= \sum_{i=1}^{n} (y_i - \hat{y}_i)^2$$

$$= \sum_{i=1}^{n} (y_i - (b_0 + b_1 x_{1i} + \cdots + b_K x_{Ki}))^2$$

This minimization is the process of finding a plane that best represents a set of points in space, as we considered in our discussion of three-dimensional graphing. To carry out the process formally, we use partial derivatives to develop a set of simultaneous normal equations that are then solved to obtain the coefficient estimators. For those with a good understanding of differential calculus, the chapter appendix presents some of the details of the process. However, one can obtain great insights by realizing that we want a linear equation that best represents the observed data, and this is accomplished by minimizing the squared deviations about the estimated regression equation. Fortunately, for the applications studied in this book, the complex computations are always performed using a statistical computer package such as Minitab, SAS, or SPSS. Our objective here is to understand how to interpret the regression results and use them to solve problems. We will do this by examining some of the intermediate algebraic results to help understand the effects of various data patterns on the coefficient estimators.

Least Squares Estimation of the Sample Multiple Regression

We begin with a sample of n observations denoted as $x_{1i}, x_{2i}, \ldots, x_{Ki}, y_i$, where $i = 1, \ldots, n$, measured for a process whose population multiple regression model is as follows:

$$y_i = \beta_0 + \beta_1 x_{1i} + \beta_2 x_{2i} + \cdots + \beta_K x_{Ki} + \varepsilon_i$$

The least squares estimates of the coefficients $\beta_1, \beta_2, \ldots, \beta_K$, are the values $b_0, b_1, \ldots, b_K$ for which the sum of the squared errors

$$SSE = \sum_{i=1}^{n} (y_i - b_0 - b_1 x_{1i} - b_2 x_{2i} - \cdots - b_K x_{Ki})^2 \qquad \text{(12.2)}$$

is a minimum.

The resulting equation

$$\hat{y}_i = b_0 + b_1 x_{1i} + b_2 x_{2i} + \cdots + b_K x_{Ki} \qquad \text{(12.3)}$$

is the sample multiple regression of Y on $X_1, X_2, \ldots, X_K$.

Let us consider again the regression model with only two predictor variables.

$$\hat{y}_i = b_0 + b_1 x_{1i} + b_2 x_{2i}$$

The coefficient estimators are computed using the following equations:

$$b_1 = \frac{s_y(r_{x_1 y} - r_{x_1 x_2} r_{x_2 y})}{s_{x_1}(1 - r_{x_1 x_2}^2)} \qquad \text{(12.4)}$$

$$b_2 = \frac{s_y(r_{x_2y} - r_{x_1x_2}r_{x_1y})}{s_{x_2}(1 - r_{x_1x_2}^2)}$$ (12.5)

$$b_0 = \bar{y} - b_1\bar{x}_1 - b_2\bar{x}_2$$ (12.6)

where

r_{x_1y} is the sample correlation between X_1 and Y
r_{x_2y} is the sample correlation between X_2 and Y
$r_{x_1x_2}$ is the sample correlation between X_1 and X_2
s_{x_1} is the sample standard deviation for X_1
s_{x_2} is the sample standard deviation for X_2
s_y is the sample standard deviation for Y

In the equations for the coefficient estimators, we see that the slope coefficient estimate, b_1, not only depends on the correlation between Y and X_1 but also is affected by the correlation between X_1 and X_2 and the correlation between X_2 and Y. If the correlation between X_1 and X_2 is equal to 0, then the coefficient estimators, b_1 and b_2, will be the same as the coefficient estimator for simple regression—we should note that this hardly ever happens in business and economic analysis. Conversely, if the correlation between the independent variables is equal to 1, the coefficient estimators will be undefined, but this will result only from poor model specification and will violate multiple regression assumption 5. If the independent variables are perfectly correlated, then they both experience simultaneous relative changes. We see that in that case it is not possible to tell which variable predicts the change in Y. In Example 12.3 we see the effect of the correlations between independent variables by considering the savings and loan association problem, whose data are shown in Table 12.1.

Example 12.3 Profit Margins of Savings and Loan Associations (Regression Coefficient Estimation)

The director of the savings and loan association has asked you to compute the coefficients for variables that predict the percent profit margin.

Solution As a first step we develop a multiple regression model specification that predicts profit margin as a linear function of the net revenue per deposit dollar and the number of offices. Using the data in Table 12.1 that are stored in the **Savings and Loan** data file, we have estimated a multiple regression model, as seen in the Minitab and Excel outputs in Figure 12.3.

The estimated coefficients are identified in the computer output. We see that each unit increase in net revenue per deposit dollar, X_1, results in a 0.237 increase in profit margin—if the other variable does not change—and a unit increase in the number of offices decreases profit margin by 0.000249. Now consider the two simple regression models in Figures 12.4 and 12.5 with Y regressed on each independent variable by itself. First, consider Y regressed on revenue, X_1, in Figure 12.4. In this simple regression the coefficient for X_1 is −0.169, which is clearly different from +0.237 in multiple regression. We see that the correlation between X_1 and X_2 is 0.941. This large correlation has a major impact on the coefficient of X_1 in the multiple regression equation.

We see that the correlation between X_1 and X_2 is 0.941. Thus, the two variables tend to move together, and it is not surprising that the multiple regression coefficients are different from the simple regression coefficients.

Figure 12.3 Regression Equation for Savings and Loan Association Profit (Minitab and Excel Output)

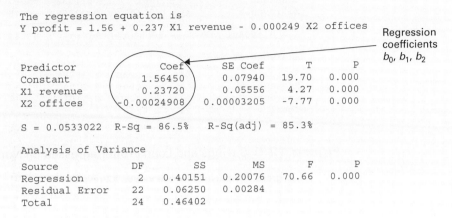

Regression Analysis: Y profit versus X1 revenue, X2 offices

```
The regression equation is
Y profit = 1.56 + 0.237 X1 revenue - 0.000249 X2 offices

                                                                Regression
                                                                coefficients
                                                                b₀, b₁, b₂
Predictor            Coef        SE Coef          T         P
Constant          1.56450       0.07940      19.70     0.000
X1 revenue        0.23720       0.05556       4.27     0.000
X2 offices       -0.00024908    0.00003205   -7.77     0.000


S = 0.0533022   R-Sq = 86.5%   R-Sq(adj) = 85.3%

Analysis of Variance

Source            DF        SS          MS         F         P
Regression         2     0.40151     0.20076    70.66     0.000
Residual Error    22     0.06250     0.00284
Total             24     0.46402
```

SUMMARY OUTPUT						
Regression Statistics						
Multiple R	0.930212915					
R Square	0.865296068					
Adjusted R Square	0.853050256					
Standard Error	0.053302217					
Observations	25					
ANOVA						
	_df_	_SS_	_MS_	_F_	_Significance F_	
Regression	2	0.40151122	0.20075561	70.66057082	2.64962E-10	
Residual	22	0.06250478	0.002841126			
Total	24	0.464016				
	Coefficients	_Standard Errors_	_t Stat_	_P-value_	_Lower 95%_	_Upper 95%_
Intercept	1.564496771	0.079395981	19.70498685	1.81733E-15	1.399839407	1.72915414
X1 revenue	0.237197475	0.055559366	4.269261695	0.000312567	0.121974278	0.35242067
X2 offices	-0.000249079	3.20485E-05	-7.771949195	9.50879E-08	-0.000315544	-0.00018261

Regression coefficients
b_0, b_1, b_2

Next, consider the regression of Y on X_2 alone in Figure 12.5. In this simple regression the slope coefficient for number of offices, X_2, is -0.000120, in contrast to -0.000249 for the multiple regression coefficient. This change in coefficients, while not quite as dramatic compared to the coefficient for X_1, also results from the high correlation between the independent variables.

The correlations between the three variables are as follows:

	Y PROFIT	X_1 REVENUE
X_1 revenue	-0.704	
X_2 offices	-0.868	0.941

Figure 12.4 Savings and Loan Profit Regressed on Revenue

Regression Analysis: Y profit versus X1 revenue

```
The regression equation is
Y profit = 1.33 - 0.169 X1 revenue


Predictor              Coef      SE Coef        T      P
Constant             1.3262       0.1386     9.57  0.000
X1 revenue          -0.16913      0.03559   -4.75  0.000
                                                             Regression
S = 0.100891   R-Sq = 49.5%   R-Sq(adj) = 47.4%             coefficient b₁

Analysis of Variance

Source          DF        SS        MS        F      P
Regression       1   0.22990   0.22990    22.59  0.000
Residual Error  23   0.23412   0.01018
Total           24   0.46402
```

Figure 12.5 Savings and Loan Profit Regressed on Number of Offices

Regression Analysis: Y profit versus X2 revenue

```
The regression equation is
Y profit = 1.55 - 0.000120 X2 offices


Predictor              Coef      SE Coef        T      P
Constant             1.5460       0.1048    14.75  0.000
X2 offices       -0.00012033   0.00001434   -8.39  0.000
                                                             Regression
S = 0.0704917  R-Sq = 75.4%   R-Sq(adj) = 74.3%             coefficient b₂

Analysis of Variance

Source          DF        SS        MS        F      P
Regression       1   0.34973   0.34973    70.38  0.000
Residual Error  23   0.11429   0.00497
Total           24   0.46402
```

We should note that the multiple regression coefficients are *conditional coefficients*; that is, the estimated coefficient b_1 depends on the other independent variables included in the model. This will always be the case in multiple regression unless two independent variables have a sample correlation of zero—a very unlikely event.

These relationships can also be studied by using a "matrix plot" from Minitab, as shown in Figure 12.6. Matrix plots are not available in Excel. Note that the simple relationship between Y and X_2 is clearly linear, whereas the simple relationship between Y and X_1 is somewhat curvilinear. This nonlinear relationship between X_1 and Y explains in part why the coefficient of X_1 changed so dramatically from simple to multiple regression. We see from this example that correlations between independent variables can have a major influence on the estimated coefficients. Thus, if one has a choice, highly correlated independent variables should be avoided. But in many cases we do not have that choice. Regression coefficient estimates are always conditional on the other predictor variables in the model. In this example, profit margin increases as a function of net revenue per deposit dollar. However, the simultaneous increase in number of offices—which reduced profit—would hide the profit increase if a simple regression analysis were used. Thus, proper model specification—that is, choice of predictor variables—is very important. Model specification requires an understanding of the problem context and appropriate theory.

Figure 12.6
Matrix Plots for
Savings and Loan
Variables

EXERCISES

 Visit www.MyStatLab.com or www.pearsonglobal editions.com to access the data files.

Basic Exercise

12.10 Compute the coefficients b_1 and b_2 for the regression model

$$\hat{y}_i = b_0 + b_1 x_{1i} + b_2 x_{2i}$$

given the following summary statistics.

a. $r_{x_1 y} = 0.80$, $r_{x_2 y} = 0.30$, $r_{x_1 x_2} = 0.90$,
   $s_{x_1} = 500$, $s_{x_2} = 400$, $s_y = 100$
b. $r_{x_1 y} = -0.80$, $r_{x_2 y} = -0.30$, $r_{x_1 x_2} = 0.90$,
   $s_{x_1} = 500$, $s_{x_2} = 400$, $s_y = 100$
c. $r_{x_1 y} = 0.40$, $r_{x_2 y} = 0.75$, $r_{x_1 x_2} = 0.90$,
   $s_{x_1} = 500$, $s_{x_2} = 400$, $s_y = 100$
d. $r_{x_1 y} = 0.80$, $r_{x_2 y} = -0.40$, $r_{x_1 x_2} = -0.10$,
   $s_{x_1} = 500$, $s_{x_2} = 400$, $s_y = 100$

Application Exercises

12.11 Consider the following estimated linear regression equations:

$$Y = a_0 + a_1 X_1 \qquad Y = b_0 + b_1 X_1 + b_2 X_2$$

a. Show in detail the coefficient estimators for a_1 and b_1 when the correlation between X_1 and X_2 is equal to 0.
b. Show in detail the coefficient estimators for a_1 and b_1 when the correlation between X_1 and X_2 is equal to 1.

The following exercises require the use of a computer.

12.12 Amalgamated Power, Inc., has asked you to estimate a regression equation to determine the effect of various predictor variables on the demand for electricity sales. You will prepare a series of regression estimates and discuss the results using the quarterly data for electrical sales during the past 17 years in the data file **Power Demand**.

a. Estimate a regression equation with electricity sales as the dependent variable, using the number of customers and the price as predictor variables. Interpret the coefficients.
b. Estimate a regression equation (electricity sales) using only number of customers as a predictor variable. Interpret the coefficient and compare the result to the result from part a.
c. Estimate a regression equation (electricity sales) using the price and degree days as predictor variables. Interpret the coefficients. Compare the coefficient for price with that obtained in part a.
d. Estimate a regression equation (electricity sales) using disposable income and degree days as predictor variables. Interpret the coefficients.

12.13 Transportation Research, Inc., has asked you to prepare some multiple regression equations to estimate the effect of variables on fuel economy. The data for this study are contained in the data file **Motors**, and the dependent variable is miles per gallon—milpgal—as established by the Department of Transportation certification.

a. Prepare a regression equation that uses vehicle horsepower—horsepower—and vehicle weight—weight—as independent variables. Interpret the coefficients.
b. Prepare a second regression equation that adds the number of cylinders—cylinder—as an independent variable to the equation from part a. Interpret the coefficients.
c. Prepare a regression equation that uses number of cylinders and vehicle weight as independent variables. Interpret the coefficients and compare the results with those from parts a and b.
d. Prepare a regression equation that uses vehicle horsepower, vehicle weight, and price as predictor variables. Interpret the coefficients.
e. Write a short report that summarizes your results.

12.14 Transportation Research, Inc., has asked you to prepare some multiple regression equations to estimate the effect of variables on vehicle horsepower. The data for this study are contained in the data file **Motors**, and the dependent variable is vehicle horsepower—horsepower—as established by the Department of Transportation certification.

a. Prepare a regression equation that uses vehicle weight—weight—and cubic inches of cylinder displacement—displacement—as predictor variables. Interpret the coefficients.

b. Prepare a regression equation that uses vehicle weight, cylinder displacement, and number of cylinders—cylinder—as predictor variables. Interpret the coefficients and compare the results with those in part a.

c. Prepare a regression equation that uses vehicle weight, cylinder displacement, and miles per gallon—milpgal—as predictor variables. Interpret the coefficients and compare the results with those in part a.

d. Prepare a regression equation that uses vehicle weight, cylinder displacement, miles per gallon, and price as predictor variables. Interpret the coefficients and compare the results with those in part c.

e. Write a short report that presents the results of your analysis of this problem.

12.3 EXPLANATORY POWER OF A MULTIPLE REGRESSION EQUATION

Multiple regression uses independent variables to explain the behavior of the dependent variable. We find that variability in the dependent variable can, in part, be explained by the linear function of the independent variables. In this section we develop a measure of the proportion of the variability in the dependent variable that can be explained by the multiple regression model.

The estimated regression model from the sample is

$$y_i = b_0 + b_1 x_{1i} + b_2 x_{2i} + \cdots + b_K x_{Ki} + e_i$$

Alternatively, we can write

$$y_i = \hat{y}_i + e_i$$

where

$$\hat{y}_i = b_0 + b_1 x_{1i} + b_2 x_{2i} + \cdots + b_K x_{Ki}$$

is the predicted value of the dependent variable and the residual, e_i, is the difference between the observed and the predicted values. Table 12.2 contains these quantities for the savings and loan example in the first three columns.

We can subtract the sample mean of the dependent variable from both sides, giving

$$(y_i - \bar{y}) = (\hat{y}_i - \bar{y}) + e_i$$
$$= (\hat{y}_i - \bar{y}) + (y_i - \hat{y}_i)$$

which can be stated as follows:

observed deviation from mean = predicted deviation from mean + residual

Then by squaring both sides and summing over the index, i, we have

$$\sum_{i=1}^{n} (y_i - \bar{y})^2 = \sum_{i=1}^{n} (\hat{y}_i - \bar{y} + y_i - \hat{y}_i)^2$$

$$= \sum_{i=1}^{n} (\hat{y}_i - \bar{y})^2 + \sum_{i=1}^{n} e_i^2$$

which is the sum-of-squares decomposition presented in Chapter 11:

$$SST = SSR + SSE$$

sum of squares total = sum of squares regression + sum of squares error

This simplified decomposition occurs because y_i and $\hat{y}_i$ are independent—y_i includes ε and $\hat{y}_i$ does not–and, thus,

$$\sum_{i=1}^{n} (\hat{y}_i - \bar{y})(y_i - \hat{y}_i) = 0$$

Table 12.2
Actual Values, Predicted Values, and Residuals for Savings and Loan Regression

y_i	$\hat{y}_i$	$e_i = y_i - \hat{y}_i$	$y_i - \bar{y}$	$\hat{y}_i - \bar{y}$
0.75	0.677	0.073	0.076	0.003
0.71	0.713	−0.003	0.036	0.039
0.66	0.699	−0.039	−0.014	0.025
0.61	0.672	−0.062	−0.064	−0.002
0.7	0.684	0.016	0.026	0.010
0.72	0.708	0.012	0.046	0.034
0.77	0.740	0.030	0.096	0.066
0.74	0.759	−0.019	0.066	0.085
0.9	0.794	0.106	0.226	0.120
0.82	0.794	0.026	0.146	0.120
0.75	0.798	−0.048	0.076	0.124
0.77	0.827	−0.057	0.096	0.153
0.78	0.802	−0.022	0.106	0.128
0.84	0.799	0.041	0.166	0.125
0.79	0.754	0.036	0.116	0.080
0.7	0.734	−0.034	0.026	0.060
0.68	0.705	−0.025	0.006	0.031
0.72	0.693	0.027	0.046	0.019
0.55	0.635	−0.085	−0.124	−0.039
0.63	0.613	0.017	−0.044	−0.061
0.56	0.570	−0.010	−0.114	−0.104
0.41	0.480	−0.070	−0.264	−0.194
0.51	0.437	0.073	−0.164	−0.237
0.47	0.395	0.075	−0.204	−0.279
0.32	0.377	−0.057	−0.354	−0.297
Sum of squares:		0.0625 (SSE)	0.4640 (SST)	0.4015 (SSR)

Sum-of-Squares Decomposition and the Coefficient of Determination

We begin with the multiple regression model fitted by least squares,

$$y_i = b_0 + b_1 x_{1i} + b_2 x_{2i} + \cdots + b_K x_{Ki} + e_i = \hat{y}_i + e_i$$

where the b_j terms are the least squares estimates of the coefficients of the population regression model and the e terms are the residuals from the estimated regression model.

The model variability can be partitioned into the components

$$SST = SSR + SSE \tag{12.7}$$

where these components are defined as follows:
Sum-of-Squares Total

$$SST = \sum_{i=1}^{n} (y_i - \bar{y})^2 \tag{12.8}$$

$$= \sum_{i=1}^{n} (\hat{y}_i - \bar{y})^2 + \sum_{i=1}^{n} (y_i - \hat{y}_i)^2 \tag{12.9}$$

Sum-of-Squares Error

$$SSE = \sum_{i=1}^{n} (y_i - \hat{y}_i)^2 = \sum_{i=1}^{n} e_i^2 \tag{12.10}$$

Sum-of-Squares Regression or Explained Sum of Squares

$$SSR = \sum_{i=1}^{n}(\hat{y}_i - \bar{y})^2 \qquad (12.11)$$

This decomposition can be interpreted as follows:

total sample variability = explained variability + unexplained variability

The coefficient of determination, R^2, of the fitted regression is defined as the proportion of the total sample variability explained by the regression

$$R^2 = \frac{SSR}{SST} = 1 - \frac{SSE}{SST} \qquad (12.12)$$

and it follows that

$$0 \leq R^2 \leq 1$$

The sum of squared errors is also used to compute the estimation for the variance of population model errors, as shown in Equation 12.13. As with simple regression, the variance of population errors is used for multiple regression statistical inference.

Estimation of Error Variance
Given the population multiple regression model

$$y_i = \beta_0 + \beta_1 x_{1i} + \beta_2 x_{2i} + \cdots + \beta_K x_{Ki} + \varepsilon_i$$

and the standard regression assumptions, let σ^2 denote the common variance of the error term, ε_i. Then an unbiased **estimate of error variance** is

$$s_e^2 = \frac{\sum_{i=1}^{n} e_i^2}{n - K - 1} = \frac{SSE}{n - K - 1} \qquad (12.13)$$

where K is the number of independent variables in the regression model. The square root of the variance, s_e, is also called the **standard error of the estimate**.

At this point we can also compute the mean square regression as follows:

$$MSR = \frac{SSR}{K}$$

We use MSR as a measure of the explained variability adjusted for the number of independent variables.

The sample mean for the savings and loan profit dependent variable is $\bar{y} = 0.674$, and we have used this value to compute the last two columns of Table 12.2. Using the data in Table 12.2 and the components, we can show that

$$SSE = 0.0625 \quad SST = 0.4640 \quad R^2 = 0.87$$

From these results we find that for this sample 87% of the variability in the savings and loan association's profit is explained by the linear relationships with net revenues and number of offices. Note that we could also compute the regression sum of squares from the identity

$$SSR = SST - SSE = 0.4640 - 0.0625 = 0.4015$$

We can also compute an estimate for the error variance σ^2 by using Equation 12.13:

$$s_e^2 = \frac{\sum_{i=1}^{n} e_i^2}{n - K - 1} = \frac{SSE}{n - K - 1} = \frac{0.0625}{25 - 1 - 2} = 0.00284$$

Figure 12.7 presents the regression output from Minitab for the savings and loan association problem, with the various computed sums of squares indicated. These quantities are routinely computed by statistical computer packages, and the detail in Table 12.2 is included only to indicate how the sums of squares are computed. In all of the work that follows, we assume that the sums of squares are calculated by a computer package.

Figure 12.7
Regression Output for the Savings and Loan Association Problem

The components of variability have associated degrees of freedom. The SST quantity has $(n-1)$ degrees of freedom because the mean of Y is required for its computation. The SSR component has K degrees of freedom because K coefficients are required for its computation. Finally, the SSE component has $(n-K-1)$ degrees of freedom because K coefficients and the mean are required for its computation. Note that in Figure 12.7 the output includes the degrees of freedom (DF) associated with each component.

We routinely use the coefficient of determination, R^2, as a descriptive statistic to describe the strength of the linear relationship between the independent X variables and the dependent variable, Y. It is important to emphasize that R^2 can be used only to compare regression models that have the same set of sample observations of y_i, where $i = 1, \ldots, n$. This result is seen from the equation form as follows:

$$R^2 = 1 - \frac{SSE}{SST}$$

Thus, we see that R^2 can be large either because SSE is small—indicating that the observed points are close to the predicted points—or because SST is large. We have seen that SSE and s_e^2 indicate the closeness of the observed points to the predicted points. With the same SST for two or more regression equations, R^2 provides a comparable measure of the goodness of fit for the equations. This is the same result that was shown in the extended example in Section 11.4.

There is a potential problem with using R^2 as an overall measure of the quality of a fitted equation. As additional independent variables are added to a multiple regression model, the explained sum of squares, SSR, will increase—in essentially all applied situations— even if the additional independent variable is not an important predictor variable. Thus, we might find that R^2 has increased spuriously after one or more nonsignificant predictor variables have been added to the multiple regression model. In such a case, the increased value of R^2 would be misleading. To avoid this problem, the adjusted coefficient of determination can be computed as shown in Equation 12.14.

Adjusted Coefficient of Determination

The **adjusted coefficient of determination**, $\bar{R}^2$, is defined as follows:

$$\bar{R}^2 = 1 - \frac{SSE/(n - K - 1)}{SST/(n - 1)} \qquad (12.14)$$

We use this measure to correct for the fact that nonrelevant independent variables will result in some small reduction in the error sum of squares. Thus, the adjusted $\bar{R}^2$ provides a better comparison between multiple regression models with different numbers of independent variables.

Returning to our savings and loan example, we see that

$$n = 25 \quad K = 2 \quad SSE = 0.0625 \quad SST = 0.4640$$

and, thus, the adjusted coefficient of determination is as follows:

$$\bar{R}^2 = 1 - \frac{0.0625/22}{0.4640/24} = 0.853$$

In this example the difference between R^2 and $\bar{R}^2$ is not very large. However, if the regression model had contained a number of independent variables that were not important conditional predictors, then the difference would be substantial. Another measure of relationship in multiple regression is the coefficient of multiple correlation.

Coefficient of Multiple Correlation

The **coefficient of multiple correlation** is the correlation between the predicted value and the observed value of the dependent variable

$$R = r(\hat{y}, y) = \sqrt{R^2} \qquad (12.15)$$

and is equal to the square root of the multiple coefficient of determination. We use R as another measure of the strength of the relationship between the dependent variable and the independent variables. Thus, it is comparable to the correlation between Y and X in simple regression.

EXERCISES

Basic Exercises

12.15 A regression analysis has produced the following analysis of variance table:

Analysis of Variance			
Source	DF	SS	MS
Regression	8	200	
Residual error	18	150	

a. Compute s_e and s_e^2.
b. Compute SST.
c. Compute R^2 and the adjusted coefficient of determination.

12.16 A regression analysis has produced the following analysis of variance table:

Analysis of Variance			
Source	DF	SS	MS
Regression	2	7,000	
Residual error	29	2,500	

a. Compute s_e and s_e^2.
b. Compute SST.

c. Compute R^2 and the adjusted coefficient of determination.

12.17 A regression analysis has produced the following analysis of variance table:

Analysis of Variance			
Source	DF	SS	MS
Regression	4	40,000	
Residual error	45	10,000	

a. Compute s_e and s_e^2.
b. Compute SST.
c. Compute R^2 and the adjusted coefficient of determination.

12.18 A regression analysis has produced the following analysis of variance table:

Analysis of Variance			
Source	DF	SS	MS
Regression	5	80,000	
Residual error	200	15,000	

a. Compute s_e and s_e^2.
b. Compute SST.
c. Compute R^2 and the adjusted coefficient of determination.

Application Exercises

12.19 Inventas Design, an architecture company in Norway, wants to predict the number of worker-hours necessary to finish the design of a new building in Oslo. Relevant explanatory variables were thought to be the number of floors in the building, the weight of materials, and the number of parts it had in common with other structures built by the company. A sample of 15 of the company's buildings was taken, and the following model was estimated:

$$y = \beta_0 + \beta_1 x_1 + \beta_2 x_2 + \beta_3 x_3 + \varepsilon$$

where
y = design effort, in millions of worker-hours
x_1 = number of floors in the building
x_2 = the weight of materials, in tons
x_3 = percentage of parts in common with other buildings

The total sum of squares and regression sum of squares were found to be as follows:

$$SST = 3.991 \quad \text{and} \quad SSR = 3.474$$

a. Compute and interpret the coefficient of determination.
b. Compute the error sum of squares.
c. Compute the adjusted coefficient of determination.
d. Compute and interpret the coefficient of multiple correlation.

12.20 The following model was fitted to a sample of 30 families in order to explain household milk consumption:

$$y = \beta_0 + \beta_1 x_1 + \beta_2 x_2 + \varepsilon$$

where
y = milk consumption, in quarts per week
x_1 = weekly income, in hundreds of dollars
x_2 = family size

The least squares estimates of the regression parameters were as follows:

$$b_0 = -0.025 \quad b_1 = 0.052 \quad b_2 = 1.14$$

The total sum of squares and regression sum of squares were found to be as follows:

$$SST = 162.1 \quad \text{and} \quad SSR = 88.2$$

a. Compute and interpret the coefficient of determination.
b. Compute the adjusted coefficient of determination.
c. Compute and interpret the coefficient of multiple correlation.

12.21 The following model was fitted to a sample of 25 students using data obtained at the end of their freshman year in college. The aim was to explain students' weight gains:

$$y = \beta_0 + \beta_1 x_1 + \beta_2 x_2 + \beta_3 x_3 + \varepsilon$$

where
y = weight gained, in pounds, during freshman year
x_1 = average number of meals eaten per week
x_2 = average number of hours of exercise per week
x_3 = average number of beers consumed per week

The least squares estimates of the regression parameters were as follows:

$$b_0 = 7.35 \quad b_1 = 0.653 \quad b_2 = -1.345 \quad b_3 = 0.613$$

The regression sum of squares and error sum of squares were found to be as follows:

$$SSR = 79.2 \quad \text{and} \quad SSE = 45.9$$

a. Compute and interpret the coefficient of determination.
b. Compute the adjusted coefficient of determination.
c. Compute and interpret the coefficient of multiple correlation.

12.22 Refer to the savings and loan association data given in Table 12.1.

a. Estimate, by least squares, the regression of profit margin on number of offices.
b. Estimate, by least squares, the regression of net revenues on number of offices.
c. Estimate, by least squares, the regression of profit margin on net revenues.
d. Estimate, by least squares, the regression of number of offices on net revenues.

12.4 CONFIDENCE INTERVALS AND HYPOTHESIS TESTS FOR INDIVIDUAL REGRESSION COEFFICIENTS

In Section 12.2 we developed and discussed the point estimators for the parameters of the multiple regression model:

$$y_i = \beta_0 + \beta_1 x_{1i} + \beta_2 x_{2i} + \cdots + \beta_K x_{Ki} + \varepsilon_i$$

Now, we will develop confidence intervals and tests of hypotheses for the estimated regression coefficients. These confidence intervals and hypothesis tests depend on the variance of the coefficients and the probability distribution of the coefficients. In Section 11.5 we showed that the simple regression coefficient is a linear function of the dependent variable, Y. Multiple regression coefficients, denoted by b_j, are also linear functions of the dependent variable, Y, but the algebra is somewhat more complex and is not presented here. In the previous multiple regression equation, we see that the dependent variable, Y, is a linear function of the X variables plus the random error, ε. For a given set of X terms the function

$$\beta_0 + \beta_1 x_{1i} + \beta_2 x_{2i} + \cdots + \beta_K x_{Ki}$$

is actually a constant. We also know from Chapters 4 and 5 that adding a constant to a random variable ε results in the random variable Y having the same probability distribution and variance as the original random variable ε. As a result, the dependent variable, Y, has the same normal distribution and variance as the error term, ε. Then it follows that the regression coefficients, b_j—which are linear functions of Y—also have a normal distribution, and their variance can be derived by using the linear relationship between the regression coefficients and the dependent variable. This computation would follow the same process as used for simple regression in Section 11.5, but the algebra is more complex.

Based on the linear relationship between the coefficients and Y, we know that the coefficient estimates are normally distributed if the model error, ε, is normally distributed. Because of the central limit theorem, we generally find that the coefficient estimates are approximately normally distributed even if ε is not normally distributed. Thus, the hypothesis tests and confidence intervals we develop are not seriously affected by departures from normality in the distribution of the error terms.

We can think of the error term, ε, in the population regression model as including the combined influences on the dependent variable of a multitude of factors not included in the list of independent variables. These factors individually may not have an important influence, but in combination their effect can be important. The fact that the error term is made up of a large number of components whose effects are random provides an intuitive argument for assuming that the coefficient errors are also normally distributed.

As we have seen previously, the coefficient estimators, b_j, are linear functions of Y, and the predicted value of Y is a linear function of the regression coefficient estimators. However, these relationships can sometimes cause interpretation problems. Thus, we will spend time gaining important insights into the variance computations. If we do not understand how the variances are computed, we will not be able to adequately understand hypothesis tests and confidence intervals.

The variance of a coefficient estimate is affected by the sample size, the spread of the X variables, the correlations between the independent variables, and the model error term. Thus, these correlations affect both confidence intervals and tests of hypotheses. Previously, we saw how the correlations between the independent variables influence the coefficient estimators. These correlations between independent variables also increase the variance of the coefficient estimators. An important conclusion is that the variance of the coefficient estimators, in addition to the coefficient estimators, is conditional on the entire set of independent variables in the regression model.

The previous discussion under three-dimensional graphing emphasized the complex effects of several variables on the coefficient variance. As the relationships between independent variables become stronger, estimates of coefficients become more unstable—that is, they have higher variance. The following discussion provides a more formal discussion of these complexities. To obtain good coefficient estimates—those that are low in variance—you should seek a wide range for the independent variables, choose independent variables that are not strongly related to each other, and find a model that is close to all data points. The reality of applied statistical work in business and economics is that we often must use data that are less than ideal, such as the data for the savings and loan example. But by knowing the effects discussed here, we can make good judgments about the applicability of our models.

To gain some understanding of the effect of independent variable correlations, we consider the variance estimators from the estimated multiple regression model with two predictor variables:

$$\hat{y}_i = b_0 + b_1 x_{1i} + b_2 x_{2i}$$

The coefficient variance estimators are

$$s_{b_1}^2 = \frac{s_e^2}{(n-1)s_{x_1}^2(1-r_{x_1x_2}^2)}$$ (12.16)

$$s_{b_2}^2 = \frac{s_e^2}{(n-1)s_{x_2}^2(1-r_{x_1x_2}^2)}$$ (12.17)

and the square roots of these variance estimators, s_{b_1} and s_{b_2}, are called the *coefficient standard errors*.

The variance of the coefficient estimators increases directly with the distance of the points from the line, measured by s_e^2, the estimated error variance. In addition, a wider spread of the independent variable values—measured by $s_{x_1}^2$ or by $s_{x_2}^2$—decreases the coefficient variance. Recall that these results also apply for simple regression coefficient estimators. We also see that the variance of the coefficient estimators increases with increases in the correlation between the independent variables in the model. As the correlation increases between two independent variables, it becomes more difficult to separate the effect of the individual variables for predicting the dependent variables. As the number of independent variables in a model increases, the influences on the coefficient variance continue to be important, but the algebraic structure becomes very complex and is not presented here. The correlation effect leads to the result that coefficient variance estimators are conditional on the other independent variables in the model. Recall that the actual coefficient estimators are also conditional on the other independent variables in the model, again because of the effect of correlations between the independent variables.

The basis for inference about population regression coefficients is summarized next. We are typically more interested in the regression coefficients β_j than in the constant or intercept β_0. Thus, we concentrate on the former, noting that inference about the latter proceeds along similar lines.

Basis for Inference about the Population Regression Parameters

Let the population regression model be as follows:

$$y_i = \beta_0 + \beta_1 x_{1i} + \beta_2 x_{1i} + \cdots + \beta_K x_{Ki} + \varepsilon_i$$

Let $b_0, b_1, \ldots, b_K$ be the least squares estimates of the population parameters and $s_{b_0}, s_{b_1}, \ldots, s_{b_K}$ be the estimated standard deviations of the least squares estimators. Then, if the standard regression assumptions hold and if the error terms, ε_i, are normally distributed,

$$t_{b_j} = \frac{b_j - \beta_j}{s_{b_j}} \quad (j = 1, 2, \ldots, K)$$ (12.18)

is distributed as a Student's t distribution with $(n - K - 1)$ degrees of freedom.

Confidence Intervals

Confidence intervals for the β_j can be derived by using Equation 12.19.

Confidence Intervals for Regression Coefficients

If the population regression errors, ε_i, are normally distributed and the standard regression assumptions hold, the $100(1 - \alpha)\%$ two-sided **confidence intervals for the regression coefficients**, β_j, are given by

$$b_j - t_{n-K-1, \alpha/2} s_{b_j} < \beta_j < b_j + t_{n-K-1, \alpha/2} s_{b_j}$$ (12.19)

where $t_{n-K-1, \alpha/2}$ is the number for which

$$P\left(t_{n-K-1} > t_{n-K-1, \alpha/2}\right) = \frac{\alpha}{2}$$

and the random variable t_{n-K-1} follows a Student's t distribution with $(n - K - 1)$ degrees of freedom.

Example 12.4 Developing the Savings and Loan Model (Confidence Interval Estimation)

We have been asked to determine confidence intervals for the coefficients of the savings and loan regression model developed in Example 12.3.

Solution The Minitab regression output for the savings and loan regression model is shown in Figure 12.8. The coefficient estimators and their standard deviations for the revenue, b_1, and number of offices, b_2, predictor variables are computed as follows:

$$b_1 = 0.2372, \quad s_{b_1} = 0.0556; \quad b_2 = -0.000249 \quad \text{and} \quad s_{b_2} = 0.00003205$$

Figure 12.8 Savings and Loan Regression: Minitab Output

Regression Analysis: Y profit versus X1 revenue, X2 offices

```
The regression equation is
Y profit = 1.56 + 0.237 X1 revenue - 0.000249 X2 offices

Predictor          Coef       SE Coef        T         P
Constant         1.56450      0.07940      19.70     0.000
X1 revenue       0.23720      0.05556       4.27     0.000
X2 offices      -0.00024908   0.00003205   -7.77     0.000

S = 0.0533022   R-Sq = 86.5%    R-Sq(adj) = 85.3%

Analysis of Variance

Source           DF        SS         MS        F         P
Regression        2      0.40151    0.20076    70.66    0.000
Residual Error    22     0.06250    0.00284
Total             24     0.46402

Source           DF      Seq SS
X1 revenue        1      0.22990
X2 offices        1      0.17161
```

Thus, we see that the standard deviation of the sampling distribution of the least squares estimator for β_1 is estimated as 0.05556 and for β_2 is estimated as 0.00003205.

To obtain the 99% confidence intervals for β_1 and β_2, we use the Student's t value from Appendix Table 8.

$$t_{n-K-1, \alpha/2} = t_{22, 0.005} = 2.819$$

Using these results, we find that the 99% coefficient confidence interval for β_1 is

$$0.237 - (2.819)(0.05556) < \beta_1 < 0.237 + (2.819)(0.05556)$$

or

$$0.080 < \beta_1 < 0.394$$

Thus, the 99% confidence interval for the expected increase in the savings and loan profit margin resulting from a one-unit increase in net revenue per dollar, given a fixed number of offices, runs from 0.080 to 0.394. The 99% coefficient confidence interval for β_2 is

$$-0.000249 - (2.819)(0.0000320) < \beta_2 < -0.000249 + (2.819)(0.0000320)$$

or

$$-0.000339 < \beta_2 < -0.000159$$

Therefore, we see that the 99% confidence interval for the expected decrease in the profit margin resulting from an increase of 1,000 offices, for a fixed level of net revenue per dollar, runs from 0.159 to 0.339.

Tests of Hypotheses

Tests of hypotheses for regression coefficients can be developed using the coefficient variance estimates. Of particular interest is the hypothesis test

$$H_0 : \beta_j = 0$$

which is frequently used to determine if a specific independent variable is conditionally important in a multiple regression model.

Tests of Hypotheses for the Regression Coefficients

If the regression errors, ε_i, are normally distributed and the standard regression assumptions hold, then the following hypothesis tests have significance level α:

1. To test either null hypothesis

$$H_0 : \beta_j = \beta^* \quad \text{or} \quad H_0 : \beta_j \leq \beta^*$$

against the alternative

$$H_1 : \beta_j > \beta^*$$

the decision rule is as follows:

$$\text{reject } H_0 \text{ if } \frac{b_j - \beta^*}{s_{b_j}} > t_{n-K-1,\alpha} \tag{12.20}$$

2. To test either null hypothesis

$$H_0 : \beta_j = \beta^* \quad \text{or} \quad H_0 : \beta_j \geq \beta^*$$

against the alternative

$$H_1 : \beta_j < \beta^*$$

the decision rule is as follows:

$$\text{reject } H_0 \text{ if } \frac{b_j - \beta^*}{s_{b_j}} < -t_{n-K-1,\alpha} \tag{12.21}$$

3. To test the null hypothesis

$$H_0 : \beta_j = \beta^*$$

against the two-sided alternative

$$H_1 : \beta_j \neq \beta^*$$

the decision rule is as follows:

$$\text{reject } H_0 \text{ if } \frac{b_j - \beta^*}{s_{b_j}} > t_{n-K-1,\alpha/2} \quad \text{or} \quad \frac{b_j - \beta^*}{s_{b_j}} < -t_{n-K-1,\alpha/2} \tag{12.22}$$

Many analysts argue that if we cannot reject the conditional hypothesis that the coefficient is 0, then we must conclude that the variable should not be included in the regression model. The Student's t statistic for this two-tailed test is typically computed in most regression programs and is printed next to the coefficient variance estimate; in addition, the p-value for the hypothesis test is typically included. These are shown in the Minitab output in Figure 12.8. Using the printed Student's t statistic or the p-value, we can immediately conclude whether or not a particular predictor variable is conditionally significant, given the other variables in the regression model.

There are clearly other procedures for deciding if an independent variable should be included in a regression model. We see that the preceding selection procedure ignores Type II error—the population coefficient is not equal to 0, but we fail to reject the null hypothesis that it is equal to 0. This is a particular problem when a model based on economic or another theory that is carefully specified to include certain independent variables. Then, because of a large error, ε, or correlations between independent variables, or both, we cannot reject the hypothesis that the coefficient is 0. In this case many analysts will include the independent variable in the model because the original model specification based on economic theory or experience is believed to dominate. This is a difficult issue and requires good judgment based on both statistical results and theory concerning the underlying relationship being modeled.

Example 12.5 Developing the Savings and Loan Model (Coefficient Hypothesis Tests)

We have been asked to determine if the coefficients in the savings and loan regression model are conditionally significant predictors of profit margin.

Solution The hypothesis test for this question will use the Minitab regression results shown in Figure 12.8. First, we wish to determine if the variable net revenue per dollar has a significant effect on increasing profit margin, conditional on or controlling for the effect of the variable number of offices. The null hypothesis is

$$H_0 : \beta_1 = 0$$

versus the alternative hypothesis

$$H_1 : \beta_1 > 0$$

The test can be performed by computing the Student's t statistic associated with the coefficient, given H_0:

$$t_{b_1} = \frac{b_1 - \beta_1}{s_{b_1}} = \frac{0.237 - 0}{0.05556} = 4.27$$

From the Student's t table, Appendix Table 8, we can determine that the critical value— for $\alpha = 0.005$– for the Student's t statistic is as follows:

$$t_{22,0.005} = 2.819$$

Figure 12.8 also indicates that the p-value for the null hypothesis test

$$H_0 : \beta_1 = 0$$

versus the alternative hypothesis

$$H_1 : \beta_1 \neq 0$$

is less than 0.005. Based on this evidence, we reject H_0 and accept H_1 and conclude that net revenue per dollar is a statistically significant predictor of increased profit margin for savings and loans, given that we have controlled for the effect of the number of offices.

Similarly, we can determine if the total number of offices has a significant effect on reducing profit margins. The null hypothesis is

$$H_0 : \beta_2 = 0$$

versus the alternative hypothesis

$$H_1 : \beta_2 < 0$$

The test can be performed by computing the Student's t statistic associated with the coefficient, given H_0:

$$t_{b_2} = \frac{b_2 - \beta_2}{s_{b_2}} = \frac{-0.000249 - 0}{0.0000320} = -7.77$$

From Appendix Table 8 we find that the critical value for the Student's t statistic is as follows:

$$t_{22, 0.005} = -2.819$$

Figure 12.8 also indicates that the p-value for the null hypothesis test

$$H_0 : \beta_2 = 0$$

versus the alternative hypothesis

$$H_1 : \beta_2 \neq 0$$

is less than 0.005. Based on this evidence, we reject H_0 and accept H_1 and conclude that number of offices is a statistically significant predictor of lower profit margin for savings and loans, given that we have controlled for the effect of net revenue per dollar.

It is important to emphasize that both of the hypothesis tests are based on the particular set of variables included in the regression model. If, for example, additional predictor variables were included, then these tests would no longer be valid. With additional variables in the model the coefficient estimates and their estimated standard deviations would be different, and, thus, the Student's t statistics would also be different.

Note that in the Minitab regression output for this problem, shown in Figure 12.8, the Student's t statistic for the null hypothesis—$H_0 : \beta_j = 0$—is computed as the ratio of the estimated coefficient divided by the estimated coefficient standard error—contained in the two columns to the left of the Student's t. The probability, or p-value, for the two-tailed hypothesis test—$H_j : \beta_j \neq 0$—is also displayed. Thus, an analyst can perform these hypothesis tests directly by examining the multiple regression output. The Student's t and the p-value are computed in every modern statistical package. Most analysts routinely look for these test results as they examine regression output from a computer statistical package.

Example 12.6 Factors Affecting Property Tax Rate (Analysis of Regression Coefficients)

A group of city managers commissioned a study to determine the factors that influence urban property-tax rates for cities with populations between 100,000 and 200,000.

Solution Using a sample of 20 U.S. cities, the following regression model was estimated:

$$\hat{y} = 1.79 + \underset{(0.000139)}{0.000567 x_1} + \underset{(0.0082)}{0.0183 x_2} - \underset{(0.000446)}{0.000191 x_3}$$

$$R^2 = 0.71 \qquad n = 20$$

where

y = effective property tax rate (actual levies divided by market value of the tax base)
x_1 = number of housing units per square mile
x_2 = percentage of total city revenue represented by grants from state and federal governments
x_3 = median per capita personal income, in dollars

The numbers in parentheses under the coefficients are the estimated coefficient standard errors.

The preceding presentation of the regression equation and variable definition provides a good format for displaying the results of a regression analysis model. The results indicate that the conditional estimates of the effects of the three predictor variables are as follows:

1. An increase of one housing unit per square mile increases the effective property tax rate by 0.000567. Note that property tax rates are typically expressed in terms of dollars per $1,000 of assessed property value. Thus, an increase of 0.000567 indicates that property tax rates are higher by $0.567 per $1,000 of assessed property value.
2. An increase of 1% of the total city revenue from state and federal grants increases the effective tax rate by 0.0183.
3. An increase of $1 in median per capita personal income leads to an expected decrease in the effective tax rate by 0.000191. Note that the ratio of 0.000191 divided by 0.000446 gives a t value less than 2.

We emphasize again that these coefficient estimates are valid only for a model with all three predictor variables included.

To better understand the accuracy of these effects, we construct conditional 95% confidence intervals. For the estimated regression model there are $(20 - 3 - 1) = 16$ degrees of freedom for error. Thus, the Student's t statistic for computing confidence intervals is, from the Appendix, $t_{16, 0.025} = 2.12$. The format for confidence intervals is as follows:

$$b_j - t_{n-K-1, \alpha/2} s_{bj} < \beta_j < b_j + t_{n-K-1, \alpha/2} s_{bj}$$

Thus, the coefficient for the number of housing units per square mile has a 95% confidence interval of

$$0.000567 - (2.12)(0.000139) < \beta_1 < 0.000567 + (2.12)(0.000139)$$
$$0.000272 < \beta_1 < 0.000862$$

The coefficient for the percentage of revenue represented by grants has a 95% confidence interval of

$$0.0183 - (2.12)(0.0082) < \beta_2 < 0.0183 + (2.12)(0.0082)$$
$$0.0009 < \beta_2 < 0.0357$$

Finally, the coefficient for median per capita personal income has a 95% confidence interval of

$$-0.000191 - (2.12)(0.000446) < \beta_3 < -0.000191 + (2.12)(0.000446)$$
$$-0.001137 < \beta_3 < 0.000755$$

Again, we emphasize that these intervals are conditional on all three predictor variables being included in the model.

We see that the 95% confidence interval for β_3 includes 0, and, thus, we could not reject the two-tailed hypothesis that this coefficient is 0. Based on this confidence interval, we conclude that X_3 is not a statistically significant predictor variable in the multiple regression model. However, the confidence intervals for the other two variables do not include 0, and, thus, we conclude that they are statistically significant.

Example 12.7 Effects of Fiscal Factors on Housing Prices (Regression Model Coefficient Estimation)

Northern City, Minnesota, was interested in the effect of local property development on the market price of houses in the city. Northern City is one of many small, nonmetropolitan, midwestern cities with populations in the range from 6,000 to 40,000. One of the objectives was to determine how increased commercial property development would influence the value of local housing. Data are stored in the data file **Citydatr**.

Solution To answer this question, data were collected from a number of cities and used to construct a regression model that estimates the effect of key variables on housing price. For this study the following variables were obtained for each city:

Y (hseval) = mean market price for houses in the city

X_1 (sizehse) = mean number of rooms in houses

X_2 (incom72) = mean household income

X_3 (taxrate) = tax rate per thousand dollars of assessed value for houses

X_4 (Comper) = percentage of taxable property that is commercial property

The multiple regression output, prepared using Minitab, is shown in Figure 12.9. The coefficient for the mean number of rooms in city houses is 7.878, with a coefficient standard deviation of 1.809. In this study housing values are in units of $1,000, with a mean of $21,000 over all cities. Thus, if the mean number of rooms in a city's houses was larger by 1.0, then the mean price would be larger by $7,878. The resulting Student's t statistic is 4.35 and the p-value is 0.000. Thus, the conditional hypothesis that this coefficient is equal to 0 is rejected. The same result occurs for the income and tax rate variables. The incom72 variable is in units of dollars, and, thus, if a city's mean income is higher by $1,000, the coefficient of 0.003666 indicates that mean housing price will be $3,666 higher. If the tax rate increases by 1%, mean housing price is reduced by $1,718. We see that the regression analysis leads to the conclusion that each of these three variables is a significant predictor of the mean house price in the cities included in this study. However, we see that the coefficient for the percent of commercial property, Comper, is −10.614, with a coefficient standard deviation of 6.491, resulting in a Student's t statistic equal to −1.64. Note that here is an important area for judgment. The coefficient would have a single-tail p-value of 0.053 or a two-tailed p-value of 0.106. Thus, it appears to have some effect in reducing the mean price of houses. Given that the effects of house size, income, and tax rate on the market price for houses have been included, we see that the percent of commercial property does not increase housing prices. Thus, the argument that the market value of houses will increase if more commercial property is developed is not supported by this analysis. That conclusion is true only for a model that includes these four predictor variables. Note also that the values of $R^2 = 47.4\%$ and s_e (standard error of the regression) = 3.677 are included in the regression output.

Figure 12.9 Housing Price Regression Model (Minitab Output)

Regression Analysis: hseval versus sizehse, income72, taxrate, Comper

```
The regression equation is
hseval = -28.1 + 7.88 sizehse + 0.00367 incom72 - 172 taxrate -10.6 Comper

Predictor          Coef      SE Coef        T       P
Constant        -28.075        9.766    -2.87   0.005
sizehse           7.878        1.809     4.35   0.000
incom72        0.003666     0.001344     2.73   0.008
taxrate         -171.80        43.09    -3.99   0.000
Comper          -10.614        6.491    -1.64   0.106


S = 3.67686     R-Sq = 47.4%     R-Sq(adj) = 45.0%

Analysis of Variance

Source            DF         SS        MS        F       P
Regression         4    1037.49    259.37    19.19   0.000
Residual Error    85    1149.14     13.52
Total             89    2186.63
```

The advocates of increased commercial development also claimed that increasing the amount of commercial property would decrease the taxes paid on owner-occupied houses. This claim was tested using the regression output in Figure 12.10, prepared using Excel. The coefficient estimators and their standard errors are indicated. The Student's t statistics for the size of house and the tax-rate coefficients are 2.65 and 6.36, indicating that these variables are important predictors. The Student's t statistic for income is 1.83, with a p-value of 0.07 for a two-tailed test. Thus, income has some influence as a predictor, but its effect is not as strong as the previous two variables. Again, we see a place for good judgment that considers the problem context. The conditional hypothesis that increased commercial property decreases taxes on owner-occupied houses can be tested using the conditional Student's t statistic for the variable "Comper" in the regression output. The conditional Student's t statistic is -1.03, with a p-value of 0.308. Thus, the hypothesis that increased commercial property does not decrease house taxes cannot be rejected. There is no evidence from this analysis that house taxes would be lowered if there was additional commercial development.

Figure 12.10 House-Tax Regression Model (Excel Output)

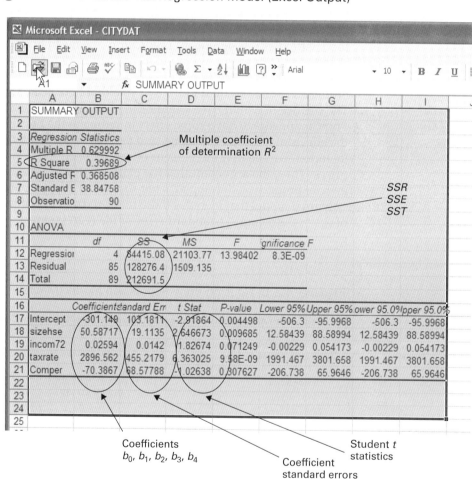

Based on the regression analyses performed in this study, the consultants concluded that there was no evidence that increased commercial property would either increase the market value of houses or lower the property taxes for a house.

Visit **www.MyStatLab.com** or **www.pearsonglobal editions.com** to access the data files.

Basic Exercises

12.23 The results from a regression model analysis are shown as follows:

$$\hat{y} = -61.50 + 21.8x_1 + 23.7x_2 - 15.4x_3$$
$$\quad\quad\quad\quad\;\; (2.1)\quad\;\;\; (22.4)\quad\;\; (32.4)$$

$$R^2 = 0.74 \quad\quad\quad n = 25$$

The numbers below the coefficient estimates are the sample standard errors of the coefficient estimates.

a. Compute two-sided 95% confidence intervals for the three regression slope coefficients.

b. For each of the slope coefficients, at the 5% level of significance, test the hypothesis

$$H_0 : \beta_j = 0$$

12.24 The following are results from a regression model analysis:

$$\hat{y} = -3.54 + 7.4x_1 + 3.2x_2 + 10.1x_3$$
$$\quad\quad\quad\; (1.8)\quad\;\; (1.4)\quad\;\; (4.3)$$

$$R^2 = 0.78 \quad\quad\quad n = 41$$

The numbers below the coefficient estimates are the sample standard errors of the coefficient estimates.

a. Compute two-sided 95% confidence intervals for the three regression slope coefficients.

b. For each of the slope coefficients, test the hypothesis

$$H_0 : \beta_j = 0$$

12.25 The following are results from a regression model analysis:

$$\hat{y} = -3.54 + 7.4x_1 + 3.2x_2 + 10.1x_3$$
$$\quad\quad\quad\; (4.2)\quad\;\; (0.7)\quad\;\; (13.2)$$

$$R^2 = 0.78 \quad\quad\quad n = 41$$

The numbers in parentheses under the coefficients are the estimated coefficient standard errors.

a. Compute two-sided 95% confidence intervals for the three regression slope coefficients.

b. For each of the slope coefficients test the hypothesis

$$H_0 : \beta_j = 0$$

12.26 The following are results from a regression model analysis:

$$\hat{y} = -9.50 + 17.8x_1 + 26.9x_2 - 9.2x_3$$
$$\quad\quad\quad\quad (7.1)\quad\;\; (13.7)\quad\;\; (3.8)$$

$$R^2 = 0.71 \quad\quad\quad n = 39$$

The numbers in parentheses under the coefficients are the estimated coefficient standard errors.

a. Compute two-sided 95% confidence intervals for the three regression slope coefficients.

b. For each of the slope coefficients test the hypothesis

$$H_0 : \beta_j = 0$$

Application Exercises

12.27 The Norwegian architecture company, Inventas Design, wants to predict the number of worker-hours necessary to finish the design of a new building in Tromsø. Relevant explanatory variables were thought to be the number of floors in the building, the weight of materials, and the number of parts it had in common with other structures built by the company. A sample of 23 of the company's structures was taken, and the following model was estimated:

$$y = \beta_0 + \beta_1x_1 + \beta_2x_2 + \beta_3x_3 + \varepsilon$$

where

$y =$ design effort, in millions of worker-hours
$x_1 =$ number of floors in the building
$x_2 =$ the weight of materials, in tons
$x_3 =$ percentage of parts in common with other buildings

The estimated regression coefficients were as follows:

$$b_1 = 0.631, \quad b_2 = 0.066, \quad b_3 = 0.017$$

The estimated standard errors were as follows:

$$s_{b_1} = 0.096, \quad s_{b_2} = 0.037, \quad s_{b_3} = 0.0023$$

a. Find 90% and 95% confidence intervals for β_1.

b. Find 95% and 99% confidence intervals for β_2.

c. Test against a two-sided alternative the null hypothesis that, all else being equal, the plane's weight has no linear influence on its design effort.

d. The error sum of squares for this regression was 0.397. Using the same data, a simple linear regression of design effort on the percentage of common parts was fitted, yielding an error sum of squares of 3.397. Test, at the 2% level, the null hypothesis that, taken together, the variable's number of floors and weight of materials contribute nothing in a linear sense to explaining the changes in the variable, design effort, given that the variable percentage of common parts is also used as an explanatory variable.

12.28 The following model was fitted to a sample of 30 families in order to explain household milk consumption:

$$y = \beta_0 + \beta_1x_1 + \beta_2x_2 + \varepsilon$$

where

$y =$ milk consumption, in quarts per week
$x_1 =$ weekly income, in hundreds of dollars
$x_2 =$ family size

The least squares estimates of the regression parameters were as follows:

$$b_0 = -0.025 \quad b_1 = 0.052 \quad b_2 = 1.14$$

The estimated standard errors were as follows:

$$s_{b_1} = 0.023 \quad s_{b_2} = 0.35$$

a. Test, against the appropriate one-sided alternative, the null hypothesis that, for fixed family size, milk consumption does not depend linearly on income.

b. Find 90%, 95%, and 99% confidence intervals for β_2.

12.29 The following model was fitted to a sample of 25 students using data obtained at the end of their freshman year in college. The aim was to explain students' weight gains:

$$y = \beta_0 + \beta_1x_1 + \beta_2x_2 + \beta_3x_3 + \varepsilon$$

where

y = weight gained, in pounds, during freshman year
x_1 = average number of meals eaten per week
x_2 = average number of hours of exercise per week
x_3 = average number of beers consumed per week

The least squares estimates of the regression parameters were as follows:

$$b_0 = 7.35 \quad b_1 = 0.653 \quad b_2 = -1.345 \quad b_3 = 0.613$$

The estimated standard errors were as follows:

$$s_{b_1} = 0.189 \quad s_{b_2} = 0.565 \quad s_{b_3} = 0.243$$

a. Test, against the appropriate one-sided alternative, the null hypothesis that, all else being equal, hours of exercise do not linearly influence weight gain.
b. Test, against the appropriate one-sided alternative, the null hypothesis that, all else being equal, beer consumption does not linearly influence weight gain.
c. Find 90%, 95%, and 99% confidence intervals for β_1.

12.30 Refer to the data of Example 12.6.

a. Test, against a two-sided alternative, the null hypothesis that, all else being equal, median per capita personal income has no influence on the effective property tax rate.
b. Test the null hypothesis that, taken together, the three independent variables do not linearly influence the effective property tax rate.

12.31 Refer to the data of Example 12.7 with the data file **Citydatr**.

a. Find 95% and 99% confidence intervals for the expected change in the market price for houses resulting from a one-unit increase in the mean number of rooms when the values of all other independent variables remain unchanged.
b. Test the null hypothesis that, all else being equal, mean household income does not influence the market price against the alternative that the higher the mean household income, the higher the market price.

12.32 In a study of revenue generated by national lotteries, the following regression equation was fitted to data from 29 countries with lotteries:

$$y = -31.323 + 0.4045x_1 + 0.8772x_2 - 365.01x_3 - 9.9298x_4$$
$$(0.00755) \quad (0.3107) \quad (263.88) \quad (3.4520)$$

$$R^2 = .51$$

where

y = dollars of net revenue per capita per year generated by the lottery
x_1 = mean per capita personal income of the country
x_2 = number of hotel, motel, inn, and resort rooms per thousand persons in the country
x_3 = spendable revenue per capita per year generated by pari-mutuel betting, racing, and other legalized gambling
x_4 = percentage of the nation's border contiguous with a state or states with a lottery

The numbers in parentheses under the coefficients are the estimated coefficient standard errors.

a. Interpret the estimated coefficient on x_1.
b. Find and interpret a 95% confidence interval for the coefficient on x_2 in the population regression.
c. Test the null hypothesis that the coefficient on x_3 in the population regression is 0 against the alternative that this coefficient is negative. Interpret your findings.

12.33 A study was conducted to determine whether certain features could be used to explain variability in the prices of furnaces. For a sample of 21 furnaces, the following regression was estimated:

$$\hat{y} = -64.64 + 0.0011x_1 + 23.799x_2 - 5.403x_3 \quad R^2 = 0.87$$
$$\phantom{\hat{y} = -64.64 + }(0.005) \quad (10.056) \quad (3.833)$$

where

y = price in euros
x_1 = the rating of the furnace in BTU per hour
x_2 = the energy efficiency ratio
x_3 = the number of settings

The numbers in parentheses under the coefficients are the estimated coefficient standard errors.

a. Find a 95% confidence interval for the expected increase in price resulting from an additional setting when the values of the rating and the energy efficiency ratio remain fixed.
b. Test the null hypothesis that, all else being equal, the energy efficiency ratio of furnaces does not affect their price against the alternative that the higher the energy efficiency ratio, the higher the price.

12.34 In a study of differences in levels of community demand for firefighters, the following sample regression was obtained, based on 46 towns in Bavaria, Germany:

$$\hat{y} = -0.00178 - 0.00035x_1 - 0.00002x_2 + 0.00036x_3$$
$$\phantom{\hat{y} = -0.00178 }(0.00010) \quad (0.000016) \quad (0.00014)$$

$$+ 0.52569x_4 + 0.05146x_5 - 0.00009x_6 + 0.00743x_7$$
$$(0.68648) \quad (0.01367) \quad (0.00004) \quad (0.00348)$$

$$\overline{R}^2 = 0.3572$$

where

y = number of full-time firefighters per capita
x_1 = maximum base salary of firefighters, in thousands of euro
x_2 = percentage of population
x_3 = estimated per capita income, in thousands of euro
x_4 = population density
x_5 = amount of intergovernmental grants per capita, in thousands of euro
x_6 = number of miles from the regional city
x_7 = percentage of the population that is male and between 12 and 21 years of age

The numbers in parentheses under the coefficients are the estimated coefficient standard errors.

a. Find and interpret a 99% confidence interval for β_5.
b. Test, against a two-sided alternative, the null hypothesis that β_4 is 0, and interpret your result.
c. Test, against a two-sided alternative, the null hypothesis that β_7 is 0, and interpret your result.

In the previous section we showed how a conditional hypothesis test can be conducted to determine if a specific variable coefficient is conditionally significant in a regression model. There are, however, situations where we are interested in the effect of the combination of several variables. For example, in a model that predicts quantity sold, we might be interested in the combined effect of both the seller's price and the competitor's price. In other cases we might be interested in knowing if the combination of all variables is a useful predictor of the dependent variable.

Tests on All Coefficients

First, we present hypothesis tests to determine if sets of several coefficients are all simultaneously equal to 0. Consider again the model:

$$y = \beta_0 + \beta_1 x_1 + \beta_2 x_1 + \cdots + \beta_K x_K + \varepsilon$$

We begin by considering the null hypothesis that all the coefficients are simultaneously equal to zero:

$$H_0 : \beta_1 = \beta_2 = \cdots = \beta_K = 0$$

Accepting this hypothesis would lead us to conclude that none of the predictor variables in the regression model is statistically significant and, thus, that they provide no useful information. If this were to occur, then we would need to go back to the model-specification process and develop a new set of predictor variables. Fortunately, in most applied regression situations this hypothesis is rejected because the specification process usually leads to identification of at least one significant predictor variable.

To test this hypothesis, we can use the partitioning of variability developed in Section 12.3:

$$SST = SSR + SSE$$

Recall that SSR is the amount of variability explained by the regression and that SSE is the amount of unexplained variability. Also recall that the variance of the regression model can be estimated by using the following:

$$s_e^2 = \frac{SSE}{(n - K - 1)}$$

If the null hypothesis that all coefficients are equal to 0 is true, then *the mean square regression,*

$$MSR = \frac{SSR}{K}$$

is also a measure of error with K degrees of freedom. As a result, the ratio

$$F = \frac{SSR/K}{SSE/(n - K - 1)}$$
$$= \frac{MSR}{s_e^2}$$

has an F distribution with K degrees of freedom for the numerator and $(n - K - 1)$ degrees of freedom for the denominator. If the null hypothesis is true, then both the numerator and the denominator provide estimates of the population variance. As noted in Section 11.5, the ratio of independent sample variances from populations with equal population variances follows an F distribution if the populations are normally distributed. The computed value of F is compared with the critical value of F from Appendix Table 9 at a significance level α. If the computed value exceeds the critical value from the table, we reject the null hypothesis and conclude that at least one coefficient is not equal to 0. This test procedure is summarized in Equation 12.23.

Test on All the Coefficients of a Regression Model

Consider the multiple regression model:

$$y = \beta_0 + \beta_1 x_1 + \beta_2 x_2 + \cdots + \beta_K x_K + \varepsilon$$

To test the null hypothesis

$$H_0: \beta_1 = \beta_2 = \cdots = \beta_K = 0$$

against the alternative hypothesis

$$H_1: \text{at least one } \beta_j \neq 0$$

at a significance level α, we use the decision rule

$$\text{reject } H_0: \text{if} \quad F_{K,n-K-1} = \frac{MSR}{s_e^2} > F_{K,n-K-1,\alpha} \tag{12.23}$$

where $F_{K,n-K-1,\alpha}$ is the critical value of F from Appendix Table 9 for which

$$P\left(F_{K,n-K-1} > F_{K,n-K-1,\alpha}\right) = \alpha$$

The computed random variable $F_{K,n-K-1}$ follows an F distribution with numerator degrees of freedom K and denominator degrees of freedom $(n - K - 1)$.

Example 12.8 Housing Price Prediction Model (Simultaneous Coefficient Testing)

During the development of the housing price prediction model for Northern City, the analysts wanted to know if there was evidence that the combination of four predictor variables was not a significant predictor of housing price. That is, they wanted to test, at a 99% confidence level, the hypothesis

$$H_0: \beta_1 = \beta_2 = \beta_3 = \beta_4 = 0$$

Solution This testing procedure can be illustrated by the housing price regression in Figure 12.9 prepared using the **Citydatr** data file. In the analysis of variance table, the computed F statistic is 19.19, with 4 degrees of freedom for the numerator and 85 degrees of freedom for the denominator. The computation of F is as follows:

$$F = \frac{259.37}{13.52} = 19.184$$

This exceeds the critical value of $F = 3.548$ for $\alpha = 0.01$ from Appendix Table 9. In addition, note that Minitab—and most statistics packages—compute the p-value, which in this example is equal to 0.000. Thus, we would reject the hypothesis that all coefficients are equal to zero.

Test on a Subset of Regression Coefficients

In the previous sections we developed hypothesis tests for individual regression parameters and for all regression parameters taken together. Next, we develop a hypothesis test for a subset of regression parameters, such as the combined price example previously discussed. We use this test to determine if the combined effect of several independent variables is significant in a regression model.

Consider a regression model that contains independent variables designated as X_j and Z_j terms:

$$y = \beta_0 + \beta_1 x_1 + \cdots + \beta_K x_K + \alpha_1 z_1 + \cdots + \alpha_R z_R + \varepsilon$$

and the null hypothesis to be tested is as follows:

$$H_0: \alpha_1 = \alpha_2 = \cdots = \alpha_R = 0 \text{ given } \beta_j \neq 0, j = 1, \dots, K$$

If H_0 is true, then the Z_j variables should not be included in the regression model because they provide nothing further to explain the behavior of the dependent variable beyond what the X_j variables provided. The procedure for performing this test is summarized in Equation 12.24, following a detailed discussion of the testing procedure.

The test is conducted by comparing the error sum of squares, SSE, from the complete regression model, which includes both the X and the Z variables, with the $SSE(R)$ from a restricted model that includes only the X variables. First, we run a regression on the complete regression model and obtain the error sum of squares, designated as SSE. Next, we run the restricted regression, which excludes the Z variables (note that the coefficients α_j are all restricted to values of 0 in this regression):

$$y = \beta_0 + \beta_1 x_1 + \cdots + \beta_K x_K + \varepsilon^*$$

From this regression we obtain the restricted error sum of squares, designated as $SSE(R)$. Then we compute the F statistic with r degrees of freedom for the numerator, where r is the number of variables removed simultaneously from the restricted model and there are $(n - K - R - 1)$ degrees of freedom for the denominator, the degrees of freedom for error in the model that includes both the X and the Z independent variables. The F statistic is

$$F = \frac{(SSE(R) - SSE)/R}{s_e^2}$$

where s_e^2 is the estimated variance of the error for the complete model. This statistic follows an F distribution with R degrees of freedom in the numerator and $(n - K - R - 1)$ degrees of freedom in the denominator. If the computed F is greater than the critical value of F, then the null hypothesis is rejected, and we conclude that the Z variables as a set should be included in the model. Note that this test does not imply that individual Z variables should not be excluded by, for example, using the Student's t test discussed previously. In addition, the test for all Z's does not imply that a subset of the Z variables cannot be excluded by using this test procedure with a different subset of Z variables.

Test on a Subset of the Regression Parameters

Given a regression model with the independent variables partitioned into X and Z subsets,

$$y = \beta_0 + \beta_1 x_1 + \cdots + \beta_K x_K + \alpha_1 z_1 + \cdots + \alpha_R z_R + \varepsilon$$

To test the null hypothesis

$$H_0: \alpha_1 = \alpha_2 = \cdots = \cdots = \alpha_R = 0$$

which states that the regression parameters in a particular subset are simultaneously equal to 0, against the alternative hypothesis

$$H_1: \text{At least one } \alpha_j \neq 0 \, (j = 1, \dots, R)$$

We compare the error sum of squares for the complete model with the error sum of squares for the restricted model. First, run a regression for the complete model, which includes all independent variables, and obtain the error sum of squares, SSE. Next, run a restricted regression, which excludes the Z variables whose coefficients are the α_i's—the number of variables excluded is R. From this regression obtain the restricted error sum of squares, $SSE(R)$. Then compute the F statistic and apply the decision rule for significance level α:

$$\text{reject } H_0 \text{ if } F = \frac{(SSE(R) - SSE)/R}{s_e^2} > F_{R, n-K-R-1, \alpha} \qquad (12.24)$$

Comparison of F and t Tests

If we used Equation 12.24 with $R = 1$, we could test the hypothesis that a single variable, X_j, does not improve the prediction of the dependent variable, given the other independent variables in the model. Thus, we have the following hypothesis test:

$$H_0 : \beta_j = 0 \,|\, \beta_l \neq 0, \quad j \neq l \quad l = 1, \ldots, K$$
$$H_1 : \beta_j \neq 0 \,|\, \beta_l \neq 0, \quad j \neq l \quad l = 1, \ldots, K$$

Previously, we saw that this test could also be performed using a Student's t test. Using methods beyond this book, we can show that the corresponding F and t tests provide exactly the same conclusions regarding the hypothesis test for a single variable. In addition, the computed t statistic for the coefficient b_j is equal to the square root of the corresponding computed F statistic. That is,

$$t_{b_j}^2 = F_{x_j}$$

where F_{x_j} is the F statistic computed using Equation 12.24 when variable x_j is excluded from the model and, thus, $R = 1$. We show this numerical result in Example 12.9.

Statistical distribution theory also shows that an F random variable with 1 degree of freedom in the numerator is the square of a t random variable with the same degrees of freedom as the denominator of the F random variable. Thus, the F and t tests will always provide the same conclusions regarding the hypothesis test for a single independent variable in a multiple regression model.

Example 12.9 Housing Price Prediction for Small Cities (Hypothesis Tests for Coefficient Subsets)

The developers of the housing price prediction model from Example 12.8 wanted to determine if the combined effect of tax rate and percent commercial property contributes to the prediction after the effects of house size and income have been previously included. Data for this example are in the data file **Citydatr**.

Solution Continuing with the problem from Examples 12.7 and 12.8, we have a conditional test of the hypothesis that two variables are not significant predictors, given that the other two are significant predictors:

$$H_0 : \beta_3 = \beta_4 = 0 \,|\, \beta_1, \beta_2 \neq 0$$

This test will be conducted using the procedure in Equation 12.24. Figure 12.9 presents the regression for the complete model with all four predictor variables. In that regression $SSE = 1{,}149.14$. In Figure 12.11 we have the reduced regression with only house size and income as predictor variables. In that regression $SSE = 1{,}426.93$. The hypothesis is tested by first computing the F statistic whose numerator is the error sum of squares for the reduced model $[SSE(R)]$ minus the SSE for the complete model:

$$F = \frac{(1426.93 - 1149.14)/2}{13.52} = 10.27$$

The F statistic has 2 degrees of freedom—for the two variables being tested simultaneously—for the numerator and 85 degrees of freedom for the denominator. Note that the variance estimator, $s_e^2 = 13.52$, is obtained from the complete model in Figure 12.9, which has 85 degrees of freedom for error. The critical value for F with $\alpha = 0.01$ and 2 and 85 degrees of freedom, from Appendix Table 9, is approximately 4.9. Since the computed value of F exceeds the critical value, we reject the null hypothesis that tax rate and percent commercial property are not in combination conditionally significant. The combined effect of these two variables does improve the model that predicts housing price. Therefore, tax rate and percent commercial property should be included in the model.

Figure 12.11 Housing-Price Regression: Reduced Model (Minitab Output)

Regression Analysis: hseval versus sizehse, income72

```
The regression equation is
hseval = -42.2 + 9.14 sizehse + 0.00393 incom72


Predictor        Coef      SE Coef        T        P
Constant      -42.208        9.810     -4.30    0.000
sizehse         9.135        1.940      4.71    0.000
incom72      0.003927     0.001473      2.67    0.009


S = 4.04987    R-Sq = 34.7%    R-Sq(adj) = 33.2%

Analysis of Variance

Source          DF        SS        MS       F       P
Regression       2    759.70    379.85   23.16   0.000
Residual Error  87   1426.93     16.40
Total           89   2186.63


Source      DF    Seq SS                    SSE(R)
sizehse      1    643.12
incom72      1    116.58
```

We also computed this regression with the variable "comper" excluded and found that the resulting *SSE* was as follows:

$$SSE(1) = 1{,}185.29$$

Then the computed F statistic for this variable was as follows:

$$F = \frac{(1185.29 - 1149.14)/1}{13.52} = 2.674$$

The square root of 2.674 is 1.64, which is the computed t statistic for the variable Comper in the regression output in Figure 12.9. Using either the computed F or the computed t, we would obtain this result for the hypotheses for this variable:

$$H_0 : \beta_{Comper} = 0 \mid \beta_l \neq 0, l \neq Comper$$
$$H_1 : \beta_{Comper} \neq 0 \mid \beta_l \neq 0, l \neq Comper$$

EXERCISES

Basic Exercise

12.35 Suppose that you have estimated coefficients for the following regression model:

$$Y = \beta_0 + \beta_1 X_1 + \beta_2 X_2 + \beta_3 X_3$$

Test the hypothesis that all three of the predictor variables are equal to 0, given the following analysis of variance table.

a. Analysis of variance ($\alpha = 0.05$)

Source	DF	SS	MS
Regression	3	3,000	
Residual Error	25	500	

b. Analysis of variance ($\alpha = 0.05$)

Source	DF	SS	MS
Regression	3	4,500	
Residual Error	21	500	

c. Analysis of variance ($\alpha = 0.05$)

Source	DF	SS	MS
Regression	3	42,000	
Residual Error	30	27,000	

d. Analysis of variance ($\alpha = 0.01$)

Source	DF	SS	MS
Regression	3	9,606	
Residual Error	21	2,300	

Application Exercises

12.36 An aircraft company wanted to predict the number of worker-hours necessary to finish the design of a new plane. Relevant explanatory variables were thought to be the plane's top speed, its weight, and the number of parts it had in common with other models built by the company. A sample of 27 of the company's planes was taken, and the following model was estimated:

$$y = \beta_0 + \beta_1 x_1 + \beta_2 x_2 + \beta_3 x_3 + \varepsilon$$

where

y = design effort, in millions of worker-hours
x_1 = plane's top speed, in miles per hour
x_2 = plane's weight, in tons
x_3 = percentage of parts in common with other models

The estimated regression coefficients were as follows:

$$b_1 = 0.661 \quad b_2 = 0.065 \quad b_3 = -0.018$$

The total sum of squares and regression sum of squares were found to be as follows:

$$SST = 3.881 \quad \text{and} \quad SSR = 3.549$$

a. Test the null hypothesis:

$$H_0 : \beta_1 = \beta_2 = \beta_3 = 0$$

b. Set out the analysis of variance table.

12.37 In a study of the influence of financial institutions on bond interest rates in Germany, quarterly data over a period of 12 years were analyzed. The postulated model was

$$y = \beta_0 + \beta_1 x_1 + \beta_2 x_2 + \varepsilon$$

where

y = change over the quarter in the bond interest rates
x_1 = change over the quarter in bond purchases by financial institutions
x_2 = change over the quarter in bond sales by financial institutions

The estimated partial regression coefficients were as follows:

$$b_1 = 0.057 \quad b_2 = -0.065$$

The corrected coefficient of determination was found to be $R^2 = 0.463$. Test the null hypothesis:

$$H_0 : \beta_1 = \beta_2 = 0$$

12.38 The following model was fitted to a sample of 30 families in order to explain household milk consumption:

$$y = \beta_0 + \beta_1 x_1 + \beta_2 x_2 + \varepsilon$$

where

y = milk consumption, in quarts per week
x_1 = weekly income, in hundreds of dollars
x_2 = family size

The least squares estimates of the regression parameters were as follows:

$$b_0 = -0.025 \quad b_1 = 0.052 \quad b_2 = 1.14$$

The estimated standard errors were as follows:

$$s_{b_1} = 0.023 \quad s_{b_2} = 0.35$$

The total sum of squares and regression sum of squares were found to be as follows:

$$SST = 162.1 \quad \text{and} \quad SSR = 88.2$$

a. Test the null hypothesis:

$$H_0 : \beta_1 = \beta_2 = 0$$

b. Set out the analysis of variance table.

12.39 The following model was fitted to a sample of 25 students using data obtained at the end of their freshman year in college. The aim was to explain students' weight gains:

$$y = \beta_0 + \beta_1 x_1 + \beta_2 x_2 + \beta_3 x_3 + \varepsilon$$

where

y = weight gained, in pounds, during freshman year
x_1 = average number of meals eaten per week
x_2 = average number of hours of exercise per week
x_3 = average number of beers consumed per week

The least squares estimates of the regression parameters were as follows:

$$b_0 = 7.35 \quad b_1 = 0.653 \quad b_2 = -1.345 \quad b_3 = 0.613$$

The estimated standard errors were as follows:

$$s_{b_1} = 0.189 \quad s_{b_2} = 0.565 \quad s_{b_3} = 0.243$$

The regression sum of squares and error sum of squares were found to be as follows:

$$SSR = 79.2 \quad \text{and} \quad SSE = 45.9$$

a. Test the null hypothesis:

$$H_0 : \beta_1 = \beta_2 = \beta_3 = 0$$

b. Set out the analysis of variance table.

12.40 A dependent variable is regressed on K independent variables, using n sets of sample observations. We denote SSE as the error sum of squares and R^2 as the coefficient of determination for this estimated regression. We want to test the null hypothesis that K_1 of these independent variables, taken together, do not linearly affect the dependent variable, given that the other $(K - K_1)$ independent variables are also to be used. Suppose that the regression is re-estimated with the K_1 independent variables of interest excluded. Let SSE^* denote the error sum of squares and R^{*2}, the coefficient of determination for this regression. Show that the statistic for testing our null hypothesis, introduced in Section 12.5, can be expressed as follows:

$$\frac{(SSE^* - SSE)/K_1}{SSE/(n - K - 1)} = \frac{R^2 - R^{*2}}{1 - R^2} \cdot \frac{n - K - 1}{K_1}$$

12.41 The following model was fitted to a sample of 28 families in order to explain household bread consumption:

$$y = \beta_0 + \beta_1 x_1 + \beta_2 x_2 + \varepsilon$$

where

> y = bread consumption, in loaves per week
> x_1 = weekly income, in hundreds of pounds
> x_2 = family size

The least squares estimates of the regression parameters were as follows:

$$b_0 = -0.022; \quad b_1 = 0.056; \quad b_2 = 1.15$$

The total sum of squares and regression sum of squares were found to be as follows:

$$SST = 162.1 \quad \text{and} \quad SSR = 91.3$$

A third independent variable—number of teenagers in the household—was added to the regression model. The sum of squared errors when this augmented model was estimated by least squares was found to be 72.6. Test the null hypothesis that, all other things being equal, the number of teenagers in the household does not linearly affect the consumption of bread.

12.42 Suppose that a dependent variable is related to K independent variables through a multiple regression model. Let R^2 denote the coefficient of determination and $\overline{R}^2$, the corrected coefficient. Suppose that n sets of observations are used to fit the regression.

a. Show that

$$\overline{R}^2 = \frac{(n-1)R^2 - K}{n - K - 1}$$

b. Show that

$$R^2 = \frac{(n - K - 1)\overline{R}^2 + K}{n - 1}$$

c. Show that the statistic for testing the null hypothesis that all the regression coefficients are 0 can be written as

$$\frac{SSR/K}{SSE/(n - K - 1)} = \frac{n - K - 1}{K} \cdot \frac{\overline{R}^2 + A}{1 - \overline{R}^2}$$

where

$$A = \frac{K}{n - K - 1}$$

12.6 PREDICTION

An important application of regression models is to predict or forecast values of the dependent variable, given values for the independent variables. Forecasts can be computed directly from the estimated regression model using the coefficient estimates in that model, as shown in Equation 12.25.

Predictions from the Multiple Regression Models
Given that the population regression model

$$y_i = \beta_0 + \beta_1 x_{1i} + \beta_2 x_{1i} + \cdots + \beta_K x_{Ki} + \varepsilon_i$$

holds and that the standard regression assumptions are valid, let $b_0, b_1, \ldots, b_K$ be the least squares estimates of the model coefficients, β_j, where $j = 1, \ldots, K$, based on the $x_1, x_2, \ldots, x_K$ $(i = 1, \ldots, n)$ data points. Then, given a new observation of a data point, $x_{1,n+1}, x_{2,n+1}, \ldots, x_{K,n+1}$ the best linear unbiased forecast of y_{n+1} is

$$\hat{y}_i = b_0 + b_1 x_{1i} + b_2 x_{1i} + \cdots + b_K x_{Ki} \quad i = n + 1 \tag{12.25}$$

It is very risky to obtain forecasts that are based on X values outside the range of the data used to estimate the model coefficients because we do not have data evidence to support the linear model at those points.

In addition to the predicted value of Y for a particular set of x_j terms, we are often interested in a confidence interval or a prediction interval associated with the prediction. As we discussed in Section 11.6, the confidence interval includes the expected value of Y with probability $1 - \alpha$. In contrast, the prediction interval includes individual predicted values—expected values of Y plus the random error term. To obtain these intervals, we need to compute estimates of the standard deviations for the expected value of Y and for the individual points. These computations are similar in form to those used in simple regression, but the estimator equations are much more complicated. The standard deviations for predicted values, $s_{\hat{y}}$, are a function of the standard error of the estimate, s_e; the standard deviation of the predictor variables; the correlations between the predictor variables; and the square of the distance between the mean of the independent variables and the X terms for the prediction. This standard deviation is similar to the standard deviation for simple regression predictions in Chapter 11. However, the equations for multiple regression are very complex and are not presented here—instead, we compute the values using Minitab. The standard deviations for the prediction interval, the confidence interval, and the corresponding intervals are computed by most good statistics packages. Excel does not have the capability to compute the standard deviation of the predicted variables.

Example 12.10 Forecast of Savings and Loan Profit Margin (Regression Model Forecasts)

You have been asked to forecast the savings and loan profit margin for a year in which the percentage net revenue is 4.50 and there are 9,000 offices, using the savings and loan regression model. Data are stored in the file **Savings and Loan**.

Solution Using the notation from Equation 12.25, we have the following variables:

$$x_{1,n+1} = 4.50 \quad x_{2,n+1} = 9,000$$

Using these values, we find that our point predictor of profit margin is as follows:

$$\hat{y}_{n+1} = b_0 + b_1 x_{1,n+1} + b_2 x_{2,n+1}$$
$$= 1.565 + (0.237)(4.50) - (0.000249)(9,000) = 0.39$$

Thus, for a year when the percentage net revenue per deposit dollar is 4.50 and the number of offices is 9,000, we predict that the profit margin for savings and loan associations will be 0.39.

Figure 12.12 Forecasts and Forecast Intervals for Multiple Regression (Minitab Output)

```
Regression Analysis: Y profit versus X1 revenue, X2 offices

The regression equation is
Y profit = 1.56 + 0.237 X1 revenue - 0.000249 X2 offices


Predictor          Coef     SE Coef      T      P
Constant        1.56450     0.07940   19.70  0.000
X1 revenue      0.23720     0.05556    4.27  0.000
X2 offices   -0.00024908  0.00003205  -7.77  0.000


S = 0.0533022    R-Sq = 86.5%    R-Sq(adj) = 85.3%


Analysis of Variance

Source          DF      SS       MS      F      P
Regression       2  0.40151  0.20076  70.66  0.000
Residual Error22  0.06250  0.00284
Total           24  0.46402
```

Predicted value
Standard error for predicted value

```
Predicted Values for New Observations

New
Obs   Fit    SE Fit    95% CI            95% PI
1   0.3902  0.0277  (0.3327, 0.4476)  (0.2656, 0.5148)
```

Prediction interval

Confidence interval

```
Values of Predictors for New Observations

New                 X2
Obs  X1 revenue   offices
1       4.50       9000
```

Predictior variable values

Predicted values, confidence intervals, and prediction intervals can be computed directly in the Minitab regression routine.

The regression output is shown in Figure 12.12. The predicted value, $\hat{y} = 0.39$, and its standard deviation, 0.0277, are presented, along with the confidence interval and the prediction interval. The confidence interval—CI—provides an interval for the expected value of Y on the linear function defined by the values of the independent variables. This interval is a function of the standard error of the regression model, the distance that the x_j values are from their individual sample means, and the correlation between the x_j variables used to fit the model. The prediction interval—PI—provides an interval for a single observed value. Thus, it includes the variability associated with the expected value plus the variability of a single point about the predicted value.

EXERCISES

 Visit www.MyStatLab.com or www.pearsonglobal editions.com to access the data files.

Basic Exercise

12.43 Given the estimated multiple regression equation

$$\hat{y} = 4.2 + 5.3x_1 - 4.4x_2 + 6.8x_3 - 0.8x_4$$

what is the predicted value of Y in each case?

a. $x_1 = 10, x_2 = 23, x_3 = 9$, and $x_4 = 12$
b. $x_1 = 23, x_2 = 18, x_3 = 10$, and $x_4 = 11$
c. $x_1 = 15, x_2 = 16, x_3 = 5$, and $x_4 = 0$
d. $x_1 = -10, x_2 = 13, x_3 = -8$, and $x_4 = -16$

Application Exercises

12.44 The following model was fitted to a sample of 25 athletes using data obtained at the end of a year. The aim was to explain atheletes' weight gains:

$$y = b_0 + b_1x_1 + b_2x_2 + b_3x_3 + \varepsilon$$

where

y = weight gained, in pounds, during the year
x_1 = average number of meals eaten per week
x_2 = average number of hours of exercise per week
x_3 = average number of sweetened beverages consumed per week

The least squares estimates of the regression parameters were as follows:

$$b_0 = 7.74 \quad b_1 = 0.684 \quad b_2 = -1.417 \quad b_3 = 0.577$$

Predict the weight gain for an athlete who eats an average of 17 meals per week, exercises an average of 8 hours per week, and consumes an average of 18 sweetened beverages per week.

12.45 The following model was fitted to a sample of 30 families in order to explain household milk consumption:

$$y = \beta_0 + \beta_1x_1 + \beta_2x_2 + \varepsilon$$

where

y = milk consumption, in quarts per week
x_1 = weekly income, in hundreds of dollars
x_2 = family size

The least squares estimates of the regression parameters were as follows:

$$b_0 = -0.025 \quad b_1 = 0.052 \quad b_2 = 1.14$$

Predict the weekly milk consumption of a family of four with an income of $600 per week.

12.46 An aircraft company wanted to predict the number of worker-hours necessary to finish the design of a new plane. Relevant explanatory variables were thought to be the plane's top speed, its weight, and the number of parts it had in common with other models built by the company. A sample of 27 of the company's planes was taken, and the following model was estimated:

$$y = \beta_0 + \beta_1x_1 + \beta_2x_2 + \beta_3x_3 + \varepsilon$$

where

y = design effort, in millions of worker-hours
x_1 = plane's top speed, in miles per hour
x_2 = plane's weight, in tons
x_3 = percentage number of parts in common with other models

The estimated regression coefficients were as follows:

$$b_1 = 0.661 \quad b_2 = 0.065 \quad b_3 = -0.018$$

and the estimated intercept was 2.0.

Predict design effort for a plane with a top speed of Mach 1.0, weighing 7 tons, and having 50% of its parts in common with other models.

12.47 A real estate agent hypothesizes that in her town the selling price of a house in dollars (y) depends on its size in square feet of floor space (x_1), the lot size in square feet (x_2), the number of bedrooms (x_3), and the number of bathrooms (x_4). For a random sample of 20 house sales, the following least squares estimated model was obtained:

$$\hat{y} = 1998.5 + 22.352x_1 + 1.4686x_2 + 6767.3x_3 + 2701.1x_4$$
$$\quad\quad\quad\quad (2.5543) \quad\quad (1.4492) \quad\quad (1820.8) \quad\quad (1996.2)$$

$$R^2 = 0.9843$$

The numbers in parentheses under the coefficients are the estimated coefficient standard errors.

  a. Interpret in the context of this model the estimated coefficient on x_2.

  b. Interpret the coefficient of determination.

  c. Assuming that the model is correctly specified, test, at the 5% level against the appropriate one-sided alternative, the null hypothesis that, all else being equal, selling price does not depend on number of bathrooms.

  d. Estimate the selling price of a house with 1,250 square feet of floor space, a lot of 4,700 square feet, 3 bedrooms, and 1 bathroom.

12.48   Transportation Research, Inc., has asked you to prepare a multiple regression equation to estimate the effect of variables on fuel economy. The data for this study are contained in the data file **Motors**,

and the dependent variable is miles per gallon—milpgal—as established by the Department of Transportation certification.

  a. Prepare a regression equation that uses vehicle horsepower—horsepower—and vehicle weight—weight—as independent variables. Determine the predicted value, the confidence interval of the prediction, and the prediction interval when the horsepower is 140 and the vehicle weight is 3,000 pounds.

  b. Prepare a second regression equation that adds the number of cylinders—cylinder—as an independent variable to the equation from part a. Determine the predicted value, the confidence interval of the prediction, and the prediction interval when the horsepower is 140, the number of cylinders is 6 and the vehicle weight is 3,000 pounds.

12.7 TRANSFORMATIONS FOR NONLINEAR REGRESSION MODELS

We have seen how regression analysis can be used to estimate linear relationships that predict a dependent variable as a function of one or more independent variables. These applications are very important. However, in addition, there are a number of economic and business relationships that are not strictly linear. In this section we develop procedures for modifying certain nonlinear model formats so that multiple regression procedures can be used to estimate the model coefficients. Thus, our objective in Sections 12.7 and 12.8 is to expand the range of problems that are adaptable to regression analysis. In this way we see that regression analysis has even broader applications.

By examining the least squares algorithm, we will see that, with careful manipulation of nonlinear models, it is possible to use least squares for a broader set of applied problems. The assumptions concerning independent variables in multiple regression are not very restrictive. Independent variables define points at which we measure a random variable Y. We assume that there is a linear relationship between the levels of the independent variables X_j, where $j = 1, \ldots, K$, and the expected value of the dependent variable Y. We can take advantage of this freedom to expand the set of models that can be estimated. Thus, we can move beyond linear models in our multiple regression applications. Three examples are shown in Figure 12.13:

Figure 12.13 Examples of Quadratic Functions

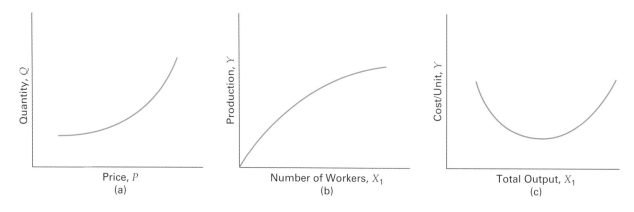

(a)   (b)   (c)

1. Supply functions may be nonlinear.
2. The increase in total output with increases in the number of workers may become flatter as more workers are added.
3. Average cost per unit produced is often minimized at an intermediate level of production.

Quadratic Transformations

We have spent considerable time developing regression analysis to estimate linear equations. There are also many processes that can best be represented by nonlinear equations. Total revenue has a quadratic relationship with price, with maximum revenue occurring at an intermediate price level if the demand function has a negative slope. In many cases the minimum production cost per unit occurs at an intermediate level of output, with cost per unit decreasing as we approach the minimum cost per unit and then increasing after passing the minimum unit cost level. We can model a number of these economic and business relationships by using a quadratic model:

$$Y = \beta_0 + \beta_1 X_1 + \beta_2 X_1^2 + \varepsilon$$

To estimate the coefficients of a quadratic model for applications such as these, we can transform or modify the variables, as shown in Equations 12.26 and 12.27. In this way a nonlinear quadratic model is converted to a model that is linear in a modified set of variables.

Quadratic Model Transformations
The quadratic function

$$Y = \beta_0 + \beta_1 X_1 + \beta_2 X_1^2 + \varepsilon \tag{12.26}$$

can be transformed into a linear multiple regression model by defining new variables:

$$z_1 = x_1$$
$$z_2 = x_1^2$$

and then specifying the model as

$$y_i = \beta_0 + \beta_1 z_{1i} + \beta_2 z_{2i} + \varepsilon_i \tag{12.27}$$

which is linear in the transformed variables. Transformed quadratic variables can be combined with other variables in a multiple regression model. Thus, we can fit a multiple quadratic regression using transformed variables. The goal is to find models that are linear in other mathematical forms of a variable.

By transforming the variables, we can estimate a linear multiple regression model and use the results as a nonlinear model. Inference procedures for transformed quadratic models are the same as those that we have previously developed for linear models. In this way we avoid confusion that would result if different statistical procedures were used for linear versus quadratic models. The coefficients must be combined for interpretation. Thus, if we have a quadratic model, then the effect of a variable, X, is indicated by the coefficients of both the linear and the quadratic terms. We can also perform a simple hypothesis test to determine if a quadratic model is an improvement over a linear model. The Z_2 or X_1^2 variable is merely an additional variable whose coefficient can be tested—$H_0 : \beta_2 = 0$—using the conditional Student's t or F statistic. If a quadratic model fits the data better than a linear model, then the coefficient of the quadratic variable—$Z_2 = X_1^2$—will be significantly different from 0. The same approach applies if we have variables such as $Z_3 = X_1^3$ or $Z_4 = X_1^2 X_2$.

Example 12.11 Production Costs (Quadratic Model Estimation)

Arnold Sorenson, production manager of New Frontiers Instruments, Inc., was interested in estimating the mathematical relationship between the number of electronic assemblies produced during an 8-hour shift and the average cost per assembly. This function would then be used to estimate cost for various production order bids and to determine the production level that would minimize average cost. Data are found in the data file **Production Cost**.

Solution Arnold collected data from nine shifts during which the number of assemblies ranged from 100 to 900. In addition, he obtained the average cost per unit for those days from the accounting department. These data are presented in a scatter plot prepared using Excel, shown in Figure 12.14. As a result of his study of economics and his experience, Arnold suspected that the function might be quadratic with an intermediate minimum average cost. He designed his analysis to consider both a linear and a quadratic average production cost function.

Figure 12.14 Mean Production Cost as a Function of Number of Units

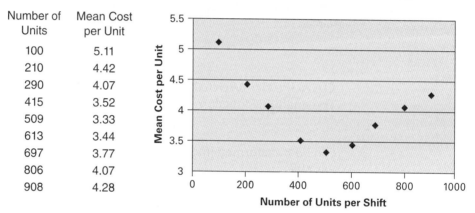

Number of Units	Mean Cost per Unit
100	5.11
210	4.42
290	4.07
415	3.52
509	3.33
613	3.44
697	3.77
806	4.07
908	4.28

Figure 12.15 is the simple regression of cost as a linear function of the number of units. We see that the linear relationship is almost flat, indicating no linear relationship

Figure 12.15 Linear Regression Average Cost on Number of Units

Regression Analysis: Mean Cost per Unit versus Number of Units

```
The regression equation is
Mean Cost per Unit = 4.43 - 0.000855 Number of Units


Predictor              Coef      SE Coef       T       P
Constant             4.4330       0.3994   11.10   0.000
Number of Units  -0.0008547    0.0007029   -1.22   0.263


S = 0.547614   R-Sq = 17.4%   R-Sq(adj) = 5.6%

Analysis of Variance

Source           DF        SS       MS       F       P
Regression        1    0.4433   0.4433    1.48   0.263
Residual Error    7    2.0992   0.2999
Total             8    2.5425
```

between average cost and number of units produced. If Arnold had simply used this relationship, he would have been led to serious errors in his cost-estimation procedures.

Figure 12.16 presents the quadratic regression that shows mean cost per unit as a nonlinear function of the number of units produced. Note that b_2 is different from 0 and thus should be included in the model. In addition, note that R^2 for the quadratic model is 0.962 compared to 0.174 for the linear model. By using the quadratic model, Arnold has produced a substantially more useful mean cost model.

Figure 12.16 Quadratic Model Analysis for Average Cost on Number of Units

```
Regression Analysis: Mean Cost per Unit versus Number of Units,
No Units Squared

The regression equation is
Mean Cost per Unit = 5.91 - 0.00884 Number of Units + 0.000008
No Units Squared

Predictor                 Coef      SE Coef       T       P
Constant                5.9084       0.1614   36.60   0.000
Number of Units      -0.0088415    0.0007344  -12.04   0.000
No Units Squared    -0.00000793   0.00000071   11.15   0.000

S = 0.126875    R-Sq = 96.2%    R-Sq(adj) = 94.9%

Analysis of Variance

Source             DF        SS        MS       F       P
Regression          2    2.4459    1.2230   75.97   0.000
Residual Error      6    0.0966    0.0161
Total               8    2.5425
```

Logarithmic Transformations

A number of economic relationships can be modeled by exponential functions. For example, if the percent change in quantity of goods sold changes linearly in response to percent changes in the price, then the demand function will have an exponential form:

$$Q = \beta_0 P^{\beta_1}$$

where Q is the quantity demanded and P is the price per unit. Exponential demand functions have constant elasticity, and, thus, a 1% change in price results in the same percent change in quantity demanded for all price levels. In contrast, linear demand models indicate that a unit change in the price variable will result in the same change in quantity demanded for all price levels. Exponential demand models are widely used in the analysis of market behavior. One important feature of exponential models is that the coefficient β_1 is the constant elasticity, e, of demand Q with respect to price P:

$$e = \frac{\partial Q/Q}{\partial P/P} = \beta_1$$

This result is developed in most microeconomics textbooks. Exponential model coefficients are estimated using logarithmic transformations, as shown in Equation 12.29.

The logarithmic transformation assumes that the random error term multiplies the true value of Y to obtain the observed value. Thus, in the exponential model the error is a percentage of the true value, and the variance of the error distribution increases with increases in Y. If this result is not true, the log transformation is not correct. In that case a much more complex nonlinear estimation technique must be used. Those techniques are considerably beyond the scope of this book.

Exponential Model Transformations

Coefficients for exponential models of the form

$$Y = \beta_0 X_1^{\beta_1} X_2^{\beta_2} \varepsilon \tag{12.28}$$

can be estimated by first taking the logarithm of both sides in order to obtain an equation that is linear in the logarithms of the variables:

$$\log(Y) = \log(\beta_0) + \beta_1 \log(X_1) + \beta_2 \log(X_2) + \log(\varepsilon) \tag{12.29}$$

Using this form, we can regress the logarithm of Y on the logarithms of the two X variables and obtain estimates for the coefficients β_1 and β_2 directly from the regression analysis. Since the coefficients are elasticities, many economists use this model form where they can assume that elasticities are constant over the range of the data. Note that this estimation procedure requires that the random errors are multiplicative in the original exponential model. Thus, the error term, ε, is expressed as a percentage increase or decrease instead of by the addition or subtraction of a random error, as we have seen for linear regression models.

Another important application of exponential models is the Cobb-Douglas production function, which has the form

$$Q = \beta_0 L^{\beta_1} K^{\beta_2}$$

where Q is the quantity produced, L is the amount of labor used, and K is the amount of capital. β_1 and β_2 are the relative contributions of changes in labor and changes in capital to changes in quantity produced. In one special case the sum of the coefficients is restricted to 1, and we have constant returns to scale. In that case β_1 and β_2 are the percent contributions of labor and capital to productivity increase.

The estimation of the coefficients when their sum is equal to 1 is one example of restricted estimation in regression models. Equation 12.29 is modified by the restriction

$$\beta_1 + \beta_2 = 1$$

and, therefore, substitution of the form

$$\beta_2 = 1 - \beta_1$$

is included, and the new estimation equation becomes

$$\log(Y) = \log(\beta_0) + \beta_1 \log(X_1) + (1 - \beta_1) \log(X_2) + \log(\varepsilon)$$
$$\log(Y) - \log(X_2) = \log(\beta_0) + \beta_1 [\log(X_1) - \log(X_2)] + \log(\varepsilon)$$
$$\log\left(\frac{Y}{X_2}\right) = \log(\beta_0) + \beta_1 \log\left(\frac{X_1}{X_2}\right) + \log(\varepsilon) \tag{12.30}$$

Thus, we see that the β_1 coefficient is obtained by regressing $\log(Y/X_2)$ on $\log(X_1/X_2)$. Then, β_2 is computed by subtracting β_1 from 1.0.

All quality computer-based statistical packages can easily compute the required transformations of the data for logarithmic models. In the following example, we used Minitab, but similar results could be obtained using many other packages.

Example 12.12 Production Function for Minong Boat Works (Exponential Model Estimation)

The Minong Boat Works began producing small fishing boats in the early 1970s for northern Wisconsin fishermen. The owners developed a low-cost production method for producing quality boats. As a result, they have experienced increased demand over the years. The production method uses a workstation with a set of jigs and power tools that can be operated by a varying number of workers. Over the years the number of workstations (units of capital) has grown from 1 to 20 to meet the demand for boats. At the same time the workforce has grown from 2 to 25 full-time workers. The owners are now considering expanding their sales to potential markets in Michigan and Minnesota. Therefore, they need to decide how much to increase the number of workstations and number of workers to achieve various levels of increased production.

Solution The owners' daughter, a senior economics major, suggests that they estimate a restricted Cobb-Douglas production function using data from previous years of operation. She explains that this production function will enable them to predict the number of boats produced for different levels of workstations and workers. The owners agree that such an analysis is a good idea and ask their daughter to prepare the analysis. She begins the analysis by collecting the production data, contained in the data file **Boat Production**, from old company records. To obtain the coefficient estimates, she first must transform the original model specification to a form that can be estimated by least squares regression. The Cobb-Douglas production function model is

$$Y = \beta_0 K^{\beta_1} L^{\beta_2}$$

with the restriction

$$\beta_1 = 1 - \beta_2$$

where Y is the number of boats produced each year, K is the number of production stations (units of capital) used each year, and L is the number of workers used each year.

The restricted Cobb-Douglas production function was transformed to the estimation form,

$$\ln\left(\frac{Y}{K}\right) = \ln(\beta_0) + \beta_2 \ln\left(\frac{L}{K}\right)$$

for least squares estimation.

The regression model estimate is shown in Figure 12.17 with the resulting equation:

$$\ln\left(\frac{Y}{K}\right) = 3.02 + 0.845 \ln\left(\frac{L}{K}\right) \tag{12.31}$$

Figure 12.17 Restricted Production Function Regression Analysis (Minitab Output)

```
The regression equation is
logbotunit = 3.02 + 0.845 logworunit


Predictor        Coef      SE Coef        T         P
Constant      3.02325      0.04387    68.92     0.000
logworun      0.84479      0.09062     9.32     0.000


S = 0.1105      R-Sq = 79.8%      R-Sq(adj) = 78.9%


Analysis of Variance

Source           DF          SS          MS        F         P
Regression        1      1.0618      1.0618    86.90     0.000
Residual Error   22      0.2688      0.0122
Total            23      1.3306
```

From this result we see that the estimated model coefficient, b_2, is 0.845. Therefore, $b_1 = 1 - 0.845 = 0.155$. Finally, $\ln(b_0) = 3.02$. This analysis shows that 84.5% of the changes in production comes from changes in labor and 15.5% comes from capital. After applying the appropriate algebraic transformations, the production function model is as follows:

$$Y = 20.49 K^{0.155} L^{0.845} \tag{12.32}$$

This production function can be used as a tool for predicting the expected output obtained by using various levels of capital and labor. In this example the model developed as Equation 12.32 would be used to compute output beyond the range of the data used to estimate the model coefficients. Thus in order to use this model, the owners of Minong Boat Works must assume that output will continue to increase at the same rate with labor and capital expansion. They strongly believe that this is a correct assumption.

Figure 12.18 presents a comparison of the observed number of boats and the forecast number of boats from the transformed regression equation. The forecast number of boats was computed using Equation 12.32. That analysis also indicates that the R^2 for the regression of the number of boats on the predicted number of boats is 0.987. This R^2 can be interpreted just as you would an R^2 for any linear regression model, and, thus, we see that the predicted number of boats provides a good fit for the observed boat production data. The R^2 for the transformed regression data in Figure 12.17 cannot be easily interpreted as an indicator of the relationship between the number of boats produced and the independent variables of labor and capital because the units are in logarithms of ratios.

Figure 12.18 Comparison of Observed and Predicted Production

EXERCISES

 Visit www.MyStatLab.com or www.pearsonglobal editions.com to access the data files.

Basic Exercises

12.49 Consider the following two equations estimated using the procedures developed in this section:
  i. $y_i = 2x^{1.4}$
  ii. $y_i = 2 + 6x_i + 1.4x_i^2$

  Compute values of y_i when $x_i = 1, 2, 4, 6, 8, 10$.

12.50 Consider the following two equations estimated using the procedures developed in this section:
  i. $y_i = 4x^{1.8}$
  ii. $y_i = 1 + 2x_i + 2x_i^2$

  Compute values of y_i when $x_i = 1, 2, 4, 6, 8, 10$.

12.51 Consider the following two equations estimated using the procedures developed in this section:
  i. $y_i = 3x^{1.2}$
  ii. $y_i = 3 + 5x_i + 1.9 x_i^2$

  Compute values of y_i when $x_i = 1, 2, 4, 6, 8, 10$.

12.52 Consider the following two equations estimated using the procedures developed in this section.
  i. $y_i = 3x^{1.2}$
  ii. $y_i = 1 + 5x_i - 1.5x_i^2$

  Compute values of y_i when $x_i = 1, 2, 4, 6, 8, 10$.

Application Exercises

12.53 Describe an example from your experience in which a quadratic model would be better than a linear model.

12.54 John Swanson, president of Market Research Inc., has asked you to estimate the coefficients of the model

$$Y = \beta_0 + \beta_1 X_1 + \beta_2 X_1^2 + \beta_3 X_2$$

where Y is the expected sales of office supplies for a large retail distributor of office supplies, X_1 is the total disposable income of residents within 5 miles of the store, and X_2 is the total number of persons employed in information-based businesses within 5 miles of the store. Recent work by a national consulting firm has concluded that the coefficients in the model must have the following restriction:

$$\beta_1 + \beta_2 = 2$$

Describe how you would estimate the model coefficients using least squares.

12.55 In a study of the determinants of household expenditures on vacation travel, data were obtained from a sample of 2,233 households (Hagermann 1981). The model estimated was

$$\log y = -4.035 + 1.1545 \log x_1 - 0.4468 \log x_2$$
$$ {\scriptstyle (0.0544)} {\scriptstyle (0.0456)}$$
$$R^2 = 0.161$$

where

y = expenditure on vacation travel
x_1 = total annual consumption expenditure
x_2 = number of members in a household

The numbers in parentheses under the coefficients are the estimated coefficient standard errors.

a. Interpret the estimated regression coefficients.
b. Interpret the coefficient of determination.
c. All else being equal, find a 95% confidence interval for the percentage increase in expenditures on vacation travel resulting from a 1% increase in total annual consumption expenditures.
d. Assuming that the model is correctly specified, test, at the 1% significance level, the null hypothesis that, all else being equal, the number of members in a household does not affect expenditures on vacation travel against the alternative that the greater the number of household members, the lower the vacation travel expenditures.

12.56 The following model was estimated for a sample of 322 supermarkets in large metropolitan areas (Macdonald and Nelson 1991):

$$\log(y) = 2.921 + 0.680 \log(x)$$
$$ {\scriptstyle (0.077)}$$
$$R^2 = 0.19$$

where

y = store size
x = median income in zip-code area in which store is located

The number in parentheses under the coefficient is the estimated coefficient standard error.

a. Interpret the estimated coefficient on $\log x$.
b. Test the null hypothesis that income has no impact on store size against the alternative that higher income tends to be associated with larger store size.

12.57 An agricultural economist believes that the amount of fish consumed (y) in tons in a year in the France depends on the price of fish (x_1) in euros per pound, the price of potatoes (x_2) in euros per pound, the price of chicken (x_3) in euros per pound, and the income per household (x_4) in thousands of euros. The following sample regression was obtained through least squares, using 30 annual observations:

$$\log y = -0.018 - 0.536 \log x_1 + 0.208 \log x_2$$
$$ {\scriptstyle (0.172)} {\scriptstyle (0.098)}$$
$$+ \ 0.205 \log x_3 + 0.425 \log x_4$$
$$ {\scriptstyle (0.121)} {\scriptstyle (0.133)}$$
$$R^2 = 0.771$$

a. Interpret the coefficient on $\log x_1$.
b. Interpret the coefficient on $\log x_2$.
c. Test, at the 1% significance level, the null hypothesis that the coefficient on $\log x_4$ in the population regression is 0 against the alternative that it is positive.
d. Test the null hypothesis that the four variables ($\log x_1, \log x_2, \log x_3, \log x_4$) do not, as a set, have any linear influence on $\log y$.
e. The economist is also concerned that, over the years, the increasing awareness of the effects of fish consumption on health may have influenced the demand for fish. If this is indeed the case, how would this influence your view of the original estimated regression?

12.58 You have been asked to develop an exponential production function—Cobb-Douglas form—that will predict the number of microprocessors produced by a manufacturer, Y, as a function of the units of capital, X_1; the units of labor, X_2; and the number of computer science staff involved in basic research, X_3. Specify the model form and then carefully and completely indicate how you would estimate the coefficients. Do this first using an unrestricted model and then a second time including the restriction that the coefficients of the three variables should sum to 1.

12.59 Consider the following nonlinear model with multiplicative errors:

$$Y = \beta_0 X_1^{\beta_1} X_2^{\beta_2} X_3^{\beta_3} X_4^{\beta_4} \varepsilon$$
$$\beta_1 + \beta_2 = 1$$
$$\beta_3 + \beta_4 = 1$$

a. Show how you would obtain the coefficient estimates. Coefficient restrictions must be satisfied. Show all your work and explain what you are doing.

b. What is the constant elasticity for Y versus X_4? Show all your work.

The following exercises require the use of a computer.

12.60 Angelica Chandra, president of Benefits Research, Inc., has asked you to study the salary structure of her firm. Benefits Research provides consulting and management for employee health care and retirement programs. Its clients are mid- to large-sized firms. As a first step you are asked to estimate a regression model that estimates expected salary as a function of years of experience in the firm. You are to consider linear, quadratic, and cubic models and determine which one would be most suitable. Estimate appropriate regression models and write a short report that recommends the best model. Use the data contained in the file **Benefits Research**.

12.61 The data file **German Imports** shows German real imports (y), real private consumption (x_1), and real exchange rate (x_2), in terms of U.S. dollars per mark, over a period of 22 years. Estimate the model

$$\log y_t = \beta_0 + \beta_1 \log x_{1t} + \beta_2 \log x_{2t} + \varepsilon_i$$

and write a report on your findings.

12.8 DUMMY VARIABLES FOR REGRESSION MODELS

In the discussion of multiple regression up to this point, we have assumed that the independent variables, x_j, have existed over a range and contained many different values. However, in the multiple regression assumptions the only restriction on the independent variables is that they are fixed values. Thus, we could have an independent variable that took on only two values: $x_j = 0$ and $x_j = 1$. This structure is commonly defined as a *dummy variable*, and we will see that it provides a valuable tool for applying multiple regression to situations involving categorical variables. One important example is a linear function that shifts in response to some influence. Consider first a simple regression equation:

$$Y = \beta_0 + \beta_1 X_1$$

Now, suppose that we introduce a dummy variable, X_2, that has values 0 and 1 and that the resulting equation is as follows:

$$Y = \beta_0 + \beta_1 X_1 + \beta_2 X_2$$

When $X_2 = 0$ in this equation, the constant is β_0, but when $X_2 = 1$, the constant is $\beta_0 + \beta_2$. Thus, we see that the dummy variable shifts the linear relationship between Y and X_1 by the value of the coefficient β_2. In this way we can represent the effect of shifts in our regression equation. Dummy variables are also called *indicator variables*. We begin our discussion with an example of an important application.

Example 12.13 Wage Discrimination Analysis (Dummy Variable Model Estimation)

The president of Investors, Ltd., wants to determine if there is any evidence of wage discrimination in the salaries of male and female financial analysts. Figure 12.19 presents an example of annual wages versus years of experience for the analysts. See the data file **Gender and Salary**.

Figure 12.19 Example of Data Pattern Indicating Wage Discrimination

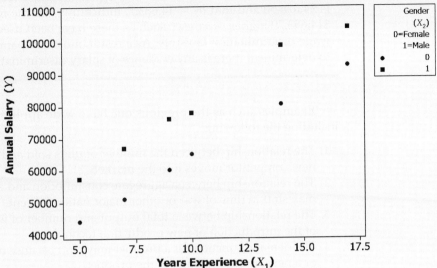

Scatterplot of Annual Salary (Y) vs Years Experience (X_1)

Solution Examining the data and the graph, we see two different subsets of salaries, and that salaries for males appears to be uniformly higher across the years of experience.

This problem can be analyzed by estimating a multiple regression model of salary, Y, versus years of experience, X_1, with a second variable, X_2, that is coded as follows:

0	Female employees
1	Male employees

The resulting multiple regression model,

$$\hat{y} = b_0 + b_1 x_1 + b_2 x_2$$

can be estimated using the procedures we have learned, noting that the coefficient b_1 is an estimate of the expected annual increase in salary per year of experience and b_2 is the shift in mean salary from male to female employees. If b_2 is positive, we have an indication that male salaries are uniformly higher.

Figure 12.20 shows the multiple regression analysis from Minitab for this problem. From this analysis we see that the coefficient of x_2—gender—has a Student's t statistic

Figure 12.20 Regression Analysis for Wage Discrimination Example Regression Analysis: Annual Salary versus Gender (X2), Years Experience

```
The regression equation is
Annual Salary (Y) = 23608 + 14684 Gender (X2) 0=Female 1=Male
                          + 4076 Years Experience (X1)


Predictor                       Coef  SE Coef      T      P
Constant                       23608     1434  16.46  0.000
Gender (X2) 0=Female 1=Male  14683.7    987.0  14.88  0.000
Year Experience (X1)          4076.5    121.3  33.61  0.000



S = 1709.48    R-Sq = 99.3%    R-Sq(adj) = 99.2%


Analysis of Variance

Source            DF          SS         MS       F      P
Regression         2  3948240796  1974120398  675.53  0.000
Residual Error     9    26300913     2922324
Total             11  3974541710
```

equal to 14.88 and a p-value of 0, which leads us to reject the null hypothesis that the coefficient is equal to 0. This result indicates that male salaries are significantly higher. We also see that $b_1 = 4{,}076.5$, indicating that the expected value for the annual increase is \$4,076.50 and that $b_2 = 14{,}683.7$, indicating that the male salaries are, on average, \$14,683.70 higher. Analyses such as these have been used successfully in a number of wage-discrimination lawsuits. As a result, most companies perform a similar analysis to determine if there is any evidence of salary discrimination.

Examples such as the previous one have wide application to a number of problems, including the following:

1. The relationship between the number of units sold and the price is likely to shift if a new competitor moves into the market.
2. The relationship between aggregate consumption and aggregate disposable income may shift in time of war or other major national event.
3. The relationship between total output and number of workers may shift as the result of the introduction of new production technology.
4. The demand function for a product may shift because of a new advertising campaign or a news release relating to the product.

The dummy variable procedure is summarized as follows.

Dummy Variable Regression Analysis

The relationship between Y and X_1,

$$Y = \beta_0 + \beta_1 X_1 + \varepsilon$$

can shift in response to a changed condition. The shift effect can be estimated by using a dummy variable that has values of 0 (condition not present) and 1 (condition present). As shown in Figure 12.19, all the observations from the upper set of data points have dummy variable $x_2 = 1$, and the observations for the lower points have $x_2 = 0$. In these cases the relationship between Y and X_1 is specified by the multiple regression model:

$$\hat{y} = b_0 + b_2 x_2 + b_1 x_1 \tag{12.33}$$

The coefficient b_2 represents the shift of the function between the upper and lower sets of points in Figure 12.19. The functions for each set of points are

$$\hat{y} = b_0 + b x_1 \quad \text{when } x_2 = 0$$

and

$$\hat{y} = (b_0 + b_2 x_2) + b_1 x_1 \quad \text{when } x_2 = 1$$

In the first function the constant is b_0, whereas in the second the constant is $b_0 + b_2$. In Chapter 13 we show how dummy variables can be used to analyze problems with more than two discrete categories.

This simple specification of the regression model is a very powerful tool for problems that involve a shift of the linear function by identifiable categorical factors. In addition, the multiple regression structure provides a direct procedure for performing a hypothesis test, as we did in Example 12.13. The hypothesis test is as follows:

$$H_0 : \beta_2 = 0 | \beta_1 \neq 0$$
$$H_1 : \beta_2 \neq 0 | \beta_1 \neq 0$$

Rejection of the null hypothesis, H_0, leads to the conclusion that the constant is different between the two subsets of data. In Example 12.13 we saw that this difference in the constant led to the conclusion that there was a significant difference in wages between the male and female subgroups after the effect of years of experience has been removed.

Differences in Slope

We can also use dummy variables to model and test for differences in the slope coefficient by adding an interaction variable. Figure 12.21 presents a typical example. To test for both differences in the constant and differences in the slope, we use a more complex regression model.

Dummy Variable Regression for Differences in Slope

To determine if there are significant differences in slopes between two discrete conditions, we need to expand our regression model to a more complex form:

$$Y = \beta_0 + \beta_2 X_2 + (\beta_1 + \beta_3 X_2) X_1 \qquad (12.34)$$

Now, we see that the slope coefficient of X_1 contains two components, β_1 and $\beta_3 X_2$. When X_2 equals 0, the slope is the usual β_1. However, when X_2 equals 1, the slope is equal to the algebraic sum of $\beta_1 + \beta_3$. To estimate the model, we actually need to create a new set of transformed variables that are linear. Therefore, the model actually used for estimation is as follows:

$$\hat{y} = b_0 + b_2 x_2 + b_1 x_1 + b_3 x_2 x_1 \qquad (12.35)$$

The resulting regression model is now linear with three variables. The new variable, $x_1 x_2$, is often called an *interaction variable*. Note that when the dummy variable $x_2 = 0$, this variable has a value of 0, but when $x_2 = 1$, this variable has the value of x_1. The coefficient b_3 is an estimate of the difference in the coefficient of x_1 when $x_2 = 1$ compared to $x_2 = 0$. Thus, the Student's t statistic for β_3 can be used to test the following hypotheses:

$$H_0 : \beta_3 = 0 \mid \beta_1 \neq 0, \beta_2 \neq 0$$
$$H_1 : \beta_3 \neq 0 \mid \beta_1 \neq 0, \beta_2 \neq 0$$

If we reject the null hypothesis, we conclude that there is a difference in the slope coefficient for the two subgroups. In many cases we will be interested in both the difference in the constant and the difference in the slope and will test both of the hypotheses presented in this section.

Example 12.14 Salary Model for Systems, Inc. (Dummy Variable Model Estimation)

The president of Systems, Inc., is interested in knowing if the annual salary increases for the female engineers in the company have maintained the same level as those for the male engineers. There have been some complaints from both male and female engineers that the salaries for female engineers have not increased at the same rate as those for male engineers.

Solution The scatter plot and regression analysis output are shown in Figure 12.21. The scatter plot suggests that the slope is higher for the upper subgroup, representing male engineers. A multiple regression analysis was run to estimate the effect of experience and gender on annual salary. This multiple regression analysis can be used to test the hypothesis that the rates of increase are the same for both subgroups of engineers. From this analysis we see that the gender-experience variable, which is an estimate of the difference between male and female annual salary increases, has a coefficient of 2,487, a Student's *t* statistic of 18.66, and a *p*-value of 0. Thus we estimate that the annual salary increases for males are $2,487 greater than the increases for females. We reject the null hypothesis that, as their experience increases, the salaries of both male and female engineers have increased at the same rate. In addition we see that the gender variable has a coefficient of 4,806 with a Student's *t* statistic of 4.04 indicating that on average male salaries are $4,806 higher. Thus, it will be important to take steps to deal with the salary discrimination that is evident in the data. The data are stored in the file **Gender and Salary**.

Figure 12.21 Regression Analysis for Annual Salary versus Experience and Gender

Scatterplot of Salary vs years experience

Regression Analysis: Salary versus years experi, Gender, gender-exper

```
The regression equation is
Salary = 36990 + 4216 years experience + 4806 Gender + 2487 gender-experience

Predictor             Coef   SE Coef      T       P
Constant            36989.6     827.2  44.72   0.000
years experience    4215.79     92.15  45.75   0.000
Gender                 4806      1188   4.04   0.000
gender-experience    2487.1     133.3  18.66   0.000


S = 1964.98    R-Sq = 99.6%    R-Sq(adj) = 99.6%


Analysis of Variance

Source          DF           SS          MS       F       P
Regression       3  32062830877  10687610292  2768.00  0.000
Residual Error  34    131278408     3861130
Total           37  32194109284
```

EXERCISES

Visit www.MyStatLab.com or www.pearsonglobal editions.com to access the data files.

Basic Exercises

12.62 What is the model constant when the dummy variable equals 1 in the following equations, where x_1 is a continuous variable and x_2 is a dummy variable with a value of 0 or 1?

a. $\hat{y} = 9 + 6x_1 + 9x_2$
b. $\hat{y} = 7 + 4x_1 + 2x_2$
c. $\hat{y} = 4 + 4x_1 + 8x_2 + 9x_1x_2$

12.63 What are the model constant and the slope coefficient of x_1 when the dummy variable equals 1 in the following equations, where x_1 is a continuous variable and x_2 is a dummy variable with a value of 0 or 1?

a. $\hat{y} = 4.5 + 9.2x_1 - 1.3x_2 + 4.3x_1x_2$
b. $\hat{y} = -6.8 + 10.4x_1 + 3.5x_2 - 1.8x_1x_2$
c. $\hat{y} = 11.3 - 3.4x_1 + 9.8x_2 + 10.5x_1x_2$

Application Exercises

12.64 The following model was fitted to observations from 1972 to 1979 in an attempt to explain oil-pricing behavior:

$$\hat{y} = 37x_1 + 5.22x_2$$
$$\quad\;\; (0.029) \quad\; (0.50)$$

where

$\hat{y}$ = difference between price in the current year and price in the previous year, in dollars per barrel

x_1 = difference between spot price in the current year and spot price in the previous year

x_2 = dummy variable taking the value 1 in 1974 and 0 otherwise to represent the specific effect of the oil embargo of that year

The numbers in parentheses under the coefficients are the estimated coefficient standard errors.

Interpret verbally and graphically the estimated coefficient on the dummy variable.

12.65 The following model was fitted to explain the selling prices of automobiles in a sample of 106 sales:

$$\hat{y} = -1{,}205 + 45.36x_1 + 3{,}325x_2 - 1{,}881x_3 + 3{,}054x_4$$
$$\quad\;\; (1.03) \qquad (480) \qquad (486) \qquad (949) \qquad (738)$$
$$+ 1{,}969\, x_5$$
$$\quad (738)$$

$$\overline{R}^2 = 0.89$$

where

$\hat{y}$ = selling price of an automobile, in euros

x_1 = the size of the car

x_2 = number of seats in the car

x_3 = age of car, in years

x_4 = dummy variable taking the value 1 if the car has a airbag and 0 otherwise

x_5 = dummy variable taking the value 1 if the car has a sunroof and 0 if it is a convertible

a. Interpret the estimated coefficient of x_4.
b. Interpret the estimated coefficient of x_5.
c. Find a 95% confidence interval for the impact of an airbag on selling price, all other things being equal.
d. Test the null hypothesis that type of roof has no impact on selling price against the alternative that, all other things equal, cars with sunroofs have a higher selling price than those with a convertible.

12.66 The following model was fitted to data on 32 insurance companies:

$$\hat{y} = 7.62 - 0.16x_1 + 1.23x_2 \qquad R^2 = 0.37$$
$$\quad\;\;\; (0.008) \quad\; (0.496)$$

where

$\hat{y}$ = price-earnings ratio

x_1 = size of insurance company assets, in billions of dollars

x_2 = dummy variable taking the value 1 for regional companies and 0 for national companies

The numbers in parentheses under the coefficients are the estimated coefficient standard errors.

a. Interpret the estimated coefficient on the dummy variable.

b. Test against a two-sided alternative. the null hypothesis that the true coefficient on the dummy variable is 0.
c. Test, at the 5% level, the null hypothesis $\beta_1 = \beta_2 = 0$, and interpret your result.

12.67 A business school dean wanted to assess the importance of factors that might help in predicting success in law school. For a random sample of 50 students, data were obtained when students graduated from law school, and the following model was fitted:

$$y = \alpha + \beta_1 x_1 + \beta_2 x_2 + \beta_3 x_3 + \varepsilon$$

where

y = score reflecting overall performance while in law school

x_1 = undergraduate grade point average

x_2 = score on GMAT

x_3 = dummy variable taking the value 1 if a student's letters of recommendation are unusually strong and 0 otherwise

Use the portion of the computer output from the estimated regression shown here to write a report summarizing the findings of this study.

Source	DF	Sum of Squares	Mean Square	F Value	R-Square
Model	3	641.04	212.68	8.48	0.356
Error	46	1,159.66	25.21		
Total	49	1,800.70			

Parameter	Estimate	t for H_0: $\beta_j = 0$	Std. Error of Estimate
Intercept	6.512		
X1	3.502	1.45	2.419
X2	0.491	4.59	0.107
X3	10.327	2.45	4.213

12.68 The following model was fitted to data on 34 states:

$$\hat{y} = -13{,}878 + 570x_1 + 5.01x_2 - 534x_3 + 30.7x_4$$
$$\qquad\qquad\quad (134.9) \quad (1.609) \quad (219.4) \quad (237)$$
$$+ 5{,}787x_5 - 2{,}630x_6$$
$$\quad (2{,}834) \qquad (1{,}630)$$

$$\overline{R}^2 = 0.55$$

where

$\hat{y}$ = annual salary of the attorney general of the state

x_1 = average annual salary of lawyers, in thousands of euros

x_2 = number of bills enacted in previous legislative session

x_3 = number of due process reviews by state courts that resulted in overturn of legislation in previous 40 years

x_4 = length of term of the attorney general of the state

x_5 = dummy variable taking value 1 if justices of the state supreme court can be removed from office by the governor, judicial review board, or majority vote of the supreme court and 0 otherwise

$x_6 =$ dummy variable taking value 1 if supreme court justices are elected on partisan ballots and 0 otherwise

The numbers in parentheses under the coefficients are the estimated coefficient standard errors.

a. Interpret the estimated coefficient on the dummy variable x_5.
b. Interpret the estimated coefficient on the dummy variable x_6.
c. Test, at the 5% level, the null hypothesis that the true coefficient on the dummy variable x_5 is 0 against the alternative that it is positive.
d. Test, at the 5% level, the null hypothesis that the true coefficient on the dummy variable x_6 is 0 against the alternative that it is negative.
e. Find and interpret a 95% confidence level for the parameter b_1.

12.69 A consulting group offers courses in financial management for executives. At the end of these courses participants are asked to provide overall ratings of the value of the course. For a sample of 25 courses, the following regression was estimated by least squares:

$$\hat{y} = 42.97 + 0.38x_1 + 0.52x_2 - 0.08x_3 + 6.21x_4 \qquad R^2 = 0.569$$
$$\quad\; (0.29) \quad\;\; (0.21) \quad\;\; (0.11) \quad\;\; (0.359)$$

where

$\hat{y} =$ average rating by participants of the course
$x_1 =$ percentage of course time spent in group discussion sessions
$x_2 =$ money, in dollars, per course member spent on preparing course material
$x_3 =$ money, in dollars, per course member spent on food and drinks
$x_4 =$ dummy variable taking the value 1 if a visiting guest lecturer is brought in and 0 otherwise

The numbers in parentheses under the coefficients are the estimated coefficient standard errors.

a. Interpret the estimated coefficient on x_4.
b. Test, against the alternative that it is positive, the null hypothesis that the true coefficient on x_4 is 0.
c. Interpret the coefficient of determination, and use it to test the null hypothesis that, taken as a group, the four independent variables do not linearly influence the dependent variable.
d. Find and interpret a 95% confidence interval for β_2.

12.70 A regression model was estimated to compare performance of students taking a business statistics course—either as a standard 14-week course or as an intensive 3-week course. The following model was estimated from observations of 350 students (Van Scyoc and Gleason 1993):

$$\hat{y} = -.7052 + 1.4170x_1 + 2.1624x_2 + .8680x_3 + 1.0845x_4$$
$$\qquad\quad (0.4568) \quad\;\; (0.3287) \quad\; (.4393) \quad\;\; (0.3766)$$

$$+ \; 0.4694x_5 + 0.0038x_6 + 0.0484x_7 \qquad R^2 = 0.344$$
$$\quad (0.0628) \qquad (0.0094) \qquad (0.0776)$$

where

$\hat{y} =$ score on a standardized test of understanding of statistics after taking the course
$x_1 =$ dummy variable taking the value 1 if the 3-week course was taken and 0 if the 14-week course was taken
$x_2 =$ student's grade point average
$x_3 =$ dummy variable taking the value 0 or 1, depending on which of two teachers had taught the course
$x_4 =$ dummy variable taking the value 1 if the student is male and 0 if female
$x_5 =$ score on a standardized test of understanding of mathematics before taking the course
$x_6 =$ number of semester credit hours the student had completed
$x_7 =$ age of student

The numbers in parentheses under the coefficients are the estimated coefficient standard errors.

Write a report discussing what can be learned from this fitted regression.

The following exercises will require a computer.

12.71 In a survey of 27 undergraduates at the University of Illinois the accompanying results were obtained with grade point averages (y), the number of hours per week spent studying (x_1), the average number of hours spent preparing for tests (x_2), the number of hours per week spent in bars (x_3), whether students take notes or mark highlights when reading texts ($x_4 = 1$ if yes, 0 if no), and the average number of credit hours taken per semester (x_5). Estimate the regression of grade point average on the five independent variables, and write a report on your findings. The data are in the data file **Student Performance**.

12.72 You have been asked to develop a model to analyze salary in a large business organization. The data for this model are stored in the file named **Salorg**; the variable names are self-explanatory.

a. Using the data in the file, develop a regression model that predicts salary as a function of the variables you select. Compute the conditional F and conditional t statistics for the coefficient of each predictor variable included in the model. Show all work and carefully explain your analysis process.
b. Test the hypothesis that female employees have a lower annual salary conditional on the variables in your model. The variable "Gender_1F" is coded 1 for female employees and 0 for male employees.
c. Test the hypothesis that the female employees have had a lower rate of salary increase conditional on the variables in the model developed for part b.

In this section we present an extended case study that indicates how a statistical study would be conducted. Careful study of this example can provide guidance in using many of the analysis procedures developed in this chapter and previous chapters.

The objective in this study is to produce a multiple regression model to predict sales of cotton fabric. Data for the project are obtained from the data file **Cotton**. The variables in the data file are as follows:

Quarter	Quarter of Year
year	Year of observation
cottonq	Quantity of cotton fabric produced
whoprice	Wholesale price index
impfab	Quantity of imported fabric
expfab	Quantity of exported fabric

Model Specification

The first step in model development is the selection of an appropriate economic theory that provides a rationale for the model analysis. This process of identifying a set of likely predictor variables and the mathematical form of the model is known as *model specification*. In this case the appropriate theory is based on that of economic demand models. Economic theory indicates that price should have an important effect—increased price reduces the quantity demanded. In addition, there are likely to be other variables that influence the quantity of cotton demanded. We would anticipate that the quantity of cotton fabric imported is likely to reduce the demand for domestic fabric and that the quantity of cotton fabric exported is likely to increase the demand for domestic fabric. In economic language, imports and exports of fabric shift the demand function. Based on this analysis, our original specification includes price with an expected negative coefficient, exported fabric with an expected positive coefficient, and imported fabric with an expected negative coefficient. All coefficients are initially specified as having linear effects. Thus, the model has the form

$$y = \beta_0 + \beta_1 x_1 + \beta_2 x_2 + \beta_3 x_3 + \varepsilon$$

where x_1 is the wholesale price, x_2 is the quantity of imported fabric, and x_3 is the quantity of exported fabric.

There is also the possibility that the quantity demanded varies over time, and, thus, the model should include the possibility of a time variable to reduce unexplained variability. For this analysis we wish to use a variable that represents time. Because time is indicated by a combination of year and quarter, we used the transformation

$$\text{time} = \text{year} + 0.25^* \text{quarter}$$

to produce a new variable for time that is continuously increasing with each quarter.

The next step in the analysis is to prepare a statistical description of the variables and their relationships. We exclude year and quarter from this analysis because they have been replaced by time and their inclusion would only add confusion to the analysis. We use Minitab to produce measures of central tendency and dispersion and also to obtain some understanding of the pattern of the observations. Figure 12.22 contains the output produced using Minitab. Examination of the mean, the standard deviation, and the minimum and maximum indicates the potential application region for the model. The estimated regression model always passes through the mean of the model variables. Predicted values of the dependent variable, cottonq, are usable over the range of the independent variables.

The next step is to examine the simple relationships between the variables, using both the correlation matrix and the matrix plots option. These should be examined together to

Results for: Cotton.MtW
Descriptive Statistics: conttonq. whoprice, impfab, expfab, time

Variable	N	N*	Mean	SE Mean	StDev	Minimum	Q1	Median	Q3
cottonq	28	0	1779.8	54.9	290.5	1277.0	1535.3	1762.5	2035 0
whoprice	28	0	106.81	1.16	6.11	98.00	100.45	107.40	112.20
impfab	28	0	7.52	1.38	7.33	1.30	2.78	4.85	9.05
expfab	28	0	274.0	20.3	107.7	80.0	190.5	277.1	358.1
time	28	0	69.625	0.389	2.056	66.250	67.813	69.625	71.438

Variable	Maximum
cottonq	2287.0
whoprice	115.80
impfab	27.00
expfab	477.0
time	73.000

determine the strength of the linear relationships (correlations) and to determine the form of the relationships (matrix plot).

Figure 12.23 contains the correlation matrix for the variables in the study prepared using Minitab. The p-value shown with each correlation indicates the probability that the hypothesis of 0 correlation between the two variables is true. Using our screening rule based on hypothesis testing, we can conclude that a p-value less than 0.05 provides evidence for a strong linear relationship between the two variables. Examining the first column, we see that there are strong linear relationships between cottonq and both whoprice and time. The variable expfab has a possible marginally significant simple relationship. A good rule to remember, as shown in Section 11.7, for examining correlation coefficients is that the absolute value of the correlation should be greater than 2 divided by the square root of the sample size, n. For this problem the screening value is $2/\sqrt{28} = 0.38$.

The second task is to determine if there are strong simple relationships between the pairs of possible predictor variables. We see a very high correlation between time and whoprice and significant relationships between impfab and both time and whoprice. These high correlations will lead to a high variance for the coefficient estimators for both time and whoprice if they are both included as predictor variables.

Figure 12.23
Minitab Output:
Correlations for
Cotton Variables

Correlations: cottonq, whoprice, impfab, expfab, time

	cottonq	whoprice	impfab	expfab
whoprice	-0.950			
	0.000			
impfab	0.291	-0.439		
	0.133	0.019		
expfab	0.370	-0.285	0.181	
	0.052	0.142	0.357	
time	-0.950	0.992	-0.392	-0.238
	0.000	0.000	0.039	0.222

Cell Contents: Pearson correlation
P-Value

We can also examine the relationships between variables by using matrix plots shown in Figure 12.24. The individual scatter plots show the relationships between a number of different variables simultaneously. Thus, they provide a display format that is similar to a correlation matrix. The advantage of the scatter plot is that it includes all the data points. Thus, one can also see if there is a simple nonlinear relationship between variables and/ or if there is some strange grouping of observations. All variables except year and quarter are included in the same order as in the correlation matrix so that there is a direct comparison between the correlation matrix and the matrix plots.

Figure 12.24
Matrix Plots for
Variables in the
Study (Minitab
Output)

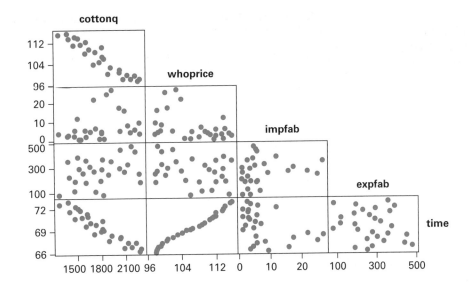

Note the correspondence between the correlations and the scatter plots. Both whoprice and time have strong negative linear relationships with cottonq. However, the strong positive linear relationship between whoprice and time will have a major influence on the estimated coefficients, as shown in Section 12.2, and on the coefficient standard errors, as shown in Section 12.4. There are no other strong simple relationships between the potential predictor variables. Neither imports nor exports are correlated with wholesale price, time, or each other.

Multiple Regression

The next step is to estimate the first multiple regression model. The economic theory for this analysis suggests that the quantity of cotton fabric produced should be inversely related to price and to the amount of fabric imported and directly related to the amount of fabric exported. In addition, the strong correlation between time and cotton fabric production indicates that production declined linearly over time but that wholesale price also increased linearly over time. The resulting very high positive correlation between time and wholesale price influences both coefficients in a multiple regression equation. We select cottonq as the dependent variable and whoprice, impfab, expfab, and time, in that order, as the independent variables. The first multiple regression analysis is shown in Figure 12.25.

Analysis of the regression statistics indicates a high R^2, and the standard error of the estimate (S) equals 78.91, compared to the standard deviation of 290.5 (Figure 12.22) for cottonq by itself. The variables impfab and expfab are both conditionally significant with signs corresponding to economic theory. The small Student's t statistics for whoprice and time indicate that, in fact, there is a serious problem. Both variables cannot be included as predictors because they both represent the same effect, as shown by the correlation between whoprice and time equal to 0.992 and by the matrix plot in Figure 12.24.

The rules for dropping variables are based on a combination of both the model theory and the statistical indicators. The statistical rule would be to drop the variable with the smallest absolute Student's t, that is, time. Economic theory would argue for including a price variable in a model to predict quantity produced or quantity demanded. We see that in this case, both rules lead to the same conclusion. This is not always the case, and, thus, good judgment and clear thinking about model objectives are very important.

It is important that we clearly state the rationale for variable selection before examining the statistical output. In economic demand or supply models such as the one considered here, we would have a very strong desire to follow economic theory and include price unless the statistical results were very strong against that prior judgment. For example, if the absolute value of the Student's t for time was greater than 2.5 or 3 and the absolute value of the Student's t for wholesale price was less than 1, there would be strong evidence against the theory that price is an important variable.

Figure 12.25
Initial Multiple
Regression Model
(Minitab Output)

Regression Analysis: cottonq versus whoprice, impfab, expfab, time

```
The regression equation is
cottonq =8876 - 24.3 whoprice - 5.57 impfab + 0.376 expfab - 65.5 time

Predictor      Coef   SE Coef       T      P
Constant       8076      2295    3.87  0.001
whoprice     -24.31     24.45   -0.99  0.331
impfab       -5.565     2.527   -2.20  0.038
expfab       0.3758    0.1595    2.36  0.027
time         -65.51     70.24   -0.93  0.361

S = 78.9141   R-Sq = 93.7%  R-Sq(adj) = 92.6%

Analysis of Variance

Source           DF        SS      MS      F      P
Regression        4   2134572  533643  85.69  0.000
Residual Error   23    143231    6227
Total            27   2277803

Source    DF   Seq SS
whoprice   1  2055110
impfab     1    44905
expfab     1    29141
time       1     5417
```

Note
This table indicates the conditional explained variability for each variable, given the order of entry used for this regression analysis.

```
Unusual Observations

Obs  Whoprice  Cottonq     Fit  SE Fit  Residual  St Resid
18        110   1810.0  1663.3    29.6     146.7      2.00R

R denotes an observation with a large standardized residual.
```

Based on this analysis, a second regression model is estimated, as shown in Figure 12.26, with time excluded as a predictor variable. We see now that whoprice is highly significant and that the s and R^2 statistics are essentially the same as those in the first regression analysis (Figure 12.25). Note also that the explained regression sum of squares (SSR) and the residual error sum of squares (SSE) are essentially the same. The standard deviation for the whoprice coefficient has dropped from 24.45 to 2.835, and, as a result, the Student's t is substantially larger. As we learned in Section 12.4, high correlations between independent variables result in much larger variances for the coefficient estimator. We see that effect here. Note also that for this regression model, the wholesale price coefficient estimate changed from −24.31 to −46.956. In Section 12.2 we saw that correlations between predictor variables have a complex effect on coefficient estimates, so there will not always be a difference that is this large. However, correlations between independent variables always increase the coefficient standard error. The standard errors for the other two coefficients have not changed substantially because the correlations with time were not large.

Minitab also provides a list of observations with extreme residuals. We see in observation 18 that the observed value of cottonq is substantially above the value predicted by the equation. In this case, we might decide to go back to the original data and try to determine if there was an error in the reported data. Such an investigation might also provide some important insights into the process being studied using multiple regression.

Effect of Dropping a Statistically Significant Variable

In this section we consider the effect of removing a conditionally significant variable from the regression model. We saw in Figure 12.26 that expfab is a statistically significant predictor of the quantity of cotton produced. However, the regression analysis in Figure 12.27 has removed expfab from the regression model in Figure 12.26 because it has the smallest absolute t value.

Figure 12.26
Final Regression
Analysis Model
(Minitab Output)

Regression Analysis: cottonq versus whoprice, impfab, expfab, time

```
The regression equation is
cottonq = 6757 - 47.0 whoprice - 6.52 impfab + 0.319 expfab


Predictor    Coef   SE Coef       T      P
Constant   6757.0     322.2   20.97  0.000
whoprice   -46.956    2.835  -16.56  0.000
impfab      -6.517    2.306   -2.83  0.009
expfab      0.3190   0.1471    2.17  0.040


S = 78.6998   R-Sq = 93.5%   R-Sq(adj) = 92.7%


Analysis of Variance


Source          DF        SS      MS       F      P
Regression       3   2129156  709719  114.59  0.000
Residual Error  24    148648    6194
Total           27   2277803
```

```
Source     DF   Seq SS
whoprice    1  2055110
impfab      1    44905
expfab      1    29141
```

> **Note**
> These sequential conditional explained sums of squares are the same as those for the regression in Figure 12.25, which included time as a predictor variable.

```
Unusual Observations

Obs  Whoprice  Cottonq     Fit  SE Fit  Residual  St Resid
18        110   1810.0  1642.0    18.7     168.0     2.20R

R denotes an observation with a large standardized residual.
```

Regression Analysis: cottonq versus whoprice, impfab, expfab, time

```
The regression equation is
cottonq = 6995 - 48.4 whoprice - 6.20 impfab


Predictor    Coef   SE Coef       T      P
Constant   6994.8     324.6   21.55  0.000
whoprice   -48.388    2.955  -16.38  0.000
impfab      -6.195    2.465   -2.51  0.019


S = 84.3299   R-Sq = 92.2%   R-Sq(adj) = 91.6%

Analysis of Variance

Source          DF        SS        MS       F      P
Regression       2   2100015   1050007  147.65  0.000
Residual Error  25    177788      7112
Total           27   2277803
```

Note that, as a result of removing expfab, the standard error of the estimate has increased from 78.70 to 84.33 and R^2 has decreased from 93.5% to 92.2%. These results indicate that the model error term is now larger and, thus, the quality of the model has been reduced.

The conditional F statistic for expfab can be computed using the analysis of variance tables from the models in Figures 12.26 and 12.27. In the following equation we define the final regression from Figure 12.26 as model 1 and the regression from Figure 12.27, with expfab removed, as model 2. Using these conventions, the conditional F statistic for the variable expfab, X_3, under the null hypothesis that its coefficient is 0, can be computed as follows:

$$F_{x_3} = \frac{SSR_1 - SSR_2}{s_e^2} = \frac{(2,129,156 - 2,100,015)}{6,194} = 4.705$$

We can also compute the conditional Student's t statistic for variable x_3 by taking the square root of the conditional F_{x_3}

$$t_{x_3} = \sqrt{4.705} = 2.17$$

and, of course, we see that this is the same as the Student's t statistic for the expfab (x_3) variable in Figure 12.26. The conditional F test for a single independent variable is always exactly the same as the conditional F because an F with 1 degree of freedom for the numerator is exactly equal to t^2.

Analysis of Residuals

After fitting the regression model, it is valuable to examine the residuals to determine how the model actually fits the data and the regression assumptions. In Section 11.9 we discussed the analysis of outliers and extreme points in simple regression. Those ideas carry over directly to multiple regression and should be part of your analysis of residuals. Recall that the residuals are computed as follows:

$$e_i = y_i - \hat{y}_i$$

A variable that contains the residuals for a particular regression analysis can be computed in Minitab or any other good statistical package. This has been done for the final regression model in Figure 12.26. The first step is to examine the pattern of the residuals by constructing a histogram, as shown in Figure 12.28. We see that the distribution of the residuals is approximately symmetric. The distribution also appears to be somewhat uniform. Note that this results in part from the small sample size used to construct the histogram.

Figure 12.28
Histogram for Residuals from Final Regression Model

Preparing a normal probability plot, as shown in Figure 12.29, is useful in determining the pattern of the residuals. The plot indicates an approximate linear relationship, and, thus, it is not possible to reject the assumption of normally distributed residuals.

Figure 12.29
Normal Probability Plot for Model Residuals

It is also a good practice to plot the residuals against each of the independent variables included in the analysis. This provides a check that there were not a few unusual data points or a complex conditional nonlinear relationship for one of the independent variables. If the model has been correctly specified and estimated, we expect that there is no pattern of relationship between the independent variables and the residuals. Figure 12.30 presents the plot of residuals versus the wholesale price variable. We do not see any unusual patterns in this plot except the large positive outlier when the wholesale price is approximately 110.

Figure 12.30
Scatter Plot of Residuals versus Wholesale Price

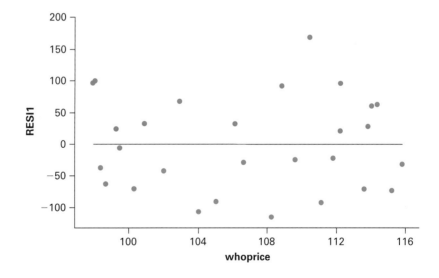

In Figure 12.31 we show the plot of residuals versus imported fabric. Again, we do not see any unusual residual patterns, but we do observe that most of the imports are concentrated between 0 and 10. Thus, the larger values of imported fabric could be having a large effect on the regression slope coefficient. Finally, in Figure 12.32, we see a plot of residuals versus exported fabric. Again, the pattern of residuals does not suggest an alternative to the linear relationship.

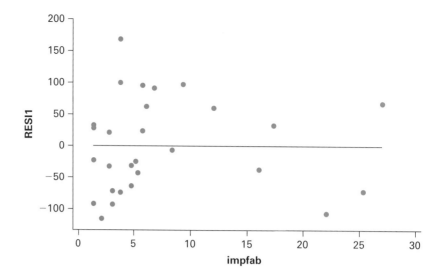

Figure 12.31
Scatter Plot of Residuals versus Imported Fabric

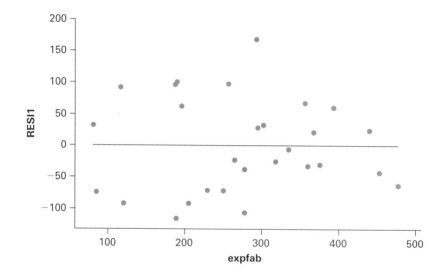

Figure 12.32
Scatter Plot of Residuals versus Exported Fabric

The final residuals analysis examines the relationship between the residuals and the dependent variable. We consider a plot of the residuals versus the observed value of the dependent variable in Figure 12.33 and versus the predicted value of the dependent variable in Figure 12.34. We can see in Figure 12.33 that there is a positive relationship between the residuals and the observed value of cottonq. There are more negative residuals at low values of cottonq and more positive residuals at high values of cottonq. It is possible to show mathematically that there is always a positive correlation between the residuals and the observed values of the dependent variable. Therefore, a plot of the residuals versus the observed value does not provide any useful information. However, one should always plot the residuals versus the predicted or fitted values of the dependent variable. This provides a way to determine if the model errors are stable over the range of predicted values. In this example note that there is not a relationship between the residuals and the predicted values. Thus, the model errors are stable over the range.

In Chapter 13 we use residuals analysis to identify two regression model situations, heteroscedasticity and autocorrelation, that violate the regression assumption that the error variance is the same over the range of the model.

Figure 12.33
Scatter Plot of
Residuals versus
Observed Value of
Cotton

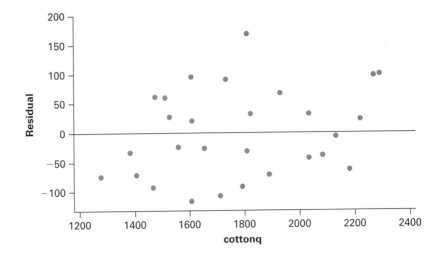

Figure 12.34
Scatter Plot of
Residuals versus
Predicted Value of
Cotton

EXERCISES

 Visit www.MyStatLab.com or www.pearsonglobal editions.com to access the data files.

Basic Exercises

12.73 Suppose that two independent variables are included as predictor variables in a multiple regression analysis. What can you expect will be the effect on the estimated slope coefficients when these two variables have each of the given correlations?

a. 0.91   b. 0.38   c. −0.64   d. −0.11

12.74 Consider a regression analysis with $n = 34$ and four potential independent variables. Suppose that one of the independent variables has a correlation of 0.23 with the dependent variable. Does this imply that this independent variable will have a very small Student's t statistic in the regression analysis with all four predictor variables?

12.75 Consider a regression analysis with $n = 58$ and four potential independent variables. Suppose that one of the independent variables has a correlation of 0.48 with the dependent variable. Does this imply that this independent variable will have a very large Student's t statistic in the regression analysis with all three predictor variables?

12.76 Consider a regression analysis with $n = 49$ and two potential independent variables. Suppose that one of the independent variables has a correlation of 0.56 with the dependent variable. Does this imply that this independent variable will have a very small Student's t statistic in the regression analysis with both predictor variables?

Application Exercises

12.77 In order to assess the effect in one state of a casualty insurance company's economic power on its political power, the following model was hypothesized and fitted to data from all 50 states:

$$Y = \beta_0 + \beta_1 X_1 + \beta_2 X_2 + \beta_3 X_3 + \beta_4 x_4 + \beta_5 X_5 + \varepsilon$$

where

$Y =$ ratio of company's payments for state and local taxes, in thousands of dollars, to total state and local tax revenues in millions of dollars

$X_1 =$ insurance company state concentration ratio (a measure of the concentration of banking resources)

X_2 = per capita income in the state in thousands of dollars

X_3 = ratio of nonfarm income to the sum of farm and nonfarm income

X_4 = ratio of insurance company's net after-tax income to insurance reserves (multiplied by 1,000)

X_5 = average of insurance reserves (divided by 10,000)

Part of the computer output from the estimated regression is shown here. Write a report summarizing the findings of this study.

R-Square = 0.515

Parameter	Estimate	Student's t for H_0: Parameter $= 0$	Std. Error of Estimate
Intercept	10.60	2.41	4.40
X1	−0.90	−0.69	1.31
X2	0.14	0.50	0.28
X3	−12.85	−2.83	4.18
X4	0.080	0.50	0.160
X5	0.100	5.00	0.020

12.78 A random sample of 93 freshmen at the University of Illinois was asked to rate, on a scale of 1 (low) to 10 (high), their overall opinion of residence hall life. They were also asked to rate their levels of satisfaction with roommates, with the floor, with the hall, and with the resident advisor. (Information on satisfaction with the room itself was obtained, but this was later discarded as it provided no useful additional power in explaining overall opinion.) The following model was estimated:

$$Y = \beta_0 + \beta_1 X_1 + \beta_2 X_2 + \beta_3 X_3 + \beta_4 X_4 + \varepsilon$$

where

Y = overall opinion of residence hall
X_1 = satisfaction with roommates
X_2 = satisfaction with floor
X_3 = satisfaction with hall
X_4 = satisfaction with resident advisor

Use the accompanying portion of the computer output from the estimated regression to write a report summarizing the findings of this study.

Dependent Variable: Y Overall Opinion

Source	DF	Sum of Squares	Mean Square	F Value	R-Square
Model	4	37.016	9.2540	9.958	0.312
Error	88	81.780	0.9293		
Total	92	118.79			

Parameter	Estimate	Student's t for H_0: Parameter $= 0$	Std. Error of Estimate
Intercept	3.950	5.84	0.676
X_1	0.106	1.69	0.063
X_2	0.122	1.70	0.072
X_3	0.092	1.75	0.053
X_4	0.169	2.64	0.064

12.79 The following model was fitted to 47 monthly observations in an attempt to explain the difference between certificate of deposit rates and commercial paper rates:

$$Y = \beta_0 + \beta_1 X_1 + \beta_2 X_2 + \varepsilon$$

where

Y = commercial paper certificate of deposit rate less commercial paper rate
X_1 = commercial paper rate
X_2 = ratio of loans and investments to capital

Use the part of the computer output from the estimated regression shown here to write a report summarizing the findings of this analysis.

R-Square = 0.730

Parameter	Estimate	Student's t for H_0: parameter $= 0$	Std. Error of Estimate
Intercept	−5.559	−4.14	1.343
X_1	0.186	5.64	0.033
X_2	0.450	2.08	0.216

12.80 You have been asked to develop a multiple regression model to predict the traffic fatality rate per 100 million miles in 2007. The data file **Vehicle Travel State** contains traffic data by state for the year 2007; the variables are described in the Chapter 11 appendix. Consider the following possible predictor variables and select only those that are conditionally significant; per capita disposable income, percent of population in urban areas, total licensed drivers, total motor vehicle registrations, percent interstate highway miles, motor vehicle fuel tax in cents per gallon, total highway expenditure divided by number of licensed drivers, doctors per 1,000 population, nurses per 1,000 population, and Medicaid enrollment as a fraction of total population.

12.81 The data file **Economic Activity** contains data for the 50 states in the United States; the variables are described in the Chapter 11 appendix. You are asked to develop a model to predict the percentage of females that are in the labor force. The possible predictor variables are per capita disposable personal income, the percentage of males unemployed, the manufacturing payroll per worker, and the unemployment rate of women (x_3). Compute the multiple regression and write a report on your findings.

12.82 The United Nations has hired you as a consultant to help identify factors that predict manufacturing growth in developing countries. You have decided to use multiple regression to develop a model and identify important variables that predict growth. You have collected the data in the data file **Developing Country** from 48 countries. The variables included are percentage manufacturing growth (y), percentage agricultural growth (x_1), percentage exports growth (x_2), and percentage rate of inflation (x_3) in 48 developing countries. Develop the multiple regression model and write a report on your findings.

KEY WORDS

DATA FILES

CHAPTER EXERCISES AND APPLICATIONS

 Visit www.MyStatLab.com or www.pearsonglobal editions.com to access the data files.

12.83 The method of least squares is used far more often than any alternative procedure to estimate the parameters of a multiple regression model. Explain the basis for this method of estimation, and discuss why its use is so widespread.

12.84 It is common practice to compute an analysis of variance table in conjunction with an estimated multiple regression. Carefully explain what can be learned from such a table.

12.85 State whether each of the following statements is true or false.

a. The error sum of squares must be smaller than the regression sum of squares.

b. Instead of carrying out a multiple regression, we can get the same information from simple linear regressions of the dependent variable on each independent variable.

c. The coefficient of determination cannot be negative.

d. The adjusted coefficient of determination cannot be negative.

e. The coefficient of multiple correlation is the square root of the coefficient of determination.

12.86 If an additional independent variable, however irrelevant, is added to a multiple regression model, a smaller sum-of-squared errors will result. Explain why this is so, and discuss the consequences for the interpretation of the coefficient of determination.

12.87 A dependent variable is regressed on two independent variables. It is possible that the hypotheses $H_0: \beta_1 = 0$ and $H_0: \beta_2 = 0$ cannot be rejected at low significance levels, yet the hypothesis $H_0: \beta_1 = \beta_2 = 0$ can be rejected at a very low significance level. In what circumstances might this result arise?

12.88 [*This exercise requires the material in the chapter appendix.*] Suppose that the regression model

$$y = \beta_0 + \beta_1 x_1 + \beta_2 x_2 + \varepsilon$$

is estimated by least squares. Show that the residuals, e_i, from the fitted model sum to 0.

12.89 A study was conducted to assess the influence of various factors on the start of new firms in the computer chip industry. For a sample of 70 countries the following model was estimated:

$$\hat{y} = -59.31 + 4.983x_1 + 2.198x_2 + 3.816x_3 - 0.310x_4$$
$$\quad\quad\quad\quad (1.156) \quad (0.210) \quad (2.063) \quad (0.330)$$

$$-0.886x_5 + 3.215x_6 + 0.85x_7$$
$$(3.055) \quad (1.568) \quad (0.354)$$

$$R^2 = 0.766$$

where

$\hat{y}$ = new business starts in the industry
x_1 = population in millions
x_2 = industry size
x_3 = measure of economic quality of life
x_4 = measure of political quality of life
x_5 = measure of environmental quality of life
x_6 = measure of health and educational quality of life
x_7 = measure of social quality of life

The numbers in parentheses under the coefficients are the estimated coefficient standard errors.

a. Interpret the estimated regression coefficients.
b. Interpret the coefficient of determination.
c. Find a 90% confidence interval for the increase in new business starts resulting from a one-unit increase in the economic quality of life, with all other variables unchanged.
d. Test, against a two-sided alternative at the 5% level, the null hypothesis that, all else remaining equal, the environmental quality of life does not influence new business starts.
e. Test, against a two-sided alternative at the 5% level, the null hypothesis that, all else remaining equal, the health and educational quality of life does not influence new business starts.
f. Test the null hypothesis that, taken together, these seven independent variables do not influence new business starts.

12.90 A survey research group conducts regular studies of households through mail questionnaires and is concerned about the factors influencing the response rate. In an experiment, 30 sets of questionnaires were mailed to potential respondents. The regression model fitted to the resulting data set was as follows:

$$Y = \beta_0 + \beta_1 X_1 + \beta_2 X_2 + \varepsilon$$

where

Y = percentage of responses received
X_1 = number of questions asked
X_2 = length of questionnaire in number of words

Part of the SAS computer output from the estimate regression is shown next.

$$R\text{-Square} = 0.637$$

Parameter	Estimate	Student's t for H_0: Parameter $= 0$	Std. Error of Estimate
Intercept	74.3652		
X1	-1.8345	-2.89	0.6349
X2	-0.0162	-1.78	0.0091

a. Interpret the estimated regression coefficients.
b. Interpret the coefficient of determination.
c. Test, at the 1% significance level, the null hypothesis that, taken together, the two independent variables do not linearly influence the response rate.
d. Find and interpret a 99% confidence interval for β_1.
e. Test the null hypothesis

$$H_0 : \beta_2 = 0$$

against the alternative

$$H_1 : \beta_2 < 0$$

and interpret your findings.

12.91 A consulting group offers courses in financial management for executives. At the end of these courses, participants are asked to provide overall ratings of the value of the course. To assess the impact of various factors on ratings, the model

$$Y = \beta_0 + \beta_1 X_1 + \beta_2 X_2 + \beta_3 X_3 + \varepsilon$$

was fitted for 25 such courses, where

Y = average rating by participants of the course
X_1 = percentage of course time spent in group discussion sessions
X_2 = amount of money (in dollars) per course member spent on the preparation of subject matter material
X_3 = amount of money per course member spent on the provision of non-course-related material (food, drinks, and so forth)

Part of the SAS computer output for the fitted regression is shown next.

$$R\text{-Square} = 0.579$$

Parameter	Estimate	Student's t for H_0: Parameter $= 0$	Std. Error of Estimate
Intercept	42.9712		
X1	0.3817	1.89	0.2018
X2	0.5172	2.64	0.1957
X3	0.0753	1.09	0.0693

a. Interpret the estimated regression coefficients.
b. Interpret the coefficient of determination.
c. Test, at the 5% level, the null hypothesis that, taken together, the three independent variables do not linearly influence the course rating.
d. Find and interpret a 90% confidence interval for β_1.
e. Test the null hypothesis

$$H_0 : \beta_2 = 0$$

against the alternative

$$H_1 : \beta_2 > 0$$

and interpret your result.

f. Test at the 10% level the null hypothesis

$$H_0 : \beta_3 = 0$$

against the alternative

$$H_1 : \beta_3 \neq 0$$

and interpret your result.

12.92 At the end of classes professors are rated by their students on a scale of 1 (poor) to 5 (excellent). Students are also asked what course grades they expect, and these are coded as A = 4, B = 3, and so on. The data file **Teacher Rating** contains, for a random sample of 20 classes, ratings of professors, the average expected grades, and the numbers of students in the classes. The variables are defined in the data file. Compute the multiple regression of rating on expected grade and number of students, and write a report on your findings.

12.93 Flyer Computer, Inc., wishes to know the effect of various variables on labor efficiency. Based on a sample of 64 observations, the following model was estimated by least squares:

$$\hat{y} = -16.528 + 28.729x_1 + .022x_2 - 0.023x_3 - 0.054x_4$$
$$-0.077x_5 + 0.411x_6 + 0.349x_7 + 0.028x_8 \quad R^2 = .467$$

where

$\hat{y}$ = index of direct labor efficiency in production plant
x_1 = ratio of overtime hours to straight-time hours worked by all production workers
x_2 = average number of hourly workers in the plant
x_3 = percentage of employees involved in some quality-of-work-life program
x_4 = number of grievances filed per 100 workers
x_5 = disciplinary action rate
x_6 = absenteeism rate for hourly workers
x_7 = salaried workers' attitudes, from low (dissatisfied) to high, as measured by questionnaire
x_8 = percentage of hourly employees submitting at least one suggestion in a year to the plant's suggestion program

Also obtained by least squares from these data was the fitted model:

$$\hat{y} = 9.062 - 10944x_1 + 0.320x_2 + 0.019x_3 \quad R^2 = 0.242$$

The variables $x_4, x_5, x_6, x_7,$ and x_8 are measures of the performance of a plant's industrial relations system. Test, at the 1% level, the null hypothesis that they do not contribute to explaining direct labor efficiency, given that $x_1, x_2,$ and x_3 are also to be used.

12.94 Based on 107 students' scores on the first examination in a course on business statistics, the following model was estimated by least squares:

$$\hat{y} = 2.178 + 0.469x_1 + 3.369x_2 + 3.054x_3$$
$$\qquad\quad (0.090) \quad\ (0.456) \quad\ (1.457)$$

$$R^2 = .686$$

where

$\hat{y}$ = student's actual score on the examination
x_1 = student's expected score on the examination
x_2 = hours per week spent working on the course
x_3 = student's grade point average

The numbers in parentheses under the coefficients are the estimated coefficient standard errors.

a. Interpret the estimate of β_1.
b. Find and interpret a 95% confidence interval for β_2.
c. Test, against a two-sided alternative, the null hypothesis that β_3 is 0, and interpret your result.
d. Interpret the coefficient of determination.
e. Test the null hypothesis that $\beta_1 = \beta_2 = \beta_3 = 0$.
f. Find and interpret the coefficient of multiple correlation.
g. Predict the score of a student who expects a score of 80, works 8 hours per week on the course, and has a grade point average of 3.0.

12.95 Based on 25 years of annual data, an attempt was made to explain savings in India. The model fitted was as follows:

$$y = \beta_0 + \beta_1 x_1 + \beta_2 x_2 + \varepsilon$$

where

y = change in real deposit rate
x_1 = change in real per capita income
x_2 = change in real interest rate

The least squares parameter estimates (with standard errors in parentheses) were (Ghatak and Deadman 1989) as follows:

$$b_1 = 0.0974(0.0215) \quad b_2 = 0.374(0.209)$$

The adjusted coefficient of determination was as follows:

$$\overline{R}^2 = .91$$

a. Find and interpret a 99% confidence interval for β_1.
b. Test, against the alternative that it is positive, the null hypothesis that β_2 is 0.
c. Find the coefficient of determination.
d. Test the null hypothesis that $\beta_1 = \beta_2 = 0$.
e. Find and interpret the coefficient of multiple correlation.

12.96 Based on data on 2,679 high school basketball players, the following model was fitted:

$$y = \beta_0 + \beta_1 x_1 + \beta_2 x_2 + \cdots + \beta_9 x_9 + \varepsilon$$

where

y = minutes played in season
x_1 = field-goal percentage
x_2 = free-throw percentage
x_3 = rebounds per minute
x_4 = points per minute
x_5 = fouls per minute
x_6 = steals per minute
x_7 = blocked shots per minute
x_8 = turnovers per minute
x_9 = assists per minute

The least squares parameter estimates (with standard errors in parentheses) were as follows:

$b_0 = 358.848\ (44.695)\ b_1 = 0.6742\ (0.0639)\ b_2 = 0.2855\ (0.0388)$

$b_3 = 303.81\ (77.73)\quad b_4 = 504.95\ (43.26)\quad b_5 = -3923.5\ (120.6)$

$b_6 = 480.04\ (224.9)\quad b_7 = 1350.3\ (212.3)\quad b_8 = -891.67\ (180.87)$

$b_9 = 722.95\ (110.98)$

The coefficient of determination was as follows:

$$R^2 = 0.5239$$

a. Find and interpret a 90% confidence interval for β_6.
b. Find and interpret a 99% confidence interval for β_7.
c. Test, against the alternative that it is negative, the null hypothesis that β_8 is 0. Interpret your result.
d. Test, against the alternative that it is positive, the null hypothesis that β_9 is 0. Interpret your result.
e. Interpret the coefficient of determination.
f. Find and interpret the coefficient of multiple correlation.

12.97 Based on data from 63 counties, the following model was estimated by least squares:

$$\hat{y} = 0.58 - .052x_1 - .005x_2 \quad R^2 = .17$$
$$\phantom{\hat{y} = 0.58 - }{\scriptstyle(.019)}{\scriptstyle(.042)}$$

where

$\hat{y}$ = growth rate in real gross domestic product
x_1 = real income per capita
x_2 = average tax rate, as a proportion of gross national product

The numbers in parentheses under the coefficients are the estimated coefficient standard errors.

a. Test against a two-sided alternative the null hypothesis that β_1 is 0. Interpret your result.
b. Test against a two-sided alternative the null hypothesis that β_2 is 0. Interpret your result.
c. Interpret the coefficient of determination.
d. Find and interpret the coefficient of multiple correlation.

12.98 The following regression model was fitted to data on 60 U.S. female amateur golfers:

$$\hat{y} = 164{,}683 + 341.10x_1 + 170.02x_2 + 495.19x_3 - 4.23x_4$$
$$\phantom{\hat{y} = 164{,}683 + }{\scriptstyle(100.59)}{\scriptstyle(167.18)}{\scriptstyle(305.48)}{\scriptstyle(90.0)}$$

$$-136{,}040x_5 - 35{,}549x_6 + 202.52x_7$$
$${\scriptstyle(25.634)}{\scriptstyle(16{,}240)}{\scriptstyle(106.20)}$$

$$\overline{R}^2 = .516$$

where

$\hat{y}$ = winnings per tournament in dollars
x_1 = average length of drive in yards
x_2 = percentage times drive ends in fairway
x_3 = percentage times green reached in regulation
x_4 = percentage times par saved after hitting into sand trap
x_5 = average number of putts taken on greens reached in regulation

x_6 = average number of putts taken on greens not reached in regulation
x_7 = number of years the golfer has played

The numbers in parentheses under the coefficients are the estimated coefficient standard errors.

Write a report summarizing what can be learned from these results.

The following exercises use a data set and require a statistical computer package to prepare the regression analysis for the problem solution.

12.99 The Economics Department wishes to develop a multiple regression model to predict student GPA for economics courses. Department faculty have collected data for 112 graduates, which include the variables economics GPA, SAT verbal, SAT mathematics, ACT English, ACT social science, and high school percentile rank. The data are stored in a file named **Student GPA** on your data disk and described in the Chapter 11 appendix.

a. Use the SAT variables and class rank to determine the best prediction model. Remove any independent variables that are not significant. What are the coefficients, their Student's t statistics, and the model?
b. Use the ACT variables and class rank to determine the best prediction model. Remove any independent variables that are not significant. What are the coefficients, their Student's t statistics, and the model?
c. Which model predicts an economics GPA better? Present the evidence to support your conclusion.

12.100 Use the data in the file **Citydatr** to estimate a regression equation that can be used to determine the marginal effect of the percent of commercial property on the market value per owner-occupied residence. Include the percent of owner-occupied residences, the percent of industrial property, the median number of rooms per residence, and the per capita income as additional predictor variables in your multiple regression equation. The variables are included on your data disk and described in the chapter appendix. Indicate which of the variables are conditionally significant. Your final equation should include only significant variables. Discuss and interpret your final regression model, including an indication of how you would select a community for your house.

12.101 The administrator of the National Highway Traffic Safety Administration (NHTSA) wants to know if the different types of vehicles in a state have a relationship to the highway death rate in the state. She has asked you to develop multiple regression analyses to determine if the average vehicle weight, the percentage of imported cars, the percentage of light trucks, and the average car age are related to crash deaths in automobiles and pickups. The data for the analysis are located in the data file named **Vehicle Travel State**. A description of the variables is contained in the Chapter 11 appendix.

a. Prepare a correlation matrix for crash deaths and the predictor variables. Note the simple relationships between crash deaths and the predictor variables. In addition, indicate any potential multicollinearity problems between the predictor variables.

b. Prepare a multiple regression analysis of crash deaths on the potential predictor variables. Remove any nonsignificant predictor variables, one at a time, from the regression model. Indicate your best final model.

c. State the conclusions from your analysis and discuss the conditional importance of the variables in terms of their relationship to crash deaths.

12.102 The Department of Transportation wishes to know if states with a larger percentage of urban population have higher automobile and pickup crash death rates. In addition, it wants to know if the variable average speed on rural roads or the variable percentage of rural roads that are surfaced is conditionally related to crash death rates, given percentage of urban population. Data for this study are included in the file **Vehicle Travel State**; the variables are defined in the Chapter 11 appendix.

a. Prepare a correlation matrix and descriptive statistics for crash deaths and the potential predictor variables. Note the relationships and any potential problems of multicollinearity.

b. Prepare a multiple regression analysis of crash deaths on the potential predictor variables. Determine which of the variables should be retained in the regression model because they have a conditionally significant relationship.

c. State the results of your analysis in terms of your final regression model. Indicate which variables are conditionally significant.

12.103 An economist wishes to predict the market value of owner-occupied homes in small midwestern cities. He has collected a set of data from 45 small cities for a 2-year period and wants you to use this as the data source for the analysis. The data are in the file **Citydatr** the variables are described in the chapter appendix. He wants you to develop a multiple regression prediction equation. The potential predictor variables include the size of the house, tax rate, percent of commercial property, per capita income, and total city government expenditures.

a. Compute the correlation matrix and descriptive statistics for the market value of residences and the potential predictor variables. Note any potential problems of multicollinearity. Define the approximate range for your regression model by the variable means ± 2 standard deviations.

b. Prepare multiple regression analyses using the predictor variables. Remove any variables that are not conditionally significant. Which variable, size of house or tax rate, has the stronger conditional relationship to the value of houses?

c. A business developer in a midwestern state has stated that local property tax rates in small towns need to be lowered because, if they are not, no one will purchase a house in these towns. Based on your analysis in this problem, evaluate the business developer's claim.

12.104 Stuart Wainwright, the vice president of purchasing for a large national retailer, has asked you to prepare an analysis of retail sales by state. He wants to know if the percent of unemployment for males and for females and the per capita disposable income are jointly related to the per capita retail sales. Data for this study are in the data file named **Economic Activity**; the variables are described in the Chapter 11 appendix. You may have to compute additional variables using the variables in the data file.

a. Prepare a correlation matrix, compute descriptive statistics, and obtain a regression analysis of per capita retail sales on unemployment and personal income. Compute 95% confidence intervals for the slope coefficients in each regression equation.

b. What is the conditional effect of a $1,000 decrease in per capita income on per capita sales?

c. Would the prediction equation be improved by adding the state population as an additional predictor variable?

12.105 A major national supplier of building materials for residential construction is concerned about total sales for next year. It is well known that the company's sales are directly related to the total national residential investment. Several New York bankers are predicting that interest rates will rise about two percentage points next year. You have been asked to develop a regression analysis that can be used to predict the effect of interest rate changes on residential investment. In addition to interest rate, you believe that the GDP, money supply, government spending, and price index for finished goods might be predictors of residential investment. Therefore, you decide that two multiple regression models will be needed. One will include prime interest rate and important additional variables. The second will include federal funds interest rate and important additional variables. The time-series data for this study are contained in the data file named **Macro2010**, which is described in the Chapter 13 appendix.

a. Develop two multiple regression models to predict residential investment using prime interest rate for one and federal funds interest rate for the other. The final regression models should include only predictor variables that have a significant conditional effect. Analyze the regression statistics and indicate which equation provides the best predictions.

b. Determine the 95% confidence interval for the interest rate conditional slope coefficient in both regression equations.

12.106 The Center for Disease Control (CDC) is interested in knowing if there are state-level population characteristics that predict the occurrence of breast cancer death rates and the occurrence of lung cancer death rates. The data file **Staten**, whose variables are described in the chapter appendix, contains a number of variables that could be possible predictors when used in combination. Your task is to develop multiple regression models that will determine which of the K variables in the data file predict the breast cancer death rate and which predict the lung cancer death rate. Interpret your final regression model, including a discussion of the coefficients, their Student's t's, the standard error of the estimate, and R^2.

12.107 You have been hired as a consultant to analyze the salary structure of Energy Futures, Inc., a firm that produces designs for solar energy applications. The company has operated for a number of years, and in recent years there have been an increasing number of complaints that the salaries paid to various workers. You have been provided data in the file **Salary Study**, whose variables are described in the Chapter 12 appendix. Your task is to determine the relationship between the various measures for each employee and the salary paid using a multiple regression analysis.

One particular complaint of great concern to the management is that female workers are paid less than male workers with the same experience and skill level. Test the hypothesis that the actual salary paid female workers and the rate of change in female salaries as a function of experience is less than the rate of change for male salaries as a function of experience. Your hypothesis test should be set up to provide strong evidence of discrimination against females if it exists. The test should be made conditional on the other significant predictor variables in your model.

12.108 Use the data in the data file named **Student GPA**, which is described in the Chapter 11 appendix, to develop a model to predict a student's grade point average in economics. Begin with the variables ACT scores, gender, and HSpct.

a. Use appropriate statistical procedures to choose a subset of statistically significant predictor variables.

Describe your strategy and carefully define your final model.

b. Discuss how this model might be used as part of the college's decision process to select students for admission.

12.109 You have been asked to develop a model that will predict home prices as a function of important economic variables. After considerable research, you locate the work of Prof. Robert Shiller, Princeton University. Shiller has compiled data for housing costs beginning in 1890. The data file **Shiller House Price Cost** is obtained from his data. The indexes for home price and building cost are developed to adjust for price changes over time. You are to develop a model using the Shiller data. Prepare a short interpretation of your model results. Variables are identified in the data file.

a. Does your model exhibit any tendency to predict high or low over the long time period? What is your evidence?

b. There was a housing price bubble in the first part of the 21st century. How could you identify this bubble using your model?

12.110 A major real estate developer has asked you to determine the effect of the interval between house sales, and the initial house sales price on second or final sales price with adjustments for the four major U.S. market areas identified in the data set. The data on housing prices are stored in the data file **House Selling Price** from the work of Robert Shiller. The data set includes the first and second sales price and the relative date of the house sales. Write a short report on the results of your analysis.

12.10 CASE STUDY PROJECTS

 Visit www.MyStatLab.com or www.pearsonglobal editions.com to access the data files.

Mini–Case Studies

12.111 A group of activists in Peaceful, Montana, are seeking increased development for this pristine enclave, which has received some national recognition on the television program *Four Dirty Old Men*. The group claims that increased commercial and industrial development will bring new prosperity and lower taxes to Peaceful. Specifically, it claims that an increased percentage of commercial and industrial development will decrease the property tax rate and increase the market value for owner-occupied residences.

You have been hired to analyze their claims. For this purpose you have obtained the data file **Citydatr**, which contains data from 45 small cities. The variables are described in the chapter appendix. From these data you will first develop regression models that predict the average value of owner-occupied housing and the property tax rate. Then you will determine if and how the addition of the percent of commercial property and then the percent of industrial property affects the variability in these regression models. The basic model for predicting market

value of houses includes the size of house, the tax rate, the per capita income, and the percent of owner-occupied residences as independent variables. The basic model for predicting tax rate includes the tax assessment base, current city expenditures per capita, and the percent of owner-occupied residences as independent variables.

Determine if the percent of commercial and the percent of industrial variables improve the explained variability in each of the two models. Perform a conditional F test for each of these additional variables. First, estimate the conditional effect of percent commercial property by itself and then the conditional effect of percent industrial property by itself. Carefully explain the results of your analysis. Include in your report an explanation of why it was important to include all the other variables in the regression model instead of just examining the effect of the direct and simple relationship between percent of commercial property and percent of industrial property on the tax rate and market value of housing.

12.112 You have been asked to develop a model that will predict the percentage of students who graduate in 4 years from highly ranked private colleges. The data file **Private Colleges** contains data collected by a national news service; descriptions of the predictor variables are contained in the Chapter 12 appendix.

a. Specify a list of potential predictor variables with a short rationale for each variable.

b. Use multiple regression to determine the conditional effect of each of these potential predictor variables.

c. Eliminate those variables that do not have a significant conditional effect to obtain your final model.

d. Prepare a short discussion regarding the conditional effects of the predictor variables in your model, based on your analysis.

12.113 You have been asked to develop a model that will predict the cost with financial aid for students at highly ranked private colleges. The data file **Private Colleges** contains data collected by a national news service. Variables are identified in the Chapter 12 appendix.

a. Specify a list of potential predictor variables with a short rationale for each variable.

b. Use multiple regression to determine the conditional effect of each of these potential predictor variables.

c. Eliminate those variables that do not have a significant conditional effect to obtain your final model.

d. Prepare a short discussion regarding the conditional effects of the predictor variables in your model, based on your analysis.

Nutrition-Based Mini-Case Studies

The following exercises are based on nutrition research done by the Economic Research Service of the U.S. Department of Agriculture. The data for these exercises are contained in the data file **HEI Cost Data Variable Subset**, which is described in the Chapter 10 appendix.

The data file **HEI Cost Data Variable Subset** contains considerable information on randomly selected individuals who participated in an extended interview and medical examination. There are two observations for each person in the study. The first observation, identified by daycode = 1, contains data from the first interview, and the second observation, daycode = 2, contains data from the second interview. This data file contains the data for the following exercises. The variables are described in the data dictionary in the Chapter 10 appendix. Each of the multiple regression models in the following exercises should contain a dummy variable that adjusts for possible additive differences between data collected during the two different interviews.

12.114 You are asked to develop a multiple regression model that indicates the relationship between a person's physical characteristics and the quality of diet consumed as measured by the Healthy Eating Index (HEI-2005). The predictor variables to be used are a doctor's diagnosis of high blood pressure (doc bp), the ratio of waist measure to obese waist measure (waistper), the body mass index (BMI), whether the subject was overweight (sr overweight), male compared to female (female), and age (age). Also, the model should include a dummy variable to indicate the effect of first versus the second interview.

a. Estimate the model using the basic specification variables indicated here.

b. Estimate the model again, but in this case include a variable that adjusts for immigrant versus native person (immigrant).

c. Estimate the model again, but in this case include a variable that adjusts for single status versus a person with a partner (single).

d. Estimate the model again, but in this case include a variable that adjusts for participation in the food stamp program (fsp).

12.115 You are asked to develop a multiple regression model that indicates the relationship between a person's behavioral characteristics and the quality of diet consumed as measured by the Healthy Eating Index (HEI-2005). The predictor variables to be used are whether subject limited weight (sr did lm wt), whether the subject was a smoker (smoker), number of hours subject spent in front of a TV or computer screen (screen hours), sedentary versus active subject (activity level; note you will need to recode to a dummy variable), percent of subject's calories from a fast-food restaurant (pff), percent of subject's calories eaten at home (P ate at Home), whether subject was a college graduate (col grad), and subject's household income (hh income est). Also, the model should include a dummy variable to indicate the effect of first versus second interview.

a. Estimate the model using the basic specification variables indicated here.

b. Estimate the model again. but in this case include a variable that adjusts for immigrant versus native person (immigrant).

c. Estimate the model again, but in this case include a variable that adjusts for single status versus a person with a partner (single).

d. Estimate the model again, but in this case include a variable that adjusts for participation in the food stamp program (fsp).

12.116 You are asked to develop a multiple regression model that indicates the relationship between a person's physical characteristics and the daily cost of food (daily cost). The predictor variables to be used are a doctor's diagnosis of high blood pressure (doc bp), the ratio of waist measure to obese waist measure (waistper), the body mass index (BMI), whether the subject was overweight (sr overweight), male compared to female (female), and age (age). Also, the model should include a dummy variable to indicate the effect of first versus the second interview.

a. Estimate the model using the basic specification variables indicated here.

b. Estimate the model again, but in this case include a variable that adjusts for immigrant versus native person (immigrant).

c. Estimate the model again, but in this case include a variable that adjusts for single status versus a person with a partner (single).

d. Estimate the model again, but in this case include a variable that adjusts for participation in the food stamp program (fsp).

12.117 You are asked to develop a multiple regression model that indicates the relationship between a person's behavioral characteristics and the daily cost of food (daily cost). The predictor variables to be used are subject's limiting weight (sr did lm wt), subject being a smoker (smoker), subject's number of hours in front of a TV or computer screen (screen hours), subject's being sedentary versus active (activity level: note that you will need to recode to a dummy variable), percent of subject's calories from a fast-food restaurant (pff), percent of subject's calories eaten at home (P ate at Home), whether the subject is a college graduate (col grad), and household income (hh income est). Also, the model should include a dummy variable to indicate the effect of first versus second interview.

a. Estimate the model using the basic specification variables indicated here.
b. Estimate the model again, but in this case include a variable that adjusts for immigrant versus native person (immigrant).
c. Estimate the model again but in this case include a variable that adjusts for single status versus a person with a partner (single).
d. Estimate the model again, but in this case include a variable that adjusts for participation in the food stamp program (fsp).

Automobile-Fuel Case Study Project

You have been asked to conduct a study to determine the variables that influence automobile fuel consumption. Your study is part of a national effort that will develop policies to reduce dependence on fossil fuels. Considerable national discussion and various economic studies have focused on this question for a number of years.

Many economists have argued that an important part of the solution is higher gasoline prices. They point to the fact that for many years European gasoline prices have been much higher, in part because of high taxes on each liter of gasoline sold for automobile consumption. And, European vehicles tend to be smaller and more fuel efficient compared to U.S. motor vehicles.

Others argue that the automobile is so important in the lives of U.S. citizens that they must drive, and higher prices will merely increase the cost of travel. The limited availability of public transportation compared to Europe is part of this argument. From this comes the argument that government regulation must be used to establish minimum fuel-consumption standards for all automobiles sold in the United States. It is argued that such CAFÉ (Corporate Average Fuel Economy) standards place manufacturers on an equal level with regard to fuel economy and avoid competitive vehicle features that would increase fuel consumption. These standards were first introduced in the late 1970s and then essentially ignored until new standards were introduced in 2010.

Another argument is that automobile driving is a central part of the U.S. society and fuel savings will really come only with changes in the overall economy. Changes would include increased use of public transportation, workers closer to work sites, working by electronic communication from home, economic recession, and other societal factors.

Your task is to conduct appropriate statistical analysis to help answer some of the questions posed here and to increase understanding of the question. Your first step was to collect data from national sources and prepare the data file **Automobile Fuel Consumption**. This data file provides monthly data for a number of measurements collected since 2005 and extending through 2010. The variables contained in this file are shown in the variable description table included in the Chapter 12 appendix.

Your assignment is to prepare a rigorous statistical analysis and to write a report that clearly presents your conclusions and explains your analysis. Your report is limited to two pages, with appropriate supporting material in selected appendices. The reader should be able to understand your work from the two-page report.

Your professor will also provide various guidelines and analysis recommendations. You might note that when data are collected over time, many analysts will present graphs that indicate the levels of key variables over time. Recall from Chapter 12 how overall price elasticity can be estimated using log transformations.

Appendix

MATHEMATICAL DERIVATIONS

1 LEAST SQUARES DERIVATION OF ESTIMATORS

The derivation of coefficient estimators for a model with two predictor variables is as follows:

$$\hat{y}_i = b_0 + b_1 x_{1i} + b_2 x_{2i}$$

Minimize

$$SSE = \sum_{i=1}^{n} [y_i - (b_0 + b_1 x_{1i} + b_2 x_{2i})]^2$$

Applying differential calculus, we obtain a set of three normal equations that can be solved for the coefficient estimators:

$$\frac{\partial SSE}{\partial b_0} = 0$$

$$2 \sum_{i=1}^{n} \left[y_i - (b_0 + b_1 x_{1i} + b_2 x_{2i}) \right] (-1) = 0$$

$$\sum_{i=1}^{n} y_i - n b_0 - b_1 \sum_{i=1}^{n} x_{1i} - b_2 \sum_{i=1}^{n} x_{2i} = 0$$

$$n b_0 + b_1 \sum_{i=1}^{n} x_{1i} + b_2 \sum_{i=1}^{n} x_{2i} = \sum_{i=1}^{n} y_i$$

$$\frac{\partial SSE}{\partial b_1} = 0$$

$$2 \sum_{i=1}^{n} \left[y_i - (b_0 + b_1 x_{1i} + b_2 x_{2i}) \right] (-x_{1i}) = 0$$

$$\sum_{i=1}^{n} x_{1i} y_i - b_0 \sum_{i=1}^{n} x_{1i} - b_1 \sum_{i=1}^{n} x_{1i}^2 - b_2 \sum_{i=1}^{n} x_{1i} x_{2i} = 0$$

$$b_0 \sum_{i=1}^{n} x_{1i} + b_1 \sum_{i=1}^{n} x_{1i}^2 + b_2 \sum_{i=1}^{n} x_{1i} x_{2i} = \sum_{i=1}^{n} x_{1i} y_i$$

$$\frac{\partial SSE}{\partial b_2} = 0$$

$$2 \sum_{i=1}^{n} \left[y_i - (b_0 + b_1 x_{1i} + b_2 x_{2i}) \right] (-x_{2i}) = 0$$

$$\sum_{i=1}^{n} x_{2i} y_i - b_0 \sum_{i=1}^{n} x_{2i} - b_1 \sum_{i=1}^{n} x_{1i} x_{2i} - b_2 \sum_{i=1}^{n} x_{2i}^2 = 0$$

$$b_0 \sum_{i=1}^{n} x_{2i} + b_1 \sum_{i=1}^{n} x_{1i} x_{2i} + b_2 \sum_{i=1}^{n} x_{2i}^2 = \sum_{i=1}^{n} x_{2i} y_i$$

As a result of applying the least squares algorithm, we have a system of three linear equations in three unknowns:

$$b_0, b_1, b_2$$

$$n b_0 + b_1 \sum_{i=1}^{n} x_{1i} + b_2 \sum_{i=1}^{n} x_{2i} = \sum_{i=1}^{n} y_i$$

$$b_0 \sum_{i=1}^{n} x_{1i} + b_1 \sum_{i=1}^{n} x_{1i}^2 + b_2 \sum_{i=1}^{n} x_{1i} x_{2i} = \sum_{i=1}^{n} x_{1i} y_i$$

$$b_0 \sum_{i=1}^{n} x_{2i} + b_1 \sum_{i=1}^{n} x_{1i} x_{2i} + b_2 \sum_{i=1}^{n} x_{2i}^2 = \sum_{i=1}^{n} x_{2i} y_i$$

The linear equations are solved for the desired coefficients by first computing the various X- and Y-squared and cross-product terms.

The intercept term is estimated by the following:

$$b_0 = \bar{y} - b_1 \bar{x}_1 - b_2 \bar{x}_2$$

2   TOTAL EXPLAINED VARIABILITY

The explained variability SSR term in multiple regression is more complex than the SSR term in simple regression.

For the two-independent-variable regression model

$$Y = \beta_0 + \beta_1 X_1 + \beta_2 X_2$$

we find that

$$SSR = \sum_{i=1}^{n} (\hat{y}_i - \bar{y})^2$$

$$= \sum_{i=1}^{n} [b_0 + b_1 x_{1i} + b_2 x_{2i} - (b_0 + b_1 \bar{x}_1 + b_2 \bar{x}_2)]^2$$

$$= \sum_{i=1}^{n} [b_1^2(x_{1i} - \bar{x}_1)^2 + b_2^2(x_{2i} - \bar{x}_2)^2 + 2b_1 b_2(x_{1i} - \bar{x}_1)(x_{2i} - \bar{x}_2)]$$

$$= (n - 1)(b_1^2 s_{x_1}^2 + b_2^2 s_{x_2}^2 + 2r_{x_1 x_2} b_1 b_2 s_{x_1} s_{x_2})$$

We see that the explained variability has a portion directly associated with each of the independent variables and a portion associated with the correlation between the two variables.

Data File Descriptions

DATA FILE AUTOMOBILE FUEL CONSUMPTION

VARIABLE	DESCRIPTION
Date	Month and Year Data Collected
Auto Miles Bi	Billions of Automobile Miles Driven Measured by U.S. Dept of Transportation
Gas Price p gal $	All Types of Gasoline, U.S. City Average Retail Price Dollars per Gallon
Population	U.S. Population Based on Census Bureau Estimates
Per cap inc R	Per Capita Income Measured in Real Dollars 2005
Daily Gas sales 1000 gal	U.S. Total Gasoline Retail Deliveries by Refiners (Thousand Gallons per Day)
Sum dum	Coded 1 for May, June, July, August 0 else
Wint dum	Coded 1 for January, February 0 else
Season	Index Coded 1–3 for 4-Month Intervals
Mile per gal	Computed Miles per Gallon
Percent Unemployment	Monthly Reported Unemployment from Bureau of Labor Statistics

DATA FILE PRIVATE COLLEGES

C1	Undergrad. Enrollment
C2	Admission Rate
C3	Student/Faculty Ratio
C4	4-year Grad. Rate
C5	6-year Grad. Rate
C6	Quality Rank
C7	Total Costs
C8	Cost After Need-Based Aid
C9	Need Met
C10	Aid From Grants
C11	Cost After Non-Need-Based Aid
C12	Average Debt
C13	Cost Rank

DATA FILE CITYDATR

This data file contains a cross-section database for project analysis. The file contains data from 45 nonmetropolitan Minnesota cities over two consecutive years. The data were collected as part of a research project to determine the effect of economic growth on local city expenditures, tax rates, and housing values. The file contains a total of 90 observations.

C1	Observation sequential number
County	County code
City	MCD code
Sizehse	Median rooms per owner-occupied house
Totexp	Total current city government expenditures
Taxbase	Assessment base in millions of real dollars
Taxrate	Tax Levy Divided by Total Assessment
Pop	Population estimate
Incom	Per capita income
Hseval	Market value per owner-occupied residence
Taxhse	Average tax per owner-occupied residence
Homper	Percent of property value: owner-occupied residence
Rentper	Percent of property value: rental residence
Comper	Percent of property value: commercial
Indper	Percent of property value: industrial property
Utilper	Percent of property value: public utility
Year	Represented as 1, 2

DATA FILE STATEN

Variable Name	Description
State	Name of state
Population	Population of state in 2008
Births	Number of live births in 2007
Police	Per capita expenditures on police 2007 Dept of Justice
Cortleg	Per capita expenditures on courts and legal 2007
Prison	Per capital expenditures on prisons 2007
Total viol Cr	Total violent crimes per 100,000 population 2007
Murder	Total number of murders per 100,000 population 2007
Rape	Total number of rapes per 100,000 population 2007
Robbery	Total number of robberies per 100,000 population 2007
Assault	Total number of assaults per 100,000 population 2007
Total Prop Cr	Total number of crimes against property per 100,000 2007
Burgularly	Total number of burglaries per 100,000 population 2007
Larceny	Total number of larcenies per 100,000 population 2007
Mtr Veh Theft	Total number of motor vehicle thefts per 100,000 2007
Doctors	Total number of doctors per 100,000 population 2007
Nurses	Total number of nurses per 100,000 population 2007
Smoker per	Percent of population who are smokers 2007
Male Smok	Percent of male population who are smokers 2007
Female Smoke	Percent of female population who are smokers 2007
Alcohol B	Percent of binge drinkers (5 or more drinks) 2007
B Cancer	Total number of breast cancer deaths in 1,000s 2007
L Cancer	Total number of lung cancer deaths in 1,000s 2007
Median Income	Household median income in 2007
G 200k	Proportion of households with income > $200,000 2007
Per Fam Pov	Percent of families with income below poverty 2007

(continued)

Variable Name	Description
HS Grad	Percent of population over age 25, high school graduates 2007
Bachelor	Percent of population over age 25 with bachelor's degree 2007
Advance	Percent of population over age 25 with advanced degree 2007
HPI2007	Housing price index (1980 = 100) 2007
HPI2008	Housing price index (1980 = 100) 2008
Exp Stu secel	Expenditures per student of elementary and secondary ed. 2007

Data File Description	Salary Study
Age	Age of person
Experience	Number of years experience at the firm
Years Jr	Number of years at junior level analyst
Years Senior	Number of years at senior level analyst
Gender	0 - male, 1 - female
Salary	Present base salary
Market	Specialized skill 1- skill has high market value, 0 - else

REFERENCES

1. Carlson, W. L., "The Effect of Growth on Small City Expenditures," Annual Meeting of the Minnesota Economic Association, St. Thomas College, November 12, 1976.

2. Ghatak, S., and D. Deadman. 1989. "Money, Prices and Stabilization Policies in Some Developing Countries," *Applied Economics* 21: 853–865.

3. Hagermann, R. P. 1981. "The Determinants of Household Vacation Travel: Some Empirical Evidence," *Applied Economics* 13: 225–234.

4. MacDonald, J. M., and P. E. Nelson. 1991. "Do the Poor Still Pay More? Food Price Variations in Large Metropolitan Areas," *Journal of Urban Economics* 30: 344–359.

5. Shiller, Robert J. 2005, 2009. *Irrational Exuberance*, 2nd ed., Princeton, NJ: Princeton University Press, 2006.

6. Shiller, Robert J. 2008. *Subprime Solution*. Princeton, NJ: Princeton University Press.

7. Spellman, L. J. 1978. "Entry and Profitability in a Rate-free Savings and Loan Market," *Quarterly Review of Economics and Business* 18 (2): 87–95.

8. United States Center for Disease Control and Prevention, National Health and Nutrition Examination Survey, 2011.

9. United States Department of Agriculture, Economic Research Service, 2011.

10. United States Department of Commerce Bureau of Economic Analysis, U.S. Economic Accounts, 2011.

11. United States Department of Labor, Bureau of Labor Statistics, 2011.

12. United States Department of Transportation Federal Highway Administration, Traffic Volume Trends, 2011.

13. United States Energy Information Administration, Petroleum and Other Liquids, 2011.

14. Van Scyoc, L. J., and J. Gleason. 1993. "Traditional or Intensive Course Lengths? A Comparison of Outcomes in Economics Learning," *Journal of Economic Education* 24: 15–22.

CHAPTER 13

Additional Topics in Regression Analysis

Introduction

In Chapters 11 and 12 we developed simple and multiple regression as tools to estimate the coefficients for linear models for business and economic applications. We now understand that the purpose of fitting a regression equation is to use information about the independent variables to explain the behavior of the dependent variables and to derive predictions of the dependent variable. The model coefficients can also be used to estimate the rate of change of the dependent variable as the result of changes in an independent variable, conditional on the particular set of other independent variables included in the model remaining fixed. In this chapter we study a set of alternative specifications. In addition, we consider situations in which the basic regression assumptions are violated.

The topics in this chapter can be selected individually to supplement your study of regression analysis. Almost everyone will be interested in the model-building discussion in the next section. The process of model building is fundamental to all regression applications, and, thus, we begin with those ideas. The section dealing with dummy variables and experimental design provides methods for extending the model applications. Sections such as those dealing with heteroscedasticity and autocorrelations indicate how to deal with violations of assumptions.

Regression models are developed in business and economic applications to increase understanding and guide decisions. Developing these models requires a good understanding of the system and process being studied. Statistical theory provides a link between the underlying process and the data observed from that process. This linking of the problem context and good statistical analysis usually requires an interdisciplinary team that can provide expertise on all aspects of the problem. In the authors' experience, these teams are successful only when all team members learn from each other—production specialists need to have a basic understanding of statistical procedures and statisticians need to understand the production process.

13.1 MODEL-BUILDING METHODOLOGY

We live in a complex world, and no one believes that we can precisely capture the complexities of economic and business behavior in one or more equations. However, we can develop a general strategy for constructing regression models. Our analysis goal is to use a relatively simple model that provides a close approximation of the complex reality to provide useful insights. The art of model building recognizes the impossibility of representing all the many individual influences on a dependent variable and tries to pick out the most influential variables. Next, we develop a model to depict relationships between these factors. We want to build a simple model that is easy to interpret but not so oversimplified that important influences are ignored.

The process of statistical model building is problem specific. Our approach will depend on what is known about the behavior of the quantities under study and what data are available. The various stages of model building are depicted in Figure 13.1.

Figure 13.1 The Stages of Statistical Model Building

Model Specification

Model building begins with **model specification**. This includes selection of the dependent and independent variables and the algebraic form of the model. We seek a specification that provides an adequate representation of the system and process under study.

The examples in Chapters 11 and 12 that dealt with retail sales, profitability of savings and loan associations, and cotton production all postulated a linear relationship between the dependent variable and the independent variables. Linear models often provide a good approximation for the problem of interest, but not always.

Model specification begins with an understanding of the theory and accumulated experience that provides the context for the model. We should carefully study the existing literature and learn what is known about the situation that we are working to model. This background study should include consultation with those that have knowledge of the context. Included would be those who have done research in the problem area and those who have developed similar models. For applied work we should also contact experienced practitioners who have been operating and working with the system being modeled. For example, if we want to model a production process, we need to learn, from the production manager, about how the process really works.

Model specification typically requires considerable thinking about the system and the process that underlies the problem. When we have complex problems involving a number of factors, it is important that we have interdisciplinary teams that will carefully analyze all aspects of the problem. It may be necessary to do additional research and perhaps include others that have important insights. Specification requires serious study and analysis. If not done properly, the entire model development will be seriously compromised. This is also the time when we need to determine the required data for the study. In many cases this may involve deciding if the available data—or data that could be obtained—will be adequate for model estimation. If we do not know what we want to do or understand the context of the problem, then sophisticated analysis tools and competent analysts will not give us the best possible answer. Inexperienced analysts often run computer-based computations before thinking carefully about the problem. Professional analysts know that such an approach leads to inferior results.

Coefficient Estimation

A statistical model, once specified, typically involves a number of unknown coefficients, or parameters. The next stage of the model-building exercise is to employ available data in the estimation of these coefficients. Both point estimates and interval estimates should be obtained for the multiple regression model:

$$y_i = \beta_0 + \beta_1 x_{1i} + \beta_2 x_{2i} + \cdots + \beta_K x_{Ki} + \varepsilon_i$$

From a statistical perspective, the regression model objectives can be divided into either a prediction of the mean of the dependent variable, Y, or an estimation of one or more of the individual coefficients, β_j. In many cases the objectives are not completely separate, but these alternatives identify important options.

If the objective is prediction, we want a model that has a small standard error of the estimate, s_e. We are not as concerned about correlated independent variables because we know that a number of different combinations of correlated variables will result in the same prediction precision. However, we do need to know that the correlations between independent variables will continue to hold in future populations. We also need to have a wide spread for the independent variables to ensure a small prediction variance over the desired range of the model application.

Alternatively, estimation of the slope coefficients leads us to consider a wider range of issues. The estimated standard deviation, s_{b_j}, of the slope coefficients is influenced directly by the standard error of the model and inversely by the spread of the independent variables and the correlations between independent variables, as seen in Section 12.4. Multicollinearity—correlations between independent variables—is a critical issue, as we discuss in Section 13.5. Also, we see in Section 13.4 that failure to include important predictor variables results in a biased estimator of the coefficients for predictor variables included in the model. These two results lead to a classic statistical problem. Do we include a predictor variable that is highly correlated with the other predictor variables and, thus, avoid a biased coefficient estimate but also substantially increase the variance of the coefficient estimator? Or do we exclude a correlated predictor variable to reduce the coefficient estimator variance but increase the bias? Selecting the proper balance between estimator bias and variance is often a problem in applied model building.

Model Verification

When developing the model specification, we incorporate insights concerning the behavior of the underlying system and process. Certain simplifications and assumptions occur when translating these insights into algebraic forms and when selecting data for model estimation. Since some of these might prove untenable, it is important to check the adequacy of the model.

After estimating a regression equation, we may find that the estimates do not make sense, given what we know about the process. For example, suppose the model indicates that the demand for cars increases as prices increase, which is counter to basic economic theory. Such a result may occur because of inadequate data or because of some high correlations between price and other predictor variables. These are possible reasons for the wrong coefficient sign. But the problem may also result from faulty model specification. Failure to include the proper set of predictor variables can lead to coefficient bias and incorrect coefficient signs. We also need to check the assumptions made about the random variables in the model. For example, the basic regression assumptions state that the error terms all have the same variance and are uncorrelated with one another. In Sections 13.6 and 13.7 we see how these assumptions can be checked by using the available data.

If we find implausible results, then it is necessary to examine our assumptions, model specification, and the data. This may lead us to consider a different model specification. Thus, in Figure 13.1 we indicate a feedback loop in the model-building process. As we develop experience with model building and other difficult problem solving, we will discover that these processes tend to be iterative, with considerable cycling back to earlier stages until a satisfactory model and problem solution are developed.

Model Interpretation and Inference

Once a model has been constructed, it can be used to learn something about the system and process being studied. In regression analysis this may involve finding confidence intervals for the model parameters, testing hypotheses of interest, or estimating future values of the dependent variable, given assumed values of the independent variables. It is important to recognize that inference of this sort is based on the assumption of appropriate model specification and estimation. The more severe any specification or estimation errors, the less reliable any inferences derived from the estimated model.

We should also recognize that some of the results from our analysis using the available data may not agree with previous understandings. When this occurs, we will need to carefully compare our results with past understandings. Differences may result from a different or improper specification of the model, errors in the data, or some other shortcoming. But we might also have discovered some important new results because of a superior problem specification or because of new data that represent a change in the environment being studied. In any case we must be prepared to either make corrections or present our new results in a logical manner.

13.2 DUMMY VARIABLES AND EXPERIMENTAL DESIGN

Dummy variables were introduced in Section 12.8 in applications involving regression models applied to two discrete categories of data. For example, we saw how they could be used to test for gender discrimination in the salary example.

In this section we expand the potential applications of dummy variables. First, we present an application in which a regression model is applied to more than two discrete categories of data. Next, we show how dummy variables can be used to estimate the seasonal effects on a regression model applied to time-series data. Finally, we show how dummy variables can be used to analyze data from experimental situations, which are defined by multiple-level categorical variables. We also provide an example that shows how dummy variables can be used for public policy analysis.

Example 13.1 Demand for Wool Products (Dummy Variable Model Analysis)

A senior marketing analyst for the American Wool Producers Association is interested in estimating the demand for wool products in various cities as a function of total disposable income in the city. Data were gathered from 30 randomly selected Standard Metropolitan Statistical Areas (SMSAs). As a first step the analyst specifies a regression model for the relationship between sales and disposable income:

$$Y = \beta_0 + \beta_1 X_1$$

where X_1 is the per capita annual disposable income for a city and Y is the per capita sales of wool products in the city. After some additional discussions, the analyst wonders if overall sales levels differ among different geographic regions: north, central, and south.

Solution The analysis begins by placing each of the cities in one of the three regions. Figure 13.2 is a scatter plot of per capita sales versus disposable income. The data appear to be separated into three distinct subgroups corresponding to geographic regions. Two dummy variables are used to identify each of the three regions:

North: $x_2 = 0, x_3 = 1$
Central: $x_2 = 1, x_3 = 0$
South: $x_2 = 0, x_3 = 0$

Figure 13.2 Per Capita Wool Sales Versus Per Capita Disposable Income

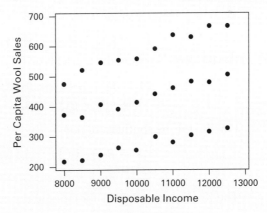

In general, K distinct regions or subsets can be identified uniquely with $K - 1$ dummy variables. If we try to use K dummy variables to represent K distinct subsets, then a linear relationship between predictor variables will result, and estimation of coefficients will be impossible, as discussed in Section 12.2. This is sometimes referred to as the "dummy variable trap."

Shifts in the model constant could be estimated using the following model:

$$Y = \beta_0 + \beta_2 X_2 + \beta_3 X_3 + \beta_1 X_1$$

Applying this model to the north, it becomes

$$Y = \beta_0 + \beta_2(0) + \beta_3(1) + \beta_1 X_1$$
$$= (\beta_0 + \beta_3) + \beta_1 X_1$$

In the central region we find the following:

$$Y = \beta_0 + \beta_2(1) + \beta_3(0) + \beta_1 X_1$$
$$= (\beta_0 + \beta_2) + \beta_1 X_1$$

Finally, for the southern region the model is as follows:

$$Y = \beta_0 + \beta_2(0) + \beta_3(0) + \beta_1 X_1$$
$$= \beta_0 + \beta_1 X_1$$

Summarizing these results, the constants for the various regions are as follows:

North: $\beta_0 + \beta_3$
Central: $\beta_0 + \beta_2$
South: β_0

This formulation defines the south as the "base" constant, with β_3 and β_2 defining the shift of the function for northern and central cities, respectively. Hypothesis tests, using the coefficient Student's t statistic, could be used to determine if there are significant differences between the constants for the different regions compared, in this case, to the constant for the southern region. For additional regions, constants could be modeled by using dummy variables that continue this pattern. We could specify the dummy variables so that any level would be the base level to which the other levels are compared. In this problem specifying the south as the base condition is natural, given the problem objectives.

The model with differences in slope coefficients and constants is as follows:

$$Y = \beta_0 + \beta_2 X_2 + \beta_3 X_3 + (\beta_1 + \beta_4 X_2 + \beta_5 X_3) X_1$$
$$= \beta_0 + \beta_2 X_2 + \beta_3 X_3 + \beta_1 X_1 + \beta_4 X_2 X_1 + \beta_5 X_3 X_1$$

Applying this model to the northern region, we see that

$$Y = \beta_0 + \beta_2(0) + \beta_3(1) + (\beta_1 + \beta_4(0) + \beta_5(1)) X_1$$
$$= (\beta_0 + \beta_3) + (\beta_1 + \beta_5) X_1$$

For the central region the model is as follows:

$$Y = \beta_0 + \beta_2(1) + \beta_3(0) + (\beta_1 + \beta_4(1) + \beta_5(0)) X_1$$
$$= (\beta_0 + \beta_2) + (\beta_1 + \beta_4) X_1$$

Finally, for the southern region

$$Y = \beta_0 + \beta_2(0) + \beta_3(0) + (\beta_1 + \beta_4(0) + \beta_5(0)) X_1$$
$$= \beta_0 + \beta_1 X_1$$

The X_1 slope coefficients for cities in different regions are as follows:

North: $\beta_1 + \beta_5$
Central: $\beta_1 + \beta_4$
South: β_1

Again, the south is the base condition with slope β_1. Hypothesis tests can be used to determine the statistical significance of slope coefficient differences compared to the base condition—in this case the southern region. Using this dummy variable regression model, the analyst can estimate the relationship between sales and disposable income by region of the country.

Figure 13.3 Dummy Variable Multiple Regression Model to Estimate Per Capita Wool Consumption (Minitab Output)

```
The regression equation is
Per Capita Wool Sales = 12.7 + 138 North X3 + 96.3 Central X2
              + 0.0252 Disposable Income + 0.0168 NorX3Inc + 0.00608 CentX2Inc


Predictor             Coef        StDev       T       P
Constant             12.73        27.74      0.53    0.600
North X3            138.46        39.22      3.53    0.022
Central X2           96.33        39.22      2.46    0.002
Disposab           0.025231     0.002680     9.42    0.000
NorX3 Inc          0.016839     0.003790     4.44    0.000
CentX2 In          0.006085     0.003790     1.61    0.121


S = 12.17      R-Sq = 99.4%    R-Sq(adj) = 99.2%

Analysis of Variance

Source            DF         SS        MS       F        P
Regression         5      553704    110741   747.71   0.000
Residual Error    24        3555       148
Total             29      557259
```

Using the sample of 30 SMSAs divided equally among the three geographic regions, a dummy variable multiple regression model was estimated using Minitab. The results are contained in Figure 13.3. From the regression model we can determine characteristics of the wool purchase patterns. Conditional hypothesis tests of the form

$$H_0 : \beta_j = 0 \,|\, \beta_l \neq 0, l = 1, \dots, K, l \neq j$$
$$H_1 : \beta_i \neq 0 \,|\, \beta_l \neq 0, l = 1, \dots, K, l \neq j$$

can be used to determine the conditional effects of the various factors on the demand for wool. The coefficient for the X_3 dummy variable, $\beta_3 = 138.46$, indicates that people in the north spend an average of \$138.46 more than people in the south. Similarly, people in the central region spend an average of \$96.33 more than people in the south. These coefficients are each conditionally significant. The coefficient for disposable income is 0.0252, indicating that for people in the south, each dollar of increased per capita income increases the purchase of wool products by 0.025, and this result is conditionally significant. For people in the north, each dollar of increased income increases expenditure for wool products by 0.042 (0.0252 + 0.0168), and the difference in the increased slope is conditionally significant. The estimated rate of increase in purchase per dollar of increased income is also greater for people in the central region compared to the south. However, that difference is not conditionally significant. Using these results, sales by region can be predicted more precisely compared to a model that combines all regions and uses only per capita income.

Example 13.2 Forecasting Sale of Wool Products (Seasonal Dummy Variables)

After finishing the regional sales analysis, the analyst decided to study the relationship between sales and disposable income using time-series data. After some discussion he realized that sales are different for each quarter of the year. For example, during the fourth quarter, sales were high in anticipation of holiday-season gifts and colder weather. Your assistance with the study is requested.

Solution After discussing the problem, you recommend that the four quarters for each year be represented by three dummy variables. In this way the multiple regression model can be used to estimate differences in sales between the different quarters. Specifically, you propose a structure that is similar to the regional dummy variable model:

First quarter: $x_2 = 0, x_3 = 0, x_4 = 0$
Second quarter: $x_2 = 1, x_3 = 0, x_4 = 0$
Third quarter: $x_2 = 0, x_3 = 1, x_4 = 0$
Fourth quarter: $x_2 = 0, x_3 = 0, x_4 = 1$

The dummy variable coefficients are estimates of shifts in the wool-consumption function between quarters in the following data model:

$$Y = \beta_0 + \beta_2 X_2 + \beta_3 X_3 + \beta_4 X_4 + \beta_1 X_1$$

where Y is the total sales of wool products and X_1 is disposable income. The constants for the various quarters are as follows:

First quarter: β_0
Second quarter: $\beta_0 + \beta_2$
Third quarter: $\beta_0 + \beta_3$
Fourth quarter: $\beta_0 + \beta_4$

Experimental Design Models

Experimental design procedures have been a major area of statistical research and practice for a number of years. Early work dealt with agricultural research. The efforts of statisticians such as R. A. Fisher and O. L. Davies in England during the 1920s provided the foundation for experimental design methodology and for statistical practice in general. Agricultural experiments require an entire growing season to obtain data. Thus, it was important to develop procedures that could answer a number of questions and ensure great precision. In addition, most of the experiments defined activity using variables with discrete as opposed to continuous levels. Experimental design methods have also been used extensively in the study of human behavior and in various industrial experiments. The recent emphasis on improving quality and productivity has spawned increased activity in this area of statistics, with important contributions from groups such as the Center for Quality and Productivity at the University of Wisconsin.

Experimental Design

Dummy variable regression can be used as a tool in experimental design work. The experiments have a single outcome variable that contains all the random error. Each experimental outcome is measured at discrete combinations of experimental (independent) variables, X_j.

There is an important difference in philosophy for experimental designs in comparison to most of the problems we have considered. Experimental design attempts to identify causes for the changes in the dependent variable. This is done by prespecifying combinations of discrete independent variables at which the dependent variable will be measured. An important objective is to choose experimental points, defined by independent variables, that provide minimum variance estimators. The order in which the experiments are performed is chosen randomly to avoid biases from variables not included in the experiment.

Experimental outcomes, Y, are measured at specific combinations of levels for treatment and blocking variables. A *treatment variable* represents a variable whose effect we are interested in estimating with minimum variance. For example, we might wish to know which of four different production machines will provide the highest productivity per hour. In that case the treatment is the production machines represented by a four-level categorical variable, Z_j. A *blocking variable* represents a variable that is part of the environment, and, thus, we cannot preselect the variable level. But we want to include the level of the blocking variable in our model so that we can remove the variability in the outcome variable, Y, that is associated with different levels of the blocking variables. We can represent a K level treatment or blocking variable by using $K - 1$ dummy variables. Let us consider a simple example that has one four-level treatment variable, Z_1, and one three-level blocking variable, Z_2. These variables could be represented by dummy variables, as shown in Table 13.1. Then, by using these dummy variables, the experimental design model could be estimated by the multiple regression model:

$$y_i = \beta_0 + \beta_1 x_{1i} + \beta_2 x_{2i} + \beta_3 x_{3i} + \beta_4 x_{4i} + \beta_5 x_{5i} + \varepsilon_i$$

Table 13.1 Example of Dummy Variable Specification for Treatment and Blocking Variables

Z_1	X_1	X_2	X_3
1	0	0	0
2	1	0	0
3	0	1	0
4	0	0	1

Z_2	X_4	X_5
1	0	0
2	1	0
3	0	1

In this model, for example, the coefficient β_3 is an estimate of the amount by which the productivity for treatment level 4 exceeds that for treatment level 1, for categorical treatment variable, Z_1. Of course, if β_3 is negative, we know that treatment level 1 has a higher productivity than treatment level 4. Following the logic of multiple regression, we know that variables X_4 and X_5 have the effect of explaining some of the variability in Y and hence result in a smaller variance estimator. This model can easily be expanded to include several treatment variables simultaneously with several other blocking variables. In addition, if there is a continuous variable—for example, ambient temperature—that affects productivity, then that variable can also be added directly to the regression model. In many cases several replications of the basic design are conducted to provide sufficient degrees of freedom for error. This process is demonstrated in Example 13.3.

Example 13.3 Worker-Training Program (Dummy Variable Model Specification)

Mary Cruz is the production manager for a large auto parts factory. She is interested in determining the effect of a new training program on worker productivity. Considerable research supports the conclusion that productivity is influenced by the machine type and by the amount of education a worker has received.

Solution Mary defines the following variables for the experiment:

Y   The number of units produced per 8-hour shift
Z_1 The type of training

    1. Traditional classroom lecture and film presentation
    2. Interactive computer-assisted instruction (CAI)

Z_2 Machine type

    1. Machine type 1
    2. Machine type 2
    3. Machine type 3

Z_3 Worker's educational level

    1. High school education
    2. At least one year of post-high school education

The variable Z_1 is called a *treatment variable* because the major study objective is an evaluation of the training program. The variables Z_2 and Z_3 are called *blocking variables* because they are included to help reduce or block out some of the unexplained variability. In this way the variance is reduced, and the test for the main treatment effects has greater power. The term *blocking variable* is a carryover from the agricultural experiments where fields were separated into small blocks, each of which had different soil conditions. It is also possible to estimate the effect of these blocking variables. Thus, one does not lose information by calling certain variables blocking variables instead of treatment variables.

Experimental design observations are predefined using the independent variables. Table 13.2 presents a listing of the observations with each observation designated using levels of the Z variables. In this design, which is called a full factorial design, there are 12 observations, one for each combination of the treatment and blocking variables. The Y_i observations represent the measured responses at each of the experimental conditions. In the data, model Y_i contains the effect of the treatment and blocking variables plus random error. In many experimental designs this pattern of 12 observations is replicated (repeated) to provide more degrees of freedom for error and lower variance estimates of the effects of the design variables. This design can also be analyzed using analysis of variance procedures. However, we show here how the analysis can be performed using dummy variable regression.

Table 13.2   Experimental Design for Productivity Study

PRODUCTION Y	TRAINING Z_1	MACHINE Z_2	EDUCATION Z_3
Y_1	1	1	1
Y_2	1	1	2
Y_3	1	2	1
Y_4	1	2	2
Y_5	1	3	1
Y_6	1	3	2
Y_7	2	1	1
Y_8	2	1	2
Y_9	2	2	1
Y_{10}	2	2	2
Y_{11}	2	3	1
Y_{12}	2	3	2

The levels for each of the three design variables—Z_1, Z_2, and Z_3—can be expressed as a set of dummy variables. Define the following dummy variables:

$$z_1 = 1 \rightarrow x_1 = 0$$
$$z_1 = 2 \rightarrow x_1 = 1$$
$$z_2 = 1 \rightarrow x_2 = 0 \text{ and } x_3 = 0$$
$$z_2 = 2 \rightarrow x_2 = 1 \text{ and } x_3 = 0$$
$$z_2 = 3 \rightarrow x_2 = 0 \text{ and } x_3 = 1$$
$$z_3 = 1 \rightarrow x_4 = 0$$
$$z_3 = 2 \rightarrow x_4 = 1$$

Using these relationships, the experimental design model in Table 13.2, which uses the Z variables, can be represented by dummy variables, as shown in Table 13.3. Using these dummy variables, we can define a multiple regression model:

$$Y = \beta_0 + \beta_1 X_1 + \beta_2 X_2 + \beta_3 X_3 + \beta_4 X_4$$

Table 13.3 Experimental Design for Productivity Study Using Dummy Variables

PRODUCTIVITY Y	X_1	X_2	X_3	X_4
Y_1	0	0	0	0
Y_2	0	0	0	1
Y_3	0	1	0	0
Y_4	0	1	0	1
Y_5	0	0	1	0
Y_6	0	0	1	1
Y_7	1	0	0	0
Y_8	1	0	0	1
Y_9	1	1	0	0
Y_{10}	1	1	0	1
Y_{11}	1	0	1	0
Y_{12}	1	0	1	1

The regression coefficients are estimated using the variables as previously specified. The 12 experiments, or observations, defined in Tables 13.2 and 13.3 are defined as one replication of the experimental design. A replication contains all the individual experiments that are included in the experimental design. Often several replications of the design are made to provide greater accuracy for the coefficient estimates and to provide sufficient degrees of freedom for estimating the variance. In the dummy variable model we estimate four coefficients and a constant, leaving $(n - 4 - 1)$ degrees of freedom for estimating the variance. With one replication, $n = 12$, we have 7 degrees of freedom for estimating the variance. With two replications of the design, $n = 24$, we have 19 degrees of freedom for estimating the variance, and with three replications we have 31 degrees of freedom. Usually, at least 15 or 20 degrees of freedom are required to obtain stable estimates of variance. Using the definitions of the dummy variables, we find that the estimated regression coefficients are interpreted as follows:

1. b_1 is the productivity increase for the new CAI training compared to the standard classroom training.
2. b_2 is the productivity increase for machine type 2 compared to machine type 1.

3. b_3 is the productivity increase for machine type 3 compared to machine type 1.
4. b_4 is the productivity increase for the post–high school education compared to high school alone.

Any of these "increases" could be negative, implying a decrease.

The significance of each of these effects can be tested using our standard hypothesis-testing procedures. Note that if an experimental observation is lost or fails, the same regression model can still be used to estimate the coefficients. However, we then have a larger variance, and, hence, the hypothesis tests have lower power.

It is also possible to add continuous variables or covariates to the model. Suppose that Mary suspects that the number of years of worker experience and the ambient temperature also influence productivity. These two continuous variables can be measured for each experiment and added to the dummy variable regression model. The regression model then becomes

$$Y = \beta_0 + \beta_1 X_1 + \beta_2 X_2 + \beta_3 X_3 + \beta_4 X_4 + \beta_5 X_5 + \beta_6 X_6$$

where X_5 is the years of experience and X_6 is the ambient temperature. If these latter variables are important, they will reduce the variance and increase the power of the hypothesis tests for the effects of other variables.

Another possible extension is the inclusion of interaction effects. Suppose that Mary suspects that the CAI training provides greater benefits for workers working with machine type 3. To test for this effect, she can include an interaction variable, $X_7 = X_1 X_3$. The values for X_7 are the product of the X_1 and the X_3 variables. Thus, in Table 13.3 we would add a column for X_7, which has 1s for the 11th and 12th observations and 0s for the remaining observations. If she also suspects that the CAI training benefits workers with more education, she can define another interaction variable, $X_8 = X_1 X_4$. This variable adds another column to Table 13.3 with 1s for the 8th, 10th, and 12th observations and 0s for the remaining observations. It is possible to add other variables and interaction terms. Thus, the number of options with these experimental designs is very large.

With all these additions the regression model is as follows:

$$Y = \beta_0 + \beta_1 X_1 + \beta_2 X_2 + \beta_3 X_3 + \beta_4 X_4 + \beta_5 X_5 + \beta_6 X_6 + \beta_7 X_7 + \beta_8 X_8$$

In this equation there are eight coefficients and a constant to estimate, leaving only 3 degrees of freedom for estimating the variance if only one replication of the design is performed. In situations where measurements can be made accurately and the various effects are large, this design, with even one replication, can provide useful information about the factors that influence productivity. In most cases more than one replication is desirable. More observations provide better coefficient estimates and a smaller coefficient variance. However, in an industrial situation, experiments may involve the entire factory and, thus, can be very expensive. Analysts try to maximize the understanding gained from each set of experiments.

In this section we introduced experimental designs and their analysis using dummy variables. Experimental design is a major area for applied statistics that can be studied in many other courses and books. Statistical software, such as Minitab, typically contains an extensive set of routines for developing various sophisticated experimental design models. These should be used only after you have learned about their specific details and interpretations. However, even with the introduction presented here, you have a powerful tool for handling some important productivity problems.

Applications of experimental design have become increasingly important in manufacturing and other business operations. Experiments to identify variables related to increased production and decreased defects are important in efforts to improve production operations. The use of dummy variables and multiple regression for experimental design analysis extends the problem types that you can handle without learning additional analysis techniques. This is an important additional advantage for dummy variable procedures.

Public Sector Applications

Applications of dummy variable regression have become increasingly popular in numerous areas of public sector research and policy analysis. Many of these projects make use of discrete policy options and work with specific subgroups. Many of these studies make use of extensive data files collected by government agencies as part of their programs to identify various public health and safety issues and to provide information for policy and legislative development. The following examples from published research provides an indication of the kind of research pursued and the size of the studies.

Example 13.4 Food Source Makes a Difference in Diet Quality

In a study to examine the relationship between diet quality and source of food, Andrea Carlson and Shirley Gerrior (2006) analyzed data from 9,407 adults contained in the 1994 Continuing Survey of Food Intake by Individuals (SFII) using the Healthy Eating Index as the measure of diet quality. The authors grouped the participants in 10 different groups, or clusters, based on where they purchased the food that they reported eating during a 24-hour period. Home Cookers represented 46.5% of the sample. They estimated a large multiple regression model that included nine sources of food intake represented as dummy variables with home cookers specified as the base condition. In addition they included a number of other variables that have been traditionally known to predict the quality of diet. These factors were included to reduce error variance and, thus, to provide more efficient coefficient estimators. For our purposes, this example indicates the extensive possibilities that result from carefully specified dummy variable regression models.

Example 13.5 Are Food Prices Lower at Discount Stores?

A study conducted by Ephraim Leibtag, Catherine Barker, and Paula Dutko at the Economic Research Service of the Department of Agriculture examined the effect of discount stores on retail food prices (Ephraim, Barker, Dutko, 2010). The study analyzed 2004–06 Nielsen Homescan data, which includes all food at-home purchases for about 40,000 households in 52 markets and selected nonmetropolitan areas. The study compared price differences at the national and market level for four broad food groups—dairy, meat, fruits and vegetables, and grains. A linear regression model was used to control for other factors that may influence the average price for a given food item or group of foods, such as region and calendar quarter when purchased.

Nielsen Homescan data—2004–06—was used in the analysis. Homescan data is household-based scanner data in which households scan the UPC of each item after every food-shopping trip. For each of the years, the data sample includes about 40,000 households in 52 markets and selected nonmetro areas. In addition to describing each purchase's product details, such as brand name and flavor, the data set includes household demographic information, such as income level and marital status.

Figure 13.4 Regression results for Yoplait Original Low-Fat Strawberry Yogurt 6 oz[1], 2006

DEPENDENT VARIABLE: PRICE PER UPC PRODUCT	PARAMETER ESTIMATE	STANDARD ERROR	t-STATISTIC
Independent variables:			
Store format			
Traditional stores	Default store type		
Nontraditional stores	−0.011	0.001	−15.92
Drug/convenience stores	0.029	0.008	3.56
Region			
East	Default region		
Central	−0.002	0.002	−1.07
South	−0.002	0.002	−1.32
West	0.003	0.002	1.82
Income	0.000	0.000	5.93
Household size	−0.001	0.000	−3.39
Race			
White	Default race		
Black	0.000	0.001	0.06
Asian	0.005	0.002	2.28
Other	0.001	0.002	0.38
Hispanic	0.002	0.002	−0.67
Quarter purchased			
First	Default quarter		
Second	0.000	0.001	0.08
Third	0.001	0.001	1.14
Fourth	0.002	0.001	2.33
Constant	0.096	0.005	18.61

Note: Observations: 5910; R-squared: 0.1168; mean of the dependent variable: 0.092 (9.2 cents/ounce).

[1]As measured by Universal Product Code (UPC); oz = ounce(s).

Source: USDA, Economic Research Service estimates using Nielsen Homescan.

A linear regression model was used to control for factors other than the store where the item was purchased. The model included region, time, household income, size, and race. Dummy variables were used to control for other differences across space, time, and demographics. Household income used the midpoints of 19 income levels ranging from below $5,000 to above $200,000 per year to construct a continuous variable. The household-size variable is treated as continuous, ranging from one-person households to nine-person households. For the dummy variables used in these regressions, the defaults are traditional for store type, East for region, White for race, and 1st quarter for quarter purchased. Almost all of the independent variables are significant for a majority of the regressions, with higher prices being associated with the East, higher incomes, and smaller households. An example of a regression at the UPC aggregation level for yogurt is presented in Figure 13.4. As in all of the national-level regressions in this study, we control for region, time, and demographics in order to estimate how much of a difference in prices can be explained by the store format chosen. In this yogurt UPC example, we find that prices are 12 percent lower in nontraditional stores as compared with traditional stores and over 30 percent higher in drug and convenience stores. Other statistically significant determinants of price are income ($+$), household size ($-$), Asian ($+$), and 4th quarter ($+$).

EXERCISES

 Visit www.MyStatLab.com or www.pearsonglobal editions.com to access the data files.

Basic Exercises

13.1 What is dummy variable? When and how it is use in a regression analysis?

13.2 By assigning dummy variables with the numbers '0' and '1' indicates the association is mutually exclusive and exhaustive in any category. What other conditions must be considered for dummy variables in a dummy variable model analysis?

13.3 The head of the statistics department at the University of Iceland needs to know the students' scores in a statistic module before and after 2015 on the basis of their gender (male and female) as the lecturers of the module have changed. Write the model specification and define the variables for a multiple regression model to predict the scores obtained based on the students' gender.

13.4 The Baltic Shipping Company, Denmark, is estimating the delivery time (Y, in minutes) for an order made to their company. The order needs to be shipped to Brofjorden (X_1), Norrköping (X_2), Stockholm (X_3). The company takes into account the total number of parcels included in the order and the age of van that will be used for delivery.

  a. Justify whether the following model is suitable for the company for dummy variable model analysis.

  $$Y = \beta_0 + \beta_1 X_1 + \beta_2 X_2 + \beta_3 X_3 + \beta_4 X_4 + \beta_5 X_5 + \varepsilon$$

where

  X_4 = Total number of parcels

  X_5 = Age of the van

  b. For a model that can be estimated is as follows:

  $$Y = \beta_0 + \beta_1 X_1 + \beta_2 X_2 + \beta_3 X_3 + \beta_4 X_4 + \varepsilon$$

  where the excluded category is Stockholm, determine the constants for each region in the model.

Application Exercises

13.5 Sharon Parsons, president of Gourmet Box Mini Pizza, has asked for your assistance in developing a model that predicts the demand for the new snack lunch pizza named Pizza1. This product competes in a market with three other brands that are named B2, B3, and B4 for identification. At present the products are sold by three major distribution chains, identified as 1, 2, and 3. These three chains have different market sizes, and, thus, sales for each distributor are likely to be different. The data file **Market** contains weekly data collected over the past 52 weeks from the three distribution chains. The variables in the data file are defined next.

Use multiple regression to develop a model that predicts the quantity of Pizza1 sold per week by each distributor. The model should contain only important predictor variables.

Distributor	Numerical identifier of the distributor 1, 2, or 3
Weeknum	Sequential number of the week in which data were collected
Sales Pizza1	Number of units of Pizza1 sold by the distributor during the week
Price Pizza1	Retail price for Pizza1 charged by the distributor during that week
Promotion	Level of promotion for the week, designated as 0, no promotion; 1, television ad; 2, store display; 3, both television and store display
Sales B2	Number of units of brand 2 sold by the distributor during the week
Price B2	Retail price for brand 2 charged by the distributor during that week
Sales B3	Number of units of brand 3 sold by the distributor during the week
Price B3	Retail price for brand 3 charged by the distributor during that week
Sales B4	Number of units of brand 4 sold by the distributor during the week
Price B4	Retail price of brand 4 charged by the distributor during that week

13.6 John Ramapujan is the plant manager for Kitchen Products, Inc. He has asked you to help identify worker factors that influence productivity. In particular, he is interested in gender differences, the effect of working on different shifts, and employee attitudes toward the present benefits plan provided by the company. As a first step in your project you have collected the time required to complete the assembly of a new coffee grinder for a number of workers in the plant. In addition you have identified the workers, by gender (1-male, 2-female), shift (1-day, 2-afternoon, 3-night), and How satisfied are you with employee benefits?

1 - Very dissatisfied
2 - Somewhat dissatisfied
3 - No opinion
4 - Somewhat satisfied
5 - Very satisfied

The data collected are a file named **Completion Times**. Prepare an appropriate analysis and write a short report on the conclusions from your analysis.

13.7 You have been asked to develop a multiple regression model to predict per capita sales of cold cereal in cities with populations over 100,000. As a first step you hold a meeting with the key marketing managers that have experience with cereal sales. From this meeting you discover that per capita sales are expected to be influenced by the cereal price, price of competing cereals, mean per capita income, percentage of college graduates, mean annual temperature, and mean annual rainfall. You also learn that the linear relationship between price and per capita sales is expected to have a different slope for cities east of the Mississippi River. Per capita sales are expected to be higher in cities with high and low per capita income compared to cities with intermediate per capita income. Per capita sales

are also expected to be different in the following four sectors of the country: Northwest, Southwest, Northeast, Southeast.

Prepare a model specification whose coefficients can be estimated using multiple regression. Define each variable completely and indicate the mathematical form of the model. Discuss your specification, indicate which variables you expect to be statistically significant, and explain the rationale for your expectation.

13.8 Maxine Makitright, president of Good Parts, Ltd., has asked you to develop a model that predicts the number of defective parts per 8-hour work shift in her factory. She believes that there are differences among the three daily shifts and among the four raw-material suppliers. In addition, higher production and a higher number of workers are thought to be related to increased number of defectives. Maxine visits the factory at various times, including all three shifts, to observe operations and to offer operating advice. She has provided you with a list of the shifts that she has visited and wants to know if the number of defectives increases or decreases when she visits the factory.

Prepare a written description of how you would develop a model to estimate and test for the various factors that might influence the number of defective parts produced per shift. Carefully define each coefficient in your model and define the test you would use. Indicate how you would collect the data and how you would define each variable used in the model. Discuss the interpretations that you would make from your model specification.

13.9 Custom Woodworking, Inc., has been in business for 40 years. The company produces high-quality custom-made wooden furniture and very high quality interior cabinet and interior woodwork for expensive homes and offices. It has been very successful in large part because of the highly skilled craftworkers, who design and produce its products in consultation with customers. Many of the company's products have won national awards for quality design and artisanship. Each custom-made product is produced by a team of two or more craftworkers who first meet with the customer, prepare an initial design, review the design with the customer, and then build the product. Customers may also meet with the craftworkers at various times during the production.

The craftworkers are well educated and have developed excellent woodworking skills. Most have liberal arts degrees and have trained with skilled craftworkers. Employees are classified at three levels: 1, apprentice; 2, professional; and 3, master. Levels 2 and 3 pay higher wages, and workers typically move through the levels as they gain experience and skill. The company now has a diverse workforce, which includes white, black, and Latino workers and both men and women. When the business started 40 years ago, all workers were white males. About 20 years ago the company began to hire black and Latino craftworkers, and about 10 years ago they hired women craftworkers. The white male workers tend to be overrepresented in the higher job classifications because, in part, they have the most experience. At present, the workforce contains 40% white males, 30% black and Latino males, 15% white females, and 15% black and Latino females.

Recently, serious concerns have been expressed concerning wage discrimination. Specifically, it is alleged that women and nonwhite workers are not receiving fair compensation based on their experience. The company management claims that every person is paid fairly based on years of experience, job classification level, and individual ability. It claims that there are no differences in wages based on either race or gender in terms of either base wage or increment for each year of experience.

Explain how you would carry out an analysis to determine if management's claim is true. Show the details of your analysis and provide a clear rationale. Indicate the data that should be collected and the names and descriptions of the variables you will use in the analysis. Clearly indicate the statistical tests that would be used to determine the true situation and indicate the decision rules based on the hypothesis tests and results from the data.

13.10 You have been asked to serve as a consultant and expert witness for a wage-discrimination lawsuit. A group of Latino and black women have filed the suit against their company, Amalgamated Distributors, Inc. The women, who have between 5 and 25 years of service

with the company, allege that the average rate of their annual wage increase has been significantly less than that of a group of white males and a group of white females. The jobs for all three groups contain a variety of administrative, analytical, and managerial components. All the employees began with a bachelor's degree, and years of experience is an important factor for predicting job performance and worker productivity. You have been provided with the present monthly wages and the years of experience for all workers in the three groups. In addition, the data indicate those in all three groups who have obtained an MBA degree. Note that you do not perform any data analysis for this problem.

a. Develop a statistical model and analysis that can be used to analyze the data. Indicate hypothesis tests that can be used to provide strong evidence of wage discrimination if wage discrimination exists. The company has also hired a statistician as a consultant and expert witness. Describe your analysis completely and clearly.

b. Assume that your hypothesis tests result in strong evidence that supports your clients' claim. Briefly summarize the key points that you will make in your expert witness testimony to the court. The company's lawyer can be expected to cross-examine you with the help of a statistician who teaches statistics at a prestigious liberal arts college.

13.3 LAGGED VALUES OF THE DEPENDENT VARIABLE AS REGRESSORS

Lagged values of the dependent variable are an important topic when time-series data are analyzed—that is, when measurements are taken over time. For example, we might have monthly observations, quarterly observations, or annual observations. Economists regularly use time-series variables such as interest rates, inflation measures, aggregate investment, and aggregate consumption for various analysis and modeling projects. We specify time-series observations using the subscript t to denote time instead of the i used to denote cross-section data. Thus, a multiple regression model would be as follows:

$$y_t = \beta_0 + \beta_t x_{1t} + \beta_2 x_{2t} + \cdots + \beta_K x_{Kt} + \varepsilon_t$$

In many time-series applications the dependent variable in time period t is also often related to the value taken by this variable in the previous time period—that is, to y_{t-1}. The value of the dependent variable in an earlier time period is called a *lagged dependent variable*.

Regressions Involving A Lagged Dependent Variable
Consider the following regression model linking a dependent variable, Y, K independent variables and a lagged dependent variable:

$$y_t = \beta_0 + \beta_t x_{1t} + \beta_2 x_{2t} + \cdots + \beta_K x_{Kt} + \gamma y_{t-1} + \varepsilon_t \tag{13.1}$$

where $\beta_0, \beta_1, \ldots, \beta_K, \gamma$ are fixed coefficients. By using data generated by this model,

1. The coefficients $\beta_0, \beta_1, \ldots, \beta_K, \gamma$ can be estimated by least squares in the usual manner.
2. Confidence intervals and hypothesis tests for the regression coefficients can be computed using the same procedure that is used for the ordinary multiple regression model. (Strictly speaking, when the regression equation contains a lagged dependent variable, these procedures are only approximately valid. The quality of the approximation improves, all other things being equal, as the number of sample observations increases.)
3. An increase of 1 unit in the independent variable X_j in time period t, with all other independent variables held fixed, leads to an expected increase in the dependent variable of β_j in period t, $\beta_j \gamma$ in period $(t + 1)$, $\beta_j \gamma^2$ in period $(t + 2)$, $\beta_j \gamma^3$ in period $(t + 3)$, and so on. The total expected increase over all current and future time periods is as follows:

$$\frac{\beta_j}{(1 - \gamma)}.$$

4. Caution should be expressed when using confidence intervals and hypothesis tests with time-series data. There is the possibility that the equation errors, ε_i, are no longer independent of one another. We consider this in Section 13.7 under autocorrelations. In particular, when the errors are correlated, the coefficient estimates are unbiased, but not efficient. Thus, confidence intervals and hypothesis tests are no longer valid. Econometricians have developed procedures for obtaining estimates under these conditions, and these are introduced in Section 13.7.

Example 13.6 illustrates the calculation of regression estimates and inference based on the fitted regression equation when the model includes a lagged dependent variable. (Dhalla, 1979).

Example 13.6 Advertising Expenditures as a Function of Retail Sales (Lagged Variable Regression Model)

A researcher was interested in forecasting advertising expenditures as a function of retail sales, while knowing that the previous year's advertising also had an influence.

Solution It is believed that local advertising per household depends on retail sales per household. Also, since advertisers may be unwilling or unable to adjust their plans to sudden changes in the level of retail sales, the value of local advertising expenditures per household in the previous year was added to the model. Thus, advertising expenditures in the current year are related to retail sales (x_t) in the current year and advertising expenditures (y_{t-1}) in the previous year. The model to be fitted is then

$$y_t = \beta_0 + \beta_1 x_t + \gamma y_{t-1} + \varepsilon_t$$

where

$$y_t = \text{local advertising per household in year } t$$
$$x_t = \text{retail sales per household in year } t$$

The data for advertising and retail sales are stored in a data file labeled **Advertising Retail**. The lagged value y_{t-1} can be generated using the lag function in your statistical package. Observation 1 for the lagged variable is omitted, and the data set has only 21 remaining observations. This is always the case when lagged variables are created. Of course, you might have access to data from the previous year—year 0 in this example—and that value could replace the missing value. The data are now ready for you to run multiple regression using the conventional procedures. The resulting regression output is shown in Figure 13.5.

Figure 13.5 Advertising Expenditure as a Function of Retail Sales and Lagged Advertising Expenditure (Minitab Output)

```
The regression equation is
Advertising Y(t) = -43.8 + 0.0188 Retail Sales X(t) + 0.479 lag advertising


21 cases used 1 cases contain missing values


Predictor        Coef      SE Coef       T        P
Constant      -43.766        9.843    -4.45    0.000
Retail S     0.018777     0.002855     6.58    0.000
lag adve      0.47906      0.08732     5.49    0.000


S = 3.451      R-Sq = 96.3%   R-Sq(adj) = 95.9%

Analysis of Variance


Source            DF          SS        MS         F        P
Regression         2      5559.1    2779.5    233.43    0.000
Residual Error    18       214.3      11.9
Total             20      5773.4


Source       DF    Seq SS
Retail S      1    5200.7
lag adve      1     358.4


Unusual observations
obs    Retail S   Advertis        Fit     SE Fit   Residual   St Resid
 4         5507    119.220    112.716      1.222      6.504      2.02R
20         6394    145.370    151.853      1.774     -6.483     -2.19R

R denotes an observation with a large standardized residual
```

The resulting regression for this problem (with the first observation eliminated) is as follows:

$$\hat{y} = -43.8 + 0.0188x_t + 0.479y_{t-1}$$
$$\qquad\qquad\quad (0.0029) \qquad (0.087)$$

The numbers below the regression coefficients are the coefficient standard deviations. The Student's t statistic for each coefficient is quite large, and the resulting p-values are 0.00, indicating that we can reject the null hypothesis that the coefficients are 0. With 18 degrees of freedom for error, the critical value for a Student's t statistic for a two-tailed hypothesis with $\alpha = 0.05$ is $t = 2.101$.

In time-series models the coefficient of determination, R^2, can be somewhat misleading. For example, the high value of $R^2 = 96.3\%$ in the present problem does not necessarily indicate a strong relationship between local advertising and retail sales. Rather, it is a well-known empirical fact that the time plots of many business and economic time series exhibit a rather smooth evolutionary pattern over time. This fact alone is enough to ensure a high value for the coefficient of determination when a lagged dependent variable is included in the regression model. As a practical matter, you are advised to pay relatively little attention to the value of R^2 for such models.

The estimated regression for this problem can be interpreted as follows. Suppose that retail sales per household increase by \$1 in the current year. The expected impact on local advertising per household is an increase of 0.0188 in the current year, a further increase of

$$(0.479)(0.0188) = \$0.0090$$

in 1 year, a further increase of

$$(0.479)^2(0.0188) = \$0.0043$$

in 2 years, and so on. The total effect on all future advertising expenditures per household is an expected increase of

$$\frac{0.0188}{1 - 0.479} = \$0.0361$$

Thus, we see that the expected effect of an increase in sales is an immediate increase in advertising expenditures, a smaller increase in the following year, a yet smaller increase 2 years ahead, and so on. Figure 13.6 illustrates this geometrically decreasing effect of an increase in sales in the current year on advertising in future years.

Figure 13.6 Expected Future Increases in Local Advertising per Household

EXERCISES

 Visit www.MyStatLab.com or www.pearsonglobal editions.com to access the data files.

Basic Exercises

13.11 Consider the following models estimated using regression analysis applied to time-series data. What is the long-term effect of a 1-unit increase in x in period t?

a. $y_t = 15 + 4x_t + 0.28y_{t-1}$
b. $y_t = 15 + 4.8x_t + 0.14y_{t-1}$
c. $y_t = 15 + 4x_t + 0.72y_{t-1}$
d. $y_t = 15 + 6.4x_t + 0.28y_{t-1}$

13.12 A market researcher is interested in the average amount of money spent per year by college students on clothing. From 25 years of annual data, the following estimated regression was obtained through least squares:

$$\hat{y}_t = 50.72 + \underset{(0.047)}{0.142x_{1t}} + \underset{(0.0021)}{0.027x_{2t}} + \underset{(0.136)}{0.432y_{t-1}}$$

where

y = expenditure per student, in dollars, on clothes
x_1 = disposable income per student, in dollars, after the payment of tuition, fees, and room and board

x_2 = index of advertising, aimed at the student market, on clothes

The numbers in parentheses below the coefficients are the coefficient standard errors.

a. Test, at the 5% level against the obvious one-sided alternative, the null hypothesis that, all else being equal, advertising does not affect expenditures on clothes in this market.

b. Find a 95% confidence interval for the coefficient on x_1 in the population regression.

c. With advertising held fixed, what would be the expected impact over time of a $1 increase in disposable income per student on clothing expenditure?

Application Exercises

13.13 Use the data from the **Retail Sales** file to estimate the regression model

$$y_t = \beta_0 + \beta_1 x_t + \gamma \, y_{t-1} + \varepsilon_t$$

and test the null hypothesis that $\gamma = 0$, where

y_t = retail sales per household
x_t = disposable income per household

13.14 The data file **Money UK** contains observations from the United Kingdom on the quantity of money in millions of pounds (Y); income, in millions of pounds (X_1); and the local authority interest rate (X_2). Estimate the model (Mills 1978)

$$y_t = \beta_0 + \beta_1 x_{1t} + \beta_2 x_{2t} + \gamma y_{t-1} + \varepsilon_t$$

and write a report on your findings.

13.15 The data file **Pension Funds** contains data on the market return (X) of stocks and the percentage (Y) of portfolios in common stocks at market value at the end of the year for private pension funds. Estimate the model

$$y_t = \beta_0 + \beta_1 x_t + \gamma y_{t-1} + \varepsilon_t$$

and write a report on your findings.

13.16 The data file **Income Canada** shows quarterly observations on income (Y) and money supply (X) in Canada. Estimate the model (Hsiao 1979)

$$y_t = \beta_0 + \beta_1 x_t + \gamma y_{t-1} + \varepsilon_t$$

and write a report on your findings.

13.17 The data file **Births Australia** shows annual observations on the first confinement resulting in a live birth of the current marriage (Y) and the number of first marriages (for females) in the previous year (X) in Australia. Estimate the model (McDonald 1981)

$$y_t = \beta_0 + \beta_1 x_t + \gamma y_{t-1} + \varepsilon_t$$

and write a report on your findings.

13.18 The data file **Thailand Consumption** shows 29 annual observations on private consumption (Y) and disposable income (X) in Thailand. Fit the regression model

$$\log y_t = \beta_0 + \beta_1 \log x_{1t} + \gamma \log y_{t-1} + \varepsilon_t$$

and write a report on your findings.

13.4 SPECIFICATION BIAS

The specification of a statistical model that adequately depicts real-world behavior is a delicate and difficult task. We know that no simple model can describe perfectly the nature of a process and the determinants of process outcomes. Our objective in model building is to discover a straightforward formulation that adequately models the underlying process for the questions of interest. However, we should also note that there are certain cases where substantial divergence of the model from reality can result in conclusions that are seriously in error.

We have seen previously some techniques for specifying a model that more appropriately models the process. Our use of dummy variables in Sections 12.8 and 13.2 and transformations of nonlinear models to linear forms in Section 12.7 are important examples. In this section we consider the implications of not including important predictor variables in our regression model.

In formulating a regression model, an investigator attempts to relate the dependent variable of interest to all of its important independent variables. Thus, if we adopt a linear model, we want to include as independent variables all variables that might markedly influence the dependent variable of interest. In formulating the regression model

$$y = \beta_0 + \beta_1 x_1 + \beta_2 x_2 + \cdots + \beta_K x_K + \varepsilon$$

we implicitly assume that the set of independent variables, $X_1, X_2, \ldots, X_K$, contains all quantities that significantly affect the behavior of the dependent variable, Y. Realistically there are likely to be additional variables that in any real applied problem also affect the dependent variable. The joint influence of these factors is absorbed within the error term, ε_i. However, a serious problem can occur if an important variable is omitted from the list of independent variables.

Bias from Excluding Significant Predictor Variables
When significant predictor variables are omitted from the model, the least squares estimates of coefficients included in the model are usually biased, and the usual inferential statements from hypothesis tests or confidence intervals can be seriously misleading. In addition, the estimated model error includes

the effect of the missing variables and, thus, is larger. In the rare case where omitted variables are uncorrelated with the other independent variables, this bias in the estimation of coefficients does not occur.

A simple example involves the retail market for gasoline. Suppose that you are the owner of store A, which sells gasoline, and that store B, 50 yards down the street, also sells gasoline. You strongly believe that if you lowered your price, unit sales would increase, and if you raised your price, unit sales would decrease. But if store B raised and lowered its price, the change in your unit sales would also be influenced by the price set at store B. Thus, if you ignored the prices set by store B and considered only your prices in attempting to predict unit sales, you would usually have large errors in your estimate of the relationship between your price and your unit sales. First, we will show this result mathematically and then present a numerical example.

We illustrate how the bias in estimating regression coefficients results by showing the effect of omitting a variable from a model with two independent variables:

$$y = \beta_0 + \beta_1 x_1 + \beta_2 x_2 + \varepsilon$$

Suppose that in this situation the analyst leaves out variable x_2 and instead estimates the following regression model:

$$y = \alpha_0 + \alpha_1 x_1 + \mu$$

Note that we have used two different symbols to emphasize the fact that the coefficient estimators will be different. For the simple regression model the estimator for the coefficient of x_1 is as follows:

$$\hat{\alpha}_1 = \frac{\sum_{i=1}^{n}(x_{1i} - \bar{x}_1)y_i}{\sum_{i=1}^{n}(x_{1i} - \bar{x}_1)^2}$$

By substituting the correct model with two predictor variables and determining the expected value, we find that

$$E[\hat{\alpha}_1] = E\left[\frac{\sum_{i=1}^{n}(x_{1i} - \bar{x}_1)y_i}{\sum_{i=1}^{n}(x_{1i} - \bar{x}_1)^2}\right] = E\left[\frac{\sum_{i=1}^{n}(x_{1i} - \bar{x}_1)(\beta_0 + \beta_1 x_{1i} + \beta_2 x_{2i} + \varepsilon_i)}{\sum_{i=1}^{n}(x_{1i} - \bar{x}_1)^2}\right]$$

When we compute the expected value, we find that

$$E[\hat{\alpha}_1] = \beta_1 + \beta_2 \left[\frac{\sum_{i=1}^{n}(x_{1i} - \bar{x}_1)x_{2i}}{\sum_{i=1}^{n}(x_{1i} - \bar{x}_1)^2}\right]$$

Thus, we see that the coefficient of the X_1 variable is biased unless the correlation between X_1 and X_2 is 0.

The previous mathematical results show the bias in coefficient estimates that occurs when an important variable is omitted. In Chapter 12 we showed mathematically and intuitively that the coefficient estimates in a multiple regression model are influenced by all the independent variables included in the model. Thus, it follows that if we omit an important independent variable, then the estimated coefficients of the remaining variables will be different. Example 13.7 shows this result numerically and should be carefully studied.

Example 13.7 Savings and Loan Regression Model with Omitted Variable (Model Specification Error)

Consider the savings and loan example used in Chapter 12. In that example the annual percentage profit margin (Y) of savings and loan associations was regressed on their net revenue per deposit dollar (X_1) and the number of offices (X_2). In Example 12.3 we estimated the regression coefficients and found that the model was as follows:

$$\hat{y} = 1.565 + 0.237x_1 - 0.000249x_2 \quad R^2 = 0.865$$
$$\quad\quad\quad\quad (0.0555) \quad\quad (0.0000320)$$

One conclusion that follows from this analysis is that for a fixed number of offices, a 1-unit increase in net revenue per deposit dollar leads to an expected increase of 0.237 unit in profit margin. What would happen if we regressed profit margin on only the net revenue per deposit dollar using the data stored in the file **Savings and Loan**?

Solution Using the data, we ran the regression of profit margin (Y) on net revenue per deposit dollar (X_1) and found the model was as follows:

$$\hat{y} = 1.326 - 0.169x_1 \quad R^2 = 0.50$$
$$\quad\quad\quad (0.036)$$

Comparing the two fitted models, we notice that one consequence of ignoring X_2 is that the percent explained variability, R^2, is substantially reduced.

There is, however, a more serious effect on the coefficient of net revenue per dollar. In the multiple regression model a 1-unit increase in net revenue increased profit by 0.237, whereas in the simple regression model the effect was a decrease of 0.169. This result is clearly counterintuitive—we should not expect an increase in net revenue to decrease profit margin. In both models we would reject the null hypothesis that there is not a relationship. Here, we see the result of the biased estimator for the coefficient that occurs when a significant variable, X_2, is not included in the model. Without including the conditional effect of the number of offices, we obtain a biased estimator.

This example nicely illustrates the point. If an important explanatory variable is not included in the regression model, any conclusions drawn about the effects of other independent variables can be seriously misleading. In this particular case we have seen that adding a relevant variable could well alter the conclusion of a significant negative association to that of a significant positive association. Further insight can be gained from inspection of the data in Table 12.1. Over the latter part of the period, at least, the profit margin fell and net revenue per dollar rose, suggesting a negative association between these variables. However, a further look at the data reveals an increase in the number of offices over this same period, suggesting the possibility that this factor could be the cause of the declining profit margin. The only legitimate way to disentangle the separate effects of the two independent variables on the dependent variable is to model them jointly in a regression equation. This example illustrates the importance of using the multiple regression model rather than simple linear regression equations when there is more than one relevant independent variable.

EXERCISES

 Visit www.MyStatLab.com or www.pearsonglobal editions.com to access the data files.

Basic Exercises

13.19 Suppose that the true linear model for a process was

$$Y = \beta_0 + \beta_1 X_1 + \beta_2 X_2 + \beta_3 X_3$$

and you incorrectly estimated the model

$$Y = \alpha_0 + \alpha_1 X_2$$

Interpret and contrast the coefficients for X_2 in the two models. Show the bias that results from using the second model.

Figure 13.19 Regression Analysis Using Transformed Variables Without Autocorrelation (Minitab Output)

Regression Analysis: Durable cons versus Disposable I, Fed Funds Ad

```
The regression equation is
Durable cons adj = - 51.8 + 0.195 Disposable Income adj - 0.93 Fed Funds Adj


112 cases used, 1 cases contain missing values


Predictor                  Coef  SE Coef      T      P
Constant                -51.820    7.599  -6.82  0.000
Disposable Income adj   0.19540  0.01124  17.38  0.000
Fed Funds Adj            -0.933    1.817  -0.51  0.609


S = 18.8067   R-Sq = 74.5%   R-Sq(adj) = 74.0%


Analysis of Variance

Source             DF      SS     MS      F      P
Regression          2  112686  56343  159.30  0.000
Residual Error    109   38552    354
Total             111  151238


Source                  DF  Seq SS
Disposable Income adj    1  112593
Fed Funds Adj            1      93


Unusual Observations

      Disposable  Durable
Obs   Income adj  cons adj    Fit  SE Fit  Residual  St Resid
  5          362     33.99  12.37   11.62     21.62    1.46 X
  9          378     33.19  24.20    6.56      8.99    0.51 X
 12          396     38.14  27.43    6.16     10.71    0.60 X
 88          616    161.72  68.95    2.53     92.77    4.98R
 89          918     85.43 128.55    4.24    -43.12   -2.35R
104          919     76.62 126.99    3.78    -50.37   -2.73R
105          878    156.42 118.95    3.41     37.47    2.03R


R denotes an observation with a large standardized residual.
X denotes an observation whose X value gives it large leverage.


Durbin-Watson statistic = 2.52246
```

The first regression has a Durbin-Watson d statistic of 0.2015, indicating strong positive autocorrelation. Based on the regression statistics for the estimated coefficients, we conclude that both disposable income ($b_1 = 0.223$) and federal funds interest rate ($b_2 = 10.439$) are statistically significant predictors of consumption expenditures for durable goods.

However, the second regression analysis—using data for the model without auto-correlated errors—provides a different conclusion:

$$\text{durable cons adj} = -51.8 + 0.195 \text{ disposable income adj} - 0.93 \text{ fed funds adj}$$

$$R^2 = 74.55$$

$$\text{D.W.} = 2.52$$

Notice that the variable names have been modified to reflect the fact that they have been transformed to variables that will produce a model that does not have autocorrelation. In addition, note that the Durbin-Watson d statistic is 2.52, indicating that autocorrelation does not exist. We see that the estimated coefficient for disposable income,

$b_1 = 0.195$, is similar to that from the first regression and that the coefficient standard error is 0.01124. The resulting Student's t statistic, 17.38, leads us to conclude that disposable income is a significant predictor of durable goods consumption. In contrast, the coefficient of federal funds interest rate is $b_2 = -0.93$ with a Student's t statistic of -0.51. Thus, we cannot reject the null hypothesis that the coefficient for federal funds interest rate is 0 and that we should eliminate that variable as a predictor in the regression model.

In this example we saw that autocorrelation led to an incorrect conclusion concerning the importance of the federal funds interest rate. Without adjusting the data to remove the correlation, we would have used the Student's t statistic from the model with the original data and that Student's t statistic from the unadjusted regression overestimates the Student's t statistic from the adjusted regression. The Student's t for the disposable income coefficient in the first regression is also overestimated. However, after adjustment to the correct estimator, we find that the coefficient is still substantially different from 0.

A number of statistical packages such as Eviews3 and SAS, which are designed for working with time-series data, have built-in routines that automatically estimate the autocorrelation coefficient and adjust for autocorrelation. Many of these routines have iterative computational routines and, as a result, generate improved estimates of model coefficients and variances compared to the routine demonstrated here. Thus, if you have access to such a package, you will find the estimation easier than using Minitab or Excel in a parallel procedure. In general, those other computer packages provide more efficient estimates of the coefficients.

Autocorrelated Errors in Models with Lagged Dependent Variables

When we have a regression model with lagged dependent variables on the right-hand side and also have autocorrelated errors, the usual least squares procedures can result in even more severe problems. In addition to the usual problems concerning the estimation of coefficient errors, we also know that the coefficient estimators are biased and not consistent. This occurs because there is a correlation between the model error and a predictor variable, and that introduces a bias in the coefficient estimate. Unfortunately, in this situation of lagged dependent variables, the previously discussed procedures for testing for autocorrelated errors are not valid. So we will briefly introduce an appropriate procedure.

Consider the model

$$y_t = \beta_0 + \beta_1 x_{1t} + \beta_2 x_{2t} + \cdots + \beta_K x_{Kt} + \gamma y_{t-1} + \varepsilon_t$$

Suppose that this model, which includes a lagged value of the dependent variable as a predictor variable, is fitted to n sets of sample observations by least squares. Let d be the usual Durbin-Watson statistic with

$$r = 1 - \frac{d}{2}$$

and let s_c denote the estimated standard deviation of the estimated coefficient γ for the lagged dependent variable. Our null hypothesis is that the autoregressive parameter ρ is 0. A test of this hypothesis, approximately valid in large samples, is based on Durbin's h statistic:

$$h = r\sqrt{n/(1 - ns_c^2)}$$

Under the null hypothesis, this statistic has a distribution that is well approximated in large samples by the standard normal. Durbin's h statistic cannot be computed if $s_c^2 > 1/T$. Thus, for example, the null hypothesis of no autocorrelation is rejected against the alternative that ρ is positive at the 5% significance level if the h statistic exceeds 1.645.

If the autoregressive error is

$$u_t = \varepsilon_t - \rho\varepsilon_{t-1}$$

then, using a modification of the procedure previously developed for autocorrelation adjustment, we can develop the following model:

$$y_t - \rho y_{t-1} = \beta_0(1 - \rho) + \beta_1(x_{1t} - \rho x_{1t-1}) + \beta_2(x_2 - \rho x_{2t-1}) + \cdots$$
$$+ \beta_K(x_{Kt} - \rho x_{Kt-1}) + \gamma(y_{t-1} - \rho y_{t-2}) + \delta_t$$

One possible approach to parameter estimation, which requires only an ordinary least squares estimation program, is to substitute, in turn, possible values of ρ—say, 0.1, 0.3, 0.5, 0.7, and 0.9—in the preceding equation. Then the regression of the dependent variable $(y_t - \rho y_{t-1})$ and the independent variables $(x_{1t} - \rho x_{1,t-1}), (x_{2t} - \rho x_{2,t-1}), \ldots, (x_{Kt} - \rho x_{K,t-1}), (y_{t-1} - \rho y_{t-2})$ is fitted by least squares for each possible ρ value. The value of ρ chosen is that for which the resulting sum of squared errors is smallest. Inference about the β_j is then based on the corresponding fitted regression.

The discussion of models that have both autocorrelation and lagged independent variables involves some important questions that are typically part of higher-level econometrics. Thus, when encountering the preceding situations, the reader might be advised to consult with a person who has knowledge of econometric methods or to study a higher-level econometrics textbook.

EXERCISES

Visit www.MyStatLab.com or www.pearsonglobal editions.com to access the data files.

Basic Exercises

13.32 In determining whether a regression model's error terms are positively correlated for the model

$$y_t = \beta_0 + \beta_1 x_{1t} + \varepsilon_t.$$

We determine $\sum_{t=1}^{30} e_t^2 = 7587.9154$ and

$$\sum_{t=1}^{30}(e_t - e_{t-1})^2 = 8195.2065$$

from its least-square residuals.

a. State the null and alternative hypothesis for the mentioned analysis.
b. Calculate the Durbin-Watson statistic.
c. Determine the decision rule.
d. What can you conclude from this analysis?

13.33 Based on the results in Exercise 13.32, answer the following questions in which a lagged dependent variable is added to the above model.

a. Write the model in which a lagged dependent variable is added.
b. Compute the estimated value for serial correlation.
c. Calculate the Durbin's h statistic with the estimated standard deviation of the estimated coefficient for the lagged dependent variable is 0.0024.
d. Justify your finding in part c.

Application Exercises

13.34 To study the pass rates of students based on the number classes missed by students and the number of cocurricular activities students enroll for, a random sample was selected from the past 40 long and short semesters. The study resulted in a Durbin-Watson statistic of 2.84.

a. Conduct a Durbin-Watson test to determine whether there is a negative autocorrelation in errors at 1% significance level.
b. How would you avoid autocorrelated errors in such a situation? Estimate the autocorrelation parameter in which it may be avoided in this problem.

13.35 The data file **Money UK** contains observations from the United Kingdom on the quantity of money in millions of pounds (Y); income, in millions of pounds (X_1); and the local authority interest rate (X_2). Estimate the model (Mills 1978)

$$y_t = \beta_0 + \beta_1 x_{1t} + \beta_2 x_{2t} + \gamma y_{t-1} + \varepsilon_t$$

and write a report on your findings.
What can be concluded from the Durbin-Watson statistic for the fitted regression?

13.36 The data file **Thailand Consumption** shows 29 annual observations on private consumption (Y) and disposable income (X) in Thailand. Fit the regression model

$$\log y_t = \beta_0 + \beta_1 \log x_{1t} + \gamma \log y_{t-1} + \varepsilon_t$$

and write a report on your findings.
Test the null hypothesis of no autocorrelated errors against the alternative of positive autocorrelation.

13.37 A farmer's yearly yield is based on the amount of rainfall received in a year and average temperature during the year. A series of observations over the past 15 years was obtained, and the model yielded the following results:

$$Yield_t = 0.767 + 0.3543 \times rainfall_t + 0.7294 \times temp_t$$
$$R^2 = 0.873, \qquad d = 0.726$$

Does it show any positive autocorrelation in the error terms at 5% significance level?

13.38 The data file **Advertising Retail** shows, for a consumer goods corporation, 22 consecutive years of data on sales (y) and advertising (x).

    a. Estimate the regression:

$$y_t = \beta_0 + \beta_1 x_t + \varepsilon_t$$

    b. Check for autocorrelated errors in this model.

    c. If necessary, re-estimate the model, allowing for autocorrelated errors.

13.39 Refer to Exercise 13.37 where a lagged variable, yield, is added to the model and suppose the estimated standard deviation of the estimated coefficient for the lagged dependent variable is 0.0639.

    Use Durbin's h statistic to construct a hypothesis test with the alternative hypothesis is $\rho > 0$ at 5% significance level.

KEY WORDS

- autocorrelated errors, 587
- Autocorrelated Errors in Models with Lagged Dependent Variables, 594
- bias from excluding significant predictor variables, 575
- dummy variables, 558
- Durbin-Watson test, 588

- estimation of regression models with autocorrelated errors, 591
- experimental design models, 562
- heteroscedasticity, 582
- lagged dependent variable, 571
- model interpretation and inference, 558

- model specification, 556
- model verification, 558
- multicollinearity, 579
- regressions involving lagged dependent variables, 571
- test for heteroscedasticity, 583

DATA FILES

- Advertising Retail, 573, 596
- Beef Veal Consumption, 600
- Births Australia, 575
- Britain Sick Leave, 599
- Citydatr, 578, 600
- East Anglica Realty, Ltd, 586
- Economic Activity, 585
- German Income, 598

- Completion Times, 570
- Health Care Cost Analysis, 601
- HEI Cost Data Variable Subset, 602
- Income Canada, 575
- Indonesia Revenue, 598
- Japan Imports, 599
- Macro2010, 591, 599, 600, 604
- Market, 569

- Metals, 599
- Money UK, 575, 586, 595
- Motors, 578
- Pension Funds, 575
- Retail Sales, 574, 585
- Savings and Loan, 577
- Thailand Consumption, 575, 595

CHAPTER EXERCISES AND APPLICATIONS

Visit www.MyStatLab.com or www.pearsonglobal editions.com to access the data files.

13.40 Joanne is the human resources manager of the University of Barcelona, Spain. She is interested in determining the effect of an academic degree (bachelor's, master's, and doctorate) on salary. She is considering the employees, of different gender, from three different faculties which are the Economics and Business, Mathematics and Computer Sciences, and Fine Arts.

    a. What is the treatment variable in an experimental design for the above situation? Why?

    b. What are the blocking variables in the experimental design? Why?

    c. Use the answers in parts a and b to create an experimental design model for Joanne that clearly defines the variables used in the model.

13.41 A market analyst, Amelia, is assessing the demand for perfume from three different brands—Adolfo Dominguez, Chanel, and Tiffany. She suspects there

are interactions between the price of the perfume and the brand in the following regression model:

$$Y = \beta_0 + \beta_1 X_1 + \beta_2 X_2 + \beta_3 X_3 + (\beta_4 X_1 + \beta_5 X_2)X_3$$
$$= \beta_0 + \beta_1 X_1 + \beta_2 X_2 + \beta_3 X_3 + \beta_4 X_1 X_3 + \beta_5 X_2 X_3$$

where

    Y = Demand
    X_1 = Adolfo Dominguez
    X_2 = Chanel
    X_3 = The price ($) of the perfume

From a random sample, Amelia estimated the constant and the slope coefficients as $\beta_0 = 19.6$, $\beta_1 = 318$, $\beta_2 = 864$, $\beta_3 = -2.896$, $\beta_4 = 0.0764$, and $\beta_5 = -1.4712$. Help Amelia interpret the estimated slope coefficient values, $\beta_1, \beta_2, \beta_3$, and $(\beta_3 + \beta_4)$.

13.42 In estimating annual food expenditure for a family based on the family's annual income and size, R^2 is 0.927 and the p-value for the family's annual income and size is 0.0567 and 0.0235, respectively. On assessing another independent variable, average meals per day, R^2 is 0.932 with p-value for the family's annual income, size, and average meals per day is 0.364, 0.0153, and 0.107 respectively. Based on what you know about multicollinearity, how would you interpret these results?

13.43 A heteroscedasticity test determines the test statistic value, $\chi^2 = 0.12$, for 20 observations.

a. Justify when heteroscedasticity might occur.
b. Define the null hypothesis and alternative for the test. What can you conclude for it at the 5% significance level?

13.44 The following regression model was fitted for an individual with a constant term and three explanatory variables, including the lagged yearly consumption y_{t-1} and two other variables, yearly income, x_{1t}, and yearly savings, x_{2t}, for over 20 years.

$$\hat{y}_t = 21.0 + \underset{(0.534)}{1.5x_{1t}} + \underset{(0.435)}{0.75x_{2t}} + \underset{(0.216)}{0.6y_{t-1}}$$

where

$\hat{y}$ = yearly consumption (€000)
x_1 = yearly income (€000)
x_2 = yearly savings (€000)

a. Test at the 5% level the null hypothesis that the coefficient on x_1 against the coefficient $\hat{y}$ is positive.
b. Determine a 95% confidence interval for the coefficient on x_1 for the entire population.
c. Calculate the total effect of the individual consumption over all current and future time period if the estimated coefficient on x_1 increases by €1,000. Interpret your result.

13.45 An autoregressive distributed lag model for a country observed by 25 yearly observations is estimated as

$$\hat{y}_t = 11 + \underset{(0.04)}{9x_{1t}} + \underset{(0.17)}{2x_{2t}} + \underset{(0.06)}{0.4x_{3t}} \underset{(0.32)}{0.7y_{t-1}}$$

$$R^2 = 0.879 \quad \text{and} \quad F = 211.654$$

where

$\hat{y}$ = inflation rate
x_1 = Consumer Price Index (CPI)
x_2 = price set by government
x_3 = demand

The numbers below the coefficients are the coefficient standard errors.

a. Interpret the coefficients of the lagged variable.
b. Test at the 5% level the null hypothesis of the effect of the previous inflation rate on the current inflation rate.
c. Interpret the coefficient of determination.
d. What do you conclude about the significance of the overall model?

13.46 The following model was fitted to a company's yearly sales ($000) on the advertising expenditure ($000),

number of sales people, distance traveled by the sales people (000km), and the previous yearly sales ($000) for the past 20 years:

$$\hat{y}_t = 138.691 + 0.3288x_{1t} + 0.2986x_{2t} + 0.0782x_{3t}$$
$$+ 0.7593y_{t-1}$$

where

$\hat{y}$ = sales
x_1 = advertising expenditure
x_2 = number of sales people
x_3 = distance traveled

The p-values for each independent variables and the lagged variable determined from the model are 0.0357, 0.0254, 07239 and 0.0038. Whereas, the R-square and the F-test value for the model is 0.9374 and 198.56 respectively. Based on the results, write a brief report for the company.

13.47 The following regression model was fitted to 30 observations:

$$\hat{y}_t = 47 + \underset{(0.254)}{0.7894x_{1t}} + \underset{(0.0157)}{0.0394x_{2t}} + \underset{(0.296)}{0.6431x_{3t}}$$

$$R^2 = 0.874$$

where

$\hat{y}$ = Temperature (°F)
x_1 = Cloud cover (%)
x_2 = Humidity (%)
x_3 = Wind (mph)

The numbers below the coefficients are the coefficient standard errors.

a. When the independent variable of cloud cover had been taken out from the model, the $R^2 = 0.679$. Justify this statement.
b. Test at the 1% level the null hypothesis, all else being equal, for the significance of the coefficient on x_1.
c. Determine whether the model has uniform variance over the predicted values at the 5% significance level.
d. Besides the method used in part c., what other method can be used in detecting heteroscedasticity? Explain how.

13.48 A company in Bulgaria is working with the local police force to develop an app to analyze the causes of crime in the region. The following regression model was fitted to 28 observations:

$$\hat{y}_t = 0.79 + \underset{(0.143)}{0.35x_1} + \underset{(0.036)}{0.57x_2} + \underset{(0.175)}{0.42x_3}$$

$$d = 1.22$$

where

$\hat{y}$ = Murder rate
x_1 = Current conviction rate
x_2 = Unemployment rate
x_3 = Fraction of young males

The numbers below the coefficients are the coefficient standard errors.

a. What will happen when autocorrelated errors appear in the model?
b. Construct an appropriate to determine whether the above model's error terms are positively autocorrelated at 5% significance level.
c. Given your result in part b, explain the reasons for such a result and the solutions, if any, for it.
d. Suppose the sample size, n, increases to 40 and $d = 1.19$. What can be concluded from the same test used in part b?

13.49 A company is modelling its revenue based on the sales make by its marketers, its summer sales, fall sales and winter sales for all the units in \$000. It determined the following regression model from a sample of 35.

$$\hat{y} = 149 + 1.59x_1 + 3.74x_2 + 1.26x_3 + 2.91x_4$$
$$\quad\quad\;\;\; (0.745)\quad\;(0.034)\quad\;(0.056)\quad\;(0.092)$$

$d = 1.09$

where

$\hat{y}$ = Revenue
x_1 = Marketers' sales
x_2 = Summer sales
x_3 = Fall sales
x_4 = Winter sales

The numbers below the coefficients are the coefficient standard errors.

a. Interpret the estimated coefficient on x_1.
b. Using the Durbin-Watson statistic, test at the 5% level the null hypothesis of positive autocorrelation of error terms.
c. Estimate the autocorrelation parameter.

13.50 The following regression model shows the cash balance for a household which based on the expenditures on food, the expenditures on entertainments and the lagged cash balance for the past 30 months.

$$\hat{y}_t = 1.6027 - 0.1024x_{1t} - 0.6869x_{2t} + 0.5284y_{t-1}$$
$$\quad\quad\;\; (1.2404)\quad\quad (0.3678)\quad\quad (0.3427)$$

$R^2 = 0.9227, \quad d = 1.8624 \quad \text{and} \quad s_c = 0.1228$

where

$\hat{y}$ = Cash balance
x_1 = Expenditures on food
x_2 = Expenditures on entertainments

a. Estimate the autocorrelation parameter.
b. What is autocorrelation?
c. Test at the 10% level the null hypothesis that, all else being equal, the model's error terms are autocorrelated.

13.51 A doctor conducted a survey to define "healthy food items" based on the amount of sugar and fats

contained in each item. From a sample of 25 items, the doctor collected the following output:

Parameter	Coefficient	Standard Deviation
Constant	59.687	1 352
Carbohydrates	− 2.124	1.053
Fats	− 2.791	0.741

The doctor also estimated the following regression model:

$$\hat{y} = \beta_0 + \beta_1 x_1 + \beta_2 x_2$$

where

$\hat{y}$ = Rating
x_1 = Amount of carbohydrates (in grams)
x_2 = Amount of fats (in grams)

$R^2 = 0.713, \quad F = 43.534 \quad d = 3.15$

a. The doctor is concerned about the possibility of multicollinearity. Explain whether it occurs in the model.
b. Use a hypothesis testing to show whether the model has uniform variance over the predicted values at 1% significance level.
c. Give one solution on how to deal with the conclusion you make in part b. and why it will happen.
d. What method can be used to check whether the error terms in a model are autocorrelated?
e. Use the suggested method in part c. to find out whether the error terms in the above model are negatively autocorrelated.

13.52 The data file **Indonesia Revenue** show 15 annual observations from Indonesia on total government tax revenues other than from oil (y), national income (x_1), and the value added by oil as a percentage of gross domestic product (x_2). Estimate by least squares the following regression:

$$\log y_t = \beta_0 + \beta_1 \log x_{1t} + \beta_2 \log x_{2t} + \varepsilon_t$$

Write a report summarizing your findings, including a test for autocorrelated errors.

13.53 The data file **German Income** shows 22 annual observations from the Federal Republic of Germany on percentage change in wages and salaries (y), productivity growth (x_1), and the rate of inflation (x_2), as measured by the gross national product price deflator. Estimate by least squares the following regression:

$$y_t = \beta_0 + \beta_1 x_{1t} + \beta_2 x_{2t} + \varepsilon_t$$

Write a report summarizing your findings, including a test for heteroscedasticity and a test for autocorrelated errors.

13.54 The data file **Japan Imports** shows 35 quarterly observations from Japan on quantity of imports (y), ratio of import prices to domestic prices (x_1), and real gross national product (x_2). Estimate by least squares the following regression:

$$\log y_t = \beta_0 + \beta_1 \log x_{1t} + \beta_2 \log x_{2t} + \gamma \log y_{t-1} + \varepsilon_t$$

Write a report summarizing your findings, including a test for autocorrelated errors.

13.55 Data providers want to investigate the time spent online (in hours) per day by an individual based on their age, gender, purpose (work, entertainment, information searching), and their relationship with other family members (poor, average, good). The model estimated model is:

$$\hat{y} = 2.43 + 0.524x_1 + 0.753x_2 + 1.062x_3 + 0.921x_4$$
$$\phantom{\hat{y} = 2.43 +}{\scriptstyle(0.075)}{\scriptstyle(0.034)}{\scriptstyle(0.056)}{\scriptstyle(0.092)}$$
$$+ 2.631x_5 - 1.352x_6$$
$${\scriptstyle(1.586)}{\scriptstyle(0.024)}$$

where

$\hat{y}$: Time spent online (in hours)
x_1 : Age
x_2 : 1 if male, 0 otherwise
x_3 : 1 if work purpose, 0 otherwise
x_4 : 1 if entertainment purpose, 0 otherwise
x_5 : 1 if poor relationship with family, 0 otherwise
x_6 : 1 if average relationship with family, 0 otherwise

The numbers in parentheses beneath coefficient estimates are the associated standard error. Write a brief report on the result.

13.56 The data file **Britain Sick Leave** shows data from Great Britain on the days of sick leave per person (Y), unemployment rate (X_1), ratio of benefits to earnings (X_2), and the real wage rate (X_3). Estimate the model

$$\log y_t = \beta_0 + \beta_1 \log x_{1t} + \beta_2 \log x_{2t} + \beta_3 \log x_{3t} + \varepsilon_t$$

and write a report on your findings. Include in your analysis a check on the possibility of autocorrelated errors and, if necessary, a correction for this problem.

13.57 The U.S. Department of Commerce has asked you to develop a regression model to predict quarterly investment in production and durable equipment. The suggested predictor variables include GDP, prime interest rate, per capita income lagged, federal government spending, and state and local government spending. The data for your analysis are found in the data file **Macro2010,** which is described in the data dictionary in the chapter appendix. Use data from the time period 1980.1 through 2010.4.

a. Estimate a regression model using only interest rate to predict the investment. Use the Durbin-Watson statistic to test for autocorrelation.
b. Find the best multiple regression equation to predict investment using the predictor variables previously indicated. Use the Durbin-Watson statistic to test for autocorrelation.

c. What are the differences between the regression models in parts a and b in terms of goodness of fit, prediction capability, autocorrelation, and contributions to understanding the investment problem?

13.58 An economist has asked you to develop a regression model to predict consumption of service goods as a function of disposable personal income and other important variables. The data for your analysis are found in the data file **Macro2010,** which is described in the data dictionary in the chapter appendix. Use data from the period 1980.1 through 2010.4.

a. Estimate a regression model using only disposable personal income to predict consumption of service goods. Test for autocorrelation using the Durbin-Watson statistic.
b. Estimate a multiple regression model using disposable personal income, total consumption lagged 1 period, and prime interest rate as additional predictors. Test for autocorrelation. Does this multiple regression model reduce the problem of autocorrelation?

13.59 Jack Wong, a Tokyo investor, is considering plans to develop a primary steel plant in Japan. After reviewing the initial design proposal, he is concerned about the proposed mix of capital and labor. He has asked you to prepare several production functions using some historical data from the United States. The data file **Metals** contains 27 observations of the value-added output, labor input, and gross value of plant and equipment per factory.

a. Use multiple regression to estimate a linear production function with value-added output regressed on labor and capital.
b. Plot the residuals versus labor and equipment. Note any unusual patterns.
c. Use multiple regression with transformed variables to estimate a Cobb-Douglas production function of the form

$$Y = \beta_0 L^{\beta_1} K^{\beta_2}$$

where y is the value added, L is the labor input, and K is the capital input.
d. Use multiple regression transformed variables to estimate a Cobb-Douglas production function with constant returns to scale. Note that this production function has the same form as the function estimated in part c, but it has the additional restriction that $\beta_1 + \beta_2 = 1$. To develop the transformed regression model, substitute β_2 as a function of β_1 and convert to a regression format.
e. Compare the three production functions using residual plots and a standard error of the estimate that is expressed in the same scale. You will need to convert the predicted values from parts c and d, which are in logarithms, back to the original units. Then you can subtract the predicted values from the original values of Y to obtain the residuals. Use the residuals to compute comparable standard errors of the estimate.

13.60 The administrator of a small city has asked you to identify variables that influence the mean market value of houses in small midwestern cities. You have obtained data from a number of small cities, which are stored in the data file **Citydatr**, with variables described in the Chapter 12 appendix. The candidate predictor variables are the median size of the house (sizehse), the property tax rate (taxrate; tax levy divided by total assessment), the total expenditures for city services (totexp), and the percent commercial property (comper).

a. Estimate the multiple regression model using all the indicated predictor variables. Select only statistically significant variables for your final equation.

b. An economist stated that since the data came from cities of different populations, your model is likely to contain heteroscedasticity. He argued that mean housing prices from larger cities would have a smaller variance because the number of houses used to compute the mean housing prices would be larger. Test for heteroscedasticity.

c. Estimate the multiple regression equation using weighted least squares with population as the weighting variable. Compare the coefficients for the weighted and unweighted multiple regression models.

13.61 The chief financial officer of a major service company has asked you to develop a regression model to predict consumption of service goods as a function of GDP and other important variables. The data for your analysis are found in the data file **Macro2010**, which is stored on your data disk and described in the data dictionary in the chapter appendix. Use data from the period 1980.1 through 2010.4.

a. Estimate a regression model using only GDP to predict consumption of service goods. Test for autocorrelation using the Durbin-Watson statistic.

b. Estimate a multiple regression model using GDP, total consumption lagged 1 period, imports or services, and prime interest rate as additional predictors. Test for autocorrelation. Does this multiple regression model reduce the problem of autocorrelation?

13.62 The marketing vice president of Consolidated Appliances has asked you to develop a regression model to predict consumption of durable goods as a function of disposable personal income and other important variables. The data for your analysis are found in the data file **Macro2010**, which is described in the data dictionary in the chapter appendix. Use data from the period 1976.1 through 2010.4.

a. Estimate a regression model using only disposable personal income to predict consumption of durable goods. Test for autocorrelation using the Durbin-Watson statistic.

b. Estimate a multiple regression model using disposable personal income, total consumption lagged 1 period, imports of goods, population, and prime interest rate as additional predictors. Test for autocorrelation. Does this multiple regression model reduce the problem of autocorrelation?

13.63 You have been asked to develop a model using multiple regression that predicts the retail sale of beef using time-series data. The data file **Beef Veal Consumption** contains a number of variables related to the beef retail markets beginning in 1935 and extending through the present. The variables are described in the Chapter 13 appendix.

a. Prepare a model that includes a test and adjustment for serial correlation. Discuss your model and indicate important factors that predict beef sales.

b. Prepare a second analysis, but this time include only data beginning in the year 1980.

c. Compare the two models estimates in a and b.

13.64 You have been asked to develop a model using multiple regression that predicts the retail sale of veal using time series data. The data file **Beef Veal Consumption** contains a number of variables related to the veal retail markets beginning in 1935 and extending through the present.

a. Prepare a model that includes a test and adjustment for serial correlation. Discuss your model and indicate important factors that predict beef sales.

b. Prepare a second analysis, but this time include only data beginning in the year 1980.

c. Compare the two models estimates in a and b.

13.65 You have been asked to develop a model using multiple regression that predicts the retail sale of beef and veal combined using time series data. The data file **Beef Veal Consumption** contains a number of variables related to the beef and veal retail markets beginning in 1935 and extending through the present.

a. Prepare a model that includes a test and adjustment for serial correlation. Discuss your model and indicate important factors that predict beef sales.

b. Prepare a second analysis, but this time include only data beginning in the year 1980.

c. Compare the two models estimates in a and b.

13.8 CASE STUDIES

Mini–Health Care Case Studies

The following can each be treated as mini–case studies or can be combined into an extended case study of health care costs.

13.66 Health care cost is an increasingly important part of the United States economy. In this exercise you are to identify variables that are predictors for the cost of physician and clinical services, either individually or in combination. Use the data file **Health Care Cost Analysis**, which contains annual health care costs for the period 1960–2008. As a first step you are to explore the simple relationships between physician and clinical services cost and individual variables using a combination of simple correlations and graphical scatter plots. You should also examine the changes in cost of physicians and clinical services and other variables over time. Medical care costs are, of course, affected by various national policies and changes in health care providers and health insurance practice. Based on these analyses, develop a multiple regression model that predicts costs of physicians and clinical services. You will probably find that the model has errors that are serially correlated and this possibility should be tested for by using the Durbin-Watson test.

If serial correlation exists in your initial model then to adjust for serial correlation, you are to use the difference variables to estimate a model that predicts the change in physician and clinical services as a function of change in the predictor variables. Again, explore the simple relationship between the change in physician and clinical services and the change in the other predictor variables using correlations and scatter plots. Using these results, develop a multiple regression model using the changes in variables to predict the change in physician and clinical services costs.

Prepare a report that identifies variables that are related to cost of physicians and clinical services individually and in combination.

13.67 Health care cost is an increasingly important part of the U.S. economy. In this exercise you are to identify variables that are predictors for hospital cost, either individually or in combination. Use the data file **Health Care Cost Analysis,** which contains annual health care costs for the period 1960–2008. As a first step you are to explore the simple relationships between hospital cost and individual variables using a combination of simple correlations and graphical scatter plots. You should also examine the changes in hospital cost and other variables over time. Medical care costs are, of course, affected by various national policies and changes in health care providers and health insurance practice. Based on these analyses, develop a multiple regression model that predicts hospital cost. You will probably find that the model has errors that are serially correlated and this possibility should be tested for by using the Durbin-Watson test.

If serial correlation exists in your initial model then use the difference variables to estimate a model that predicts the change as a function of change in the predictor variables. Again, explore the simple relationship between the change in hospital cost and the change in the other predictor variables using correlations and scatter plots. Using these results develop a multiple regression model using the changes in variables to predict the change in hospital care costs.

Prepare a report that identifies variables that are related to hospital cost individually and in combination.

13.68 Health care cost is an increasingly important part of the U.S. economy. In this exercise you are to identify variables that are predictors for drug cost, either individually or in combination. Use the data file **Health Care Cost Analysis**, which contains annual health care costs for the period 1960–2008. As a first step you are to explore the simple relationships between drug cost and individual variables using a combination of simple correlations and graphical scatter plots. You should also examine the changes in drug cost and other variables over time. Medical care costs are, of course, affected by various national policies and changes in health care providers and health insurance practice. Based on these analyses, develop a multiple regression model that predicts drug costs. You will probably find that the model has errors that are serially correlated and this possibility should be tested for by using the Durbin-Watson test.

If serial correlation exists in your initial model then use the difference variables to estimate a model that predicts the change in drug costs as a function of change in the predictor variables. Again, explore the simple relationship between the change in drug cost and the change in the other predictor variables using correlations and scatter plots. Using these results, develop a multiple regression model using the changes in variables to predict the change in drug cost.

Prepare a report that identifies variables that are related to drug cost individually and in combination.

Health Care Cost Analysis Data File Description

(*Source:* National Health Expenditures by Type Of Service and Source of Funds: Calendar Years 2008 to 1960, NHE08-60.

United States Dept. of Health and Human Services, Centers for Medicare and Medicaid Services)

C1	Year
C2	National Health Expenditures
C3	Medicare
C4	Hospital Care
C5	Physician and Clinical Services
C6	Prescription Drugs
C7	Admin. & Net Cost of Priv. Hlth
C8	Income Low 5th
C9	Income Median
C10	Income High 5th
C11	Income High 5%
C12	Population
C13	Unemployment
C14	Percent 65 plus
C15	Per age <5
C16	Lag Hosp care
C17	Difference Hosp Care
C18	Difference Physician
C19	Difference Drugs
C20	Difference Population
C21	Difference % >65
C22	Difference % <5
C23	Difference Medicare Cost
C24	Difference Income >5%
C25	Difference Income Median
C26	Lag Diff % Age >65

Nutrition Model Analysis Case Study

Emily Carlsperger, Program Director for Nutrition Studies, has asked you to conduct a statistical analysis study to identify variables that are related to a healthy diet. In addition, she has asked you to develop a model that shows the combined effect of a set of variables on the prediction of the quality of various diet combinations. The results of your analysis and report will be used as part of the knowledge base to identify the characteristics that are related to a healthy diet. In addition the results will be used as part of an education program to promote healthy diets. Your research will use the Healthy Eating Index as a measure of a healthy diet and a data file that was developed from extensive interviews of randomly selected individuals.

The U.S. Department of Agriculture (USDA) developed the Healthy Eating Index (HEI) to monitor the diet quality of the U.S. population, particularly how well it conforms to dietary guidance. The HEI–2005 measures how well the population follows the recommendations of the *2005 Dietary Guidelines for Americans*. In particular, it measures, on a 100-point scale, the adequacy of consumption of vegetables, fruits, grains, milk,

meat and beans, and liquid oils. Full credit for these groups is given only when the individual consumes some whole fruit; vegetables from the dark green, orange, and legume subgroup; and whole grains. In addition the HEI–2005 measures how well the U.S. population limits consumption of saturated fat, sodium, and extra calories from solid fats, added sugars, and alcoholic beverages. You will use the total HEI–2005 score as the measure of the quality of a diet. Further background on the HEI and important research on nutrition can be found at the government Web sites indicated at the end of this case study.

To begin this study you should explore the important research literature and prepare a one-page summary of your findings. You should also prepare a one-page summary of the Healthy Eating Index that will be included as an important appendix in the study report. This summary can then be used to guide your analysis and the variables that you will consider in the statistical analysis.

The data file **HEI Cost Data Variable Subset** contains a subset of the variables from a large national sample of randomly selected individuals who participated in an extended interview and medical examination. Included is the HEI–2005 total score for each person and an extensive list of variables obtained from the medical examination and interviews. Your task is to determine which of these variables have significant and important relationships with a healthy diet. The analysis should explore both the simple relationships and the combined relationships of many variables with HEI–2005.

Note that all participants in the study had two interviews; an initial 4-hour interview in person and a second interview by telephone 2 to 10 days later. You might want to consider analyzing the first and second interview responses separately (identified by variable daycode equal to 1 or 2). Also you will find that there are missing responses for variables that resulted for some subjects.

Your analysis is to consider a number of variables that influence diet both individually and in combination. There is an increasing emphasis on healthy diets. However, a number of commentators claim that one can obtain a healthier diet only by purchasing more-expensive foods. For example, references are often made to organic food markets that charge a higher price for food items compared to the large supermarkets. Diet cost is an important question, but your analysis needs to have much greater depth by considering many possible variables.

Requirements

You are to prepare a report to the director that indicates important factors that contribute to an improved diet. Some of these factors will be part of personal behavior, and your recommendations could become part of an education program to help individuals improve their diet. Other results might contribute to policies and guidelines that enable federal and state agencies to improve overall health and quality of life. There may be specific recommendations that apply to subsets of the population. Your professor may also provide additional specific guidelines for your case study analysis.

Your work on this case provides considerable flexibility regarding direction and focus. However, it is fundamentally important that your conclusions and recommendations are supported by rigorous statistical analysis of the data provided for this case. You are to avoid results based upon your personal opinions, newspaper reports, political commentary, or opinions from so-called experts in this field unless these results are supported by your statistical analysis. Careful analysis includes both correct use of appropriate statistical procedures and a clear explanation and interpretation of the statistical results that support your recommendations and conclusions. You are providing your report to people who do not have your level of statistical expertise. Your

project will be graded on both the depth and quality of the statistical analysis and the quality of the communication in your report.

Use the Internet to find the following government sites to begin your search of appropriate sources:

National Health and Nutrition Examination Survey
Center for Nutrition Policy and Promotion
Dietary Guidelines for Americans

Appendix

VARIABLE LIST FOR DATA FILE BEEF VEAL CONSUMPTION

VARIABLE	LABEL
Year	Year represented by the data
Beef Veal CPI	Price index for beef and veal
Beef Retail	Total retail sales of beef in tons
U.S. Population	Population of United States
Beef Production	Total production of beef in tons
Veal Retail	Total retail sales of veal in tons
Veal Production	Total production of veal in tons
Beef Veal Slaughter PPI	Producer price index for beef and veal slaughter operations
Red Meat Retail	Total retail sales of red meat in tons
Beef Veal Retail	Total combined retail sales of beef and veal in tons
Beef Veal Production	Total production of beef and veal in tons

VARIABLE LIST FOR DATA FILE HEI COST DATA VARIABLE SUBSET

	VARIABLE	LABEL
1	Suppl	take supplements
2	doc_bp	1 - Doctor-diagnosed high blood pressure
3	daycode	1 - First interview day, 2 - Second interview day
4	sr_overweight	1 - Subject reported was overweight
5	try_wl	1 - Tried to lose weight
6	try_mw	1 - Trying to maintain weight, active
7	sr_did_lm_wt	1 - Subject reported did limit weight
8	daily_cost	One day_adjusted_food_cost
9	HEI2005	TOTAL HEI-2005 SCORE
10	daily_cost2	Daily food cost squared
11	Friday	1 - Dietary_recall_occurred_on_Friday
12	weekend_ss	1 - Dietary_recall_occurred_on_Sat_or
13	week_mth	1 - Dietary recall occurred Mon through Thur
14	keeper	1 - Data are complete for 2 days
15	WIC	1 - Someone_in_the_HH_particpates_in
16	fsp	1 - Someone_in_the_HH_approved_for_food stamps (SNAP program)
17	fsec	1 - Family_has_high_food_security
18	PIR_p	Poverty_income_ratio_as_percent (family income / poverty-level income)
19	PIR_grp	Poverty_income_ratio_group
20	nhw	1 - Non_Hispanic_White, 0 - Else
21	hisp	1 - Hispanic
22	nhb	1 - Non_Hispanic_Black
23	single	1 - Single__no_partner_in_the_home
24	female	1 - Subject is female

(continued)

	VARIABLE	LABEL
25	waist_cir	Waist circumference (cm) separate by male and female)
26	waistper	Ratio of subject waist measure to waist cutoff for obese
27	age	Age at screening adjudicated - recode
28	hh_size	Total number of people in the household
29	WTINT2YR	Full sample 2-year interview weight
30	WTMEC2YR	Full sample 2-year MEC exam weight
31	immigrant	1 - immigrant
32	citizen	1 - U.S citizen
33	native_born	1 - Native born
34	hh_income_est	Household income estimated by subject
35	English	1 - Primary language spoken in home is English
36	Spanish	1 - Primary language spoken in home is Spanish
37	Smoker	1- Currently smokes
38	doc_chol	1 - Doctor diagnosis of high cholesterol that was made before interview
39	BMI	Body mass index (kg/m**2) 20–25 Healthy, 26–30 Overweight, >30 Obese
40	doc_dib	1 - Doctor diagnosis diabeties
41	no_days_ph_ng	No. of days physical health was not good
42	no_days_mh_ng	No. of days mental health was not good
43	doc_ow	1 - Doctor diagnosis overweight was made before interview
44	screen_hours	Number of hours in front of computer or TV screen
45	activity_level	1 = Sedentary, 2 = Active, 3 = Very Active
46	total_active_min	Active minutes per day
47	waist_large	Waist circumferance > cut_off
48	Pff	Percent of calories from fast food, deli, pizza restaurant
49	Prest	Percent of calories from table service restaurant
50	P_Ate_At_Home	Percent of calories eaten at home
51	Hs	1 = High school graduate
52	Col_grad	1 = College graduate or higher
53	Pstore	Percent of calories purchased at store for consumption at home

Data File **Macro2010**

Economic Series in Real Dollars

Quarterly data are available from the first quarter of 1947 through the fourth quarter of 2010 except where indicated. The data are in 2005 dollars (index numbers [2005 = 100]), seasonally adjusted. Bureau of Economic Analysis.

Downloaded on 4/10/2011 Last revised 3/25/2011

FBPr	Bank Prime Loan Rate	1949 01
FFED	Effective Federal Funds Rate	1954 03
FM1	Money Stock M1	1959 01
FM2	M2 Money Stock	1959 01
GDP	Gross Domestic Product	1947 01
C	Personal Consumption Expenditures	1947 01
CD	Durable Goods	1947 01
CN	Nondurable Goods	1947 01
CS	Services	1947 01
I	Gross Private Domestic Investment	1947 01
IF	Fixed Investment	1947 01
IN	Nonresidential	1947 01
IS	Structures	1947 01
IES	Equipment and Software	1947 01
IR	Residential	1947 01

X	Exports	1947 01
XG	Goods	1947 01
XS	Services	1947 01
M	Imports	1947 01
MG	Goods	1947 01
MS	Services	1947 01
G	Government Spending	1947 01
GF	Federal	1947 01
GD	National Defense	1947 01
GN	Nondefense	1947 01
GSL	State and Local	1947 01
YPI	Personal Income	1947 01
YTAX	Less: Personal Current Taxes	1947 01
YDPI	Equals: Disposable Personal Income	1947 01
YPO	Less: Personal Outlays	1947 01
YPCE	Personal Consumption Expenditures	1947 01
YPS	Equals: Personal Saving	1947 01
POP	Population (Midperiod, Thousands)	1947 01

REFERENCES

1. Carlson, A., D. Dong, and M. Lino. 2010. "Are the Total Daily Cost of Food and Diet Quality Related: A Random Effects Panel Data Analysis." Paper presented at 1st Joint EAAE/AAEA Seminar "The Economics of Food, Food Choice and Health." Freising, Germany, September 15–17, 2010.

2. Carlson, A., and G. Gerrior. 2006. "Food Source Makes a Difference in Diet Quality." *Journal of Nutrition Education and Behavior* 38(4): 238–243.

3. Dhalla, N. K. 1979. "Short-Term Forecasts of Advertising Expenditures." *Journal of Advertising Research* 19 (1): 7–13.

4. Greene, W. H., *Econometric Analysis*, 7th Ed. Englewood Cliffs, NJ: Prentice Hall, 2005.

5. Hsiao, C. 1979. "Autoregressive Modeling of Canadian Money and Income Data." *Journal of American Statistical Association* 74: 553–560.

6. Leibtag, Ephraim, Catherine Barker, and Paula Dutko. *How Much Lower Are Prices at Discount Stores? An Examination of Retail Food Prices*, ERR-105.

7. U.S. Dept. of Agri., Econ. Res. Serv. September 2010.

8. McDonald, J. 1981. "Modeling Demographic Relationships: An Analysis of Forecast Functions for Australian Births." *Journal of the American Statistical Association* 76: 782–792.

9. Mills, T. C. 1978. "The Functional Form of the UK Demand for Money." *Applied Statistics* 27: 52–57.

10. United States Center for Disease Control and Prevention, National Health and Nutrition Examination Survey, 2011.

11. United States Department of Agriculture, Economic Research Service, 2011.

12. United States Department of Commerce, Bureau of Economic Analysis, U.S. Economic Accounts, 2011.

13. United States Department of Labor, Bureau of Labor Statistics, 2011.

14. United States Department of Transportation Federal Highway Administration, Traffic Volume Trends, 2011.

15. United States Energy Information Adminstration, Petroleum and Other Liquids, 2011.

16. Waldauer, C., V. G. Duggal, and M. L. Willliams. 1992. "Gender Differences in Economic Knowledge: A Further Extension of the Analysis." *Quarterly Review of Economics and Finance* 32 (4): 138–143.

CHAPTER 14

Analysis of Categorical Data

Introduction

Do customers have a preference for any of several soft drinks, flavors of ice cream, toppings for pizza, or even Internet browsers or social networks? Are people's preferences for a particular political candidate based on some characteristic such as age, gender, or location of residence? Do students at a particular university prefer any of three faculty members who all teach an introductory accounting course? Based on a survey of recent university graduates, is the median starting salary significantly different from (or greater than or less than) some specified value? Is there an overall tendency of a panel of judges to prefer a new pizza sauce over the original pizza sauce? These are only a few of the types of questions that we address in this chapter.

We introduce *nonparametric* tests, which are often the appropriate procedure needed to make statistical conclusions about qualitative data (nominal or ordinal data) or numerical data when the normality assumption cannot be made about the probability distribution of the population. Such data are frequently obtained in many settings, including marketing research studies, business surveys, and questionnaires.

First we discuss certain tests that are based on the chi-square distribution, such as a test of the hypothesis that data are generated by a *fully specified* probability distribution. This technique is often used by market researchers to determine if products are equally preferred by potential customers or to check if the market shares for several brands of a product have changed over a given period of time.

Next, we test the hypothesis that data are generated by some distribution, such as the binomial, the Poisson, or the normal, without assuming the parameters of that distribution to be known. In these circumstances the available data can be used to estimate the unknown population parameters. A goodness-of-fit test is used when population parameters are estimated. The chi-square test can be extended to deal with a problem in which a sample is taken from a population, each of whose members can be uniquely cross-classified according to a pair of characteristics. The hypothesis to be tested is of no association in the population between possessions of these characteristics. Marketing professionals frequently use this procedure. For larger contingency tables it is convenient to use a software package to determine the test statistic and *p*-value.

We consider next nonparametric alternatives to various procedures introduced earlier in the book. It is not our intention here to attempt to describe the entire wide array of such nonparametric procedures that are available. Rather, our objective is the more modest one of providing a flavor of selected nonparametric procedures, including the sign test, the Wilcoxon signed rank test, the Mann-Whitney U test, the Wilcoxon rank sum test, and the Spearman rank correlation test.

We conclude this introduction to nonparametric statistics with a discussion of the *runs test* for randomness applied to time-series data with a small sample size and time-series data with a large sample size.

14.1 GOODNESS-OF-FIT TESTS: SPECIFIED PROBABILITIES

The most straightforward test of this type is illustrated with a study that observed a random sample of 300 subjects purchasing a soft drink. Of these subjects, 75 selected brand A, 110 selected brand B, and the remainder selected brand C. This information is displayed in Table 14.1.

Table 14.1
Brand Selection

CATEGORY (BRAND)	A	B	C	TOTAL
Number of subjects	75	110	115	300

More generally, consider a random sample of n observations that can be classified according to K categories. If the numbers of observations falling into each category are $O_1, O_2, \ldots, O_K$, the setup is as shown in Table 14.2.

Table 14.2 Classification of n Observations into K Categories

CATEGORY	1	2	...	K	TOTAL
Number of observations	O_1	O_2	...	O_K	n

The sample data are to be used to test a null hypothesis specifying the probabilities that an observation falls in each of the categories. In the example of 300 subjects purchasing a soft drink, the null hypothesis (H_0) might be that a randomly chosen subject is equally likely to select any of the three different varieties. This null hypothesis, then, specifies that the probability is 1/3 that a sample observation falls into each of the three categories. To test this hypothesis, it is natural to compare the sample numbers *observed* with what would be *expected* if the null hypothesis were true. Given a total of 300 sample observations, the expected number of subjects in each category under the null hypothesis would be $(300)(1/3) = 100$. This information is summarized in Table 14.3.

Table 14.3 Observed and Expected Number of Purchases for Three Brands of Soft Drink

Category (Brand)	A	B	C	Total
Observed number of subjects	75	110	115	300
Probability (under H_0)	1/3	1/3	1/3	1
Expected number of subjects (under H_0)	100	100	100	300

In the general case of K categories, suppose that the null hypothesis specifies $P_1, P_2, \ldots, P_K$ for the probabilities that an observation falls into the categories. Assume that these possibilities are mutually exclusive and collectively exhaustive—that is, each sample observation must belong to one of the categories and cannot belong to more than one. In this case, the hypothesized probabilities must sum to 1—that is,

$$P_1 + P_2 + \cdots + P_K = 1$$

Then, if there are n sample observations, the expected numbers in each category, under the null hypothesis, will be as follows:

$$E_i = nP_i \quad \text{for } i = 1, 2, \ldots, K$$

This is shown in Table 14.4.

Table 14.4 Observed and Expected Numbers for n Observations and K Categories

Category	1	2	...	K	Total
Observed number	O_1	O_2	...	O_K	n
Probability (under H_0)	P_1	P_2	...	P_K	1
Expected number (under H_0)	$E_1 = nP_1$	$E_2 = nP_2$	...	$E_K = nP_K$	n

The null hypothesis about the population specifies the probabilities that a sample observation will fall into each possible category. The sample observations are to be used to check this hypothesis. If the null hypothesis were true, we would think that the observed data in each category would be close in value to the expected numbers in each category. In such circumstances the data provide a close *fit* to the assumed population distribution of probabilities. A test of the null hypothesis is based on an assessment of the closeness of this fit and is generally referred to as a **goodness-of-fit test**.

Now, in order to test the null hypothesis, it is natural to look at the magnitudes of the discrepancies between what is observed and what is expected. The larger these discrepancies are in absolute value, the more suspicious we are of the null hypothesis. The random variable in Equation 14.2 is known as the chi-square random variable.

Chi-Square Random Variable

A random sample of n observations, each of which can be classified into exactly one of K categories, is selected. Suppose the observed numbers in each category are $O_1, O_2, \ldots, O_K$. If a null hypothesis (H_0) specifies probabilities $P_1, P_2, \ldots, P_K$ for an observation falling into each of these categories, the expected numbers in the categories, under H_0, would be as follows:

$$E_i = nP_i \quad \text{for } i = 1, 2, \ldots, K \tag{14.1}$$

If the null hypothesis is true and the sample size is large enough that the expected values are at least 5, then the random variable associated with

$$\chi^2 = \sum_{i=1}^{K} \frac{(O_i - E_i)^2}{E_i} \tag{14.2}$$

is known as a **chi-square random variable**, and has, to a good approximation, a chi-square distribution with $(K - 1)$ degrees of freedom.

Intuitively, the number of degrees of freedom follows from the fact that the O_i must sum to n. Hence, if the number of sample members, n, and the numbers of observations falling in any $K - 1$ of the categories are known, then the number in the Kth category is also known. The null hypothesis will be rejected when the observed numbers differ substantially from the expected numbers—that is, for unusually large values of the statistic in Equation 14.2. The appropriate goodness-of-fit test follows.

A Goodness-of-Fit Test: Specified Probabilities

A **goodness-of-fit test with specified probabilites**, of significance level α, of H_0 against the alternative that the specified probabilities are not correct is based on the decision rule

$$\text{reject } H_0 \text{ if } \sum_{i=1}^{K} \frac{(O_i - E_i)^2}{E_i} > \chi^2_{K-1,\alpha}$$

where $\chi^2_{K-1,\alpha}$ is the number for which

$$P(\chi^2_{K-1} > \chi^2_{K-1,\alpha}) = \alpha$$

and the random variable χ^2_{K-1} follows a chi-square distribution with $K - 1$ degrees of freedom.

To illustrate this test, consider again the data of Table 14.3 on brand selection. The null hypothesis is that the probabilities are the same for the three categories. The test of this hypothesis is based on the following:

$$\chi^2 = \sum_{i=1}^{3} \frac{(O_i - E_i)^2}{E_i} = \frac{(75 - 100)^2}{100} + \frac{(110 - 100)^2}{100} + \frac{(115 - 100)^2}{100} = 9.50$$

There are three $(K = 3)$ categories, so $K - 1 = 2$ degrees of freedom are associated with the chi-square distribution. From Appendix Table 7,

$$\chi^2_{2,0.01} = 9.210$$

Therefore, according to our decision rule, the null hypothesis is rejected at the 1% significance level. These data contain strong evidence against the hypothesis that a randomly chosen subject is equally likely to select any of the three soft drink brands.

Example 14.1 Do Customers Have a Preference for Any of Four Hershey Chocolate Bars? (Chi-Square)

Suppose that the Hershey Company wants to determine if customers have a preference for any of the following four candy bars: A, Mr. Goodbar; B, Hershey's Milk Chocolate; C, Hershey's Special Dark Mildly Sweet Chocolate; or D, Krackel. From a random sample of 200 people, it was found that 43 preferred Mr. Goodbar; 53 preferred Hershey's Milk Chocolate; 60 preferred Hershey's Special Dark Mildly Sweet Chocolate, and the remainder preferred Krackel. Test the null hypothesis that customers have no preference for any of the four candy bars against the alternative hypothesis that customers have a preference for at least one of the candy bars.

Solution The null hypothesis states that customers have *no preference* for any of the four candy bars (A, B, C, and D). That is, all four candy bars are equally preferred:

$$H_0 : P_A = P_B = P_C = P_D = 0.25$$

Since the null hypothesis states that each candy bar is preferred by 25% of the customers, it follows that each of the expected values will be 50:

$$E_i = nP_i = 200(0.25) = 50$$

The chi-square test statistic is calculated in Table 14.5.

Table 14.5 Do Customers Have a Preference for Any of Four Hershey Chocolate Bars?

Type of Candy Bar	O_i	E_i	$(O_i - E_i)$	$(O_i - E_i)^2$	$(O_i - E_i)^2 / E_i$
A. Mr. Goodbar	43	50	−7	49	49/50 = 0.98
B. Hershey's Milk Chocolate	53	50	3	9	9/50 = 0.18
C. Hershey's Special Dark	60	50	10	100	100/50 = 2.00
D. Krackel	44	50	−6	36	36/50 = 0.72
					$\chi^2 = 3.88$

The chi-square test statistic is $\chi^2 = \Sigma[(O_i - E_i)^2 / E_i] = 3.88$. From Appendix Table 7 with df $= K - 1 = 3$, we find that the test statistic falls between 0.584 and 6.251; it follows that $0.10 < p$-value < 0.90. We fail to reject the null hypothesis and conclude that the data are not statistically significant to conclude that customers have a preference for at least one of these candy bars. We must be careful not to conclude that all four candy bars are equally preferred; we can state only that the evidence does not support a preference.

Another marketing question that Hershey might address concerns whether the current customer preferences differ from historically known preferences.

Example 14.2 Is There a Change in Customer Preferences? (Chi-Square)

From historical data, such as sales records, the Hershey Company knows that 30% of its customers prefer Mr. Goodbar, 50% prefer Hershey's Milk Chocolate, 15% prefer Hershey's Special Dark Mildly Sweet Chocolate, and the remainder prefer Krackel. Suppose that marketing analysts sample 200 people and find that 50 prefer Mr. Goodbar, 93 prefer Hershey's Milk Chocolate, 45 prefer Hershey's Special Dark Mildly Sweet Chocolate, and the remainder prefers Krackel. Have current preferences for these products changed from the known preferences?

Solution The null hypothesis is that current customer preferences follow the same pattern. That is, the customer preferences do not differ from that known to the Hershey Company:

$$H_0 : P_A = 0.30; P_B = 0.50; P_C = 0.15; P_D = 0.05$$

The expected number of customers who prefer Mr. Goodbar is as follows:

$$E_A = nP_A = 200(0.30) = 60$$

The expected number of customers who prefer each of the other candy bars is computed similarly and the test statistic (Table 14.6) is found to be as follows:

$$\chi^2 = \sum_{i=1}^{K} \frac{(O_i - E_i)^2}{E_i} = 10.06$$

Table 14.6 Have Customer Preferences Changed?

TYPE OF CANDY BAR	O_i	E_i	$(O_i - E_i)$	$(O_i - E_i)^2$	$(O - E_i)^2/E_i$
A. Mr. Goodbar	50	60	−10	100	100/60 = 1.67
B. Hershey's Milk Chocolate	93	100	−7	49	49/100 = 0.49
C. Hershey's Special Dark	45	30	15	225	225/30 = 7.50
D. Krackel	12	10	2	4	4/10 = 0.40
					$\chi^2 = 10.06$

From Appendix Table 7 with df $= K - 1 = 3$, we find that the test statistic falls between 9.348 and 11.345; it follows that $0.01 < p\text{-value} < 0.025$.

We reject the null hypothesis and conclude that the data provide considerable evidence to suggest that current customer preferences differ from the given pattern of preferences. Market researchers could now look into the specific differences and recommend appropriate marketing strategies.

Example 14.3 Gas Company (Chi-Square)

A gas company has determined from past experience that at the end of winter 80% of its accounts are fully paid, 10% are 1 month in arrears, 6% are 2 months in arrears, and 4% are more than 2 months in arrears. At the end of this winter the company checked a random sample of 400 of its accounts, finding 287 to be fully paid, 49 to be 1 month in arrears, 30 to be 2 months in arrears, and 34 to be more than 2 months in arrears. Do these data suggest that the pattern of previous years is not being followed this winter?

Solution Under the null hypothesis that the proportions in the present winter conform to the historical record, the respective probabilities for the four categories are 0.80, 0.10, 0.06, and 0.04. Under that hypothesis the expected numbers of accounts in each category, for a random sample of 400 accounts, would be as follows:

$$400(0.80) = 320; \quad 400(0.10) = 40; \quad 400(0.06) = 24; \quad 400(0.04) = 16$$

The observed and expected numbers are as follows:

NUMBER OF MONTHS IN ARREARS	0	1	2	MORE THAN 2	TOTAL
Observed number	287	49	30	34	400
Probability (under H_0)	0.80	0.10	0.06	0.04	1
Expected number (under H_0)	320	40	24	16	400

The test of the null hypothesis (H_0) is based on the following:

$$\chi^2 = \sum_{i=1}^{4} \frac{(O_i - E_i)^2}{E_i} = \frac{(287 - 320)^2}{320} + \frac{(49 - 40)^2}{40} + \frac{(30 - 24)^2}{24} + \frac{(34 - 16)^2}{16}$$

$$= 27.178$$

Here there are $K = 4$ categories, so there are $K - 1 = 3$ degrees of freedom. From Appendix Table 7 we have the following:

$$\chi^2_{3, 0.001} = 16.266$$

Since 27.178 is much larger than 16.266, the null hypothesis is very clearly rejected, even at the 0.1% significance level. Certainly, these data provide considerable evidence to suspect that the pattern of payments of gas bills this year differs from the historical norm. Inspection of the numbers in the table shows that more accounts are in arrears over a longer time period than is usually the case.

A word of caution is in order. The values used in calculating the test statistic in Equation 14.2 must be the observed and expected numbers in each category. It is not correct, for example, to use the percentages of sample members in each category instead.

EXERCISES

Application Exercises

14.1 A business manager wants to improve employee satisfaction in his company. He asked a random sample of 100 employees from four departments if they were satisfied with the working conditions of the company. The results obtained are shown in the following table. Test the null hypothesis that for this population their satisfaction are evenly distributed over the four departments.

Department	Sales	Marketing	Human Resources	IT
Satisfaction	41	19	24	16

14.2 Campbell's Soup Company is going to produce a new flavor for their soup product. They conducted a survey to ask users to vote on their favorite soup flavor. It found that 40% voted for creamy seafood, 35% voted for tom yam chicken, and the remaining voted for herbal chicken. Campbell's invited 150 testers to a soup testing campaign and found that 75 preferred creamy seafood, 30 preferred tom yam chicken, and the rest preferred herbal chicken. Based on the data, can Campbell's conclude that the preferences in the survey are the same when compared with the campaign at the 5% level?

14.3 Assume the 2018 enrollment records for Stockholm University showed that 55% of applicants were for the business program, 25% for the science program, 10% for the law program, and the rest for other programs. In the current enrollment record, the university found that out of 1,500 enrollments, 850 are for the business program, 350 for the science program, 155 for the law program, and the rest for other programs.

a. Explain why goodness-of-fit test is suitable to use for the above situation.

b. State the null and alternative hypothesis for conducting a goodness-of-fit test.

c. Are the enrollments for the previous and the current enrollment record the same at the 1% level? Give a reason for your conclusion.

14.4 Anna Sui is a fashion designer known for her innovative packaging and product designs like those for her fragrance collection. According to the brand, 65% of its customers prefer the design of Sui Love, 20% prefer Peace and Love, and 15% prefer Dolly Girl. From a random sample of 400 consumers, 250 chose the Sui Love bottle design; 95 chose Peace and Love; and 55 selected Dolly Girl. Test, at the 5% level, the null hypothesis that consumer preferences conform to the claims made by Anna Sui.

14.5 TMaker is a Malaysian t-shirt printing and design company. Each month it receives orders for each size—10% for large, 55% for medium, and 35% for small. The company wants to compare the proportion of sizes ordered to the number of t-shirts printed. The observed number of printed t-shirts were 385 large t-shirts, 907 medium, and 708 small. Test at the 10% level to help TMaker determine whether there is any difference in the number of t-shirts printed in proportion to t-shirts ordered.

14.6 Steven and his friends are playing a board game that involves rolling two dice. He is interested in the number of times a 6 is rolled. Based on each player's records, he found that 52 rolls did not get a 6; 43 rolls produce one 6; and five rolls get a 6 twice. By using the binomial distribution, Steven estimated that 69% of the rolls did not get a 6, 28% produce one, and about 3% produce a 6 twice. Does the data show Steven's estimated pattern for the number of times a 6 is thrown at the 1% level?

14.7   Several types of puddings are sold in a small general store in London. From a past study of customer selections, the owner knows that 25% of the customers ordered strawberry pudding; 30% ordered chocolate; 19% ordered lemon; 12% ordered mango; and the remainder, vanilla. Now the owner, who thinks customer preferences have changed, uses a random sample of 80 customers to find that 17 prefer strawberry, 17 prefer chocolate, 30 prefer lemon, 7 prefer vanilla, and the remainder prefer mango. Determine if the customers' preferences have changed from the last study.

14.8   The chef of Brew'd café is calculating the cost of baking a cake. He pays $2 for sugar, $1.30 for flour, $5.80 for butter, $3.20 for milk, and $10 for labor cost. The past records indicate that 11% of his total costs was for sugar, 4% for flour, 21% for butter, 16% for milk, and the remaining for labor. Does the data indicate that the costs today differ from those of the previous month?

14.9   The cafeteria at the University of Barcelona, Spain, hired a group of analysts to determine the pizza best liked by students enrolled in the university. Two years ago a similar study was conducted, and it was found that 35% of all students at the university preferred La Pizzateca, 25% chose Grosso Napoletano, 15% selected Massa Pizza, and the rest selected Picsa. A random sample of 180 students were asked to indicate their pizza preferences. The results were as follows: 42 selected Massa Pizza, 33 chose Picsa, 80 preferred La Pizzateca, and the remainder selected Grosso Napoletano. Do the data indicate that the preferences today differ from those from the last study?

14.10 In a blood donation camp, out of 168 donors, 57 are of blood type O; 77 are blood type A; 25 are blood type B; and 9 are blood type AB. The expected distribution in the entire population is 43% for type O, 41% for type A, 11% for type B, and 5% for type AB. Is there any significant difference between the types of blood donors in the sample and those in the entire camp? Use a 5% level of significance.

14.2 GOODNESS-OF-FIT TESTS: POPULATION PARAMETERS UNKNOWN

In Section 14.1 the hypothesis concerned data that are generated by a *fully specified* probability distribution. The null hypothesis in this test specifies the probability that a sample observation will fall in any category. However, it is often required to test the hypothesis that data are generated by some distribution, such as the binomial, the Poisson, or the normal, without assuming the parameters of that distribution to be known. In these circumstances Section 14.1 is not applicable, but the available data can be used to estimate the unknown population parameters. The goodness-of-fit test used when population parameters are estimated is stated next.

Goodness-of-Fit Tests When Population Parameters Are Estimated

Suppose that a null hypothesis specifies category probabilities that depend on the estimation (from the data) of m unknown population parameters. The appropriate **goodness-of-fit test with estimated population parameters** is precisely as in Section 14.1, except that the number of degrees of freedom for the chi-square random variable is

$$\text{degrees of freedom} = (K - m - 1) \tag{14.3}$$

where K is the number of categories and m is the number of unknown population parameters.

A Test for the Poisson Distribution

Consider a test to determine if data are generated by the Poisson distribution. One procedure for attempting to resolve questions of disputed authorship is to count the number of occurrences of particular words in blocks of text. These can be compared with results from passages whose authorship is known; often this comparison can be achieved through the assumption that the number of occurrences follows a Poisson distribution. An example of this type of research involves the study of *The Federalist Papers* (Mosteller and Wallace 1964).

Example 14.4 Federalist Papers (Chi-Square)

For a sample of 262 blocks of text (each approximately 200 words in length) from *The Federalist Papers* (Mosteller and Wallace 1964), the mean number of occurrences of the word *may* was 0.66. Table 14.7 shows the observed frequencies of occurrence of this word in the 262 sampled blocks of text. Test the null hypothesis that the population distribution of occurrences is Poisson, without assuming prior knowledge of the mean of this distribution.

Table 14.7   Occurrences of the Word *may* in 262 Blocks of Text in *The Federalist Papers*

NUMBER OF OCCURRENCES	0	1	2	3 OR MORE
Observed frequency	156	63	29	14

Solution Recall that, if the Poisson distribution is appropriate, the probability of x occurrences is

$$P(x) = \frac{e^{-\lambda}\lambda^x}{x!}$$

where λ is the mean number of occurrences. Although this population mean is unknown, it can be estimated by the sample mean 0.66. It is then possible, by substituting 0.66 for λ, to estimate the probability for any number of occurrences under the null hypothesis that the population distribution is Poisson. For example, the probability of two occurrences is as follows:

$$P(2) = \frac{e^{-0.66}(0.66)^2}{2!}$$
$$= \frac{(0.5169)(0.66)^2}{2} = 0.1126$$

Similarly, the probabilities for zero and one occurrence can be found, so the probability of three or more occurrences is as follows:

$$P(X \geq 3) = 1 - P(0) - P(1) - P(2)$$

These probabilities are shown in the second row of Table 14.8.

Table 14.8   Observed and Expected Frequencies for *The Federalist Papers*

NUMBER OF OCCURENCES	0	1	2	3 OR MORE	TOTAL
Observed frequencies	156	63	29	14	262
Probabilities	0.5169	0.3411	0.1126	0.0294	1
Expected frequencies under H_0	135.4	89.4	29.5	7.7	262

Then, exactly as before, the expected frequencies under the null hypothesis are obtained from the following:

$$E_i = nP_i \quad \text{for } i = 1, 2, \ldots, K$$

Thus, for example, the expected frequency of two occurrences of the word *may* in 262 blocks of text is $(262)(0.1126) = 29.5$. Even though the variable itself is an integer, it is best not to round these expected values to integer values. The bottom row of Table 14.8 shows these expected frequencies. The test statistic is then as follows:

$$\chi^2 = \sum_{i=1}^{4} \frac{(O_i - E_i)^2}{E_i} = \frac{(156 - 135.4)^2}{135.4} + \frac{(63 - 89.4)^2}{89.4} + \frac{(29 - 29.5)^2}{29.5} + \frac{(14 - 7.7)^2}{7.7}$$
$$= 16.08$$

Since there are four categories and one parameter has been estimated, the approximate number of degrees of freedom for the test is 2. From Appendix Table 7, we have the following:

$$\chi^2_{2,\,0.001} = 13.816$$

Thus, the null hypothesis that the population distribution is Poisson can be rejected at the 0.1% significance level. The evidence in the data against that hypothesis is, then, very strong indeed.

A Test for the Normal Distribution

The normal distribution plays an important role in statistics, and many practical procedures rely for their validity, or for particular optimality properties, on an assumption that sample data are from a normal distribution. In Chapter 5 we looked at the normal probability plot to check for evidence of nonnormality. Also, in Chapter 7 (Figures 7.2 and 7.9) we visually tested for evidence of nonnormality by determining if the dots in the normal probability plots were "close" to the straight line. Next, we consider a test of the normality assumption through an adaptation of the chi-square procedure. This test is both easy to carry out and likely to be more powerful.

The Jarque-Bera test for normality, which is an adaptation of the chi-square procedure, relies on two descriptive measures, skewness (Equation 14.5) and kurtosis (Equation 14.6). We discussed skewness in both Chapter 1 and in the Chapter 2 appendix. Skewness, a measure of symmetry, is known to be 0 for the normal distribution. Kurtosis provides a measure of the weight in the tails of a probability density function. It is known that for the normal distribution, the population kurtosis is 3. Therefore, the Jarque-Bera test for a normal distribution is based on the closeness to 0 of the sample skewness and the closeness to 3 of the sample kurtosis. The Jarque-Bera test statistic is given in Equation 14.4.

Jarque-Bera Test for Normality

Suppose that we have a random sample $x_1, x_2, \ldots, x_n$ of n observations from a population. The test statistic for the **Jarque-Bera test for normality** is

$$JB = n\left[\frac{(\text{skewness})^2}{6} + \frac{(\text{kurtosis} - 3)^2}{24} \right] \tag{14.4}$$

where using sample information, **skewness** of a population is estimated by

$$\text{skewness} = \frac{\sum_{i=1}^{n}(x_i - \bar{x})^3}{ns^3} \tag{14.5}$$

and **kurtosis** is estimated by

$$\text{kurtosis} = \frac{\sum_{i=1}^{n}(x_i - \bar{x})^4}{ns^4} \tag{14.6}$$

It is known that as the number of sample observations becomes very large, this statistic has, under the null hypothesis that the population distribution is normal, a chi-square distribution with 2 degrees of freedom. The null hypothesis is, of course, rejected for large values of the test-statistic.

Unfortunately, the chi-square approximation to the distribution of the Jarque-Bera test statistic, JB, is close only for very large sample sizes. Table 14.9 (Bera and Jarque 1981) shows significance points appropriate for a range of sample sizes for tests at the 5% and 10% levels. The recommended procedure, then, is to calculate the statistic, JB, in Equation 14.4 and reject the null hypothesis of normality if the test statistic exceeds the appropriate value tabulated in Table 14.9.

Table 14.9 Significance Points of the Jarque–Bera Statistic (Bera and Jarque 1981)

SAMPLE SIZE n	10% POINT	5% POINT	SAMPLE SIZE n	10% POINT	5% POINT
20	2.13	3.26	200	3.48	4.43
30	2.49	3.71	250	3.54	4.51
40	2.70	3.99	300	3.68	4.60
50	2.90	4.26	400	3.76	4.74
75	3.09	4.27	500	3.91	4.82
100	3.14	4.29	800	4.32	5.46
125	3.31	4.34	∞	4.61	5.99
150	3.43	4.39			

Example 14.5 Daily Stock Market Rates of Return (Test of the Normal Distribution)

Daily closing prices of shares of a particular stock for the past year are contained in the data file **Closing Stock Prices**. The sample has $n = 251$ trading days. Compute the daily rates of return and test the null hypothesis that the true distribution for these rates of return is normal.

Solution From the data file **Closing Stock Prices**, we first calculate the daily rates of return, r_i, for each of the $n = 251$ trading days as follows:

$$r_i = \frac{p_i - p_{i-1} + d_i}{p_{i-1}} \quad \text{for } i = 1, \ldots, n \tag{14.7}$$

where p_i is the closing price on day i and d_i is any dividend paid on day i. No dividends were paid in the past year. Once the daily rates of return are calculated, the following intermediate calculations are found:

$$\sum_{i=1}^{251} (r_i - \bar{r})^2 = 0.0835496$$

$$\sum_{i=1}^{251} (r_i - \bar{r})^3 = -0.002158324$$

$$\sum_{i=1}^{251} (r_i - \bar{r})^4 = 0.000329593$$

From Equation 14.5, skewness is calculated as follows:

$$\text{skewness} = \frac{\sum_{i=1}^{n}(r_i - \bar{r})^3}{ns^3} = \frac{-0.002158324}{251(0.00000610951)} \cong -1.41$$

and by Equation 14.6, kurtosis is as follows:

$$\text{kurtosis} = \frac{\sum_{i=1}^{n}(r_i - \bar{r})^4}{ns^4} = \frac{0.000329593}{251(0.000000111688)} \cong 11.76$$

Next, we find the Jarque-Bera test statistic, JB:

$$JB \cong 251\left[\frac{(-1.41)^2}{6} + \frac{(8.76)^2}{24}\right] \cong 886$$

Comparison of this result with the significance points in Table 14.9 certainly provides ground to think that the population distribution is not normal.

It is often the case with real data that questions arise concerning unusual data points, such as the outlier seen in the normal probability plot in Figure 14.1. So what can we say about that point? Did it really happen or was there a recording error? Except for this outlier, the other rates of return fluctuate between −0.05 and +0.05. If no recording error occurred, analysts would look for extenuating circumstances or very unusual conditions that might lead to this unusually low rate of return.

Figure 14.1 Daily Rates of Return (Probability Plot)

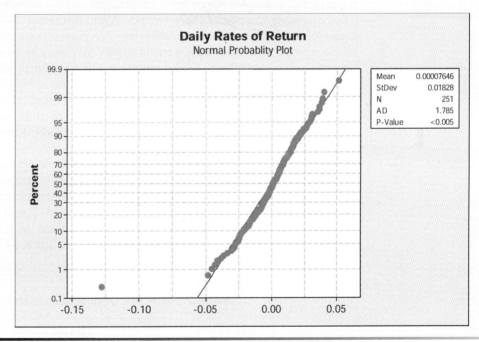

Skewness and kurtosis are included in the standard output of most statistical software packages; however, it is possible that an alternative formula may be used to compute these descriptive measures. Other nonparametric tests of normality such as the Kolmogorov-Smirnov test, Anderson-Darling test, Ryan-Joiner test, Shapiro-Wilk test, and the Lilliefors test are beyond the scope of this book.

Basic Exercises

14.11 The number of times a machine broke down each week was observed over a period of 100 weeks and recorded in the accompanying table. It was found that the average number of breakdowns per week over this period was 2.4. Test at the 10% level the null hypothesis that the population distribution of breakdowns is Poisson.

Number of breakdowns	0	1	2	3	4	5 or more
Number of weeks	11	23	33	22	5	6

14.12 In a specific book of 150 pages various typo errors are observed and recorded. The following table shows the number pages and the number of typo errors across the book with an average of 1.5. Test the null hypothesis that it is distributed Poisson.

Number of typo errors per page	0	1	2	3	4 or more
Observed number of pages	46	52	25	11	16

14.13 A random sample of 50 students was asked to estimate how much money they spent on textbooks in a year. The sample skewness of these amounts was found to be 0.47 and the sample kurtosis was 4.14. Test at the 10% level the null hypothesis that the population distribution of amounts spent is normal.

14.14 Australia's traffic department was tracing the speed of different automobiles at one spot on the highway. They found that with a random sample of 125 automobiles, the skewness of the sample was 0.36 and the kurtosis was 2.94. Determine whether the null hypothesis for the population is normally distributed.

14.15 What test is used to determine whether a data set matches a normal distribution? Give two examples of the form of data may use this test.

14.16 A random sample of 50 children appearing for an IQ test was taken. The sample skewness in their IQ results was 0.73 and the sample kurtosis was 1.15. Test the null hypothesis that the IQ results distribution is normal.

14.3 CONTINGENCY TABLES

Suppose that a sample is taken from a population and the members can be uniquely cross-classified according to a pair of characteristics, A and B. The hypothesis to be tested is of no association or dependence in the population between possession of characteristic A and possession of characteristic B. For example, a travel agency may want to know if there is any relationship between a client's gender and the method used to make an airline reservation. An accounting firm may want to examine the relationship between the age of people and the type of income tax return filed by these individuals. Or, perhaps, in a medical study, a pharmaceutical company may want to know if the success of a drug used to control cholesterol depends on a person's weight. A marketing research company may test if a customer's choice of cereal is in some way dependent on the color of the cereal box. Perhaps there is an association between political affiliation and support for a particular amendment that is to appear on the next election's ballot.

Assume that there are r categories for A and c categories for B, so a total of rc cross-classifications is possible. The number of sample observations belonging to both the ith category of A and the jth category of B will be denoted as O_{ij}, where $i = 1, 2, \ldots, r$ and $j = 1, 2, \ldots, c$. Table 14.10 is called an $r \times c$ contingency table. For convenience, row and column totals were added to Table 14.10, denoted respectively as $R_1, R_2, \ldots, R_r$ and $C_1, C_2, \ldots, C_c$.

Table 14.10 Cross-Classification of n Observations in an $r \times c$ Contingency Table

	CHARACTERISTIC B				
Characteristic A	1	2	...	c	Total
1	O_{11}	O_{12}	...	O_{1c}	R_1
2	O_{21}	O_{22}	...	O_{2c}	R_2
⋮	⋮	⋮	...	⋮	⋮
r	O_{r1}	O_{r2}	...	O_{rc}	R_r
Total	C_1	C_2	...	C_c	n

To test the null hypothesis of no association between characteristics A and B, we ask how many observations we would expect to find in each cross-classification if that hypothesis were true. This question becomes meaningful when the row and column totals are *fixed*. Consider, then, the joint classification corresponding to the ith row and jth column of the table. There is a total of C_j observations in the jth column, and, given no association, we would expect each of these column totals to be distributed among the rows in proportion to the total number of observations in each ith row. Thus, we would expect a proportion R_i/n of these C_j observations to be in the ith row. Hence, the estimated expected number of observations in the cross-classifications is

$$E_{ij} = \frac{R_i C_j}{n} \text{ for } i = 1, 2, \ldots, r; j = 1, 2, \ldots, c$$

where R_i and C_j are the corresponding row and column totals.

Our test of the null hypothesis of no association is based on the magnitudes of the discrepancies between the observed numbers and those that would be expected if that hypothesis was true. The random variable given in Equation 14.8 is a generalized version of that introduced in Section 14.1.

Chi-Square Random Variable for Contingency Tables

It can be shown that under the null hypothesis, the random variable associated with

$$\chi^2 = \sum_{i=1}^{r} \sum_{j=1}^{c} \frac{(O_{ij} - E_{ij})^2}{E_{ij}} \tag{14.8}$$

has, to a good approximation, a chi-square distribution with $(r-1)(c-1)$ degrees of freedom. The approximation works well if no more than 20% of the estimated expected numbers E_{ij} is less than 5. Sometimes adjacent classes can be combined in order to meet this assumption.

The double summation in Equation 14.8 implies that the summation extends over all rc cells of the table. Clearly, the null hypothesis of no association will be rejected for large absolute discrepancies between observed and expected numbers—that is, for high values of the statistic in Equation 14.8. The test procedure is summarized as follows.

A Test of Association in Contingency Tables

Suppose that a sample of n observations is cross-classified according to two characteristics in an $r \times c$ contingency table. Denote by O_{ij} the number of observations in the cell that is in the ith row and jth column. If the null hypothesis is H_0: No association exists between the two characteristics in the population, then the estimated expected number of observations in each cell under H_0 is

$$E_{ij} = \frac{R_i C_j}{n} \tag{14.9}$$

where R_i and C_j are the corresponding row and column totals. A **test of association** at a significance level α is based on the following decision rule:

$$\text{reject } H_0 \text{ if } = \sum_{i=1}^{r} \sum_{j=1}^{c} \frac{(O_{ij} - E_{ij})^2}{E_{ij}} > \chi^2_{(r-1)(c-1),\alpha}$$

Example 14.6 Market Differentiation (Test of Association)

When marketers position products or establish new brands, they aim to differentiate their product from its competition. To investigate the consumer's perception, spontaneous associations are frequently used. That means consumers are exposed to different products and asked what comes to their mind when they see or hear of this product. For example, suppose a study was conducted to determine whether "safety" or "sporty" comes to a person's mind when they see or hear of a particular type of automobile: BMW, Mercedes, or Lexus. Associations and products can be organized in a cross table, such as Table 14.11. The number in a cell thereby equals the frequency of a certain combination occurring (e.g., 256 people named BMW as sporty). Use a chi-square test to evaluate whether the products mentioned differ in their associations and are, thus, perceived as dissimilar (which is most likely desired by the marketer).

Table 14.11 Automobile by Consumer Perception

AUTOMOBILE	SPORTY	SAFETY	TOTAL
BMW	256	74	330
Mercedes	41	42	83
Lexus	66	34	100
Total	**363**	**150**	**513**

Solution The null hypothesis to be tested implies that, in the population, the three types of automobiles are perceived as similar; that is, there is no association between the automobile type and customers' perception of the car as being known for being sporty or being known for its safety. To test the null hypothesis of no association, we again ask how many observations we would expect to find in each cross-classification if that hypothesis were true.

For example, if there were no association between these characteristics, the expected number of customers who perceived a BMW as sporty would be as follows:

$$E_{11} = \frac{(330)(363)}{513} = 233.5$$

The other expected numbers are calculated in the same way and are shown in Table 14.12, alongside the corresponding observed numbers.

Table 14.12 Observed (and Expected) Number of Customers in Each Cross-Classification

AUTOMOBILE	SPORTY	SAFETY	TOTAL
BMW	256 (233.5)	74 (96.5)	330
Mercedes	41 (58.7)	42 (24.3)	83
Lexus	66 (70.8)	34 (29.2)	100

The test of the null hypothesis of no association is based on the magnitudes of the discrepancies between the observed numbers and those that would be expected if that hypothesis was true. Extending Equation 14.2 to include each of the six cross-classifications gives the following value of the chi-square test statistic:

$$\chi^2 = \frac{(256 - 233.5)^2}{233.5} + \frac{(74 - 96.5)^2}{96.5} + \frac{(41 - 58.7)^2}{58.7} + \frac{(42 - 24.3)^2}{24.3}$$

$$+ \frac{(66 - 70.8)^2}{70.8} + \frac{(34 - 29.2)^2}{29.2} = 26.8$$

The degrees of freedom are $(r - 1)(c - 1)$. Here, there are $r = 3$ rows and $c = 2$ columns in the table, so the appropriate number of degrees of freedom is as follows:

$$(r - 1)(c - 1) = (3 - 1)(2 - 1) = 2$$

From Appendix Table 7, we find the following:

$$\chi^2_{2, 0.001} = 13.816$$

Therefore, the null hypothesis of no association is very clearly rejected, even at the 0.1% level. The evidence against this hypothesis is overwhelming.

It should be noted, as was the case for the goodness-of-fit tests in earlier sections, that the figures used in calculating the statistic must be the *actual numbers* observed and not, for example, percentages of the total.

Example 14.7 Sarbanes-Oxley Act of 2002 (Test of Association)

Regulatory agencies and the U.S. Congress are recognizing both the values and emerging issues for small firms as the Sarbanes-Oxley Act of 2002 (SOX) is implemented. On April 23, 2006, the Advisory Committee on Smaller Public Companies issued a final report to the Security and Exchange Commission assessing the impact of the Sarbanes-Oxley Act of 2002 on smaller public companies (Final Report of the Advisory Committee on Smaller Public Companies to the U.S. Securities and Exchange Commission, April 23, 2006). In Exercise 1.54 we introduced a study that was conducted among a random sample of CEOs, CFOs, and board members of corporations since the implementation of the Sarbanes-Oxley Act of 2002 (Michelson, Stryker and Thorne 2009). Based on the data contained in Table 14.13, is there an association between the firm's opinion as to the overall impact of Sarbanes-Oxley implementation and the firm's size?

Table 14.13   Overall Impact of Sarbanes-Oxley Implementation and Size of the Firm

IMPACT OF SOX	SMALL FIRMS	MEDIUM SIZE FIRMS	LARGE FIRMS
Little or no impact	17	13	6
Moderate to very major impact	13	41	22

Solution   In this study the size of the firm was measured by annual revenue, not number of employees or some other factor. Small firms are corporations with annual revenue not exceeding $250 million; large firms had annual revenue above $750 million. We calculate each of the expected number of firms for each cell as

$$E_{11} = \frac{(36)(30)}{112} = 9.64$$

and then use Equation 14.8 to obtain a test statistic of 11.358. With 2 degrees of freedom and $\chi^2_{2, 0.01} = 9.210$ (Appendix Table 7), we conclude that the p-value < 0.01 and that the data are statistically significant to believe that there is an association between opinion on the overall impact of the Sarbanes-Oxley Act of 2002 and the size of the firm. From Figure 14.2 (obtained using SPSS), we see the same conclusion with p-value $= 0.003$.

Figure 14.2 Overall Impact of Sarbanes-Oxley Act of 2002 by Size of Firm (SPSS)

Overall Impact of SOX			Small	Medium	Large	Total
			Size			Total
Little or no impact		Count	17	13	6	36
		Expected count	9.6	17.4	9.0	36.0
Major impact		Count	13	41	22	76
		Expected count	20.4	36.6	19.0	76.0
Total		Count	30	28	54	112

chi-Square Tests

	Value	df	Asymp. Sig. (2-sided)
Pearson Chi-Square	**11.358(a)**	2	.003
Likelihood Ratio	10.900	2	.004
Linear-by-Linear Association	7.907	1	.005
N of Valid Cases	112		

a 0 cells (.0%) have expected count less than 5. The minimum expected count is 9.00.

Although the use of the chi-square test for association may indicate that there is a relationship between two variables, this procedure does not indicate the direction or strength of the relationship.

EXERCISES

Visit www.MyStatLab.com or www.pearsonglobal editions.com to access the data files.

Application Exercises

14.17 The **Baby Walking** data file contains information on 98 babies about several variables concerning their birth and first steps. One of the variables measured is the "first walk timeline", coded as 1 = soon (up to 9 months old), 2 = regular (between 10 and 13 months old), and 3 = late (14 months or older). The following table shows the baby's first walk timeline by gender. Determine if there is an association between a baby's first walk and gender.

First walk	Male	Female
Soon	2	4
Regular	43	26
Late	11	12

14.18 University administrators have collected the following information concerning student grade point average and the school of the student's major.

Determine if there is any association between GPA and major.

School	GPA < 3.0	GPA 3.0 or Higher
Arts and Sciences	50	35
Business	45	30
Music	15	25

14.19 An increasing number of public school districts are utilizing the iPad as a teaching tool. Suppose Calandlyceum, a high school in Amsterdam, recently distributed 47 iPads to the students and teachers in two humanities classes, with expectations that in time all 1,100 students will be provided with iPads (Hu 2011). Educators are divided on their opinion as to the academic benefit of iPads. Much research is needed to determine if iPads are an enhancement to learning or just another technological fad. Assume that a random sample of high school teachers (math, history, science, and language teachers) were surveyed and asked, Do you think the iPad will enhance learning? Determine if there is an association between the subject taught and the response to this question.

	iPad Enhances Learning?	
Subject	Yes	No
Math	71	39
History	70	20
Science	40	60
Language	60	40

14.20 How do customers first hear about a new product? A random sample of 200 users of a new product was surveyed to determine the answer to this question. Other demographic data such as age were also collected. The respondents included 50 people under the age of 21 and 90 people between the ages of 21 and 35; the remainder was over 35 years of age. Of those under 21, 60% heard about the product from a friend, and the remainder saw an advertisement in the local paper. One-third of the people in the age category from 21 to 35 saw the advertisement in the local paper. The other two-thirds heard about it from a friend. Of those over 35, only 30% heard about it from a friend, while the remainder saw the local newspaper advertisement. Set up the contingency table for the variables age and method of learning about the product. Is there an association between the consumer's age and the method by which the customer heard about the new product?

14.21 In January 2019, local organizations in Nigeria held several presidential debates before the general elections in February. Suppose after one debate related to the main presidential candidates—Muhammadu Buhari and Atiku Abubakar—the Nigerians were asked how they might vote in the forthcoming election. At the 5% significance level, is there any association between the voter's gender and the choice of candidate?

	Gender	
Candidate Preference	Male	Female
Buhari	300	280
Abubakar	200	220

14.4 NONPARAMETRIC TESTS FOR PAIRED OR MATCHED SAMPLES

The simplest nonparametric test to carry out is the **sign test**. It is most frequently employed in testing hypotheses about analyzing data from paired or matched samples. The sign test is used in market research studies to determine if consumer preference exists for one of two products. Since respondents simply name their preference, the data are nominal and lend themselves to nonparametric procedures. The sign test is also useful to test the median of a population.

Sign Test for Paired or Matched Samples

Suppose that paired or matched samples are taken from a population and the differences equal to 0 are discarded, leaving n observations. The sign test can be used to test the null hypothesis that the population median of the differences is 0 (which would be true, for example, if the differences came from a population whose distribution was symmetric about a mean of 0). Let $+$ indicate a positive difference and $-$ indicate a negative difference. If the null hypothesis were true, our sequence of $+$ and $-$ differences could be regarded as a random sample from a population in which the probabilities for $+$ and $-$ were each 0.5. In that case, the observations would constitute a random sample from a binomial population in which the probability of $+$ was 0.5. Thus, if P denotes the true proportion of $+$ signs in the population (that is, the true proportion of positive differences), the null hypothesis is simply

$$H_0 : P = 0.5$$

The sign test is then based on the fact that the number of positive observations, S, in the sample has a binomial distribution (with $P = 0.5$ under the null hypothesis).

Sign Test

Suppose that paired or matched random samples are taken from a population and the differences equal to 0 are discarded, leaving n observations. Calculate the difference for each pair of observations and record the sign of this difference. The **sign test** is used to test

$$H_0 : P = 0.5$$

where P is the proportion of nonzero observations in the population that are positive. The test statistic S for the sign test for paired samples is simply

$$S = \text{the number of pairs with a positive difference}$$

where S has a binomial distribution with $P = 0.5$ and $n =$ the number of nonzero differences.

After determining the null and alternative hypotheses and finding a test statistic, the next step is to determine the p-value and draw conclusions based on a decision rule.

Determining p-Value for a Sign Test

The p-value for a sign test is found using the binomial distribution with $n =$ number of nonzero differences, $S =$ number of positive differences, and $P = 0.5$.

a. For an upper-tail test

$$H_1 : P > 0.5 \quad p\text{-value} = P(x \geq S) \tag{14.10}$$

b. For a lower-tail test

$$H_1 : P < 0.5 \quad p\text{-value} = P(x \leq S) \tag{14.11}$$

c. For a two-tail test, let $S = \max(S_+, S_-)$, where S_+ is the number of positive differences and S_- is the number of negative differences. Then,

$$H_1 : P \neq 0.5 \quad p\text{-value} = 2P(x \geq S) \tag{14.12}$$

Example 14.8 Product Preference (Sign Test)

An Italian restaurant close to a college campus contemplated a new recipe for the sauce used on its pizza. A random sample of eight students was chosen, and each was asked to rate the tastes of the original sauce and the proposed new one on a scale of 1 to 10. The scores of the taste comparison are shown in Table 14.14, with higher numbers indicating a greater liking of the product.

Do the data indicate an overall tendency to prefer the new pizza sauce over the original pizza sauce?

Solution Also shown in Table 14.14 are the differences in the scores for every taster and the signs of these differences. Thus, + is assigned if the original product is preferred, − if the new product is preferred, and 0 if the two products are rated equally. In this particular experiment, two tasters preferred the original pizza sauce, five preferred the new recipe, and one rated them equal.

The null hypothesis of interest is that in the population at large, there is no overall tendency to prefer one product to the other. In assessing this hypothesis, we compare the numbers expressing a preference for each product, discarding those who rated the products equally. In the present example, the values for taster G are omitted in further analysis, and the effective sample size is reduced to $n = 7$. The only sample information on which our test is based is that two of the seven tasters preferred the original product. Hence, the test statistic is $S = 2$.

Table 14.14 Student Ratings for Pizza Sauce

| | RATING | | | |
STUDENT	ORIGINAL PIZZA SAUCE	NEW PIZZA SAUCE	DIFFERENCE (ORIGINAL − NEW)	SIGN OF DIFFERENCE
A	6	8	−2	−
B	4	9	−5	−
C	5	4	1	+
D	8	7	1	+
E	3	9	−6	−
F	6	9	−3	−
G	7	7	0	0
H	5	9	−4	−

The null hypothesis can be viewed as the hypothesis that the population median of the differences is 0. If the null hypothesis were true, our sequence of + and − differences could be regarded as a random sample from a population in which the probabilities for + and − were each 0.5. In that case, the observations would constitute a random sample from a binomial population in which the probability of + was 0.5. Thus, if P denotes the true proportion of + signs in the population (that is, the true proportion of the population that prefers the original pizza sauce), the null hypothesis is simply as follows:

$H_0 : P = 0.5$ There is no overall tendency to prefer one sauce to the other.

A one-tailed test is used to determine if there is an overall tendency to prefer the new pizza sauce to the original pizza sauce. The alternative of interest is that in the population the majority of preferences are for the new product. This alternative is expressed as follows:

$H_1 : P < 0.5$ Fewer than 50% prefer the old pizza sauce.

Next, we find the probability of observing a sample result as extreme as or more extreme than that found if the null hypothesis were, in fact, true. This value is the p-value of the test. If we denote by $P(x)$ the probability of observing x "successes" (+) in $n = 7$ binomial trials, each with probability of success 0.5, then the cumulative binomial probability of observing two or fewer + signs can be obtained by Appendix Table 3. Thus, the p-value is as follows:

$$p\text{-value} = P(x \le 2) = 0.227$$

With a p-value this large, we are unable to reject the null hypothesis, and we conclude that the data are not sufficient to suggest that the students have a preference for the new sauce. Similarly, we could have said that if we adopt the decision rule reject H_0 if two or fewer + signs occur in the sample, then the probability is 0.227 that the null hypothesis will be rejected when it is, in fact, true. Hence, such a test has a p-value of 22.7%. Since the p-value is the smallest significance level at which the null hypothesis can be rejected, for the present example the null hypothesis can be rejected at 22.7% or higher. It is unlikely that we would be willing to accept such a high significance level. Again, we conclude that the data are not statistically significant to recommend a change in the pizza sauce. Perhaps our decision is a consequence of our having such a small number of sample observations.

Wilcoxon Signed Rank Test for Paired or Matched Samples

One disadvantage of the sign test is that it takes into account only a very limited amount of information—namely, the signs of the differences. For example, in Table 14.14 the sign test simply records which product is preferred, *ignoring the strengths of the preferences*. When the sample size is small, it might be suspected that the test would not be very powerful. The Wilcoxon signed rank test provides a method for incorporating information about the magnitude of the differences between matched pairs. It is still a distribution-free test. Like many nonparametric tests, it is based on *ranks*.

The Wilcoxon Signed Rank Test for Paired Samples

The **Wilcoxon signed rank test** can be employed when a random sample of matched pairs of observations is available. Assume that the population distribution of the differences in these paired samples is symmetric and that we want to test the null hypothesis that this distribution is centered at 0. Discarding pairs for which the difference is 0, we rank the remaining n absolute differences in ascending order, with ties assigned the average of the ranks they occupy. The sums of the ranks corresponding to positive and negative differences are calculated, and the smaller of these sums is the Wilcoxon signed rank statistic T—that is,

$$T = \min(T_+, T_-)$$

(14.13)

where

T_+ = sum of the positive ranks
T_- = sum of the negative ranks
n = number of nonzero differences

The null hypothesis is rejected if T is less than or equal to the value in Appendix Table 10.

Example 14.9 Product Preference (Wilcoxon Signed Rank Test)

Consider again Example 14.8, the student ratings for pizza sauce. Use the Wilcoxon signed rank test to determine if the data indicate an overall tendency to prefer the new pizza sauce to the original pizza sauce.

Solution As with the sign test, we ignore any difference of 0, so taster G is removed from the study and the sample size is reduced to $n = 7$. The nonzero absolute differences are then ranked in ascending order of magnitude. That is, the smallest absolute value is given a rank of 1. If two or more values are equal, they are assigned the average of the next available ranks. In our example the two smallest absolute differences are equal. The rank assigned to them is, therefore, the average of ranks 1 and 2—that is, 1.5. The next absolute value is assigned rank 3, and so on. We rank all differences and obtain Table 14.15.

The ranks for positive and negative differences are summed separately. The smaller of these sums is the Wilcoxon signed rank statistic T. Here, $T = 3$.

We now suppose that the population distribution of the paired differences is symmetric. The null hypothesis to be tested is that the center of this distribution is 0. In our example, then, we are assuming that differences in the ratings of the two products have a symmetric distribution, and we want to test whether that distribution is centered on 0—that is, no difference between ratings. We would be suspicious of the null hypothesis

Table 14.15 Calculation of Wilcoxon Test Statistic for Taste Preference Data

TASTER	DIFFERENCE	RANK (+)	RANK (−)
A	−2		3
B	−5		6
C	1	1.5	
D	1	1.5	
E	−6		7
F	−3		4
G	0		
H	−4		5
		Rank sum 3	25

Wilcoxon signed rank statistic T = minimum $(3, 25)$ = 3

if the sum of the ranks for positive differences were very different from that for negative differences. Hence, the null hypothesis will be rejected for low values of the statistic T.

Cutoff points for the distribution of this random variable are given in Appendix Table 10 for tests against a one-sided alternative that the population distribution of the paired differences is specified either to be centered on some number greater than 0 or to be centered on some number less than 0. For sample size n, Table 10 shows, for selected probabilities α, the number T_α such that $P(T \leq T_\alpha) = \alpha$. For example, if we let $\alpha = 0.05$, we read in the table for $n = 7$ that $P(T \leq 4) = 0.05$. Since the Wilcoxon signed rank test statistic is $T = 3$, the null hypothesis is rejected against the one-sided alternative at the 5% level. It appears likely that, overall, ratings are higher for the new product.

Normal Approximation to the Sign Test

As a consequence of the central limit theorem, the normal distribution can be used to approximate the binomial distribution if the sample size is large. Experts differ on the exact definition of "large." We suggest that the normal approximation is acceptable if the sample size exceeds 20. A continuity correction factor in the test statistic compensates for estimating discrete data with a continuous distribution and provides a closer approximation to the p-value.

The Sign Test: Normal Approximation (Large Samples)

If the number n of nonzero sample observations is large, then the sign test is based on the *normal approximation* to the binomial with the following mean and standard deviation:

$$\text{mean: } \mu = np = 0.5n;$$

$$\text{standard deviation: } \sigma = \sqrt{np(1-p)} = \sqrt{0.25n} = 0.5\sqrt{n}$$

The test statistic is

$$Z = \frac{S^* - \mu}{\sigma} = \frac{S^* - 0.5n}{0.5\sqrt{n}} \tag{14.14}$$

where S^* is the test statistic corrected for continuity, defined as follows:

a. For a two-tail test:

$$S^* = S + 0.5 \text{ if } S < \mu \quad \text{or} \quad S^* = S - 0.5 \text{ if } S > \mu \tag{14.15}$$

b. For an upper-tail test:

$$S^* = S - 0.5 \tag{14.16}$$

c. For a lower-tail test:

$$S^* = S + 0.5 \tag{14.17}$$

Example 14.10 Ice Cream (Sign Test: Normal Approximation)

A random sample of 100 children was asked to compare two new ice cream flavors—peanut butter ripple and bubblegum surprise. Fifty-six sample members preferred peanut butter ripple, 40 preferred bubblegum surprise, and 4 expressed no preference. Use the *normal approximation* to determine if there is an overall preference for either flavor.

Solution To test if there is an overall preference in this population for one flavor over the other, the hypotheses are as follows:

$$H_0: P = 0.5 \quad \text{Children have no preference for either flavor.}$$

$$H_1: P \neq 0.5 \quad \text{Children have a preference for one flavor.}$$

Let P be the population proportion that prefers bubblegum surprise, giving $S = 40$ (we could just as well have chosen P to be the population proportion that prefers peanut butter ripple, with $S = 56$). Using Equations 14.14 and 14.15,

$$\mu = np = 0.5n = 0.5(96) = 48$$

$$\sigma = 0.5\sqrt{96} = 4.899$$

$$z = \frac{S^* - \mu}{\sigma} = \frac{40.5 - 48}{4.899} = -1.53 \quad \text{since} \quad 40 < 48, S^* = 40.5$$

From the standard normal distribution, it follows that the approximate p-value $= 2(0.0630) = 0.126$. Hence, the null hypothesis can be rejected at all significance levels greater than 12.6%. If no continuity correction factor is used, the value Z becomes $Z = -1.633$, giving a slightly smaller p-value of 0.1024.

Normal Approximation to the Wilcoxon Signed Rank Test

When the number n of nonzero differences in the sample is large ($n > 20$), the normal distribution provides a good approximation to the distribution of the Wilcoxon statistic T under the null hypothesis that the population differences are centered on 0. When this hypothesis is true, the mean and variance of this distribution are given in Equations 14.18 and 14.19.

The Wilcoxon Signed Rank Test: Normal Approximation (Large Samples)

Under the null hypothesis that the population differences are centered on 0, the Wilcoxon signed rank test has mean and variance given by

$$E(T) = \mu_T = \frac{n(n+1)}{4} \tag{14.18}$$

and

$$Var(T) = \sigma_T^2 = \frac{n(n + 1)(2n + 1)}{24} \tag{14.19}$$

Then, for large n, the distribution of the random variable, Z, is approximately standard normal where

$$Z = \frac{T - \mu_T}{\sigma_T} \tag{14.20}$$

If the number, n, of nonzero differences is large and T is the observed value of the Wilcoxon statistic, then the following tests have significance level α.

1. If the alternative hypothesis is one-sided, reject the null hypothesis if

$$\frac{T - \mu_T}{\sigma_T} < -z_\alpha$$

2. If the alternative hypothesis is two-sided, reject the null hypothesis if

$$\frac{T - \mu_T}{\sigma_T} < -z_{\alpha/2}$$

Example 14.11 Postaudit Procedures (Wilcoxon Signed Rank Test)

Suppose that a study compared firms with and without sophisticated postaudit procedures. A random sample of 31 matched pairs of firms was examined. For each firm the ratio of market valuation to replacement cost of assets was computed as a measure of firm performance. In each of the 31 pairs, one firm employed sophisticated postaudit procedures and the other did not. The 31 differences in ratios were calculated, and the absolute differences were ranked. The smaller of the rank sums, 189, was for those pairs where the ratio was higher for the firm without sophisticated postaudit procedures. Test the null hypothesis that the distribution of differences in ratios is centered on 0 against the alternative that the ratio of market valuation to replacement cost of assets tends to be lower for firms without sophisticated postaudit procedures

Solution Given a random sample of $n = 31$ matched pairs, the Wilcoxon statistic has, under the null hypothesis, the mean

$$\mu_T = \frac{n(n + 1)}{4} = \frac{(31)(32)}{4} = 248$$

and variance

$$Var(T) = \sigma_T^2 = \frac{n(n + 1)(2n + 1)}{24} = \frac{(31)(32)(63)}{24} = 2,604$$

so that the standard deviation is as follows:

$$\sigma_T = 51.03$$

The observed value of the statistic is $T = 189$. It follows from Equations 14.18–14.20 that the null hypothesis is rejected against the one-sided alternative if

$$Z = \frac{T - \mu_T}{\sigma_T} = \frac{189 - 248}{51.03} = \frac{-59}{51.03} = -1.16 < z_\alpha$$

For $\alpha = 0.05$,

$$z_\alpha = -1.645$$

The test result is not sufficient to reject the null hypothesis. Using the standard normal distribution, the null hypothesis could be rejected only at all significance levels of 12.3% or higher. Such a large p-value indicates that the data are not statistically significant to indicate that the ratio of market valuation to replacement cost of assets tends to be lower for firms without sophisticated postaudit procedures.

Sign Test for a Single Population Median

The sign test can also be used to test hypotheses about the central location (median) of a population distribution.

Example 14.12 Starting Incomes of Recent College Graduates (Sign Test)

The starting incomes of a random sample of 23 recent graduates are given in Table 14.16.

Table 14.16 Starting Salaries

29,250	29,900	28,070	31,400	31,100	29,000	33,000	50,000	28,500	31,000
34,800	42,100	33,200	36,000	65,800	34,000	29,900	32,000	31,500	29,900
32,890	36,000	35,000							

Do the data indicate that the median starting income differs from $35,000? The data for this problem can be found in the data file **Income**.

Solution Since the distribution of incomes is often skewed, the sign test will be used. The null and alternative hypotheses are as follows:

$$H_0 : \text{median} = \$35{,}000$$

$$H_1 : \text{median} \neq \$35{,}000$$

Here, we test the null hypothesis using a binomial distribution with $P = 0.50$. First, we approximate the answer using Equations 14.14 and 14.15. Notice that there are 17 students who indicated income less than $35,000 and 5 who indicated income greater than $35,000, with 1 student having a starting income of $35,000. The sample size is reduced to $n = 22$ and $S = 5$. The mean and the standard deviation are found to be as follows:

$$\mu = np = 0.5n = 0.5(22) = 11$$

$$\sigma = 0.5\sqrt{22} = 2.345$$

Since $S = 5 < \mu = 11$, the test statistic for the normal approximation is as follows:

$$Z = \frac{5.5 - 11}{2.345} = -2.35$$

Using the table for the standard normal distribution, the *approximate* p-value is $2(0.0094) = 0.0188$. Therefore, the null hypothesis is rejected at 1.88% or higher.

Application Exercises

14.22 A random sample of 12 financial analysts was asked to predict the percentage increases in the prices of two common stocks over the next year. The results obtained are shown in the table. Use the sign test to test the null hypothesis that for the population of analysts there is no overall preference for increases in one stock over the other.

Analyst	Stock 1	Stock 2
A	6.8	7.2
B	9.8	12.3
C	2.1	5.3
D	6.2	6.8
E	7.1	7.2
F	6.5	6.2
G	9.3	10.1
H	1.0	2.7
I	−0.2	1.3
J	9.6	9.8
K	12.0	12.0
L	6.3	8.9

14.23 An organization offers a program designed to increase the level of comprehension achieved by students when reading technical material quickly. Each member of a random sample of 10 students was given 30 minutes to read an article. A test of the level of comprehension achieved was then administered. This process was repeated after these students had completed the program. The accompanying table shows comprehension scores before and after completion of the program. Use the sign test to test the null hypothesis that for this population there is no overall improvement in comprehension levels following completion of the program.

Student	Before	After
A	79	87
B	57	68
C	87	83
D	85	85
E	77	89
F	60	67
G	92	106
H	83	85
I	73	70
J	77	85

14.24 A sample of 11 managers in retail stores having self-checkout was asked if customers have a positive attitude about the scanning process. Seven managers answered yes, and four answered no. Test against a two-sided alternative the null hypothesis that, for the population of managers, responses would be equally divided between yes and no.

14.25 A sample of 75 corporations buying back franchises was examined. Of these cases, returns on common stock around the buyback announcement date were positive 52 times, negative 15 times, and zero 8 times. Test the null hypothesis that positive and negative returns are equally likely against the alternative that positive returns are more likely.

14.26 Of a random sample of 130 voters, 44 favored a state tax increase to raise funding for education, 68 opposed the tax increase, and 18 expressed no opinion. Test, against a two-sided alternative, the null hypothesis that voters in the state are evenly divided on the issue of this tax increase.

14.27 A random sample of 60 professional economists was asked to predict whether next year's inflation rate would be higher than, lower than, or about the same as that in the current year. The results are shown in the following table. Test the null hypothesis that the profession is evenly divided on the question.

Prediction	Number
Higher	20
Lower	29
About the same	11

14.28 A random sample of 160 shoppers was asked to compare two new energy bars. From the sample, 91 shoppers preferred energy bar A, 61 preferred energy bar B, and 8 expressed no preference. Use the normal approximation to determine, at the 1% level, if there is an overall preference for either energy bar.

14.29 A random sample of 10 students was asked to rate, in a blind taste test, the quality of two brands of ice cream, one reduced-sugar and one regular ice cream. Ratings were based on a scale of 1 (poor) to 10 (excellent). The accompanying table gives the results. Use the Wilcoxon test to test, at the 5% level, the null hypothesis that the distribution of the paired differences is centered on 0 against the alternative that the population of all student ice cream consumers prefer the regular brand.

Student	Reduced Sugar	Regular
A	3	9
B	3	4
C	8	6
D	4	4
E	5	4
F	2	8
G	2	9
H	2	3
I	7	5
J	3	7

14.30 Sixteen freshmen on a college campus were grouped into eight pairs in such a way that the two members of any pair were as similar as possible in academic backgrounds—as measured by high school class rank and achievement test scores—and also in social backgrounds. The major difference within pairs was that one student was an in-state student and the other was from out of state. At the end of the first year of college, grade point averages of these students were recorded, yielding the results shown in the table. Use the Wilcoxon test to analyze the data. Discuss the implications of the test results.

Pair	In State	Out of State
A	3.4	2.8
B	3.0	3.1
C	2.4	2.7
D	3.8	3.3
E	3.9	3.7
F	2.3	2.8
G	2.6	2.6
H	3.7	3.3

14.31 A random sample of 40 business majors who had just completed introductory courses in both statistics and accounting was asked to rate each class in terms of level of interest on a scale of 1 (very uninteresting) to 10 (very interesting). The 40 differences in the pairs of ratings were calculated and the absolute differences ranked. The smaller of the rank sums, which was for those finding accounting the more interesting, was 281. Test the null hypothesis that the population of business majors would rate these courses equally against the alternative that the statistics course is viewed as the more interesting.

14.32 A consultant is interested in the impact of the introduction of a total-quality management program on job satisfaction of employees. A random sample of 30 employees was asked to assess level of satisfaction on a scale from 1 (very dissatisfied) to 10 (very satisfied) three months before the introduction of the program. These same sample members were asked to make this assessment again 3 months after the introduction of the program. The 30 differences in the pairs of ratings were calculated and the absolute differences ranked. The smaller of the rank sums, which was for those more satisfied before the introduction of the program, was 169. What can be concluded from this finding?

14.33 A random sample of 80 owners of videocassette recorders was taken. Each sample member was asked to assess the amounts of time in a month spent watching material he or she had recorded from television broadcasts and watching purchased or rented commercially recorded tapes. The 80 differences in times spent were then calculated and their absolute values ranked. The smaller of the rank sums, for material recorded from television, was 1,502. Discuss the implications of this sample result.

14.5 NONPARAMETRIC TESTS FOR INDEPENDENT RANDOM SAMPLES

In this section we introduce two tests that compare the central locations of two population distributions when *independent random samples* are taken from the two populations. The two tests are the Mann-Whitney U test and the Wilcoxon rank sum test.

Mann-Whitney U Test

The distribution of the Mann-Whitney statistic, U, approaches the normal distribution quite rapidly as the number of sample observations increases. The approximation is adequate if each sample contains at least 10 observations. Thus, we consider here only samples with $n_1 \geq 10$ and $n_2 \geq 10$. To test the null hypothesis that the central locations of the two population distributions are the same, we assume that, apart from any possible differences in central location, the two population distributions are identical.

The Mann-Whitney U Statistic

Assume that, apart from any possible differences in central location, the two population distributions are identical. Suppose that n_1 observations are available from the first population and n_2 observations from the second. The two samples are pooled, and the observations are ranked in ascending order with ties assigned the average of the next available ranks. Let R_1 denote the sum of the ranks of the observations from the first population. The **Mann-Whitney U test** is based on the Mann-Whitney U statistic defined as follows:

$$U = n_1 n_2 + \frac{n_1(n_1 + 1)}{2} - R_1 \qquad (14.21)$$

It can be shown then that if the null hypothesis is true, the random variable U has mean and variance as defined in Equations 14.22 and 14.23.

Mann-Whitney U Test: Normal Approximation

Assuming as the null hypothesis that the central locations of the two population distributions are the same, the Mann-Whitney U has the following mean and variance:

$$E(U) = \mu_U = \frac{n_1 n_2}{2} \qquad (14.22)$$

$$Var(U) = \sigma_U^2 = \frac{n_1 n_2(n_1 + n_2 + 1)}{12} \qquad (14.23)$$

Then, for large sample sizes (both at least 10), the distribution of the random variable

$$Z = \frac{U - \mu_U}{\sigma_U} \qquad (14.24)$$

is approximated by the normal distribution.

Example 14.13 Hours of Study (Mann-Whitney U Test)

Table 14.17 shows the numbers of hours per week students claim to spend studying for introductory finance and accounting courses. The data are from independent random samples of 10 finance students and 12 accounting students.

Do the data indicate a difference in the median number of hours per week that students spend studying for introductory finance and accounting courses? The name of the data file is **Hours**.

Solution Our null hypothesis is that the central locations (medians) of the two population distributions are identical.

H_0 : median (1) = median (2); Students spend the same median number of hours studying for introductory finance and accounting courses.

The two samples are pooled, and the observations are ranked in ascending order with ties being treated in the same way as previously. These ranks are shown in Table 14.18.

Now, if the null hypothesis were true, we would expect the average ranks for the two samples to be quite close. In the particular example the average rank for the finance students is 9.35, whereas that for the accounting students is 13.29. As usual, when testing hypotheses, we want to know how likely a discrepancy of this magnitude would be if the null hypothesis were true.

Table 14.17 Number of Hours per Week Spent Studying for Introductory Finance and Accounting Courses

Finance	10	6	8	10	12	13	11	9	5	11		
Accounting	13	17	14	12	10	9	15	16	11	8	9	7

Table 14.18 Mann-Whitney U Test Ranks for Hours of Study per Week

FINANCE	(RANK)	ACCOUNTING	(RANK)
10	(10)	13	(17.5)
6	(2)	17	(22)
8	(4.5)	14	(19)
10	(10)	12	(15.5)
12	(15.5)	10	(10)
13	(17.5)	9	(7)
11	(13)	15	(20)
9	(7)	16	(21)
5	(1)	11	(13)
11	(13)	8	(4.5)
		9	(7)
		7	(3)
Rank Sum = 93.5		Rank Sum = 159.5	

It is not necessary to calculate both rank sums, because if we know one, we can deduce the other. In this example, for instance, the ranks must sum to the sum of the integers 1 through 22—that is, to 253. Thus, any test of the hypothesis can be based on just one of the rank sums. If finance is the first sample, then

$$n_1 = 10 \quad n_2 = 12 \quad R_1 = 93.5$$

so the value observed for the Mann-Whitney statistic is, by Equation 14.21,

$$U = n_1 n_2 + \frac{n_1(n_1 + 1)}{2} - R_1 = (10)(12) + \frac{(10)(11)}{2} - 93.5 = 81.5$$

Using the null hypothesis that the central locations of the two population distributions are the same and Equation 14.22, the distribution of the statistic has mean

$$E(U) = \mu_U = \frac{n_1 n_2}{2} = \frac{(10)(12)}{2} = 60$$

and variance

$$Var(U) = \sigma_U^2 = \frac{n_1 n_2(n_1 + n_2 + 1)}{12} = \frac{(10)(12)(23)}{12} = 230$$

It follows that

$$Z = \frac{U - \mu_U}{\sigma_U} = \frac{81.5 - 60}{\sqrt{230}} = 1.42 \text{ and } p\text{-value} = 0.1556.$$

With the usual 0.05 significance level, the test result is not sufficient to conclude that students spend more time studying for one of these subjects than the other. We could have used a continuity correction factor in the normal approximation. The p-value will be slightly higher than 0.1556.

If accounting is population 1 with $n_1 = 12$ and $R_1 = 159.5$, the outcome will be the same, since $Z = -1.42$. The p-value will still be 0.1556.

Wilcoxon Rank Sum Test

The **Wilcoxon rank sum test** is similar to the Mann-Whitney U test. The results will be the same for both tests. We include it here for completeness, since this test may be preferred for its ease. Similar to the Mann-Whitney U test, the distribution of the Wilcoxon rank sum test approaches the normal distribution quite rapidly as the number of sample observations increases. The approximation is adequate if each sample contains at least 10 observations.

Wilcoxon Rank Sum Statistic T

Suppose that n_1 observations are available from the first population and n_2 observations from the second. The two samples are pooled, and the observations are ranked in ascending order with ties assigned the average of the next available ranks. Let T denote the sum of the ranks of the observations from the first population (T in the Wilcoxon rank sum test is the same as R_1 in the Mann-Whitney U test). Assuming that the null hypothesis to be true, the Wilcoxon rank sum statistic, T, has mean

$$E(T) = \mu_T = \frac{n_1(n_1 + n_2 + 1)}{2} \qquad (14.25)$$

$$\text{Var}(T) = \sigma_T^2 = \frac{n_1 n_2(n_1 + n_2 + 1)}{12} \qquad (14.26)$$

Then, for large samples ($n_1 \geq 10$ and $n_2 \geq 10$), the distribution of the random variable

$$Z = \frac{T - \mu_T}{\sigma_T} \qquad (14.27)$$

is approximated by the normal distribution. For a large number of ties, Equation 14.26 may not be correct.

For the data in Table 14.18, $T = R_1 = 93.5$ with

$$E(T) = \mu_T = \frac{n_1(n_1 + n_2 + 1)}{2} = \frac{10(23)}{2} = 115$$

and

$$\text{Var}(T) = \sigma_T^2 = \frac{n_1 n_2(n_1 + n_2 + 1)}{12} = 230$$

Notice that the variance of the sampling distribution of the Wilcoxon rank sum statistic, T, is the same as the variance of the sampling distribution of the Mann-Whitney statistic, U. It follows that

$$Z = \frac{T - \mu_T}{\sigma_T} = \frac{93.5 - 115}{\sqrt{230}} = -1.42 \Rightarrow p\text{-value} = 0.1556.$$

Example 14.14 Earnings for Two Firms (Wilcoxon Rank Sum Test)

In a study designed to compare the performance of firms that give management forecasts of earnings with the performances of those that do not, independent random samples of 80 firms from each of the populations were taken. The variability of the growth rate of earnings over the previous 10 periods was measured for each of the 160 firms, and these variabilities were ranked. The sum of the ranks for firms not disclosing management earnings forecasts was 7,287 (Jaggi and Grier 1980). Test, against a two-sided alternative, the null hypothesis that the central locations of the population distributions of earnings variabilities are the same for these two types of firms. Show that the results are the same with both the Mann-Whitney U test and the Wilcoxon rank sum test.

Solution Since we have $n_1 = 80, n_2 = 80,$ and $R_1 = 7,287,$ the calculated value of the Mann-Whitney statistic is as follows:

$$U = n_1 n_2 + \frac{n_1(n_1 + 1)}{2} - R_1 = (80)(80) + \frac{(80)(81)}{2} - 7,287 = 2,353$$

Under the null hypothesis the Mann-Whitney statistic has mean

$$\mu_U = \frac{n_1 n_2}{2} = \frac{(80)(80)}{2} = 3,200$$

and variance

$$\sigma_U^2 = \frac{n_1 n_2 (n_1 + n_2 + 1)}{12} = \frac{(80)(80)(161)}{12} = 85,867$$

Here, we have the following:

$$Z = \frac{2,353 - 3,200}{\sqrt{85,867}} = -2.89$$

From the standard normal distribution, Appendix Table 1, we see that the value of $\alpha/2$ corresponding to a Z-value of 2.89 is 0.0019, so the p-value is 0.0038. Hence, the null hypothesis can be rejected at all levels higher than 0.38%.

The Wilcoxon rank sum test uses Equations 14.25–14.27. The mean of T is as follows:

$$E(T) = \frac{n_1(n_1 + n_2 + 1)}{2} = \frac{80(161)}{2} = 6,440$$

The variance of T is the same as the variance of U (Equation 14.23 is the same as Equation 14.26). Thus, by Equation 14.27,

$$Z = \frac{T - \mu_T}{\sigma_T} = \frac{7,287 - 6,440}{\sqrt{85,867}} = 2.89$$

and, again, the null hypothesis can be rejected at all levels higher than 0.38%. The results are the same whether using either the Mann-Whitney U test or the Wilcoxon rank sum test. These data, then, present very strong evidence against the hypothesis that the central locations of the distributions of population variability in earnings growth rates are the same for firms that give management earnings forecasts as for those that do not.

Now, if we had been given the actual data rather than just the ranks, we could have carried out a test of the null hypothesis using the methods of Chapter 10. However, using the Mann-Whitney test, we have found that the null hypothesis can be rejected *without the assumption of population normality.*

Application Exercises

14.34 A study compared firms with and without an audit committee. For samples of firms of each type, the extent of directors' ownership was measured using the number of shares owned by the board as a proportion of the total number of shares issued. In the sample, directors' ownership was, overall, higher for firms without an audit committee. To test for statistical significance, the Mann-Whitney U statistic was calculated. It follows that $(U - \mu_U)/\sigma_U$ was found to be 2.12. What can we conclude from this result?

14.35 At the beginning of the year, a stock market analyst produced a list of stocks to buy and another list of stocks to sell. For a random sample of 12 stocks from the buy list, percentage returns over the year were as follows:

2.8	4.7	1.2	3.2	4.8	1.4
2.1	3.0	1.7	3.3	3.1	3.4

For an independent random sample of 12 stocks from the sell list, percentage returns over the year were as follows:

9.2	7.0	5.0	5.4	3.6	10.0
5.2	7.4	9.8	4.4	8.2	2.2

Use the Mann-Whitney test to interpret these data at the 5% level.

14.36 The human resources department of Alfa Laval, Sweden, is analyzing on the number of years of work experience of employees in the marketing and finance departments. For a random sample of 12 marketing staff members, the number of years of work experience were as follows:

4	15	6	8	2	3
5	7	13	14	11	20

For the finance department, 10 employees were selected and the corresponding years of work experience were as follows:

11	7	9	15	3
6	3	10	7	11

Use the Mann-Whitney test to analyze the data and comment on the results.

14.37 GreenEnergy, a manufacturing company in Finland, wants to know the consumer satisfaction level for two products—A and B. A random sample of 12 consumers are invited to participate in a survey. The participants are divided into two equal groups and are asked to rate the satisfaction they received from each of the two products. The products are then ranked from 1 (extremely unsatisfied) to 10 (extremely satisfied). The participants' results are shown in the following table. Test the null hypothesis to help GreenEnergy to identify which product offers consumers more satisfaction.

Product A		Product B	
Participant	Rating	Participant	Rating
1	3	1	9
2	4	2	7
3	2	3	5
4	6	4	10
5	2	5	6
6	5	6	8

14.38 Two different drugs for deliberating headaches are being analyzed for effectiveness. The analyst uses a random selection of 15 patients to test the first drug and 13 patients for the second drug. For each patient, the analyst records the number of hours of relief from headache as follows:

Drug 1	3.5	5.7	2.9	2.4	1.9	3.3	4.3	3.5
	2.1	2.4	4.7	1.1	2.7	3.9	2.1	
Drug 2	1.7	4.0	3.5	2.4	5.2	4.3	2.2	4.5
	3.2	1.8	0.7	3.7	4.1			

Test the null hypothesis that number of hours of relief from a headache is equal for both drugs.

14.39 A newsletter rates mutual funds. Independent random samples of 12 funds with the highest rating and 12 funds with the lowest rating were chosen. The following figures are percentage rates of return achieved by these 24 funds in the next year.

Highest rated	8.8	10.8	8.4	9.0	5.4	5.0	6.8	11.2	8.2	7.4	4.6	6.0
Lowest rated	4.6	2.7	2.5	1.7	4.0	1.4	4.0	1.7	2.0	2.8	1.2	4.0

Test at the 1% level the null hypothesis of no difference between the central locations of the population distributions of rates of return against the alternative that the highestrated funds tended to achieve higher rates of return than the lowest-rated funds.

14.40 JW Intelligent proposed a new moisturizing cream that includes herbal essence as a key ingredient. A random sample of 15 women were selected for a pilot trial of the new product. The women used the product and evaluated its effectiveness using a skin test machine to see whether their skin was more moisturized compared to another independent random sample of 15 women who use a different product. The test results were then assimilated and ranked from 1 (worst) to 10 (best). The sum of the ranks for the results is 274.5. Test the null hypothesis that there is a difference in skin test results for women using the new moisturizing cream against those who use another product at 5% significance level.

14.41 An investment company is going to make decision on which mobile app they are to invest from two different mobile application developments. The company accesses the ability on the two apps by monitoring the daily number of users downloading the apps for 20 days. The company ranked the daily downloading numbers from the lowest to the highest and found that first app has the sum of rank of 478. Test the null hypothesis for the company to determine if there is any difference between the two apps.

The sample correlation coefficient can be seriously affected by odd extreme observations. Moreover, tests based on it rely for their validity on an assumption of normality. A measure of correlation that is not susceptible to serious influence by extreme values and on which valid tests can be based for very general population distributions is obtained through the use of ranks. The resulting test is then nonparametric.

Spearman Rank Correlation

Suppose that a random sample $(x_1, y_1), \ldots, (x_n, y_n)$ of n pairs of observations is taken. If the x_i and y_i are each ranked in ascending order and the sample correlation of these ranks is calculated, the resulting coefficient is called the **Spearman rank correlation coefficient**. If there are no tied X or Y ranks, an equivalent formula for computing this coefficient is

$$r_s = 1 - \frac{6 \sum_{i=1}^{n} d_i^2}{n(n^2 - 1)} \tag{14.28}$$

where the d_i are the differences of the ranked pairs.

The following tests of the null hypothesis H_0 of no association in the population have a significance level α.

1. To test against the alternative of positive association, the decision rule is as follows:

$$\text{reject } H_0 \text{ if } r_s > r_{s,\alpha} \tag{14.29}$$

2. To test against the alternative of negative association, the decision rule is as follows:

$$\text{reject } H_0 \text{ if } r_s < -r_{s,\alpha} \tag{14.30}$$

3. To test against the two-sided alternative of some association, the decision rule is as follows:

$$\text{reject } H_0 \text{ if } r_s < -r_{s,\alpha/2} \quad \text{or} \quad r_s > r_{s,\alpha/2} \tag{14.31}$$

Example 14.15 Cruise Industry Promotion (Spearman Rank Correlation)

To promote the cruise industry in Florida, suppose that James Thorne of the Cruise Emporium of Ormond Beach ran an advertisement in 17 tourism magazines. Readers were invited to write for additional brochures and literature. The two variables to be related are

    X: cost of advertising and circulation, in thousands of dollars
    Y: return-on-inquiry cost

where the latter is defined as

    $Y =$ (estimated revenue from inquiries $-$ cost of advertisement) $\div$ cost of advertisement

Table 14.19 lists the ranks of these two variables for the 17 magazine advertisements. Calculate the Spearman rank correlation coefficient and test for association between the variables.

Table 14.19 Rank Correlation Calculations for the Cruise Example

MAGAZINE	RANK(X_i)	RANK(Y_i)	$d_i = $ RANK(x_i) $-$ RANK(Y_i)	d_i^2
1	14	2	12	144
2	8	4	4	16
3	1	16	-15	225
4	16	1	15	225
5	17	5	12	144
6	13	6	7	49
7	15	8	7	49
8	2	11	-9	81
9	7	9	-2	4
10	3	13	-10	100
11	6	12	-6	36
12	9	17	-8	64
13	5	3	2	4
14	4	7	-3	9
15	11	14	-3	9
16	12	15	-3	9
17	10	10	0	0
				Sum 1,168

Solution Although Magazine 17 has an X rank of 10 and a Y rank of 10, ties are considered only within the X ranks, or within the Y ranks, and not between the X and Y ranks. Since there are no ties in the X or the Y ranks, we use Equation 14.28 and obtain the following:

$$r_s = 1 - \frac{6\sum_{i=1}^{n} d_i^2}{n(n^2 - 1)} = 1 - \frac{6(1,168)}{17[(17)^2 - 1]} = -0.431$$

Since there are 17 pairs of observations, the cutoff points (see Appendix Table 11) for 10% level and 5% level tests are, respectively,

$$r_{s,0.05} = 0.412 \quad \text{and} \quad r_{s,0.025} = 0.490$$

The null hypothesis of no association can be rejected against the two-sided alternative, according to the decision rule, at the 10% level but not at the 5% level. Our conclusions are not based on the assumption of population normality. The negative correlation coefficient indicates that the more one spends for advertising the lower the rate of return.

If there are no ties in the X or the Y ranks, then to calculate the Spearman rank correlation with either Minitab or Excel is straightforward. If there are ties, we compute the simple correlation (Section 11.7) between the ranks.

Application Exercises

14.42 Petron has formulated a new chemical to be added in their petrol. To determine the effectiveness of the new formulated chemical, they recorded the amount of chemical had been added in the petrol (in liter) and the distances traveled (in km) by 10 automobiles in the follow table:

Chemical	1.8	1.2	2	1	1	1.2	0.8	0.6	1	0.85
Distance	50	75	120	40	48	50	40	41	45	50

a. Calculate the Spearman rank correlation coefficient.

b. Carry out a test of the null hypothesis for Petron to determine the association between the amount of chemical added and distances traveled.

14.43 The accompanying table shows, for a random sample of 20 long-term-growth mutual funds, percentage return over a period of 12 months and total assets (in millions of pounds).

Return	Assets	Return	Assets	Return	Assets
26.4	300	17.5	421	11.5	75
23.4	70	16.7	99	14.9	610
28.7	3004	18.8	756	8.4	264
24.5	161	17.9	730	6.2	27
25.5	827	12.7	436	9.3	71
19.9	295	12.3	143	3.7	719
17.3	29	14.3	117		

a. Calculate the Spearman rank correlation coefficient.

b. Carry out a nonparametric test of the null hypothesis of no association in the population against a two-sided alternative.

c. Discuss the advantages of a nonparametric test for these data.

14.7 A NONPARAMETRIC TEST FOR RANDOMNESS

In Chapter 1 we presented graphs to plot time-series data. In this section we consider the **runs test**, a nonparametric test for randomness in time series. Time-series analysis and forecasting are presented in Chapter 16.

Runs Test: Small Sample Size

First we consider a time series of n observations with $n \leq 20$. We denote observations above the median with + signs and observations below the median with − signs. These signs are used to define the sequence of observations in the series.

Runs Test: Small Sample Size

Let R denote the number of runs in the sequence of n observations with $n \leq 20$. The null hypothesis is that the series is a set of random variables. Appendix Table 14 gives the smallest significance level at which this null hypothesis can be rejected against the alternative of positive association between adjacent observations, as a function of R and n.

If the alternative is the two-sided hypothesis on nonrandomness, the significance level must be doubled if it is less than 0.5. Alternatively, if the significance level read from the table is greater than 0.5, the appropriate significance level for the test against the two-sided alternative is $2(1 - \alpha)$.

Example 14.16 illustrates a time series with $n = 16$ daily observations on an index of the volume of shares traded on the New York Stock Exchange. If this series were random, then the volume traded on one day would be independent of the volume traded on any other day. In particular, a high-volume day would be no more likely to be followed by another high-volume day than would any other day.

Example 14.16 New York Stock Exchange (Runs Test: Small Sample Size)

A series of 16 daily observations on an index of the volume of shares traded on the New York Stock Exchange is shown in Table 14.20. Test the null hypothesis of randomness. Data are stored in the data file **Shares Traded**.

Table 14.20   Index of Volume of Shares Traded

DAY	VOLUME	DAY	VOLUME	DAY	VOLUME	DAY	VOLUME
1	98	5	113	9	114	13	109
2	93	6	111	10	107	14	108
3	82	7	104	11	111	15	128
4	103	8	103	12	109	16	92

Solution First, we compute the median. For an even number of observations, the median is the average of the middle pair when the observations are arranged in ascending order. Here, that is

$$\text{median} = \frac{107 + 108}{2} = 107.5$$

The runs test developed here separates the observations into a subgroup above the median and a subgroup below the median. Notice that a line was drawn on Figure 14.3 at the median of 107.5.

Figure 14.3 Index of Volume of Shares Traded versus Day (Runs Test)

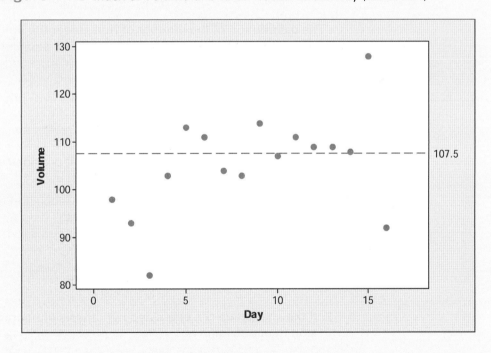

Then, letting a + denote observations above the median and a − denote observations below the median, we find the following pattern over the sequential days:

$$- - - - + + - - - + - + + + + + -$$

This sequence consists of a run of four $-$ signs, followed by a run of two $+$ signs, a run of two $-$ signs, a run of one $+$ sign, a run of one $-$ sign, a run of five $+$ signs, and finally a run of one $-$ sign. In total, there are $R = 7$ runs.

If, as might be suspected here, there was a positive association between adjacent observations in time, we would expect to find relatively few runs. We ask how likely it is to observe 7 or fewer runs if the series is truly random. This requires knowledge of the distribution of the number of runs when the null hypothesis of randomness is true. The cumulative distribution is tabulated in Appendix Table 14. From the table, we see that, for $n = 16$ observations, the probability under the null hypothesis of finding 7 or fewer runs is 0.214. Therefore, the null hypothesis of randomness can be rejected only against the alternative of positive association between adjacent observations at the $\alpha = 0.214$ significance level. This is not small enough to reasonably reject the null hypothesis. We have merely failed to find strong evidence to reject it. Tests of randomness based on small samples such as this have quite low power.

Runs Test: Large Sample Size

Next we consider the runs test for large samples of n observations with $n > 20$. In this situation the normal approximation given in Equation 14.32 is appropriate.

Runs Test: Large Sample Size

Given that we have a time series with n observations and $n > 20$, define the number of runs, R, as the number of sequences above or below the median. We want to test the null hypothesis

$$H_0 : \text{the series is random}$$

The distribution of the number of runs under the null hypothesis can be approximated by a normal distribution. It can be shown that under the null hypothesis,

$$Z = \frac{R - \dfrac{n}{2} - 1}{\sqrt{\dfrac{n^2 - 2n}{4(n - 1)}}} \tag{14.32}$$

has a standard normal distribution. This result provides a test for randomness. The following tests have significance level α.

1. If the alternative hypothesis is positive association between adjacent observations, the decision rule is as follows:

$$\text{reject } H_0 \text{ if } Z = \frac{R - \dfrac{n}{2} - 1}{\sqrt{\dfrac{n^2 - 2n}{4(n - 1)}}} < -z_\alpha \tag{14.33}$$

2. If the alternative is a two-sided hypothesis of nonrandomness, the decision rule is as follows:

$$\text{reject } H_0 \text{ if } Z = \frac{R - \dfrac{n}{2} - 1}{\sqrt{\dfrac{n^2 - 2n}{4(n - 1)}}} < -z_{\alpha/2} \quad \text{or} \quad Z = \frac{R - \dfrac{n}{2} - 1}{\sqrt{\dfrac{n^2 - 2n}{4(n - 1)}}} > z_{\alpha/2} \tag{14.34}$$

Example 14.17 Analysis of Sales Data (Runs Test: Large Sample Size)

You have been asked to determine if 30 weeks of sales follow a random pattern from one observation to the next in a time series. The data are stored in the data file **Weekly Sales**.

Solution Figure 14.4 is a time-series plot of the data with the median drawn on the graph. Examination of the plot shows that the series has eight ($R = 8$) runs and suggests that the observations are not independent, since they appear to follow a pattern.

Figure 14.4 Weekly Sales Data over Time (Runs Test)

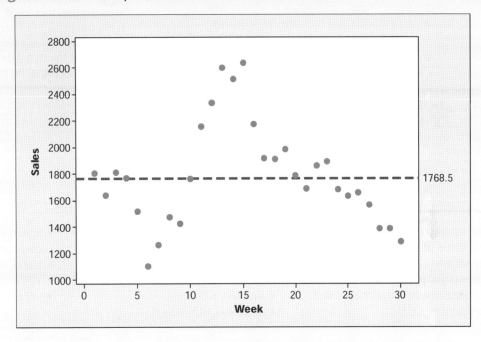

The runs test statistic can be computed using Equation 14.32 as follows:

$$Z = \frac{R - \frac{n}{2} - 1}{\sqrt{\frac{n^2 - 2n}{4(n - 1)}}} = \frac{8 - 15 - 1}{\sqrt{\frac{900 - 60}{116}}} = -2.97$$

The resulting p-value for a two-tailed test is 0.0030 from the standard normal distribution table, Appendix Table 1. Similarly using Equation 14.34 with a significance level of 0.01, it follows that:

$$z = -2.97 < -2.576$$

and the null hypothesis of randomness is rejected. Thus, we see the evidence in favor of nonrandom series is quite overwhelming.

EXERCISES

 Visit www.MyStatLab.com or www.pearsonglobal editions.com to access the data files.

Basic Exercises

14.44 Given a sequence 0.16, 0.27, 0.58, 0.63, 0.45, 0.21, 0.72, 0.87, 0.27, 0.15, 0.92, 0.85.

    a. How many runs for the sequence in total?

    b. What is the probability the number of run is less than 6?

14.45 A time series contains 10 and 16 observations. Determine the probability of the number of runs for the following.

    a. n = 10, P(R > 5)

    b. n = 16, P(4 < R < 7)

14.46 A time series contains 50 observations. What is the probability that the number of runs is

a. no more than 13?
b. fewer than 15?
c. greater than 34?

14.47 Use the runs test to test for randomness the number of miles traveled per week for a car in three months.

Week	Distance (miles)	Week	Distance (miles)
1	253	7	450
2	452	8	678
3	308	9	529
4	414	10	120
5	386	11	379
6	197	12	298

Application Exercises

14.48 The data file **Euribor 12 Months** shows an average annual interest rate of certain European banks over 18 consecutive years. Use the runs test to test this series for randomness.

14.49 The data file **Inventory Sales** shows the inventory-sales ratio for manufacturing and trade in the United States over a period of 12 years. Test this series for randomness using the runs test.

14.50 The **Tesla Stock Prices** data file shows the closing price of Tesla's stocks in the first day of each month for a period of 12 consecutive months. Test for randomness using the runs test.

14.51 On October 18, 2018, the fuel prices in Portugal went down after having risen to a five-year high the previous week. The **Fuel Prices** data file contains the price per liter of gasoline and of diesel, in Portugal, recorded every Monday for two consecutive years. Test the two data sets stored in the data file for randomness using the runs test.

CHAPTER EXERCISES AND APPLICATIONS

14.52 Suppose that a random sample of firms with impaired assets was classified according to whether discretionary write-downs of these assets were taken, and also according to whether there was evidence of subsequent merger or acquisition activity. Using the data in the accompanying table, test the null hypothesis of no association between these characteristics.

Write-Down	Merger or Acquisition Activity?	
	Yes	No
Yes	32	48
No	25	57

14.53 A manufacturer of a certain product has three factories located across the United States. There are three major causes of defects in this product, which we will identify as A, B, and C. During a recent week the reported occurrences of product defects in the three factories were as follows:

Factory 1	A, 15;	B, 25;	C, 23
Factory 2	A, 10;	B, 12;	C, 21
Factory 3	A, 32;	B, 28;	C, 44

Based on these frequencies, can we conclude that the defect patterns in the different factories are the same?

14.54 The human resources department is attempting to determine if employees' undergraduate majors influence their performance. The majors considered are business, economics, mathematics, and all others. Personnel ratings are grouped as excellent, strong, and average. The classifications are based on employees with two to four years of experience, as follows:

Business major	excellent, 21;	strong, 18;	average, 10
Economics major	excellent, 19;	strong, 15;	average, 5
Mathematics major	excellent, 10;	strong, 5;	average, 5
Other major	excellent, 5;	strong, 15;	average, 13

Do these data indicate that there is a difference in ratings based on undergraduate major?

14.55 A random sample of people from three different job classifications labeled A, B, and C was asked to indicate preferences for three brands of camping lanterns: Big Star, Lone Star, and Bright Star. The preferences were as follows:

Group A	Big Star, 54;	Lone Star, 67;	Bright Star, 39
Group B	Big Star, 23;	Lone Star, 13;	Bright Star, 44
Group C	Big Star, 69;	Lone Star, 53;	Bright Star, 59

Do these data indicate that there is a difference in ratings for the three different groups?

14.56 A liberal arts college was interested in determining if there were different graduate school patterns for students with undergraduate majors in history and economics. The college surveyed a random sample of recent graduates and found that a large number obtained graduate degrees in business, law, and theology. The frequency of persons in the various combinations is shown next. Based on these results, is there evidence that undergraduate economics and history majors pursue different graduate school programs?

	Graduate Studies		
Undergraduate	Business	Law	Theology
Economics	30	20	10
History	6	34	20

14.57 Suppose that you have collected market survey data for gender and product purchase. Perform a chi-square test to determine if there is a different probability of purchase among men and women. Include in your answer the expected cell values under the null hypothesis.

	Gender	
Decision	Male	Female
Purchase	150	150
No purchase	50	250

14.58 Sally Smith is a long-time political campaign manager from Chicago. In the primary election there are four candidates. She wishes to determine if voter preference is different over the four major districts. A random sample survey results in the candidate preference frequencies by district and is shown in the following

contingency table. Perform an appropriate statistical test to determine if candidate preference is related to the district.

	Preference for Candidates in Primary Election				
District	A	B	C	D	Total
1	52	34	80	34	200
2	33	15	78	24	150
3	66	54	141	39	300

14.59 A manufacturer of household appliances wanted to determine if there was a relationship between family size and the size of washing machine purchased. The manufacturer was preparing guidelines for sales personnel and wanted to know if the sales staff should make specific recommendations to customers. A random sample of 300 families was asked about family size and size of washing machine. For the 40 families with one or two people, 25 had an 8-pound washer, 10 had a 10-pound washer, and 5 had a 12-pound washer. The 140 families with three or four people included 37 with the 8-pound washer, 62 with the 10-pound washer, and 41 with the 12-pound washer. For the remaining 120 families with five or more people, 8 had an 8-pound washer, 53 had a 10-pound washer, and 59 had a 12-pound washer. Based on these results, what can be concluded about family size and size of washer? Construct a two-way table, state the hypothesis, compute the statistics, and state your conclusion.

14.60 The gear-cutting department in a large manufacturing firm produces high-quality gears. The number produced per hour by a single machinist is 1, 2, or 3, as shown in the table. Company management is interested in determining the effect of worker experience on the number of units produced per hour. Worker experience is classified in three subgroups: 1 year or less, 2 to 5 years, and more than 5 years. Use the data in the table to determine if experience and number of parts produced per hour are independent.

	Units Produced/Hour			
Experience	1	2	3	Total
≤1 year	10	30	10	50
2–5 years	10	20	20	50
>5 years	10	10	30	50
Total	30	60	60	150

14.61 Aurica Sabou has been working on a plan for new store locations as part of her regional expansion. In the city proposed for expansion there are three possible locations: north, east, and west. From past experience she knows that the three major profit centers in her stores are tools, lumber, and paint. In selecting a location, the demand patterns in the different parts of the city were important. She commissioned a sampling study of the city that resulted in a two-way table for the variables residential location and product purchased. This table was prepared by the market research department using data obtained from the random sample of households in the three major residential areas of the city. Each residential area had a separate phone number prefix, and the last four digits were chosen using a computer random number generator. Is there a difference in the demand patterns for the three major items among the different areas of the city?

	Product Demand		
Area	Tools	Lumber	Paint
East	100	50	50
North	50	95	45
West	65	70	75

14.62 The Speedi-Flex delivery service is conducting a study of its delivery operations. As part of this study it collected data on package type by originating source for one day's operation for one district office in the Southeast. These data are shown in the table. The major originating sources were identified as (1) small cities (towns), (2) central business districts (CBDs), (3) light-manufacturing districts (factories), and (4) suburban residential communities (suburbs). Three major size and rate categories classify the items handled. Overnight envelopes must weigh 3 pounds or less and have a fixed charge of $12 anywhere in the United States. Small packages weigh from 4 to 10 pounds and have dimension restrictions. Large packages can weigh from 11 to 75 pounds and have the lowest rate per pound and the longest delivery time.

	Package Size (LB)			
Package Source	≤ 3	4–10	11–75	Total
Towns	40	40	20	100
CBDs	119	63	18	200
Factories	18	71	111	200
Suburbs	69	64	17	150

a. Are there any differences in the patterns of packages originated at the various locations?
b. Which two combinations have the largest percentage deviation from a uniform pattern?

14.63 A travel agent randomly sampled individuals in her target market and asked, Did you use a travel agent to book your last airline flight? By cross-referencing the answers to this question with the responses to the rest of the questionnaire, the agent obtained data such as that in the following contingency table:

	Did You Use a Travel Agent to Book Your Last Flight?	
Age	Yes	No
Under 30	15	30
30 to 39	20	42
40 to 49	47	42
50 to 59	36	50
60 or older	45	20

Determine if there is an association between the respondent's age and use of a travel agent to make reservations for the respondent's last flight.

14.64 Suppose the operations manager at a Honda service center conducts a survey on the level of satisfaction for the quality of workmanship based on the customer's gender. A random sample of 200 customers who recently availed of Honda's services were selected and the manager summarized the satisfaction levels into three categories (poor, average and perfect). Of the 90 female customers who participated in the survey, 13 rated the quality of workmanship as being poor, and 34 felt it was average. Among the male customers, 50% felt that the services were average, 20% rated it as poor, and 30% felt the quality of workmanship was perfect. Is there a relationship between the satisfaction rating and the customer's gender?

14.65   A random sample of companies was surveyed and asked to indicate if they had used an Internet career service site to search for prospective employees. The companies were also asked questions concerning the posting fee for use of such a site. Is there a relationship between use of such a site and management's opinion on the posting fee?

	Have You Used an Internet Career Service Site?	
Posting Fee	Yes	No
Fee is too high	36	50
Fee is about right	82	28

14.66 Suppose that a random sample of businesses that relocated in Florida within the last 3 years is surveyed. Do the data in the following contingency table show any relationship between the primary reason for the company's move to Florida and the industry type?

	Industry Type		
Primary Reason	Manufacturing	Retail	Tourism
Emerging technology	53	25	10
Tax credits	67	36	20
Labor force	30	40	33

14.67 Should large retailers offer banking services? Small community banks may be concerned about their future if more retailers enter the world of banking. Suppose that a market research company conducted a national survey for one retailer that is considering offering banking services to its customers. The respondents were asked to indicate the provider (bank, retail store, other) that they most likely would use for certain banking services (assuming that rate is not a factor). Is there a relationship between these two variables?

Service	Provider		
	Bank	Retail Store	Other
Checking account	100	45	10
Savings account	85	25	45
Home mortgage	30	10	80

14.68 Many easy-weight-loss products are just gimmicks that attract people with the hope of a fast way to a slimmer body. Suppose that a random sample of residents in one community was asked if they had ever tried a quick-weight-loss product. They were also asked if they thought that there should be stricter advertising controls to prohibit deceptive weight-loss advertising. Are respondents' views on advertising controls dependent on whether or not they had ever used a quick-weight-loss product?

Advertising	Used a Quick-Weight-Loss Product?	
	Yes	No
Stricter controls needed	85	40
Stricter controls not needed	25	64

14.69 Downsizing is one method companies may use in an attempt to reduce costs. Suppose that the following contingency table shows the number of layoffs in three manufacturing plants during the last 4 months and the length of service (in months) by those employees that were laid off. Is there any relationship between theses two variables?

Months of Service	Company		
	A	B	C
Less than 6 months	13	30	15
6 months to 1 year	15	11	10
More than 1 year	10	9	4

14.70 Two years ago the manager of a local supermarket that sells three national brands (brands A, B, and C) and one store brand (brand D) of orange juice found that brands A and C were equally preferred, 33% preferred brand B, and 27% preferred the store brand, D. Now, the manager thinks that there has been a change in customer preferences and that the preference for store-brand orange juice has increased and perhaps will positively contribute to increased profits. The results from a recent random sample of shoppers indicate the following preferences.

Favorite brand	A	B	C	D (store brand)
Number	56	70	28	126

Has there been a change in customer preferences from the study 2 years ago?

14.71 In Example 14.2 a random sample of 200 people was asked to indicate candy bar preference. Suppose that we also gathered demographic data such as gender. From the 50 who preferred Mr. Goodbar, it was found that 20% were female; from the 93 who preferred Hershey's Milk Chocolate, 70 were female; from the 45 who preferred Hershey's Special Dark, 80% were male;

and from the remainder who preferred Krackel, two-thirds were male. Do the data indicate that there is an association between candy bar preference and gender?

14.72 What does it mean to say that a test is nonparametric? What are the relative advantages of such tests?

14.73 In a random sample of 12 analysts, 7 believed that automobile sales in the United States were likely to be significantly higher next year than in the present year, 2 believed that sales would be significantly lower, and the others anticipated that next year's sales would be roughly the same as those in the current year. What can we conclude from these data?

14.74 In a random sample of 16 exchange rate analysts, 8 believed that the Japanese yen would be an excellent investment this year, 5 believed that it would be a poor investment, and 3 had no strong opinion on the question. What conclusions can be drawn from these data?

14.75 Of a random sample of 100 college students, 35 expected to achieve a higher standard of living than their parents, 43 expected a lower standard of living, and 22 expected about the same standard of living as their parents. Do these data present strong evidence that, for the population of students, more expect a lower standard of living compared with their parents than expect a higher standard of living?

14.76 Of a random sample of 120 business school professors, 48 believed students' analytical skills had improved over the last decade, 35 believed these skills had deteriorated, and 37 saw no discernible change. Evaluate the strength of the sample evidence suggesting that, for all business school professors, more believe that analytical skills have improved than believe that these skills have deteriorated.

14.77 A random sample of 10 corporate analysts was asked to rate, on a scale from 1 (very poor) to 10 (very high), the prospects for their own corporations and for the economy at large in the current year. The results obtained are shown in the accompanying table. Using the Wilcoxon signed rank test, discuss the proposition that in the aggregate corporate analysts are more optimistic about the prospects for their own companies than for the economy at large.

Analyst	Own Corporation	Economy at Large
1	8	8
2	7	5
3	6	7
4	5	4
5	8	4
6	6	9
7	7	7
8	5	2
9	4	6
10	9	6

14.78 Nine pairs of hypothetical profiles were constructed for corporate employees applying for admission to an executive MBA program. Within each pair, these profiles were identical, except that one candidate was male and the other female. For interviews for employment of these graduates, evaluations on a scale of 1 (low) to

10 (high) were made of the candidates' suitability for employment. The results are shown in the accompanying table. Analyze these data using the Wilcoxon signed rank test test.

Interview	Male	Female
1	8	8
2	9	10
3	7	5
4	4	7
5	8	8
6	9	9
7	5	3
8	4	5
9	6	2

14.79 Suppose that a random sample of 513 individuals were randomly sampled and information was collected about the method a subject used to make an airline reservation (last reservation for either business or pleasure) and the subject's gender. Test the null hypothesis of no association between these two characteristics. The data are summarized as follows:

Reservation Method	Female	Male
Used a travel agent	56	74
Booked on the Internet	148	142
Called the airline's toll-free number	66	34

REFERENCES

1. Bera, A. K., and C. M. Jarque. 1981. "An Efficient Large-Sample Test for Normality of Observations and Regression Residuals." *Working Papers in Economics and Econometrics* 40, Australian National University.

2. Butcher, Richard, Marketing Assistant. *RELEVANT Magazine*. 2011. www.RELEVANTmagazine.com.

3. Guenther, P. M., J. Reedy, S. M. Krebs-Smith, B. B. Reeve, and P. P. Basiotis. 2007. *Development and Evaluation of the Healthy Eating Index–2005: Technical Report*. Center for Nutrition Policy and Promotion, U.S. Department of Agriculture. Available at http://www.cnpp.usda.gov/HealthyEatingIndex.htm.

4. Hu, Winnie. "Math That Moves: Schools Embrace the iPad." *New York Times*, January 5, 2011, A16. Also available at http://www.nytimes.com/2011/01/05/education/05tablets.html (accessed April 23, 2011).

5. Jaggi, B., and P. Grier. 1980. "A Comparative Analysis of Forecast Disclosing and Nondisclosing Firms." *Financial Management* 9 (2): 38–43.

6. Michelson, Stuart, J. Stryker, and B. Thorne. 2009. "The Sarbanes-Oxley Act of 2002: What Impact Has It Had on Small Business Firms?" *Managerial Auditing Journal/Emerald Group Publishing Limited*, 24 (8): 743-766. www.emeraldinsight.com/maj.htm.

7. Mosteller, F., and D. L. Wallace. 1994. *Interference and Disputed Authorship: The Federalist*, Reading, Mass: Addison-Wesley. Tables 2.3 and 2.4. Reprinted with permission.

15

Analysis of Variance

Introduction

In modern business applications of statistical analysis, there are a number of situations that require comparisons of processes at more than two levels. For example, the manager of Integrated Circuits, Inc., would like to determine if any of five different processes for assembling components results in higher productivity per hour and/or in fewer defective components. Analyses to answer such questions come under the general heading of experimental design. An important tool for organizing and analyzing the data from this experiment is called *analysis of variance*, the subject of this chapter. The experiment might also be extended to a design that includes the question of which of four sources of raw materials leads to the highest productivity in combination with the different manufacturing processes. This question could be answered by using two-way analysis of variance. In another example the president of Prairie Flower Cereal is interested in comparing product sales per week of four different brands over three different stores. Again, we have a problem design that can be analyzed using analysis of variance. In Section 13.2 we showed that dummy variables could also be used for analysis of experimental design problems.

15.1 COMPARISON OF SEVERAL POPULATION MEANS

In Sections 10.1 and 10.2 we saw how to test the hypothesis of equality of two population means. In fact, two distinct tests were developed, the appropriate test depending on the mechanism employed in the generation of sample observations. Specifically, our tests assumed either paired observations or independent random samples. This distinction is important; to clarify it, we pause to consider a simple illustration. Suppose that it is our objective to compare the fuel consumption recorded for two different makes of automobile, A-cars and B-cars. We could randomly select 10 people to drive these cars over a specified distance, each driver being assigned to a car of each type, so that any particular driver will drive both an A-car and a B-car. The 20 resulting fuel-consumption figures obtained will consist of 10 pairs, each pair corresponding to a single driver. This is the matched pairs design, and its attraction lies in its ability to produce a comparison between the quantities of interest (in this case fuel consumption for the two types of car), while controlling for the possible importance of an additional relevant factor (individual driver differences). Thus, if a significant difference between the performance of A-cars and that of B-cars is found, we have some assurance that this is not a result of differences in driver behavior. An alternative design would be to take 20 drivers and randomly assign 10 of them to A-cars and 10 to B-cars (though, in fact, there is no need to have equal numbers of trials for each type of car). The 20 resulting fuel-consumption figures would then constitute a pair of independent random samples of 10 observations each on A-cars and B-cars.

For these two types of design, we discussed in Chapter 10 the appropriate procedures for testing the null hypothesis of equality of a pair of population means. In this chapter our aim is to extend these procedures to the development of tests for the equality of more than two population means. Suppose, for example, that our study included a third make of automobile, the C-car. The null hypothesis of interest would then be that the population mean fuel consumption is the same for all three makes of car. We show how tests for such hypotheses can be constructed, beginning with the case where independent random samples are taken. Suppose that out of 20 drivers, 7 are randomly assigned to A-cars, 7 to B-cars, and 6 to C-cars. Using the data in Table 15.1, we computed the following:

$$\text{sample mean for A-cars} = \frac{146.3}{7} = 20.9$$

$$\text{sample mean for B-cars} = \frac{162.4}{7} = 23.2$$

$$\text{sample mean for C-cars} = \frac{137.4}{6} = 22.9$$

Table 15.1 Fuel-Consumption Figures from Three Independent Random Samples, in Miles per Gallon

	A-CARS	B-CARS	C-CARS
	22.2	24.6	22.7
	19.9	23.1	21.9
	20.3	22.0	23.2
	21.4	23.5	24.1
	21.2	23.6	22.1
	21.0	22.1	23.4
	20.3	23.5	—
Sums	146.3	162.4	137.4

Naturally, these sample means are not all the same. As always, however, when testing hypotheses, we are interested in the likelihood of such differences arising by chance if, in fact, the null hypothesis was true. If it is concluded that such discrepancies would be very unlikely to arise by chance, we would have reason to reject the null hypothesis.

To clarify the issues involved, consider Figure 15.1, which depicts two hypothetical sets of data. The sample means in part (a) of the figure are precisely the same as those in part (b). The crucial difference is that in the former, the observations are tightly clustered about their respective sample means, whereas in the latter there is much greater dispersion. Visual inspection of part (a) suggests very strongly the conjecture that the data, in fact, arise from three populations with different means. Looking at part (b) of the figure, by contrast, we would not be terribly surprised to learn that these data came from a common population.

Figure 15.1 Two Sets of Sample Fuel-Consumption Data on Three Makes of Automobile

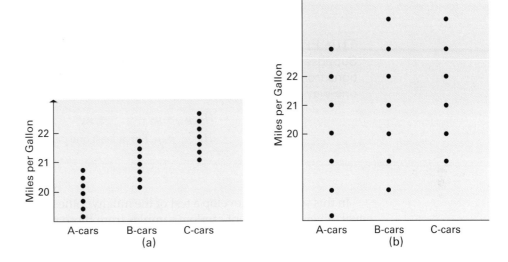

This illustration serves to point out the very essence of the test for equality of population means. The critical factor is the *variability* involved in the data. If the variability *around* the sample means is small compared with the variability *among* the sample means, as in Figure 15.1(a), we are inclined to doubt the null hypothesis that the population means are equal. If, as in Figure 15.1(b), the variability around the sample means is large compared with the variability among them, the evidence against the null hypothesis is rather weak. This being the case, it seems reasonable to expect that an appropriate test will be based on assessments of variation. This is indeed the case, and for this reason the general technique employed is referred to as the analysis of variance.

15.2 ONE-WAY ANALYSIS OF VARIANCE

The problem introduced in Section 15.1 can be treated quite generally. Suppose that we want to compare the means of K populations, *each of which is assumed to have the same variance*. Independent random samples of $n_1, n_2, \ldots, n_K$ observations are taken from these populations. We use the symbol x_{ij} to denote the jth observation in the ith population. Then, using the format of Table 15.1, we can display the sample data as in Table 15.2.

The procedure for testing the equality of population means in this setup is called **one-way analysis of variance**, a term that will become clearer when we discuss other analysis of variance models.

Table 15.2 Sample Observations from Independent Random Samples of K Populations

	POPULATION		
1	2	...	K
x_{11}	x_{21}	...	x_{K1}
x_{12}	x_{22}	...	x_{K2}
.	.		.
.	.		.
.	.		.
x_{1n}	x_{2n}	...	x_{Kn}

The Framework for One-Way Analysis of Variance

Suppose that we have independent random samples of $n_1, n_2, \ldots, n_K$ observations from K populations. If the population means are denoted $\mu_1, \mu_2, \ldots, \mu_K$, the one-way analysis of variance framework is designed to test the null hypothesis:

$$H_0 : \mu_1 = \mu_2 = \cdots = \mu_K$$
$$H_1 : \mu_i \neq \mu_j \text{ For at least one pair } \mu_i, \mu_j$$

In this section we develop a test of the null hypothesis that the K population means are equal, given independent random samples from those populations. The obvious first step is to calculate the sample means for the k groups of observations. These sample means are denoted $\bar{x}_1, \bar{x}_2, \ldots, \bar{x}_k$. Formally, then

$$\bar{x}_i = \frac{\sum_{j=1}^{n_i} x_{ij}}{n_i} (i = 1, 2, \ldots, K)$$

where n_i denotes the number of sample observations in group i. In this notation we have already found for the data of Table 15.1:

$$\bar{x}_1 = 20.9 \quad \bar{x}_2 = 23.2 \quad \bar{x}_3 = 22.9$$

Now, the null hypothesis of interest specifies that the K populations have a common mean. A logical step, then, is to form an estimate of that common mean from the sample observations. This is just the sum of all of the sample values divided by their total number. If we let n denote the total number of sample observations, then

$$n = \sum_{i=1}^{K} n_i$$

In our example $n = 20$. The overall mean of the sample observations can then be expressed as

$$\bar{\bar{x}} = \frac{\sum_{i=1}^{K} \sum_{j=1}^{n_i} x_{ij}}{n}$$

where the double summation notation indicates that we sum over all observations within each group and over all groups; that is, we sum all of the available observations. An equivalent expression is as follows:

$$\bar{\bar{x}} = \frac{\sum_{i=1}^{K} n_i \bar{x}_i}{n}$$

For the fuel consumption data of Table 15.1, the overall mean is as follows:

$$\bar{\bar{x}} = \frac{(7)(20.9) + (7)(23.2) + (6)(22.9)}{20} = 22.3$$

If, in fact, the population mean fuel consumption is the same for A-cars, B-cars, and C-cars, we then estimate that common mean to be 22.3 miles per gallon.

As indicated in Section 15.1, the test of equality of population means is based on a comparison of two types of variability exhibited by the sample members. The first is variability about the individual sample means within the K groups of observations. It is convenient to refer to this as *within-groups variability*. Second, we are interested in the variability among the K group means. This is called *between-groups variability*. We now seek measures, based on the sample data, of these two types of variability.

To begin, consider variability within groups. To measure variability in the first group, we calculate the sum of squared deviations of the observations about their sample mean $\bar{x}_1$, that is,

$$SS_1 = \sum_{j=1}^{n_1} (x_{1j} - \bar{x}_1)^2$$

Similarly, for the second group, whose sample mean is $\bar{x}_2$, we calculate

$$SS_2 = \sum_{j=1}^{n_2} (x_{2j} - \bar{x}_2)^2$$

and so on. The total within-groups variability, denoted SSW, is then the sum of the sums of squares over all K groups—that is,

$$SSW = SS_1 + SS_2 + \cdots + SS_K$$

or

$$SSW = \sum_{i=1}^{K} \sum_{j=1}^{n_i} (x_{ij} - \bar{x}_i)^2$$

For the data on fuel consumption we have the following:

$$SS_1 = (22.2 - 20.9)^2 + (19.9 - 20.9)^2 + \cdots + (20.3 - 20.9)^2 = 3.76$$
$$SS_2 = (24.6 - 23.2)^2 + (23.1 - 23.2)^2 + \cdots + (23.5 - 23.2)^2 = 4.96$$
$$SS_3 = (22.7 - 22.9)^2 + (21.9 - 22.9)^2 + \cdots + (23.4 - 22.9)^2 = 3.46$$

The within-group sum of squares is, therefore,

$$SSW = SS_1 + SS_2 + SS_3 = 3.76 + 4.96 + 3.46 = 12.18$$

Next, we need a measure of variability between groups. A natural measure is based on the discrepancies between the individual group means and the overall mean. In fact, as before, these discrepancies are squared, giving

$$(\bar{x}_1 - \bar{\bar{x}})^2, (\bar{x}_2 - \bar{\bar{x}})^2, \ldots, (\bar{x}_K - \bar{\bar{x}})^2$$

In computing the total between-group sum of squares, SSG, we weight each squared discrepancy by the number of sample observations in the corresponding group (so that the most weight is given to the squared discrepancies in groups with most observations), giving

$$SSG = \sum_{i=1}^{K} n_i (\bar{x}_i - \bar{\bar{x}})^2$$

Thus, for our fuel-consumption data,

$$SSG = (7)(20.9 - 22.3)^2 + (7)(23.2 - 22.3)^2 + (6)(22.9 - 22.3)^2$$
$$= 21.55$$

Another sum of squares is often calculated. This is the sum of squared discrepancies of *all* the sample observations about their *overall* mean. This is called the *total sum of squares* and is expressed as follows:

$$SST = \sum_{i=1}^{K} \sum_{j=1}^{n_i} (x_{ij} - \bar{\bar{x}})^2$$

In fact, we show in the appendix to this chapter that the total sum of squares is the sum of the within-group and between-group sums of squares—that is,

$$SST = SSW + SSG$$

Hence, for the fuel consumption data we have the following:

$$SST = 12.18 + 21.55 = 33.73$$

Sum of Squares Decomposition for One-Way Analysis of Variance

Suppose that we have independent random samples of $n_1, n_2, \ldots, n_K$ observations from K populations. Denote by $\bar{x}_1, \bar{x}_2, \ldots, \bar{x}_K$ the K group sample means and by $\bar{\bar{x}}$ the overall sample mean. We define the following **sums of squares**:

$$\text{within groups: } SSW = \sum_{i=1}^{K} \sum_{j=1}^{n_i} (x_{ij} - \bar{x}_i)^2 \qquad (15.1)$$

$$\text{between groups: } SSG = \sum_{i=1}^{K} n_i (\bar{x}_i - \bar{\bar{x}})^2 \qquad (15.2)$$

$$\text{total: } SST = \sum_{i=1}^{K} \sum_{j=1}^{n_i} (x_{ij} - \bar{\bar{x}})^2 \qquad (15.3)$$

where x_{ij} denotes the jth sample observation in the ith group.
Then,

$$SST = SSW + SSG \qquad (15.4)$$

The decomposition of the total sum of squares into the sum of two components—within-groups and between-groups sums of squares—provides the basis for the analysis of variance test of equality of group population means. We can view this decomposition as expressing the total variability of all the sample observations about their overall mean as the sum of variability within groups and variability between groups. Schematically, this is shown in Figure 15.2.

Figure 15.2
Sum of Squares
Decomposition for
One-Way Analysis
of Variance

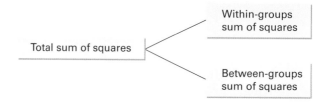

Our test of the equality of population means is based on the assumption that the K populations have a common variance. If the null hypothesis that the population means are all the same is true, each of the sums of squares, SSW and SSG, can be used as the basis for an estimate of the common population variance. To obtain these estimates, the sums of squares must be divided by the appropriate number of degrees of freedom.

First, we show in the chapter appendix that an unbiased estimator of the population variance results if SSW is divided by $(n - K)$. The resulting estimate is called the *within-groups mean square*, denoted MSW, so that

$$MSW = \frac{SSW}{n - K}$$

For our data we have the following:

$$MSW = \frac{12.18}{20 - 3} = 0.71647$$

If the population means are equal, another unbiased estimator of the population variance is obtained by dividing SSG by $(K - 1)$, also shown in the chapter appendix. The resulting quantity is called the *between-groups mean square*, denoted MSG, and, hence,

$$MSG = \frac{SSG}{K - 1}$$

For the fuel-consumption data,

$$MSG = \frac{21.55}{3 - 1} = 10.775$$

When the population means are *not* equal, the between-groups mean square does *not* provide an unbiased estimate of the common population variance. Rather, the expected value of the corresponding random variable exceeds the common population variance, as it also carries information about the squared differences of the true population means.

If the null hypothesis were true, we would now be in possession of two unbiased estimates of the same quantity, the common population variance. It would be reasonable to expect these estimates to be quite close to each other. The greater the discrepancy between these two estimates, all else being equal, the stronger our suspicion that the null hypothesis is not true. The test of the null hypothesis is based on the ratio of mean squares (see the chapter appendix):

$$F = \frac{MSG}{MSW}$$

If this ratio is quite close to 1, there is little cause to doubt the null hypothesis of equality of population means. However, as already noted, if the variability between groups is large compared to the variability within groups, we suspect the null hypothesis to be false. This is the case where a value considerably larger than 1 arises for the F ratio. The null hypothesis is rejected for large values of this ratio.

A formal test follows from the fact that, if the null hypothesis of equality of population means is true, the random variable follows the F distribution (discussed in Section 10.4) with numerator degrees of freedom $(K - 1)$ and denominator degrees of freedom $(n - K)$, assuming the population distributions to be normal.

Hypothesis Test for One-Way Analysis of Variance

Suppose that we have independent random samples of $n_1, n_2, \ldots, n_K$ observations from K populations. Denote by n the total sample size, so that

$$n = n_1 + n_2 + \cdots + n_K$$

We define the **mean squares** as follows:

$$\text{within groups}: MSW = \frac{SSW}{n - K} \qquad (15.5)$$

$$\text{between groups}: MSG = \frac{SSG}{K - 1} \qquad (15.6)$$

The null hypothesis to be tested is that the K population means are equal—that is,

$$H_0 : \mu_1 = \mu_2 = \cdots = \mu_K$$

We make the following additional assumptions:

1. The population variances are equal.
2. The population distributions are normal.

A test of significance level α is provided by the decision rule

$$\text{reject } H_0 \text{ if } \frac{\text{MSG}}{\text{MSW}} > F_{K-1, n-K, \alpha} \tag{15.7}$$

where $F_{K-1, n-K, \alpha}$ is the number for which

$$P(F_{K-1, n-K} > F_{K-1, n-K, \alpha}) = \alpha$$

and the random variable $F_{K-1, n-K}$ follows an F distribution with numerator degrees of freedom $(K-1)$ and denominator degrees of freedom $(n-K)$.

The p-value for this test is the smallest significance value that would allow us to reject the null hypothesis.

For the fuel-consumption data, we find the following:

$$\frac{\text{MSG}}{\text{MSW}} = \frac{10.775}{0.71647} = 15.039$$

The numerator and denominator degrees of freedom are, respectively, $(K-1) = 2$ and $(n-K) = 17$. Thus, for a 1% significance level test, from Appendix Table 9, we have the following:

$$F_{2,17,0.01} = 6.112$$

Hence, these data allow us to reject, at the 1% significance level, the null hypothesis that population mean fuel consumption is the same for all three types of automobiles.

The computations involved in carrying out this test are very conveniently summarized in a **one-way analysis of variance table**. The general form of the table is set out in Table 15.3. For the fuel consumption data the analysis of variance is set out in Table 15.4. Note that in some expositions the within-groups sum of squares is referred to as the *error sum of squares*.

Table 15.3
General Format of One-Way Analysis of Variance Table

SOURCE OF VARIATION	SUM OF SQUARES	DEGREES OF FREEDOM	MEAN SQUARES	F RATIO
Between groups	SSG	$K-1$	$\text{MSG} = \dfrac{\text{SSG}}{K-1}$	$\dfrac{\text{MSG}}{\text{MSW}}$
Within groups	SSW	$n-K$	$\text{MSW} = \dfrac{\text{SSW}}{n-K}$	
Total	SST	$n-1$		

Table 15.4
One-Way Analysis of Variance Table for Fuel-Consumption Data

SOURCE OF VARIATION	SUM OF SQUARES	DEGREES OF FREEDOM	MEAN SQUARES	F RATIO
Between groups	21.55	2	10.78	15.05
Within groups	12.18	17	0.7165	
Total	33.73	19		

Example 15.1 Reading Difficulty of Magazine Advertisements (One-Way Analysis of Variance)

The *fog index* is used to measure the reading difficulty of a written text: The higher the value of the index, the more difficult the reading level. We want to know if the reading difficulty index is different for three magazines: *Scientific American, Fortune,* and the *New Yorker*.

Solution Independent random samples of 6 advertisements were taken from *Scientific American, Fortune,* and the *New Yorker,* and the fog indices for the 18 advertisements were measured, as recorded in Table 15.5 (Shuptrine and McVicker 1981).

Table 15.5 Fog Index of Reading Difficulty for Three Magazines

SCIENTIFIC AMERICAN	FORTUNE	NEW YORKER
15.75	12.63	9.27
11.55	11.46	8.28
11.16	10.77	8.15
9.92	9.93	6.37
9.23	9.87	6.37
8.20	9.42	5.66

From these data we can derive the analysis of variance table using a statistical program such as Minitab. Figure 15.3 contains the analysis of variance output. To test the null hypothesis that the population mean fog indices are the same, the computed F ratio—$F = 6.97$—in the analysis of variance table must be compared with tabulated values of the F distribution with $(2, 15)$ degrees of freedom. From Appendix Table 9 we find the following:

$$F_{2,15,0.01} = 6.359$$

Figure 15.3 One-Way Analysis of Variance for Reading Difficulty in *Scientific American, Fortune,* and the *New Yorker* (Minitab Output)

One-way ANOVA: SCIENTIFIC AMERICAN, FORTUNE, NEW YORKER

```
Source    DF       SS     MS      F      P
Factor     2    48.53  24.26   6.97  0.007
Error     15    52.22   3.48
Total     17   100.75

S = 1.866    R-Sq = 48.17%    R-Sq(adj) = 41.26%


                                 Individual 95% CIs For Mean Based on
                                 Pooled StDev
Level              N    Mean   StDev   -+-------+-------+-------+----
SCIENTIFIC AMERI   6  10.968   2.647               (------*------)
FORTUNE            6  10.680   1.202             (------*------)
NEW YORKER         6   7.350   1.412   (------*------)
                                       -+-------+-------+-------+----
                                      6.0     8.0    10.0    12.0

Pooled StDev = 1.866
```

Thus, the null hypothesis of equality of the three population mean fog indices is rejected at the 1% significance level. Note also that the computed *p*-value as found in Figure 15.3 is 0.007. We have strong evidence that the reading difficulty is different, with the *New Yorker* having the lowest index. Note that the Minitab output provides a graphical display of subgroup means and their confidence intervals. This output provides a visual display of the differences between subgroup means, noting in this case that the *New Yorker* differs substantially from *Scientific American* and *Fortune*.

Multiple Comparisons Between Subgroup Means

After we have concluded that subgroup means are different by rejecting the null hypothesis, we might naturally ask which subgroup means are different from others. Thus, we would like to have a minimal interval that could be used to decide if two subgroup means are different in a statistical sense. Or, more precisely, can we reject a hypothesis that certain of the subgroup means are not different from others when we have concluded that at least one of the subgroup means is different from others? This is an important question for applied analysis—but one that leads to certain additional complications.

If we have two subgroups, then we can use the hypothesis-testing methods developed in Chapter 10 to compute a minimum significant difference (MSD) between two sample means that would lead us to reject the hypothesis that the population means are equal and, thus, that we have evidence to conclude that the population means are different. In those cases we would compute a common estimate of variance s_p and the resulting MSD can be computed as follows:

$$\text{MSD} = t_{\alpha/2} s_p \sqrt{\frac{1}{n_1} + \frac{1}{n_2}}$$

Although this procedure, based on hypothesis tests with probability of error α, works well for two subgroups, it does not work well when there are K subgroups. In that case the number of paired comparisons can be computed using the combinations equation developed in Chapter 3:

$$C_2^K = \frac{K!}{(K-2)!\,2!}$$

Where n_1 and n_2 are the subgroup sample sizes. Thus, the probability of error α would no longer hold.

A number of procedures have been developed to deal with the multiple-comparisons question. Essentially, they involve developing intervals that are somewhat wider than those for the two-subgroup case. These intervals are developed using advanced mathematical statistics analysis that provides intervals with the correct α levels for many subgroups. We present here a procedure developed by John Tukey, which uses an extended form of the Student's t distribution. Factors identified as Q are presented in Appendix Table 13 for various numbers of subgroups, degrees of freedom, and α equal to 0.01 and 0.05.

Multiple-Comparison Procedure
The minimum significant difference between K subgroups is computed using

$$\text{MSD}(K) = Q \frac{s_p}{\sqrt{n}}$$

with

$$s_p = \sqrt{\text{MSW}}$$

with the factor q selected from Table 13 for the appropriate level of α (0.01, 0.05), the number of subgroups K, and the degrees of freedom for MSW. To obtain the value of Q from Table 13, note that in Table 13 the columns are based on the number of subgroups and the rows indicate the degrees of freedom for error. The resulting MSD can be used to indicate which subgroup means are different and, thus, provides a very useful screening device that can be used to extend the results from the analyses we have discussed here.

Population Model for One-Way Analysis of Variance

It is instructive to view the one-way analysis of variance model in a different light. Let the random variable X_{ij} denote the jth observation from the ith population, and let μ_i stand for the mean of this population. Then X_{ij} can be viewed as the sum of two parts—its mean and a random variable ε_{ij} having a mean of 0. Therefore, we can write the following:

$$X_{ij} = \mu_i + \varepsilon_{ij}$$

Now, because independent random samples are taken, the random variables ε_{ij} will be uncorrelated with one another. Moreover, given our assumption that the population variances are all the same, it follows that the ε_{ij} all have the same variances. This equation can be viewed as such a model, with unknown parameters $\mu_1, \mu_2, \ldots, \mu_K$. The null hypothesis of interest is as follows:

$$H_0 : \mu_1 = \mu_2 = \cdots = \mu_K$$

A test on these parameters is facilitated by the further assumption of normality.

The model can be written in a slightly different manner. Let μ denote the overall mean of the K combined populations and G_i be the discrepancy between the population mean for the ith group and this overall mean, so that

$$G_i = \mu_i - \mu \ \text{ or } \ \mu_i = \mu + G_i$$

Substituting into the original equation gives

$$X_{ij} = \mu + G_i + \varepsilon_{ij}$$

so that an observation is made up of the sum of an overall mean μ, a group-specific term G_i, and a random error ε_{ij}. Then, our null hypothesis is that every population mean μ_i is the same as the overall mean, or

$$H_0 : G_1 = G_2 = \cdots = G_K = 0$$

This population model and some of the assumptions are illustrated in Figure 15.4. For the fuel-consumption data, each type of car's, actual fuel consumption recorded in any trial can be represented by a normally distributed random variable. The population means of fuel consumption, μ_1, μ_2, and μ_3, for A-cars, B-cars, and C-cars, respectively, determine the centers of these distributions. According to our assumption these population distributions must have the same variances. Figure 15.4 also shows the mean μ of the three combined populations and the differences G_i between the individual population means and the overall mean. Finally, for B-cars, we have marked by a dot the ith sample observation. The random variable ε_{ij} is then the difference between the observed value and the mean of the sub-population i from which it is drawn.

Figure 15.4
Illustration of the
Population Model
for the One-Way
Analysis of Variance

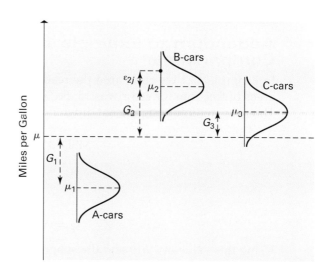

Basic Exercises

15.1 Given the following analysis of variance table, compute mean squares for between groups and within groups. Compute the F ratio and test the hypothesis that the group means are equal.

Source of Variation	Sum of Squares	Degrees of Freedom
Between groups	1,728	4
Within groups	624	13
Total	2,352	17

15.2 Given the following analysis of variance table, compute mean squares for between groups and within groups. Compute the F ratio and test the hypothesis that the group means are equal.

Source of Variation	Sum of Squares	Degrees of Freedom
Between groups	879	3
Within groups	798	16
Total	1,677	19

15.3 Given the information in the following table, compute the F ratio and test the hypothesis that the group means are equal. The SST = 378.

	Group 1	Group 2	Group 3
Size, n_i	18	12	13
Mean, $\bar{x}_i$	2.1	6.4	5.6
SS_i	33	68	49

Application Exercises

15.4 A manufacturer of cereal is considering three alternative box colors—red, yellow, and blue. To check whether such a consideration has any effect on sales, 16 stores of approximately equal size are chosen. Red boxes are sent to 6 of these stores, yellow boxes to 5 others, and blue boxes to the remaining 5. After a few days a check is made on the number of sales in each store. The results (in tens of boxes) shown in the following table were obtained.

Red	Yellow	Blue
43	52	61
52	37	29
59	38	38
76	64	53
61	74	79
81		

a. Calculate the within-groups, between-groups, and total sum of squares.
b. Complete the analysis of variance table, and test the null hypothesis that the population mean sales levels are the same for all three box colors.

15.5 An instructor at the University of Liège, Belgium, teaches a class of 28 students. At the beginning of the semester, each student is randomly assigned to one of four teaching assistants—Lucas, Emma, Arthur, or Sofia. The students are encouraged to meet with their assigned teaching assistant to discuss difficult course material. At the end of the semester, a common examination is administered. The scores obtained by students working with the teaching assistants are shown in the accompanying table.

Lucas	Emma	Arthur	Sofia
29	53	23	37
42	40	34	38
33	39	24	50
22	32	43	48
46	49	30	41
24	36	27	35
55	45	31	38

a. Calculate the within-groups, between-groups, and total sum of squares.
b. Complete the analysis of variance table and test the null hypothesis of equality of population mean scores for the teaching assistants.

15.6 Three suppliers provide parts in shipments of 500 units. Random samples of six shipments from each of the three suppliers were carefully checked, and the numbers of parts not conforming to standards were recorded. These numbers are listed in the following table:

Supplier A	Supplier B	Supplier C
28	22	33
37	27	29
34	29	39
29	20	33
31	18	37
33	30	38

a. Prepare the analysis of variance table for these data.
b. Test the null hypothesis that the population mean numbers of parts per shipments not conforming to standards are the same for all three suppliers.
c. Compute the minimum significant difference and indicate which subgroups have different means.

15.7 Starbucks is launching their new member cards in three different designs for this coming Christmas. A branch manager would like to know whether the average sales of the three cards are the same for 5 consecutive weeks. The accompanying sales records of the three cards for her branch were obtained.

Week	Card 1	Card 2	Card 3
1	22	14	13
2	13	36	27
3	6	19	14
4	21	5	30
5	18	23	22

a. Prepare the analysis of variance table for these data.
b. Test the null hypothesis that the population mean that the average sale of the three cards are the same for the five consecutive weeks.
c. Compute the minimum significant difference for the three cards.

15.8 Random samples of seven freshmen, seven sophomores, and seven juniors taking a business statistics class were drawn. The accompanying table shows scores on the final examination.

Freshmen	Sophomores	Juniors
82	71	64
93	62	73
61	85	87
74	94	91
69	78	56
70	66	78
53	71	87

a. Prepare the analysis of variance table.
b. Test the null hypothesis that the three population mean scores are equal.
c. Compute the minimum significant difference and indicate which subgroups have different means.

15.9 Samples of four salespeople from each of four regions were asked to predict percentage increases in sales volume for their territories in the next 12 months. The predictions are shown in the accompanying table.

West	Midwest	South	East
6.8	7.2	4.2	9.0
4.2	6.6	4.8	8.0
5.4	5.8	5.8	7.2
5.0	7.0	4.6	7.6

a. Prepare the analysis of variance table.
b. Test the null hypothesis that the four population mean sales growth predictions are equal.

15.10 Independent random samples of six assistant professors, four associate professors, and five full professors were asked to estimate the amount of time outside the classroom spent on teaching responsibilities in the last week. Results, in hours, are shown in the accompanying table.

Assistant	Associate	Full
7	15	11
12	12	7
11	15	6
15	8	9
9		7
14		

a. Prepare the analysis of variance table.
b. Test the null hypothesis that the three population mean times are equal.

15.11 Two tutoring services offer crash courses in preparation for the CPA exam. To check on the effectiveness of these services, twenty-one students were chosen. Seven students were randomly assigned to service A, seven were assigned to service B, and the remaining seven did not take a crash course. Their scores on the examination, expressed as percentages, are given in the following table.

Service A	Service B	No Course
61	91	99
65	88	83
71	74	75
52	56	95
67	76	62
58	81	69
78	66	80

a. Prepare the analysis of variance table.
b. Test the null hypothesis that the three population mean operating cost are the same.
c. Compute the minimum significant difference and indicate which subgroups have different means.

15.12 In the study of Example 15.1, independent random samples of six advertisements from *True Confessions*, *People Weekly*, and *Newsweek* were taken. The fog indices for these advertisements are given in the accompanying table. Test the null hypothesis that the population mean fog indices are the same for advertisements in these three magazines and compute the minimum significant difference and indicate which subgroups have different means.

True Confessions	People Weekly	Newsweek
12.89	9.50	10.21
12.69	8.60	9.66
11.15	8.59	7.67
9.52	6.50	5.12
9.12	4.79	4.88
7.04	4.29	3.12

15.13 Independent random samples of 6 advertisements were taken from three different magazines: *EuroScientist*, *Focus*, and *Science Reporter*. The fog indices, measuring the reading difficulty of a written text, were taken and are given in the accompanying table. For the one-way analysis of variance model, we write the *j*th observation from the *i*th group as

$$X_{ij} = \mu + G_i + \varepsilon_{ij}$$

where μ is the overall mean, G_i is the effect specific to the *i*th group, and ε_{ij} is a random error for the *j*th observation from the *i*th group.

EuroScientist	Focus	Science Reporter
12.53	9.46	11.15
11.95	9.26	10.41
10.65	7.88	9.27
9.07	5.99	8.22
8.11	5.32	6.61
5.61	4.82	6.25

a. Estimate μ.
b. Estimate G_i for each of the three magazines.
c. Estimate ε_{13}, the error term corresponding to the thrid observation (10.65) for *EuroScience*.

15.14 Use the model for the one-way analysis of variance for the data of Exercise 15.12.

a. Estimate μ.
b. Estimate G_i for each of the three magazines.
c. Estimate ε_{13}, the error term corresponding to the thrid observation (11.15) for *True Confessions*.

15.3 THE KRUSKAL-WALLIS TEST

As we have already noted, the one-way analysis of variance test of Section 15.2 generalizes to the multipopulation case for the *t* test comparing two population means when independent random samples are available. The test is based on an assumption that the underlying population distributions are normal. In Section 14.6 we introduced the Mann-Whitney test, a nonparametric test that is valid for the comparison of the central locations of two populations based on independent random samples, even when the population distributions are not normal. It is also possible to develop a nonparametric alternative to the one-way analysis of variance test. This is known as the **Kruskal-Wallis test**, employed when an investigator has strong grounds for suspecting that the parent population distributions may be markedly different from the normal.

Like the majority of the nonparametric tests we have already encountered, the Kruskal-Wallis test is based on the *ranks* of the sample observations. We illustrate the computation of the test statistic by reference to the fuel-consumption data of Table 15.1. The sample values are all pooled together and ranked in ascending order, as in Table 15.6, using the average of adjacent ranks in the case of ties.

Table 15.6 Fuel-Consumption Figures (in Miles per Gallon) and Ranks from Three Independent Random Samples

A-Cars	Rank	B-Cars	Rank	C-Cars	Rank
22.2	11	24.6	20	22.7	12
19.9	1	23.1	13	21.9	7
20.3	2.5	22.0	8	23.2	14
21.4	6	23.5	16.5	24.1	19
21.2	5	23.6	18	22.1	9.5
21.0	4	22.1	9.5	23.4	15
20.3	2.5	23.5	16.5		
Rank sum	**32**		**101.5**		**76.5**

The test is based on the sums of the ranks $R_1, R_2, \ldots, R_K$ for the K samples. In the fuel-consumption example,

$$R_1 = 32 \quad R_2 = 101.5 \quad R_3 = 76.5$$

Now, the null hypothesis to be tested is that the three population means are the same. We would be suspicious of that hypothesis if there were substantial differences among the average ranks for the K samples. In fact, our test is based on the statistic where n_i are the sample sizes in the K groups and n is the total number of sample observations. Define W as follows:

$$W = \frac{12}{n(n+1)} \sum_{i=1}^{k} \frac{R_i^2}{n_i} - 3(n+1)$$

The null hypothesis would be in doubt if a large value for W were observed. The basis for the test follows from the fact that, unless the sample sizes are very small, the random variable corresponding to the test statistic has, under the null hypothesis, a distribution that is well approximated by the χ^2 distribution with $(K-1)$ degrees of freedom.

The Kruskal-Wallis Test

Suppose that we have independent random samples of $n_1, n_2, \ldots n_K$ observations from K populations. Let

$$n = n_1 + n_2 + \cdots + n_K$$

denote the total number of sample observations. Denote by $R_1, R_2, \ldots, R_K$ the sums of ranks for the K samples when the sample observations are pooled together and ranked in ascending order. The test of the null hypothesis, H_0, of equality of the population means is based on the statistic

$$W = \frac{12}{n(n+1)} \sum_{i=1}^{k} \frac{R_i^2}{n_i} - 3(n+1) \tag{15.8}$$

A test of significance level α is given by the decision rule

$$\text{reject } H_0 \text{ if } W > \chi^2_{k-1,\alpha} \tag{15.9}$$

where $\chi^2_{K-1,\alpha}$ is the number that is exceeded with probability α by a χ^2 random variable with $(K-1)$ degrees of freedom.

This test procedure is approximately valid, provided that the sample contains at least five observations from each population.

For our fuel-consumption data, we find the following:

$$W = \frac{12}{(20)(21)} \left[\frac{(32)^2}{7} + \frac{(101.5)^2}{7} + \frac{(76.5)^2}{6} \right] - (3)(21) = 11.10$$

Here, we have $(K-1) = 2$ degrees of freedom, so for a 1% significance level test, we find from Appendix Table 7 that

$$\chi^2_{2,0.01} = 9.210$$

Hence, the null hypothesis that the population mean fuel consumption is the same for the three types of automobiles can be rejected even at the 1% significance level. Of course, we also rejected this hypothesis using the analysis of variance test of Section 15.2. However, here we have been able to do so without imposing the assumption of normality of the population distributions.

Example 15.2 Importance of Brand Names (Kruskal-Wallis Test)

A research study was designed to determine if women from different occupational subgroups assign different levels of importance to brand names when purchasing soft drinks.

Solution Independent random samples of 101 clerical, 112 administrative, and 96 professional women were asked to rate, on a scale from 1 to 7, the importance attached to brand name when purchasing soft drinks. The value of the Kruskal-Wallis statistic for this study was reported as 25.22. Test the null hypothesis that the population mean ratings are the same for these three subgroups.

The calculated test statistic is as follows:

$$W = 25.22$$

Since there are $K = 3$ groups, we have, for a 1% test,

$$\chi^2_{k-1,\alpha} = \chi^2_{2,0.01} = 9.210$$

Thus, the null hypothesis that the three population mean ratings are the same is very clearly rejected on the evidence of this sample, even at the 1% level of significance. We have strong evidence that women from different occupational subgroups assign different levels of importance to brand names.

EXERCISES

Basic Exercises

15.15 Consider a problem with three subgroups with different subgroup sizes of $n_1 = 8$, $n_2 = 7$, and $n_3 = 6$. The sum of ranks in each of these subgroups equal to 131, 58, and 42. Complete the Kruskal-Wallis test and test the null hypothesis to determine whether the three subgroups equal mean at 5% significance level.

15.16 Consider a problem with three subgroups with the ranks in each subgroup shown as follows. Complete the Kruskal-Wallis test and test the null hypothesis to determine whether the subgroups have equal mean at 10% significance level.
Sample 1 rankings: 7, 2.5, 9.5, 6, 4, 12, 19
Sample 2 rankings: 1, 8, 18, 9.5, 15, 5, 13, 20
Sample 3 rankings: 16, 14, 2.5, 17, 11

15.17 Consider a problem with four subgroups with the sum of ranks in each of the subgroups equal to 227, 151, 198, and 271 and with subgroup sizes equal to 5, 9, 15, and 12. Complete the Kruskal-Wallis test and test the null hypothesis to determine whether the subgroups have equal means at 1% significance level.

Application Exercises

15.18 For the data of Exercise 15.4, use the Kruskal-Wallis test of the null hypothesis that the population mean sales levels are identical for three box colors.

15.19 Using the data of Exercise 15.5, perform a Kruskal-Wallis test of the null hypothesis that the population mean test scores are the same for students assigned to the four teaching assistants.

15.20 Using the data of Exercise 15.6, carry out a test of the null hypothesis of equality of the three population mean numbers of parts per shipment not conforming to standards without assuming normality of population distributions.

15.21 For the data of Exercise 15.7, test the null hypothesis that the population mean operating costs per mile are the same for all three types of cards without assuming normal population distributions.

15.22 Using the data of Exercise 15.8, carry out a nonparametric test of the null hypothesis of equality of population mean examination scores for freshmen, sophomores, and juniors.

15.23 Based on the data of Exercise 15.9, use the Kruskal-Wallis method to test the null hypothesis of equality of growth predictions for population mean sales for the four regions.

15.24 Refer to Exercise 15.10. Without assuming normal population distributions, test the null hypothesis that the population mean times spent outside the classroom on teaching responsibilities are the same for assistant, associate, and full professors.

15.25 Based on the data of Exercise 15.11, perform the Kruskal-Wallis test of the null hypothesis of equal population mean scores on the CPA exam for students using no tutoring services and using services A and B.

15.26 A pharmacist randomly selected a group of 45 individuals with a similar level of back pain. The participants randomly distributed into three treatment groups in which using three different medicines (M1, M2 and M3) to treat their back pain for a period of one month. During the treatment, the daily amounts of the medicines taken by the participants are recorded. The pharmacist wants to compare the levels of pain experienced by the different groups at the end of the treatment.

a. What test is suitable for the pharmacist to achieve his goal? Why?

b. Give two assumptions for conducting the suggest test.

15.4 Two-Way Analysis of Variance: One Observation per Cell, Randomized Blocks

Although our primary interest lies in the analysis of one particular feature of an experiment, we may suspect that a second factor could exert an important influence on the outcome. In the earliest sections of this chapter we discussed an experiment in which the objective was to compare the fuel consumption of three types of automobiles. Data were collected from three independent random samples of trials and analyzed through a one-way analysis of variance. It was assumed that the variability in the sample data was due to two causes—genuine differences between the performance characteristics of these three types of car and random variation. In fact, we might suspect that part of the observed random variability could be explained by differences in driver habits. Now, if this last factor could be isolated, the amount of random variability in the experiment would be reduced accordingly. This might, in turn, make it easier to detect differences in the performance of the automobiles. In other words, by designing an experiment to account for differences in driver characteristics, we hope to achieve a more powerful test of the null hypothesis that population mean fuel consumption is the same for all types of automobiles.

In fact, it is quite straightforward to design an experiment in such a way that the influence of a second factor of this kind can be taken into account. Suppose, once again, that we have three makes of automobile (say, α-cars, β-cars, and γ-cars) whose fuel economies we wish to compare. We consider an experiment in which six trials are to be run with each type of car. If these trials are conducted using six drivers, each of whom drives a car of all three types, it will be possible, since every car type will have been tested by every driver, to extract from the results information about driver variability as well as information about the differences among the three types of car. The additional variable—in this case, drivers—is sometimes called a *blocking variable*. The experiment is said to be arranged in *blocks*; in our example there would be six blocks, one for each driver.

This kind of blocked design can be used to obtain information about two factors simultaneously. For example, suppose that we want to compare fuel economy obtained not only by different types of automobiles, but also by different types of drivers. In particular, we may be interested in the effect of driver age on fuel economy. To do this, drivers can be subdivided into age categories. We might use the following six age classes (in years):

1. 25 and under
2. 26–35
3. 36–45
4. 46–55
5. 56–65
6. Over 65

Then we can arrange our experiment so that an automobile from each group is driven by a driver from each age class. In this way, in addition to testing the hypothesis that population mean fuel consumption is the same for each automobile type, we can test the hypothesis that population mean fuel consumption is the same for each age class.

In fact, whether a car of each type is driven by each of six drivers or a car of each type is driven by a driver from each of six age classes, the procedure for testing equality of population mean fuel consumption for the automobile types is the same. In this section we use the latter design for purposes of illustration.

Table 15.7 gives results for an experiment involving three automobile types and six driver age classes. The comparison of automobile types is the main focus of interest, and driver ages are used as a blocking variable.

This kind of design is called a **randomized blocks design**. The randomization arises because we randomly select one driver from the first age class to drive an α-car, one driver from the second age class to drive an α-car, and so on. This procedure is repeated for each driver class and for each of the car types. If possible, the trials should be carried out in random order rather than block by block.

Table 15.7   Sample Observations on Fuel Consumption Recorded for Three Types of Automobiles Driven by Drivers in Six Classes

	Automobile Type			
Driver Class	α-Cars	β-Cars	γ-Cars	Sum
1	25.1	23.9	26.0	75.0
2	24.7	23.7	25.4	73.8
3	26.0	24.4	25.8	76.2
4	24.3	23.3	24.4	72.0
5	23.9	23.6	24.2	71.7
6	24.2	24.5	25.4	74.1
Sum	148.2	143.4	151.2	442.8

Suppose that we have K groups and that there are H blocks. We use x_{ij} to denote the sample observation corresponding to the ith group and the jth block. Then, the sample data may be set out as in Table 15.8.

Table 15.8
Sample Observation on K Groups and H Blocks

	Group			
Block	1	2	. . .	K
1	x_{11}	x_{21}	. . .	x_{K1}
2	x_{12}	x_{22}	. . .	x_{K2}
.	.	.		.
.	.	.		.
.	.	.		.
H	x_{1H}	x_{2H}	. . .	x_{KH}

To develop a test of the hypothesis that the population means are the same for all K groups, we require the sample means for these groups. For the mean of the ith group, we use the notation $\bar{x}_{i\cdot}$, so

$$\bar{x}_{i\cdot} = \frac{\sum_{j=1}^{H} x_{ij}}{H} \quad (i = 1, 2, \ldots, K)$$

From Table 15.7 we obtain the following:

$$\bar{x}_{1\cdot} = \frac{148.2}{6} = 24.7 \quad \bar{x}_{2\cdot} = \frac{143.4}{6} = 23.9 \quad \bar{x}_{3\cdot} = \frac{151.2}{6} = 25.2$$

We are also interested in the differences in the population block means. Hence, we require the sample means for the H blocks. We use $\bar{x}_{\cdot j}$ to denote the sample mean for the jth block, so

$$\bar{x}_{\cdot j} = \frac{\sum_{i=1}^{K} x_{ij}}{K} \quad (j = 1, 2, \ldots, H)$$

For the fuel-consumption data of Table 15.7, we have the following:

$$\bar{x}_{\cdot 1} = \frac{75.0}{3} = 25.0 \quad \bar{x}_{\cdot 2} = \frac{73.8}{3} = 24.6 \quad \bar{x}_{\cdot 3} = \frac{76.2}{3} = 25.4$$

$$\bar{x}_{\cdot 4} = \frac{72.0}{3} = 24.0 \quad \bar{x}_{\cdot 5} = \frac{71.7}{3} = 23.9 \quad \bar{x}_{\cdot 6} = \frac{74.1}{3} = 24.7$$

Finally, we require the overall mean of the sample observations. If n denotes the total number of observations, then

$$n = HK$$

and the sample mean observation is as follows:

$$\bar{\bar{x}} = \frac{\sum\limits_{i=1}^{K}\sum\limits_{j=1}^{H} x_{ij}}{n} = \frac{\sum\limits_{i=1}^{K} \bar{x}_{i\cdot}}{K} = \frac{\sum\limits_{j=1}^{H} x_{\cdot j}}{H}$$

For the data of Table 15.7,

$$\bar{\bar{x}} = \frac{442.8}{18} = 24.6$$

Before considering the form of an appropriate test for the hypothesis of interest, it is useful to examine the population model that is implicitly being assumed. Let the random variable X_{ij} correspond to the observation for the ith group and jth block. This value is then regarded as the sum of the following four components:

1. An "overall" mean μ
2. A parameter G_i, which is specific to the ith group and measures the discrepancy between the mean for that group and the overall mean
3. A parameter B_j, which is specific to the ith block and measures the discrepancy between the mean for that block and the overall mean
4. A random variable ε_{ij}, which represents experimental error, or that part of the observation not explained by either the overall mean or the group or block membership

We can therefore write the following:

$$X_{ij} = \mu + G_i + B_j + \varepsilon_{ij}$$

The error term ε_{ij} is taken to obey the standard assumptions of the multiple regression model. In particular, then, we assume independence and equality of variances.

We can now write this as follows:

$$X_{ij} - \mu = G_i + B_j + \varepsilon_{ij}$$

Now, given sample data, the overall mean μ is estimated by the overall sample mean $\bar{\bar{x}}$, so an estimate of the left-hand side is provided by $(x_{ij} - \bar{\bar{x}})$. The difference G_i between the population mean for the ith group and the overall population mean is estimated by the corresponding difference in sample means, $(\bar{x}_{i\cdot} - \bar{\bar{x}})$. Similarly, B_j is estimated by $(\bar{x}_{\cdot j} - \bar{\bar{x}})$. Finally, by subtraction, we estimate the error term by

$$(x_{ij} - \bar{\bar{x}}) - (\bar{x}_{i\cdot} - \bar{\bar{x}}) - (\bar{x}_{\cdot j} - \bar{\bar{x}}) = x_{ij} - \bar{x}_{i\cdot} - \bar{x}_{\cdot j} + \bar{\bar{x}}$$

Thus, we have for the sample members

$$(x_{ij} - \bar{\bar{x}}) = (\bar{x}_{i\cdot} - \bar{\bar{x}}) - (\bar{x}_{\cdot j} - \bar{\bar{x}}) + (x_{ij} - \bar{x}_{i\cdot} - \bar{x}_{\cdot j} + \bar{\bar{x}})$$

To illustrate, consider the fuel consumption recorded by a driver from the third class with an α-car. From Table 15.7,

$$x_{13} = 26.0$$

The term on the left-hand side is as follows:

$$x_{13} - \bar{\bar{x}} = 26.0 - 24.6 = 1.4$$

For the group (automobile) effect, we have the following:

$$\bar{x}_{1\cdot} - \bar{\bar{x}} = 24.7 - 24.6 = 0.1$$

(Notice that this term will result whenever the α-car is driven.) For the block (driver) effect, we have the following:

$$\bar{x}_{\cdot 3} - \bar{\bar{x}} = 25.4 - 24.6 = 0.8$$

Finally, the error term is as follows:

$$x_{13} - \bar{x}_1. - \bar{x}_{.3} + \bar{\bar{x}} = 26.0 - 24.7 - 25.4 + 24.6 = 0.5$$

Thus, we have, for this observation,

$$1.4 = 0.1 + 0.8 + 0.5$$

We can interpret this equation as follows: When a driver from the third age class tested the α-car, he consumed 1.4 miles per gallon more than the average for all cars and drivers. Of this amount, it is estimated that 0.1 is due to the automobile, 0.8 is due to the driver age class, and the remaining 0.5 results from other factors, which we put down to chance variability or experimental error.

Now, if both sides are squared and summed over all n sample observations, it can be shown that the result is as follows:

$$\sum_{i=1}^{K}\sum_{j=1}^{H}(x_{ij} - \bar{\bar{x}})^2 = H\sum_{i=1}^{K}(\bar{x}_i. - \bar{\bar{x}})^2 + K\sum_{j=1}^{H}(\bar{x}_{.j} - \bar{\bar{x}})^2 + \sum_{i=1}^{K}\sum_{j=1}^{H}(x_{ij} - \bar{x}_i. - \bar{x}_{.j} + \bar{\bar{x}})^2$$

This equation expresses the total sample variability of the observations about their overall mean as the sum of variabilities due to differences among groups, differences among blocks, and error, respectively. It is on the decomposition of these sums of squares that the analysis of experiments of this type is based. The analysis is called two-way analysis of variance, since the data are categorized in two ways, according to groups and blocks.

We illustrate this important sum of squares decomposition in Figure 15.5. Notice, by contrast with the decomposition for the one-way analysis of variance, that the total sum of squares of the sample observations about their overall mean is broken down here into *three* components. We summarize the components in Equations 15.10 to 15.14; the extra component arises because of our ability to extract from the data information about differences among blocks.

Figure 15.5 Sum of Squares Decomposition for Two-Way Analysis of Variance with One Observation per Cell

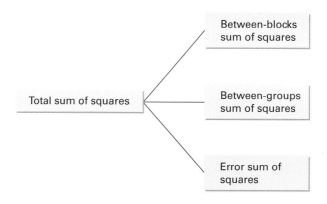

For the fuel-consumption data of Table 15.7, we find

$$\text{SST} = (25.1 - 24.6)^2 + (24.7 - 24.6)^2 + \cdots + (25.4 - 24.6)^2 = 11.88$$
$$\text{SSG} = 6[(24.7 - 24.6)^2 + (23.9 - 24.6)^2 + (25.2 - 24.6)^2] = 5.16$$
$$\text{SSB} = 3[(25.0 - 24.6)^2 + (24.6 - 24.6)^2 + \cdots + (24.7 - 24.6)^2] = 4.98$$

so, by subtraction,

$$\text{SSE} = \text{SST} - \text{SSG} - \text{SSB} = 11.88 - 5.16 - 4.98 = 1.74$$

Sum of Squares Decomposition for Two-Way Analysis of Variance

Suppose that we have a sample of observations with x_{ij} denoting the observation in the ith group and jth block. Suppose that there are K groups and H blocks, for a total of

$$n = KH$$

observations. Denote the group sample means by $\bar{x}_{i\cdot}(i = 1, 2, \ldots, K)$ the block sample means by $\bar{x}_{\cdot j}(j = 1, 2, \ldots, H)$ and the overall sample mean by $\bar{\bar{x}}$.

We define the following sum of squares:

$$\text{total}: \text{SST} = \sum_{i=1}^{K} \sum_{j=1}^{H} (x_{ij} - \bar{\bar{x}})^2 \qquad (15.10)$$

$$\text{between groups}: \text{SSG} = H \sum_{i=1}^{K} (\bar{x}_{i\cdot} - \bar{\bar{x}})^2 \qquad (15.11)$$

$$\text{between blocks}: \text{SSB} = K \sum_{j=1}^{H} (\bar{x}_{\cdot j} - \bar{\bar{x}})^2 \qquad (15.12)$$

$$\text{error}: \text{SSE} = \sum_{i=1}^{K} \sum_{j=1}^{H} (x_{ij} - \bar{x}_{i\cdot} - \bar{x}_{\cdot j} + \bar{\bar{x}})^2 \qquad (15.13)$$

Then,

$$\text{SST} = \text{SSG} + \text{SSB} + \text{SSE} \qquad (15.14)$$

From this point, the tests associated with the two-way analysis of variance proceed in a fashion similar to the one-way analysis of Section 15.2. First, the mean squares are obtained by dividing each sum of squares by the appropriate number of degrees of freedom. For the total sum of squares, the degrees of freedom are 1 less than the total number of observations, that is, $(n - 1)$. For the sum of squares between groups, the degrees of freedom are 1 less than the number of groups, or $(K - 1)$. Similarly, for the sum of squares between blocks, the number of degrees of freedom is $(H - 1)$. Hence, by subtraction, the degrees of freedom associated with the sum of squared errors are as follows:

$$(n - 1) - (K - 1) - (H - 1) = n - K - H + 1$$
$$= KH - K - H + 1$$
$$= (K - 1)(H - 1)$$

The null hypothesis that the population group means are equal can then be tested through the ratio of the mean square for groups to the mean square error, as shown in Equation 15.18. Very often a blocking variable is included in the analysis simply to reduce variability due to experimental error. However, sometimes the hypothesis that the block population means are equal is also of interest. This can be tested through the ratio of the mean square for blocks to the mean square error from Equation 15.19. As in the case of the one-way analysis of variance, the relevant standard for comparison is obtained from a tail probability of the F distribution.

For the fuel-consumption data, the mean squares are as follows:

$$\text{MSG} = \frac{\text{SSG}}{K - 1} = \frac{5.16}{2} = 2.58$$

$$\text{MSB} = \frac{\text{SSB}}{H - 1} = \frac{4.98}{5} = 0.996$$

$$\text{MSE} = \frac{\text{SSE}}{(K - 1)(H - 1)} = \frac{1.74}{10} = 0.174$$

To test the null hypothesis that the population mean fuel consumption is the same for all three types of automobiles, we require the following:

$$\frac{\text{MSG}}{\text{MSE}} = \frac{2.58}{0.174} = 14.83$$

For a 1% significance level test, we have from Appendix Table 9,

$$F_{K-1,(K-1)(H-1),\alpha} = F_{2,10,0.01} = 7.559$$

Hypothesis Tests for Two-Way Analysis of Variance

Suppose that we have a sample observation for each group-block combination in a design containing K groups and H blocks:

$$x_{ij} = \mu + G_i + B_j + \varepsilon_{ij}$$

where G_i is the group effect and B_j is the block effect.

Define the following mean squares:

$$\text{between groups}: \text{MSG} = \frac{\text{SSG}}{K-1} \qquad (15.15)$$

$$\text{between blocks}: \text{MSB} = \frac{\text{SSB}}{H-1} \qquad (15.16)$$

$$\text{error}: \text{MSE} = \frac{\text{SSE}}{(K-1)(H-1)} \qquad (15.17)$$

We assume that the error terms ε_{ij} in the model are independent of one another and have the same variance. We further assume that these errors are normally distributed.

Then, a test of significance level α of the null hypothesis, H_0, that the K population group means are all the same is provided by the following decision rule:

$$\text{reject } H_0 \text{ if } \frac{\text{MSG}}{\text{MSE}} > F_{K-1,(K-1)(H-1),\alpha} \qquad (15.18)$$

A test of significance level α of the null hypothesis, H_0, that the H population block means are all the same is provided by the decision rule

$$\text{reject } H_0 \text{ if } \frac{\text{MSB}}{\text{MSE}} > F_{H-1,(K-1)(H-1),\alpha} \qquad (15.19)$$

Here, $F_{v_1,v_2,\alpha}$ is the number exceeded with probability α by a random variable following an F distribution with numerator degrees of freedom v_1 and denominator degrees of freedom v_2.

Therefore, on the evidence of these data, the hypothesis of equal mean population performances for the three types of automobiles is clearly rejected at the 1% significance level.

In this particular example, the null hypothesis of equality of the population block means is the hypothesis that population values of mean fuel consumption are the same for each driver age class. The test is based on the following:

$$\frac{\text{MSB}}{\text{MSE}} = \frac{0.996}{0.174} = 5.724$$

For a 1% test we have, from Appendix Table 9,

$$F_{H-1,(K-1)(H-1),\alpha} = F_{5,10,0.01} = 5.636$$

Hence, the null hypothesis of equal population means for the six driver age classes is also rejected at the 1% significance level.

Once again, it is very convenient to summarize the computations in tabular form. The general setup for the **two-way analysis of variance table** is shown in Table 15.9. For the fuel-consumption data, this analysis of variance is set out in Figure 15.6. The numbers of degrees of freedom are determined by the numbers of groups and blocks. The mean squares are obtained by dividing the sums of squares by their associated degrees of freedom. The mean square error is then the denominator in the calculation of the two F ratios on which our tests are based.

Table 15.9   General Format of Two-Way Analysis of Variance Table

SOURCE OF VARIATION	SUM OF SQUARES	DEGREES OF FREEDOM	MEAN SQUARES	F RATIO
Between groups	SSG	$K - 1$	$MSG = \dfrac{SSG}{K - 1}$	$\dfrac{MSG}{MSE}$
Between blocks	SSB	$H - 1$	$MSB = \dfrac{SSB}{H - 1}$	$\dfrac{MSB}{MSE}$
Error	SSE	$(K - 1)(H - 1)$	$MSE = \dfrac{SSE}{(K - 1)(H - 1)}$	
Total	SST	$n - 1$		

Example 15.3 Automobile Fuel Consumption (Two-Way Analysis of Variance)

We wish to determine if there is strong evidence to conclude that there is a difference in automobile fuel consumption for different cars used by different drivers.

Solution The gas-mileage data from Table 15.7 can be analyzed using Minitab, and the output is shown in Figure 15.6. Figure 15.6 also shows the various sums of squares and F ratios. The computed F ratio for the car of 14.83 results in a rejection of the null hypothesis that there are no differences between cars. Similarly the computed F ratio for the driver of 5.72 results in a rejection of the null hypothesis that there are no differences between drivers. Thus, both car and driver have significant effects on fuel consumption.

Figure 15.6 Results for Two-Way Analysis of Variance (Minitab Output)

```
Two-way ANOVA: Mileage versus Car, Driver

Source   DF      SS      MS       F       P
Car       2    5.16   2.580   14.83   0.001
Driver    5    4.98   0.996    5.72   0.009
Error    10    1.74   0.174
Total    17   11.88

S = 0.4171     R-Sq = 85.35%     R-Sq(adj) = 75.10%

                Individual 95% CIs For Mean Based on
                Pooled StDev
Car   Mean    -------+---------+---------+---------+-
 1    24.7                   (-----*-----)
 2    23.9           (-----*-----)
 3    25.2                       (-----*-----)
                -------+---------+---------+---------+-
                    24.00      24.60     25.20     25.80


                Individual 95% CIs For Mean Based on
                Pooled StDev
Driver  Mean   -----+---------+---------+---------+---
 1      25.0                 (------*------)
 2      24.6            (------*------·)
 3      25.4                    (------*------)
 4      24.0         (------*------)
 5      23.9         (------*------·)
 6      24.7                  (------*------·)
               -----+---------+---------+---------+---
                  23.80      24.50     25.20     25.90
```

Exercises

Basic Exercises

15.27 Consider a two-way analysis of variance with one observation per cell and randomized blocks with the following results:

Source of Variation	Sum of Squares	Degrees of Freedom
Between groups	3636	33
Between blocks	7575	66
Error	9999	1818
Total	210210	2727

Compute the mean squares and test the hypotheses that between-group means are equal and betweenblock means are equal.

15.28 Consider a two-way analysis of variance with one observation per cell and randomized blocks with the following results:

Source of Variation	Sum of Squares	Degrees of Freedom
Between groups	380	6
Between blocks	232	5
Error	387	30
Total	989	41

Compute the mean squares and test the hypotheses that between-group means are equal and between-block means are equal.

15.29 Consider a two-way analysis of variance with one observation per cell and randomized blocks with the following results:

Source of Variation	Sum of Squares	Degrees of Freedom
Between groups	131	3
Between blocks	287	6
Error	360	18
Total	778	27

Compute the mean squares and test the hypotheses that between-group means are equal and between-block means are equal.

Application Exercises

15.30 Four financial analysts were asked to predict earnings growth over the coming year for five oil companies. Their forecasts, as projected percentage increases in earnings, are given in the accompanying table.

a. Prepare the two-way analysis of variance table.
b. Test the null hypothesis that the population mean growth forecasts are the same for all oil companies.

Oil Company	Analyst			
	A	B	C	D
1	8	12	7	13
2	9	9	8	12
3	12	10	9	10
4	11	10	10	12
5	9	8	10	14

15.31 In Greece, an agricultural experiment designed to assess differences in yields of olives for four different varieties (Athenolia, Black olives, Green olives, and Koroneiki), using six different fertilizers, produced the results (in kilos per acre) shown in the following table:

Fertilizer	Athenolia	Black	Green	Koroneiki
1	23	22	21	22
2	22	22	24	27
3	17	21	20	28
4	23	20	24	28
5	19	22	21	23
6	22	20	22	29

a. Prepare the two-way analysis of variance table.
b. Test the null hypothesis that the population mean yields are identical for all four varieties of corn.
c. Test the null hypothesis that population mean yields are the same for all three brands of fertilizer.

15.32 A company has test-marketed three new types of soup in selected stores over a period of 1 year. The following table records sales achieved (in thousands of dollars) for each of the three soups in each quarter of the year.

Quarter	Soup		
	A	B	C
1	47	57	65
2	63	63	76
3	79	67	54
4	52	50	49

a. Prepare the two-way analysis of variance table.
b. Test the null hypothesis that population mean sales are the same for all three types of soup.

15.33 A diet soda manufacturer wants to compare the effects on sales of three can colors—red, yellow, and blue. Four regions are selected for the test, and three stores are randomly chosen from each region, each to display one color of cans. The accompanying table shows sales (in tens of cans) at the end of the experimental period.

Region	Can Color		
	Red	Yellow	Blue
East	47	52	60
South	56	54	52
Midwest	49	63	55
West	41	44	48

a. Prepare the appropriate analysis of variance table.
b. Test the null hypothesis that population mean sales are the same for each can color.

15.34 An instructor in an economics class is considering three different texts. He is also considering three types of examinations—multiple choice, essay, and a mix of multiple choice and essay questions. During the year he teaches nine sections of the course and randomly assigns a text–examination type combination of each section. At the end of the course he obtained students' evaluations for each section. These ratings are shown in the accompanying table.

Examination	Text		
	A	B	C
Multiple choice	4.8	5.3	4.9
Essays	4.6	5.0	4.3
Mix	4.6	5.1	4.8

a. Prepare the analysis of variance table.
b. Test the null hypothesis of equality of population mean ratings for the three texts.
c. Test the null hypothesis of equality of population mean ratings for the three examination types.

15.35 We introduced for the two-way analysis of variance the population model

$$X_{ij} - \mu = G_i + \beta_j + \varepsilon_{ij}$$

For the data of Exercise 15.33, obtain sample estimates for each term on the right-hand side of this equation for the east region–red can combination.

15.36 For the data of Exercise 15.34, obtain sample estimates for each term on the right-hand side of the equation used in the previous exercise for the text C–multiple choice combination.

15.37 Four real estate agents were asked to appraise the values of 10 houses in a particular neighborhood. The appraisals were expressed in thousands of dollars, with the results shown in the following table.

Source of variation	Sum of Squares
Between agents	304
Between houses	1330
Error	2055

15.38 Four brands of fertilizer were evaluated. Each brand was applied to each six plots of land containing soils of different types. Percentage increases in corn yields were then measured for the 24 brand-soil-type combinations. The results obtained are summarized in the accompanying table.

Source of Variation	Sum of Squares
Between fertilizers	135.6
Between soil types	81.7
Error	111.3

a. Complete the analysis of variance table.
b. Test the null hypothesis that population mean yield increases are the same for the four fertilizers.
c. Test the null hypothesis that population mean yield increases are the same for the six soil types.

15.39 Three television pilots for potential situation-comedy series were shown to audiences in four regions of the country—the East, the South, the Midwest, and the West Coast. Based on audience reactions, a score (on a scale from 0 to 100) was obtained for each show. The sums of squares between groups (shows) and between blocks (regions) were found to be

$$\text{SSG} = 95.2 \quad \text{and} \quad \text{SSB} = 69.5$$

and the error sum of squares was as follows:

$$\text{SSE} = 79.3$$

Prepare the analysis of variance table, and test the null hypothesis that the population mean scores for audience reactions are the same for all three shows.

15.40 Suppose that, in the two-way analysis of variance setup with one observation per cell, there are just two groups. Show in this case that the F ratio for testing the equality of the group population means is precisely the square of the test-statistic discussed in Section 10.1 for testing equality of population means, given a sample of matched pairs. Hence, deduce that the two tests are equivalent in this particular case.

In the two-way analysis of variance layout of Section 15.4, we can view the tabulated raw data (as in Tables 15.7 and 15.8) as being broken down into cells, where each cell refers to a particular group-block combination. Thus, for example, the results obtained when a driver from the fourth age class drives a β-car constitute a single cell. A feature of the design analyzed in Section 15.4 is that each cell contains just a single sample observation. Thus, a driver from the fourth age class tests a β-car only once.

In this section we consider the possibility of replicating the experiment so that, for example, β-cars would be driven by more than one driver from the fourth age class. The data resulting from such a design would then involve more than just a single observation per cell. There are two major advantages in extending the sample in this way. First, when more sample data are available, the resulting estimates will be more precise, and we will be better able to distinguish differences among the population means. Second, a design with more than one observation per cell allows the isolation of a further source of variability—the **interaction** between groups and blocks. Such interactions occur when differences in group effects are not distributed uniformly across blocks. For example, drivers who achieve better-than-average fuel consumption figures may be considerably more successful in getting better fuel economy than other drivers when driving an α-car than when driving a β-car. Thus, this better-than-average performance is not uniformly spread over all types of cars but rather is more manifest in some types than others. This possibility of driver-car interaction can be taken into account in an analysis based on more than one observation per cell.

To illustrate the kind of data that can be analyzed, Table 15.10 contains results on fuel consumption recorded for drivers from five age classes with three types of automobiles: X-cars, Y-cars, and Z-cars. The three observations in each cell refer to independent trials by drivers from a given age class with automobiles of a particular type.

Table 15.10 Sample Observations on Fuel Consumption Recorded for Three Types of Automobiles Driven by Five Classes of Drivers; Three Observations per Cell

DRIVER CLASS	AUTOMOBILE TYPE								
	X-CARS			Y-CARS			Z-CARS		
1	25.0	25.4	25.2	24.0	24.4	23.9	25.9	25.8	25.4
2	24.8	24.8	24.5	23.5	23.8	23.8	25.2	25.0	25.4
3	26.1	26.3	26.2	24.6	24.9	24.9	25.7	25.9	25.5
4	24.1	24.4	24.4	23.9	24.0	23.8	24.0	23.6	23.5
5	24.0	23.6	24.1	24.4	24.4	24.1	25.1	25.2	25.3

To denote the individual sample observations, we require a triple subscript, so x_{ijl} will denote the lth observation in the ijth cell—that is, the lth observation in the cell corresponding to the ith group and the jth block. As before, we will let K denote the number of groups and H, the number of blocks. We denote by m the number of observations per cell. Hence, in the example of Table 15.10, $K = 3$, $H = 5$, and $m = 3$. This notation is illustrated in Table 15.11.

Based on the results of an experiment of this type, there are three null hypotheses that can be tested: no difference between group means, no difference between block means, and no group-block interaction. In order to carry out these tests, we will again calculate various sample means, defined and calculated as follows:

Table 15.11

Sample Observations on K Groups and H Blocks; m Observations per Cell

BLOCK	GROUP			
	1	2	...	K
1	$x_{111}x_{112}\ldots x_{11m}$	$x_{211}x_{212}\ldots x_{21m}$	...	$x_{K11}x_{K12}\ldots x_{K1m}$
2	$x_{121}x_{122}\ldots x_{12m}$	$x_{221}x_{222}\ldots x_{22m}$		$x_{K21}x_{K22}\ldots x_{K2m}$
.	.	.		.
.	.	.		.
.	.	.		.
H	$x_{1H1}x_{1H2}\ldots x_{1Hm}$	$x_{2H1}x_{2H2}\ldots x_{2Hm}$	...	$x_{KH1}x_{KH2}\ldots x_{KHm}$

1. *Group Means*

   The mean of *all* the sample observations in the ith group is denoted $\bar{x}_{i..}$, so

   $$\bar{x}_{i..} = \frac{\sum_{j=1}^{H}\sum_{l=1}^{m} x_{ijl}}{Hm}$$

   From Table 15.10 we find the following:

   $$\bar{x}_{1..} = \frac{25.0 + 25.4 + \cdots + 23.6 + 24.1}{15} = 24.86$$

   $$\bar{x}_{2..} = \frac{24.0 + 24.4 + \cdots + 24.4 + 24.1}{15} = 24.16$$

   $$\bar{x}_{3..} = \frac{25.9 + 25.8 + \cdots + 25.2 + 25.3}{15} = 25.10$$

2. *Block Means*

   The mean for all the sample observations in the jth block is denoted $\bar{x}_{.j.}$, so

   $$\bar{x}_{.j.} = \frac{\sum_{i=1}^{K}\sum_{l=1}^{m} x_{ijl}}{Km}$$

   From Table 15.10 we find the following:

   $$\bar{x}_{.1.} = \frac{25.0 + 25.4 + \cdots + 25.8 + 25.4}{9} = 25.00$$

   $$\bar{x}_{.2.} = \frac{24.8 + 24.8 + \cdots + 25.0 + 25.4}{9} = 24.53$$

   $$\bar{x}_{.3.} = \frac{26.1 + 26.3 + \cdots + 25.9 + 25.5}{9} = 25.57$$

   $$\bar{x}_{.4.} = \frac{24.1 + 24.4 + \cdots + 23.6 + 23.5}{9} = 23.97$$

   $$\bar{x}_{.5.} = \frac{24.0 + 23.6 + \cdots + 25.2 + 25.3}{9} = 24.47$$

3. *Cell Means*

   To check the possibility of group-block interactions, it is necessary to calculate the sample mean for each cell. Let $\bar{x}_{ij.}$ denote the sample mean for the (ij)th cell. Then,

   $$\bar{x}_{ij.} = \frac{\sum_{l=1}^{m} x_{ijl}}{m}$$

Hence, we find for the data from Table 15.10,

$$\bar{x}_{11\cdot} = \frac{25.0 + 25.4 + 25.2}{3} = 25.2$$

$$\bar{x}_{12\cdot} = \frac{24.8 + 24.8 + 24.5}{3} = 24.7$$

and, similarly,

$$\bar{x}_{13\cdot} = 26.2 \quad \bar{x}_{14\cdot} = 24.3 \quad \bar{x}_{15\cdot} = 23.9$$

$$\bar{x}_{21\cdot} = 24.1 \quad \bar{x}_{22\cdot} = 23.7 \quad \bar{x}_{23\cdot} = 24.8 \quad \bar{x}_{24\cdot} = 23.9 \quad \bar{x}_{25\cdot} = 24.3$$

$$\bar{x}_{31\cdot} = 25.7 \quad \bar{x}_{32\cdot} = 25.2 \quad \bar{x}_{33\cdot} = 25.7 \quad \bar{x}_{34\cdot} = 23.7 \quad \bar{x}_{35\cdot} = 25.2$$

4. *Overall Mean*

We denote the mean of all the sample observations by $\bar{\bar{x}}$, so

$$\bar{\bar{x}} = \frac{\sum_{i=1}^{K} \sum_{j=1}^{H} \sum_{l=1}^{m} x_{ijl}}{KHm}$$

For our data, this quantity is simplest to calculate as the average of the three group sample means, as follows:

$$\bar{\bar{x}} = \frac{24.86 + 24.16 + 25.10}{3} = 24.71$$

Now, to get a feeling for the analysis, it is convenient to think in terms of the assumed population model. Let X_{ijl} denote the random variable corresponding to the lth observation in the ijth cell. Then the model assumed in our analysis is as follows:

$$X_{ijl} = \mu + G_i + B_j + L_{ij} + \varepsilon_{ijl}$$

The first three terms on the right-hand side are precisely the same as those in the model without replication. As before, they represent an overall mean, a group-specific factor, and a block-specific factor. The next term, L_{ij}, represents the effect of being in the ijth cell, given that the overall, group, and block effects are already accounted for. If there were no group-block interaction, this term would be 0. Its presence in the model allows us to test for interaction. Finally, the error term, ε_{ijl}, is a random variable representing experimental error.

We will rewrite the model in deviation form:

$$X_{ijl} - \mu = G_i + B_j + L_{ij} + \varepsilon_{ijl}$$

It is shown that the total sum of squares can be decomposed as the sum of four terms, representing variability due to groups, blocks, interaction between groups and blocks, and error.

Without providing detailed derivations the decomposition on which the tests are based is shown in Equations 15.20–15.25.

Two-Way Analysis of Variance: Several Observations per Cell

Suppose that we have a sample of observations on k groups and h blocks, with m observations per cell. Let x_{ijl} denote the lth observation in the cell for the ith group and jth block. Let $\bar{\bar{x}}$ denote the overall sample mean, $\bar{x}_{i\cdot\cdot}$ be the group sample means, $\bar{x}_{\cdot j}$ be the block sample means, and $\bar{x}_{ij}$ be the cell sample means.

Then we define the following sums of squares and associated degrees of freedom:

	Sum of Squares	Degrees of Freedom	
Total:	$\text{SST} = \sum_i \sum_j \sum_l (x_{ijl} - \bar{\bar{x}})^2$	$KHm - 1$	(15.20)
Between groups:	$\text{SSG} = Hm \sum_{i=1}^{K} (\bar{x}_{i\cdot\cdot} - \bar{\bar{x}})^2$	$K - 1$	(15.21)
Between blocks:	$\text{SSB} = Km \sum_{i=1}^{H} (\bar{x}_{\cdot j} - \bar{\bar{x}})^2$	$H - 1$	(15.22)
Interaction:	$\text{SSI} = m \sum_{i=1}^{K} \sum_{j=1}^{H} (\bar{x}_{ij\cdot} - \bar{x}_{i\cdot\cdot} - \bar{x}_{\cdot j} + \bar{\bar{x}})$	$(K-1)(H-1)$	(15.23)
Error:	$\text{SSE} = \sum_i \sum_j \sum_l (x_{ijl} - \bar{x}_{ij\cdot})^2$	$HK(m-1)$	(15.24)

Then,

$$\text{SST} = \text{SSG} + \text{SSB} + \text{SSI} + \text{SSE} \tag{15.25}$$

Division of the component sums of squares by their corresponding degrees of freedom yields the mean squares MSG, MSB, MSI, and MSE. Tests of the hypotheses of no effects for groups, blocks, and interaction are based on the respective F ratios:

$$\frac{\text{MSG}}{\text{MSE}} \quad \frac{\text{MSB}}{\text{MSE}} \quad \frac{\text{MSI}}{\text{MSE}}$$

The tests are carried out with reference to the F distributions with the corresponding numerator and denominator degrees of freedom. Their validity rests on the assumption that the ε_{ijl} behave as a random variable from a normal distribution.

Figure 15.7 depicts the decomposition of the total sum of squares of the sample observations about their overall mean as the sum of four components. It differs from Figure 15.5 in that, as the experiment is replicated, we are now able to isolate an interaction sum of squares.

Figure 15.7
Sum of Squares Decomposition for a Two-Way Analysis of Variance with More than One Observation per Cell

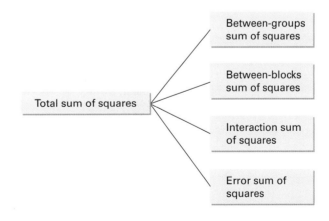

As before, the calculations involved can be conveniently summarized in an analysis of variance table. The general form of the table when there are m observations per cell in a two-way analysis of variance is shown in Table 15.12.

Table 15.12
General Format of the
Two-Way Analysis of
Variance Table with m
Observations per Cell

Source of Variation	Sum of Squares	Degrees of Freedom	Mean Squares	F Ratio
Between groups	SSG	$K - 1$	$MSG = \dfrac{SSG}{K - 1}$	$\dfrac{MSG}{MSE}$
Between blocks	SSB	$H - 1$	$MSB = \dfrac{SSB}{H - 1}$	$\dfrac{MSB}{MSE}$
Interaction	SSI	$(K - 1)(H - 1)$	$MSI = \dfrac{SSI}{(K - 1)(H - 1)}$	$\dfrac{MSI}{MSE}$
Error	SSE	$KH(m - 1)$	$MSE = \dfrac{SSE}{KH(m - 1)}$	
Total	SST			

In fact, formulas that are computationally simpler exist for the calculation of the various sums of squares. Nevertheless, the arithmetic involved is still rather tedious and should be performed using a computer. We will not go into further detail here but will simply report in Figure 15.8 the results of the calculations for our data. In practice, analysis of variance computations are typically carried out using a statistical computer package such as Minitab. Thus, considerations of arithmetic complexity rarely impose any constraint on practical analyses.

Two-way ANOVA: Mileage versus Car, Driver

```
Source        DF        SS       MS       F        P
Car            2     7.156  3.57800  92.53   0.000
Driver         4    13.148  3.28700  85.01   0.000
Interaction    8     6.604  0.82550  21.35   0.000
Error         30     1.160  0.03867
Total         44    28.068

S = 0.1966     R-Sq = 95.87%     R-Sq(adj) = 93.94%


                    Individual 95% CIs For Mean Based on
                    Pooled StDev
Car    Mean   -------+---------+---------+---------+-
1      24.86                                (--.*--.)
2      24.16   (--.*--.)
3      25.10                                     (--.*--.)
              -------+---------+---------+---------+-
                  24.30     24.60     25.90     25.20


                    Indiviual 95% CIs For Mean Based on
                    Pooled StDev
Driver    Mean   ---+---------+---------+---------+-----
1         25.0000                       (--*--)
2         24.5333                 (--*-)
3         25.5667                               (-*--)
4         23.9667   (-.*--)
5         24.4667            (-.*--)
                 ---+---------+---------+---------+-----
                 24.00     24.50     25.00     25.50
```

The degrees of freedom in Figure 15.8 follow from the fact that for these data we have the following:

$$K = 3 \quad H = 5 \quad m = 3$$

The mean squares are obtained by dividing the sums of squares by their associated degrees of freedom. Finally, the F ratios follow from dividing, in turn, each of the first three mean squares by the error mean square.

Using the material in Figure 15.8, we can test the three null hypotheses of interest. First, we test the null hypothesis of no interaction between drivers and automobile type. This test is based on the calculated F ratio 21.35 and the p-value of 0.000. Since the numerator and denominator degrees of freedom are 8 and 30, respectively, we have, from Appendix Table 9,

$$F_{8,30,0.01} = 3.173$$

The null hypothesis of no interaction between car type and driver is very clearly rejected at the 1% level of significance, since 21.35 is greater than 3.173.

Next, we test the null hypothesis that the population mean fuel consumption is the same for X-cars, Y-cars, and Z-cars. The test is based on the calculated F ratio 92.53. From Appendix Table 9, we find for a 1% test with numerator and denominator degrees of freedom 2 and 30, respectively,

$$F_{2,30,0.01} = 5.390$$

Hence, the null hypothesis of equality of the population means for automobile types is overwhelmingly rejected at the 1% significance level.

Finally, we test the null hypothesis that the population mean fuel consumption is the same for all five driver age classes. From Figure 15.8 the test is based on the calculated F ratio 85.01. The numerator and denominator degrees of freedom are 4 and 30, respectively, so for a 1% significance level test,

$$F_{4,30,0.01} = 4.018$$

The null hypothesis of equality of population means for the driver age classes is very clearly rejected at the 1% significance level.

The evidence of our data points very firmly to the following three conclusions:

1. Average fuel consumption is not the same for X-cars, Y-cars, and Z-cars.
2. The average performance levels are not the same for all driver classes.
3. The differences in driver performance are not spread evenly over all three types of automobiles. Rather, compared with other drivers, a driver from a particular age class is likely to do relatively better in one automobile type than in another.

So far in this section, we have assumed that the number of observations in each cell is the same. However, this restriction is not necessary and may, on occasion, be inconvenient for an investigator. In fact, the formulas for the computation of sums of squares can be modified to allow for unequal cell contents. We are not concerned here with the technical details of the calculation of appropriate sums of squares. Generally, an investigator will have available a computer package for this purpose. Rather, our interest lies in the analysis of the results.

Example 15.4 Worker Satisfaction Level (Two-Way Analysis of Variance)

A study (Kim 1980) was designed to compare the satisfaction levels of introverted and extroverted workers performing stimulating and nonstimulating tasks. For the purpose of this study, there are two worker types and two task types, producing four combinations. The sample mean satisfaction levels reported by workers in these four combinations were as follows:

Introverted worker, nonstimulating task (16 observations):	2.78
Extroverted worker, nonstimulating task (15 observations):	1.85
Introverted worker, stimulating task (17 observations):	3.87
Extroverted worker, stimulating task (19 observations):	4.12

The following table shows the calculated sums of squares and associated degrees of freedom. Complete the analysis of variance table and analyze the results of this experiment.

Source of Variation	Sum of Squares	Degrees of Freedom
Task	62.04	1
Worker type	0.06	1
Interaction	1.85	1
Error	23.31	63
Total	87.26	66

Solution Once again, the mean squares are obtained from division of the sums of squares by their associated degrees of freedom. The F ratios then follow from division of the task, worker type, and interaction mean squares by the error mean square. The analysis of variance table may now be completed as shown.

Source of Variation	Sum of Squares	Degrees of Freedom	Mean Squares	F Ratios
Task	62.04	1	62.04	167.68
Worker type	0.06	1	0.06	0.16
Interaction	1.85	1	1.85	5.00
Error	23.31	63	0.37	
Total	87.26	66		

The analysis of variance table can be used as the basis for testing three null hypotheses. For the null hypothesis of equal mean population satisfaction levels with the two types of task, the calculated F ratio is 167.68. We have numerator degrees of freedom 1 and denominator degrees of freedom 63, so by using Minitab for a 1% test,

$$F_{1,63,0.01} = 7.055$$

Hence, the null hypothesis of equal population mean satisfaction levels for stimulating and nonstimulating tasks is very clearly rejected. This result is not surprising. We would naturally expect workers to be more satisfied when performing stimulating rather than nonstimulating tasks.

Next, we test the null hypothesis that the population mean satisfaction levels are the same for introverted and extroverted workers. Here, the calculated F ratio is 0.16. Again, the degrees of freedom are 1 and 63, so for a 5% test,

$$F_{1,63,0.05} = 3.993$$

The null hypothesis of equal mean levels of satisfaction for introverted and extroverted workers cannot be rejected at the 5% level of significance.

In many studies the interaction term is not, in itself, of any great importance. The main reason for including it in the analysis is to "soak up" some of the variability in the data, rendering any differences between population means easier to detect. However, in this particular study the interaction is of major interest. The null hypothesis of no interaction between task and worker type in determining worker satisfaction levels is tested through the calculated F ratio equal to 5.00. Once again, the numerator and denominator degrees of freedom are 1 and 63, respectively. Hence, comparison with the tabulated values of the F distribution reveals that the null hypothesis of no interaction can be rejected at the 5% level but not at the 1% level of significance.

Exercises

Basic Exercises

15.41 Consider an experiment with treatment factors A and B, with factor A having four levels and factor B having three levels. The results of the experiment are summarized in the following analysis of variance table.

Compute the mean squares and test the null hypotheses of no effect from either treatment and no interaction effect.

Source of Variation	Sum of Squares	Degrees of Freedom
Treatment A groups	90	4
Treatment B groups	82	2
Interaction	26	8
Error	260	60
Total	458	74

15.42 The partial output for an experiment with treatment factors A and B are summarized in the following table.

Source of Variation	Sum of Squares	Degrees of Freedom	Degrees of Freedom
Treatment A groups	740		370
Treatment B groups		1	30
Interaction		2	130
Error	178	24	
Total	1208		

Compute the F ratios and test the null hypotheses of any effect from either treatment and any interaction effect.

15.43 Consider an experiment with treatment factors A and B, with factor A having three levels and factor B having seven levels. The results of the experiment are summarized in the following analysis of variance table:

Source of Variation	Sum of Squares	Degrees of Freedom
Treatment A groups	21	2
Treatment B groups	96	6
Interaction	29	12
Error	390	100
Total	536	120

Compute the mean squares and test the null hypotheses of no effect from either treatment and no interaction effect.

Application Exercises

15.44 Suppose that scores given by judges to competitors in the ski-jumping events of the Winter Olympics were analyzed. For the men's ski-jumping competition,

suppose there were 22 contestants and 9 judges. Each judge in seven subevents assessed each contestant. The scores given can, thus, be treated in the framework of a two-way analysis of variance with 198 contestant-judge cells, seven observations per cell. The sums of squares are given in the following table:

Source of Variation	Sum of Squares
Between contestants	364.50
Between judges	0.81
Interaction	4.94
Error	1,069.94

a. Complete the analysis of variance table.
b. Carry out the associated F tests and interpret your findings.

15.45 Refer to Exercise 15.44. Twelve pairs were entered in the ice-dancing competition. Once again, there were 9 judges, and contestants were assessed in seven subevents. The sums of squares between groups (pairs of contestants) and between blocks (judges) were found to be

$$SSG = 60.10 \quad \text{and} \quad SSB = 1.65$$

while the interaction and error sums of squares were as follows:

$$SSI = 3.35 \quad \text{and} \quad SSE = 31.61$$

Analyze these results and verbally interpret the conclusions.

15.46 A researcher randomly collected the annually income (in thousand) in a village for three different age range (less than 20 years old, 20 to 30 years old and above 30 years old) based on gender (male and female). She recorded her findings in the following table.

Subject Type	Male					Female				
< 20	54	49	59	39	55	25	29	47	26	28
20–30	53	72	43	56	52	46	51	33	47	41
>30	33	30	26	25	29	18	21	34	40	24

a. Set up the analysis of variance table for the data collected by the researcher.
b. Test the null hypothesis of the effects are significant at 5% significance level.

15.47 Random samples of two freshmen, two sophomores, two juniors, and two seniors each from four dormitories were asked to rate, on a scale of 1 (poor) to 10 (excellent), the quality of the dormitory environment for studying. The results are shown in the following table:

Year	Dormitory							
	A		B		C		D	
Freshman	7	6	8	7	9	8	9	8
Sophomore	6	7	6	6	6	9	9	6
Junior	4	3	6	5	6	8	6	9
Senior	6	2	6	8	6	5	6	8

a. Set up the analysis of variance table.
b. Test the null hypothesis that the population mean ratings are the same for the four dormitories.
c. Test the null hypothesis that the population mean ratings are the same for the four student years.
d. Test the null hypothesis of no interaction between student year and dormitory rating.

15.48 In some experiments with several observations per cell the analyst is prepared to assume that there is no interaction between groups and blocks. Any apparent interaction found is then attributed to random error. When such an assumption is made, the analysis is carried out in the usual way, except that what were previously the interaction and error sums of squares are now added together to form a new error sum of squares. Similarly, the corresponding degrees of freedom are added. If the assumption of no interaction is correct, this approach has the advantage of providing more error degrees of freedom and, hence, more powerful tests of the equality of group and block means. For the study of Exercise 15.47, suppose that we now make the assumption of no interaction between dormitory ratings and student years.

a. State, in your own words, what is implied by this assumption.
b. Given this assumption, set up the new analysis of variance table.
c. Test the null hypothesis that the population mean ratings are the same for all dormitories.
d. Test the null hypothesis that the population mean ratings are the same for all four student years.

15.49 Refer to Exercise 15.31. Having carried out the experiment to compare mean yields per acre of four varieties of corn and three brands of fertilizer, an agricultural researcher suggested that there might be some interaction between variety and fertilizer. To check this

possibility, another set of trials was carried out, producing the yields in the table.

Fertilizer	Variety			
	A	B	C	D
1	80	88	73	88
2	94	91	79	93
3	81	78	83	83

a. What would be implied by an interaction between variety and fertilizer?
b. Combine the data from the two sets of trials and set up an analysis of variance table.
c. Test the null hypothesis that the population mean yield is the same for all four varieties of corn.
d. Test the null hypothesis that the population mean yield is the same for all three brands of fertilizer.
e. Test the null hypothesis of no interaction between variety of corn and brand of fertilizer.

15.50 Refer to Exercise 15.33. Suppose that a second store for each region–can color combination is added to the study, yielding the results shown in the following table. Combining these results with those of Exercise 15.33, carry out the analysis of variance calculations and discuss your findings.

Region	Can Color		
	Red	Yellow	Blue
East	45	50	54
South	49	51	58
Midwest	43	60	50
West	38	49	44

15.51 Having carried out the study of Exercise 15.34, the instructor decided to replicate the study the following year. The results obtained are shown in the table. Combining these results with those of Exercise 15.34, carry out the analysis of variance calculations and discuss your findings.

Examination	Text		
	A	B	C
Multiple choice	4.7	5.1	4.8
Essays	4.4	4.6	4.0
Mix	4.5	5.3	4.9

KEY WORDS

- interaction, 674
- Kruskal-Wallis test, 662
- mean squares, 655
- one-way analysis of variance, 651
- one-way analysis of variance table, 656
- randomized blocks design, 665
- sums of squares, 654

- sum of squares decomposition for one-way analysis of variance, 654
- sum of squares decomposition for two-way analysis of variance, 669
- two-way analysis of variance: one observation per cell, randomized blocks, 665

- two-way analysis of variance: several observations per cell, 676
- two-way analysis of variance table, 670

15.52 Briefly discuss the analysis of variance (ANOVA) by defining what ANOVA is. Give examples to explain when ANOVA analysis is used and what it delivers.

15.53 List three common assumptions in conducting the one-way analysis of variance and the two-way analysis of variance.

15.54 Case is a car assessor shop provides the car windows tinting. The shop ordered three different types of film from a manufacturer. According to the manufacturer, the dyed window tint film is the most economical film that blocks the UV rays to some extent. The metalized window film has a better UV-blocking effect compared to the first one. The ceramic tinted film is most effective in blocking UV rays. To ensure this information is true, Case randomly selected three cars with tinted windows for each type of film in conducting a test on the UV-blocking strength. The outcome is recorded in the following table. Conduct an appropriate test to justify the manufacturer's claim.

Source of Variation	Sum of Squares	Degrees of Freedom
Between groups	86,050	2
Within groups	10,254	6
Total	96,304	8

15.55 ReduX Corporation is planning to change their management program. The company needs to choose on one out of four different management programs provided by four different programming companies. Before making decision, ReduX sent eight employees to attend the training provided by the four programming companies. At the end of each training, the employees had to record the time taken (in minutes) to complete the same task. The results show that the sum of squares time taken is 61.467 and the mean of squares time taken within a programming company is 275.539. ReduX then compares the results to see if there are any differences in the average time taken to complete the same task.

   a. Use the provided information to prepare the analysis of variance table.
   b. Test the null hypothesis that the population mean time taken to complete a task are the same for all the four different programming.

15.56 Susan, a school teacher in Norway, is planning on traveling overseas during her holidays in December. Since most schools are shut in December, the holiday season, Susan wants to determine if there is any difference in the average price of air tickets sold during December. She recorded the 7 days' air ticket prices for each week in December and determined that the sum of squares flight ticket price between the 4 weeks is 1205.89 and the sum of squares air ticket price within a week is 24789.32.

   a. Use the provided information to prepare the analysis of variance table.
   b. Test the null hypothesis that the population mean flight ticket prices are the same in these four groups.

15.57 Zhang Shan Cai is a researcher in Taiwan. She wants to know if there is any difference in the average hours spent on reading each day for people aged 21 to 30 years, 31 to 40 years, and 41 to 50 years. Shan Cai conducted a survey by randomly recording 15 adults' reading time for the three groups. From the data collected, she determines that the sum of squares reading time between the groups is 568.94 and the sum of squares reading time within a group is 187.67.

   a. Prepare the complete analysis variance table.
   b. Test the null hypothesis of equality of the three population mean average hours spent on reading each day.

15.58 Professor Sui predicts that students will learn better with adding animations and sound effects in the PowerPoint slides. She randomly puts 21 students into three different groups to complete one assignment. The first group of students study with PowerPoint slides without any animations and sound effects; the second group uses the PowerPoint slides with animations but without any sound effects; and the third group studies using PowerPoint slides that have both animations and sound effects. After the assignment is completed, the students are asked to take an MCQ test for 10 points. Their results are recorded in the accompanying table. Test the null hypothesis that Professor Sui's claim is true.

Source of Variation	Sum of Squares	Degrees of Freedom
Between groups	50.62	2
Within groups	85.78	18
Total	136.3	20

15.59 Independent random samples of the selling prices of houses in four districts were taken. The selling prices (in thousands of dollars) are shown in the accompanying table. Test the null hypothesis that population mean selling prices are the same in all four districts.

District A	District B	District C	District D
73	85	97	61
63	59	86	67
89	84	76	84
75	70	78	67
70	80	76	69

15.60 For the data of Exercise 15.59, use the Kruskal-Wallis test to test the null hypothesis that the population mean selling prices of houses are the same in the four districts.

15.61 Bong Soon owns a tire shop and wants to compare the longevity of four different brands of tires that he sells in his shop. He collected 20 observations and measured the mileage (in miles) covered by the cars using each brand. From the data, he determined that the sum of squares of mileages covered between the four brands is 384.4 and the sum of squares of mileages covered within brands is 318.6.

a. Prepare the complete analysis of variance table.
b. Test the null hypothesis of equality of the four brands at 1% significance level.

15.62 Consider the one-way analysis of variance setup.

a. Show that the within-groups sum of squares can be written as follows:

$$SSW = \sum_{i=1}^{K} \sum_{j=1}^{n_i} x_{ij}^2 - \sum_{i=1}^{K} n_i \bar{x}_i^2$$

b. Show that the between-groups sum of squares can be written as follows:

$$SSG = \sum_{i=1}^{K} n_i \bar{x}_i^2 - n\bar{\bar{x}}^2$$

c. Show that the total sum of squares can be written as follows:

$$SST = \sum_{i=1}^{K} \sum_{j=1}^{n_i} x_{ij}^2 - n\bar{\bar{x}}^2$$

15.63 Consider the two-way analysis of variance setup, with one observation per cell.

a. Show that the between-groups sum of squares can be written as follows:

$$SSG = H \sum_{i=1}^{K} \bar{x}_{i\cdot}^2 - n\bar{\bar{x}}^2$$

b. Show that the between-blocks sum of squares can be written as follows:

$$SSB = K \sum_{j=1}^{H} \bar{x}_{\cdot j}^2 - n\bar{\bar{x}}^2$$

c. Show that the total sum of squares can be written as follows:

$$SST = \sum_{i=1}^{K} \sum_{j=1}^{H} x_{ij}^2 - n\bar{\bar{x}}^2$$

d. Show that the error sum of squares can be written as follows:

$$SSE = \sum_{i=1}^{K} \sum_{j=1}^{H} x_{ij}^2 - H \sum_{i=1}^{K} \bar{x}_{i\cdot}^2 - K \sum_{j=1}^{H} \bar{x}_{\cdot j}^2 + n\bar{\bar{x}}^2$$

15.64 A delivery company manager needs information on the mean delivery time (in minutes) for five different locations in Sichuan, China—Chengdu, Leshan City, Garze, Jiuzhaigou County, and Daocheng County. He randomly selected 25 delivery records of his staff members. The sum of squares delivery time between and within the 5 locations are given in the accompanying table. Complete the analysis of variance table and write a conclusion for your answer at the 1% significance level.

Source of Variation	Sum of Squares
Between locations	53.96
Within locations	46.23
Total	100.19

15.65 Three real estate agents were each asked to assess the values of five houses in a neighborhood. The results, in thousands of dollars, are given in the table. Prepare the analysis of variance table, and test the null hypothesis that population mean valuations are the same for the three real estate agents.

House	Agent A	Agent B	Agent C
1	210	218	226
2	192	190	198
3	183	187	185
4	227	223	237
5	242	240	237

15.66 Students were classified according to three parental income groups and also according to three possible score ranges on the SAT examination. One student was chosen randomly from each of the nine cross-classifications, and the grade point averages of those sample members at the end of the sophomore year were recorded. The results are shown in the accompanying table.

Sat Score	Income Group High	Moderate	Low
Very high	3.7	3.6	3.6
High	3.4	3.5	3.2
Moderate	2.9	2.8	3.0

a. Prepare the analysis of variance table.
b. Test the null hypothesis that the population mean grade point averages are the same for all three income groups.
c. Test the null hypothesis that the population mean grade point averages are the same for all three SAT score groups.

15.67 For the two-way analysis of variance model with one observation per cell, write the observation from the ith group and jth block as

$$X_{ij} = \mu + G_i + B_j + \varepsilon_{ij}$$

Refer to Exercise 15.65 and consider the observation on agent B and house 1 ($x_{21} = 218$).

a. Estimate μ.
b. Estimate and interpret G_2.
c. Estimate and interpret B_1.
d. Estimate ε_{21}.

15.68 Refer to Exercise 15.66 and consider the observation on moderate-income group and high SAT score ($x_{22} = 3.5$).

a. Estimate μ.
b. Estimate and interpret G_2.
c. Estimate and interpret B_2.
d. Estimate ε_{22}.

15.69 Consider the two-way analysis of variance setup, with m observations per cell.

a. Show that the between-groups sum of squares can be written as follows:

$$SSG = Hm \sum_{i=1}^{K} \bar{x}_{i\cdot\cdot}^2 - HKm\bar{\bar{x}}^2$$

b. Show that the between-blocks sum of squares can be written as follows:

$$SSB = Km \sum_{j=1}^{H} \bar{x}_{\cdot j\cdot}^2 - HKm\bar{\bar{x}}^2$$

c. Show that the error sum of squares can be written as follows:

$$SSE = \sum_{i=1}^{K}\sum_{j=1}^{H}\sum_{l=1}^{m} x_{ijl}^2 - m \sum_{i=1}^{K}\sum_{j=1}^{H} \bar{x}_{ij\cdot}^2$$

d. Show that the total sum of squares can be written as follows:

$$SST = \sum_{i=1}^{K}\sum_{j=1}^{H}\sum_{l=1}^{m} x_{ijl}^2 - HKm\bar{\bar{x}}^2$$

e. Show that the interaction sum of squares can be written as follows:

$$SSI = m \sum_{i=1}^{K}\sum_{j=1}^{H} \bar{x}_{ij\cdot}^2 - Hm \sum_{i=1}^{K} \bar{x}_{i\cdot\cdot}^2 - Km \sum_{j=1}^{H} \bar{x}_{\cdot j\cdot}^2 + HKm\bar{\bar{x}}^2$$

15.70 Purchasing agents were given information about a cellular phone system and asked to assess its quality. The information given was identical except for two factors—price and country of origin. For price there were three possibilities: $150, $80, and no price given. For country of origin there were also three possibilities: United States, Taiwan, and no country given. Part of the analysis of variance table for the quality assessments of the purchasing agents is shown here. Complete the analysis of variance table and provide a full analysis of these data.

Source of Variation	Sum of Squares	Degrees of Freedom
Between prices	0.178	2
Between countries	4.365	2
Interaction	1.262	4
Error	93.330	99

15.71 In the study of Exercise 15.70, information on the cellular phone system was also shown to MBA students. Part of the analysis of variance table for their quality assessments is shown here. Complete the analysis of variance table and provide a full analysis of these data.

Source of Variation	Sum of Squares	Degrees of Freedom
Between prices	0.042	2
Between countries	17.319	2
Interaction	2.235	4
Error	70.414	45

15.72 Having carried out the study of Exercise 15.66, the investigator decided to take a second independent random sample of one student from each of the nine income–SAT score categories. The grade point averages found are given in the accompanying table.

	Income Group		
Sat Score	High	Moderate	Low
Very high	3.9	3.7	3.8
High	3.2	3.6	3.4
Moderate	2.7	3.0	2.8

a. Prepare the analysis of variance table.
b. Test the null hypothesis that the population mean grade point averages are the same for all three income groups.
c. Test the null hypothesis that the population mean grade point averages are the same for all three SAT score groups.
d. Test the null hypothesis of no interaction between income group and SAT score.

15.73 Catherine Tate owns a restaurant in Maltby Street Market, London, and serves four different main dishes. She randomly recorded the time (in hours) spent at her restaurant by customers, grouped according to their age, who order the different dishes—20 years or younger, 21 to 40 years, and 41 years or older. Her observations are recorded in the following table.

Main Dishes	Time Spent (in hours)					
	< 20		21 to 40		> 40	
1	2	2.1	1.5	0.4	0.3	0.5
	3	1.8	2.5	2.8	2	1.4
2	2.8	1.5	3.2	2.4	2.6	1.5
	1.1	4	1.6	3.2	1.5	2
3	2.7	1.6	2.1	3.5	0.4	2.1
	3.1	2.3	1.4	0.6	0.7	3.1
4	3.5	1.6	0.5	0.8	1.5	1.1
	2.1	1.5	2.1	1.3	0.8	2.1

a. Prepare the complete analysis of variance table for the record.
b. Justify which of the main effects are significant at the 5% significance level.
c. Is the interaction effect significant at the 5% significance level?

Appendix: Mathematical Derivations

1   TOTAL SUM OF SQUARES

$$\text{SST} = \sum_{i=1}^{K} \sum_{j=1}^{n_i} (x_{ij} - \bar{\bar{x}})^2$$

$$= \sum_{i=1}^{K} \sum_{j=1}^{n_i} (x_{ij} - \bar{x}_i + \bar{x}_i - \bar{\bar{x}})^2$$

$$= \sum_{i=1}^{K} \sum_{j=1}^{n_i} (x_{ij} - \bar{x}_i)^2 + \sum_{i=1}^{K} \sum_{j=1}^{n_i} (\bar{x}_i - \bar{\bar{x}})^2 + 2 \sum_{i=1}^{K} (\bar{x}_i - \bar{\bar{x}}) \sum_{j=1}^{n_i} (x_{ij} - \bar{x}_i)$$

$$= \sum_{i=1}^{K} \sum_{j=1}^{n_i} (x_{ij} - \bar{x}_i)^2 + \sum_{i=1}^{K} n_i (\bar{x}_i - \bar{\bar{x}})^2$$

$$\text{SST} = \text{SSW} + \text{SSG}$$

$$\text{Note: } \sum_{j=1}^{n_i} (x_{ij} - \bar{x}) = 0$$

2   WITHIN-GROUPS MEAN SQUARE (MSW)

For each subgroup i:

$$\sigma^2 = E\left[\frac{\sum_{j=1}^{n_i} (x_{ij} - \mu_i)^2}{n_i} \right]$$

$$= E\left[\frac{\sum_{j=1}^{n_i} (x_{ij} - \bar{x}_i + \bar{x}_i - \mu_i)^2}{n_i} \right]$$

$$= E\left[\frac{\sum_{j=1}^{n_i} (x_{ij} - \bar{x}_i)^2}{n_i} \right] + \frac{\sigma^2}{n_i}$$

$$\frac{(n_i - 1)\sigma^2}{n_i} = E\left[\frac{\sum_{j=1}^{n_i} (x_{ij} - \bar{x}_i)^2}{n_i} \right]$$

$$\hat{\sigma}^2 = \frac{\sum_{j=1}^{n_i} (x_{ij} - \bar{x}_i)^2}{n_i - 1}$$

Summing over k subgroups:

$$\hat{\sigma}^2 = \frac{\sum_{i=1}^{K} \sum_{j=1}^{n_i} (x_{ij} - \bar{x}_i)^2}{n - K} = \frac{\text{SSW}}{n - K}$$

$$\hat{\sigma}^2 = \text{MSW}$$

3   BETWEEN-GROUPS MEAN SQUARE (MSG)

$$\mu_i = \mu \quad i = 1, \ldots, K$$

Then,

$$\hat{\sigma}^2 = E\left[\frac{\sum_{i=1}^{K}\sum_{j=1}^{n_i}(x_{ij} - \bar{\bar{x}})^2}{n-1}\right]$$

$$= E\left[\frac{\sum_{i=1}^{K}\sum_{j=1}^{n_i}(x_{ij} - \bar{x}_i + \bar{x}_i - \bar{\bar{x}})^2}{n-1}\right]$$

$$= E\left[\frac{\sum_{i=1}^{K}\sum_{j=1}^{n_i}(x_{ij} - \bar{x}_i)^2}{n-1} + \frac{\sum_{i=1}^{K}\sum_{j=1}^{n_i}(\bar{x}_i - \bar{\bar{x}})^2}{n-1}\right]$$

$$= \frac{(n-K)\hat{\sigma}^2}{n-1} + \frac{\sum_{i=1}^{K}n_i(\bar{x}_i - \bar{\bar{x}})^2}{n-1}$$

$$\frac{(K-1)\hat{\sigma}^2}{n-1} = \frac{\sum_{i=1}^{K}n_i(\bar{x}_i - \bar{\bar{x}})^2}{n-1}$$

$$\hat{\sigma}^2 = \frac{\sum_{i=1}^{K}n_i(\bar{x}_i - \bar{\bar{x}})^2}{K-1}$$

$$\hat{\sigma}^2 = MSG = \frac{SSG}{K-1}$$

4 RATIO OF MEAN SQUARES

If

$$H_0 : \mu_1 = \mu_2 = \cdots = \mu_K$$

is true, then MSG—with $(K-1)$ degrees of freedom—is an estimator of σ^2 and

$$\chi_{K-1}^2 = \frac{(K-1)MSG}{\sigma^2}$$

In addition, MSW with $(n-K)$ degrees is an estimator of σ^2, and, therefore,

$$\chi_{n-K}^2 = \frac{(n-K)MSW}{\sigma^2}$$

Thus,

$$F_{K-1,n-K} = \frac{\dfrac{\chi_{K-1}^2}{K-1}}{\dfrac{\chi_{n-K}^2}{n-K}} = \frac{MSG}{MSW}$$

REFERENCES

1. Kim, J. S. 1980. Relationships of Personality of Perceptual and Behavioral Responses in Stimulating and Nonstimulating Tasks. *Academy of Management Journal* 23: 307–319.
2. Shuptrine, F. K., and D. D. McVicker. 1981. Readability Levels of Magazine Advertisements. *Journal of Advertising Research* 21 (5): 45–50.

Time-Series Analysis and Forecasting

Introduction

In this chapter we develop procedures for analyzing data sets that contain measurements over time for various variables. Examples of time-series data include monthly product sales and interest rates, quarterly corporate earnings and aggregate consumption, and daily closing prices for shares of common stock.

Time Series

A **time series** is a set of measurements, ordered over time, on a particular quantity of interest. In a time series, the sequence of the observations is important, in contrast to cross-section data for which the sequence of observations is not important.

Time-series data typically possess special characteristics—associated with the sequence of the observations—that necessitate the development of special statistical analysis methods. Virtually all the procedures of data analysis and inference that we have developed are based on the assumption that samples are random—in particular, that the observation's errors are independent. Only very rarely will the assumption of independence be realistic for time-series data. For example, consider a series of monthly sales for a manufactured product and note possible reasons for lack of independence. If sales were higher than average last month, then it is reasonable to expect that high sales will continue because the strong underlying economic and business conditions are not likely to change abruptly. Thus, we can expect similarity in sales during adjacent months. We also note that sales of many products have a seasonal pattern—shorts and swimsuits have higher sales in spring and early summer compared to winter. Many retail stores have peak sales during the fourth quarter because of holiday gift purchases. These and many other examples establish the case for lack of independence.

The lack of independence between time-series observations leads to serious problems if conventional statistical procedures—which assume independence—are used with time-series data. We saw the problem in Section 13.7 when examining the problems of using conventional regression procedures when the errors are correlated between observations. The independence assumption is crucial, and other serious problems can occur if conventional procedures are used when the observations are dependent. In this chapter we focus on examining time-series analysis procedures that apply to a single time series. In particular there are many situations in which we want to forecast future values of the series. Forecasting is a major objective of this chapter.

We have considered the negative aspect of the kinds of dependency patterns likely to occur in time-series data. These are real problems and require special procedures. However, this dependency can also be exploited to produce lower-variance forecasts of future time-series values. For example, if there is a correlation between adjacent-month errors in a retail series, then that correlation can be used to provide a better forecast for the next month compared to a forecast based on a random sample. We will develop procedures based on the assumption that past patterns of relationship between measurements in a time series will continue into the future and can be used for forecasting—this is rather like arguing that we can, in fact, learn from a study of history.

The important assumption that enables us to forecast using the methods that follow is that the relationships between variables continue into the future. Thus, if there is a correlation between observations that are separated by one or more places, we assume that correlation continues. If the mean levels increase, decrease, or stay the same, we assume that pattern continues. However, it is certainly possible that the pattern will not continue into the future. A war or major disaster may occur. Unanticipated "bubbles" may not be recognized, such as the housing price bubble that occurred in 2005 and resulted from poor business behavior that was not part of the previous historical pattern. Thus, the economic forecaster in applied situations needs to be aware of the broader issues beyond the particular series that is being forecast. Unusual situations—such as "Black Swans"—do occur.

16.1 COMPONENTS OF A TIME SERIES

As a first step, in Sections 16.1 through 16.3 we develop some descriptive procedures for analyzing time-series data. The series of interest is denoted by $X_1, X_2, \ldots, X_n$, and at time t the series value is X_t.

A standard model for the behavior of time series identifies various components of the series. Traditionally, four components are represented, at least in part, in most time series:

1. Trend component
2. Seasonality component
3. Cyclical component
4. Irregular component

Many time series exhibit a tendency to grow or decrease rather steadily over long periods of time, indicating a trend component. For example, measures of national wealth, such as gross domestic product, have typically grown over time. Trends often hold up over time, and, when they do, this provides an important component for developing forecasts. Figure 16.1 shows the time series for quarterly gross domestic product for more

Figure 16.1 Gross Domestic Product by Quarter Indicating a Trend

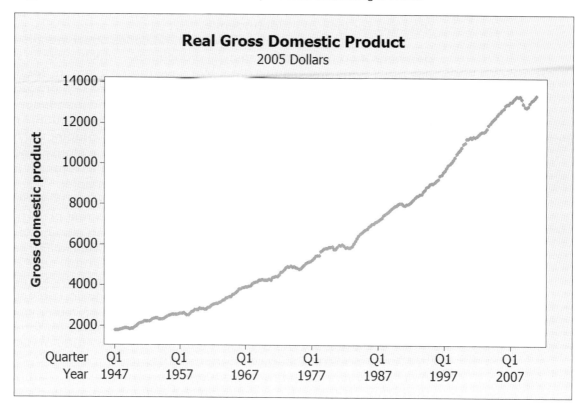

than 60 years, from the data file **Macro2010**. This pattern clearly shows a strong upward-trend component that is stronger in some periods than in others. This time plot reveals a major trend component that is important for initial analysis and is usually followed by more sophisticated analyses, as we show in future sections.

Another important component is the seasonal pattern. Figure 16.2 shows quarterly earnings per share of a corporation. The fourth-quarter earnings are substantially higher, and the second-quarter earnings are somewhat higher compared to the other periods. Note how this pattern continues to repeat over the four-quarter cycle representing each year. In addition to the seasonality component, there is also a noticeable upward trend in earnings per share. Our treatment of seasonality depends on our objectives. For example, if it is important to forecast each quarter as precisely as possible, then we include a seasonality component in our model. In Section 13.2, for instance, we showed how dummy variables can be used to estimate a seasonality component in a time series. Thus, if we anticipate that the seasonality pattern will continue, then the estimation of the seasonality component must be included in our forecasting model.

For some other purposes, seasonality can be a nuisance. In many applications the analyst requires an assessment of overall movements in a time series, uncontaminated by the influence of seasonal factors. For instance, suppose that we have just received the most recent fourth-quarter earnings figures of the corporation in Figure 16.2. We already know that these will very likely probably be a good deal higher than those of the previous quarter. What we would like to do is assess how much of this increase in earnings is due to purely seasonal factors and how much represents real underlying growth. In other words, we would like to produce a time series free from seasonal influence. Such a series is said to be seasonally adjusted. We will say a little more about seasonal adjustment in Section 16.2.

Seasonal patterns in a time series constitute one form of regular, oscillatory behavior. In addition, many business and economic time series exhibit oscillatory or cyclical patterns not related to seasonal behavior. For example, many economic series follow business cycle patterns of upswings and downswings. Figure 16.3 shows a cyclical

Figure 16.2 Revised Quarterly Earnings per Share of a Corporation Indicating a Seasonality Component

Figure 16.3 Shiller Home Price Index Indicating Cyclical Behavior

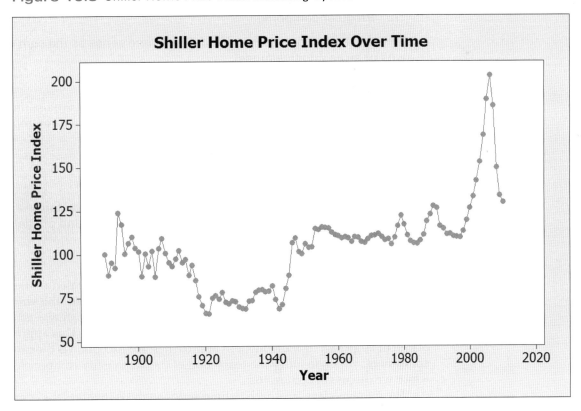

pattern for the Shiller home price index, going back to 1890. In the early part of the 20th century there were numerous cycles, followed by a major drop and then various cycles during the 1920s and 1930s. After a large increase during World War II, we saw a decrease in sales to a trough in 1949, followed by an upswing to a peak in the mid-1950s, and, thereafter, a slow steady decline. The most dramatic change began in the late 1990s and led to the housing bubble, which finally started to collapse in 2007, contributing substantially to the largest major recession since the 1930s. Those who correctly predicted the bubble collapse and took appropriate action experienced significant gains. However, most investors and homeowners did not, and there were major losses by large investment banking firms. This pattern is a common business-cycle time series, and we can describe historical behavior by cyclical movements. However, we are not suggesting that there is sufficient regularity in such historical patterns to allow the reliable prediction of future peaks and troughs—as we have seen in our recent history. Indeed, the available evidence suggests that this is not the case.

We have discussed three sources of variability in a time series. If we could characterize time series primarily in terms of trend, seasonal, and cyclical components, then the series would vary smoothly over time, and forecasts could be made using these components. However, actual data do not behave in that way. In addition to the major components, the series will exhibit irregular components, induced by a multitude of factors influencing the behavior of any actual series and exhibiting patterns that look rather unpredictable on the basis of past experience. These patterns can be thought of as similar to the random error term in a regression model. In all of the component examples that we have plotted so far, we can see the irregular component clearly on top of the structural components.

Time-Series Component Analysis
A time series can be described by models based on the following components:

T_t Trend component
S_t Seasonality component
C_t Cyclical component
I_t Irregular component

Using these components, we can define a time series as the sum of its components or as an additive model:

$$X_t = T_t + S_t + C_t + I_t$$

Alternatively, in other circumstances we might define a time series as the product of its components or as a multiplicative model—often represented as a logarithmic additive model:

$$X_t = T_t S_t C_t I_t$$
$$ln(X_t) = ln(T_t) + ln(S_t) + ln(C_t) + ln(I_t)$$

We do not have to restrict ourselves to these two structural forms. For example, in some cases we might have a combination of additive and multiplicative forms.

Much of the early work in time-series analysis concentrated on the isolation of the individual components from a series. Thus, at any point in time, the series value could be expressed as a function of the components. Often this approach was achieved by the use of moving averages, as we discuss in the next two sections. This approach has been replaced in large part by more modern approaches. An exception is the problem of seasonal adjustment, which requires the extraction of the seasonality component from the series, which we discuss in Section 16.2.

The more modern approach to time-series analysis involves the construction of a formal model, in which various components are either explicitly or implicitly present, to describe the behavior of a data series. In model building there are two possible treatments of series components. One is to regard them as being fixed over time, so that, for example, a trend might be represented by a straight line. This approach is often valuable in the analysis of physical data but is far less appropriate in business and economic applications, where experience suggests that any apparently fixed effects are all too often illusory on closer examination. To illustrate the point, suppose that we consider the Shiller home price index data for only the years 1946–2010. We see in Figure 16.3 that over the period 1950 through 1990, there appears to be a slow upward trend with a number of cycles, especially toward the later part of this period. However, had this "trend" been projected forward a few years, the resulting forecasts of future sales would have been highly inaccurate—the bubble would have been missed. It is only when we look at the picture in future years that we see just how inappropriate a fixed-trend model would have been.

For business and economic data another treatment of the regular components of a time series is preferable. Rather than regarding them as being fixed for all time, it is generally more sensible to think of them as steadily evolving over time. Thus, we need not be committed to fixed trend or seasonal patterns but can allow for the possibility that these components change with time. Models of this sort are considered after we have looked at moving averages. Finally, it is important to note that looking at time series plots such as those in Figures 16.1–16.3 can provide valuable insights into time-related changes.

EXERCISES

Application Exercises

16.1   The data file **Housing Starts** shows private housing units started per thousand of population in the United States over a period of 24 years. Use a computer to prepare a time plot of this series and comment on the components of the series revealed by this plot.

16.2 The data file **Earnings per Share** shows earnings per share of a corporation over a period of 28 years.

Use a computer to prepare a time plot of this series and comment on the components of the series revealed by this plot.

16.2 MOVING AVERAGES

The irregular component in some time series may be so large that it obscures any underlying component effects; thus, any visual interpretation of the time plot is very difficult. In these circumstances the actual plot will appear rather jagged, and we may want to smooth it to achieve a clearer picture. We can smooth the series by using a moving average.

The method of moving averages utilizes the idea that any large irregular component at any point in time will exert a smaller effect if we average the point with its immediate neighbors. The simplest procedure we can use is a simple, centered $(2m + 1)$-point moving average. That is, we replace each observation x_t by the average of itself and its neighbors, as follows:

$$x_t^* = \frac{1}{2m + 1} \sum_{j=-m}^{m} x_{t+j}$$

$$= \frac{x_{t-m} + x_{t-m+1} + \cdots + x_t + \cdots + x_{t+m-1} + x_{t+m}}{2m + 1}$$

For example, if we set m at 2, the 5-point moving average is

$$x_t^* = \frac{x_{t-2} + x_{t-1} + x_t + x_{t+1} + x_{t+2}}{5}$$

Since the first observation is x_1, the first moving average term is

$$x_3^* = \frac{x_1 + x_2 + x_3 + x_4 + x_5}{5}$$

This is the average of the first five observations. For the Shiller home price index data in Table 16.1, we have, for 1948,

$$x_3^* = \frac{106.5 + 109.3 + 101.2 + 100.0 + 105.9}{5} = 104.6$$

Similarly, x_4^* for 1949 is the average of the second through the sixth observations, and so on. Table 16.1 gives the original and smoothed series. Notice that for centered moving averages, we lose the first m and last m observations. Thus, while the original series runs from 1946 through 2010, the smoothed series goes from 1948 through 2008.

Table 16.1 Shiller Real Home Price Index with the Simple Centered 5-Point Moving Average

YEAR	SHILLER REAL HOME PRICE INDEX	MOVING AVERAGE 5-POINT CENTERED	YEAR	SHILLER REAL HOME PRICE INDEX	MOVING AVERAGE 5 POINT CENTERED
1946	106.5		1979	122.1	115.2
1947	109.3		1980	117.1	114.7
1948	101.2	104.6	1981	110.8	112.7
1949	100.0	104.1	1982	107.3	109.4
1950	105.9	103.0	1983	106.1	107.6
1951	103.9	105.7	1984	105.9	107.6
1952	104.0	108.5	1985	107.7	110.0
1953	114.7	110.4	1986	111.2	113.3
1954	114.2	112.7	1987	118.9	117.6
1955	115.5	115.0	1988	122.8	121.4
1956	115.3	114.6	1989	127.5	122.4
1957	115.1	113.9	1990	126.5	121.6
1958	112.7	112.9	1991	116.3	119.3
1959	111.0	111.7	1992	114.7	116.1
1960	110.5	110.6	1993	111.3	112.8
1961	109.2	109.9	1994	111.5	111.5
1962	109.7	109.1	1995	110.3	110.5
1963	109.4	109.0	1996	109.9	110.9
1964	107.0	109.0	1997	109.6	112.5
1965	109.7	108.5	1998	113.1	115.7
1966	109.4	107.9	1999	119.5	120.3
1967	107.2	108.3	2000	126.3	126.8
1968	106.4	108.4	2001	133.0	134.8
1969	108.6	108.7	2002	142.0	144.6
1970	110.4	109.5	2003	153.1	157.1
1971	110.7	110.2	2004	168.4	171.1
1972	111.6	110.1	2005	189.1	179.8
1973	109.9	109.8	2006	202.8	179.1
1974	108.1	108.8	2007	185.5	172.2
1975	108.6	108.3	2008	149.7	160.3
1976	105.7	109.6	2009	133.6	*
1977	109.4	112.4	2010	129.7	*
1978	116.3	114.1			

Simple Centered $(2m + 1)$-Point Moving Averages

Let $x_1, x_2, x_3, \ldots, x_n$ be n observations on a time series of interest. A smoothed series can be obtained by using a simple centered $(2m + 1)$-point moving average:

$$x_t^* = \frac{1}{2m + 1} \sum_{j=-m}^{m} x_{t+j} \qquad (t = m + 1, m + 2, \ldots, n - m) \tag{16.1}$$

A moving average can be generated using Minitab, as shown in Figure 16.4. We see both the original series and the smoothed series—the 5-point moving average series—plotted versus time. As we can see, the moving average series is, indeed, smoother than the original series. Thus, the moving average series has removed the underlying irregular component from the series to reveal the structural components more clearly.

Figure 16.4 Simple Centered 5-Point Moving Average of Shiller Home Price Index Data

The kind of moving average discussed in this section is just one of many that might have been used. It is often deemed desirable to use a weighted average, in which most weight is given to the central observation, with weights for other values decreasing as their distance from the central observation increases. For example, we might use a weighted average such as

$$x_t^* = \frac{x_{t-2} + 2x_{t-1} + 4x_t + 2x_{t+1} + x_{t+2}}{10}$$

In any event, the objective in using moving averages remains the smoothing out of the irregular component in order to allow us to form a clearer picture of the underlying irregularities in a time series. The technique is perhaps of most value for descriptive purposes, in the production of graphs such as Figure 16.4.

Extraction of the Seasonal Component Through Moving Averages

We now move to develop a procedure for using moving averages to extract seasonal components from business and economic series. Seasonal components can be a nuisance, and the analyst may want to remove them from the series to obtain a keener appreciation of the behavior of other components. Recall also that in Section 13.2 we showed how dummy variables could be used to estimate and control seasonal effects.

Consider a quarterly time series with a seasonal component. Our strategy to remove seasonality will be to produce four-period moving averages so that the various seasonal values are brought together in a single seasonal moving average. For example, using the earnings-per-share data in Table 16.2, the first member of the series is

$$\frac{0.300 + 0.460 + 0.345 + 0.910}{4} = 0.50375$$

and the second member is

$$\frac{0.460 + 0.345 + 0.910 + 0.330}{4} = 0.51125$$

The complete series is shown in Table 16.2.

Table 16.2
Actual Earnings per Share of a Corporation and Centered 4-Point Moving Average

YEAR QUARTER	EARNINGS	4-POINT MOVING AVERAGES	CENTERED 4-POINT MOVING AVERAGES
1.1	0.3	*	*
1.2	0.46	*	*
1.3	0.345	0.50375	0.5075
1.4	0.91	0.51125	0.5219
2.1	0.33	0.53250	0.5444
2.2	0.545	0.55625	0.5725
2.3	0.44	0.58875	0.6094
2.4	1.04	0.63000	0.6469
3.1	0.495	0.66375	0.6769
3.2	0.68	0.69000	0.7206
3.3	0.545	0.75125	0.7581
3.4	1.285	0.76500	0.7888
4.1	0.55	0.81250	0.8269
4.2	0.87	0.84125	0.8781
4.3	0.66	0.91500	0.9200
4.4	1.58	0.92500	0.9400
5.1	0.59	0.95500	0.9763
5.2	0.99	0.99750	1.0163
5.3	0.83	1.03500	1.0375
5.4	1.73	1.04000	1.0475
6.1	0.61	1.05500	1.0663
6.2	1.05	1.07750	1.1163
6.3	0.92	1.15500	1.1663
6.4	2.04	1.17750	1.2000
7.1	0.7	1.22250	1.2400
7.2	1.23	1.25750	1.2925
7.3	1.06	1.32750	1.3425
7.4	2.32	1.35750	1.3800
8.1	0.82	1.40250	1.4263
8.2	1.41	1.45000	1.5013
8.3	1.25	1.55250	*
8.4	2.73	*	*

This new series of moving averages should be free from seasonality, but there is still a problem. The location in time of the members of the series of moving averages does not correspond precisely with that of the members of the original series. The first term is the average of the first four observations, and, thus, we might regard it as being centered between the second and third observations:

$$x_{2.5}^* = \frac{x_1 + x_2 + x_3 + x_4}{4}$$

Similarly, the second term could be written as follows:

$$x_{3.5}^* = \frac{x_2 + x_3 + x_4 + x_5}{4}$$

This problem can be overcome by centering our series of 4-point moving averages. This can be done by calculating the averages of adjacent pairs, which for the first value is

$$x_3^* = \frac{x_{2.5}^* + x_{3.5}^*}{2} = \frac{0.50375 + 0.51125}{2} = 0.5075$$

This value is the centered moving average corresponding to the third observation of the original series. The remainder of the series of centered moving averages is in the final column of Table 16.2. Note again that this procedure results in the loss of two observations from each end of the series.

The series of centered moving averages is plotted in Figure 16.5, along with the original series. Clearly, the seasonality component has been removed. In addition, because we have used moving averages, the irregular component has also been smoothed. The resulting picture thus allows us to judge the nonseasonal regularities in the data. We see that the smoothed series is dominated by an upward trend. Closer examination reveals steady earnings growth in the early part of the series, a central portion of rather slower growth, and resumption in the last part of the period of a pattern similar to the early one.

Figure 16.5 Centered 4-Point Moving Averages and Original Series for Earnings per Share of a Corporation

A Simple Moving Average Procedure for Seasonal Adjustment

Let x_t $(t = 1, 2, \ldots, n)$ be a seasonal time series of period s ($s = 4$ for quarterly data and $s = 12$ for monthly data). A centered s-point moving average series, x_{t}^{*}, is obtained through the following steps, where it is assumed that s is even:

1. Form the s-point moving averages:

$$x_{t+0.5}^{*} = \frac{\sum_{j=-(s/2)+1}^{s/2} x_{t+j}}{s} \qquad \left(t = \frac{s}{2}, \frac{s}{2} + 1, \ldots, n - \frac{s}{2} \right) \qquad (16.2)$$

2. Form the centered s-point moving averages:

$$x_{t}^{*} = \frac{x_{t-0.5}^{*} + x_{t+0.5}^{*}}{2} \qquad \left(t = \frac{s}{2} + 1, \frac{s}{2} + 2, \ldots, n - \frac{s}{2} \right) \qquad (16.3)$$

We have seen that the series of centered s-point moving averages can be a useful tool for gaining descriptive insight into the structure of a time series. Since it is largely free from seasonality and embodies a smoothing of the irregular component, it is well suited for the identification of a trend and/or cyclical component. This series of moving averages also forms the basis for many practical seasonal adjustment procedures. The specific procedure depends on a number of factors, including the amount of stability one assumes in the seasonal pattern and whether seasonality is viewed as additive or multiplicative. In the latter case we often take logarithms of the data.

Next, we discuss a seasonal-adjustment approach that is based on the implicit assumption of a stable seasonal pattern over time. The procedure is known as the *seasonal index method*. We assume that for any month or quarter in each year, the effect of seasonality is to increase or decrease the series by the same percentage.

We illustrate the seasonal index method using the corporate earnings data. The seasonally adjusted series is computed in Table 16.3. The first two columns contain the original series and the centered 4-point moving average. To assess the influence of seasonality, we express the original series as a percentage of the centered 4-point moving average series. Thus, for example, for the third quarter of year 1, we have the following:

$$100\left(\frac{x_3}{x_3^{*}}\right) = 100\left(\frac{0.345}{0.5075}\right) = 67.98$$

These percentages are also entered into Table 16.4, where the calculation of the seasonal index is shown. To assess the effect of seasonality in the first quarter, we find the median of the seven percentages for that quarter. This is the fourth value when they are arranged in ascending order—that is, 60.43. In a similar way we find the median of x_t as a percentage of x_t^{*} for each of the other quarters.

Table 16.3

Seasonal Adjustment of Earnings per Share of a Corporation by the Seasonal Index Method

YEAR QUARTER	x_t	x_t^{*}	$100\left(\dfrac{x_t}{x_t^{*}}\right)$	SEASONAL INDEX	ADJUSTED SERIES
1.1	0.300*			61.06	0.4913
1.2	0.460*			96.15	0.4784
1.3	0.345	0.5075	67.98	72.95	0.4729
1.4	0.910	0.5219	174.36	169.84	0.5358

(continued)

Table 16.3
(*continued*)

YEAR QUARTER	x_t	x_t^*	$100\left(\dfrac{x_t}{x_t^*}\right)$	SEASONAL INDEX	ADJUSTED SERIES
2.1	0.330	0.5444	60.62	61.06	0.5405
2.2	0.545	0.5725	95.20	96.15	0.5668
2.3	0.440	0.6094	72.20	72.95	0.6032
2.4	1.040	0.6469	160.77	169.84	0.6123
3.1	0.495	0.6769	73.13	61.06	0.8107
3.2	0.680	0.7206	94.37	96.15	0.7072
3.3	0.545	0.7581	71.89	72.95	0.7471
3.4	1.285	0.7888	162.91	169.84	0.7566
4.1	0.550	0.8269	66.51	61.06	0.9008
4.2	0.870	0.8781	99.08	96.15	0.9048
4.3	0.660	0.9200	71.74	72.95	0.9047
4.4	1.580	0.9400	168.09	169.84	0.9303
5.1	0.590	0.9763	60.43	61.06	0.9663
5.2	0.990	1.0163	97.41	96.15	1.0296
5.3	0.830	1.0375	80.00	72.95	1.1378
5.4	1.730	1.0475	165.16	169.84	1.0186
6.1	0.610	1.0663	57.21	61.06	0.9990
6.2	1.050	1.1163	94.06	96.15	1.0920
6.3	0.920	1.1663	78.88	72.95	1.2611
6.4	2.040	1.2000	170.00	169.84	1.2011
7.1	0.700	1.2400	56.45	61.06	1.1464
7.2	1.230	1.2925	95.16	96.15	1.2793
7.3	1.060	1.3425	78.96	72.95	1.4531
7.4	2.320	1.3800	168.12	169.84	1.3660
8.1	0.820	1.4263	57.49	61.06	1.3429
8.2	1.410	1.5013	93.92	96.15	1.4665
8.3	1.250*			72.95	1.7135
8.4	2.730*			169.84	1.6074

Table 16.4
Calculation of Seasonal Index for Earnings per Share Data of a Corporation

YEAR	QUARTER 1	QUARTER 2	QUARTER 3	QUARTER 4	SUMS
1			67.98	174.36	
2	60.62	95.20	72.20	160.77	
3	73.13	94.37	71.89	162.91	
4	66.51	99.08	71.74	168.09	
5	60.43	97.41	80.00	165.16	
6	57.21	94.06	78.88	170.00	
7	56.45	95.16	78.96	168.12	
8	57.49	93.92			
Median	60.43	95.16	72.20	168.09	395.88
Seasonal index	61.06	96.15	72.95	169.84	400

To obtain seasonal indices, we also adjust the indices so that their average is 100. In Table 16.4, we see that the four medians sum only to 395.88. We can obtain the final indices—that have a mean of 100—by multiplying each median by (400/395.88). For the first quarter we have

$$\text{seasonal index} = 60.43\left(\frac{400}{395.88}\right) - 61.06$$

We interpret this figure as estimating that the effect of seasonality is to lower first-quarter earnings to 61.06% of what they would have been in the absence of seasonal factors.

The seasonal indices, from the last row of Table 16.4, are entered in the fifth column of Table 16.3. Notice that the same index is used for any particular quarter in every year. Finally, we obtain our seasonally adjusted value:

$$\text{adjusted value} = \text{original value}\left(\frac{100}{\text{seasonal index}}\right)$$

For example, for the third quarter of year 1 the seasonally adjusted value is

$$0.345\left(\frac{100}{72.95}\right) = 0.4729$$

The complete seasonally adjusted series obtained in this way is given in the final column of Table 16.3 and graphed in Figure 16.6. Notice that there is a suggestion of a little remaining seasonality in the latter part of the period. This suggests that a more elaborate approach, allowing for changing seasonal patterns, may be desirable.

Figure 16.6
Seasonally Adjusted Earnings per Share of a Corporation

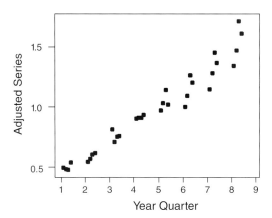

The seasonal-index method presented here provides one simple solution to the index problem. Many important time series—such as gross domestic product and its components, employment and unemployment, prices, and wages—have strong seasonal components. Generally, data on such quantities are published by government agencies in both unadjusted and adjusted forms. Although they are more complex than the method described here, official adjustment procedures are typically based on moving averages. The seasonal-adjustment procedure most commonly employed in official U.S. government publications is the Census X-11 method. It differs from the seasonal-index method in allowing for a steadily evolving seasonal pattern over time. It can be shown that in its additive version of X-11 estimates the seasonal component of a monthly time series to a close approximation by

$$S_t = \frac{z_{t-36} + 2z_{t-24} + 3z_{t-12} + 3z_t + 3z_{t+12} + 2z_{t+24} + z_{t+36}}{15}$$

where

$$z_t = x_t - x_t^*$$

with x_t the original value of the series at time t and x_t^* the corresponding centered 12-point moving average. Of course, if such a procedure is used, some special treatment is needed for values toward the end of the series because the expression for the seasonal factor involves values in the time series that have not yet occurred. A possible way of accomplishing this is to replace unknown future values of a series in the moving average by forecasts based on the available data.

EXERCISES

 Visit www.MyStatLab.com or www.pearsonglobal editions.com to access the data files.

Application Exercises

16.3 The data file **Fargo Electronics Earnings** shows quarterly sales of a corporation over a period of 6 years.

   a. Draw a time plot of this series and discuss its features.
   b. Use the seasonal-index method to seasonally adjust this series. Graph the seasonally adjusted series and discuss its features.

16.4 The data file **Fargo Electronics Sales** shows quarterly sales of a corporation over a period of 6 years.

   a. Draw a time plot of this series and discuss its features.
   b. Use the seasonal-index method to seasonally adjust this series. Graph the seasonally adjusted series and discuss its features.

16.5 The data file **Gold Price** shows the year-end price of gold (in dollars) over 14 consecutive years. Compute a simple, centered 3-point moving average series for the gold price data. Plot the smoothed series and discuss the resulting graph.

16.6 The data file **Housing Starts** shows private housing units started per thousand of population in the United States over a period of 24 years. Compute a simple, centered 5-point moving average series for the housing starts data. Draw a time plot of the smoothed series and comment on your results.

16.7 The data file **Earnings per Share** shows earnings per share of a corporation over a period of 28 years. Compute a simple, centered 7-point moving average series for the corporate earnings data. Based

on a time plot of the smoothed series, what can be said about its regular components?

16.8 Let

$$x_t^* = \frac{1}{2m+1} \sum_{j=-m}^{m} x_{t+j}$$

be a simple, centered $(2m+1)$-point moving average. Show that

$$x_{t+1}^* = x_t^* \frac{x_{t+m+1} - x_{t-m}}{2m+1}$$

How might this result be used in the efficient computation of series of centered moving averages?

16.9 The data file **Acme LLC Earnings per Share** shows earnings per share of a corporation over a period of 7 years.

   a. Draw a time plot of these data. Does your graph suggest the presence of a strong seasonal component in this earnings series?
   b. Using the seasonal index method, obtain a seasonally adjusted earnings series. Graph this series and comment on its behavior.

16.10 a. Show that the centered s-point moving average series of Section 16.2 can be written as follows:

$$x_t^* = \frac{x_{t-(s/2)} + 2(x_{t-(s/2)+1} + \cdots + x_{t+(s/2)-1}) + x_{t+(s/2)}}{2s}$$

   b. Show that

$$x_{t+1}^* = x_t^* + \frac{x_{t+(s/2)+1} + x_{t+(s/2)} - x_{t-(s/2)+1} - x_{t-(s/2)}}{2s}$$

Discuss the computational advantages of this formula in the seasonal adjustment of monthly time series.

16.3 EXPONENTIAL SMOOTHING

We now examine some procedures for using the current and past values of a time series to forecast future values of the series. This easily stated problem can be very difficult to resolve satisfactorily. A vast array of forecasting methods are in common use, and, to a great extent, the eventual choice will be problem specific, depending on the resources and objectives of the analyst and the nature of the available data.

   Our aim is to use the available observations, $x_1, x_2, \ldots, x_n$, of a series to predict the unknown future values $x_{t+1}, x_{t+2}, \ldots$. Forecasting is of crucial importance in the business environment as a rational basis for decision making. For example, monthly product sales are predicted as a basis for inventory-control policy. Forecasts of future earnings are used when making investment decisions.

In this section we introduce a forecasting method known as **simple exponential smoothing**, which performs quite effectively in a number of forecasting applications. In addition, it forms the basis for some more elaborate forecasting methods. Exponential smoothing is appropriate when the series is nonseasonal and has no consistent upward or downward trend.

In the absence of trend and seasonality, the objective is to estimate the current level of the time series and then use this estimate to forecast future values. Our position is that we are standing at time t, we are looking back on the series of observations $x_t, x_{t-1}, x_{t-2}, \ldots,$ and we want to make a forecast of future values based on the history that we know. As a prelude, we consider two extreme possibilities. First, we might simply use the most recent observation to forecast all future observations. In some cases, such as prices in speculative markets, this may be the best we can do, but the result is often not very successful. However, in many series with irregular components, we would probably want to use a number of previous observations in the series. This would identify any patterns that might exist in the time series and avoid using only a random fluctuation as the basis of our forecast.

At the opposite extreme, we might use the average of all past values as our estimate of the current level. A moment's reflection suggests that often this would not be useful because all past values would be treated equally. Thus, for example, if we tried to predict future sales by this procedure, we would be assigning equal importance to sales many years ago and to recent sales. It seems reasonable that more recent experience should have a greater impact on our forecast.

Simple exponential smoothing allows a compromise between these extremes, providing a forecast based on a weighted average of current and past values. In forming this average, most weight is given to the most recent observation, rather less to the immediately preceding value, less to the one before that, and so on. We estimate the level at the current time t by

$$\hat{x}_t = \alpha x_t + \alpha(1 - \alpha)x_{t-1} + \alpha(1 - \alpha)^2 x_{t-2} + \cdots$$

where α is a number between 0 and 1. For example, with $\alpha = 0.5$, the forecast of future observations is

$$\hat{x}_t = .5x_t + .25x_{t-1} + .125x_{t-2} + \cdots$$

so that a weighted average, with declining weights, is applied to current and past observations in computing the forecasts.

From this model we see that the forecast of the series at any time t is estimated by

$$\hat{x}_t = \alpha x_t + \alpha(1 - \alpha)x_{t-1} + \alpha(1 - \alpha)^2 x_{t-2} + \cdots$$

and, similarly, the level at the previous time period $(t - 1)$ is estimated by

$$\hat{x}_{t-1} = \alpha x_{t-1} + \alpha(1 - \alpha)x_{t-2} + \alpha(1 - \alpha)^2 x_{t-3} + \cdots$$

Multiplying through by $1 - \alpha$, we have the following:

$$(1 - \alpha)\hat{x}_{t-1} = \alpha(1 - \alpha)x_{t-1} + \alpha(1 - \alpha)^2 x_{t-2} + \alpha(1 - \alpha)^3 x_{t-3} + \cdots$$

Hence, on subtracting these two equations, we obtain

$$\hat{x}_t - (1 - \alpha)\hat{x}_{t-1} = \alpha x_t$$

And by simple manipulation, we have the equation for computing the simple exponential smoothing forecast:

$$\hat{x}_t = (1 - \alpha)\,\hat{x}_{t-1} + \alpha x_t \quad \text{for } 0 < \alpha < 1$$

This provides a convenient recursive algorithm for calculating forecasts. The forecast value, $\hat{x}_t$, at time t is a weighted average of the previous period forecast $\hat{x}_{t-1}$ and the latest observation x_t. The weights given to each depend on the choice of α, which is defined as the smoothing constant. Note that a small value of α gives greater weight to $\hat{x}_{t-1}$, which is based on the past history of the series, and less weight to x_t, which represents the most recent data.

We can illustrate the procedure using the Shiller home price index data shown in Table 16.1 with a value of $\alpha = 0.6$. The process begins by setting the first element of the series:

$$\hat{x}_1 = x_1 = 106.5$$

The second value in the forecast is then

$$\hat{x}_2 = .4\hat{x}_1 + .6x_2$$
$$= (.4)(106.5) + (.6)(109.3) = 108.2$$

This process continues through the series so that

$$\hat{x}_3 = .4\hat{x}_2 + .6x_3$$
$$= (.4)(108.2) + (.6)(101.2) = 104.0$$

Forecasting Through Simple Exponential Smoothing

Let $x_1, x_2, \ldots, x_n$ be a set of observations on a nonseasonal time series with no consistent upward or downward trend. **Forecasting though simple exponential smoothing** then proceeds as follows:

1. We obtain the smoothed series $\hat{x}_t$, as

$$\hat{x}_1 = x_1$$

$$\hat{x}_t = (1 - \alpha)\hat{x}_{t-1} + \alpha x_t \quad (0 < \alpha < 1; t = 2, 3, \ldots, n) \tag{16.4}$$

where α is a smoothing constant whose value is fixed between 0 and 1.

2. Standing at time n, we obtain forecasts of future values, x_{n+h}, of the series by

$$\hat{x}_{n+h} = \hat{x}_n \quad (h = 1, 2, 3, \ldots)$$

So far we have said little about the choice of the smoothing constant, α, in practical applications. In applications this choice may be based on either subjective or objective grounds. One possibility is to rely on experience or judgment. For instance, an analyst who wants to predict product demand may have had considerable experience in working with data on similar product lines and may use that experience to select an appropriate α. Visual inspection of a graph of the available data can also be useful in suggesting an appropriate value for the smoothing constant. If the series appears to contain a substantial irregular element, we do not want to give too much weight to the most recent observation alone since it might not indicate what we expect in the future. This would suggest a relatively low value for the smoothing constant, α. But if the series is rather smooth, we would use a higher value for α in order to give more weight to the most recent observation.

A more objective approach is to try several different values and see which would have been most successful in predicting historical movements in the time series. We might, for example, compute the smoothed series at values of α of 0.8, 0.6, 0.4, and 0.2 and choose the value that provides the best forecast in the historical series. We would compute the error for each forecast as follows:

$$e_t = x_t - \hat{x}_{t-1}$$

One possibility is to compute, for each trial value of α, the sum of squared forecast errors:

$$SS = \sum_{t=2}^{n} e_t^2 = \sum_{t=2}^{n} (x_t - \hat{x}_{t-1})^2$$

The value of α that minimizes the sum of squared forecast errors will be used for future predictions. Simple exponential smoothing can be performed using Minitab. Figure 16.7 shows a plot for the Shiller home price index of the original and smoothed

Figure 16.7 Shiller Home Price Index with Original and Simple Exponential Smoothing Values

series using $\alpha = 0.9$, which was established by trying different values and finding the value that provided a satisfactory fit.

Whatever value of the smoothing constant is used, Equation 16.4 can be regarded as an updating mechanism. At time $(t - 1)$ the level of the series is estimated by $\hat{x}_{t-1}$. Then, in the next period, the new observation x_t is used to update this estimate so that the new estimate of level is a weighted average of the previous estimate and the new observation.

The Holt-Winters Exponential Smoothing Forecasting Model

Many business forecasting procedures are based on extensions of simple exponential smoothing. The Holt-Winters exponential smoothing procedure allows for trend, and possibly also seasonality, in a time series.

First, we consider a nonseasonal time series. We want to estimate not only the current level of the series but also the trend—regarded as the difference between the current level and the preceding level.

We denote x_t as the observed value and $\hat{x}_t$ as the estimate of the level. The trend estimate is represented as T_t. The principle behind the estimation of these two quantities is much the same as in the simple exponential smoothing algorithm. The two estimating equations are

$$\hat{x}_t = (1 - \alpha)(\hat{x}_{t-1} + T_{t-1}) + \alpha x_t \quad (0 < \alpha < 1)$$
$$T_t = (1 - \beta)T_{t-1} + \beta(\hat{x}_t - \hat{x}_{t-1}) \quad (0 < \beta < 1)$$

where α and β are smoothing constants whose values are set between 0 and 1.

Comparable to simple exponential smoothing, the Holt-Winters procedure uses these equations to update previous estimates using a new observation. The estimate of level $\hat{x}_{t-1}$ made at time $(t - 1)$, taken in conjunction with the trend estimate, T_{t-1}, suggests for time t a level $(\hat{x}_{t-1} + T_{t-1})$. This estimate is modified, in light of the new observation, x_t, to obtain an updated estimate of level, $\hat{x}_t$, using the given equation.

Similarly, trend at time $(t-1)$ is estimated as T_{t-1}. However, once the new observation, x_t, is available, an estimate of trend is suggested as the difference between the two most recent estimates of level. The trend estimate at time t is then the weighted average as given.

We begin the computations by setting the following:

$$T_2 = x_2 - x_1 \quad \text{and} \quad \hat{x}_2 = x_2$$

Then, the previous equations are applied, in turn, for $t = 3, 4, \ldots, n$. We demonstrate these calculations in Example 16.1. The entire procedure is summarized next.

Forecasting with the Holt-Winters Method: Nonseasonal Series

Let $x_1, x_2, \ldots, x_n$ be a set of observations on a nonseasonal time series. **Forecasting with the Holt-Winters method: nonseasonal series** proceeds as follows.

1. Obtain estimates of level $\hat{x}_t$ and trend T_t as

$$\hat{x}_2 = x_2 \quad T_2 = x_2 - x_1$$

$$\hat{x}_t = (1 - \alpha)(\hat{x}_{t-1} + T_{t-1}) + \alpha x_t \quad (0 < \alpha < 1; t = 3, 4, \ldots, n)$$

$$T_t = (1 - \beta)T_{t-1} + \beta(\hat{x}_t - \hat{x}_{t-1}) \quad (0 < \beta < 1; t = 3, 4, \ldots, n) \tag{16.5}$$

where α and β are smoothing constants whose values are fixed between 0 and 1.

2. Standing at time n, we obtain forecasts of future values, x_{n+h}, of the series by

$$\hat{x}_{n+h} = \hat{x}_n + hT_n \tag{16.6}$$

where h is the number of periods in the future.

Example 16.1 Forecasting Consumer Credit (Holt-Winters Exponential Smoothing)

You are asked to obtain a forecast for outstanding consumer credit using the Holt-Winters exponential smoothing procedure.

Solution The calculations that follow use the consumer credit data in Table 16.5, which also includes the calculations for the Holt-Winters procedure.

Table 16.5 Holt-Winters Calculations for Consumer Credit Outstanding ($\alpha = 0.7, \beta = 0.6$)

t	x_t	$\hat{x}_t$	T_t
1	133		
2	155	155	22
3	165	169	17
4	171	175	11
5	194	192	14
6	231	223	25
7	274	266	36
8	312	309	40
9	313	324	25
10	333	338	18
11	343	347	13

The initial estimates of level and trend in year 2 are

$$\hat{x}_2 = x_2 = 155$$

and

$$T_2 = x_2 - x_1 = 155 - 133 = 22$$

This smoothing application uses $\alpha = 0.7, \beta = 0.6$, and the following equations:

$$\hat{x}_t = 0.3(\hat{x}_{t-1} + T_{t-1}) + 0.7x_t$$
$$T_t = 0.4T_{t-1} + 0.6(\hat{x}_t - \hat{x}_{t-1})$$

Then, for $t = 3$,

$$\hat{x}_3 = 0.3(\hat{x}_2 + T_2) + 0.7x_3$$
$$= (0.3)(155 + 22) + (0.7)(165)$$
$$= 168.6$$

and, in addition,

$$T_3 = 0.4T_2 + 0.6(\hat{x}_3 - \hat{x}_2)$$
$$= (0.4)(22) + (0.6)(168.6 - 155)$$
$$= 16.96$$

Then, for $t = 4$,

$$\hat{x}_4 = 0.3(\hat{x}_3 + T_3) + 0.7x_4$$
$$= (0.3)(168.6 + 16.96) + (0.7)(171)$$
$$= 175.4$$

and, in addition,

$$T_4 = 0.4T_3 + 0.6(\hat{x}_4 - \hat{x}_3)$$
$$= (0.4)(16.96) + (0.6)(175.4 - 168.6)$$
$$= 10.86$$

The remaining calculations continue in the same way, setting, in turn, $t = 5, 6, \ldots, 11$. The results of these calculations are shown in Table 16.5.

Now let us use these level and trend estimates to forecast future observations. Given a series $x_1, x_2, \ldots, x_n$, the most recent level and trend estimates are $\hat{x}_t$ and T_n, respectively. In the production of forecasts it is assumed that this latest trend will continue from the most recent level. Thus, we forecast using the relationship

$$\hat{x}_{n+1} = \hat{x}_n + T_n$$

and, for the following one,

$$\hat{x}_{n+2} = \hat{x}_n + 2T_n$$

In general, for h periods ahead,

$$\hat{x}_{n+h} = \hat{x}_n + hT_n$$

From Table 16.5 the most recent level and trend estimates are

$$\hat{x}_{11} = 347$$
$$T_{11} = 13$$

Then, the forecasts for the next three periods are as follows:

$$\hat{x}_{12} = 347 + 13 = 360$$
$$\hat{x}_{13} = 347 + (2)(13) = 373$$
$$\hat{x}_{14} = 347 + (3)(13) = 386$$

The Holt-Winters procedure can be computed in Minitab, and Figure 16.8 shows the time-series graph and the forecasts.

Figure 16.8 Consumer Credit Outstanding Observed and Forecasts Using Minitab Calculations

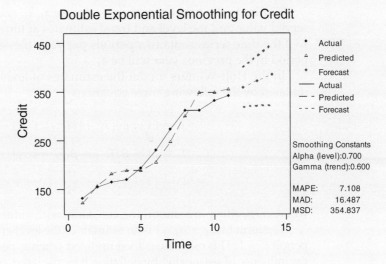

The Minitab procedure differs slightly from the procedure just described. Minitab computes an estimate for the first period using the following procedure:

1. Minitab fits a linear regression model to time-series data (y variable) versus time (x variable).
2. The constant from this regression is the initial estimate of the level component; the slope coefficient is the initial estimate of the trend component.

As a result, the values calculated by the Minitab program differ slightly from those in Table 16.5. The comparable values computed by the Minitab procedure are shown in Table 16.6. The Minitab procedure generally provides slightly better forecasts compared to the more simplified procedure we have shown. For other statistical packages, check the specific computational algorithms to ensure that you understand what is being computed. Usually this can be done by clicking the Help option.

Table 16.6 Minitab Calculations for Consumer Credit Outstanding ($\alpha = 0.7, \beta = 0.6$)

TIME	OBSERVED CONSUMER CREDIT	LEVEL EXPECTED VALUE	TREND	FORECASTS
1	133	130	28	
2	155	156	27	
3	165	170	19	
4	171	177	12	
5	194	192	14	
6	231	224	24	
7	274	266	35	
8	312	309	40	
9	313	324	25	
10	333	338	18	
11	343	347	13	
12				360
13				373
14				385

Forecasting Seasonal Time Series

We now examine an extension of the Holt-Winters method that allows for seasonality. In most practical problems, the seasonal factor is taken to be multiplicative, so that, for example, in dealing with monthly sales figures, we might think of January in terms of a proportion of average monthly sales. As before, the trend component is assumed to be additive.

Similar to the nonseasonal case, we use x_t, $\hat{x}_t$, and T_t to denote, respectively, the observed value and the level and trend estimates at time t. The seasonal factor is denoted F_t, so if the time series contains s periods per year, the seasonal factor for the corresponding period in the previous year will be F_{t-s}.

In the Holt-Winters model the estimates of level, trend, and the seasonal factor are updated by the following three equations

$$\hat{x}_t = (1 - \alpha)(\hat{x}_{t-1} + T_{t-1}) + \alpha \frac{x_t}{F_{t-s}} \quad (0 < \alpha < 1)$$

$$T_t = (1 - \beta)T_{t-1} + \beta(\hat{x}_t - \hat{x}_{t-1}) \quad (0 < \beta < 1)$$

$$F_t = (1 - \gamma)F_{t-s} + \gamma \frac{x_t}{\hat{x}_t} \quad (0 < \gamma < 1)$$

where α, β, and γ are smoothing constants with values between 0 and 1.

The term $(\hat{x}_{t-1} + T_{t-1})$ is an estimate of the level at time t computed at the previous time period $t - 1$. This estimate is then updated when x_t becomes available. But we also remove the influence of seasonality by deflating it by the latest available estimate, F_{t-s}, of the seasonal factor for that period. The updating equation for trend, T_t, is the same as used previously.

Finally, the seasonal factor, F_t, is estimated using the third equation. The most recent estimate of the factor, available from the previous year, is F_{t-s}. However, dividing the new observation, x_t, by the level estimate, $\hat{x}_t$, suggests a seasonal factor $x_t/\hat{x}_t$. The new estimate of the seasonal factor is then a weighted average of these two quantities.

Forecasting with the Holt-Winters Method: Seasonal Series

Let $x_1, x_2, \ldots, x_n$ be a set of observations on a seasonal time series of period s (with $s = 4$ for quarterly data and $s = 12$ for monthly data). **Forecasting with the Holt–Winters method: seasonal series** uses a set of recursive estimates from the historical series. These estimates utilize a level factor, α; a trend factor, β; and a multiplicative seasonal factor, γ. The recursive estimates are based on the following equations:

$$\hat{x}_t = (1 - \alpha)(\hat{x}_{t-1} + T_{t-1}) + \alpha \frac{x_t}{F_{t-s}} \quad (0 < \alpha < 1)$$

$$T_t = (1 - \beta)T_{t-1} + \beta(\hat{x}_t - \hat{x}_{t-1}) \quad (0 < \beta < 1)$$

$$F_t = (1 - \gamma)F_{t-s} + \gamma \frac{x_t}{\hat{x}_t} \quad (0 < \gamma < 1) \quad (16.7)$$

where $\hat{x}_t$ is the smoothed level of the series, T_t is the smoothed trend of the series, and F_t is the smoothed seasonal adjustment for the series. The computational details are tedious and best left to a computer. We have demonstrated the algorithm used by Minitab, but numerous quality statistical packages have similar procedures. These computer procedures may differ in the way they handle the generation of factors for the initial periods of an observed time series, and, thus, you should consult the documentation for the package to determine the exact procedure used. Minitab uses a dummy variable regression procedure to obtain estimates for the initial periods.

After the initial procedure generates the level, trend, and seasonal factors from a historical series, we can use the results to forecast future values at h time periods ahead from the last observation, x_n, in the historical series. The forecast equation is as follows:

$$\hat{x}_{n+h} = (\hat{x}_n + hT_n)F_{n+h-s} \tag{16.8}$$

We note that the seasonal factor, F, is the one generated for the most recent seasonal time period.

The procedure that we have developed here can be implemented using the Minitab procedure labeled "Winters method" smoothing forecast. Specifically, the method described here uses the multiplicative option. The Winters method employs a level component, a trend component, and a seasonal component at each period. It uses three weights, or smoothing parameters, to update the components at each period. Initial values for the level and trend components are obtained from a linear regression on time. Initial values for the seasonal component are obtained from a dummy variable regression using detrended data. The Winters method smoothing equations for the multiplicative model are those previously used.

Figure 16.9

History and Forecast of Corporate Earnings Using Holt–Winters Method: Seasonal Series

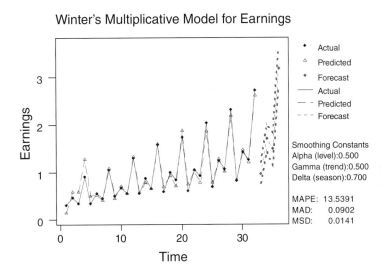

This procedure is demonstrated using the corporate earnings per share in Minitab. A plot of observed and fitted values, along with forecasts for the next four periods, is shown in Figure 16.9. Forecasts are obtained by using the most recent trend and level estimates and then adjusting for the particular seasonal factor. Given a season containing s time periods, the forecast for one period ahead would be as follows:

$$\hat{x}_{n+1} = (\hat{x}_n + T_n)F_{n+1-s}$$

Our example data contain 32 time periods and a seasonal factor $s = 4$, indicating quarterly data. Thus, to forecast the next observation beyond the end of the series, we use the following:

$$\hat{x}_{33} = (\hat{x}_{32} + T_{32})F_{29}$$

Table 16.7 Computational Results: Minitab Application of Holt-Winters Smoothing Procedure: Seasonal Series

Year Quarter	Corporate Earnings	Smoothed Value	Level Estimate	Trend Estimate	Seasonal Estimate	Forecast
1.1	0.300	0.043	0.387	0.242	0.713	
1.2	0.460	0.360	0.562	0.208	0.851	
1.3	0.345	0.433	0.609	0.128	0.628	
1.4	0.910	1.055	0.631	0.075	1.529	
2.1	0.330	0.450	0.584	0.014	0.609	
2.2	0.545	0.498	0.619	0.024	0.872	
2.3	0.440	0.389	0.672	0.039	0.646	
2.4	1.040	1.028	0.696	0.031	1.505	
3.1	0.495	0.424	0.770	0.053	0.633	
3.2	0.680	0.671	0.801	0.042	0.856	
3.3	0.545	0.518	0.843	0.042	0.646	
3.4	1.285	1.269	0.869	0.034	1.486	
4.1	0.550	0.550	0.886	0.025	0.624	
4.2	0.870	0.758	0.964	0.052	0.888	
4.3	0.660	0.623	1.019	0.053	0.648	
4.4	1.580	1.514	1.067	0.051	1.482	
5.1	0.590	0.666	1.032	0.008	0.588	
5.2	0.990	0.916	1.077	0.026	0.910	
5.3	0.830	0.697	1.193	0.071	0.681	
5.4	1.730	1.767	1.215	0.047	1.441	
6.1	0.610	0.714	1.150	−0.009	0.548	
6.2	1.050	1.047	1.147	−0.006	0.914	
6.3	0.920	0.782	1.246	0.046	0.721	
6.4	2.040	1.795	1.354	0.077	1.487	
7.1	0.700	0.741	1.355	0.039	0.526	
7.2	1.230	1.238	1.370	0.027	0.902	
7.3	1.060	0.988	1.433	0.045	0.734	
7.4	2.320	2.131	1.519	0.066	1.515	
8.1	0.820	0.799	1.572	0.059	0.523	
8.2	1.410	1.419	1.597	0.042	0.889	
8.3	1.250	1.172	1.671	0.058	0.744	
8.4	2.730	2.531	1.765	0.076	1.537	
9.1						0.963
9.2						1.705
9.3						1.48
9.4						3.18

This forecast is for the first quarter; thus, we use the most recent first-quarter seasonal factor, which is F_{29}. In general, if we are forecasting h periods into the future, we obtain the forecast as follows:

$$\hat{x}_{n+h} = (\hat{x}_n + hT_n)F_{n+h-s}$$

The forecast here uses a level factor, $\alpha = 0.5$; a trend factor, $\beta = 0.5$; and a seasonal factor, $\gamma = 0.7$.

Finally, in Table 16.7 we show the detailed results of the computation of trend, level, and seasonal factors for each period.

The actual forecasts obtained through the Holt-Winters approach will depend on the specific values chosen for the smoothing constants. As in our earlier discussion of exponential smoothing, this choice could be based on either subjective or objective criteria. The analyst's experience with similar data sets might suggest suitable values of the smoothing constants. Alternatively, several different sets of possible values could be tried on the available historical data, and the set that would have yielded the best forecasts for that data could be used to generate the forecasts. This strategy is easy to implement by using a statistical computer package, as shown by the example we demonstrated using Minitab.

EXERCISES

Visit www.MyStatLab.com or www.pearsonglobal editions.com to access the data files.

Application Exercises

16.11 The data file **Inventory Sales** shows the inventory-sales ratio for manufacturing and trade in the United States over a period of 12 years. Use the method of simple exponential smoothing to obtain forecasts of the inventory-sales ratio over the next 4 years. Use a smoothing constant of $\alpha = 0.6$. Graph the observed time series and the forecasts.

16.12 The data file **Gold Price** shows the year-end price of gold (in dollars) over 14 consecutive years. Use the method of simple exponential smoothing, with a smoothing constant of $\alpha = 0.7$, to obtain forecasts of the price of gold in the next 5 years.

16.13 The data file **Housing Starts** shows private housing units started per thousand of population in the United States over a period of 24 years. Using the data, employ the method of simple exponential smoothing with smoothing constant $\alpha = 0.5$ to predict housing starts in the next 3 years.

16.14 The data file **Earnings per Share** shows earnings per share of a corporation over a period of 18 years.

a. Using smoothing constants $\alpha = 0.8, 0.6, 0.4$, and 0.2, find forecasts based on simple exponential smoothing.

b. Which of the forecasts would you choose to use?

16.15 a. If forecasts are based on simple exponential smoothing, with $\hat{x}_t$ denoting the smoothed value of the series at time t, show that the error made in forecasting x_t, standing at time $(t - 1)$, can be written as follows:

$$e_t = x_t - \hat{x}_{t-1}$$

b. Hence, show that we can write $\hat{x}_t = x_t - (1 - \alpha)e_t$, from which we see that the most recent observation and the most recent forecast error are used to compute the next forecast.

16.16 Suppose that in the simple exponential smoothing method, the smoothing constant α is set equal to 1. What forecasts will result?

16.17 Comment on the following statement: We know that all business and economic time series exhibit variability through time. Yet if simple exponential smoothing is used, the same forecast results for all future values of the time series. Since we know that all future values will not be the same, this is absurd.

16.18 The data file **Industrial Production Canada** shows an index of industrial production for Canada over a period of 15 years. Use the Holt-Winters procedure with smoothing constants $\alpha = 0.7$ and $\beta = 0.5$ to obtain forecasts over the next 5 years.

16.19 The data file **Hourly Earnings** shows manufacturing hourly earnings in the United States over 24 months. Use the Holt-Winters procedure with smoothing constants $\alpha = 0.7$ and $\beta = 0.6$ to obtain forecasts for the next 3 months.

16.20 The data file **Food Prices** shows an index of food prices, seasonally adjusted, over a period of 14 months in the United States. Use the Holt-Winters method with smoothing constants $\alpha = 0.5$ and $\beta = 0.5$ to obtain forecasts for the next 3 months.

16.21 The data file **Profit Margins** shows percentages of profit margins of a corporation over a period of 11 years. Obtain forecasts for the next 2 years, using the Holt-Winters method with smoothing constants $\alpha = 0.4$ and $\beta = 0.4$.

16.22 The data file **Quarterly Earnings** shows quarterly sales of a corporation over a period of 6 years. Use the Holt-Winters seasonal method to obtain forecasts of sales up to eight quarters ahead. Employ smoothing constants $\alpha = 0.4, \beta = 0.5$, and $\gamma = 0.6$. Graph the data and the forecasts.

16.23 The data file **Quarterly Sales** shows quarterly sales of a corporation over a period of 6 years. Use the Holt-Winters seasonal method to obtain forecasts of sales up to eight quarters ahead. Employ smoothing constants $\alpha = 0.5, \beta = 0.6$, and $\gamma = 0.7$. Graph the data and the forecasts.

In this section we present a different approach to time-series forecasting. This approach involves using the available data to estimate parameters of a model of the process that might have generated the time series. In this section we consider one widely used procedure, *autoregressive models*, that is based on the model-building approach.

In Section 13.3 we introduced the use of lagged dependent variables in multiple regression models, and that approach is the basis of the models we discuss here. Essentially, the idea is to regard a time series as a series of random variables. For practical purposes we might often be prepared to assume that these random variables all have the same means and variances. However, we cannot assume that they are independent of each other. Certainly, if we consider a series of product sales, it is very likely that sales in adjacent periods are correlated with each other. Correlation patterns such as those between adjacent periods are sometimes referred to as *autocorrelation*.

In principle, any number of autocorrelation patterns are possible. However, some are considerably more likely to arise than others. A particularly attractive possibility arises when we think of a fairly strong correlation between adjacent observations in time: a less-strong correlation between observations two time periods apart, a weaker correlation yet between values three time periods apart, and so on. A very simple autocorrelation pattern of this sort arises when the correlation between adjacent values in the time series is some number—say, $\phi_1(0 \leq |\phi_1| \leq 1)$—that between values two time periods apart is ϕ_1^2, that between values three time periods apart is ϕ_1^3, and so on. Thus, if we let x_t denote the value of the series at time t, we have, under this model of autocorrelation,

$$Corr(x_t, x_{t-j}) = \phi_1^j \qquad (j = 1, 2, 3, \dots)$$

This autocorrelation structure gives rise to a time-series model of the form

$$x_t = \gamma + \phi_1 x_{t-1} + \varepsilon_t$$

where γ and ϕ_1 are fixed parameters, and the random variables ε_t have means 0 and fixed variances for all t and are not correlated with each other. The purpose of the parameter γ is to allow for the possibility that the series x_t has some mean other than 0. Otherwise, this is the model we used in Section 13.7 to represent autocorrelation in the error terms of a regression equation. It is called a *first-order autoregressive model*.

The first-order autoregressive model expresses the current value, x_t, of a series in terms of the previous value, x_{t-1}, and a nonautocorrelated random variable, ε_t. Since the random variable ε_t is not autocorrelated, it is unpredictable. For series generated by the first-order autoregressive model, forecasts of future values depend only on the most recent value of the series. However, in many applications we would want to use more than this one observation as a basis for forecasting. An obvious extension of the model would be to make the current value of the series dependent on the two most recent observations. Thus, we could use a model

$$x_t = \gamma + \phi_1 x_{t-1} + \phi_2 x_{t-2} + \varepsilon_t$$

where γ, ϕ_1, and ϕ_2 are fixed parameters. This is called a *second-order autoregressive model*.

More generally, for any positive integer p, the current value of the series can be made (linearly) dependent on the p previous values through the autoregressive model of order p:

$$x_t = \gamma + \phi_1 x_{t-1} + \phi_2 x_{t-2} + \cdots + \phi_p x_{t-p} + \varepsilon_t$$

where γ, ϕ_1, ϕ_2, $\dots$, ϕ_p are fixed parameters. This equation depicts the general autoregressive model. In the remainder of this section we consider the fitting of such models and their use in forecasting future values.

Suppose that we have a series of observations $x_1, x_2, \dots, x_t$. We want to use these to estimate the unknown parameters γ, ϕ_1, ϕ_2, $\dots$, ϕ_p for which the sum of squared discrepancies

$$SS = \sum_{t=p+1}^{n} (x_t - \gamma - \phi_1 x_{t-1} - \phi_2 x_{t-2} - \cdots - \phi_p x_{t-p})^2$$

is smallest. Hence, the estimation can be carried out using a multiple regression program. We demonstrate this procedure in Example 16.2 using the Shiller home price index data.

Autoregressive Models and Their Estimation

Let x_t $(t = 1, 2, \ldots, n)$ be a time series. A model that can often be used effectively to represent that series is the **autoregressive model** of order p:

$$x_t = \gamma + \phi_1 x_{t-1} + \phi_2 x_{t-2} + \cdots + \phi_p x_{t-p} + \varepsilon_t \tag{16.9}$$

where $\gamma, \phi_1, \phi_2, \ldots, \phi_p$ are fixed parameters and the ε_t are random variables that have means 0 and constant variances and are uncorrelated with one another.

The parameters of the autoregressive model are estimated through a least squares algorithm, as the values of $\gamma, \phi_1, \phi_2, \ldots, \phi_p$, for which the sum of squares

$$SS = \sum_{t=p+1}^{n} (x_t - \gamma - \phi_1 x_{t-1} - \phi_2 x_{t-2} - \cdots - \phi_0 x_{t-p})^2 \tag{16.10}$$

is a minimum.

Forecasting from Estimated Autoregressive Models

Suppose that we have observations $x_1, x_2, \ldots, x_n$ from a time series and that an autoregressive model of order p has been fitted to these data. Write the estimated model as follows:

$$x_t = \hat{\gamma} + \hat{\phi}_1 x_{t-1} + \hat{\phi}_2 x_{t-2} + \cdots + \hat{\phi}_p x_{t-p} + \varepsilon_t \tag{16.11}$$

Standing at time n, we obtain forecasts of future values of the series from

$$\hat{x}_{n+h} = \hat{\gamma} + \hat{\phi}_1 \hat{x}_{n+h-1} + \hat{\phi}_2 \hat{x}_{n+h-2} + \cdots + \hat{\phi}_p \hat{x}_{n+h-p} \qquad (h = 1, 2, 3, \ldots) \tag{16.12}$$

where for $h > 0$, $\hat{x}_{n+h}$ is the forecast of x_{t+h} standing at time n, and for $h \le 0$, $\hat{x}_{t+h}$, it is simply the observed value of x_{t+h}.

Example 16.2 Forecasting Sales Data (Autoregressive Model)

You have been asked to develop an autoregressive model to forecast the Shiller real home price index data. This index is contained in the data file **Shiller House Price Cost**.

Solution To use an autoregressive model to generate forecasts of future values, it is necessary to fix a value for p, the order of the autoregression. In making this choice we must choose p large enough to account for all the important autocorrelation behavior of the series. But, in addition, we do not want p to be so large that we are including irrelevant parameters and, as a result, having inefficient estimation of the important parameters. In general, parsimonious—simple but sufficient to accomplish the objective—models are preferred for good time-series forecasting.

One possibility is to fix the value of p arbitrarily, perhaps on the basis of past experience, with similar data sets. An alternative approach is to set some maximal order, K, of the autoregression and fit, in turn, models of order $p = K, K - 1, K - 2, \ldots$. For each value of p, the null hypothesis that the final autoregression parameter, φ_p, of the model is 0 is tested against a two-sided alternative. The procedure terminates when we find a value of p for which this null hypothesis is not rejected. Our aim, then, is to test the null hypothesis

$$H_0 : \phi_p = 0$$

against the alternative

$$H_1 : \phi_p \ne 0$$

In Chapter 11 we developed procedures for testing the null hypothesis, H_0. Basically, we know that the ratio of the coefficient estimate divided by the estimated coefficient standard error follows a Student's t distribution. The Minitab regression output (and the regression output from any statistical package) includes that Student's t calculation and, in addition, the probability of the null hypothesis being true (the p-value for the null hypothesis) given the computed Student's t.

Figure 16.10 presents abbreviated copies of Minitab regression output for autoregressive models using the Shiller home price index data with $p = 1, 2, 3, 4$.

Figure 16.10
Autoregressive Models for the Shiller Home Price Index

61 cases used, 4 cases contain missing values

Predictor	Coef	SE Coef	T	P
Constant	12.415	5.387	2.30	0.025
indexlag1	1.8421	0.1312	14.04	0.000
indexlag2	-1.4409	0.2713	-5.31	0.000
indexlag3	0.7445	0.3227	2.31	0.025
indexlag4	-0.2500	0.1993	-1.25	0.215

S = 5.42799   R-Sq = 93.6%   R-Sq(adj) = 93.2%

Regression with p = 3
Shiller Real Home Price Index = 9.60 + 1.77 indexlag1 - 1.19 indexlag2
                          + 0.349 indexlag3
62 cases used, 3 cases contain missing values

Predictor	Coef	SE Coef	T	P
Constant	9.598	4.496	2.13	0.037
indexlag1	1.7653	0.1221	14.45	0.000
indexlag2	-1.1915	0.2141	-5.57	0.000
indexlag3	0.3487	0.1281	2.72	0.009

S = 5.44949   R-Sq = 93.5%   R-Sq(adj) = 93.1%

Regression with p = 2
Shiller Real Home Price Index = 13.9 + 1.54 indexlag1 - 0.654 indexlag2
63 cases used, 2 cases contain missing values

Predictor	Coef	SE Coef	T	P
Constant	13.850	4.407	3.14	0.003
indexlag1	1.53819	0.09791	15.71	0.000
indexlag2	-0.65442	0.09806	-6.67	0.000

S = 5.87141   R-Sq = 92.2%   R-Sq(adj) = 92.0%

Regression with p = 1
Shiller Real Home Price Index = 8.70 + 0.930 indexlag1
64 cases used, 1 cases contain missing values

Predictor	Coef	SE Coef	T	P
Constant	8.705	5.607	1.55	0.126
indexlag1	0.92966	0.04658	19.96	0.000

S = 7.62692   R-Sq = 86.5%   R-Sq(adj) = 86.3%

We apply this approach for the Shiller home price index data, using a 5% significance level for our tests. We use the results in Figure 16.10, which include autoregressive regressions for $p = 1, 2, 3, 4$. For the regression with $p = 4$, we find that the coefficient of x_{t-4} has a Student's t statistic of -1.25 and a p-value of 0.215. Thus, we cannot reject the null hypothesis that the coefficient is 0, and we move on to the regression with $p = 3$. Here we see that the coefficient of x_{t-3} has a Student's t statistic equal to 2.72 and a p-value of 0.009. We can reject the null hypothesis that this coefficient is 0. Our chosen model, then, is the one with three lagged values, $p = 3$. Note that the standard error of the estimate is somewhat larger for the models with $p = 1$ and $p = 2$. The final equation is as follows:

$$\hat{x}_t = 9.60 + 1.77x_{t-1} - 1.19x_{t-2} + 0.349x_{t-3}$$

Now that we have the model, we want to apply it to obtain forecasts for the Shiller home price index data. We prepared a forecast for the $p = 3$ model using the Minitab Arima time-series analysis model. The results are shown in Figure 16.11. The coefficients are slightly different from those prepared using lagged regressions in Figure 16.10. This occurs because the Arima routine uses a slightly different algorithm for the computation. However, the forecast results are essentially the same.

Figure 16.11
Predicted Values from Autoregressive Model for the Shiller Home Price Index

Home Price Index

ARIMA Model: Shiller Real Home Price Index

Unable to reduce sum of squares any further

Final Estimates of Parameters

Type		Coef	SE Coef	T	P
AR	1	1.7865	0.1225	14.58	0.000
AR	2	-1.2241	0.2145	-5.71	0.000
AR	3	0.3712	0.1281	2.90	0.005
Constant		7.8766	0.6839	11.52	0.000
Mean		118.64	10.30		

Number of observations: 65
Residuals: SS = 1827.79 (backforecasts excluded)
              MS = 29.96 DF = 61

Forecasts from period 59

		95% Limits		
Period	Forecast	Lower	Upper	Actual
60	173.990	163.259	184.721	189.147
61	169.440	147.470	191.410	202.830
62	160.100	129.631	190.569	185.520
63	151.071	115.563	186.578	149.709
64	144.684	106.573	182.796	133.584
65	140.861	101.394	180.327	129.685

Forecasts from period 55

		95% Limits		
Period	Forecast	Lower	Upper	Actual
56	129.227	118.496	139.958	133.042
57	128.489	106.520	150.459	142.049
58	126.120	95.651	156.589	153.096
59	123.876	88.368	159.383	168.368
60	122.494	84.383	160.606	189.147
61	121.893	82.426	161.360	202.830
62	121.677	81.380	161.974	185.520
63	121.514	80.591	162.437	149.709

In Figure 16.11 we show how a forecast compares with actual data for the home price index. In the face of the housing bubble, we see that the the actual housing bubble data were substantially above the forecast interval. Thus, we see that in this situation, with housing prices deviating greatly from past patterns, the forecast using the autoregressive Arima model does not provide a good forecast. We should also note that most forecasters were not successful in the actual market and hence the entire economy suffered when the bubble collapsed.

Graphical depiction of the forecasts for the home price index beyond 2010 are shown in Figure 16.12. The forecast extends the most recent data and shows a small increase in the index followed by some decline. Note also that the prediction interval becomes much wider as the forecast moves further into the future.

Figure 16.12 Forecasts of Shiller Home Price Index Using a Fitted Third-Order Autoregressive Model

EXERCISES

Application Exercises

16.24 Using the data in the data file **Earnings per Share**, estimate a first-order autoregressive model for the earnings per share. Use the fitted model to obtain forecasts for the next 4 days.

16.25 The data file **Trading Volume** shows the volume of transactions (in hundreds of thousands) in shares of a corporation over a period of 12 weeks. Using these data, estimate a first-order autoregressive model, and use the fitted model to obtain forecasts of volume for the next 3 weeks.

16.26 Using the data file **Housing Starts**, estimate autoregressive models of orders 1 through 4. Use the method of this section to test the hypothesis that the order of the autoregression is $p - 1$ against the alternative that the order is p, with a significance level of 10%. Select one of these models, and calculate forecasts of housing starts for the next 5 years. Draw a time plot showing the original observations together with the forecasts. Would different forecasts result if a significance level of 5% was used for the tests of autoregressive order?

16.27 From the data file **Earnings per Share** on corporate earnings per share, fit autoregressive models of orders 1 through 4. Use the procedure of this section to test the hypothesis that the order of the autoregression is $p - 1$ against the alternative that the true order is p, with a 10% significance level. Choose one of these models, and compute forecasts of earnings per share for the next 5 years. Draw a graph showing the original data along with these forecasts. Would the results differ if a 5% significance level was used for the tests?

16.28 In Figure 16.10, fitted autoregressive models of orders 1 through 4 are given for annual sales data. We then selected a model by testing the null hypothesis of autoregression of order $p - 1$ against the alternative of autoregression of order p at the 5% significance level. Repeat this procedure, but test at the 10% significance level.

a. What autoregressive model is now selected?

b. Obtain forecasts of sales for the next 3 years, based on this selected model.

16.29 For a certain product it was found that annual sales volume could be well described by a third-order autoregressive model. The estimated model obtained was as follows:

$$x_t = 188 + 1.90x_{t-1} - 0.46x_{t-2} + 0.16x_{t-3} + \varepsilon_t$$

For 2015, 2016, and 2017, sales were 858, 904, and 966, respectively. Calculate sales forecasts for the years 2018 through 2020.

16.30 For many time series, particularly prices in speculative markets, the *random walk* model has been found to give a good representation of actual data. This model is written as follows:

$$x_t = x_{t-1} + \varepsilon_t$$

Show that, if this model is appropriate, forecasts of x_{n+h}, standing at time n, are given by

$$\hat{x}_{n+h} = x_n \quad (h = 1, 2, 3, \dots)$$

16.31 Refer to the data file **Hourly Earnings**, showing earnings over 24 months. Denote the observations x_t ($t = 1, 2, \dots, 24$). Now, form the series of first differences:

$$z_t = x_t - x_{t-1} \quad (t = 2, 3, \dots, 24)$$

Fit autoregressive models of orders 1–4 to the series z_t. Using the approach of this section for testing the hypothesis that the autoregressive order is $p - 1$ against the alternative of order p, with a 10% significance level, select one of these models. Using the selected model, find forecasts for z_t, where $t = 25, 26$, and 27. Hence, obtain forecasts of earnings for the next 3 months.

16.5 AUTOREGRESSIVE INTEGRATED MOVING AVERAGE MODELS

In this section we briefly introduce an approach to time-series forecasting that is widely used in business applications. The models to be discussed include, as special cases, the autoregressive models discussed in Section 16.4.

In a classic book, George Box and Gwilyn Jenkins (1979) introduced a methodology sufficiently versatile to provide a moderately skillful user with good results for a wide range of forecasting problems that occur in practice. The Box-Jenkins approach requires that we first define a very broad class of models from which forecasts can be derived. Next we develop a methodology for picking, on the basis of the characteristics of the available data, a suitable model for any forecasting problem.

The general class of models is the class of autoregressive integrated moving average models, or **ARIMA models**. These are rather natural extensions of the autoregressive models of Section 16.4. Moreover, the simple exponential smoothing and Holt-Winters predictors of Section 16.3 can be derived from specific members of this general class, as can many other widely used forecasting algorithms. The models and the Box-Jenkins time-series analysis techniques can be generalized to allow for seasonality and also to deal with related time series so that future values of one series can be predicted from information not only on its own past, but also on the past of other relevant series. This last possibility allows an approach to forecasting that generalizes the regression procedures discussed in Chapters 11–13.

It is not possible in the space available to provide a full discussion of the Box-Jenkins methodology. (For an introduction to this methodology, see Newbold and Bos (1994) or Greene (2012).) In essence, it involves three stages:

1. Based on summary statistics that are readily calculated from the available data, the analyst selects a specific model that might be appropriate from the general class. This is not simply a matter of automatically following a set of rules but rather requires a certain amount of judgment and experience. However, one is not forever committed to the model chosen at this stage but can abandon it in favor of some alternative at a later stage of the analysis if that appears desirable.

2. The specific model chosen will almost invariably have some unknown coefficients. These must be estimated from the available data using efficient statistical techniques, such as least squares.

3. Finally, checks are applied to determine whether the estimated model provides an adequate representation of the available time-series data. Any inadequacies revealed at this stage may suggest some alternative specification, and the process of model selection, coefficient estimation, and model checking is iterated until a satisfactory model is found.

The Box-Jenkins approach to forecasting has the great advantage of flexibility—a wide range of predictors is available, and choice among them is based on data evidence. Moreover, when this approach to forecasting has been compared with other methods, using actual economic and business time series, it has usually been found to perform very well. Thus, the procedure can be said to have survived the acid test: In practice, it works!

In concluding this brief discussion, note that computer programs for performing a time-series analysis through the fitting to data of ARIMA models are widely available—including a set of procedures in Minitab. However, the method does have a drawback compared with other simpler procedures discussed in earlier sections of this chapter. Because flexibility is allowed in choosing an appropriate model from the general class, the Box-Jenkins approach is more costly in terms of skilled worker time than methods that force a single model structure onto every time series.

Key Words

- ARIMA models, 717
- autoregressive model, 713
- forecasting from estimated autoregressive models, 713
- forecasting through simple exponential smoothing, 703
- forecasting with the Holt-Winters method: nonseasonal series, 705
- forecasting with the Holt-Winters method: seasonal series, 708
- simple exponential smoothing, 702
- time series, 688
- time series component analysis, 692

Data Files

- Acme LLC Earnings per Share, 701
- Earnings per Share, 693, 701, 711, 716
- Fargo Electronics Earnings, 701
- Fargo Electronics Sales, 701
- Food Prices, 711
- Gold Price, 701
- Hourly Earnings, 711, 717
- Housing Starts, 693, 701, 711, 716
- Industrial Production Canada, 711
- Inventory Sales, 711
- Macro2010, 690, 719
- Product Sales, 719
- Profit Margins, 711
- Quarterly Earnings, 711, 718, 719
- Quarterly Sales, 711
- Shiller House Price Cost, 713
- Trading Volume, 716

Chapter Exercises and Applications

 Visit www.MyStatLab.com or www.pearsonglobal editions.com to access the data files.

16.32 Explain the statement that a time series can be viewed as being made up of a number of components. Provide examples of business and economic time series for which you would expect particular components to be important.

16.33 In many business applications, forecasts for future values of time series, such as sales and earnings, are made exclusively on the basis of past information on the time series in question. What features of time-series behavior are exploited in the production of such forecasts?

16.34 A manager in charge of inventory control requires sales forecasts for several products, on a monthly basis, over the next 6 months. This manager has available monthly sales records over the past 4 years for each of these products. He decides to use, as forecasts for each of the next 6 months, the average monthly sales over the previous 4 years. Do you think this is a good strategy? Provide reasons.

16.35 What is meant by the seasonal adjustment of a time series? Explain why government agencies expend a large amount of effort on the seasonal adjustment of economic time series.

16.36 The data file **Quarterly Earnings** shows quarterly earnings per share of a corporation over 7 years.

  a. Draw a time plot of these data. Does this graph suggest the presence of a strong seasonal component?
  b. Use the seasonal index method to obtain a seasonally adjusted series.

16.37　The data file **Product Sales** shows 24 annual observations on sales of a product. Use simple exponential smoothing with smoothing constant $\alpha = 0.5$ to obtain forecasts of sales for the next 3 years.

16.38　Refer to the data file **Quarterly Earnings**. Use the Holt-Winters seasonal method with smoothing constants $\alpha = 0.6, \beta = 0.6$, and $\gamma = 0.8$ to obtain forecasts of this earnings-per-share series for the next four quarters.

16.39　Using the data file **Product Sales**, estimate autoregressive models of orders 1–4 for product sales. Using the procedure of Section 16.4 for testing the hypothesis that the autoregressive order is $p - 1$ against the alternative that the order is p, with a significance level of 10%, choose one of these models. Compute forecasts for the next 3 years from the chosen model.

16.40　Using the data in the file **Macro2010**, develop and autoregressive model for the prime interest rate. First, use the data for the period 1980, first quarter, through 2000, fourth quarter, to forecast for the quarters in years 2001–2003. Then use the data from 1980, first quarter, through 2007, fourth quarter, to forecast the quarters in the years 2008 and 2009. Discuss the differences in the accuracy of the forecasts compared to the actual results and indicate reasons for these differences.

16.41　Using the data in the file **Macro2010** develop an autoregressive model for the Personal Consumption Expenditures. First, use the data for the period 1980, first quarter, through 2000, fourth quarter, to forecast for the quarters in years 2001–2003. Then use the data from 1980, first quarter, through 2007, fourth quarter, to forecast the quarters in the years 2008 and 2009. Discuss the differences in the accuracy of the forecasts compared to the actual results and indicate reasons for these differences.

16.42　Using the data in the file **Macro2010** develop an autoregressive model for fixed investment. First, use the data for the period 1965, first quarter, through 2000, fourth quarter, to forecast for the quarters in years 2001–2003. Then use the data from 1965, first quarter, through 2007, fourth quarter, to forecast the quarters in the years 2008 and 2009.

Discuss the differences in the accuracy of the forecasts compared to the actual results and indicate reasons for these differences.

16.43　Using the data in the file **Macro2010**, develop an autoregressive model for imports. First, use the data for the period 1970, first quarter, through 2000, fourth quarter, to forecast for the quarters in years 2001–2003. Then use the data from 1970, first quarter, through 2007, fourth quarter, to forecast the quarters in the years 2008 and 2009. Discuss the differences in the accuracy of the forecasts compared to the actual results and indicate reasons for these differences.

REFERENCES

1. Box, G. E. P., and G. M. Jenkins. 1970. *Time Series Analysis, Forecasting, and Control.* San Francisco: Holden-Day.

2. Granger, C. W., and P. Newbold. 1986. *Forecasting Economic Time Series*, 2nd ed. Orlando, FL: Academic Press.

3. Greene, W. H. 2012. *Econometric Analysis*, 7th ed. Upper Saddle River, NJ: Prentice Hall.

3. Newbold, P., and T. Bos. 1994. *Introductory Business Forecasting*, 2nd ed. Cincinnati, OH: South-Western.

4. Taleb, N. N. 2005. *Fooled by Randomness*. New York: Random House.

CHAPTER

17

Additional Topics in Sampling

Introduction

In some situations it is desirable to break down the population into subgroups called strata, so that each individual member of the population belongs to one, and only one, of the strata. The basis of the stratum might be some particular identifiable characteristic of the population of special interest to the researcher. This type of sampling is called stratified sampling. In this chapter we introduce confidence interval estimation of a population mean, population total, and population proportion for stratified sampling, and we consider allocation of sample size under proportional and optimal allocation. A brief discussion of cluster sampling, two-phase sampling, and nonprobabilistic sampling methods is also presented.

17.1 STRATIFIED SAMPLING

Suppose that you decide to investigate the views of students on your campus concerning some sensitive topic, and the framing of appropriately worded questions could be difficult. It is likely that you would want to ask several questions of every sample member and so, given limited resources, would be able to take only a fairly small sample. You would presumably select a simple random sample of, say, 100 students from a list of all students on campus. Suppose, however, that, on closer inspection of the records of the sample members, you find that only two of them are business majors, although the population proportion of business majors is far higher than this. Your problem at this stage is twofold. First, you may well be interested in comparing the views of business majors with those of the rest of the student population. This is hardly feasible, given their minimal representation in your sample. Second, you may suspect that the views of business majors on this question will differ from those of their fellow students. If that was the case, you would worry about the reliability of inference based on a sample in which this group is seriously underrepresented.

You could perhaps console yourself with the thought that, since you have taken a random sample, any estimators derived in the usual way will be unbiased, and the resulting inference, in the statistical sense, will be strictly valid. However, a little reflection should convince you that this is scant consolation indeed! All that unbiasedness indicates is that, if the sampling procedure is repeated a very large number of times and the estimator is calculated, its average will be equal to the corresponding population value. But, in fact, you are *not* going to repeat the sampling procedure a large number of times. You have to base your conclusions on *just a single sample*, and the fact that business majors could have been overrepresented in other samples you might have drawn, so that things "average out" in the long run, is not terribly useful.

There is a second tempting possibility, one that is in many ways preferable to proceeding with the original sample. You could simply discard the original sample and take another. If the constitution of the sample achieved at the second attempt looks more representative of the population at large, you may well be better off to proceed with it. The difficulty now is that the sampling procedure you have adopted—where the population is to be sampled until you achieve a sample you like the looks of—is very difficult to formalize; consequently, the sample results are very hard to analyze with any statistical validity. This is no longer simple random sampling, and the procedures of Chapter 7 are not, therefore, strictly valid.

Fortunately, a third alternative sampling scheme exists to afford protection against just this type of problem. If it is suspected at the outset that particular identifiable characteristics of population members are germane to the subject of inquiry or if particular subgroups of the population are of special interest to the investigator, it is not necessary (and probably not desirable) to be content with simple random sampling as a means of selecting the sample members. Instead, the population can be broken down into subgroups, or *strata*, and a simple random sample can be taken from each stratum. The only requirement is that each individual member of the population be identifiable as belonging to one, and only one, of the strata.

Stratified Random Sampling

Suppose that a population of N individuals can be subdivided into K mutually exclusive and collectively exhaustive groups, or strata. **Stratified random sampling** is the selection of independent simple random samples from each stratum of the population. If the K strata in the population contain $N_1, N_2, \ldots, N_K$ members, then

$$N_1 + N_2 + \cdots + N_K = N$$

There is no need to take the same number of sample members from every stratum. Denote the numbers in the sample by $n_1, n_2, \ldots, n_K$. Then the total number of sample members is as follows:

$$n_1 + n_2 + \cdots + n_K = n$$

The population of students whose views are to be canvassed could be divided into two strata—business majors and nonbusiness majors. Less straightforward stratification is also possible. Suppose that, on some other topic, you believe that gender and class year (senior, junior, sophomore, or first-year) are both potentially relevant. In that case, to satisfy the requirement that the strata be mutually exclusive and collectively exhaustive, eight strata—senior women, senior men, and so on—are needed.

Later in this section the question of how to allocate the sampling effort among the strata is considered. An attractive possibility, often employed in practice, is *proportional allocation*: The proportion of sample members from any stratum is the same as the proportion of population members in that stratum.

Analysis of Results from Stratified Random Sampling

The analysis of the results of a stratified random sample is relatively straightforward. Let $\mu_1, \mu_2, \ldots, \mu_K$ denote the population means in the K strata and $\bar{x}_1, \bar{x}_2, \ldots, \bar{x}_K$ be the corresponding sample means. Consider a particular stratum—say, the jth stratum. Then, since a simple random sample has been taken in this stratum, the stratum sample mean is an unbiased estimator of the population mean μ_j. Also, from an unbiased estimation procedure for the variance of the stratum sample mean, the point estimate is

$$\hat{\sigma}_{\bar{x}_j}^2 = \frac{s_j^2}{n_j} \times \frac{(N_j - n_j)}{N_j - 1}$$

where s_j^2 is the sample variance in the jth stratum. Inference about individual strata can, therefore, be made in the same way as in Section 7.6.

Generally, inferences about the overall population mean μ are of interest where

$$\mu = \frac{N_1\mu_1 + N_2\mu_2 + \cdots + N_K\mu_K}{N} = \frac{1}{N}\sum_{j=1}^{K}N_j\mu_j$$

A natural point estimate is provided by the following:

$$\bar{x}_{st} = \frac{1}{N}\sum_{j=1}^{K}N_j\bar{x}_j$$

An unbiased estimator of the variance of the estimator of μ follows from the fact that the samples in each stratum are independent of one another, and the point estimate is given by the following:

$$\hat{\sigma}_{\bar{x}_{st}}^2 = \frac{1}{N^2}\sum_{j=1}^{K}N_j^2\hat{\sigma}_{\bar{x}_j}^2$$

Inferences about the overall population mean can be based on these results.

Estimation of the Population Mean Using Stratified Random Samples

Suppose that random samples of n_j individuals are taken from strata containing N_j individuals ($j = 1, 2, \ldots, K$). Let

$$\sum_{j=1}^{K}N_j = N \qquad \text{and} \qquad \sum_{j=1}^{K}n_j = n$$

Denote the sample means and variances in the strata by $\bar{x}_j$ and s_j^2 ($j = 1, 2, \ldots, K$) and the overall population mean by μ.

1. An unbiased estimation procedure for the overall population mean μ yields the following point estimate:

$$\bar{x}_{st} = \frac{1}{N}\sum_{j=1}^{K}N_j\bar{x}_j \qquad (17.1)$$

2. An unbiased estimation procedure for the variance of our estimator of the overall population mean yields the point estimate

$$\hat{\sigma}_{\bar{x}_{st}}^2 = \frac{1}{N^2}\sum_{j=1}^{K}N_j^2\hat{\sigma}_{\bar{x}_j}^2 \qquad (17.2)$$

where

$$\hat{\sigma}_{\bar{x}_j}^2 = \frac{s_j^2}{n_j} \times \frac{(N_j - n_j)}{N_j - 1} \qquad (17.3)$$

3. Provided the sample size is large, a $100(1 - \alpha)\%$ confidence interval **estimation of the population mean using stratified random samples**, is obtained from the following:

$$\bar{x}_{st} \pm z_{\alpha/2}\hat{\sigma}_{\bar{x}_{st}} \tag{17.4}$$

Example 17.1 Restaurant Chain (Estimation)

A popular restaurant chain in the Benelux has 75 restaurants in Belgium, including 30 in the Netherlands, and 28 in Luxembourg. Management is considering adding Waterzooi, a creamy fish stew, to the menu. To test the likely demand for this item, it was introduced on the menus of random samples of 15 restaurants in Belgium, 8 in the Netherlands, and 5 in Luxembourg. Using the subscripts 1, 2, and 3 to denote Belgium, the Netherlands, and Luxembourg, respectively, the sample means and standard deviations for numbers of orders received for this item per restaurant in the three states in a week were as follows:

$$\bar{x}_1 = 21.2 \quad s_1 = 12.8$$

$$\bar{x}_2 = 13.3 \quad s_2 = 11.4$$

$$\bar{x}_3 = 26.1 \quad s_3 = 9.2$$

Estimate the mean number of weekly orders per restaurant, μ, for all restaurants in this chain.

Solution We know that

$$N_1 = 75 \quad N_2 = 30 \quad N_3 = 20 \quad N = 125$$

$$n_1 = 15 \quad n_2 = 8 \quad n_3 = 2 \quad n = 25$$

Our estimate of the population mean is as follows:

$$\bar{x}_{st} = \frac{1}{N}\sum_{j=1}^{K}N_j\bar{x}_j = \frac{(75)(21.2) + (30)(13.3) + (20)(26.1)}{125} = 20.09$$

Thus, the estimated mean number of weekly orders per restaurant is 20.09.

The next step is to calculate the quantities:

$$\hat{\sigma}_{\bar{x}_1}^2 = \frac{s_1^2}{n_1} \times \frac{(N_1 - n_1)}{N_1 - 1} = \frac{(12.8)^2}{15} \times \frac{60}{74} = 8.856$$

$$\hat{\sigma}_{\bar{x}_2}^2 = \frac{s_2^2}{n_2} \times \frac{(N_2 - n_2)}{N_2 - 1} = \frac{(11.4)^2}{8} \times \frac{22}{29} = 12.324$$

$$\hat{\sigma}_{\bar{x}_3}^2 = \frac{s_3^2}{n_3} \times \frac{(N_3 - n_3)}{N_3 - 1} = \frac{(9.2)^2}{2} \times \frac{18}{19} = 40.093$$

Together with the individual stratum sample means, these quantities can be used to compute confidence intervals for the population means of the three strata. However, our concentration here is on the overall population mean. To obtain confidence intervals for this quantity,

$$\hat{\sigma}_{\bar{x}_{st}}^2 = \frac{1}{N^2}\sum_{j=1}^{K}N_j^2\sigma_{\bar{x}_j}^2$$

$$= \frac{(75)^2(8.856) + (30)^2(12.324) + (20)^2(40.093)}{(125)^2} = 4.924$$

On taking the square root,

$$\hat{\sigma}_{\bar{x}_{st}} = 2.22$$

Thus, the 95% confidence interval for the mean number of orders per restaurant received in a week is

$$20.09 \pm (1.96)(2.22)$$

The 95% confidence interval runs from 15.74 to 24.44 orders per restaurant.

Since the population total is the product of the population mean and the number of population members, these procedures can be readily modified to allow its estimation, as described next.

Estimation of the Population Total Using Stratified Random Samples

Suppose that random samples of n_j individuals from strata containing N_j individuals ($j = 1, 2, \ldots, K$) are selected and that the quantity to be estimated is the population total, $N\mu$.

1. An unbiased estimation procedure for $N\mu$ leads to the following point estimate:

$$N\bar{x}_{st} = \sum_{j=1}^{K} N_j \bar{x}_j \tag{17.5}$$

2. An unbiased estimation procedure for the variance of our estimator of the population total yields the following estimate:

$$N^2 \hat{\sigma}_{\bar{x}_{st}}^2 = \sum_{j=1}^{K} N_j^2 \hat{\sigma}_{\bar{x}_j}^2 \tag{17.6}$$

3. Provided the sample size is large, a $100(1 - \alpha)\%$ confidence interval **estimation of the population total using stratified random samples** is obtained from the following:

$$N\bar{x}_{st} \pm z_{\alpha/2} N\hat{\sigma}_{\bar{x}_{st}} \tag{17.7}$$

Example 17.2 Total Annual Enrollment in Business Statistics (Estimation)

The publisher of a business statistics text wants an estimate of the total number of students taking business statistics courses in all U.S. colleges. Suppose that there are 1,395 colleges in the United States, 364 have 2-year programs and 1,031 are 4-year schools. A simple random sample of 40 two-year schools and an independent simple random sample of 60 four-year schools were taken. The sample means and standard deviations of numbers of students enrolled in the past year in business statistics courses are given in the table. Estimate the total annual enrollment in business statistics courses.

	2-YEAR SCHOOLS	4-YEAR SCHOOLS
Mean	154.3	411.8
Standard deviation	87.3	219.9

Solution We know that

$$N_1 = 364 \quad n_1 = 40 \quad \bar{x}_1 = 154.3 \quad s_1 = 87.3$$

$$N_2 = 1{,}031 \quad n_2 = 60 \quad \bar{x}_2 = 411.8 \quad s_2 = 219.9$$

Our estimate of the population total is as follows:

$$N\bar{x}_{st} = \sum_{j=1}^{K} N_j\bar{x}_j = (364)(154.3) + (1{,}031)(411.8) = 480{,}731$$

Next,

$$\hat{\sigma}_{\bar{x}_1}^2 = \frac{s_1^2}{n_1} \times \frac{(N_1 - n_1)}{N_1 - 1} = \frac{(87.3)^2}{40} \times \frac{324}{363} = 170.06$$

$$\hat{\sigma}_{\bar{x}_2}^2 = \frac{s_2^2}{n_2} \times \frac{(N_2 - n_2)}{N_2 - 1} = \frac{(219.9)^2}{60} \times \frac{971}{1{,}030} = 759.77$$

Finally,

$$N^2\hat{\sigma}_{\bar{x}_{st}}^2 = \sum_{j=1}^{K} N_j^2\hat{\sigma}_{\bar{x}_{st}}^2 = (364)^2(170.06) + (1{,}031)^2(759.77) = 830{,}138{,}148.73$$

and, on taking the square root,

$$N\hat{\sigma}_{\bar{x}_{st}}^2 = 28{,}812$$

For a 95% confidence interval,

$$z_{\alpha/2} = z_{0.025} = 1.96$$

The required 95% interval is, therefore,

$$480{,}731 \pm (1.96)(28{,}812)$$

Thus, our 95% confidence interval runs from 424,259 to 537,203 students enrolled.

Next, consider the problem of estimating a population proportion based on a stratified random sample. Let $P_1, P_2, \ldots, P_K$ be the population proportions in the K strata and $\hat{p}_1, \hat{p}_2, \ldots, \hat{p}_K$ be the corresponding sample proportions. If P denotes the overall population proportion, its estimate is based on the fact that

$$P = \frac{N_1 P_1 + N_2 P_2 + \cdots + N_K P_K}{N} = \frac{1}{N}\sum_{j=1}^{K} N_j P_j$$

Procedures to develop an estimation of the population proportion from a stratified random sample follow.

Estimation of the Population Proportion Using Stratified Random Samples

Suppose that random samples of n_j individuals from strata containing N_j individuals ($j = 1, 2, \ldots, K$) are obtained. Let P_j be the population proportion and $\hat{p}_j$ be the sample proportion, in the jth stratum, of those possessing a particular characteristic. If P is the overall population proportion, then

1. An unbiased estimation procedure for P yields the following:

$$\hat{p}_{st} = \frac{1}{N}\sum_{j=1}^{K} N_j\hat{p}_j \tag{17.8}$$

2. An unbiased estimation procedure for the variance of our estimator of the overall population proportion is

$$\hat{\sigma}^2_{\hat{p}_{st}} = \frac{1}{N^2}\sum_{j=1}^{K} N_j^2 \hat{\sigma}^2_{\hat{p}_j} \tag{17.9}$$

where

$$\hat{\sigma}^2_{\hat{p}_j} = \frac{\hat{p}_j(1 - \hat{p}_j)}{n_j - 1} \times \frac{(N_j - n_j)}{N_j - 1} \tag{17.10}$$

is the estimate of the variance of the sample proportion in the jth stratum.

3. Provided the sample size is large, a $100(1 - \alpha)\%$ confidence interval **estimation of the population proportion using stratified random samples** is obtained from the following:

$$\hat{p}_{st} \pm z_{\alpha/2}\hat{\sigma}_{\hat{p}_{st}} \tag{17.11}$$

Example 17.3 Statistics Taught in Economics Departments (Estimation)

In the study of Example 17.2, suppose that it was found that business statistics was taught by members of the economics department in 7 of the 2-year colleges and 13 of the 4-year colleges in the sample. Estimate the proportion of all colleges in which this course is taught in the economics department.

Solution We know that

$$N_1 = 364 \qquad n_1 = 40 \qquad \hat{p}_1 = \frac{7}{40} = 0.175$$

$$N_2 = 1{,}031 \qquad n_2 = 60 \qquad \hat{p}_2 = \frac{13}{60} = 0.217$$

Our estimate of the population proportion is as follows:

$$\hat{p}_{st} = \frac{1}{N}\sum_{j=1}^{K} N_j\hat{p}_j = \frac{(364)(0.175) + (1{,}031)(0.217)}{1{,}395} = 0.206$$

Thus, it is estimated that in 20.6% of all colleges, the economics department teaches the course.

Next,

$$\hat{\sigma}^2_{\hat{p}_1} = \frac{\hat{p}_1(1 - \hat{p}_1)}{n_1 - 1} \times \frac{(N_1 - n_1)}{N_1 - 1} = \frac{(0.175)(0.825)}{39} \times \frac{324}{363} = 0.003304$$

$$\hat{\sigma}^2_{\hat{p}_2} = \frac{\hat{p}_2(1 - \hat{p}_2)}{n_2 - 1} \times \frac{(N_2 - n_2)}{N_2 - 1} = \frac{(0.217)(0.783)}{59} \times \frac{971}{1{,}030} = 0.002715$$

Together with the individual stratum sample proportions, these values can be used to calculate confidence intervals for the two stratum population proportions. However, here, focus is given to interval estimation for the overall population proportion, for which

$$\hat{\sigma}^2_{\hat{p}_{st}} = \frac{1}{N^2}\sum_{j=1}^{K} N_j^2 \hat{\sigma}^2_{\hat{p}_j} = \frac{(364)^2(0.003304) + (1{,}031)^2(0.002715)}{(1{,}395)^2} = 0.001708$$

so taking the square root yields the following:

$$\hat{\sigma}_{\hat{p}_{st}} = 0.0413$$

For a 90% confidence level,

$$z_{\alpha/2} = z_{0.05} = 1.645$$

and the 90% confidence interval for the population proportion from a stratified random sample is

$$(0.206) \pm (1.645)(0.0413)$$

This interval runs from 13.8% to 27.4% of all colleges.

Allocation of Sample Effort Among Strata

The question of the allocation of the sample effort among the various strata remains to be discussed. Assuming that a total of n sample members is to be selected, how many of these sample observations should be allocated to each stratum? In fact, the survey in question may have multiple objectives, meaning that no clear-cut answer is available. Nevertheless, it is possible to specify criteria for choice that the investigator might keep in mind. If little or nothing is known beforehand about the population and if there are no strong requirements for the production of information about sparsely populated individual strata, a natural choice is *proportional allocation*.

Proportional Allocation: Sample Size

The proportion of sample members in any stratum is the same as the proportion of population members in that stratum. Thus, for the jth stratum

$$\frac{n_j}{n} = \frac{N_j}{N} \tag{17.12}$$

so that the **sample size for the jth stratum using proportional allocation** is as follows:

$$n_j = \frac{N_j}{N} \times n \tag{17.13}$$

This intuitively reasonable allocation mechanism is frequently employed and generally provides a satisfactory analysis. Notice that proportional allocation was used in Example 17.1. A total of $N = 125$ restaurants was divided into three strata (Belgium, the Netherlands, and Luxembourg). A sample of $n = 25$ was selected with

$$n_1 = \frac{75}{125} \times 25 = 12 \qquad n_2 = \frac{30}{125} \times 25 = 6 \qquad n_3 = \frac{20}{125} \times 25 = 5$$

Sometimes strict adherence to proportional allocation will produce relatively few observations in strata in which the investigator is particularly interested. In that case inference about the population parameters of these particular strata could be quite imprecise. In these circumstances one might prefer to allocate more observations to such strata than is dictated by proportional allocation. In Examples 17.2 and 17.3, 364 of the 1,395 colleges are 2-year schools, and a sample of 100 observations is to be taken. If proportional allocation had been used, the number of 2-year schools in the sample would have been as follows:

$$n_1 = \frac{N_1}{N} \times n = \frac{364}{1,395} \times 100 = 26$$

Since the publisher in Example 17.2 was particularly interested in acquiring information about this market, it was thought that a sample of only 26 observations would be inadequate. For this reason, 40 of the 100 sample observations were allocated to this stratum.

If the sole objective of a survey is to estimate as precisely as possible an overall population parameter, such as the mean, total, or proportion, and if enough is known about the population, it is possible to derive an *optimal allocation*.

Optimal Allocation: Sample Size for jth Stratum, Overall Population Mean or Total

If it is required to estimate an overall population mean or total and if the population variances in the individual strata are denoted σ_j^2, it can be shown that the most precise estimators are obtained with optimal allocation. The **sample size for the jth stratum for overall mean or total using optimal allocation** is as follows:

$$n_j = \frac{N_j \sigma_j}{\sum_{i=1}^{K} N_i \sigma_i} \times n \tag{17.14}$$

This formula is intuitively plausible. Compared with proportional allocation, it allocates relatively more sample effort to strata in which the population variance is highest. That is to say, a larger sample size is required where the greater population variability exists. Thus, in Example 17.1, where proportional allocation was used, if the differences observed in the sample standard deviations correctly reflect differences in the population quantities, it would have been preferable to take fewer observations in the third stratum and more in the first.

An immediate objection arises to the use of Equation 17.14. It requires knowledge of the population standard deviations, σ_j, whereas very often we do not even have worthwhile estimates of these values before the sample is taken. This point is considered in the final section of the chapter.

Now, consider the sample size required under optimal allocation for a population proportion.

Optimal Allocation: Sample Size for jth Stratum, Population Proportion

For estimating the overall population proportion, estimators with the smallest possible variance are obtained by optimal allocation. The **sample size for the jth stratum for population proportion using optimal allocation** is as follows:

$$n_j = \frac{N_j \sqrt{P_j(1 - P_j)}}{\sum_{i=1}^{K} N_i \sqrt{P_i(1 - P_i)}} \times n \tag{17.15}$$

Compared with the proportional allocation, Equation 17.15 allocates more sample observations to strata in which the true population proportions are closest to 0.50. The difficulty in using Equation 17.15 is that it involves the unknown proportions P_j for $(j = 1, 2, \ldots, K)$, the very quantities that the survey is designed to estimate.

Nevertheless, sometimes prior knowledge about the population can provide at least a rough idea as to which strata have proportions closest to 0.5. In Example 17.3 the sample proportions suggest that the number of 2-year colleges in the sample should have been less than the number resulting from proportional allocation. The same conclusion holds for this study when we compare the sample standard deviations of Example 17.2 with Equation 17.14. In spite of this, it was decided that *more*, rather than fewer, 2-year colleges should be included in the sample. The reason for this decision was that, in this particular study, the publisher in Example 17.2 was eager to obtain reliable information about both the 2-year and the 4-year college markets.

This illustration serves as an example of an important point. Although the division of sample effort suggested by Equations 17.14 and 17.15 is often referred to as the *optimum allocation*, it is optimal only with regard to the narrow criterion of efficient estimation of overall population parameters. Frequently, surveys have broader objectives than this, in which case it may well be reasonable to depart from the optimum allocation.

Determining Sample Sizes for Stratified Random Sampling with Specified Degree of Precision

It is also possible to derive formulas for the sample size needed to yield a specified degree of precision when stratified random sampling is employed.

Variance of Estimator of Population Mean, Stratified Sampling

Let the random variable $\overline{X}_{st}$ denote the estimator of the population mean from stratified sampling and $\overline{X}_j$ $(j = 1, 2, \ldots, K)$ be the sample means for the individual strata. It then follows, since

$$\overline{X}_{st} = \frac{1}{N}\sum_{j=1}^{K} N_j \overline{X}_j \tag{17.16}$$

that the variance of $\overline{X}_{st}$ is

$$Var(\overline{X}_{st}) = \sigma^2_{\overline{X}_{st}} = \frac{1}{N^2}\sum_{j=1}^{K} N_j^2\, Var(\overline{X}_j) = \frac{1}{N^2}\sum_{j=1}^{K} N_j^2 \frac{\sigma_j^2}{n_j} \times \frac{(N_j - n_j)}{N_j - 1} \tag{17.17}$$

where the σ_j^2 are the population variances for the K strata.

Now, for any choice of $n_1, n_2, \ldots, n_K$, Equation 17.17 can be used to derive the corresponding variance of the estimator of the population mean. However, the actual total sample size, n, required to achieve a particular value for this variance will depend on the manner in which the sample observations are allocated among the strata. We have already discussed two frequently used procedures, proportional allocation and optimum allocation. In either case, by substituting for n_j in Equation 17.17, you can solve the resulting equation and obtain the sample size, n. The results are given in Equation 17.18 and Equation 17.19.

Total Sample Size to Estimate Overall Mean (Stratum Population Variances Specified), Stratified Random Sampling

Suppose that a population of N members is subdivided in K strata containing $N_1, N_2, \ldots, N_K$ members. Let σ_j^2 denote the population variance in the jth stratum, and suppose that an estimate of the overall population mean is desired. If the desired variance, $\sigma^2_{\overline{X}_{st}}$, of the sample estimator is specified, the required total sample size, n, is as follows:

1. *Proportional allocation*

$$n = \frac{\displaystyle\sum_{j=1}^{K} N_j \sigma_j^2}{N\sigma^2_{\overline{X}_{st}} + \dfrac{1}{N}\displaystyle\sum_{j=1}^{K} N_j \sigma_j^2} \tag{17.18}$$

2. *Optimal allocation*

$$n = \frac{\frac{1}{N}\left(\sum_{j=1}^{K} N_j \sigma_j\right)^2}{N\sigma_{\bar{X}_{st}}^2 + \frac{1}{N}\sum_{j=1}^{K} N_j \sigma_j^2} \tag{17.19}$$

Example 17.4 Restaurant in the Benelux (Sample Size)

As in Example 17.1, take a stratified random sample to estimate the mean number of orders per restaurant of a new food item when the numbers of restaurants in the three states are as follows:

$$N_1 = 75 \quad N_2 = 30 \quad N_3 = 20$$

Suppose also that the experience of the restaurant chain suggests that the population standard deviations for the three states are likely to be approximately

$$\sigma_1 = 13 \quad \sigma_2 = 11 \quad \sigma_3 = 9$$

If a 95% confidence interval is required for the population mean that extends three orders per restaurant on each side of the sample-point estimate, how many sample observations are needed in all?

Solution Note that

$$1.96\sigma_{\bar{X}_{st}} = 3, \qquad \text{so} \qquad \sigma_{\bar{X}_{st}} = 1.53$$

$$\sum_{j=1}^{K} N_j \sigma_j^2 = (75)(13)^2 + (30)(11)^2 + (20)(9)^2 = 17{,}925$$

and

$$\frac{1}{N}\left(\sum_{j=1}^{K} N_j \sigma_j\right)^2 = \frac{[(75)(13) + (30)(11) + (20)(9)]^2}{125} = 17{,}641.8$$

For proportional allocation, the sample size needed is as follows:

$$n = \frac{\sum_{j=1}^{K} N_j \sigma_j^2}{N\sigma_{\bar{X}_{st}}^2 + \frac{1}{N}\sum_{j=1}^{K} N_j \sigma_j^2} = \frac{17{,}925}{(125)(1.53)^2 + 17{,}925/125} = 41.1$$

Thus, a sample of 41 observations will suffice to produce the required level of precision. If optimal allocation is to be used, the sample size needed is

$$n = \frac{\frac{1}{N}\left(\sum_{j=1}^{K} N_j \sigma_j\right)^2}{N\sigma_{\bar{X}_{st}}^2 + \frac{1}{N}\sum_{j=1}^{K} N_j \sigma_j^2} = \frac{17{,}641.8}{(125)(1.53)^2 + 17{,}925/125} = 40.5$$

so the same degree of reliability can be obtained with 40 observations if this method of allocation is used. In this particular case, since the population standard deviations are quite close, this represents only a very small savings compared with proportional allocation.

EXERCISES

Application Exercises

17.1 A small town contains a total of 1,800 households. The town is divided into three districts, containing 820, 540, and 440 households, respectively. A stratified random sample of 300 households contains 120, 90, and 90 households, respectively, from these three districts. Sample members were asked to estimate their total energy bills for the winter months. The respective sample means were $290, $352, and $427, and the respective sample standard deviations were $47, $61, and $93.

  a. Use an unbiased estimation procedure to estimate the mean winter energy bill for all households in this town.

  b. Use an unbiased estimation procedure to find an estimate of the variance of the estimator of part a.

  c. Find a 95% confidence interval for the population mean winter energy bill for households in this town.

17.2 A researcher in Denmark is studying the reading habits of the people in the country. His sample that comprises three different cities—Aarhus, Esbjerg, and Copenhagen. Assume there are 150 households in Aarhus, 40 in Esbjerg, and 85 in Copenhagen. The researcher randomly selected 20 households from Aarhus, 10 from Esbjerg, and 15 from Copenhagen and recorded the weekly average reading times (in hours) for each households. From the record, he found that the weekly average reading time for Aarhus is 35.73 hours, Esbjerg is 26.24 hours, and Copenhagen is 18.31 hours. The sample standard deviations for Aarhus, Esbjerg, and Copenhagen were 1.56 hours, 4.78 hours, and 2.49 hours, respectively.

  a. Estimate the mean reading time spent by the households in the city using an unbiased estimation procedure.

  b. Find a 90% confidence interval for the mean reading time spent in the city.

  c. Find the 95% confidence interval for the total amount of time spent by the people of each city in reading.

17.3 A teacher would like to know the average height (in inches) of the students in her school. She divided the students into 4 groups based on their ages from the youngest to the oldest. The total number of students for group 1 is 125, for group 2 is 118, for group 3 is 132, and for group 4 is 123. Random samples of heights of students are taken from each group where the sample size, sample mean, and sample standard deviation are summarized in the following table.

	Group 1	Group 2	Group 3	Group 4
n_i	45	34	41	30
$\bar{x}_i$	58	64	63.5	65
s_i	0.3	0.1	1.1	0.8

  a. Using an unbiased estimation procedure, estimate the mean height of students in the school.

  b. Find a 90% confidence interval for the mean height of students in group 1.

  c. Find a 90% confidence interval for the mean height of students in the whole school.

17.4 In a stratified random sample of individuals—male and female—in Porvoo, Finland, sample members were asked to share the amount of time they spent on reading (in hours) per week. The results had been recorded and are shown in the accompanying table.

	Male (M)	Female (M)
N_i	450	550
n_i	25	25
$\bar{x}_i$	8.75	14.6
s_i	1.25	0.94

  a. Find a 90% confidence interval for the mean reading time provided by all the male members.

  b. Find a 95% confidence interval for the mean reading time provided by all the female members.

  c. Find a 99% confidence interval for the mean reading time that is given by all the individuals in Porvoo, Finland.

17.5 A college has 152 assistant professors, 127 associate professors, and 208 full professors. The college administration is investigating the amount of time these faculty members spend in meetings in a semester. Random samples of 40 assistant professors, 40 associate professors, and 50 full professors were asked to keep records of time spent in meetings during a semester. The sample means were 27.6 hours for assistant professors, 39.2 hours for associate professors, and 43.3 hours for full professors. The sample standard deviations were 7.1 hours for assistant professors, 9.9 hours for associate professors, and 12.3 hours for full professors.

  a. Find a 90% confidence interval for the total amount of time spent in meetings by all full professors in this college in the semester.

  b. Find a 90% confidence interval for the total amount of time spent in meetings by all faculty members in this college in the semester.

17.6 JM Property, a Nordic property developer, is considering the price for three housing subdivisions (apartment, single storey, and double storey) in Malmö, Sweden. Random samples of prices were taken for the three different types of houses by using the stratified random sampling method and determined the following statistical results.

	Apartment	Single Storey	Double Storey
N_i	520	875	605
n_i	173	201	126
$\bar{x}_i$ (in $000)	429	621	958
s_i	1.2	0.86	1.15

a. Using an unbiased estimation procedure, find the average selling price for the three different types of houses in Malmö.

b. Find a 95% confidence interval for the total selling price for the three housing subdivisions in Malmö.

17.7 Of the 1,395 colleges in the United States, 364 have 2-year schools. In a random sample of 40 two-year schools, it was found that the text *Statistics Can Be Fun* was used in 10 of the schools. In an independent random sample of 60 four-year schools, this text was used by 8 of the sample members.

a. Find an estimate of the proportion of all colleges using this text, using an unbiased estimation procedure.

b. Find a 95% confidence interval for the proportion of all colleges using this text.

17.8 Bónus, an Icelandic supermarket chain, wants to know the level of consumer satisfaction derived from its four products—A, B, C, and D. The company's sales records showed that 10,000 customers purchased product A, 18,000 customers purchased product B, 9,000 customers purchased product C, and 14,000 customers purchased product D. Bónus decided to investigate samples of 200 customers, 110 customers, 180 customers, and 150 customers for products A, B, C, and D respectively. From each sample group it was found that that 40% were satisfied with product A, 35% were satisfied with product B, 55% were satisfied with product C, and 15% with product D.

a. Find an estimate of the proportion of customers who were satisfied with the company's products.

b. Construct a 95% confidence interval for this population proportion.

17.9 66°North, an outdoor apparel store in Iceland, is analyzing the defective items three items—parkas, trousers, and sweaters. From a total of 500 parkas, 780 trousers, and 720 sweaters, it sampled 75, 35, and 43 respectively. The company found that the defective ratio for each product is 0.15 for parkas, 0.2 for trousers, and 0.05 for sweaters.

a. Calculate the population ratio for defective item for the three products.

b. Find the 90% confidence interval for the proportion of the defective items for all three products.

17.10 Refer to Exercise 17.2. If a total sample of 130 faculty members is to be taken, determine how many of these should be full professors under each of the following schemes.

a. Proportional allocation

b. Optimum allocation, assuming the stratum population standard deviations are the same as the corresponding sample values

17.11 Refer to the data in Exercise 17.3. Determine the sample size for Group 1 under each of the following schemes.

a. Proportional allocation

b. Optimum allocation for the overall population mean

17.12 Refer to the data in Exercise 17.4. Determine the sample size for female individuals in Porvoo, Finland, by under each of the following schemes.

a. Proportional allocation

b. Optimum allocation for the overall population mean

17.13 A company has three divisions. To estimate the total amounts of the company's accounts receivable, random samples of these accounts were taken for each of the three divisions, yielding the results shown in the following table:

	Division 1	Division 2	Division 3
N_i	120	150	180
n_i	40	45	50
$\bar{x}_i$	$237	$198	$131
s_i	$93	$64	$47

If a total sample of 135 accounts receivable is to be taken, determine how many of these should be from Division 1 under each of the following schemes.

a. Proportional allocation

b. Optimum allocation, assuming the stratum population standard deviations are the same as the corresponding sample values

17.14 Refer to the data in Exercise 17.2. Determine the sample size for Copenhagen under each of the following schemes.

a. Proportional allocation

b. Optimum allocation for the overall population mean

17.15 The program director for Aarhus School of Business, Denmark, is analyzing the marks obtained by students from three different modules—Business Economics, and Political Science. For Business, he sampled 58 students' results from the total of 472, 66 out of 687 for Economics, and 57 out of 461 for Political Science. He estimated the standard deviations for each module from the previous results to be 34, 56, and 21, respectively. Determine the total sample size under both proportional allocation and optimal allocation when a 95% confidence interval for the overall population mean extended to 20 points for both side of the sample estimate.

17.16 Mean household income must be estimated for a town that can be divided into three districts. The relevant information is shown in the table.

District	Population Size	Estimated Standard Deviation ($)
1	1,150	4,000
2	2,120	6,000
3	930	8,000

If a 95% confidence interval for the population mean extending $500 on each side of the sample estimate is required, determine how many sample observations in total are needed under proportional allocation and optimal allocation.

17.2 OTHER SAMPLING METHODS

Simple random sampling and stratified random sampling have been discussed briefly. These are not the only procedures used for choosing a sample. Some alternative methods are discussed in this section.

Cluster Sampling

Suppose that an investigator wants to survey a population spread over a wide geographical area, such as a large city or a state. If either a simple random sample or a stratified random sample is to be used, two immediate problems will arise. First, in order to draw the sample, the investigator will need a reasonably accurate listing of the population members. Such a list may not be available or could perhaps be obtained only at a prohibitively high cost. Second, even if the investigator does possess a list of the population, the resulting sample members will almost inevitably be thinly spread over a large area. In that case, having interviewers contact each individual sample member would be quite costly. Of course, if a mail questionnaire is to be used, this latter problem does not arise. However, this means of contact may lead to an unacceptably high rate of nonresponse, leading the investigator to prefer personal interviews.

Faced with the dilemma of either not having a reliable population listing or wanting to set up personal interviews with sample members when budget resources are tight, the investigator may use an alternative sampling procedure known as **cluster sampling**. This approach is attractive when a population can conveniently be subdivided into relatively small, geographically compact units called *clusters*. For example, a city might be subdivided into political wards or residential blocks. This can generally be achieved even when a complete listing of residents or households is unavailable.

In cluster sampling a simple random sample of clusters is selected from the population, and every individual in each of the sampled clusters is contacted; that is, a complete census is carried out in each of the chosen clusters. In the following equations procedures for deriving valid inferences about the population mean and proportion from the results of a cluster sample are given.

Estimators for Cluster Sampling

A population is subdivided into M clusters, a simple random sample of m of these clusters is selected, and information is obtained from every member of the sampled clusters. Let $n_1, n_2, \ldots, n_m$ denote the numbers of population members in the m sampled clusters. Denote the means of these clusters by $\bar{x}_1, \bar{x}_2, \ldots, \bar{x}_m$ and the proportions of cluster members possessing an attribute of interest by $\hat{p}_1, \hat{p}_2, \ldots, \hat{p}_m$. The objective is to estimate the overall population mean μ and proportion $\hat{p}$.

1. Unbiased estimation procedures give

$$\bar{x}_c = \frac{\sum_{i=1}^{m} n_i \bar{x}_i}{\sum_{i=1}^{m} n_i} \tag{17.20}$$

and

$$\hat{p}_c = \frac{\sum_{i=1}^{m} n_i \hat{p}_i}{\sum_{i=1}^{m} n_i} \tag{17.21}$$

2. Estimates of the variance of these estimators, following from unbiased estimation procedures, are

$$\hat{\sigma}_{\bar{x}_c}^2 = \frac{M - m}{Mm\bar{n}^2}\left(\frac{\sum_{i=1}^{m} n_i^2(\bar{x}_i - \bar{x}_c)^2}{m - 1}\right) \tag{17.22}$$

and

$$\hat{\sigma}_{\hat{p}_c}^2 = \frac{M - m}{Mm\bar{n}^2}\left(\frac{\sum_{i=1}^{m} n_i^2(\hat{p}_i - \hat{p}_c)^2}{m - 1}\right) \tag{17.23}$$

where $\bar{n} = \sum_{i=1}^{m} n_i/m$ is the average number of individuals in the sampled clusters.

Based on these estimators, the confidence intervals with cluster sampling follow.

Estimation of Population Mean Using Cluster Sampling

Provided the sample size is large, a $100(1 - \alpha)\%$ confidence interval **estimation of the population mean using cluster sampling** is as follows:

$$\bar{x}_c \pm z_{\alpha/2}\hat{\sigma}_{\bar{x}_c} \tag{17.24}$$

Similarly, confidence intervals for the population proportion based on cluster sampling are established.

Estimation of Population Proportion Using Cluster Sampling

Provided the sample size is large, a $100(1 - \alpha)\%$ confidence interval **estimation of the population proportion using cluster sampling** is as follows:

$$\hat{p}_c \pm z_{\alpha/2}\hat{\sigma}_{\hat{p}_c} \tag{17.25}$$

Notice that inferences can be made with relatively little prior information about the population. All that is required is a breakdown into identifiable clusters. It is not necessary to know the total number of population members. It is sufficient to know the numbers in each of the *sampled* clusters, and these can be determined during the course of the survey, since a full census is taken in each cluster in the sample. In addition, since sample members will be geographically close to one another within clusters, their contact by interviewers is relatively inexpensive.

Example 17.5 Cluster Sampling for Family Incomes (Estimation)

A simple random sample of 20 blocks is taken from a residential area containing a total of 1,000 blocks. Each household in the sampled blocks is then contacted, and information is obtained about family incomes. The mean annual incomes and the proportion of families with incomes below $15,000 per year in the sampled blocks are contained in the data file **Income Clusters**. For this residential area estimate the mean family income and the proportion of families with incomes below $15,000 per year.

Solution It is known that

$$m = 20 \quad \text{and} \quad M = 1,000$$

The total number of households in the sample is as follows:

$$\sum_{i=1}^{m} n_i = (23 + 31 + \cdots + 41) = 607$$

To obtain point estimates,

$$\sum_{i=1}^{m} n_i \bar{x}_i = (23)(26,823) + (31)(19,197) + \cdots + (41)(16,493) = 15,848,158$$

and

$$\sum_{i=1}^{m} n_i \hat{p}_i = (23)(0.1304) + (31)(0.4516) + \cdots + (41)(0.3659) = 153$$

Our point estimates are, therefore,

$$\bar{x}_c = \frac{\sum_{i=1}^{m} n_i \bar{x}_i}{\sum_{i=1}^{m} n_i} = \frac{15,848,158}{607} = 26,109$$

$$\hat{p}_c = \frac{\sum_{i=1}^{m} n_i \hat{p}_i}{\sum_{i=1}^{m} n_i} = \frac{153}{607} = 0.2521$$

Thus, on the basis of this sample evidence it is estimated that for this residential area, mean annual household income is $26,109 and 25.21% of households have incomes below $15,000 per year.

To obtain interval estimates of the population mean, the average cluster size is needed where

$$\bar{n} = \frac{\sum_{i=1}^{m} n_i}{m} = \frac{607}{20} = 30.35$$

Also,

$$\frac{\sum_{i=1}^{m} n_i^2 (\bar{x}_i - \bar{x}_c)^2}{m - 1} = \frac{(23)^2(26,283 - 26,109)^2 + \cdots + (41)^2(16,493 - 26,109)^2}{19}$$

$$= 69,270,562,244$$

so

$$\hat{\sigma}_{\bar{x}_c}^2 = \frac{M - m}{Mm\bar{n}^2} \times \frac{\sum_{i=1}^{m} n_i^2 (\bar{x}_i - \bar{x}_c)^2}{m - 1} = \frac{(980)(69,270,562,244)}{(1,000)(20)(30.35)^2} = 3,684,914$$

and, taking the square root,

$$\hat{\sigma}_{\bar{x}} = 1,920$$

A 95% confidence interval for the population mean is

$$26,109 \pm (1.96)(1,920)$$

A 95% confidence interval for the mean income of all families in this area, therefore, runs from $22,346 to $29,872.

To obtain interval estimates for the population proportion,

$$\frac{\sum_{i=1}^{m} n_i^2 (\hat{p}_i - \hat{p}_c)^2}{m - 1} = \frac{(23)^2(0.1304 - 0.2521)^2 + \cdots + (41)^2(0.3659 - 0.2521)^2}{19} = 38.1547$$

Then,

$$\hat{\sigma}_{\hat{p}_c}^2 = \frac{M - m}{Mm\bar{n}^2} \left(\frac{\sum_{i=1}^{m} n_i^2 (\hat{p}_i - \hat{p}_c)^2}{m - 1} \right)$$

$$= \frac{(980)(38.1547)}{(1,000)(20)(30.35)^2} = 0.0020297$$

and, taking the square root,

$$\hat{\sigma}_{\hat{p}_c} = 0.0451$$

The 95% confidence interval for the population proportion is

$$(0.2521) \pm (1.96)(0.0451)$$

Our 95% confidence interval for the percentage of households with annual incomes below $15,000 runs from 16.4% to 34.0%.

Cluster sampling has a superficial resemblance to stratified sampling. In both, the population is first divided into subgroups. However, the similarity is rather illusory. In stratified random sampling, a sample is taken from *every stratum* of the population in an attempt to ensure that important segments of the population are given due weight. By contrast, in cluster sampling a random sample of *clusters* is taken, so that some clusters will have no members in the sample. Since, within clusters, population members will probably be fairly homogeneous, the danger is that important subgroups of the population may be either not represented at all or grossly underrepresented in the final sample. In consequence, while the great advantage of cluster sampling lies in its convenience, this convenience may well be at the cost of additional imprecision in the sample estimates. A further distinction between cluster sampling and stratified sampling is that in the former a *complete census* of cluster members is taken, while in the latter a *random sample* of stratum members is drawn. This difference, however, is not essential. Indeed, on occasions an investigator may draw a random sample of cluster members rather than take a full census.

Two-Phase Sampling

In many investigations the population is not surveyed in a single step. Rather, it is often convenient to carry out an initial pilot study in which a relatively small proportion of the sample members are contacted. The results obtained are then analyzed prior to conducting the bulk of the survey. The chief disadvantage of such a procedure is that it can be quite time consuming. However, this factor may be outweighed by several advantages. One important benefit is that the investigator is able, at modest cost, to try out the proposed questionnaire in order to ensure that the various questions can be thoroughly understood. The pilot study may also suggest additional questions whose potential importance had previously been overlooked. Moreover, this study should also provide an estimate of the likely rate of nonresponse. Should this prove unacceptably high, some modification in the method of soliciting responses might appear desirable.

Conducting a survey in two stages, beginning with a pilot study, is known as **two-phase sampling**. This approach has two further advantages. First, if stratified random sampling is employed, the pilot study can be used to provide estimates of the individual stratum variances. These, in turn, can be employed to estimate the optimum allocation of the sample among the various strata. Second, the results of the pilot study can be used to estimate the number of observations needed to obtain estimators of population parameters with a specified level of precision. The following examples serve to illustrate these points. Consider a straightforward situation in which a simple random sample is to be used to estimate a population mean. At the outset, relatively little is known about this population, so an initial pilot survey is to be carried out to get some idea of the sample size required.

Example 17.6 Mean Value of Accounts Receivable (Sample Size)

An auditor wishes to estimate the mean value of accounts receivable in a total population of 1,120 accounts. He wants to produce a 95% confidence interval for the population mean, extending approximately $4 on each side of the sample mean. To begin, he takes a simple random sample of 100 accounts, finding a sample standard deviation of $30.27. How many more accounts should be sampled?

Solution Using Equation 7.23, the required sample size is found to be

$$n = \frac{N\sigma^2}{(N-1)\sigma_{\bar{X}}^2 + \sigma^2}$$

where $N = 1,120$ is the number of population members in this case. In order for the 95% confidence interval to be the required width,

$$1.96\sigma_{\bar{x}} = 4$$

so that $\sigma_{\bar{x}}$, the standard deviation of the sample mean, must be as follows:

$$\sigma_{\bar{x}} = \frac{4}{1.96} = 2.04$$

The population standard deviation, σ, is unknown. However, as a result of the initial study of 100 accounts receivable, it is estimated to be 30.27. The total number of sample observations needed is, therefore,

$$n = \frac{N\sigma^2}{(N-1)\sigma_{\bar{x}}^2 + \sigma^2} = \frac{(1,120)(30.27)^2}{(1,119)(2.04)^2 + (30.27)^2} = 184.1$$

Since 100 observations have already been taken, an additional 85 will suffice to satisfy the auditor's objective.

Example 17.7 Income (Sample Size)

An investigator intends to take a stratified random sample to estimate mean family income in a town where the numbers in the three stratum districts are as follows:

$$N_1 = 1,150 \quad N_2 = 2,120 \quad N_3 = 930$$

To begin, the investigator conducts a pilot study, sampling 30 households from each district and obtaining the sample standard deviations $3,657, $6,481, and $8,403, respectively. Suppose that the objective is to obtain, with as small a size as possible, a 95% confidence interval for the population mean extending $500 on each side of the sample estimate. How many additional observations should be taken in each district?

Solution The requirement that a specified degree of precision be obtained with as few sample observations as possible implies that optimal allocation must be used. Recall from Equation 17.14 that the numbers n_1, n_2, and n_3 to be sampled in the three strata are as follows:

$$n_j = \frac{N_j \sigma_j}{\sum_{i=1}^{K} N_i \sigma_i} \times n \qquad (j = 1, 2, 3)$$

where the σ_i are the stratum population standard deviations. Using our sample estimates in place of these quantities,

$$n_1 = \frac{(1,150)(3,657)}{(1,150)(3,657) + (2,120)(6,481) + (930)(8,403)} \times n = 0.163n$$

$$n_2 = \frac{(2,120)(6,481)}{(1,150)(3,657) + (2,120)(6,481) + (930)(8,403)} \times n = 0.533n$$

$$n_3 = \frac{(930)(8,403)}{(1,150)(3,657) + (2,120)(6,481) + (930)(8,403)} \times n = 0.303n$$

The properties of the total sample to be allocated to each stratum under the optimal scheme are now specified. It remains to determine the total number n of sample observations.

Nonprobabilistic Sampling Methods

Various sampling schemes for which it is possible to specify the probability that any particular sample will be drawn from the population have been considered. Because of this feature of the sampling methods, valid statistical inferences based on the sample results can be made. Otherwise, the derivation of unbiased point estimates and confidence intervals with specified probability content could not be achieved with strict statistical validity.

Nevertheless, in many practical applications, **nonprobabilistic methods** are used for selecting sample members, primarily as a matter of convenience. For example, suppose that you want to assess the reactions of students on your campus to some issue of topical interest. One possibility would be to ask all your friends how they feel about it. This group would not constitute a random sample from the population of all students. Accordingly, if you proceed to analyze the data as if they were obtained from a random sample, the resulting inference would lack proper statistical validity.

A more sophisticated version of the approach just described, called **quota sampling**, is commonly used by polling organizations. Interviewers are assigned to a particular locale and instructed to contact specified numbers of people of certain age, race, and gender characteristics. These assigned quotas represent what are thought to be appropriate proportions for the population at large. However, once the quotas are determined, interviewers are granted flexibility in the choice of sample members. Their choice is typically not random. Quota sampling can, and often does, produce quite accurate estimates of population parameters. The drawback is that, since the sample is not chosen using probabilistic methods, there is no valid way of determining the reliability of the resulting estimates.

EXERCISES

Application Exercises

17.17 An economist is studying the average profit earned by companies in Stuttgart, Germany. Assume that Stuttgart consists of 576 companies. A simple random sample of 10 companies was selected, and each company stated down its average annual profits earned and number of sales staff in each company. The following table shows the results.

a. Find the average annual profit earned by the companies in Stuttgart.
b. Find a 95% confidence interval for the average annual profit earned by companies in the entire city.

Sampled Company	Number of Sales Staff Members	Average Annual Profit (€000)
1	34	342
2	21	432
3	43	539
4	12	524
5	23	743
6	32	342
7	24	443
8	29	432
9	37	545
10	16	195

17.18 A property agent is investigating the average renting price per month for the factories in an area. In his study area, totally there are 8 types of factories. He randomly selected 4 different types of factories and stated down their average renting price per month and the numbers of factories as below.

Type of Factory	Number of Factories	Average Renting Price per Month ($000)
1	31	5
2	12	1.5
3	83	3
4	26	2.5

a. Estimate the average annual renting prices for the factories in that area.
b. Find a 90% confidence interval for the average renting prices for the factories in that area.

17.19 In the survey of Exercise 17.17, the households were asked if they had cable television. The numbers having cable are given in the accompanying table.

Precinct	1	2	3	4	5	6	7	8	9	10
Number	12	11	10	29	15	13	20	14	9	26

a. Find a point estimate of the proportion of all households in the city having cable television.
b. Find a 90% confidence interval for this population proportion.

17.20 In the survey of Exercise 17.18, the clerical employees in the eight sampled subdivisions were asked if they were satisfied with the operation of the bonus plan. The results obtained are listed in the following table:

Subdivision	1	2	3	4	5	6	7	8
Number satisfied	24	25	11	21	35	44	30	34

a. Find a point estimate of the proportion of all clerical employees satisfied with the bonus plan.
b. Find a 95% confidence interval for this population proportion.

17.21 A city is divided into 50 geographic subdivisions. An estimate was required of the proportion of households in the city interested in a new lawn-care service. A random sample of three subdivisions contained 611, 521, and 734 households, respectively. The numbers expressing interest in the service were 128, 131, and 172, respectively. Find a 90% confidence interval for the proportion of all households in this city interested in the lawn-care service.

17.22 A bank holds 720 delinquent mortgages in residential properties. It required an estimate of the mean current appraised value of these properties. Initially, a random sample of 20 was appraised, and a sample standard deviation of $37,600 was found. If the bank requires a 90% confidence interval for the population mean extending $5,000 on each side of the sample mean, how many more properties must be appraised?

17.23 A cellphone technician wishes to estimate the average lifetime (in years) of a cellphone battery in the current market. In total there are 1183 different brands of cellphone battery selling in the market. He would like to have a 95% confidence interval for the population average lifetime of a cellphone battery, which extended to 3 years on both side of the sample average. A simple random sample of 19 battery brands were taken. The technician found the sample standard deviation is 5.78 years. Estimate the smallest total number of sample observations needed to achieve his goal.

17.24 Alex Perry is an Australian fashion designer and television presenter, known for his womenswear. To estimate the mean time (in hours) taken by a tailor to create a woman's gown, which will be part of his new evening wear collection, he selected a random sample of 45 tailors from 243 tailors in Sydney. The sample standard deviation for tailoring a gown is 47.13 hours. He requires a 90% confidence interval for the population mean time spent extended to 10 hours on each side of the sample point estimate. What is the additional number of samples Alex needs to achieve his objective?

DATA FILE

CHAPTER EXERCISES AND APPLICATIONS

17.25 Carefully explain the distinction between stratified random sampling and cluster sampling. Provide illustrations of sampling problems where each of these techniques might be useful.

17.26 A researcher at Procter & Gamble (P&G) wants to determine the consumers' satisfaction proportion on 3 different fabric softener brands—Downy (United States), Cuddly (Australia), and Makom (China). For Downy, 30% of a random sample of 50 consumers out of 200 were satisfied with it. For Cuddly, 60% of a sample of 30 out of 450 consumers were satisfied. For Makom, 45% of a sample of 45 out of 350 consumers were satisfied.

  a. Find a 95% confidence interval for the population proportion of consumers who are satisfied with the brands they are using.
  b. What is the conclusion you have derived based on your answer in part (a)?

17.27 The University of Jordan, the Middle East, is counting the mean research papers published per year by its faculty members—professors, senior lecturers, and lecturers. The university has 55 professors, 250 senior lecturers, and 845 lecturers. Random samples of 20 professors, 80 senior lecturers, and 150 lecturers were selected. The sample means of published research papers were 110 professors, 95 senior lecturers, and 100 lecturers. The sample standard deviations were 1.05, 2.52, and 1.58, respectively.

  a. Using an unbiased estimation procedure, find the mean number of research paper published by the university per year.
  b. Find a 90% confidence interval for the mean research papers published per year by the university.

17.28 Of the 300 pages in a particular book, 180 pages are primarily nontechnical, while the remainder of the pages are technical. Independent random samples of technical and nontechnical pages were taken, and the numbers of errors per page were recorded. The results are summarized in the following table:

	Technical	Nontechnical
N_i	120	180
n_i	20	20
$\bar{x}_i$	1.6	0.74
s_i	0.98	0.56

  a. Find a 95% confidence interval for the mean number of errors per page in this book.
  b. Find a 99% confidence interval for the total number of errors in the book.

17.29 In the analysis of Exercise 17.28, it was found that 9 of the sampled technical pages and 15 of the sampled nontechnical pages contained no errors. Find a 90% confidence interval for the proportion of all pages in this book that have no errors.

17.30 Refer to the data of Exercise 17.27. If 80 managers were sampled, determine how many sample members would be from subdivision 1 under each of the following schemes.

  a. Proportional allocation
  b. Optimum allocation, assuming that the stratum population standard deviations are the same as the corresponding sample quantities

17.31 Refer to the data of Exercise 17.28. If 40 pages are to be sampled, determine how many sampled pages would be technical under each of the following schemes.

  a. Proportional allocation
  b. Optimum allocation, assuming that the stratum population standard deviations are the same as the corresponding sample quantities

17.32 You intend to sample the students in your university to assess their views on the adequacy of space in the library. You decide to use a stratified sample by year—first-year students, sophomores, and so forth. Discuss the factors you would take into account in deciding how many sample observations to take in each stratum.

17.33 Suppose that you were asked by your state office of elections to assist in resolving an election dispute between two candidates, or perhaps you were asked to be a statistical expert in a lawsuit concerning the outcome of a close election (such as the 2000 U.S. presidential election). Many questions arise. Should all ballots in the state be recounted? Should only ballots in certain counties be recounted? If only certain ballots are recounted, which ballots? These and other similar questions were asked during the 2000 U.S. presidential election. Discuss the advantages and disadvantages of various sampling designs that might be used to select ballots to be recounted.

APPENDIX TABLES

Table 1 Cumulative Distribution Function, $F(z)$, of the Standard Normal Distribution Table

z	0	0.01	0.02	0.03	0.04	0.05	0.06	0.07	0.08	0.09
0.0	0.5000	0.5040	0.5080	0.5120	0.5160	0.5199	0.5239	0.5279	0.5319	0.5359
0.1	0.5398	0.5438	0.5478	0.5517	0.5557	0.5596	0.5636	0.5675	0.5714	0.5753
0.2	0.5793	0.5832	0.5871	0.5910	0.5948	0.5987	0.6026	0.6064	0.6103	0.6141
0.3	0.6179	0.6217	0.6255	0.6293	0.6331	0.6368	0.6406	0.6443	0.6480	0.6517
0.4	0.6554	0.6591	0.6628	0.6664	0.6700	0.6736	0.6772	0.6808	0.6844	0.6879
0.5	0.6915	0.6950	0.6985	0.7019	0.7054	0.7088	0.7123	0.7157	0.7190	0.7224
0.6	0.7257	0.7291	0.7324	0.7357	0.7389	0.7422	0.7454	0.7486	0.7517	0.7549
0.7	0.7580	0.7611	0.7642	0.7673	0.7704	0.7734	0.7764	0.7794	0.7823	0.7852
0.8	0.7881	0.7910	0.7939	0.7967	0.7995	0.8023	0.8051	0.8078	0.8106	0.8133
0.9	0.8159	0.8186	0.8212	0.8238	0.8264	0.8289	0.8315	0.8340	0.8365	0.8389
1.0	0.8413	0.8438	0.8461	0.8485	0.8508	0.8531	0.8554	0.8577	0.8599	0.8621
1.1	0.8643	0.8665	0.8686	0.8708	0.8729	0.8749	0.8770	0.8790	0.8810	0.8830
1.2	0.8849	0.8869	0.8888	0.8907	0.8925	0.8944	0.8962	0.8980	0.8997	0.9015
1.3	0.9032	0.9049	0.9066	0.9082	0.9099	0.9115	0.9131	0.9147	0.9162	0.9177
1.4	0.9192	0.9207	0.9222	0.9236	0.9251	0.9265	0.9279	0.9292	0.9306	0.9319
1.5	0.9332	0.9345	0.9357	0.9370	0.9382	0.9394	0.9406	0.9418	0.9429	0.9441
1.6	0.9452	0.9463	0.9474	0.9484	0.9495	0.9505	0.9515	0.9525	0.9535	0.9545
1.7	0.9554	0.9564	0.9573	0.9582	0.9591	0.9599	0.9608	0.9616	0.9625	0.9633
1.8	0.9641	0.9649	0.9656	0.9664	0.9671	0.9678	0.9686	0.9693	0.9699	0.9706
1.9	0.9713	0.9719	0.9726	0.9732	0.9738	0.9744	0.9750	0.9756	0.9761	0.9767
2.0	0.9772	0.9778	0.9783	0.9788	0.9793	0.9798	0.9803	0.9808	0.9812	0.9817
2.1	0.9821	0.9826	0.9830	0.9834	0.9838	0.9842	0.9846	0.9850	0.9854	0.9857
2.2	0.9861	0.9864	0.9868	0.9871	0.9875	0.9878	0.9881	0.9884	0.9887	0.9890
2.3	0.9893	0.9896	0.9898	0.9901	0.9904	0.9906	0.9909	0.9911	0.9913	0.9916
2.4	0.9918	0.9920	0.9922	0.9925	0.9927	0.9929	0.9931	0.9932	0.9934	0.9936
2.5	0.9938	0.9940	0.9941	0.9943	0.9945	0.9946	0.9948	0.9949	0.9951	0.9952
2.6	0.9953	0.9955	0.9956	0.9957	0.9959	0.9960	0.9961	0.9962	0.9963	0.9964
2.7	0.9965	0.9966	0.9967	0.9968	0.9969	0.9970	0.9971	0.9972	0.9973	0.9974
2.8	0.9974	0.9975	0.9976	0.9977	0.9977	0.9978	0.9979	0.9979	0.9980	0.9981
2.9	0.9981	0.9982	0.9982	0.9983	0.9984	0.9984	0.9985	0.9985	0.9986	0.9986
3.0	0.9987	0.9987	0.9987	0.9988	0.9988	0.9989	0.9989	0.9989	0.9990	0.9990
3.1	0.9990	0.9991	0.9991	0.9991	0.9992	0.9992	0.9992	0.9992	0.9993	0.9993
3.2	0.9993	0.9993	0.9994	0.9994	0.9994	0.9994	0.9994	0.9995	0.9995	0.9995
3.3	0.9995	0.9995	0.9995	0.9996	0.9996	0.9996	0.9996	0.9996	0.9996	0.9997

Dr. William L. Carlson, prepared using Minitab 16.

Table 2 Probability Function of the Binomial Distribution

The table shows the probability of x successes in n independent trials, each with probability of success P. For example, the probability of four successes in eight independent trials, each with probability of success .35, is .1875.

n	x	.05	.10	.15	.20	.25	.30	.35	.40	.45	.50
1	0	.9500	.9000	.8500	.8000	.7500	.7000	.6500	.6000	.5500	.5000
	1	.0500	.1000	.1500	.2000	.2500	.3000	.3500	.4000	.4500	.5000
2	0	.9025	.8100	.7225	.6400	.5625	.4900	.4225	.3600	.3025	.2500
	1	.0950	.1800	.2550	.3200	.3750	.4200	.4550	.4800	.4950	.5000
	2	.0025	.0100	.0225	.0400	.0625	.0900	.1225	.1600	.2025	.2500
3	0	.8574	.7290	.6141	.5120	.4219	.3430	.2746	.2160	.1664	.1250
	1	.1354	.2430	.3251	.3840	.4219	.4410	.4436	.4320	.4084	.3750
	2	.0071	.0270	.0574	.0960	.1406	.1890	.2389	.2880	.3341	.3750
	3	.0001	.0010	.0034	.0080	.0156	.0270	.0429	.0640	.0911	.1250
4	0	.8145	.6561	.5220	.4096	.3164	.2401	.1785	.1296	.0915	.0625
	1	.1715	.2916	.3685	.4096	.4219	.4116	.3845	.3456	.2995	.2500
	2	.0135	.0486	.0975	.1536	.2109	.2646	.3105	.3456	.3675	.3750
	3	.0005	.0036	.0115	.0256	.0469	.0756	.1115	.1536	.2005	.2500
	4	.0000	.0001	.0005	.0016	.0039	.0081	.0150	.0256	.0410	.0625
5	0	.7738	.5905	.4437	.3277	.2373	.1681	.1160	.0778	.0503	.0312
	1	.2036	.3280	.3915	.4096	.3955	.3602	.3124	.2592	.2059	.1562
	2	.0214	.0729	.1382	.2048	.2637	.3087	.3364	.3456	.3369	.3125
	3	.0011	.0081	.0244	.0512	.0879	.1323	.1811	.2304	.2757	.3125
	4	.0000	.0004	.0022	.0064	.0146	.0284	.0488	.0768	.1128	.1562
	5	.0000	.0000	.0001	.0003	.0010	.0024	.0053	.0102	.0185	.0312
6	0	.7351	.5314	.3771	.2621	.1780	.1176	.0754	.0467	.0277	.0156
	1	.2321	.3543	.3993	.3932	.3560	.3025	.2437	.1866	.1359	.0938
	2	.0305	.0984	.1762	.2458	.2966	.3241	.3280	.3110	.2780	.2344
	3	.0021	.0146	.0415	.0819	.1318	.1852	.2355	.2765	.3032	.3125
	4	.0001	.0012	.0055	.0154	.0330	.0595	.0951	.1382	.1861	.2344
	5	.0000	.0001	.0004	.0015	.0044	.0102	.0205	.0369	.0609	.0938
	6	.0000	.0000	.0000	.0001	.0002	.0007	.0018	.0041	.0083	.0156
7	0	.6983	.4783	.3206	.2097	.1335	.0824	.0490	.0280	.0152	.0078
	1	.2573	.3720	.3960	.3670	.3115	.2471	.1848	.1306	.0872	.0547
	2	.0406	.1240	.2097	.2753	.3115	.3177	.2985	.2613	.2140	.1641
	3	.0036	.0230	.0617	.1147	.1730	.2269	.2679	.2903	.2918	.2734
	4	.0002	.0026	.0109	.0287	.0577	.0972	.1442	.1935	.2388	.2734
	5	.0000	.0002	.0012	.0043	.0115	.0250	.0466	.0774	.1172	.1641
	6	.0000	.0000	.0001	.0004	.0013	.0036	.0084	.0172	.0320	.0547
	7	.0000	.0000	.0000	.0000	.0001	.0002	.0006	.0016	.0037	.0078
8	0	.6634	.4305	.2725	.1678	.1001	.0576	.0319	.0168	.0084	.0039
	1	.2793	.3826	.3847	.3355	.2670	.1977	.1373	.0896	.0548	.0312
	2	.0515	.1488	.2376	.2936	.3115	.2965	.2587	.2090	.1569	.1094
	3	.0054	.0331	.0839	.1468	.2076	.2541	.2786	.2787	.2568	.2188
	4	.0004	.0046	.0185	.0459	.0865	.1361	.1875	.2322	.2627	.2734
	5	.0000	.0004	.0026	.0092	.0231	.0467	.0808	.1239	.1719	.2188
	6	.0000	.0000	.0002	.0011	.0038	.0100	.0217	.0413	.0703	.1094
	7	.0000	.0000	.0000	.0001	.0004	.0012	.0033	.0079	.0164	.0312
	8	.0000	.0000	.0000	.0000	.0000	.0001	.0002	.0007	.0017	.0039

(continued)

Table 2 Probability Function of the Binomial Distribution (*Continued*)

n	x	P									
		.05	.10	.15	.20	.25	.30	.35	.40	.45	.50
9	0	.6302	.3874	.2316	.1342	.0751	.0404	.0207	.0101	.0046	.0020
	1	.2985	.3874	.3679	.3020	.2253	.1556	.1004	.0605	.0339	.0176
	2	.0629	.1722	.2597	.3020	.3003	.2668	.2162	.1612	.1110	.0703
	3	.0077	.0446	.1069	.1762	.2336	.2668	.2716	.2508	.2119	.1641
	4	.0006	.0074	.0283	.0661	.1168	.1715	.2194	.2508	.2600	.2461
	5	.0000	.0008	.0050	.0165	.0389	.0735	.1181	.1672	.2128	.2461
	6	.0000	.0001	.0006	.0028	.0087	.0210	.0424	.0743	.1160	.1641
	7	.0000	.0000	.0000	.0003	.0012	.0039	.0098	.0212	.0407	.0703
	8	.0000	.0000	.0000	.0000	.0001	.0004	.0013	.0035	.0083	.0176
	9	.0000	.0000	.0000	.0000	.0000	.0000	.0001	.0003	.0008	.0020
10	0	.5987	.3487	.1969	.1074	.0563	.0282	.0135	.0060	.0025	.0010
	1	.3151	.3874	.3474	.2684	.1877	.1211	.0725	.0403	.0207	.0098
	2	.0746	.1937	.2759	.3020	.2816	.2335	.1757	.1209	.0763	.0439
	3	.0105	.0574	.1298	.2013	.2503	.2668	.2522	.2150	.1665	.1172
	4	.0010	.0112	.0401	.0881	.1460	.2001	.2377	.2508	.2384	.2051
	5	.0001	.0015	.0085	.0264	.0584	.1029	.1536	.2007	.2340	.2461
	6	.0000	.0001	.0012	.0055	.0162	.0368	.0689	.1115	.1596	.2051
	7	.0000	.0000	.0001	.0008	.0031	.0090	.0212	.0425	.0746	.1172
	8	.0000	.0000	.0000	.0001	.0004	.0014	.0043	.0106	.0226	.0439
	9	.0000	.0000	.0000	.0000	.0000	.0001	.0004	.0016	.0042	.0098
	10	.0000	.0000	.0000	.0000	.0000	.0000	.0000	.0001	.0003	.0010
11	0	.5688	.3138	.1673	.0859	.0422	.0198	.0088	.0036	.0014	.0005
	1	.3293	.3835	.3248	.2362	.1549	.0932	.0518	.0266	.0125	.0054
	2	.0867	.2131	.2866	.2953	.2581	.1998	.1395	.0887	.0513	.0269
	3	.0137	.0710	.1517	.2215	.2581	.2568	.2254	.1774	.1259	.0806
	4	.0014	.0158	.0536	.1107	.1721	.2201	.2428	.2365	.2060	.1611
	5	.0001	.0025	.0132	.0388	.0803	.1321	.1830	.2207	.2360	.2256
	6	.0000	.0003	.0023	.0097	.0268	.0566	.0985	.1471	.1931	.2256
	7	.0000	.0000	.0003	.0017	.0064	.0173	.0379	.0701	.1128	.1611
	8	.0000	.0000	.0000	.0002	.0011	.0037	.0102	.0234	.0462	.0806
	9	.0000	.0000	.0000	.0000	.0001	.0005	.0018	.0052	.0126	.0269
	10	.0000	.0000	.0000	.0000	.0000	.0000	.0002	.0007	.0021	.0054
	11	.0000	.0000	.0000	.0000	.0000	.0000	.0000	.0000	.0002	.0005
12	0	.5404	.2824	.1422	.0687	.0317	.0138	.0057	.0022	.0008	.0002
	1	.3413	.3766	.3012	.2062	.1267	.0712	.0368	.0174	.0075	.0029
	2	.0988	.2301	.2924	.2835	.2323	.1678	.1088	.0639	.0339	.0161
	3	.0173	.0852	.1720	.2362	.2581	.2397	.1954	.1419	.0923	.0537
	4	.0021	.0213	.0683	.1329	.1936	.2311	.2367	.2128	.1700	.1208
	5	.0002	.0038	.0193	.0532	.1032	.1585	.2039	.2270	.2225	.1934
	6	.0000	.0005	.0040	.0155	.0401	.0792	.1281	.1766	.2124	.2256
	7	.0000	.0000	.0006	.0033	.0015	.0291	.0591	.1009	.1489	.1934
	8	.0000	.0000	.0001	.0005	.0024	.0078	.0199	.0420	.0762	.1208
	9	.0000	.0000	.0000	.0001	.0004	.0015	.0048	.0125	.0277	.0537
	10	.0000	.0000	.0000	.0000	.0000	.0002	.0008	.0025	.0068	.0161
	11	.0000	.0000	.0000	.0000	.0000	.0000	.0001	.0003	.0010	.0029
	12	.0000	.0000	.0000	.0000	.0000	.0000	.0000	.0000	.0001	.0002

Table 2 Probability Function of the Binomial Distribution (*Continued*)

n	x	P									
		.05	.10	.15	.20	.25	.30	.35	.40	.45	.50
13	0	.5133	.2542	.1209	.0550	.0238	.0097	.0037	.0013	.0004	.0001
	1	.3512	.3672	.2774	.1787	.1029	.0540	.0259	.0113	.0045	.0016
	2	.1109	.2448	.2937	.2680	.2059	.1388	.0836	.0453	.0220	.0095
	3	.0214	.0997	.1900	.2457	.2517	.2181	.1651	.1107	.0660	.0349
	4	.0028	.0277	.0838	.1535	.2097	.2337	.2222	.1845	.1350	.0873
	5	.0003	.0055	.0266	.0691	.1258	.1803	.2154	.2214	.1989	.1571
	6	.0000	.0008	.0063	.0230	.0559	.1030	.1546	.1968	.2169	.2095
	7	.0000	.0001	.0011	.0058	.0186	.0442	.0833	.1312	.1775	.2095
	8	.0000	.0000	.0001	.0011	.0047	.0142	.0336	.0656	.1089	.1571
	9	.0000	.0000	.0000	.0001	.0009	.0034	.0101	.0243	.0495	.0873
	10	.0000	.0000	.0000	.0000	.0001	.0006	.0022	.0065	.0162	.0349
	11	.0000	.0000	.0000	.0000	.0000	.0001	.0003	.0012	.0036	.0095
	12	.0000	.0000	.0000	.0000	.0000	.0000	.0000	.0001	.0005	.0016
	13	.0000	.0000	.0000	.0000	.0000	.0000	.0000	.0000	.0000	.0001
14	0	.4877	.2288	.1028	.0440	.0178	.0068	.0024	.0008	.0002	.0001
	1	.3593	.3559	.2539	.1539	.0832	.0407	.0181	.0073	.0027	.0009
	2	.1229	.2570	.2912	.2501	.1802	.1134	.0634	.0317	.0141	.0056
	3	.0259	.1142	.2056	.2501	.2402	.1943	.1366	.0845	.0462	.0222
	4	.0037	.0348	.0998	.1720	.2202	.2290	.2022	.1549	.1040	.0611
	5	.0004	.0078	.0352	.0860	.1468	.1963	.2178	.2066	.1701	.1222
	6	.0000	.0013	.0093	.0322	.0734	.1262	.1759	.2066	.2088	.1833
	7	.0000	.0002	.0019	.0092	.0280	.0618	.1082	.1574	.1952	.2095
	8	.0000	.0000	.0003	.0020	.0082	.0232	.0510	.0918	.1398	.1833
	9	.0000	.0000	.0000	.0003	.0018	.0066	.0183	.0408	.0762	.1222
	10	.0000	.0000	.0000	.0000	.0003	.0014	.0049	.0136	.0312	.0611
	11	.0000	.0000	.0000	.0000	.0000	.0002	.0010	.0033	.0093	.0222
	12	.0000	.0000	.0000	.0000	.0000	.0000	.0001	.0005	.0019	.0056
	13	.0000	.0000	.0000	.0000	.0000	.0000	.0000	.0001	.0002	.0009
	14	.0000	.0000	.0000	.0000	.0000	.0000	.0000	.0000	.0000	.0001
15	0	.4633	.2059	.0874	.0352	.0134	.0047	.0016	.0005	.0001	.0000
	1	.3658	.3432	.2312	.1319	.0668	.0305	.0126	.0047	.0016	.0005
	2	.1348	.2669	.2856	.2309	.1559	.0916	.0476	.0219	.0090	.0032
	3	.0307	.1285	.2184	.2501	.2252	.1700	.1110	.0634	.0318	.0139
	4	.0049	.0428	.1156	.1876	.2252	.2186	.1792	.1268	.0780	.0417
	5	.0006	.0105	.0449	.1032	.1651	.2061	.2123	.1859	.1404	.0916
	6	.0000	.0019	.0132	.0430	.0917	.1472	.1906	.2066	.1914	.1527
	7	.0000	.0003	.0030	.0138	.0393	.0811	.1319	.1771	.2013	.1964
	8	.0000	.0000	.0005	.0035	.0131	.0348	.0710	.1181	.1647	.1964
	9	.0000	.0000	.0001	.0007	.0034	.0116	.0298	.0612	.1048	.1527
	10	.0000	.0000	.0000	.0001	.0007	.0030	.0096	.0245	.0515	.0916
	11	.0000	.0000	.0000	.0000	.0001	.0006	.0024	.0074	.0191	.0417
	12	.0000	.0000	.0000	.0000	.0000	.0001	.0004	.0016	.0052	.0139
	13	.0000	.0000	.0000	.0000	.0000	.0000	.0001	.0003	.0010	.0032
	14	.0000	.0000	.0000	.0000	.0000	.0000	.0000	.0000	.0001	.0005
	15	.0000	.0000	.0000	.0000	.0000	.0000	.0000	.0000	.0000	.0000
16	0	.4401	.1853	.0743	.0281	.0100	.0033	.0010	.0003	.0001	.0000
	1	.3706	.3294	.2097	.1126	.0535	.0228	.0087	.0030	.0009	.0002
	2	.1463	.2745	.2775	.2111	.1336	.0732	.0353	.0150	.0056	.0018

(continued)

Table 2 Probability Function of the Binomial Distribution (*Continued*)

n	x	.05	.10	.15	.20	.25	.30	.35	.40	.45	.50
	3	.0359	.1423	.2285	.2463	.2079	.1465	.0888	.0468	.0215	.0085
	4	.0061	.0514	.1311	.2001	.2552	.2040	.1553	.1014	.0572	.0278
	5	.0008	.0137	.0555	.1201	.1802	.2099	.2008	.1623	.1123	.0667
	6	.0001	.0028	.0180	.0550	.1101	.1649	.1982	.1983	.1684	.1222
	7	.0000	.0004	.0045	.0197	.0524	.1010	.1524	.1889	.1969	.1746
	8	.0000	.0001	.0009	.0055	.0197	.0487	.0923	.1417	.1812	.1964
	9	.0000	.0000	.0001	.0012	.0058	.0185	.0442	.0840	.1318	.1746
	10	.0000	.0000	.0000	.0002	.0014	.0056	.0167	.0392	.0755	.1222
	11	.0000	.0000	.0000	.0000	.0002	.0013	.0049	.0142	.0337	.0667
	12	.0000	.0000	.0000	.0000	.0000	.0002	.0011	.0040	.0115	.0278
	13	.0000	.0000	.0000	.0000	.0000	.0000	.0002	.0008	.0029	.0085
	14	.0000	.0000	.0000	.0000	.0000	.0000	.0000	.0001	.0005	.0018
	15	.0000	.0000	.0000	.0000	.0000	.0000	.0000	.0000	.0001	.0002
	16	.0000	.0000	.0000	.0000	.0000	.0000	.0000	.0000	.0000	.0000
17	0	.4181	.1668	.0631	.0225	.0075	.0023	.0007	.0002	.0000	.0000
	1	.3741	.3150	.1893	.0957	.0426	.0169	.0060	.0019	.0005	.0001
	2	.1575	.2800	.2673	.1914	.1136	.0581	.0260	.0102	.0035	.0010
	3	.0415	.1556	.2359	.2393	.1893	.1245	.0701	.0341	.0144	.0052
	4	.0076	.0605	.1457	.2093	.2209	.1868	.1320	.0796	.0411	.0182
	5	.0010	.0175	.0068	.1361	.1914	.2081	.1849	.1379	.0875	.0472
	6	.0001	.0039	.0236	.0680	.1276	.1784	.1991	.1839	.1432	.0944
	7	.0000	.0007	.0065	.0267	.0668	.1201	.1685	.1927	.1841	.1484
	8	.0000	.0001	.0014	.0084	.0279	.0644	.1134	.1606	.1883	.1855
	9	.0000	.0000	.0003	.0021	.0093	.0276	.0611	.1070	.1540	.1855
	10	.0000	.0000	.0000	.0004	.0025	.0095	.0263	.0571	.1008	.1484
	11	.0000	.0000	.0000	.0001	.0005	.0026	.0090	.0242	.0525	.0944
	12	.0000	.0000	.0000	.0000	.0001	.0006	.0024	.0081	.0215	.0472
	13	.0000	.0000	.0000	.0000	.0000	.0001	.0005	.0021	.0068	.0182
	14	.0000	.0000	.0000	.0000	.0000	.0000	.0001	.0004	.0016	.0052
	15	.0000	.0000	.0000	.0000	.0000	.0000	.0000	.0001	.0003	.0010
	16	.0000	.0000	.0000	.0000	.0000	.0000	.0000	.0000	.0000	.0001
	17	.0000	.0000	.0000	.0000	.0000	.0000	.0000	.0000	.0000	.0000
18	0	.3972	.1501	.0536	.0180	.0056	.0016	.0004	.0001	.0000	.0000
	1	.3763	.3002	.1704	.0811	.0338	.0126	.0042	.0012	.0003	.0001
	2	.1683	.2835	.2556	.1723	.0958	.0458	.0190	.0069	.0022	.0006
	3	.0473	.1680	.2406	.2297	.1704	.1046	.0547	.0246	.0095	.0031
	4	.0093	.0700	.1592	.2153	.2130	.1681	.1104	.0614	.0291	.0117
	5	.0014	.0218	.0787	.1507	.1988	.2017	.1664	.1146	.0666	.0327
	6	.0002	.0052	.0301	.0816	.1436	.1873	.1941	.1655	.1181	.0708
	7	.0000	.0010	.0091	.0350	.0820	.1376	.1792	.1892	.1657	.1214
	8	.0000	.0002	.0022	.0120	.0376	.0811	.1327	.1734	.1864	.1669
	9	.0000	.0000	.0004	.0033	.0139	.0386	.0794	.1284	.1694	.1855
	10	.0000	.0000	.0001	.0008	.0042	.0149	.0385	.0771	.1248	.1669
	11	.0000	.0000	.0000	.0001	.0010	.0046	.0151	.0374	.0742	.1214
	12	.0000	.0000	.0000	.0000	.0002	.0012	.0047	.0145	.0354	.0708
	13	.0000	.0000	.0000	.0000	.0000	.0002	.0012	.0044	.0134	.0327
	14	.0000	.0000	.0000	.0000	.0000	.0000	.0002	.0011	.0039	.0117
	15	.0000	.0000	.0000	.0000	.0000	.0000	.0000	.0002	.0009	.0031

Table 2 Probability Function of the Binomial Distribution (*Continued*)

n	x	P									
		.05	.10	.15	.20	.25	.30	.35	.40	.45	.50
	16	.0000	.0000	.0000	.0000	.0000	.0000	.0000	.0000	.0001	.0006
	17	.0000	.0000	.0000	.0000	.0000	.0000	.0000	.0000	.0000	.0001
	18	.0000	.0000	.0000	.0000	.0000	.0000	.0000	.0000	.0000	.0000
19	0	.3774	.1351	.0456	.0144	.0042	.0011	.0003	.0001	.0000	.0000
	1	.3774	.2852	.1529	.0685	.0268	.0093	.0029	.0008	.0002	.0000
	2	.1787	.2852	.2428	.1540	.0803	.0358	.0138	.0046	.0013	.0003
	3	.0533	.1796	.2428	.2182	.1517	.0869	.0422	.0175	.0062	.0018
	4	.0112	.0798	.1714	.2182	.2023	.1419	.0909	.0467	.0203	.0074
	5	.0018	.0266	.0907	.1636	.2023	.1916	.1468	.0933	.0497	.0222
	6	.0002	.0069	.0374	.0955	.1574	.1916	.1844	.1451	.0949	.0518
	7	.0000	.0014	.0122	.0443	.0974	.1525	.1844	.1797	.1443	.0961
	8	.0000	.0002	.0032	.0166	.0487	.0981	.1489	.1797	.1771	.1442
	9	.0000	.0000	.0007	.0051	.0198	.0514	.0980	.1464	.1771	.1762
	10	.0000	.0000	.0001	.0013	.0066	.0220	.0528	.0976	.1449	.1762
	11	.0000	.0000	.0000	.0003	.0018	.0077	.0233	.0532	.0970	.1442
	12	.0000	.0000	.0000	.0000	.0004	.0022	.0083	.0237	.0529	.0961
	13	.0000	.0000	.0000	.0000	.0001	.0005	.0024	.0085	.0233	.0518
	14	.0000	.0000	.0000	.0000	.0000	.0001	.0006	.0024	.0082	.0222
	15	.0000	.0000	.0000	.0000	.0000	.0000	.0001	.0005	.0022	.0074
	16	.0000	.0000	.0000	.0000	.0000	.0000	.0000	.0001	.0005	.0018
	17	.0000	.0000	.0000	.0000	.0000	.0000	.0000	.0000	.0001	.0003
	18	.0000	.0000	.0000	.0000	.0000	.0000	.0000	.0000	.0000	.0000
	19	.0000	.0000	.0000	.0000	.0000	.0000	.0000	.0000	.0000	.0000
20	0	.3585	.1216	.0388	.0115	.0032	.0008	.0002	.0000	.0000	.0000
	1	.3774	.2702	.1368	.0576	.0211	.0068	.0020	.0005	.0001	.0000
	2	.1887	.2852	.2293	.1369	.0669	.0278	.0100	.0031	.0008	.0002
	3	.0596	.1901	.2428	.2054	.1339	.0716	.0323	.0123	.0040	.0011
	4	.0133	.0898	.1821	.2182	.1897	.1304	.0738	.0350	.0139	.0046
	5	.0022	.0319	.1028	.1746	.2023	.1789	.1272	.0746	.0365	.0148
	6	.0003	.0089	.0454	.1091	.1686	.1916	.1712	.1244	.0746	.0370
	7	.0000	.0020	.0160	.0545	.1124	.1643	.1844	.1659	.1221	.0739
	8	.0000	.0004	.0046	.0222	.0609	.1144	.1614	.1797	.1623	.1201
	9	.0000	.0001	.0011	.0074	.0271	.0654	.1158	.1597	.1771	.1602
	10	.0000	.0000	.0002	.0020	.0099	.0308	.0686	.1171	.1593	.1762
	11	.0000	.0000	.0000	.0005	.0030	.0120	.0336	.0710	.1185	.1602
	12	.0000	.0000	.0000	.0001	.0008	.0039	.0136	.0355	.0727	.1201
	13	.0000	.0000	.0000	.0000	.0002	.0010	.0045	.0146	.0366	.0739
	14	.0000	.0000	.0000	.0000	.0000	.0002	.0012	.0049	.0150	.0370
	15	.0000	.0000	.0000	.0000	.0000	.0000	.0003	.0013	.0049	.0148
	16	.0000	.0000	.0000	.0000	.0000	.0000	.0000	.0003	.0013	.0046
	17	.0000	.0000	.0000	.0000	.0000	.0000	.0000	.0000	.0002	.0011
	18	.0000	.0000	.0000	.0000	.0000	.0000	.0000	.0000	.0000	.0002
	19	.0000	.0000	.0000	.0000	.0000	.0000	.0000	.0000	.0000	.0000
	20	.0000	.0000	.0000	.0000	.0000	.0000	.0000	.0000	.0000	.0000

From National Bureau of Standards, *Tables of the Binomial Probability Distribution*, United States Department of Commerce (1950).

Table 3 Cumulative Binomial Probabilities

The table shows the probability of x or fewer successes in n independent trials each with probability of success P. For example, the probability of two or less successes in four independent trials, each with probability of success 0.35, is 0.874.

n	x	P									
		.05	.10	.15	.20	.25	.30	.35	.40	.45	.500
2	0	.902	.81	.722	.64	.562	.49	.422	.36	.302	.25
	1	.998	.99	.978	.96	.937	.91	.877	.84	.797	.75
	2	1.00	1.00	1.00	1.00	1.00	1.00	1.00	1.00	1.00	1.00
3	0	.857	.729	.614	.512	.422	.343	.275	.216	.166	.125
	1	.993	.972	.939	.896	.844	.784	.718	.648	.575	.500
	2	1.00	.999	.997	.992	.984	.973	.957	.936	.909	.875
	3	1.00	1.00	1.00	1.00	1.00	1.00	1.00	1.00	1.00	1.000
4	0	.815	.656	.522	.41	.316	.24	.179	.13	.092	.062
	1	.986	.948	.89	.819	.738	.652	.563	.475	.391	.312
	2	1.00	.996	.988	.973	.949	.916	.874	.821	.759	.687
	3	1.00	1.00	.999	.998	.996	.992	.985	.974	.959	.937
	4	1.00	1.00	1.00	1.00	1.00	1.00	1.00	1.00	1.00	1.000
5	0	.774	.59	.444	.328	.237	.168	.116	.078	.05	.031
	1	.977	.919	.835	.737	.633	.528	.428	.337	.256	.187
	2	.999	.991	.973	.942	.896	.837	.765	.683	.593	.500
	3	1.00	1.00	.998	.993	.984	.969	.946	.913	.869	.812
	4	1.00	1.00	1.00	1.00	.999	.998	.995	.99	.982	.969
	5	1.00	1.00	1.00	1.00	1.00	1.00	1.00	1.00	1.00	1.000
6	0	.735	.531	.377	.262	.178	.118	.075	.047	.028	.016
	1	.967	.886	.776	.655	.534	.42	.319	.233	.164	.109
	2	.998	.984	.953	.901	.831	.744	.647	.544	.442	.344
	3	1.00	.999	.994	.983	.962	.93	.883	.821	.745	.656
	4	1.00	1.00	1.00	.998	.995	.989	.978	.959	.931	.891
	5	1.00	1.00	1.00	1.00	1.00	.999	.998	.996	.992	.984
	6	1.00	1.00	1.00	1.00	1.00	1.00	1.00	1.00	1.00	1.000
7	0	.698	.478	.321	.21	.133	.082	.049	.028	.015	.008
	1	.956	.85	.717	.577	.445	.329	.234	.159	.102	.062
	2	.996	.974	.926	.852	.756	.647	.532	.42	.316	.227
	3	1.00	.997	.988	.967	.929	.874	.80	.71	.608	.500
	4	1.00	1.00	.999	.995	.987	.971	.944	.904	.847	.773
	5	1.00	1.00	1.00	1.00	.999	.996	.991	.981	.964	.937
	6	1.00	1.00	1.00	1.00	1.00	1.00	.999	.998	.996	.992
	7	1.00	1.00	1.00	1.00	1.00	1.00	1.00	1.00	1.00	1.000
8	0	.663	.43	.272	.168	.10	.058	.032	.017	.008	.004
	1	.943	.813	.657	.503	.367	.255	.169	.106	.063	.035
	2	.994	.962	.895	.797	.679	.552	.428	.315	.22	.145
	3	1.00	.995	.979	.944	.886	.806	.706	.594	.477	.363
	4	1.00	1.00	.997	.99	.973	.942	.894	.826	.74	.637
	5	1.00	1.00	1.00	.999	.996	.989	.975	.95	.912	.855
	6	1.00	1.00	1.00	1.00	1.00	.999	.996	.991	.982	.965
	7	1.00	1.00	1.00	1.00	1.00	1.00	1.00	.999	.998	.996
	8	1.00	1.00	1.00	1.00	1.00	1.00	1.00	1.00	1.00	1.000
9	0	.63	.387	.232	.134	.075	.04	.021	.01	.005	.002
	1	.929	.775	.599	.436	.30	.196	.121	.071	.039	.020
	2	.992	.947	.859	.738	.601	.463	.337	.232	.15	.090

Table 3 Cumulative Binomial Probabilities (*Continued*)

n	*x*	.05	.10	.15	.20	.25	.30	.35	.40	.45	.500
						P					
	3	.999	.992	.966	.914	.834	.73	.609	.483	.361	.254
	4	1.00	.999	.994	.98	.951	.901	.828	.733	.621	.500
	5	1.00	1.00	.999	.997	.99	.975	.946	.901	.834	.746
	6	1.00	1.00	1.00	1.00	.999	.996	.989	.975	.95	.910
	7	1.00	1.00	1.00	1.00	1.00	1.00	.999	.996	.991	.980
	8	1.00	1.00	1.00	1.00	1.00	1.00	1.00	1.00	.999	.998
	9	1.00	1.00	1.00	1.00	1.00	1.00	1.00	1.00	1.00	1.000
10	0	.599	.349	.197	.107	.056	.028	.013	.006	.003	.001
	1	.914	.736	.544	.376	.244	.149	.086	.046	.023	.011
	2	.988	.93	.82	.678	.526	.383	.262	.167	.10	.055
	3	.999	.987	.95	.879	.776	.65	.514	.382	.266	.172
	4	1.00	.998	.99	.967	.922	.85	.751	.633	.504	.377
	5	1.00	1.00	.999	.994	.98	.953	.905	.834	.738	.623
	6	1.00	1.00	1.00	.999	.996	.989	.974	.945	.898	.828
	7	1.00	1.00	1.00	1.00	1.00	.998	.995	.988	.973	.945
	8	1.00	1.00	1.00	1.00	1.00	1.00	.999	.998	.995	.989
	9	1.00	1.00	1.00	1.00	1.00	1.00	1.00	1.00	1.00	.999
	10	1.00	1.00	1.00	1.00	1.00	1.00	1.00	1.00	1.00	1.000
11	0	.569	.314	.167	.086	.042	.02	.009	.004	.001	.000
	1	.898	.697	.492	.322	.197	.113	.061	.03	.014	.006
	2	.985	.91	.779	.617	.455	.313	.20	.119	.065	.033
	3	.998	.981	.931	.839	.713	.57	.426	.296	.191	.113
	4	1.00	.997	.984	.95	.885	.79	.668	.533	.397	.274
	5	1.00	1.00	.997	.988	.966	.922	.851	.753	.633	.500
	6	1.00	1.00	1.00	.998	.992	.978	.95	.901	.826	.726
	7	1.00	1.00	1.00	1.00	.999	.996	.988	.971	.939	.887
	8	1.00	1.00	1.00	1.00	1.00	.999	.998	.994	.985	.967
	9	1.00	1.00	1.00	1.00	1.00	1.00	1.00	.999	.998	.994
	10	1.00	1.00	1.00	1.00	1.00	1.00	1.00	1.00	1.00	1.000
	11	1.00	1.00	1.00	1.00	1.00	1.00	1.00	1.00	1.00	1.000
12	0	.54	.282	.142	.069	.032	.014	.006	.002	.001	.000
	1	.882	.659	.443	.275	.158	.085	.042	.02	.008	.003
	2	.98	.889	.736	.558	.391	.253	.151	.083	.042	.019
	3	.998	.974	.908	.795	.649	.493	.347	.225	.134	.073
	4	1.00	.996	.976	.927	.842	.724	.583	.438	.304	.194
	5	1.00	.999	.995	.981	.946	.882	.787	.665	.527	.387
	6	1.00	1.00	.999	.996	.986	.961	.915	.842	.739	.613
	7	1.00	1.00	1.00	.999	.997	.991	.974	.943	.888	.806
	8	1.00	1.00	1.00	1.00	1.00	.998	.994	.985	.964	.927
	9	1.00	1.00	1.00	1.00	1.00	1.00	.999	.997	.992	.981
	10	1.00	1.00	1.00	1.00	1.00	1.00	1.00	1.00	.999	.997
	11	1.00	1.00	1.00	1.00	1.00	1.00	1.00	1.00	1.00	1.000
	12	1.00	1.00	1.00	1.00	1.00	1.00	1.00	1.00	1.00	1.000
13	0	.513	.254	.121	.055	.024	.01	.004	.001	.00	.000
	1	.865	.621	.398	.234	.127	.064	.03	.013	.005	.002
	2	.975	.866	.692	.502	.333	.202	.113	.058	.027	.011
	3	.997	.966	.882	.747	.584	.421	.278	.169	.093	.046
	4	1.00	.994	.966	.901	.794	.654	.501	.353	.228	.133

(*continued*)

Table 3 Cumulative Binomial Probabilities (*Continued*)

n	x	.05	.10	.15	.20	.25	.30	.35	.40	.45	.500
								P			
	5	1.00	.999	.992	.97	.92	.835	.716	.574	.427	.291
	6	1.00	1.00	.999	.993	.976	.938	.871	.771	.644	.50
	7	1.00	1.00	1.00	.999	.994	.982	.954	.902	.821	.709
	8	1.00	1.00	1.00	1.00	.999	.996	.987	.968	.93	.867
	9	1.00	1.00	1.00	1.00	1.00	.999	.997	.992	.98	.954
	10	1.00	1.00	1.00	1.00	1.00	1.00	1.00	.999	.996	.989
	11	1.00	1.00	1.00	1.00	1.00	1.00	1.00	1.00	.999	.998
	12	1.00	1.00	1.00	1.00	1.00	1.00	1.00	1.00	1.00	1.000
14	0	.488	.229	.103	.044	.018	.007	.002	.001	.00	.000
	1	.847	.585	.357	.198	.101	.047	.021	.008	.003	.001
	2	.97	.842	.648	.448	.281	.161	.084	.04	.017	.006
	3	.996	.956	.853	.698	.521	.355	.22	.124	.063	.029
	4	1.00	.991	.953	.87	.742	.584	.423	.279	.167	.090
	5	1.00	.999	.988	.956	.888	.781	.641	.486	.337	.212
	6	1.00	1.00	.998	.988	.962	.907	.816	.692	.546	.395
	7	1.00	1.00	1.00	.998	.99	.969	.925	.85	.741	.605
	8	1.00	1.00	1.00	1.00	.998	.992	.976	.942	.881	.788
	9	1.00	1.00	1.00	1.00	1.00	.998	.994	.982	.957	.910
	10	1.00	1.00	1.00	1.00	1.00	1.00	.999	.996	.989	.971
	11	1.00	1.00	1.00	1.00	1.00	1.00	1.00	.999	.998	.994
	12	1.00	1.00	1.00	1.00	1.00	1.00	1.00	1.00	1.00	.999
	13	1.00	1.00	1.00	1.00	1.00	1.00	1.00	1.00	1.00	1.000
15	0	.463	.206	.087	.035	.013	.005	.002	.00	.00	.000
	1	.829	.549	.319	.167	.08	.035	.014	.005	.002	.000
	2	.964	.816	.604	.398	.236	.127	.062	.027	.011	.004
	3	.995	.944	.823	.648	.461	.297	.173	.091	.042	.018
	4	.999	.987	.938	.836	.686	.515	.352	.217	.12	.059
	5	1.00	.998	.983	.939	.852	.722	.564	.403	.261	.151
	6	1.00	1.00	.996	.982	.943	.869	.755	.61	.452	.304
	7	1.00	1.00	.999	.996	.983	.95	.887	.787	.654	.500
	8	1.00	1.00	1.00	.999	.996	.985	.958	.905	.818	.696
	9	1.00	1.00	1.00	1.00	.999	.996	.988	.966	.923	.849
	10	1.00	1.00	1.00	1.00	1.00	.999	.997	.991	.975	.941
	11	1.00	1.00	1.00	1.00	1.00	1.00	1.00	.998	.994	.982
	12	1.00	1.00	1.00	1.00	1.00	1.00	1.00	1.00	.999	.996
	13	1.00	1.00	1.00	1.00	1.00	1.00	1.00	1.00	1.00	1.000
16	0	.44	.185	.074	.028	.01	.003	.001	.00	.00	.000
	1	.811	.515	.284	.141	.063	.026	.01	.003	.001	.000
	2	.957	.789	.561	.352	.197	.099	.045	.018	.007	.002
	3	.993	.932	.79	.598	.405	.246	.134	.065	.028	.011
	4	.999	.983	.921	.798	.63	.45	.289	.167	.085	.038
	5	1.00	.997	.976	.918	.81	.66	.49	.329	.198	.105
	6	1.00	.999	.994	.973	.92	.825	.688	.527	.366	.227
	7	1.00	1.00	.999	.993	.973	.926	.841	.716	.563	.402
	8	1.00	1.00	1.00	.999	.993	.974	.933	.858	.744	.598
	9	1.00	1.00	1.00	1.00	.998	.993	.977	.942	.876	.773
	10	1.00	1.00	1.00	1.00	1.00	.998	.994	.981	.951	.895
	11	1.00	1.00	1.00	1.00	1.00	1.00	.999	.995	.985	.962

Table 3 Cumulative Binomial Probabilities (*Continued*)

n	x	P									
		.05	.10	.15	.20	.25	.30	.35	.40	.45	.500
	12	1.00	1.00	1.00	1.00	1.00	1.00	1.00	.999	.997	.989
	13	1.00	1.00	1.00	1.00	1.00	1.00	1.00	1.00	.999	.998
	14	1.00	1.00	1.00	1.00	1.00	1.00	1.00	1.00	1.00	1.000
17	0	.418	.167	.063	.023	.008	.002	.001	.00	.00	.000
	1	.792	.482	.252	.118	.05	.019	.007	.002	.001	.000
	2	.95	.762	.52	.31	.164	.077	.033	.012	.004	.001
	3	.991	.917	.756	.549	.353	.202	.103	.046	.018	.006
	4	.999	.978	.901	.758	.574	.389	.235	.126	.06	.025
	5	1.00	.995	.968	.894	.765	.597	.42	.264	.147	.072
	6	1.00	.999	.992	.962	.893	.775	.619	.448	.29	.166
	7	1.00	1.00	.998	.989	.96	.895	.787	.641	.474	.315
	8	1.00	1.00	1.00	.997	.988	.96	.901	.801	.663	.500
	9	1.00	1.00	1.00	1.00	.997	.987	.962	.908	.817	.685
	10	1.00	1.00	1.00	1.00	.999	.997	.988	.965	.917	.834
	11	1.00	1.00	1.00	1.00	1.00	.999	.997	.989	.97	.928
	12	1.00	1.00	1.00	1.00	1.00	1.00	.999	.997	.991	.975
	13	1.00	1.00	1.00	1.00	1.00	1.00	1.00	1.00	.998	.994
	14	1.00	1.00	1.00	1.00	1.00	1.00	1.00	1.00	1.00	.999
	15	1.00	1.00	1.00	1.00	1.00	1.00	1.00	1.00	1.00	1.00
18	0	.397	.15	.054	.018	.006	.002	.00	.00	.00	.000
	1	.774	.45	.224	.099	.039	.014	.005	.001	.00	.000
	2	.942	.734	.48	.271	.135	.06	.024	.008	.003	.001
	3	.989	.902	.72	.501	.306	.165	.078	.033	.012	.004
	4	.998	.972	.879	.716	.519	.333	.189	.094	.041	.015
	5	1.00	.994	.958	.867	.717	.534	.355	.209	.108	.048
	6	1.00	.999	.988	.949	.861	.722	.549	.374	.226	.119
	7	1.00	1.00	.997	.984	.943	.859	.728	.563	.391	.240
	8	1.00	1.00	.999	.996	.981	.94	.861	.737	.578	.407
	9	1.00	1.00	1.00	.999	.995	.979	.94	.865	.747	.593
	10	1.00	1.00	1.00	1.00	.999	.994	.979	.942	.872	.760
	11	1.00	1.00	1.00	1.00	1.00	.999	.994	.98	.946	.881
	12	1.00	1.00	1.00	1.00	1.00	1.00	.999	.994	.982	.952
	13	1.00	1.00	1.00	1.00	1.00	1.00	1.00	.999	.995	.985
	14	1.00	1.00	1.00	1.00	1.00	1.00	1.00	1.00	.999	.996
	15	1.00	1.00	1.00	1.00	1.00	1.00	1.00	1.00	1.00	.999
	16	1.00	1.00	1.00	1.00	1.00	1.00	1.00	1.00	1.00	1.000
19	0	.377	.135	.046	.014	.004	.001	.00	.00	.00	.000
	1	.755	.42	.198	.083	.031	.01	.003	.001	.00	.000
	2	.933	.705	.441	.237	.111	.046	.017	.005	.002	.000
	3	.987	.885	.684	.455	.263	.133	.059	.023	.008	.002
	4	.998	.965	.856	.673	.465	.282	.15	.07	.028	.010
	5	1.00	.991	.946	.837	.668	.474	.297	.163	.078	.032
	6	1.00	.998	.984	.932	.825	.666	.481	.308	.173	.084
	7	1.00	1.00	.996	.977	.923	.818	.666	.488	.317	.180
	8	1.00	1.00	.999	.993	.971	.916	.815	.667	.494	.324
	9	1.00	1.00	1.00	.998	.991	.967	.913	.814	.671	.500
	10	1.00	1.00	1.00	1.00	.998	.989	.965	.912	.816	.676
	11	1.00	1.00	1.00	1.00	1.00	.997	.989	.965	.913	.820

(continued)

Table 3   Cumulative Binomial Probabilities (*Continued*)

n	x	P									
		.05	.10	.15	.20	.25	.30	.35	.40	.45	.500
	12	1.00	1.00	1.00	1.00	1.00	.999	.997	.988	.966	.916
	13	1.00	1.00	1.00	1.00	1.00	1.00	.999	.997	.989	.968
	14	1.00	1.00	1.00	1.00	1.00	1.00	1.00	.999	.997	.990
	15	1.00	1.00	1.00	1.00	1.00	1.00	1.00	1.00	.999	.998
	16	1.00	1.00	1.00	1.00	1.00	1.00	1.00	1.00	1.00	1.000
20	0	.358	.122	.039	.012	.003	.001	.00	.00	.00	.000
	1	.736	.392	.176	.069	.024	.008	.002	.001	.00	.000
	2	.925	.677	.405	.206	.091	.035	.012	.004	.001	.000
	3	.984	.867	.648	.411	.225	.107	.044	.016	.005	.001
	4	.997	.957	.83	.63	.415	.238	.118	.051	.019	.006
	5	1.00	.989	.933	.804	.617	.416	.245	.126	.055	.021
	6	1.00	.998	.978	.913	.786	.608	.417	.25	.13	.058
	7	1.00	1.00	.994	.968	.898	.772	.601	.416	.252	.132
	8	1.00	1.00	.999	.99	.959	.887	.762	.596	.414	.252
	9	1.00	1.00	1.00	.997	.986	.952	.878	.755	.591	.412
	10	1.00	1.00	1.00	.999	.996	.983	.947	.872	.751	.588
	11	1.00	1.00	1.00	1.00	.999	.995	.98	.943	.869	.748
	12	1.00	1.00	1.00	1.00	1.00	.999	.994	.979	.942	.868
	13	1.00	1.00	1.00	1.00	1.00	1.00	.998	.994	.979	.942
	14	1.00	1.00	1.00	1.00	1.00	1.00	1.00	.998	.994	.979
	15	1.00	1.00	1.00	1.00	1.00	1.00	1.00	1.00	.998	.994
	16	1.00	1.00	1.00	1.00	1.00	1.00	1.00	1.00	1.00	.999
	17	1.00	1.00	1.00	1.00	1.00	1.00	1.00	1.00	1.00	1.000

Reproduced with permission from National Bureau of Standards, *Tables of the Binomial Probability Distribution*, United States Department of Commerce (1950).

Table 4 Values of $e^{-\lambda}$

λ	$e^{-\lambda}$	λ	$e^{-\lambda}$	λ	$e^{-\lambda}$	λ	$e^{-\lambda}$
0.00	1.000000	2.60	.074274	5.10	.006097	7.60	.000501
0.10	.904837	2.70	.067206	5.20	.005517	7.70	.000453
0.20	.818731	2.80	.060810	5.30	.004992	7.80	.000410
0.30	.740818	2.90	.055023	5.40	.004517	7.90	.000371
0.40	.670320	3.00	.049787	5.50	.004087	8.00	.000336
0.50	.606531	3.10	.045049	5.60	.003698	8.10	.000304
0.60	.548812	3.20	.040762	5.70	.003346	8.20	.000275
0.70	.496585	3.30	.036883	5.80	.003028	8.30	.000249
0.80	.449329	3.40	.033373	5.90	.002739	8.40	.000225
0.90	.406570	3.50	.030197	6.00	.002479	8.50	.000204
1.00	.367879	3.60	.027324	6.10	.002243	8.60	.000184
1.10	.332871	3.70	.024724	6.20	.002029	8.70	.000167
1.20	.301194	3.80	.022371	6.30	.001836	8.80	.000151
1.30	.272532	3.90	.020242	6.40	.001661	8.90	.000136
1.40	.246597	4.00	.018316	6.50	.001503	9.00	.000123
1.50	.223130	4.10	.016573	6.60	.001360	9.10	.000112
1.60	.201897	4.20	.014996	6.70	.001231	9.20	.000101
1.70	.182684	4.30	.013569	6.80	.001114	9.30	.000091
1.80	.165299	4.40	.012277	6.90	.001008	9.40	.000083
1.90	.149569	4.50	.011109	7.00	.000912	9.50	.000075
2.00	.135335	4.60	.010052	7.10	.000825	9.60	.000068
2.10	.122456	4.70	.009095	7.20	.000747	9.70	.000061
2.20	.110803	4.80	.008230	7.30	.000676	9.80	.000056
2.30	.100259	4.90	.007447	7.40	.000611	9.90	.000050
2.40	.090718	5.00	.006738	7.50	.000553	10.00	.000045
2.50	.082085						

Table 5 Individual Poisson Probabilities

	0.1	0.2	0.3	0.4	0.5	0.6	0.7	0.8	0.9	1.0
0	.9048	.8187	.7408	.6703	.6065	.5488	.4966	.4493	.4066	.3679
1	.0905	.1637	.2222	.2681	.3033	.3293	.3476	.3595	.3659	.3679
2	.0045	.0164	.0333	.0536	.0758	.0988	.1217	.1438	.1647	.1839
3	.0002	.0011	.0033	.0072	.0126	.0198	.0284	.0383	.0494	.0613
4	.0	.0001	.0003	.0007	.0016	.0030	.0050	.0077	.0111	.0153
5	.0	.0	.0	.0001	.0002	.0004	.0007	.0012	.0020	.0031
6	.0	.0	.0	.0	.0	.0	.0001	.0002	.0003	.0005
7	.0	.0	.0	.0	.0	.0	.0	.0	.0	.0001

MEAN ARRIVAL RATE λ

	1.1	1.2	1.3	1.4	1.5	1.6	1.7	1.8	1.9	2.0
0	.3329	.3012	.2725	.2466	.2231	.2019	.1827	.1653	.1496	.1353
1	.3662	.3614	.3543	.3452	.3347	.3230	.3106	.2975	.2842	.2707
2	.2014	.2169	.2303	.2417	.2510	.2584	.2640	.2678	.2700	.2707
3	.0738	.0867	.0998	.1128	.1255	.1378	.1496	.1607	.1710	.1804
4	.0203	.0260	.0324	.0395	.0471	.0551	.0636	.0723	.0812	.0902
5	.0045	.0062	.0084	.0111	.0141	.0176	.0216	.0260	.0309	.0361
6	.0008	.0012	.0018	.0026	.0035	.0047	.0061	.0078	.0098	.0120
7	.0001	.0002	.0003	.0005	.0008	.0011	.0015	.0020	.0027	.0034
8	.0	.0	.0001	.0001	.0001	.0002	.0003	.0005	.0006	.0009
9	.0	.0	.0	.0	.0	.0	.0001	.0001	.0001	.0002

MEAN ARRIVAL RATE λ

	2.1	2.2	2.3	2.4	2.5	2.6	2.7	2.8	2.9	3.0
0	.1225	.1108	.1003	.0907	.0821	.0743	.0672	.0608	.0550	.0498
1	.2572	.2438	.2306	.2177	.2052	.1931	.1815	.1703	.1596	.1494
2	.2700	.2681	.2652	.2613	.2565	.2510	.2450	.2384	.2314	.2240
3	.1890	.1966	.2033	.2090	.2138	.2176	.2205	.2225	.2237	.2240
4	.0992	.1082	.1169	.1254	.1336	.1414	.1488	.1557	.1622	.1680
5	.0417	.0476	.0538	.0602	.0668	.0735	.0804	.0872	.0940	.1008
6	.0146	.0174	.0206	.0241	.0278	.0319	.0362	.0407	.0455	.0504
7	.0044	.0055	.0068	.0083	.0099	.0118	.0139	.0163	.0188	.0216
8	.0011	.0015	.0019	.0025	.0031	.0038	.0047	.0057	.0068	.0081
9	.0003	.0004	.0005	.0007	.0009	.0011	.0014	.0018	.0022	.0027
10	.0001	.0001	.0001	.0002	.0002	.0003	.0004	.0005	.0006	.0008
11	.0	.0	.0	.0	.0	.0001	.0001	.0001	.0002	.0002
12	.0	.0	.0	.0	.0	.0	.0	.0	.0	.0001

MEAN ARRIVAL RATE λ

	3.1	3.2	3.3	3.4	3.5	3.6	3.7	3.8	3.9	4.0
0	.0450	.0408	.0369	.0334	.0302	.0273	.0247	.0224	.0202	.0183
1	.1397	.1304	.1217	.1135	.1057	.0984	.0915	.0850	.0789	.0733
2	.2165	.2087	.2008	.1929	.1850	.1771	.1692	.1615	.1539	.1465
3	.2237	.2226	.2209	.2186	.2158	.2125	.2087	.2046	.2001	.1954
4	.1733	.1781	.1823	.1858	.1888	.1912	.1931	.1944	.1951	.1954
5	.1075	.1140	.1203	.1264	.1322	.1377	.1429	.1477	.1522	.1563
6	.0555	.0608	.0662	.0716	.0771	.0826	.0881	.0936	.0989	.1042
7	.0246	.0278	.0312	.0348	.0385	.0425	.0466	.0508	.0551	.0595

Table 5   Individual Poisson Probabilities (*Continued*)

				MEAN ARRIVAL RATE λ					
	3.1	3.2	3.3	3.4	3.5	3.6	3.7	3.8	3.9	4.0
8	.0095	.0111	.0129	.0148	.0169	.0191	.0215	.0241	.0269	.0298
9	.0033	.0040	.0047	.0056	.0066	.0076	.0089	.0102	.0116	.0132
10	.0010	.0013	.0016	.0019	.0023	.0028	.0033	.0039	.0045	.0053
11	.0003	.0004	.0005	.0006	.0007	.0009	.0011	.0013	.0016	.0019
12	.0001	.0001	.0001	.0002	.0002	.0003	.0003	.0004	.0005	.0006
13	.0	.0	.0	.0	.0001	.0001	.0001	.0001	.0002	.0002
14	.0	.0	.0	.0	.0	.0	.0	.0	.0	.0001

				MEAN ARRIVAL RATE λ					
	4.1	4.2	4.3	4.4	4.5	4.6	4.7	4.8	4.9	5.0
0	.0166	.0150	.0136	.0123	.0111	.0101	.0091	.0082	.0074	.0067
1	.0679	.0630	.0583	.0540	.0500	.0462	.0427	.0395	.0365	.0337
2	.1393	.1323	.1254	.1188	.1125	.1063	.1005	.0948	.0894	.0842
3	.1904	.1852	.1798	.1743	.1687	.1631	.1574	.1517	.1460	.1404
4	.1951	.1944	.1933	.1917	.1898	.1875	.1849	.1820	.1789	.1755
5	.1600	.1633	.1662	.1687	.1708	.1725	.1738	.1747	.1753	.1755
6	.1093	.1143	.1191	.1237	.1281	.1323	.1362	.1398	.1432	.1462
7	.0640	.0686	.0732	.0778	.0824	.0869	.0914	.0959	.1002	.1044
8	.0328	.0360	.0393	.0428	.0463	.0500	.0537	.0575	.0614	.0653
9	.0150	.0168	.0188	.0209	.0232	.0255	.0281	.0307	.0334	.0363
10	.0061	.0071	.0081	.0092	.0104	.0118	.0132	.0147	.0164	.0181
11	.0023	.0027	.0032	.0037	.0043	.0049	.0056	.0064	.0073	.0082
12	.0008	.0009	.0011	.0013	.0016	.0019	.0022	.0026	.0030	.0034
13	.0002	.0003	.0004	.0005	.0006	.0007	.0008	.0009	.0011	.0013
14	.0001	.0001	.0001	.0001	.0002	.0002	.0003	.0003	.0004	.0005

				MEAN ARRIVAL RATE λ					
	5.1	5.2	5.3	5.4	5.5	5.6	5.7	5.8	5.9	6.0
0	.0061	.0055	.0050	.0045	.0041	.0037	.0033	.0030	.0027	.0025
1	.0311	.0287	.0265	.0244	.0225	.0207	.0191	.0176	.0162	.0149
2	.0793	.0746	.0701	.0659	.0618	.0580	.0544	.0509	.0477	.0446
3	.1348	.1293	.1239	.1185	.1133	.1082	.1033	.0985	.0938	.0892
4	.1719	.1681	.1641	.1600	.1558	.1515	.1472	.1428	.1383	.1339
5	.1753	.1748	.1740	.1728	.1714	.1697	.1678	.1656	.1632	.1606
6	.1490	.1515	.1537	.1555	.1571	.1584	.1594	.1601	.1605	.1606
7	.1086	.1125	.1163	.1200	.1234	.1267	.1298	.1326	.1353	.1377
8	.0692	.0731	.0771	.0810	.0849	.0887	.0925	.0962	.0998	.1033
9	.0392	.0423	.0454	.0486	.0519	.0552	.0586	.0620	.0654	.0688
10	.0200	.0220	.0241	.0262	.0285	.0309	.0334	.0359	.0386	.0413
11	.0093	.0104	.0116	.0129	.0143	.0157	.0173	.0190	.0207	.0225
12	.0039	.0045	.0051	.0058	.0065	.0073	.0082	.0092	.0102	.0113
13	.0015	.0018	.0021	.0024	.0028	.0032	.0036	.0041	.0046	.0052
14	.0006	.0007	.0008	.0009	.0011	.0013	.0015	.0017	.0019	.0022

				MEAN ARRIVAL RATE λ					
	6.1	6.2	6.3	6.4	6.5	6.6	6.7	6.8	6.9	7.0
0	.0022	.0020	.0018	.0017	.0015	.0014	.0012	.0011	.0010	.0009
1	.0137	.0126	.0116	.0106	.0098	.0090	.0082	.0076	.0070	.0064
2	.0417	.0390	.0364	.0340	.0318	.0296	.0276	.0258	.0240	.0223

(continued)

Table 5 Individual Poisson Probabilities (*Continued*)

| | \multicolumn{10}{c}{Mean Arrival Rate λ} |
	6.1	6.2	6.3	6.4	6.5	6.6	6.7	6.8	6.9	7.0
3	.0848	.0806	.0765	.0726	.0688	.0652	.0617	.0584	.0552	.0521
4	.1294	.1249	.1205	.1162	.1118	.1076	.1034	.0992	.0952	.0912
5	.1579	.1549	.1519	.1487	.1454	.1420	.1385	.1349	.1314	.1277
6	.1605	.1601	.1595	.1586	.1575	.1562	.1546	.1529	.1511	.1490
7	.1399	.1418	.1435	.1450	.1462	.1472	.1480	.1486	.1489	.1490
8	.1066	.1099	.1130	.1160	.1188	.1215	.1240	.1263	.1284	.1304
9	.0723	.0757	.0791	.0825	.0858	.0891	.0923	.0954	.0985	.1014
10	.0441	.0469	.0498	.0528	.0558	.0588	.0618	.0649	.0679	.0710
11	.0244	.0265	.0285	.0307	.0330	.0353	.0377	.0401	.0426	.0452
12	.0124	.0137	.0150	.0164	.0179	.0194	.0210	.0227	.0245	.0263
13	.0058	.0065	.0073	.0081	.0089	.0099	.0108	.0119	.0130	.0142
14	.0025	.0029	.0033	.0037	.0041	.0046	.0052	.0058	.0064	.0071

| | \multicolumn{10}{c}{Mean Arrival Rate λ} |
	7.1	7.2	7.3	7.4	7.5	7.6	7.7	7.8	7.9	8.0
0	.0008	.0007	.0007	.0006	.0006	.0005	.0005	.0004	.0004	.0003
1	.0059	.0054	.0049	.0045	.0041	.0038	.0035	.0032	.0029	.0027
2	.0208	.0194	.0180	.0167	.0156	.0145	.0134	.0125	.0116	.0107
3	.0492	.0464	.0438	.0413	.0389	.0366	.0345	.0324	.0305	.0286
4	.0874	.0836	.0799	.0764	.0729	.0696	.0663	.0632	.0602	.0573
5	.1241	.1204	.1167	.1130	.1094	.1057	.1021	.0986	.0951	.0916
6	.1468	.1445	.1420	.1394	.1367	.1339	.1311	.1282	.1252	.1221
7	.1489	.1486	.1481	.1474	.1465	.1454	.1442	.1428	.1413	.1396
8	.1321	.1337	.1351	.1363	.1373	.1381	.1388	.1392	.1395	.1396
9	.1042	.1070	.1096	.1121	.1144	.1167	.1187	.1207	.1224	.1241
10	.0740	.0770	.08	.0829	.0858	.0887	.0914	.0941	.0967	.0993
11	.0478	.0504	.0531	.0558	.0585	.0613	.0640	.0667	.0695	.0722
12	.0283	.0303	.0323	.0344	.0366	.0388	.0411	.0434	.0457	.0481
13	.0154	.0168	.0181	.0196	.0211	.0227	.0243	.0260	.0278	.0296
14	.0078	.0086	.0095	.0104	.0113	.0123	.0134	.0145	.0157	.0169
15	.0037	.0041	.0046	.0051	.0057	.0062	.0069	.0075	.0083	.0090
16	.0016	.0019	.0021	.0024	.0026	.0030	.0033	.0037	.0041	.0045
17	.0007	.0008	.0009	.0010	.0012	.0013	.0015	.0017	.0019	.0021
18	.0003	.0003	.0004	.0004	.0005	.0006	.0006	.0007	.0008	.0009
19	.0001	.0001	.0001	.0002	.0002	.0002	.0003	.0003	.0003	.0004

| | \multicolumn{10}{c}{Mean Arrival Rate λ} |
	8.1	8.2	8.3	8.4	8.5	8.6	8.7	8.8	8.9	9.0
0	.0003	.0003	.0002	.0002	.0002	.0002	.0002	.0002	.0001	.0001
1	.0025	.0023	.0021	.0019	.0017	.0016	.0014	.0013	.0012	.0011
2	.01	.0092	.0086	.0079	.0074	.0068	.0063	.0058	.0054	.0050
3	.0269	.0252	.0237	.0222	.0208	.0195	.0183	.0171	.0160	.0150
4	.0544	.0517	.0491	.0466	.0443	.0420	.0398	.0377	.0357	.0337
5	.0882	.0849	.0816	.0784	.0752	.0722	.0692	.0663	.0635	.0607
6	.1191	.1160	.1128	.1097	.1066	.1034	.1003	.0972	.0941	.0911
7	.1378	.1358	.1338	.1317	.1294	.1271	.1247	.1222	.1197	.1171
8	.1395	.1392	.1388	.1382	.1375	.1366	.1356	.1344	.1332	.1318
9	.1256	.1269	.1280	.1290	.1299	.1306	.1311	.1315	.1317	.1318
10	.1017	.1040	.1063	.1084	.1104	.1123	.1140	.1157	.1172	.1186
11	.0749	.0776	.0802	.0828	.0853	.0878	.0902	.0925	.0948	.0970

Table 5 Individual Poisson Probabilities (*Continued*)

	MEAN ARRIVAL RATE λ									
	8.1	8.2	8.3	8.4	8.5	8.6	8.7	8.8	8.9	9.0
12	.0505	.0530	.0555	.0579	.0604	.0629	.0654	.0679	.0703	.0728
13	.0315	.0334	.0354	.0374	.0395	.0416	.0438	.0459	.0481	.0504
14	.0182	.0196	.0210	.0225	.0240	.0256	.0272	.0289	.0306	.0324
15	.0098	.0107	.0116	.0126	.0136	.0147	.0158	.0169	.0182	.0194
16	.0050	.0055	.0060	.0066	.0072	.0079	.0086	.0093	.0101	.0109
17	.0024	.0026	.0029	.0033	.0036	.0040	.0044	.0048	.0053	.0058
18	.0011	.0012	.0014	.0015	.0017	.0019	.0021	.0024	.0026	.0029
19	.0005	.0005	.0006	.0007	.0008	.0009	.0010	.0011	.0012	.0014

	MEAN ARRIVAL RATE λ									
	9.1	9.2	9.3	9.4	9.5	9.6	9.7	9.8	9.9	10.0
0	.0001	.0001	.0001	.0001	.0001	.0001	.0001	.0001	.0001	.0000
1	.0010	.0009	.0009	.0008	.0007	.0007	.0006	.0005	.0005	.0005
2	.0046	.0043	.0040	.0037	.0034	.0031	.0029	.0027	.0025	.0023
3	.0140	.0131	.0123	.0115	.0107	.01	.0093	.0087	.0081	.0076
4	.0319	.0302	.0285	.0269	.0254	.0240	.0226	.0213	.0201	.0189
5	.0581	.0555	.0530	.0506	.0483	.0460	.0439	.0418	.0398	.0378
6	.0881	.0851	.0822	.0793	.0764	.0736	.0709	.0682	.0656	.0631
7	.1145	.1118	.1091	.1064	.1037	.1010	.0982	.0955	.0928	.0901
8	.1302	.1286	.1269	.1251	.1232	.1212	.1191	.1170	.1148	.1126
9	.1317	.1315	.1311	.1306	.13	.1293	.1284	.1274	.1263	.1251
10	.1198	.1210	.1219	.1228	.1235	.1241	.1245	.1249	.1250	.1251
11	.0991	.1012	.1031	.1049	.1067	.1083	.1098	.1112	.1125	.1137
12	.0752	.0776	.0799	.0822	.0844	.0866	.0888	.0908	.0928	.0948
13	.0526	.0549	.0572	.0594	.0617	.0640	.0662	.0685	.0707	.0729
14	.0342	.0361	.0380	.0399	.0419	.0439	.0459	.0479	.05	.0521
15	.0208	.0221	.0235	.0250	.0265	.0281	.0297	.0313	.0330	.0347
16	.0118	.0127	.0137	.0147	.0157	.0168	.0180	.0192	.0204	.0217
17	.0063	.0069	.0075	.0081	.0088	.0095	.0103	.0111	.0119	.0128
18	.0032	.0035	.0039	.0042	.0046	.0051	.0055	.0060	.0065	.0071
19	.0015	.0017	.0019	.0021	.0023	.0026	.0028	.0031	.0034	.0037

	MEAN ARRIVAL RATE λ									
	10.1	10.2	10.3	10.4	10.5	10.6	10.7	10.8	10.9	11.0
0	.00	.00	.00	.00	.00	.00	.00	.00	.00	.0000
1	.0004	.0004	.0003	.0003	.0003	.0003	.0002	.0002	.0002	.0002
2	.0021	.0019	.0018	.0016	.0015	.0014	.0013	.0012	.0011	.0010
3	.0071	.0066	.0061	.0057	.0053	.0049	.0046	.0043	.0040	.0037
4	.0178	.0168	.0158	.0148	.0139	.0131	.0123	.0116	.0109	.0102
5	.0360	.0342	.0325	.0309	.0293	.0278	.0264	.0250	.0237	.0224
6	.0606	.0581	.0558	.0535	.0513	.0491	.0470	.0450	.0430	.0411
7	.0874	.0847	.0821	.0795	.0769	.0743	.0718	.0694	.0669	.0646
8	.1103	.1080	.1057	.1033	.1009	.0985	.0961	.0936	.0912	.0888
9	.1238	.1224	.1209	.1194	.1177	.1160	.1142	.1124	.1105	.1085
10	.1250	.1249	.1246	.1241	.1236	.1230	.1222	.1214	.1204	.1194
11	.1148	.1158	.1166	.1174	.1180	.1185	.1189	.1192	.1193	.1194
12	.0966	.0984	.1001	.1017	.1032	.1047	.1060	.1072	.1084	.1094
13	.0751	.0772	.0793	.0814	.0834	.0853	.0872	.0891	.0909	.0926
14	.0542	.0563	.0584	.0604	.0625	.0646	.0667	.0687	.0708	.0728

(*continued*)

Table 5 Individual Poisson Probabilities (*Continued*)

| | | | | MEAN ARRIVAL RATE λ | | | | | |
	10.1	10.2	10.3	10.4	10.5	10.6	10.7	10.8	10.9	11.0
15	.0365	.0383	.0401	.0419	.0438	.0457	.0476	.0495	.0514	.0534
16	.0230	.0244	.0258	.0272	.0287	.0303	.0318	.0334	.0350	.0367
17	.0137	.0146	.0156	.0167	.0177	.0189	.0200	.0212	.0225	.0237
18	.0077	.0083	.0089	.0096	.0104	.0111	.0119	.0127	.0136	.0145
19	.0041	.0045	.0048	.0053	.0057	.0062	.0067	.0072	.0078	.0084
20	.0021	.0023	.0025	.0027	.0030	.0033	.0036	.0039	.0043	.0046

| | | | | MEAN ARRIVAL RATE λ | | | | | |
	11.1	11.2	11.3	11.4	11.5	11.6	11.7	11.8	11.9	12.0
0	.0000	.0000	.0000	.0000	.0000	.0000	.0000	.0000	.0000	.0000
1	.0002	.0002	.0001	.0001	.0001	.0001	.0001	.0001	.0001	.0001
2	.0009	.0009	.0008	.0007	.0007	.0006	.0006	.0005	.0005	.0004
3	.0034	.0032	.0030	.0028	.0026	.0024	.0022	.0021	.0019	.0018
4	.0096	.0090	.0084	.0079	.0074	.0069	.0065	.0061	.0057	.0053
5	.0212	.0201	.0190	.0180	.0170	.0160	.0152	.0143	.0135	.0127
6	.0393	.0375	.0358	.0341	.0325	.0310	.0295	.0281	.0268	.0255
7	.0623	.0600	.0578	.0556	.0535	.0514	.0494	.0474	.0455	.0437
8	.0864	.0840	.0816	.0792	.0769	.0745	.0722	.0700	.0677	.0655
9	.1065	.1045	.1024	.1003	.0982	.0961	.0939	.0917	.0895	.0874
10	.1182	.1170	.1157	.1144	.1129	.1114	.1099	.1082	.1066	.1048
11	.1193	.1192	.1189	.1185	.1181	.1175	.1169	.1161	.1153	.1144
12	.1104	.1112	.1120	.1126	.1131	.1136	.1139	.1142	.1143	.1144
13	.0942	.0958	.0973	.0987	.1001	.1014	.1025	.1036	.1046	.1056
14	.0747	.0767	.0786	.0804	.0822	.0840	.0857	.0874	.0889	.0905
15	.0553	.0572	.0592	.0611	.0630	.0649	.0668	.0687	.0706	.0724
16	.0384	.0401	.0418	.0435	.0453	.0471	.0489	.0507	.0525	.0543
17	.0250	.0264	.0278	.0292	.0306	.0321	.0336	.0352	.0367	.0383
18	.0154	.0164	.0174	.0185	.0196	.0207	.0219	.0231	.0243	.0255
19	.0090	.0097	.0104	.0111	.0119	.0126	.0135	.0143	.0152	.0161
20	.0050	.0054	.0059	.0063	.0068	.0073	.0079	.0084	.0091	.0097

| | | | | MEAN ARRIVAL RATE λ | | | | | |
	12.1	12.2	12.3	12.4	12.5	12.6	12.7	12.8	12.9	13.0
4	.0050	.0046	.0043	.0041	.0038	.0035	.0033	.0031	.0029	.0027
5	.0120	.0113	.0107	.0101	.0095	.0089	.0084	.0079	.0074	.0070
6	.0242	.0230	.0219	.0208	.0197	.0187	.0178	.0169	.0160	.0152
7	.0419	.0402	.0385	.0368	.0353	.0337	.0323	.0308	.0295	.0281
8	.0634	.0612	.0591	.0571	.0551	.0531	.0512	.0493	.0475	.0457
9	.0852	.0830	.0808	.0787	.0765	.0744	.0723	.0702	.0681	.0661
10	.1031	.1013	.0994	.0975	.0956	.0937	.0918	.0898	.0878	.0859
11	.1134	.1123	.1112	.1100	.1087	.1074	.1060	.1045	.1030	.1015
12	.1143	.1142	.1139	.1136	.1132	.1127	.1121	.1115	.1107	.1099
13	.1064	.1072	.1078	.1084	.1089	.1093	.1096	.1098	.1099	.1099
14	.0920	.0934	.0947	.0960	.0972	.0983	.0994	.1004	.1013	.1021
15	.0742	.0759	.0777	.0794	.0810	.0826	.0841	.0856	.0871	.0885
16	.0561	.0579	.0597	.0615	.0633	.0650	.0668	.0685	.0702	.0719
17	.0399	.0416	.0432	.0449	.0465	.0482	.0499	.0516	.0533	.0550
18	.0268	.0282	.0295	.0309	.0323	.0337	.0352	.0367	.0382	.0397
19	.0171	.0181	.0191	.0202	.0213	.0224	.0235	.0247	.0259	.0272
20	.0103	.0110	.0118	.0125	.0133	.0141	.0149	.0158	.0167	.0177

Table 5   Individual Poisson Probabilities (*Continued*)

	MEAN ARRIVAL RATE λ									
	13.1	13.2	13.3	13.4	13.5	13.6	13.7	13.8	13.9	14.0
5	.0066	.0062	.0058	.0055	.0051	.0048	.0045	.0042	.0040	.0037
6	.0144	.0136	.0129	.0122	.0115	.0109	.0103	.0097	.0092	.0087
7	.0269	.0256	.0245	.0233	.0222	.0212	.0202	.0192	.0183	.0174
8	.0440	.0423	.0407	.0391	.0375	.0360	.0345	.0331	.0318	.0304
9	.0640	.0620	.0601	.0582	.0563	.0544	.0526	.0508	.0491	.0473
10	.0839	.0819	.0799	.0779	.0760	.0740	.0720	.0701	.0682	.0663
11	.0999	.0983	.0966	.0949	.0932	.0915	.0897	.0880	.0862	.0844
12	.1091	.1081	.1071	.1060	.1049	.1037	.1024	.1011	.0998	.0984
13	.1099	.1098	.1096	.1093	.1089	.1085	.1080	.1074	.1067	.1060
14	.1028	.1035	.1041	.1046	.1050	.1054	.1056	.1058	.1060	.1060
15	.0898	.0911	.0923	.0934	.0945	.0955	.0965	.0974	.0982	.0989
16	.0735	.0751	.0767	.0783	.0798	.0812	.0826	.0840	.0853	.0866
17	.0567	.0583	.0600	.0617	.0633	.0650	.0666	.0682	.0697	.0713
18	.0412	.0428	.0443	.0459	.0475	.0491	.0507	.0523	.0539	.0554
19	.0284	.0297	.0310	.0324	.0337	.0351	.0365	.0380	.0394	.0409
20	.0186	.0196	.0206	.0217	.0228	.0239	.0250	.0262	.0274	.0286

	MEAN ARRIVAL RATE λ									
	14.1	14.2	14.3	14.4	14.5	14.6	14.7	14.8	14.9	15.0
6	.0082	.0078	.0073	.0069	.0065	.0061	.0058	.0055	.0051	.0048
7	.0165	.0157	.0149	.0142	.0135	.0128	.0122	.0115	.0109	.0104
8	.0292	.0279	.0267	.0256	.0244	.0234	.0223	.0213	.0204	.0194
9	.0457	.0440	.0424	.0409	.0394	.0379	.0365	.0351	.0337	.0324
10	.0644	.0625	.0607	.0589	.0571	.0553	.0536	.0519	.0502	.0486
11	.0825	.0807	.0789	.0771	.0753	.0735	.0716	.0698	.0681	.0663
12	.0970	.0955	.0940	.0925	.0910	.0894	.0878	.0861	.0845	.0829
13	.1052	.1043	.1034	.1025	.1014	.1004	.0992	.0981	.0969	.0956
14	.1060	.1058	.1057	.1054	.1051	.1047	.1042	.1037	.1031	.1024
15	.0996	.1002	.1007	.1012	.1016	.1019	.1021	.1023	.1024	.1024
16	.0878	.0889	.0900	.0911	.0920	.0930	.0938	.0946	.0954	.0960
17	.0728	.0743	.0757	.0771	.0785	.0798	.0811	.0824	.0836	.0847
18	.0570	.0586	.0602	.0617	.0632	.0648	.0663	.0677	.0692	.0706
19	.0423	.0438	.0453	.0468	.0483	.0498	.0513	.0528	.0543	.0557
20	.0298	.0311	.0324	.0337	.0350	.0363	.0377	.0390	.0404	.0418
21	.0200	.0210	.0220	.0231	.0242	.0253	.0264	.0275	.0287	.0299
22	.0128	.0136	.0143	.0151	.0159	.0168	.0176	.0185	.0194	.0204
23	.0079	.0084	.0089	.0095	.0100	.0106	.0113	.0119	.0126	.0133
24	.0046	.0050	.0053	.0057	.0061	.0065	.0069	.0073	.0078	.0083

	MEAN ARRIVAL RATE λ									
	15.1	15.2	15.3	15.4	15.5	15.6	15.7	15.8	15.9	16.0
7	.0098	.0093	.0088	.0084	.0079	.0075	.0071	.0067	.0063	.0060
8	.0186	.0177	.0169	.0161	.0153	.0146	.0139	.0132	.0126	.0120
9	.0311	.0299	.0287	.0275	.0264	.0253	.0243	.0232	.0223	.0213
10	.0470	.0454	.0439	.0424	.0409	.0395	.0381	.0367	.0354	.0341
11	.0645	.0628	.0611	.0594	.0577	.0560	.0544	.0527	.0512	.0496
12	.0812	.0795	.0778	.0762	.0745	.0728	.0711	.0695	.0678	.0661
13	.0943	.0930	.0916	.0902	.0888	.0874	.0859	.0844	.0829	.0814
14	.1017	.1010	.1001	.0993	.0983	.0974	.0963	.0953	.0942	.0930

(*continued*)

Table 5   Individual Poisson Probabilities (*Continued*)

					Mean Arrival Rate λ					
	15.1	15.2	15.3	15.4	15.5	15.6	15.7	15.8	15.9	16.0
15	.1024	.1023	.1021	.1019	.1016	.1012	.1008	.1003	.0998	.0992
16	.0966	.0972	.0977	.0981	.0984	.0987	.0989	.0991	.0992	.0992
17	.0858	.0869	.0879	.0888	.0897	.0906	.0914	.0921	.0928	.0934
18	.0720	.0734	.0747	.0760	.0773	.0785	.0797	.0808	.0819	.0830
19	.0572	.0587	.0602	.0616	.0630	.0645	.0659	.0672	.0686	.0699
20	.0432	.0446	.0460	.0474	.0489	.0503	.0517	.0531	.0545	.0559
21	.0311	.0323	.0335	.0348	.0361	.0373	.0386	.0400	.0413	.0426
22	.0213	.0223	.0233	.0244	.0254	.0265	.0276	.0287	.0298	.0310
23	.0140	.0147	.0155	.0163	.0171	.0180	.0188	.0197	.0206	.0216
24	.0088	.0093	.0099	.0105	.0111	.0117	.0123	.0130	.0137	.0144
25	.0053	.0057	.0061	.0064	.0069	.0073	.0077	.0082	.0087	.0092

					Mean Arrival Rate λ					
	16.1	16.2	16.3	16.4	16.5	16.6	16.7	16.8	16.9	17.0
7	.0057	.0054	.0051	.0048	.0045	.0043	.0040	.0038	.0036	.0034
8	.0114	.0108	.0103	.0098	.0093	.0088	.0084	.0080	.0076	.0072
9	.0204	.0195	.0187	.0178	.0171	.0163	.0156	.0149	.0142	.0135
10	.0328	.0316	.0304	.0293	.0281	.0270	.0260	.0250	.0240	.0230
11	.0481	.0466	.0451	.0436	.0422	.0408	.0394	.0381	.0368	.0355
12	.0645	.0628	.0612	.0596	.0580	.0565	.0549	.0534	.0518	.0504
13	.0799	.0783	.0768	.0752	.0736	.0721	.0705	.0690	.0674	.0658
14	.0918	.0906	.0894	.0881	.0868	.0855	.0841	.0828	.0814	.0800
15	.0986	.0979	.0971	.0963	.0955	.0946	.0937	.0927	.0917	.0906
16	.0992	.0991	.0989	.0987	.0985	.0981	.0978	.0973	.0968	.0963
17	.0939	.0944	.0949	.0952	.0956	.0958	.0960	.0962	.0963	.0963
18	.0840	.0850	.0859	.0868	.0876	.0884	.0891	.0898	.0904	.0909
19	.0712	.0725	.0737	.0749	.0761	.0772	.0783	.0794	.0804	.0814
20	.0573	.0587	.0601	.0614	.0628	.0641	.0654	.0667	.0679	.0692
21	.0439	.0453	.0466	.0480	.0493	.0507	.0520	.0533	.0547	.0560
22	.0322	.0333	.0345	.0358	.0370	.0382	.0395	.0407	.0420	.0433
23	.0225	.0235	.0245	.0255	.0265	.0276	.0287	.0297	.0309	.0320
24	.0151	.0159	.0166	.0174	.0182	.0191	.0199	.0208	.0217	.0226
25	.0097	.0103	.0108	.0114	.0120	.0127	.0133	.0140	.0147	.0154

					Mean Arrival Rate λ					
	17.1	17.2	17.3	17.4	17.5	17.6	17.7	17.8	17.9	18.0
8	.0068	.0064	.0061	.0058	.0055	.0052	.0049	.0046	.0044	.0042
9	.0129	.0123	.0117	.0112	.0107	.0101	.0097	.0092	.0088	.0083
10	.0221	.0212	.0203	.0195	.0186	.0179	.0171	.0164	.0157	.0150
11	.0343	.0331	.0319	.0308	.0297	.0286	.0275	.0265	.0255	.0245
12	.0489	.0474	.0460	.0446	.0432	.0419	.0406	.0393	.0380	.0368
13	.0643	.0628	.0612	.0597	.0582	.0567	.0553	.0538	.0524	.0509
14	.0785	.0771	.0757	.0742	.0728	.0713	.0699	.0684	.0669	.0655
15	.0895	.0884	.0873	.0861	.0849	.0837	.0824	.0812	.0799	.0786
16	.0957	.0951	.0944	.0936	.0929	.0920	.0912	.0903	.0894	.0884
17	.0963	.0962	.0960	.0958	.0956	.0953	.0949	.0945	.0941	.0936
18	.0914	.0919	.0923	.0926	.0929	.0932	.0934	.0935	.0936	.0936
19	.0823	.0832	.0840	.0848	.0856	.0863	.0870	.0876	.0882	.0887
20	.0704	.0715	.0727	.0738	.0749	.0760	.0770	.0780	.0789	.0798
21	.0573	.0586	.0599	.0612	.0624	.0637	.0649	.0661	.0673	.0684

Table 5 Individual Poisson Probabilities (*Continued*)

					Mean Arrival Rate λ					
	17.1	17.2	17.3	17.4	17.5	17.6	17.7	17.8	17.9	18.0
22	.0445	.0458	.0471	.0484	.0496	.0509	.0522	.0535	.0547	.0560
23	.0331	.0343	.0354	.0366	.0378	.0390	.0402	.0414	.0426	.0438
24	.0236	.0246	.0255	.0265	.0275	.0286	.0296	.0307	.0318	.0328
25	.0161	.0169	.0177	.0185	.0193	.0201	.0210	.0218	.0227	.0237

					Mean Arrival Rate λ					
	18.1	18.2	18.3	18.4	18.5	18.6	18.7	18.8	18.9	19.0
9	.0079	.0075	.0072	.0068	.0065	.0061	.0058	.0055	.0053	.0050
10	.0143	.0137	.0131	.0125	.0120	.0114	.0109	.0104	.0099	.0095
11	.0236	.0227	.0218	.0209	.0201	.0193	.0185	.0178	.0171	.0164
12	.0356	.0344	.0332	.0321	.0310	.0299	.0289	.0278	.0269	.0259
13	.0495	.0481	.0468	.0454	.0441	.0428	.0415	.0403	.0390	.0378
14	.0640	.0626	.0611	.0597	.0583	.0569	.0555	.0541	.0527	.0514
15	.0773	.0759	.0746	.0732	.0719	.0705	.0692	.0678	.0664	.0650
16	.0874	.0864	.0853	.0842	.0831	.0820	.0808	.0796	.0785	.0772
17	.0931	.0925	.0918	.0912	.0904	.0897	.0889	.0881	.0872	.0863
18	.0936	.0935	.0934	.0932	.0930	.0927	.0924	.0920	.0916	.0911
19	.0891	.0896	.0899	.0902	.0905	.0907	.0909	.0910	.0911	.0911
20	.0807	.0815	.0823	.0830	.0837	.0844	.0850	.0856	.0861	.0866
21	.0695	.0706	.0717	.0727	.0738	.0747	.0757	.0766	.0775	.0783
22	.0572	.0584	.0596	.0608	.0620	.0632	.0643	.0655	.0666	.0676
23	.0450	.0462	.0475	.0487	.0499	.0511	.0523	.0535	.0547	.0559
24	.0340	.0351	.0362	.0373	.0385	.0396	.0408	.0419	.0431	.0442
25	.0246	.0255	.0265	.0275	.0285	.0295	.0305	.0315	.0326	.0336

					Mean Arrival Rate λ					
	19.1	19.2	19.3	19.4	19.5	19.6	19.7	19.8	19.9	20.0
10	.0090	.0086	.0082	.0078	.0074	.0071	.0067	.0064	.0061	.0058
11	.0157	.0150	.0144	.0138	.0132	.0126	.0121	.0116	.0111	.0106
12	.0249	.0240	.0231	.0223	.0214	.0206	.0198	.0191	.0183	.0176
13	.0367	.0355	.0344	.0333	.0322	.0311	.0301	.0291	.0281	.0271
14	.0500	.0487	.0474	.0461	.0448	.0436	.0423	.0411	.0399	.0387
15	.0637	.0623	.0610	.0596	.0582	.0569	.0556	.0543	.0529	.0516
16	.0760	.0748	.0735	.0723	.0710	.0697	.0684	.0671	.0659	.0646
17	.0854	.0844	.0835	.0825	.0814	.0804	.0793	.0782	.0771	.0760
18	.0906	.0901	.0895	.0889	.0882	.0875	.0868	.0860	.0852	.0844
19	.0911	.0910	.0909	.0907	.0905	.0903	.0900	.0896	.0893	.0888
20	.0870	.0874	.0877	.0880	.0883	.0885	.0886	.0887	.0888	.0888
21	.0791	.0799	.0806	.0813	.0820	.0826	.0831	.0837	.0842	.0846
22	.0687	.0697	.0707	.0717	.0727	.0736	.0745	.0753	.0761	.0769
23	.0570	.0582	.0594	.0605	.0616	.0627	.0638	.0648	.0659	.0669
24	.0454	.0466	.0477	.0489	.0500	.0512	.0523	.0535	.0546	.0557
25	.0347	.0358	.0368	.0379	.0390	.0401	.0412	.0424	.0435	.0446

					Mean Arrival Rate λ					
	20.1	20.2	20.3	20.4	20.5	20.6	20.7	20.8	20.9	21.0
10	.0055	.0053	.0050	.0048	.0045	.0043	.0041	.0039	.0037	.0035
11	.0101	.0097	.0092	.0088	.0084	.0080	.0077	.0073	.0070	.0067
12	.0169	.0163	.0156	.0150	.0144	.0138	.0132	.0127	.0122	.0116

(continued)

Table 5 Individual Poisson Probabilities (*Continued*)

	MEAN ARRIVAL RATE λ									
	20.1	20.2	20.3	20.4	20.5	20.6	20.7	20.8	20.9	21.0
13	.0262	.0253	.0244	.0235	.0227	.0219	.0211	.0203	.0195	.0188
14	.0376	.0365	.0353	.0343	.0332	.0322	.0311	.0301	.0292	.0282
15	.0504	.0491	.0478	.0466	.0454	.0442	.0430	.0418	.0406	.0395
16	.0633	.0620	.0607	.0594	.0581	.0569	.0556	.0543	.0531	.0518
17	.0748	.0736	.0725	.0713	.0701	.0689	.0677	.0665	.0653	.0640
18	.0835	.0826	.0817	.0808	.0798	.0789	.0778	.0768	.0758	.0747
19	.0884	.0879	.0873	.0868	.0861	.0855	.0848	.0841	.0834	.0826
20	.0888	.0887	.0886	.0885	.0883	.0881	.0878	.0875	.0871	.0867
21	.0850	.0854	.0857	.0860	.0862	.0864	.0865	.0866	.0867	.0867
22	.0777	.0784	.0791	.0797	.0803	.0809	.0814	.0819	.0824	.0828
23	.0679	.0688	.0698	.0707	.0716	.0724	.0733	.0741	.0748	.0756
24	.0568	.0579	.0590	.0601	.0611	.0622	.0632	.0642	.0652	.0661
25	.0457	.0468	.0479	.0490	.0501	.0512	.0523	.0534	.0545	.0555

Table 6 Cumulative Poisson Probabilities

					MEAN ARRIVAL RATE λ					
	0.1	0.2	0.3	0.4	0.5	0.6	0.7	0.8	0.9	1.0
0	.9048	.8187	.7408	.6703	.6065	.5488	.4966	.4493	.4066	.3679
1	.9953	.9825	.9631	.9384	.9098	.8781	.8442	.8088	.7725	.7358
2	.9998	.9989	.9964	.9921	.9856	.9769	.9659	.9526	.9371	.9197
3	1.0000	.9999	.9997	.9992	.9982	.9966	.9942	.9909	.9865	.9810
4	1.0000	1.0000	1.0000	.9999	.9998	.9996	.9992	.9986	.9977	.9963
5	1.0000	1.0000	1.0000	1.0000	1.0000	1.0000	.9999	.9998	.9997	.9994
6	1.0000	1.0000	1.0000	1.0000	1.0000	1.0000	1.0000	1.0000	1.0000	.9999
7	1.0000	1.0000	1.0000	1.0000	1.0000	1.0000	1.0000	1.0000	1.0000	1.0000

					MEAN ARRIVAL RATE λ					
	1.1	1.2	1.3	1.4	1.5	1.6	1.7	1.8	1.9	2.0
0	.3329	.3012	.2725	.2466	.2231	.2019	.1827	.1653	.1496	.1353
1	.6990	.6626	.6268	.5918	.5578	.5249	.4932	.4628	.4337	.4060
2	.9004	.8795	.8571	.8335	.8088	.7834	.7572	.7306	.7037	.6767
3	.9743	.9662	.9569	.9463	.9344	.9212	.9068	.8913	.8747	.8571
4	.9946	.9923	.9893	.9857	.9814	.9763	.9704	.9636	.9559	.9473
5	.9990	.9985	.9978	.9968	.9955	.9940	.9920	.9896	.9868	.9834
6	.9999	.9997	.9996	.9994	.9991	.9987	.9981	.9974	.9966	.9955
7	1.0000	1.0000	.9999	.9999	.9998	.9997	.9996	.9994	.9992	.9989
8	1.0000	1.0000	1.0000	1.0000	1.0000	1.0000	.9999	.9999	.9998	.9998
9	1.0000	1.0000	1.0000	1.0000	1.0000	1.0000	1.0000	1.0000	1.0000	1.0000

					MEAN ARRIVAL RATE λ					
	2.1	2.2	2.3	2.4	2.5	2.6	2.7	2.8	2.9	3.0
0	.1225	.1108	.1003	.0907	.0821	.0743	.0672	.0608	.0550	.0498
1	.3796	.3546	.3309	.3084	.2873	.2674	.2487	.2311	.2146	.1991
2	.6496	.6227	.5960	.5697	.5438	.5184	.4936	.4695	.4460	.4232
3	.8386	.8194	.7993	.7787	.7576	.7360	.7141	.6919	.6696	.6472
4	.9379	.9275	.9162	.9041	.8912	.8774	.8629	.8477	.8318	.8153
5	.9796	.9751	.9700	.9643	.9580	.9510	.9433	.9349	.9258	.9161
6	.9941	.9925	.9906	.9884	.9858	.9828	.9794	.9756	.9713	.9665
7	.9985	.9980	.9974	.9967	.9958	.9947	.9934	.9919	.9901	.9881
8	.9997	.9995	.9994	.9991	.9989	.9985	.9981	.9976	.9969	.9962
9	.9999	.9999	.9999	.9998	.9997	.9996	.9995	.9993	.9991	.9989
10	1.0000	1.0000	1.0000	1.0000	.9999	.9999	.9999	.9998	.9998	.9997
11	1.0000	1.0000	1.0000	1.0000	1.0000	1.0000	1.0000	1.0000	.9999	.9999
12	1.0000	1.0000	1.0000	1.0000	1.0000	1.0000	1.0000	1.0000	1.0000	1.0000

					MEAN ARRIVAL RATE λ					
	3.1	3.2	3.3	3.4	3.5	3.6	3.7	3.8	3.9	4.0
0	.0450	.0408	.0369	.0334	.0302	.0273	.0247	.0224	.0202	.0183
1	.1847	.1712	.1586	.1468	.1359	.1257	.1162	.1074	.0992	.0916
2	.4012	.3799	.3594	.3397	.3208	.3027	.2854	.2689	.2531	.2381
3	.6248	.6025	.5803	.5584	.5366	.5152	.4942	.4735	.4532	.4335
4	.7982	.7806	.7626	.7442	.7254	.7064	.6872	.6678	.6484	.6288
5	.9057	.8946	.8829	.8705	.8576	.8441	.8301	.8156	.8006	.7851
6	.9612	.9554	.9490	.9421	.9347	.9267	.9182	.9091	.8995	.8893
7	.9858	.9832	.9802	.9769	.9733	.9692	.9648	.9599	.9546	.9489
8	.9953	.9943	.9931	.9917	.9901	.9883	.9863	.9840	.9815	.9786

(continued)

Table 6   Cumulative Poisson Probabilities (*Continued*)

					MEAN ARRIVAL RATE λ					
	3.1	3.2	3.3	3.4	3.5	3.6	3.7	3.8	3.9	4.0
9	.9986	.9982	.9978	.9973	.9967	.9960	.9952	.9942	.9931	.9919
10	.9996	.9995	.9994	.9992	.9990	.9987	.9984	.9981	.9977	.9972
11	.9999	.9999	.9998	.9998	.9997	.9996	.9995	.9994	.9993	.9991
12	1.0000	1.0000	1.0000	.9999	.9999	.9999	.9999	.9998	.9998	.9997
13	1.0000	1.0000	1.0000	1.0000	1.0000	1.0000	1.0000	1.0000	.9999	.9999
14	1.0000	1.0000	1.0000	1.0000	1.0000	1.0000	1.0000	1.0000	1.0000	1.0000

					MEAN ARRIVAL RATE λ					
	4.1	4.2	4.3	4.4	4.5	4.6	4.7	4.8	4.9	5.0
0	.0166	.0150	.0136	.0123	.0111	.0101	.0091	.0082	.0074	.0067
1	.0845	.0780	.0719	.0663	.0611	.0563	.0518	.0477	.0439	.0404
2	.2238	.2102	.1974	.1851	.1736	.1626	.1523	.1425	.1333	.1247
3	.4142	.3954	.3772	.3594	.3423	.3257	.3097	.2942	.2793	.2650
4	.6093	.5898	.5704	.5512	.5321	.5132	.4946	.4763	.4582	.4405
5	.7693	.7531	.7367	.7199	.7029	.6858	.6684	.6510	.6335	.6160
6	.8786	.8675	.8558	.8436	.8311	.8180	.8046	.7908	.7767	.7622
7	.9427	.9361	.9290	.9214	.9134	.9049	.8960	.8867	.8769	.8666
8	.9755	.9721	.9683	.9642	.9597	.9549	.9497	.9442	.9382	.9319
9	.9905	.9889	.9871	.9851	.9829	.9805	.9778	.9749	.9717	.9682
10	.9966	.9959	.9952	.9943	.9933	.9922	.9910	.9896	.9880	.9863
11	.9989	.9986	.9983	.9980	.9976	.9971	.9966	.9960	.9953	.9945
12	.9997	.9996	.9995	.9993	.9992	.9990	.9988	.9986	.9983	.9980
13	.9999	.9999	.9998	.9998	.9997	.9997	.9996	.9995	.9994	.9993
14	1.0000	1.0000	1.0000	.9999	.9999	.9999	.9999	.9999	.9998	.9998

					MEAN ARRIVAL RATE λ					
	5.1	5.2	5.3	5.4	5.5	5.6	5.7	5.8	5.9	6.0
0	.0061	.0055	.0050	.0045	.0041	.0037	.0033	.0030	.0027	.0025
1	.0372	.0342	.0314	.0289	.0266	.0244	.0224	.0206	.0189	.0174
2	.1165	.1088	.1016	.0948	.0884	.0824	.0768	.0715	.0666	.0620
3	.2513	.2381	.2254	.2133	.2017	.1906	.1800	.1700	.1604	.1512
4	.4231	.4061	.3895	.3733	.3575	.3422	.3272	.3127	.2987	.2851
5	.5984	.5809	.5635	.5461	.5289	.5119	.4950	.4783	.4619	.4457
6	.7474	.7324	.7171	.7017	.6860	.6703	.6544	.6384	.6224	.6063
7	.8560	.8449	.8335	.8217	.8095	.7970	.7841	.7710	.7576	.7440
8	.9252	.9181	.9106	.9027	.8944	.8857	.8766	.8672	.8574	.8472
9	.9644	.9603	.9559	.9512	.9462	.9409	.9352	.9292	.9228	.9161
10	.9844	.9823	.9800	.9775	.9747	.9718	.9686	.9651	.9614	.9574
11	.9937	.9927	.9916	.9904	.9890	.9875	.9859	.9841	.9821	.9799
12	.9976	.9972	.9967	.9962	.9955	.9949	.9941	.9932	.9922	.9912
13	.9992	.9990	.9988	.9986	.9983	.9980	.9977	.9973	.9969	.9964
14	.9997	.9997	.9996	.9995	.9994	.9993	.9991	.9990	.9988	.9986

					MEAN ARRIVAL RATE λ					
	6.1	6.2	6.3	6.4	6.5	6.6	6.7	6.8	6.9	7.0
0	.0022	.0020	.0018	.0017	.0015	.0014	.0012	.0011	.0010	.0009
1	.0159	.0146	.0134	.0123	.0113	.0103	.0095	.0087	.0080	.0073
2	.0577	.0536	.0498	.0463	.0430	.0400	.0371	.0344	.0320	.0296
3	.1425	.1342	.1264	.1189	.1118	.1052	.0988	.0928	.0871	.0818

Table 6 Cumulative Poisson Probabilities (*Continued*)

	Mean Arrival Rate λ									
	6.1	6.2	6.3	6.4	6.5	6.6	6.7	6.8	6.9	7.0
4	.2719	.2592	.2469	.2351	.2237	.2127	.2022	.1920	.1823	.1730
5	.4298	.4141	.3988	.3837	.3690	.3547	.3406	.3270	.3137	.3007
6	.5902	.5742	.5582	.5423	.5265	.5108	.4953	.4799	.4647	.4497
7	.7301	.7160	.7017	.6873	.6728	.6581	.6433	.6285	.6136	.5987
8	.8367	.8259	.8148	.8033	.7916	.7796	.7673	.7548	.7420	.7291
9	.9090	.9016	.8939	.8858	.8774	.8686	.8596	.8502	.8405	.8305
10	.9531	.9486	.9437	.9386	.9332	.9274	.9214	.9151	.9084	.9015
11	.9776	.9750	.9723	.9693	.9661	.9627	.9591	.9552	.9510	.9467
12	.9900	.9887	.9873	.9857	.9840	.9821	.9801	.9779	.9755	.9730
13	.9958	.9952	.9945	.9937	.9929	.9920	.9909	.9898	.9885	.9872
14	.9984	.9981	.9978	.9974	.9970	.9966	.9961	.9956	.9950	.9943

	Mean Arrival Rate λ									
	7.1	7.2	7.3	7.4	7.5	7.6	7.7	7.8	7.9	8.0
0	.0008	.0007	.0007	.0006	.0006	.0005	.0005	.0004	.0004	.0003
1	.0067	.0061	.0056	.0051	.0047	.0043	.0039	.0036	.0033	.0030
2	.0275	.0255	.0236	.0219	.0203	.0188	.0174	.0161	.0149	.0138
3	.0767	.0719	.0674	.0632	.0591	.0554	.0518	.0485	.0453	.0424
4	.1641	.1555	.1473	.1395	.1321	.1249	.1181	.1117	.1055	.0996
5	.2881	.2759	.2640	.2526	.2414	.2307	.2203	.2103	.2006	.1912
6	.4349	.4204	.4060	.3920	.3782	.3646	.3514	.3384	.3257	.3134
7	.5838	.5689	.5541	.5393	.5246	.5100	.4956	.4812	.4670	.4530
8	.7160	.7027	.6892	.6757	.6620	.6482	.6343	.6204	.6065	.5925
9	.8202	.8096	.7988	.7877	.7764	.7649	.7531	.7411	.7290	.7166
10	.8942	.8867	.8788	.8707	.8622	.8535	.8445	.8352	.8257	.8159
11	.9420	.9371	.9319	.9265	.9208	.9148	.9085	.9020	.8952	.8881
12	.9703	.9673	.9642	.9609	.9573	.9536	.9496	.9454	.9409	.9362
13	.9857	.9841	.9824	.9805	.9784	.9762	.9739	.9714	.9687	.9658
14	.9935	.9927	.9918	.9908	.9897	.9886	.9873	.9859	.9844	.9827
15	.9972	.9969	.9964	.9959	.9954	.9948	.9941	.9934	.9926	.9918
16	.9989	.9987	.9985	.9983	.9980	.9978	.9974	.9971	.9967	.9963
17	.9996	.9995	.9994	.9993	.9992	.9991	.9989	.9988	.9986	.9984
18	.9998	.9998	.9998	.9997	.9997	.9996	.9996	.9995	.9994	.9993
19	.9999	.9999	.9999	.9999	.9999	.9999	.9998	.9998	.9998	.9997
20	1.0000	1.0000	1.0000	1.0000	1.0000	1.0000	.9999	.9999	.9999	.9999

	Mean Arrival Rate λ									
	8.1	8.2	8.3	8.4	8.5	8.6	8.7	8.8	8.9	9.0
0	.0003	.0003	.0002	.0002	.0002	.0002	.0002	.0002	.0001	.0001
1	.0028	.0025	.0023	.0021	.0019	.0018	.0016	.0015	.0014	.0012
2	.0127	.0118	.0109	.0100	.0093	.0086	.0079	.0073	.0068	.0062
3	.0396	.0370	.0346	.0323	.0301	.0281	.0262	.0244	.0228	.0212
4	.0940	.0887	.0837	.0789	.0744	.0701	.0660	.0621	.0584	.0550
5	.1822	.1736	.1653	.1573	.1496	.1422	.1352	.1284	.1219	.1157
6	.3013	.2896	.2781	.2670	.2562	.2457	.2355	.2256	.2160	.2068
7	.4391	.4254	.4119	.3987	.3856	.3728	.3602	.3478	.3357	.3239
8	.5786	.5647	.5507	.5369	.5231	.5094	.4958	.4823	.4689	.4557
9	.7041	.6915	.6788	.6659	.6530	.6400	.6269	.6137	.6006	.5874
10	.8058	.7955	.7850	.7743	.7634	.7522	.7409	.7294	.7178	.7060

(*continued*)

Table 6   Cumulative Poisson Probabilities (*Continued*)

	MEAN ARRIVAL RATE λ									
	8.1	8.2	8.3	8.4	8.5	8.6	8.7	8.8	8.9	9.0
11	.8807	.8731	.8652	.8571	.8487	.8400	.8311	.8220	.8126	.8030
12	.9313	.9261	.9207	.9150	.9091	.9029	.8965	.8898	.8829	.8758
13	.9628	.9595	.9561	.9524	.9486	.9445	.9403	.9358	.9311	.9261
14	.9810	.9791	.9771	.9749	.9726	.9701	.9675	.9647	.9617	.9585
15	.9908	.9898	.9887	.9875	.9862	.9848	.9832	.9816	.9798	.9780
16	.9958	.9953	.9947	.9941	.9934	.9926	.9918	.9909	.9899	.9889
17	.9982	.9979	.9977	.9973	.9970	.9966	.9962	.9957	.9952	.9947
18	.9992	.9991	.9990	.9989	.9987	.9985	.9983	.9981	.9978	.9976
19	.9997	.9997	.9996	.9995	.9995	.9994	.9993	.9992	.9991	.9989
20	.9999	.9999	.9998	.9998	.9998	.9998	.9997	.9997	.9996	.9996

	MEAN ARRIVAL RATE λ									
	9.1	9.2	9.3	9.4	9.5	9.6	9.7	9.8	9.9	10.0
0	.0001	.0001	.0001	.0001	.0001	.0001	.0001	.0001	.0001	.0000
1	.0011	.0010	.0009	.0009	.0008	.0007	.0007	.0006	.0005	.0005
2	.0058	.0053	.0049	.0045	.0042	.0038	.0035	.0033	.0030	.0028
3	.0198	.0184	.0172	.0160	.0149	.0138	.0129	.0120	.0111	.0103
4	.0517	.0486	.0456	.0429	.0403	.0378	.0355	.0333	.0312	.0293
5	.1098	.1041	.0986	.0935	.0885	.0838	.0793	.0750	.0710	.0671
6	.1978	.1892	.1808	.1727	.1649	.1574	.1502	.1433	.1366	.1301
7	.3123	.3010	.2900	.2792	.2687	.2584	.2485	.2388	.2294	.2202
8	.4426	.4296	.4168	.4042	.3918	.3796	.3676	.3558	.3442	.3328
9	.5742	.5611	.5479	.5349	.5218	.5089	.4960	.4832	.4705	.4579
10	.6941	.6820	.6699	.6576	.6453	.6329	.6205	.6080	.5955	.5830
11	.7932	.7832	.7730	.7626	.7520	.7412	.7303	.7193	.7081	.6968
12	.8684	.8607	.8529	.8448	.8364	.8279	.8191	.8101	.8009	.7916
13	.9210	.9156	.9100	.9042	.8981	.8919	.8853	.8786	.8716	.8645
14	.9552	.9517	.9480	.9441	.9400	.9357	.9312	.9265	.9216	.9165
15	.9760	.9738	.9715	.9691	.9665	.9638	.9609	.9579	.9546	.9513
16	.9878	.9865	.9852	.9838	.9823	.9806	.9789	.9770	.9751	.9730
17	.9941	.9934	.9927	.9919	.9911	.9902	.9892	.9881	.9870	.9857
18	.9973	.9969	.9966	.9962	.9957	.9952	.9947	.9941	.9935	.9928
19	.9988	.9986	.9985	.9983	.9980	.9978	.9975	.9972	.9969	.9965
20	.9995	.9994	.9993	.9992	.9991	.9990	.9989	.9987	.9986	.9984

	MEAN ARRIVAL RATE λ									
	10.1	10.2	10.3	10.4	10.5	10.6	10.7	10.8	10.9	11.0
0	.0000	.0000	.0000	.0000	.0000	.0000	.0000	.0000	.0000	.0000
1	.0005	.0004	.0004	.0003	.0003	.0003	.0003	.0002	.0002	.0002
2	.0026	.0023	.0022	.0020	.0018	.0017	.0016	.0014	.0013	.0012
3	.0096	.0089	.0083	.0077	.0071	.0066	.0062	.0057	.0053	.0049
4	.0274	.0257	.0241	.0225	.0211	.0197	.0185	.0173	.0162	.0151
5	.0634	.0599	.0566	.0534	.0504	.0475	.0448	.0423	.0398	.0375
6	.1240	.1180	.1123	.1069	.1016	.0966	.0918	.0872	.0828	.0786
7	.2113	.2027	.1944	.1863	.1785	.1710	.1636	.1566	.1498	.1432
8	.3217	.3108	.3001	.2896	.2794	.2694	.2597	.2502	.2410	.2320
9	.4455	.4332	.4210	.4090	.3971	.3854	.3739	.3626	.3515	.3405
10	.5705	.5580	.5456	.5331	.5207	.5084	.4961	.4840	.4719	.4599
11	.6853	.6738	.6622	.6505	.6387	.6269	.6150	.6031	.5912	.5793

Table 6 Cumulative Poisson Probabilities (*Continued*)

	MEAN ARRIVAL RATE λ									
	10.1	10.2	10.3	10.4	10.5	10.6	10.7	10.8	10.9	11.0
12	.7820	.7722	.7623	.7522	.7420	.7316	.7210	.7104	.6996	.6887
13	.8571	.8494	.8416	.8336	.8253	.8169	.8083	.7995	.7905	.7813
14	.9112	.9057	.9	.8940	.8879	.8815	.8750	.8682	.8612	.8540
15	.9477	.9440	.9400	.9359	.9317	.9272	.9225	.9177	.9126	.9074
16	.9707	.9684	.9658	.9632	.9604	.9574	.9543	.9511	.9477	.9441
17	.9844	.9830	.9815	.9799	.9781	.9763	.9744	.9723	.9701	.9678
18	.9921	.9913	.9904	.9895	.9885	.9874	.9863	.9850	.9837	.9823
19	.9962	.9957	.9953	.9948	.9942	.9936	.9930	.9923	.9915	.9907
20	.9982	.9980	.9978	.9975	.9972	.9969	.9966	.9962	.9958	.9953

	MEAN ARRIVAL RATE λ									
	11.1	11.2	11.3	11.4	11.5	11.6	11.7	11.8	11.9	12.0
0	.0000	.0000	.0000	.0000	.0000	.0000	.0000	.0000	.0000	.0000
1	.0002	.0002	.0002	.0001	.0001	.0001	.0001	.0001	.0001	.0001
2	.0011	.0010	.0009	.0009	.0008	.0007	.0007	.0006	.0006	.0005
3	.0046	.0042	.0039	.0036	.0034	.0031	.0029	.0027	.0025	.0023
4	.0141	.0132	.0123	.0115	.0107	.0100	.0094	.0087	.0081	.0076
5	.0353	.0333	.0313	.0295	.0277	.0261	.0245	.0230	.0217	.0203
6	.0746	.0708	.0671	.0636	.0603	.0571	.0541	.0512	.0484	.0458
7	.1369	.1307	.1249	.1192	.1137	.1085	.1035	.0986	.0940	.0895
8	.2232	.2147	.2064	.1984	.1906	.1830	.1757	.1686	.1617	.1550
9	.3298	.3192	.3089	.2987	.2888	.2791	.2696	.2603	.2512	.2424
10	.4480	.4362	.4246	.4131	.4017	.3905	.3794	.3685	.3578	.3472
11	.5673	.5554	.5435	.5316	.5198	.5080	.4963	.4847	.4731	.4616
12	.6777	.6666	.6555	.6442	.6329	.6216	.6102	.5988	.5874	.5760
13	.7719	.7624	.7528	.7430	.7330	.7230	.7128	.7025	.6920	.6815
14	.8467	.8391	.8313	.8234	.8153	.8069	.7985	.7898	.7810	.7720
15	.9020	.8963	.8905	.8845	.8783	.8719	.8653	.8585	.8516	.8444
16	.9403	.9364	.9323	.9280	.9236	.9190	.9142	.9092	.9040	.8987
17	.9654	.9628	.9601	.9572	.9542	.9511	.9478	.9444	.9408	.9370
18	.9808	.9792	.9775	.9757	.9738	.9718	.9697	.9674	.9651	.9626
19	.9898	.9889	.9879	.9868	.9857	.9845	.9832	.9818	.9803	.9787
20	.9948	.9943	.9938	.9932	.9925	.9918	.9910	.9902	.9893	.9884

	MEAN ARRIVAL RATE λ									
	12.1	12.2	12.3	12.4	12.5	12.6	12.7	12.8	12.9	13.0
5	.0191	.0179	.0168	.0158	.0148	.0139	.0130	.0122	.0115	.0107
6	.0433	.0410	.0387	.0366	.0346	.0326	.0308	.0291	.0274	.0259
7	.0852	.0811	.0772	.0734	.0698	.0664	.0631	.0599	.0569	.0540
8	.1486	.1424	.1363	.1305	.1249	.1195	.1143	.1093	.1044	.0998
9	.2338	.2254	.2172	.2092	.2014	.1939	.1866	.1794	.1725	.1658
10	.3368	.3266	.3166	.3067	.2971	.2876	.2783	.2693	.2604	.2517
11	.4502	.4389	.4278	.4167	.4058	.3950	.3843	.3738	.3634	.3532
12	.5645	.5531	.5417	.5303	.5190	.5077	.4964	.4853	.4741	.4631
13	.6709	.6603	.6495	.6387	.6278	.6169	.6060	.5950	.5840	.5730
14	.7629	.7536	.7442	.7347	.7250	.7153	.7054	.6954	.6853	.6751
15	.8371	.8296	.8219	.8140	.8060	.7978	.7895	.7810	.7724	.7636
16	.8932	.8875	.8816	.8755	.8693	.8629	.8563	.8495	.8426	.8355
17	.9331	.9290	.9248	.9204	.9158	.9111	.9062	.9011	.8959	.8905
18	.9600	.9572	.9543	.9513	.9481	.9448	.9414	.9378	.9341	.9302

(*continued*)

Table 6   Cumulative Poisson Probabilities (*Continued*)

					Mean Arrival Rate λ					
	12.1	12.2	12.3	12.4	12.5	12.6	12.7	12.8	12.9	13.0
19	.9771	.9753	.9734	.9715	.9694	.9672	.9649	.9625	.9600	.9573
20	.9874	.9863	.9852	.9840	.9827	.9813	.9799	.9783	.9767	.9750
21	.9934	.9927	.9921	.9914	.9906	.9898	.9889	.9880	.9870	.9859
22	.9966	.9963	.9959	.9955	.9951	.9946	.9941	.9936	.9930	.9924
23	.9984	.9982	.9980	.9978	.9975	.9973	.9970	.9967	.9964	.9960

					Mean Arrival Rate λ					
	13.1	13.2	13.3	13.4	13.5	13.6	13.7	13.8	13.9	14.0
5	.0101	.0094	.0088	.0083	.0077	.0072	.0068	.0063	.0059	.0055
6	.0244	.0230	.0217	.0204	.0193	.0181	.0171	.0161	.0151	.0142
7	.0513	.0487	.0461	.0438	.0415	.0393	.0372	.0353	.0334	.0316
8	.0953	.0910	.0868	.0828	.0790	.0753	.0718	.0684	.0652	.0621
9	.1593	.1530	.1469	.1410	.1353	.1297	.1244	.1192	.1142	.1094
10	.2432	.2349	.2268	.2189	.2112	.2037	.1964	.1893	.1824	.1757
11	.3431	.3332	.3234	.3139	.3045	.2952	.2862	.2773	.2686	.2600
12	.4522	.4413	.4305	.4199	.4093	.3989	.3886	.3784	.3684	.3585
13	.5621	.5511	.5401	.5292	.5182	.5074	.4966	.4858	.4751	.4644
14	.6649	.6546	.6442	.6338	.6233	.6128	.6022	.5916	.5810	.5704
15	.7547	.7456	.7365	.7272	.7178	.7083	.6987	.6890	.6792	.6694
16	.8282	.8208	.8132	.8054	.7975	.7895	.7813	.7730	.7645	.7559
17	.8849	.8791	.8732	.8671	.8609	.8545	.8479	.8411	.8343	.8272
18	.9261	.9219	.9176	.9130	.9084	.9035	.8986	.8934	.8881	.8826
19	.9546	.9516	.9486	.9454	.9421	.9387	.9351	.9314	.9275	.9235
20	.9732	.9713	.9692	.9671	.9649	.9626	.9601	.9576	.9549	.9521
21	.9848	.9836	.9823	.9810	.9796	.9780	.9765	.9748	.9730	.9712
22	.9917	.9910	.9902	.9894	.9885	.9876	.9866	.9856	.9845	.9833
23	.9956	.9952	.9948	.9943	.9938	.9933	.9927	.9921	.9914	.9907

					Mean Arrival Rate λ					
	14.1	14.2	14.3	14.4	14.5	14.6	14.7	14.8	14.9	15.0
6	.0134	.0126	.0118	.0111	.0105	.0098	.0092	.0087	.0081	.0076
7	.0299	.0283	.0268	.0253	.0239	.0226	.0214	.0202	.0191	.0180
8	.0591	.0562	.0535	.0509	.0484	.0460	.0437	.0415	.0394	.0374
9	.1047	.1003	.0959	.0918	.0878	.0839	.0802	.0766	.0732	.0699
10	.1691	.1628	.1566	.1507	.1449	.1392	.1338	.1285	.1234	.1185
11	.2517	.2435	.2355	.2277	.2201	.2127	.2054	.1984	.1915	.1848
12	.3487	.3391	.3296	.3203	.3111	.3021	.2932	.2845	.2760	.2676
13	.4539	.4434	.4330	.4227	.4125	.4024	.3925	.3826	.3728	.3632
14	.5598	.5492	.5387	.5281	.5176	.5071	.4967	.4863	.4759	.4657
15	.6594	.6494	.6394	.6293	.6192	.6090	.5988	.5886	.5783	.5681
16	.7472	.7384	.7294	.7204	.7112	.7020	.6926	.6832	.6737	.6641
17	.8200	.8126	.8051	.7975	.7897	.7818	.7737	.7656	.7573	.7489
18	.8770	.8712	.8653	.8592	.8530	.8466	.8400	.8333	.8265	.8195
19	.9193	.9150	.9106	.9060	.9012	.8963	.8913	.8861	.8807	.8752
20	.9492	.9461	.9430	.9396	.9362	.9326	.9289	.9251	.9211	.9170
21	.9692	.9671	.9650	.9627	.9604	.9579	.9553	.9526	.9498	.9469
22	.9820	.9807	.9793	.9779	.9763	.9747	.9729	.9711	.9692	.9673
23	.9899	.9891	.9882	.9873	.9863	.9853	.9842	.9831	.9818	.9805
24	.9945	.9941	.9935	.9930	.9924	.9918	.9911	.9904	.9896	.9888
25	.9971	.9969	.9966	.9963	.9959	.9956	.9952	.9947	.9943	.9938

Table 6 Cumulative Poisson Probabilities (*Continued*)

	MEAN ARRIVAL RATE λ									
	15.1	15.2	15.3	15.4	15.5	15.6	15.7	15.8	15.9	16.0
7	.0170	.0160	.0151	.0143	.0135	.0127	.0120	.0113	.0106	.0100
8	.0355	.0337	.0320	.0304	.0288	.0273	.0259	.0245	.0232	.0220
9	.0667	.0636	.0607	.0579	.0552	.0526	.0501	.0478	.0455	.0433
10	.1137	.1091	.1046	.1003	.0961	.0921	.0882	.0845	.0809	.0774
11	.1782	.1718	.1657	.1596	.1538	.1481	.1426	.1372	.1320	.1270
12	.2594	.2514	.2435	.2358	.2283	.2209	.2137	.2067	.1998	.1931
13	.3537	.3444	.3351	.3260	.3171	.3083	.2996	.2911	.2827	.2745
14	.4554	.4453	.4353	.4253	.4154	.4056	.3959	.3864	.3769	.3675
15	.5578	.5476	.5374	.5272	.5170	.5069	.4968	.4867	.4767	.4667
16	.6545	.6448	.6351	.6253	.6154	.6056	.5957	.5858	.5759	.5660
17	.7403	.7317	.7230	.7141	.7052	.6962	.6871	.6779	.6687	.6593
18	.8123	.8051	.7977	.7901	.7825	.7747	.7668	.7587	.7506	.7423
19	.8696	.8638	.8578	.8517	.8455	.8391	.8326	.8260	.8192	.8122
20	.9128	.9084	.9039	.8992	.8944	.8894	.8843	.8791	.8737	.8682
21	.9438	.9407	.9374	.9340	.9304	.9268	.9230	.9190	.9150	.9108
22	.9652	.9630	.9607	.9583	.9558	.9532	.9505	.9477	.9448	.9418
23	.9792	.9777	.9762	.9746	.9730	.9712	.9694	.9674	.9654	.9633
24	.9880	.9871	.9861	.9851	.9840	.9829	.9817	.9804	.9791	.9777
25	.9933	.9928	.9922	.9915	.9909	.9902	.9894	.9886	.9878	.9869

	MEAN ARRIVAL RATE λ									
	16.1	16.2	16.3	16.4	16.5	16.6	16.7	16.8	16.9	17.0
8	.0208	.0197	.0186	.0176	.0167	.0158	.0149	.0141	.0133	.0126
9	.0412	.0392	.0373	.0355	.0337	.0321	.0305	.0290	.0275	.0261
10	.0740	.0708	.0677	.0647	.0619	.0591	.0565	.0539	.0515	.0491
11	.1221	.1174	.1128	.1084	.1041	.0999	.0959	.0920	.0883	.0847
12	.1866	.1802	.1740	.1680	.1621	.1564	.1508	.1454	.1401	.1350
13	.2664	.2585	.2508	.2432	.2357	.2285	.2213	.2144	.2075	.2009
14	.3583	.3492	.3402	.3313	.3225	.3139	.3054	.2971	.2889	.2808
15	.4569	.4470	.4373	.4276	.4180	.4085	.3991	.3898	.3806	.3715
16	.5560	.5461	.5362	.5263	.5165	.5067	.4969	.4871	.4774	.4677
17	.6500	.6406	.6311	.6216	.6120	.6025	.5929	.5833	.5737	.5640
18	.7340	.7255	.7170	.7084	.6996	.6908	.6820	.6730	.6640	.6550
19	.8052	.7980	.7907	.7833	.7757	.7681	.7603	.7524	.7444	.7363
20	.8625	.8567	.8508	.8447	.8385	.8321	.8257	.8191	.8123	.8055
21	.9064	.9020	.8974	.8927	.8878	.8828	.8777	.8724	.8670	.8615
22	.9386	.9353	.9319	.9284	.9248	.9210	.9171	.9131	.9090	.9047
23	.9611	.9588	.9564	.9539	.9513	.9486	.9458	.9429	.9398	.9367
24	.9762	.9747	.9730	.9713	.9696	.9677	.9657	.9637	.9616	.9594
25	.9859	.9849	.9839	.9828	.9816	.9804	.9791	.9777	.9763	.9748
26	.9920	.9913	.9907	.9900	.9892	.9884	.9876	.9867	.9858	.9848

	MEAN ARRIVAL RATE λ									
	17.1	17.2	17.3	17.4	17.5	17.6	17.7	17.8	17.9	18.0
8	.0119	.0112	.0106	.0100	.0095	.0089	.0084	.0079	.0075	.0071
9	.0248	.0235	.0223	.0212	.0201	.0191	.0181	.0171	.0162	.0154
10	.0469	.0447	.0426	.0406	.0387	.0369	.0352	.0335	.0319	.0304
11	.0812	.0778	.0746	.0714	.0684	.0655	.0627	.0600	.0574	.0549
12	.1301	.1252	.1206	.1160	.1116	.1074	.1033	.0993	.0954	.0917

(*continued*)

Table 6 Cumulative Poisson Probabilities (*Continued*)

	MEAN ARRIVAL RATE λ									
	17.1	17.2	17.3	17.4	17.5	17.6	17.7	17.8	17.9	18.0
13	.1944	.1880	.1818	.1758	.1699	.1641	.1585	.1531	.1478	.1426
14	.2729	.2651	.2575	.2500	.2426	.2354	.2284	.2215	.2147	.2081
15	.3624	.3535	.3448	.3361	.3275	.3191	.3108	.3026	.2946	.2867
16	.4581	.4486	.4391	.4297	.4204	.4112	.4020	.3929	.3839	.3751
17	.5544	.5448	.5352	.5256	.5160	.5065	.4969	.4875	.4780	.4686
18	.6458	.6367	.6275	.6182	.6089	.5996	.5903	.5810	.5716	.5622
19	.7281	.7199	.7115	.7031	.6945	.6859	.6773	.6685	.6598	.6509
20	.7985	.7914	.7842	.7769	.7694	.7619	.7542	.7465	.7387	.7307
21	.8558	.8500	.8441	.8380	.8319	.8255	.8191	.8126	.8059	.7991
22	.9003	.8958	.8912	.8864	.8815	.8765	.8713	.8660	.8606	.8551
23	.9334	.9301	.9266	.9230	.9193	.9154	.9115	.9074	.9032	.8989
24	.9570	.9546	.9521	.9495	.9468	.9440	.9411	.9381	.9350	.9317
25	.9732	.9715	.9698	.9680	.9661	.9641	.9621	.9599	.9577	.9554
26	.9838	.9827	.9816	.9804	.9791	.9778	.9764	.9749	.9734	.9718
27	.9905	.9898	.9891	.9883	.9875	.9866	.9857	.9848	.9837	.9827

	MEAN ARRIVAL RATE λ									
	18.1	18.2	18.3	18.4	18.5	18.6	18.7	18.8	18.9	19.0
9	.0146	.0138	.0131	.0124	.0117	.0111	.0105	.0099	.0094	.0089
10	.0289	.0275	.0262	.0249	.0237	.0225	.0214	.0203	.0193	.0183
11	.0525	.0502	.0479	.0458	.0438	.0418	.0399	.0381	.0363	.0347
12	.0881	.0846	.0812	.0779	.0748	.0717	.0688	.0659	.0632	.0606
13	.1376	.1327	.1279	.1233	.1189	.1145	.1103	.1062	.1022	.0984
14	.2016	.1953	.1891	.1830	.1771	.1714	.1658	.1603	.1550	.1497
15	.2789	.2712	.2637	.2563	.2490	.2419	.2349	.2281	.2214	.2148
16	.3663	.3576	.3490	.3405	.3321	.3239	.3157	.3077	.2998	.2920
17	.4593	.4500	.4408	.4317	.4226	.4136	.4047	.3958	.3870	.3784
18	.5529	.5435	.5342	.5249	.5156	.5063	.4970	.4878	.4786	.4695
19	.6420	.6331	.6241	.6151	.6061	.5970	.5879	.5788	.5697	.5606
20	.7227	.7146	.7064	.6981	.6898	.6814	.6729	.6644	.6558	.6472
21	.7922	.7852	.7781	.7709	.7636	.7561	.7486	.7410	.7333	.7255
22	.8494	.8436	.8377	.8317	.8256	.8193	.8129	.8065	.7998	.7931
23	.8944	.8899	.8852	.8804	.8755	.8704	.8652	.8600	.8545	.8490
24	.9284	.9249	.9214	.9177	.9139	.9100	.9060	.9019	.8976	.8933
25	.9530	.9505	.9479	.9452	.9424	.9395	.9365	.9334	.9302	.9269
26	.9701	.9683	.9665	.9646	.9626	.9606	.9584	.9562	.9539	.9514
27	.9816	.9804	.9792	.9779	.9765	.9751	.9736	.9720	.9704	.9687

	MEAN ARRIVAL RATE λ									
	19.1	19.2	19.3	19.4	19.5	19.6	19.7	19.8	19.9	20.0
10	.0174	.0165	.0157	.0149	.0141	.0134	.0127	.0120	.0114	.0108
11	.0331	.0315	.0301	.0287	.0273	.0260	.0248	.0236	.0225	.0214
12	.0580	.0556	.0532	.0509	.0488	.0467	.0446	.0427	.0408	.0390
13	.0947	.0911	.0876	.0842	.0809	.0778	.0747	.0717	.0689	.0661
14	.1447	.1397	.1349	.1303	.1257	.1213	.1170	.1128	.1088	.1049
15	.2084	.2021	.1959	.1899	.1840	.1782	.1726	.1671	.1617	.1565
16	.2844	.2768	.2694	.2621	.2550	.2479	.2410	.2342	.2276	.2211
17	.3698	.3613	.3529	.3446	.3364	.3283	.3203	.3124	.3047	.2970
18	.4604	.4514	.4424	.4335	.4246	.4158	.4071	.3985	.3899	.3814

Table 6 Cumulative Poisson Probabilities (*Continued*)

	MEAN ARRIVAL RATE λ									
	19.1	19.2	19.3	19.4	19.5	19.6	19.7	19.8	19.9	20.0
19	.5515	.5424	.5333	.5242	.5151	.5061	.4971	.4881	.4792	.4703
20	.6385	.6298	.6210	.6122	.6034	.5946	.5857	.5769	.5680	.5591
21	.7176	.7097	.7016	.6935	.6854	.6772	.6689	.6605	.6521	.6437
22	.7863	.7794	.7724	.7653	.7580	.7507	.7433	.7358	.7283	.7206
23	.8434	.8376	.8317	.8257	.8196	.8134	.8071	.8007	.7941	.7875
24	.8888	.8842	.8795	.8746	.8697	.8646	.8594	.8541	.8487	.8432
25	.9235	.9199	.9163	.9126	.9087	.9048	.9007	.8965	.8922	.8878
26	.9489	.9463	.9437	.9409	.9380	.9350	.9319	.9288	.9255	.9221
27	.9670	.9651	.9632	.9612	.9591	.9570	.9547	.9524	.9500	.9475

	MEAN ARRIVAL RATE λ									
	20.1	20.2	20.3	20.4	20.5	20.6	20.7	20.8	20.9	21.0
10	.0102	.0097	.0092	.0087	.0082	.0078	.0074	.0070	.0066	.0063
11	.0204	.0194	.0184	.0175	.0167	.0158	.0150	.0143	.0136	.0129
12	.0373	.0356	.0340	.0325	.0310	.0296	.0283	.0270	.0257	.0245
13	.0635	.0609	.0584	.0560	.0537	.0515	.0493	.0473	.0453	.0434
14	.1010	.0973	.0938	.0903	.0869	.0836	.0805	.0774	.0744	.0716
15	.1514	.1464	.1416	.1369	.1323	.1278	.1234	.1192	.1151	.1111
16	.2147	.2084	.2023	.1963	.1904	.1847	.1790	.1735	.1682	.1629
17	.2895	.2821	.2748	.2676	.2605	.2536	.2467	.2400	.2334	.2270
18	.3730	.3647	.3565	.3484	.3403	.3324	.3246	.3168	.3092	.3017
19	.4614	.4526	.4438	.4351	.4265	.4179	.4094	.4009	.3926	.3843
20	.5502	.5413	.5325	.5236	.5148	.5059	.4972	.4884	.4797	.4710
21	.6352	.6267	.6181	.6096	.6010	.5923	.5837	.5750	.5664	.5577
22	.7129	.7051	.6972	.6893	.6813	.6732	.6651	.6569	.6487	.6405
23	.7808	.7739	.7670	.7600	.7528	.7456	.7384	.7310	.7235	.7160
24	.8376	.8319	.8260	.8201	.8140	.8078	.8016	.7952	.7887	.7822
25	.8833	.8787	.8739	.8691	.8641	.8591	.8539	.8486	.8432	.8377
26	.9186	.9150	.9114	.9076	.9037	.8997	.8955	.8913	.8870	.8826
27	.9449	.9423	.9395	.9366	.9337	.9306	.9275	.9242	.9209	.9175

	MEAN ARRIVAL RATE λ									
	21.1	21.2	21.3	21.4	21.5	21.6	21.7	21.8	21.9	22.0
11	.0123	.0116	.0110	.0105	.0099	.0094	.0090	.0085	.0080	.0076
12	.0234	.0223	.0213	.0203	.0193	.0184	.0175	.0167	.0159	.0151
13	.0415	.0397	.0380	.0364	.0348	.0333	.0318	.0304	.0291	.0278
14	.0688	.0661	.0635	.0610	.0586	.0563	.0540	.0518	.0497	.0477
15	.1072	.1034	.0997	.0962	.0927	.0893	.0861	.0829	.0799	.0769
16	.1578	.1528	.1479	.1432	.1385	.1340	.1296	.1253	.1211	.1170
17	.2206	.2144	.2083	.2023	.1965	.1907	.1851	.1796	.1743	.1690
18	.2943	.2870	.2798	.2727	.2657	.2588	.2521	.2454	.2389	.2325
19	.3760	.3679	.3599	.3519	.3440	.3362	.3285	.3209	.3134	.3060
20	.4623	.4537	.4452	.4367	.4282	.4198	.4115	.4032	.3950	.3869
21	.5490	.5403	.5317	.5230	.5144	.5058	.4972	.4887	.4801	.4716
22	.6322	.6238	.6155	.6071	.5987	.5902	.5818	.5733	.5648	.5564
23	.7084	.7008	.6930	.6853	.6774	.6695	.6616	.6536	.6455	.6374
24	.7755	.7687	.7619	.7550	.7480	.7409	.7337	.7264	.7191	.7117
25	.8321	.8264	.8206	.8146	.8086	.8025	.7963	.7900	.7836	.7771
26	.8780	.8734	.8686	.8638	.8588	.8537	.8486	.8433	.8379	.8324
27	.9139	.9103	.9065	.9027	.8988	.8947	.8906	.8863	.8820	.8775

Table 7a Upper Critical Values of Chi-Square Distribution with ν Degrees of Freedom

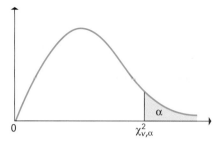

For selected probabilities α, the table shows the values $\chi^2_{\nu,\alpha}$ such that $P(\chi^2_\nu > \chi^2_{\nu,\alpha}) = \alpha$, where χ^2_ν is a chi-square random variable with ν degress of freedom. For example, the probability is .100 that a chi-square random variable with 10 degrees of freedom is greater than 15.987.

	PROBABILITY OF EXCEEDING THE CRITICAL VALUE				
ν	0.10	0.05	0.025	0.01	0.001
1	2.706	3.841	5.024	6.635	10.828
2	4.605	5.991	7.378	9.210	13.816
3	6.251	7.815	9.348	11.345	16.266
4	7.779	9.488	11.143	13.277	18.467
5	9.236	11.070	12.833	15.086	20.515
6	10.645	12.592	14.449	16.812	22.458
7	12.017	14.067	16.013	18.475	24.322
8	13.362	15.507	17.535	20.090	26.125
9	14.684	16.919	19.023	21.666	27.877
10	15.987	18.307	20.483	23.209	29.588
11	17.275	19.675	21.920	24.725	31.264
12	18.549	21.026	23.337	26.217	32.910
13	19.812	22.362	24.736	27.688	34.528
14	21.064	23.685	26.119	29.141	36.123
15	22.307	24.996	27.488	30.578	37.697
16	23.542	26.296	28.845	32.000	39.252
17	24.769	27.587	30.191	33.409	40.790
18	25.989	28.869	31.526	34.805	42.312
19	27.204	30.144	32.852	36.191	43.820
20	28.412	31.410	34.170	37.566	45.315
21	29.615	32.671	35.479	38.932	46.797
22	30.813	33.924	36.781	40.289	48.268
23	32.007	35.172	38.076	41.638	49.728
24	33.196	36.415	39.364	42.980	51.179
25	34.382	37.652	40.646	44.314	52.620
26	35.563	38.885	41.923	45.642	54.052
27	36.741	40.113	43.195	46.963	55.476
28	37.916	41.337	44.461	48.278	56.892
29	39.087	42.557	45.722	49.588	58.301
30	40.256	43.773	46.979	50.892	59.703
40	51.805	55.758	59.342	63.691	73.402
50	63.167	67.505	71.420	76.154	86.661
60	74.397	79.082	83.298	88.379	99.607
70	85.527	90.531	95.023	100.425	112.317
80	96.578	101.879	106.629	112.329	124.839
90	107.565	113.145	118.136	124.116	137.208
100	118.498	124.342	129.561	135.807	149.449

NIST/SEMATECH e-Handbook of Statistical Methods, http://www.itl.nist.gov/div898/handbook/, September 2011.

Table 7b   Lower Critical Values of Chi-Square Distribution with ν Degrees of Freedom

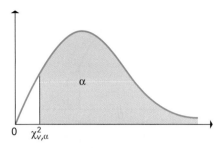

For selected probabilities α, the table shows the values $\chi^2_{\nu,\alpha}$ such that $P(\chi^2_\nu > \chi^2_{\nu,\alpha}) = \alpha$, where χ^2_ν is a chi-square random variable with ν degress of freedom. For example, the probability is 0.90 that a chi-square variable with 10 degrees of freedom is greater than 4.865.

	PROBABILITY OF EXCEEDING THE CRITICAL VALUE				
ν	0.90	0.95	0.975	0.99	0.999
1	.016	.004	.001	.000	.000
2	.211	.103	.051	.020	.002
3	.584	.352	.216	.115	.024
4	1.064	.711	.484	.297	.091
5	1.610	1.145	.831	.554	.210
6	2.204	1.635	1.237	.872	.381
7	2.833	2.167	1.690	1.239	.598
8	3.490	2.733	2.180	1.646	.857
9	4.168	3.325	2.700	2.088	1.152
10	4.865	3.940	3.247	2.558	1.479
11	5.578	4.575	3.816	3.053	1.834
12	6.304	5.226	4.404	3.571	2.214
13	7.042	5.892	5.009	4.107	2.617
14	7.790	6.571	5.629	4.660	3.041
15	8.547	7.261	6.262	5.229	3.483
16	9.312	7.962	6.908	5.812	3.942
17	10.085	8.672	7.564	6.408	4.416
18	10.865	9.390	8.231	7.015	4.905
19	11.651	10.117	8.907	7.633	5.407
20	12.443	10.851	9.591	8.260	5.921
21	13.240	11.591	10.283	8.897	6.447
22	14.041	12.338	10.982	9.542	6.983
23	14.848	13.091	11.689	10.196	7.529
24	15.659	13.848	12.401	10.856	8.085
25	16.473	14.611	13.120	11.524	8.649
26	17.292	15.379	13.844	12.198	9.222
27	18.114	16.151	14.573	12.879	9.803
28	18.939	16.928	15.308	13.565	10.391
29	19.768	17.708	16.047	14.256	10.986
30	20.599	18.493	16.791	14.953	11.588
40	29.051	26.509	24.433	22.164	17.916
50	37.689	34.764	32.357	29.707	24.674
60	46.459	43.188	40.482	37.485	31.738
70	55.329	51.739	48.758	45.442	39.036
80	64.278	60.391	57.153	53.540	46.520
90	73.291	69.126	65.647	61.754	54.155
100	82.358	77.929	74.222	70.065	61.918

NIST/SEMATECH e-Handbook of Statistical Methods, http://www.itl.nist.gov/div898/handbook/, September 2011.

Table 8 Upper Critical Values of Student's t Distribution with ν Degrees of Freedom

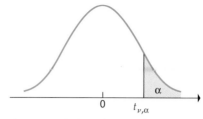

For selected probabilities, α, the table shows the values $t_{\nu,\alpha}$ such that $P(t_\nu > t_{\nu,\alpha}) = \alpha$, where t_ν is a Student's t random variable with ν degress of freedom. For example, the probability is .10 that a Student's t random variable with 10 degrees of freedom exceeds 1.372.

ν	\multicolumn{6}{c}{PROBABILITY OF EXCEEDING THE CRITICAL VALUE}					
	0.10	0.05	0.025	0.01	0.005	0.001
1	3.078	6.314	12.706	31.821	63.657	318.313
2	1.886	2.920	4.303	6.965	9.925	22.327
3	1.638	2.353	3.182	4.541	5.841	10.215
4	1.533	2.132	2.776	3.747	4.604	7.173
5	1.476	2.015	2.571	3.365	4.032	5.893
6	1.440	1.943	2.447	3.143	3.707	5.208
7	1.415	1.895	2.365	2.998	3.499	4.782
8	1.397	1.860	2.306	2.896	3.355	4.499
9	1.383	1.833	2.262	2.821	3.250	4.296
10	1.372	1.812	2.228	2.764	3.169	4.143
11	1.363	1.796	2.201	2.718	3.106	4.024
12	1.356	1.782	2.179	2.681	3.055	3.929
13	1.350	1.771	2.160	2.650	3.012	3.852
14	1.345	1.761	2.145	2.624	2.977	3.787
15	1.341	1.753	2.131	2.602	2.947	3.733
16	1.337	1.746	2.120	2.583	2.921	3.686
17	1.333	1.740	2.110	2.567	2.898	3.646
18	1.330	1.734	2.101	2.552	2.878	3.610
19	1.328	1.729	2.093	2.539	2.861	3.579
20	1.325	1.725	2.086	2.528	2.845	3.552
21	1.323	1.721	2.080	2.518	2.831	3.527
22	1.321	1.717	2.074	2.508	2.819	3.505
23	1.319	1.714	2.069	2.500	2.807	3.485
24	1.318	1.711	2.064	2.492	2.797	3.467
25	1.316	1.708	2.060	2.485	2.787	3.450
26	1.315	1.706	2.056	2.479	2.779	3.435
27	1.314	1.703	2.052	2.473	2.771	3.421
28	1.313	1.701	2.048	2.467	2.763	3.408
29	1.311	1.699	2.045	2.462	2.756	3.396
30	1.310	1.697	2.042	2.457	2.750	3.385
40	1.303	1.684	2.021	2.423	2.704	3.307
60	1.296	1.671	2.000	2.390	2.660	3.232
100	1.290	1.660	1.984	2.364	2.626	3.174
∞	1.282	1.645	1.960	2.326	2.576	3.090

NIST/SEMATECH e-Handbook of Statistical Methods, http://www.itl.nist.gov/div898/handbook/, September 2011.

Table 9a   Upper Critical Values of the F Distribution

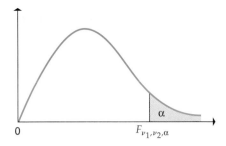

For probabilities $\alpha = 0.5$ and $\alpha = .01$, the tables show the values $F_{\nu_1,\nu_2,\alpha}$ such that $P(F_{\nu_1,\nu_2} > F_{\nu_1,\nu_2,\alpha}) = \alpha$, where F_{ν_1,ν_2} is an F random variable, with numerator degrees of freedom ν_1 and denominator degrees of freedom ν_2. For example, the probability is .05 that an $F_{3,7}$ random variables exceeds 4.347.

For ν_1 Numerator Degrees of Freedom and ν_2 Denominator Degrees of Freedom 5% Significance Level $F_{.05}(\nu_1, \nu_2)$

ν_2/ν_1	1	2	3	4	5	6	7	8	9	10
1	161.448	199.500	215.707	224.583	230.162	233.986	236.768	238.882	240.543	241.882
2	18.513	19.000	19.164	19.247	19.296	19.330	19.353	19.371	19.385	19.396
3	10.128	9.552	9.277	9.117	9.013	8.941	8.887	8.845	8.812	8.786
4	7.709	6.944	6.591	6.388	6.256	6.163	6.094	6.041	5.999	5.964
5	6.608	5.786	5.409	5.192	5.050	4.950	4.876	4.818	4.772	4.735
6	5.987	5.143	4.757	4.534	4.387	4.284	4.207	4.147	4.099	4.060
7	5.591	4.737	4.347	4.120	3.972	3.866	3.787	3.726	3.677	3.637
8	5.318	4.459	4.066	3.838	3.687	3.581	3.500	3.438	3.388	3.347
9	5.117	4.256	3.863	3.633	3.482	3.374	3.293	3.230	3.179	3.137
10	4.965	4.103	3.708	3.478	3.326	3.217	3.135	3.072	3.020	2.978
11	4.844	3.982	3.587	3.357	3.204	3.095	3.012	2.948	2.896	2.854
12	4.747	3.885	3.490	3.259	3.106	2.996	2.913	2.849	2.796	2.753
13	4.667	3.806	3.411	3.179	3.025	2.915	2.832	2.767	2.714	2.671
14	4.600	3.739	3.344	3.112	2.958	2.848	2.764	2.699	2.646	2.602
15	4.543	3.682	3.287	3.056	2.901	2.790	2.707	2.641	2.588	2.544
16	4.494	3.634	3.239	3.007	2.852	2.741	2.657	2.591	2.538	2.494
17	4.451	3.592	3.197	2.965	2.810	2.699	2.614	2.548	2.494	2.450
18	4.414	3.555	3.160	2.928	2.773	2.661	2.577	2.510	2.456	2.412
19	4.381	3.522	3.127	2.895	2.740	2.628	2.544	2.477	2.423	2.378
20	4.351	3.493	3.098	2.866	2.711	2.599	2.514	2.447	2.393	2.348
21	4.325	3.467	3.072	2.840	2.685	2.573	2.488	2.420	2.366	2.321
22	4.301	3.443	3.049	2.817	2.661	2.549	2.464	2.397	2.342	2.297
23	4.279	3.422	3.028	2.796	2.640	2.528	2.442	2.375	2.320	2.275
24	4.260	3.403	3.009	2.776	2.621	2.508	2.423	2.355	2.300	2.255
25	4.242	3.385	2.991	2.759	2.603	2.490	2.405	2.337	2.282	2.236
26	4.225	3.369	2.975	2.743	2.587	2.474	2.388	2.321	2.265	2.220
27	4.210	3.354	2.960	2.728	2.572	2.459	2.373	2.305	2.250	2.204
28	4.196	3.340	2.947	2.714	2.558	2.445	2.359	2.291	2.236	2.190
29	4.183	3.328	2.934	2.701	2.545	2.432	2.346	2.278	2.223	2.177
30	4.171	3.316	2.922	2.690	2.534	2.421	2.334	2.266	2.211	2.165
40	4.085	3.232	2.839	2.606	2.449	2.336	2.249	2.180	2.124	2.077
60	4.001	3.150	2.758	2.525	2.368	2.254	2.167	2.097	2.040	1.993
100	3.936	3.087	2.696	2.463	2.305	2.191	2.103	2.032	1.975	1.927

(continued)

For ν_1 Numerator Degrees of Freedom and ν_2 Denominator Degrees of Freedom 5% Significance Level $F_{.05}(\nu_1, \nu_2)$

ν_2/ν_1	11	12	13	14	15	16	17	18	19	20
1	242.983	243.906	244.690	245.364	245.950	246.464	246.918	247.323	247.686	248.013
2	19.405	19.413	19.419	19.424	19.429	19.433	19.437	19.440	19.443	19.446
3	8.763	8.745	8.729	8.715	8.703	8.692	8.683	8.675	8.667	8.660
4	5.936	5.912	5.891	5.873	5.858	5.844	5.832	5.821	5.811	5.803
5	4.704	4.678	4.655	4.636	4.619	4.604	4.590	4.579	4.568	4.558
6	4.027	4.000	3.976	3.956	3.938	3.922	3.908	3.896	3.884	3.874
7	3.603	3.575	3.550	3.529	3.511	3.494	3.480	3.467	3.455	3.445
8	3.313	3.284	3.259	3.237	3.218	3.202	3.187	3.173	3.161	3.150
9	3.102	3.073	3.048	3.025	3.006	2.989	2.974	2.960	2.948	2.936
10	2.943	2.913	2.887	2.865	2.845	2.828	2.812	2.798	2.785	2.774
11	2.818	2.788	2.761	2.739	2.719	2.701	2.685	2.671	2.658	2.646
12	2.717	2.687	2.660	2.637	2.617	2.599	2.583	2.568	2.555	2.544
13	2.635	2.604	2.577	2.554	2.533	2.515	2.499	2.484	2.471	2.459
14	2.565	2.534	2.507	2.484	2.463	2.445	2.428	2.413	2.400	2.388
15	2.507	2.475	2.448	2.424	2.403	2.385	2.368	2.353	2.340	2.328
16	2.456	2.425	2.397	2.373	2.352	2.333	2.317	2.302	2.288	2.276
17	2.413	2.381	2.353	2.329	2.308	2.289	2.272	2.257	2.243	2.230
18	2.374	2.342	2.314	2.290	2.269	2.250	2.233	2.217	2.203	2.191
19	2.340	2.308	2.280	2.256	2.234	2.215	2.198	2.182	2.168	2.155
20	2.310	2.278	2.250	2.225	2.203	2.184	2.167	2.151	2.137	2.124
21	2.283	2.250	2.222	2.197	2.176	2.156	2.139	2.123	2.109	2.096
22	2.259	2.226	2.198	2.173	2.151	2.131	2.114	2.098	2.084	2.071
23	2.236	2.204	2.175	2.150	2.128	2.109	2.091	2.075	2.061	2.048
24	2.216	2.183	2.155	2.130	2.108	2.088	2.070	2.054	2.040	2.027
25	2.198	2.165	2.136	2.111	2.089	2.069	2.051	2.035	2.021	2.007
26	2.181	2.148	2.119	2.094	2.072	2.052	2.034	2.018	2.003	1.990
27	2.166	2.132	2.103	2.078	2.056	2.036	2.018	2.002	1.987	1.974
28	2.151	2.118	2.089	2.064	2.041	2.021	2.003	1.987	1.972	1.959
29	2.138	2.104	2.075	2.050	2.027	2.007	1.989	1.973	1.958	1.945
30	2.126	2.092	2.063	2.037	2.015	1.995	1.976	1.960	1.945	1.932
40	2.038	2.003	1.974	1.948	1.924	1.904	1.885	1.868	1.853	1.839
60	1.952	1.917	1.887	1.860	1.836	1.815	1.796	1.778	1.763	1.748
100	1.886	1.850	1.819	1.792	1.768	1.746	1.726	1.708	1.691	1.676

NIST/SEMATECH e-Handbook of Statistical Methods, http://www.itl.nist.gov/div898/handbook/, September 2011.

Table 9b Upper Critical Values of the F Distribution

For ν_1 Numerator Degrees of Freedom and ν_2 Denominator Degrees of Freedom 1% Significance Level $F_{.01}(\nu_1, \nu_2)$

ν_2/ν_1	1	2	3	4	5	6	7	8	9	10
1	4052.19	4999.52	5403.34	5624.62	5763.65	5858.97	5928.33	5981.10	6022.50	6055.85
2	98.502	99.000	99.166	99.249	99.300	99.333	99.356	99.374	99.388	99.399
3	34.116	30.816	29.457	28.710	28.237	27.911	27.672	27.489	27.345	27.229
4	21.198	18.000	16.694	15.977	15.522	15.207	14.976	14.799	14.659	14.546
5	16.258	13.274	12.060	11.392	10.967	10.672	10.456	10.289	10.158	10.051
6	13.745	10.925	9.780	9.148	8.746	8.466	8.260	8.102	7.976	7.874
7	12.246	9.547	8.451	7.847	7.460	7.191	6.993	6.840	6.719	6.620
8	11.259	8.649	7.591	7.006	6.632	6.371	6.178	6.029	5.911	5.814
9	10.561	8.022	6.992	6.422	6.057	5.802	5.613	5.467	5.351	5.257
10	10.044	7.559	6.552	5.994	5.636	5.386	5.200	5.057	4.942	4.849
11	9.646	7.206	6.217	5.668	5.316	5.069	4.886	4.744	4.632	4.539
12	9.330	6.927	5.953	5.412	5.064	4.821	4.640	4.499	4.388	4.296
13	9.074	6.701	5.739	5.205	4.862	4.620	4.441	4.302	4.191	4.100
14	8.862	6.515	5.564	5.035	4.695	4.456	4.278	4.140	4.030	3.939
15	8.683	6.359	5.417	4.893	4.556	4.318	4.142	4.004	3.895	3.805
16	8.531	6.226	5.292	4.773	4.437	4.202	4.026	3.890	3.780	3.691
17	8.400	6.112	5.185	4.669	4.336	4.102	3.927	3.791	3.682	3.593
18	8.285	6.013	5.092	4.579	4.248	4.015	3.841	3.705	3.597	3.508
19	8.185	5.926	5.010	4.500	4.171	3.939	3.765	3.631	3.523	3.434
20	8.096	5.849	4.938	4.431	4.103	3.871	3.699	3.564	3.457	3.368
21	8.017	5.780	4.874	4.369	4.042	3.812	3.640	3.506	3.398	3.310
22	7.945	5.719	4.817	4.313	3.988	3.758	3.587	3.453	3.346	3.258
23	7.881	5.664	4.765	4.264	3.939	3.710	3.539	3.406	3.299	3.211
24	7.823	5.614	4.718	4.218	3.895	3.667	3.496	3.363	3.256	3.168
25	7.770	5.568	4.675	4.177	3.855	3.627	3.457	3.324	3.217	3.129
26	7.721	5.526	4.637	4.140	3.818	3.591	3.421	3.288	3.182	3.094
27	7.677	5.488	4.601	4.106	3.785	3.558	3.388	3.256	3.149	3.062
28	7.636	5.453	4.568	4.074	3.754	3.528	3.358	3.226	3.120	3.032
29	7.598	5.420	4.538	4.045	3.725	3.499	3.330	3.198	3.092	3.005
30	7.562	5.390	4.510	4.018	3.699	3.473	3.305	3.173	3.067	2.979
40	7.314	5.179	4.313	3.828	3.514	3.291	3.124	2.993	2.888	2.801
60	7.077	4.977	4.126	3.649	3.339	3.119	2.953	2.823	2.718	2.632
100	6.895	4.824	3.984	3.513	3.206	2.988	2.823	2.694	2.590	2.503

(continued)

For ν_1 Numerator Degrees of Freedom and ν_2 Denominator Degrees of Freedom 1% Significance Level $F_{.01}(\nu_1, \nu_2)$

ν_2/ν	11	12	13	14	15	16	17	18	19	20
1	6083.35	6106.35	6125.86	6142.70	6157.28	6170.12	6181.42	6191.52	6200.58	6208.74
2	99.408	99.416	99.422	99.428	99.432	99.437	99.440	99.444	99.447	99.449
3	27.133	27.052	26.983	26.924	26.872	26.827	26.787	26.751	26.719	26.690
4	14.452	14.374	14.307	14.249	14.198	14.154	14.115	14.080	14.048	14.020
5	9.963	9.888	9.825	9.770	9.722	9.680	9.643	9.610	9.580	9.553
6	7.790	7.718	7.657	7.605	7.559	7.519	7.483	7.451	7.422	7.396
7	6.538	6.469	6.410	6.359	6.314	6.275	6.240	6.209	6.181	6.155
8	5.734	5.667	5.609	5.559	5.515	5.477	5.442	5.412	5.384	5.359
9	5.178	5.111	5.055	5.005	4.962	4.924	4.890	4.860	4.833	4.808
10	4.772	4.706	4.650	4.601	4.558	4.520	4.487	4.457	4.430	4.405
11	4.462	4.397	4.342	4.293	4.251	4.213	4.180	4.150	4.123	4.099
12	4.220	4.155	4.100	4.052	4.010	3.972	3.939	3.909	3.883	3.858
13	4.025	3.960	3.905	3.857	3.815	3.778	3.745	3.716	3.689	3.665
14	3.864	3.800	3.745	3.698	3.656	3.619	3.586	3.556	3.529	3.505
15	3.730	3.666	3.612	3.564	3.522	3.485	3.452	3.423	3.396	3.372
16	3.616	3.553	3.498	3.451	3.409	3.372	3.339	3.310	3.283	3.259
17	3.519	3.455	3.401	3.353	3.312	3.275	3.242	3.212	3.186	3.162
18	3.434	3.371	3.316	3.269	3.227	3.190	3.158	3.128	3.101	3.077
19	3.360	3.297	3.242	3.195	3.153	3.116	3.084	3.054	3.027	3.003
20	3.294	3.231	3.177	3.130	3.088	3.051	3.018	2.989	2.962	2.938
21	3.236	3.173	3.119	3.072	3.030	2.993	2.960	2.931	2.904	2.880
22	3.184	3.121	3.067	3.019	2.978	2.941	2.908	2.879	2.852	2.827
23	3.137	3.074	3.020	2.973	2.931	2.894	2.861	2.832	2.805	2.781
24	3.094	3.032	2.977	2.930	2.889	2.852	2.819	2.789	2.762	2.738
25	3.056	2.993	2.939	2.892	2.850	2.813	2.780	2.751	2.724	2.699
26	3.021	2.958	2.904	2.857	2.815	2.778	2.745	2.715	2.688	2.664
27	2.988	2.926	2.871	2.824	2.783	2.746	2.713	2.683	2.656	2.632
28	2.959	2.896	2.842	2.795	2.753	2.716	2.683	2.653	2.626	2.602
29	2.931	2.868	2.814	2.767	2.726	2.689	2.656	2.626	2.599	2.574
30	2.906	2.843	2.789	2.742	2.700	2.663	2.630	2.600	2.573	2.549
40	2.727	2.665	2.611	2.563	2.522	2.484	2.451	2.421	2.394	2.369
60	2.559	2.496	2.442	2.394	2.352	2.315	2.281	2.251	2.223	2.198
100	2.430	2.368	2.313	2.265	2.223	2.185	2.151	2.120	2.092	2.067

NIST/SEMATECH e-Handbook of Statistical Methods, http://www.itl.nist.gov/div898/handbook/, September 2011.

Table 10 Cutoff Points for the Distribution of the Wilcoxon Test Statistic

For sample size n, the table shows, for selected probabilities α, the numbers T_α such that $P(T < T_\alpha) = \alpha$, where the distribution of the random variable T is that of the Wilcoxon test statistic under the null hypothesis.

n	α				
	.005	.010	.025	.050	.100
4	0	0	0	0	1
5	0	0	0	1	3
6	0	0	1	3	4
7	0	1	3	4	6
8	1	2	4	6	9
9	2	4	6	9	11
10	4	6	9	11	15
11	6	8	11	14	18
12	8	10	14	18	22
13	10	13	18	22	27
14	13	16	22	26	32
15	16	20	26	31	37
16	20	24	30	36	43
17	24	28	35	42	49
18	28	33	41	48	56
19	33	38	47	54	63
20	38	44	53	61	70

From R. L. McCormack, "Extended tables of the Wilcoxon matched pairs signed rank statistics," *Journal of the American Statistical Association* 60 (1965).

Table 11   Cutoff Points for the Distribution of Spearman Rank Correlation Coefficient

For sample size n, the table shows, for selected probabilities α, the numbers $r_{s,\alpha}$ such that $P(r_s > r_{s,\alpha}) = \alpha$, where the distribution of the random variable r_s is that of Spearman rank correlation coefficient under the null hypothesis of no association.

n	α			
	.050	.025	.010	.005
5	.900	—	—	—
6	.829	.886	.943	—
7	.714	.786	.893	—
8	.643	.738	.833	.881
9	.600	.683	.783	.833
10	.564	.648	.745	.794
11	.523	.623	.736	.818
12	.497	.591	.703	.780
13	.475	.566	.673	.745
14	.457	.545	.646	.716
15	.441	.525	.623	.689
16	.425	.507	.601	.666
17	.412	.490	.582	.645
18	.399	.476	.564	.625
19	.388	.462	.549	.608
20	.377	.450	.534	.591
21	.368	.438	.521	.576
22	.359	.428	.508	.562
23	.351	.418	.496	.549
24	.343	.409	.485	.537
25	.336	.400	.475	.526
26	.329	.392	.465	.515
27	.323	.385	.456	.505
28	.317	.377	.448	.496
29	.311	.370	.440	.487
30	.305	.364	.432	.478

Reproduced with permission from E. G. Olds, "Distribution of sums of squares of rank differences for small samples," *Annals of Mathematical Statistics* 9 (1938).

Table 12 Cutoff Points for the Distribution of the Durbin-Watson Test Statistic

Let d_α be the number such that $P(d < d_\alpha) = \alpha$, where the random variable d has the distribution of the Durbin-Watson statistic under the null hypothesis of no autocorrelation in the regression errors. For probabilities $\alpha = .05$ and $\alpha = .01$, the tables show, for numbers of independent variables, K, values d_L and d_U such that $d_L < d_\alpha < d_U$, for numbers n of observations.

	$\alpha = 0.05$									
n	K									
	1		2		3		4		5	
	d_L	d_U	d_L	d_U	d_L	d_U	d_L	d_U	d_L	d_U
15	1.08	1.36	0.95	1.54	0.82	1.75	0.69	1.97	0.56	2.21
16	1.10	1.37	0.98	1.54	0.86	1.73	0.74	1.93	0.62	2.15
17	1.13	1.38	1.02	1.54	0.90	1.71	0.78	1.90	0.67	2.10
18	1.16	1.39	1.05	1.53	0.93	1.69	1.82	1.87	0.71	2.06
19	1.18	1.40	1.08	1.53	0.97	1.68	0.86	1.85	0.75	2.02
20	1.20	1.41	1.10	1.54	1.00	1.68	0.90	1.83	0.79	1.99
21	1.22	1.42	1.13	1.54	1.03	1.67	0.93	1.81	0.83	1.96
22	1.24	1.43	1.15	1.54	1.05	1.66	0.96	1.80	0.86	1.94
23	1.26	1.44	1.17	1.54	1.08	1.66	0.99	1.79	0.90	1.92
24	1.27	1.45	1.19	1.55	1.10	1.66	1.01	1.78	0.93	1.90
25	1.29	1.45	1.21	1.55	1.12	1.66	1.04	1.77	0.95	1.89
26	1.30	1.46	1.22	1.55	1.14	1.65	1.06	1.76	0.98	1.88
27	1.32	1.47	1.24	1.56	1.16	1.65	1.08	1.76	1.01	1.86
28	1.33	1.48	1.26	1.56	1.18	1.65	1.10	1.75	1.03	1.85
29	1.34	1.48	1.27	1.56	1.20	1.65	1.12	1.74	1.05	1.84
30	1.35	1.49	1.28	1.57	1.21	1.65	1.14	1.74	1.07	1.83
31	1.36	1.50	1.30	1.57	1.23	1.65	1.16	1.74	1.09	1.83
32	1.37	1.50	1.31	1.57	1.24	1.65	1.18	1.73	1.11	1.82
33	1.38	1.51	1.32	1.58	1.26	1.65	1.19	1.73	1.13	1.81
34	1.39	1.51	1.33	1.58	1.27	1.65	1.21	1.73	1.15	1.81
35	1.40	1.52	1.34	1.58	1.28	1.65	1.22	1.73	1.16	1.80
36	1.41	1.52	1.35	1.59	1.29	1.65	1.24	1.73	1.18	1.80
37	1.42	1.53	1.36	1.59	1.31	1.66	1.25	1.72	1.19	1.80
38	1.43	1.54	1.37	1.59	1.32	1.66	1.26	1.72	1.21	1.79
39	1.43	1.54	1.38	1.60	1.33	1.66	1.27	1.72	1.22	1.79
40	1.44	1.54	1.39	1.60	1.34	1.66	1.29	1.72	1.23	1.79
45	1.48	1.57	1.43	1.62	1.38	1.67	1.34	1.72	1.29	1.78
50	1.50	1.59	1.46	1.63	1.42	1.67	1.38	1.72	1.34	1.77
55	1.53	1.60	1.49	1.64	1.45	1.68	1.41	1.72	1.38	1.77
60	1.55	1.62	1.51	1.65	1.48	1.69	1.44	1.73	1.41	1.77
65	1.57	1.63	1.54	1.66	1.50	1.70	1.47	1.73	1.44	1.77
70	1.58	1.64	1.55	1.67	1.52	1.70	1.49	1.74	1.46	1.77
75	1.60	1.65	1.57	1.68	1.54	1.71	1.51	1.74	1.49	1.77
80	1.61	1.66	1.59	1.69	1.56	1.72	1.53	1.74	1.51	1.77
85	1.62	1.67	1.60	1.70	1.57	1.72	1.55	1.75	1.52	1.77
90	1.63	1.68	1.61	1.70	1.59	1.73	1.57	1.75	1.54	1.78
95	1.64	1.69	1.62	1.71	1.60	1.73	1.58	1.75	1.56	1.78
100	1.65	1.69	1.63	1.72	1.61	1.74	1.59	1.76	1.57	1.78

(*continued*)

	$\alpha = 0.05$									
n	K									
	1		2		3		4		5	
	d_L	d_U	d_L	d_U	d_L	d_U	d_L	d_U	d_L	d_U
15	0.81	1.07	0.70	1.25	0.59	1.46	0.49	1.70	0.39	1.96
16	0.84	1.09	0.74	1.25	0.63	1.44	0.53	1.66	0.44	1.90
17	0.87	1.10	0.77	1.25	0.67	1.43	0.57	1.63	0.48	1.85
18	0.90	1.12	0.80	1.26	0.71	1.42	0.61	1.60	0.52	1.80
19	0.93	1.13	0.83	1.26	0.74	1.41	0.65	1.58	0.56	1.77
20	0.95	1.15	0.86	1.27	0.77	1.41	0.68	1.57	0.60	1.74
21	0.97	1.16	0.89	1.27	0.80	1.41	0.72	1.55	0.63	1.71
22	1.00	1.17	0.91	1.28	0.83	1.40	0.75	1.54	0.66	1.69
23	1.02	1.19	0.94	1.29	0.86	1.40	0.77	1.53	0.70	1.67
24	1.04	1.20	0.96	1.30	0.88	1.41	0.80	1.53	0.72	1.66
25	1.05	1.21	0.98	1.30	0.90	1.41	0.83	1.52	0.75	1.65
26	1.07	1.22	1.00	1.31	0.93	1.41	0.85	1.52	0.78	1.64
27	1.09	1.23	1.02	1.32	0.95	1.41	0.88	1.51	0.81	1.63
28	1.10	1.24	1.04	1.32	0.97	1.41	0.90	1.51	0.83	1.62
29	1.12	1.25	1.05	1.33	0.99	1.42	0.92	1.51	0.85	1.61
30	1.13	1.26	1.07	1.34	1.01	1.42	0.94	1.51	0.88	1.61
31	1.15	1.27	1.08	1.34	1.02	1.42	0.96	1.51	0.90	1.60
32	1.16	1.28	1.10	1.35	1.04	1.43	0.98	1.51	0.92	1.60
33	1.17	1.29	1.11	1.36	1.05	1.43	1.00	1.51	0.94	1.59
34	1.18	1.30	1.13	1.36	1.07	1.43	1.01	1.51	0.95	1.59
35	1.19	1.31	1.14	1.37	1.08	1.44	1.03	1.51	0.97	1.59
36	1.21	1.32	1.15	1.38	1.10	1.44	1.04	1.51	0.99	1.59
37	1.22	1.32	1.16	1.38	1.11	1.45	1.06	1.51	1.00	1.59
38	1.23	1.33	1.18	1.39	1.12	1.45	1.07	1.52	1.02	1.58
39	1.24	1.34	1.19	1.39	1.14	1.45	1.09	1.52	1.03	1.58
40	1.25	1.34	1.20	1.40	1.15	1.46	1.10	1.52	1.05	1.58
45	1.29	1.38	1.24	1.42	1.20	1.48	1.16	1.53	1.11	1.58
50	1.32	1.40	1.28	1.45	1.24	1.49	1.20	1.54	1.16	1.59
55	1.36	1.43	1.32	1.47	1.28	1.51	1.25	1.55	1.21	1.59
60	1.38	1.45	1.35	1.48	1.32	1.52	1.28	1.56	1.25	1.60
65	1.41	1.47	1.38	1.50	1.35	1.53	1.31	1.57	1.28	1.61
70	1.43	1.49	1.40	1.52	1.37	1.55	1.34	1.58	1.31	1.61
75	1.45	1.50	1.42	1.53	1.39	1.56	1.37	1.59	1.34	1.62
80	1.47	1.52	1.44	1.54	1.42	1.57	1.39	1.60	1.36	1.62
85	1.48	1.53	1.46	1.55	1.43	1.58	1.41	1.60	1.39	1.63
90	1.50	1.54	1.47	1.56	1.45	1.59	1.43	1.61	1.41	1.64
95	1.51	1.55	1.49	1.57	1.47	1.60	1.45	1.62	1.42	1.64
100	1.52	1.56	1.50	1.58	1.48	1.60	1.46	1.63	1.44	1.65

Computed from TSP 4.5 based on R. W. Farebrother, "A Remark on Algorithms AS106, AS153, and AS155: The Distribution of a Linear Combination of Chi-Square Random Variables", Journal of the Royal Statistical Society, Series C (Applied Statistics), 1984, 29, pp. 323–333.

Table 13 Critical Values of Studentized Range Q ($\alpha = 0.05$)

The Studentized Range Upper Quantiles $Q(k, df, 0.05)$

df	k→ 2	3	4	5	6	7	8	9	10	11	12	13	14	15	16	17	18	19	20
1	17.969	26.976	32.819	37.082	40.408	43.119	45.397	47.357	49.071	50.592	51.957	53.194	54.323	55.361	56.320	57.212	58.044	58.824	59.558
2	6.085	8.331	9.798	10.881	11.734	12.435	13.027	13.539	13.988	14.389	14.749	15.076	15.375	15.650	15.905	16.143	16.365	16.573	16.769
3	4.501	5.910	6.825	7.502	8.037	8.478	8.852	9.177	9.462	9.717	9.946	10.155	10.346	10.522	10.686	10.838	10.980	11.114	11.240
4	3.926	5.040	5.757	6.287	6.706	7.053	7.347	7.602	7.826	8.027	8.208	8.373	8.524	8.664	8.793	8.914	9.027	9.133	9.233
5	3.635	4.602	5.218	5.673	6.033	6.330	6.582	6.801	6.995	7.167	7.323	7.466	7.596	7.716	7.828	7.932	8.030	8.122	8.208
6	3.460	4.339	4.896	5.305	5.628	5.895	6.122	6.319	6.493	6.649	6.789	6.917	7.034	7.143	7.244	7.338	7.426	7.508	7.586
7	3.344	4.165	4.681	5.060	5.359	5.606	5.815	5.997	6.158	6.302	6.431	6.550	6.658	6.759	6.852	6.939	7.020	7.097	7.169
8	3.261	4.041	4.529	4.886	5.167	5.399	5.596	5.767	5.918	6.053	6.175	6.287	6.389	6.483	6.571	6.653	6.729	6.801	6.869
9	3.199	3.948	4.415	4.755	5.024	5.244	5.432	5.595	5.738	5.867	5.983	6.089	6.186	6.276	6.359	6.437	6.510	6.579	6.643
10	3.151	3.877	4.327	4.654	4.912	5.124	5.304	5.460	5.598	5.722	5.833	5.935	6.028	6.114	6.194	6.269	6.339	6.405	6.467
11	3.113	3.820	4.256	4.574	4.823	5.028	5.202	5.353	5.486	5.605	5.713	5.811	5.901	5.984	6.062	6.134	6.202	6.265	6.325
12	3.081	3.773	4.199	4.508	4.750	4.950	5.119	5.265	5.395	5.510	5.615	5.710	5.797	5.878	5.953	6.023	6.089	6.151	6.209
13	3.055	3.734	4.151	4.453	4.690	4.884	5.049	5.192	5.318	5.431	5.533	5.625	5.711	5.789	5.862	5.931	5.995	6.055	6.112
14	3.033	3.701	4.111	4.407	4.639	4.829	4.990	5.130	5.253	5.364	5.463	5.554	5.637	5.714	5.785	5.852	5.915	5.973	6.029
15	3.014	3.673	4.076	4.367	4.595	4.782	4.940	5.077	5.198	5.306	5.403	5.492	5.574	5.649	5.719	5.785	5.846	5.904	5.958
16	2.998	3.649	4.046	4.333	4.557	4.741	4.896	5.031	5.150	5.256	5.352	5.439	5.519	5.593	5.662	5.726	5.786	5.843	5.896
17	2.984	3.628	4.020	4.303	4.524	4.705	4.858	4.991	5.108	5.212	5.306	5.392	5.471	5.544	5.612	5.675	5.734	5.790	5.842
18	2.971	3.609	3.997	4.276	4.494	4.673	4.824	4.955	5.071	5.173	5.266	5.351	5.429	5.501	5.567	5.629	5.688	5.743	5.794
19	2.960	3.593	3.977	4.253	4.468	4.645	4.794	4.924	5.037	5.139	5.231	5.314	5.391	5.462	5.528	5.589	5.647	5.701	5.752
20	2.950	3.578	3.958	4.232	4.445	4.620	4.768	4.895	5.008	5.108	5.199	5.282	5.357	5.427	5.492	5.553	5.610	5.663	5.714
21	2.941	3.565	3.942	4.213	4.424	4.597	4.743	4.870	4.981	5.081	5.170	5.252	5.327	5.396	5.460	5.520	5.576	5.629	5.679
22	2.933	3.553	3.927	4.196	4.405	4.577	4.722	4.847	4.957	5.056	5.144	5.225	5.299	5.368	5.431	5.491	5.546	5.599	5.648
23	2.926	3.542	3.914	4.180	4.388	4.558	4.702	4.826	4.935	5.033	5.121	5.201	5.274	5.342	5.405	5.464	5.519	5.571	5.620
24	2.919	3.532	3.901	4.166	4.373	4.541	4.684	4.807	4.915	5.012	5.099	5.179	5.251	5.319	5.381	5.439	5.494	5.545	5.594
25	2.913	3.523	3.890	4.153	4.358	4.526	4.667	4.789	4.897	4.993	5.079	5.158	5.230	5.297	5.359	5.417	5.471	5.522	5.570
26	2.907	3.514	3.880	4.141	4.345	4.511	4.652	4.773	4.880	4.975	5.061	5.139	5.211	5.277	5.339	5.396	5.450	5.500	5.548
27	2.902	3.506	3.870	4.130	4.333	4.498	4.638	4.758	4.864	4.959	5.044	5.122	5.193	5.259	5.320	5.377	5.430	5.480	5.528
28	2.897	3.499	3.861	4.120	4.322	4.486	4.625	4.745	4.850	4.944	5.029	5.106	5.177	5.242	5.302	5.359	5.412	5.462	5.509
29	2.892	3.493	3.853	4.111	4.311	4.475	4.613	4.732	4.837	4.930	5.014	5.091	5.161	5.226	5.286	5.342	5.395	5.445	5.491
30	2.888	3.486	3.845	4.102	4.301	4.464	4.601	4.720	4.824	4.917	5.001	5.077	5.147	5.211	5.271	5.327	5.379	5.429	5.475

(continued)

Table 13 Critical Values of Studentized Range Q ($\alpha = 0.05$) (Continued)

df $k\to$	2	3	4	5	6	7	8	9	10	11	12	13	14	15	16	17	18	19	20
31	2.884	3.481	3.838	4.094	4.292	4.454	4.591	4.709	4.812	4.905	4.988	5.064	5.134	5.198	5.257	5.313	5.365	5.414	5.460
32	2.881	3.475	3.832	4.086	4.284	4.445	4.581	4.698	4.802	4.894	4.976	5.052	5.121	5.185	5.244	5.299	5.351	5.400	5.445
33	2.877	3.470	3.825	4.079	4.276	4.436	4.572	4.689	4.791	4.883	4.965	5.040	5.109	5.173	5.232	5.287	5.338	5.386	5.432
34	2.874	3.465	3.820	4.072	4.268	4.428	4.563	4.680	4.782	4.873	4.955	5.030	5.098	5.161	5.220	5.275	5.326	5.374	5.420
35	2.871	3.461	3.814	4.066	4.261	4.421	4.555	4.671	4.773	4.863	4.945	5.020	5.088	5.151	5.209	5.264	5.315	5.362	5.408
36	2.868	3.457	3.809	4.060	4.255	4.414	4.547	4.663	4.764	4.855	4.936	5.010	5.078	5.141	5.199	5.253	5.304	5.352	5.397
37	2.865	3.453	3.804	4.054	4.249	4.407	4.540	4.655	4.756	4.846	4.927	5.001	5.069	5.131	5.189	5.243	5.294	5.341	5.386
38	2.863	3.449	3.799	4.049	4.243	4.400	4.533	4.648	4.749	4.838	4.919	4.993	5.060	5.122	5.180	5.234	5.284	5.331	5.376
39	2.861	3.445	3.795	4.044	4.237	4.394	4.527	4.641	4.741	4.831	4.911	4.985	5.052	5.114	5.171	5.225	5.275	5.322	5.367
40	2.858	3.442	3.791	4.039	4.232	4.388	4.521	4.634	4.735	4.824	4.904	4.977	5.044	5.106	5.163	5.216	5.266	5.313	5.358
48	2.843	3.420	3.764	4.008	4.197	4.351	4.481	4.592	4.690	4.777	4.856	4.927	4.993	5.053	5.109	5.161	5.210	5.256	5.299
60	2.829	3.399	3.737	3.977	4.163	4.314	4.441	4.550	4.646	4.732	4.808	4.878	4.942	5.001	5.056	5.107	5.154	5.199	5.241
80	2.814	3.377	3.711	3.947	4.129	4.277	4.402	4.509	4.603	4.686	4.761	4.829	4.892	4.949	5.003	5.052	5.099	5.142	5.183
120	2.800	3.356	3.685	3.917	4.096	4.241	4.363	4.468	4.560	4.641	4.714	4.781	4.842	4.898	4.950	4.998	5.043	5.086	5.126
240	2.786	3.335	3.659	3.887	4.063	4.205	4.324	4.427	4.517	4.596	4.668	4.733	4.792	4.847	4.897	4.944	4.988	5.030	5.069
Inf	2.772	3.314	3.633	3.858	4.030	4.170	4.286	4.387	4.474	4.552	4.622	4.685	4.743	4.796	4.845	4.891	4.934	4.974	5.012

The Studentized Range Upper Quantiles $Q(k, df, 0.01)$

df $k\to$	2	3	4	5	6	7	8	9	10	11	12	13	14	15	16	17	18	19	20
1	90.024	135.041	164.258	185.575	202.210	215.769	227.166	236.966	245.542	253.151	259.979	266.165	271.812	277.003	281.803	286.263	290.426	294.328	297.997
2	14.036	19.019	22.294	24.717	26.629	28.201	29.530	30.679	31.689	32.589	33.398	34.134	34.806	35.426	36.000	36.534	37.034	37.502	37.943
3	8.260	10.619	12.170	13.324	14.241	14.998	15.641	16.199	16.691	17.130	17.526	17.887	18.217	18.522	18.805	19.068	19.315	19.546	19.765
4	6.511	8.120	9.173	9.958	10.583	11.101	11.542	11.925	12.264	12.567	12.840	13.090	13.318	13.530	13.726	13.909	14.081	14.242	14.394
5	5.702	6.976	7.804	8.421	8.913	9.321	9.669	9.971	10.239	10.479	10.696	10.894	11.076	11.244	11.400	11.545	11.682	11.811	11.932
6	5.243	6.331	7.033	7.556	7.972	8.318	8.612	8.869	9.097	9.300	9.485	9.653	9.808	9.951	10.084	10.208	10.325	10.434	10.538
7	4.949	5.919	6.542	7.005	7.373	7.678	7.939	8.166	8.368	8.548	8.711	8.860	8.997	9.124	9.242	9.353	9.456	9.553	9.645
8	4.745	5.635	6.204	6.625	6.959	7.237	7.474	7.680	7.863	8.027	8.176	8.311	8.436	8.552	8.659	8.760	8.854	8.943	9.027
9	4.596	5.428	5.957	6.347	6.657	6.915	7.134	7.325	7.494	7.646	7.784	7.910	8.025	8.132	8.232	8.325	8.412	8.495	8.573
10	4.482	5.270	5.769	6.136	6.428	6.669	6.875	7.054	7.213	7.356	7.485	7.603	7.712	7.812	7.906	7.993	8.075	8.153	8.226
11	4.392	5.146	5.621	5.970	6.247	6.476	6.671	6.841	6.992	7.127	7.250	7.362	7.464	7.560	7.648	7.731	7.809	7.883	7.952
12	4.320	5.046	5.502	5.836	6.101	6.320	6.507	6.670	6.814	6.943	7.060	7.166	7.265	7.356	7.441	7.520	7.594	7.664	7.730
13	4.260	4.964	5.404	5.726	5.981	6.192	6.372	6.528	6.666	6.791	6.903	7.006	7.100	7.188	7.269	7.345	7.417	7.484	7.548
14	4.210	4.895	5.322	5.634	5.881	6.085	6.258	6.409	6.543	6.663	6.772	6.871	6.962	7.047	7.125	7.199	7.268	7.333	7.394

15	4.167	4.836	5.252	5.556	5.796	5.994	6.162	6.309	6.438	6.555	6.660	6.756	6.845	6.927	7.003	7.074	7.141	7.204	7.264
16	4.131	4.786	5.192	5.489	5.722	5.915	6.079	6.222	6.348	6.461	6.564	6.658	6.744	6.823	6.897	6.967	7.032	7.093	7.151
17	4.099	4.742	5.140	5.430	5.659	5.847	6.007	6.147	6.270	6.380	6.480	6.572	6.656	6.733	6.806	6.873	6.937	6.997	7.053
18	4.071	4.703	5.094	5.379	5.603	5.787	5.944	6.081	6.201	6.309	6.407	6.496	6.579	6.655	6.725	6.791	6.854	6.912	6.967
19	4.046	4.669	5.054	5.334	5.553	5.735	5.889	6.022	6.141	6.246	6.342	6.430	6.510	6.585	6.654	6.719	6.780	6.837	6.891
20	4.024	4.639	5.018	5.293	5.510	5.688	5.839	5.970	6.086	6.190	6.285	6.370	6.449	6.523	6.591	6.654	6.714	6.770	6.823
21	4.004	4.612	4.986	5.257	5.470	5.646	5.794	5.924	6.038	6.140	6.233	6.317	6.395	6.467	6.534	6.596	6.655	6.710	6.762
22	3.986	4.588	4.957	5.225	5.435	5.608	5.754	5.882	5.994	6.095	6.186	6.269	6.346	6.417	6.482	6.544	6.602	6.656	6.707
23	3.970	4.566	4.931	5.195	5.403	5.573	5.718	5.844	5.955	6.054	6.144	6.226	6.301	6.371	6.436	6.497	6.553	6.607	6.658
24	3.955	4.546	4.907	5.168	5.373	5.542	5.685	5.809	5.919	6.017	6.105	6.186	6.261	6.330	6.394	6.453	6.510	6.562	6.612
25	3.942	4.527	4.885	5.144	5.347	5.513	5.655	5.778	5.886	5.983	6.070	6.150	6.224	6.292	6.355	6.414	6.469	6.522	6.571
26	3.930	4.510	4.865	5.121	5.322	5.487	5.627	5.749	5.856	5.951	6.038	6.117	6.190	6.257	6.319	6.378	6.432	6.484	6.533
27	3.918	4.495	4.847	5.101	5.300	5.463	5.602	5.722	5.828	5.923	6.008	6.087	6.158	6.225	6.287	6.344	6.399	6.450	6.498
28	3.908	4.481	4.830	5.082	5.279	5.441	5.578	5.697	5.802	5.896	5.981	6.058	6.129	6.195	6.256	6.314	6.367	6.418	6.465
29	3.898	4.467	4.814	5.064	5.260	5.420	5.556	5.674	5.778	5.871	5.955	6.032	6.103	6.168	6.228	6.285	6.338	6.388	6.435
30	3.889	4.455	4.799	5.048	5.242	5.401	5.536	5.653	5.756	5.848	5.932	6.008	6.078	6.142	6.202	6.258	6.311	6.361	6.407
31	3.881	4.443	4.786	5.032	5.225	5.383	5.517	5.633	5.736	5.827	5.910	5.985	6.055	6.119	6.178	6.234	6.286	6.335	6.381
32	3.873	4.433	4.773	5.018	5.210	5.367	5.500	5.615	5.716	5.807	5.889	5.964	6.033	6.096	6.155	6.211	6.262	6.311	6.357
33	3.865	4.423	4.761	5.005	5.195	5.351	5.483	5.598	5.698	5.789	5.870	5.944	6.013	6.076	6.134	6.189	6.240	6.289	6.334
34	3.859	4.413	4.750	4.992	5.181	5.336	5.468	5.581	5.682	5.771	5.852	5.926	5.994	6.056	6.114	6.169	6.220	6.268	6.313
35	3.852	4.404	4.739	4.980	5.169	5.323	5.453	5.566	5.666	5.755	5.835	5.908	5.976	6.038	6.096	6.150	6.200	6.248	6.293
36	3.846	4.396	4.729	4.969	5.156	5.310	5.439	5.552	5.651	5.739	5.819	5.892	5.959	6.021	6.078	6.132	6.182	6.229	6.274
37	3.840	4.388	4.720	4.959	5.145	5.298	5.427	5.538	5.637	5.725	5.804	5.876	5.943	6.004	6.061	6.115	6.165	6.212	6.256
38	3.835	4.381	4.711	4.949	5.134	5.286	5.414	5.526	5.623	5.711	5.790	5.862	5.928	5.989	6.046	6.099	6.148	6.195	6.239
39	3.830	4.374	4.703	4.940	5.124	5.275	5.403	5.513	5.611	5.698	5.776	5.848	5.914	5.974	6.031	6.084	6.133	6.179	6.223
40	3.825	4.367	4.695	4.931	5.114	5.265	5.392	5.502	5.599	5.685	5.764	5.835	5.900	5.961	6.017	6.069	6.118	6.165	6.208
48	3.793	4.324	4.644	4.874	5.052	5.198	5.322	5.428	5.522	5.606	5.681	5.750	5.814	5.872	5.926	5.977	6.024	6.069	6.111
60	3.762	4.282	4.594	4.818	4.991	5.133	5.253	5.356	5.447	5.528	5.601	5.667	5.728	5.784	5.837	5.886	5.931	5.974	6.015
80	3.732	4.241	4.545	4.763	4.931	5.069	5.185	5.284	5.372	5.451	5.521	5.585	5.644	5.698	5.749	5.796	5.840	5.881	5.920
120	3.702	4.200	4.497	4.709	4.872	5.005	5.118	5.214	5.299	5.375	5.443	5.505	5.561	5.614	5.662	5.708	5.750	5.790	5.827
240	3.672	4.160	4.450	4.655	4.814	4.943	5.052	5.145	5.227	5.300	5.366	5.426	5.480	5.530	5.577	5.621	5.661	5.699	5.735
Inf	3.643	4.120	4.403	4.603	4.757	4.882	4.987	5.078	5.157	5.227	5.290	5.348	5.400	5.448	5.493	5.535	5.574	5.611	5.645

Source: Agriculture, Forestry and Fisheries Research Information Technology Center, https://itcweb.cc.affrc.go.jp/affrit/doku.php

Table 14 Cumulative Distribution Function of the Runs Test Statistic

For a given number n of observations, the table shows the probability, for a random time series, that the number of runs will not exceed K.

n	K																		
	2	3	4	5	6	7	8	9	10	11	12	13	14	15	16	17	18	19	20
6	.100	.300	.700	.900	1.000														
8	.029	.114	.371	.629	.886	.971	1.000												
10	.008	.040	.167	.357	.643	.833	.960	.992	1.000										
12	.002	.013	.067	.175	.392	.608	.825	.933	.987	.998	1.000								
14	.001	.004	.025	.078	.209	.383	.617	.791	.922	.975	.996	.999	1.000						
16	.000	.001	.009	.032	.100	.214	.405	.595	.786	.900	.968	.991	.999	1.000					
18	.000	.000	.003	.012	.044	.109	.238	.399	.601	.762	.891	.956	.988	.997	1.000	1.000			
20	.000	.000	.001	.004	.019	.051	.128	.242	.414	.586	.758	.872	.949	.981	.996	.999	1.000	1.000	1.000

Reproduced with permission from F. Swed and C. Eisenhart, "Tables for testing randomness of grouping in a sequence of alternatives," *Annals of Mathematical Statistics* 14 (1943).

INDEX

Distribution shape, 66–67. *See also* specific distributions
Diversifiable risk, 460–462
Dummy variables, 526–530, 558–569
  experimental design models, 562–567
  public sector applications, 567–569
  for regression models, 526–530, 562–569
Durbin-Watson test, 588–590
  cut-off points, 781–782

Efficient estimators, 292
Empirical rule, 80–81
Equality, 407–409
  of variances between two normally distributed populations, 407–409
Errors, 55–58, 499, 581–585
  data presentation, 55–59
  nonsampling, 28–29
  reducing margin of, 299–300
  sampling, 28, 297, 353
  standard error, estimate, 494
  Type I, 354, 355, 411
  Type II, 354, 355, 373–377, 411
Error sum of squares, 431–432, 436–437, 493, 656
Error variance, estimation of, 494
Estimated regression model, 428
Estimates, 289
  confidence interval, 295
  explanation of, 289
  point, 290
  standard error, 494
Estimation. *See also* Confidence intervals
  of beta coefficients, 460–462
  coefficient, 557–558
  of error variance, 494
  least squares, 473–474, 487
  of model error variance, 441
  of multiple regression coefficients, 485–491
  of population proportion, 317
  of regressions with autocorrelated errors, 590–594
Estimators, 289
  biased, 291
  confidence interval, 295
  consistent, 330
  efficient, 292
  examples of, 292
  explanation of, 289
  least squares, 473–474

least squares coefficient, 431–434, 443
least squares derivation of, 550–551
point, 289–293
of population mean, 729
unbiased, 290–291, 293
Events, 100–105
  collectively exhaustive, 102
  complements, 102–104
  independent, 129–130
  intersection of, 100–104, 148–149
  mutually exclusive, 100–101, 121
  union, 101–104, 148–149
Excel, 91. *See also* Minitab
  confidence intervals using, 305–306, 335–336
  covariance and correlation using, 187
  jointly distributed discrete random variables, 184
  regression analysis using, 433
  shape of a distribution, 66
Expected value
  of continuous random variables, 207–209
  of discrete random variables, 156–157
  of functions of random variables, 159, 185, 188
  of sample mean, 254
Experimental design models, 562–567
Exploratory data analysis (EDA), 50
Exponential distribution, 229–231
Exponential model transformations, 522–524
Exponential smoothing, 701–711
Extreme points, 463, 465, 468

Failure to reject, 354, 355
F distribution, 407, 775–778
Financial investment portfolios, 236–240
Financial risk, beta measure of, 460–462
Finite population correction factor, 255, 313
Finite populations, confidence interval estimation for, 313–317
First-order autoregressive models, 712–713
First quartile, 68–69
Fisher, R. A., 562
Five-number summary, 69

Forecasting
  from autoregressive models, 713–716
  regression models and, 450–454
  seasonal time series, 708–711
  simple exponential smoothing and, 701–711
  trends and, 690
F probability distribution
  hypothesis test for population slope coefficient using, 447–449
Frequency distributions, 32, 44
  class width, 45
  construction of, 45
  cumulative, 46
  inclusive and nonoverlapping classes, 45–46
  interval width, 45
  number of classes for, 45
  for numerical data, 44–47
  relative, 32, 46
F tests
  for simple regression coefficient, 448–449
  t tests vs., 512–513
Functions, of random variables, 159–161

Geometric mean, 67–68
Geometric mean rate of return, 67
Goodness-of-fit tests
  explanations of, 607
  population parameters unknown, 613–617
  specified probabilities, 607–612
Gosset, William Sealy, 301, 330
Graphical analysis, 462–468
Graphs
  for categorical variables, 32–39
  data presentation errors, 55–58
  to describe relationships between variables, 51–53
  distribution shape, 48–50
  histograms, 48
  of multiple regression model, 484
  for numerical variables, 44–54
  ogives, 48
  scatter plots, 51–53
  stem-and-leaf displays, 50–51
  for time-series data, 39–44
Grouped data, measures of, 85–86
Group means, 675

analysis of variance and, 437
coefficient of determination R², 437–438
Linear regression model, 425–430
  assumptions, 426–427
  examples using, 429–430
  outcomes, 428
  population, 427
Linear regression population equation model, 427
Linear relationships, 422–423
Linear sum of random variables, 284
Line charts, 39–43
Logarithmic transformations, 521–522
Lower confidence limit, 297
Lower tail test, 624

Mann-Whitney *U* statistic, 632–633
Mann-Whitney *U* test, 632–634
Marginal distributions, 233
Marginal probabilities, 127–129, 183–184
Marginal probability distribution, 181–182
Margin of error, 297, 303, 308
  reducing, 299–300
Matched pairs, 391–392
Mathematical derivations, 550–552, 686–687
Matrix plots, 490–491
Mean, 64–68
  approximate, 85–86
  of Bernoulli random variable, 164
  of binomial distribution, 166, 199–200
  conditional, 184
  of continuous random variables, 208
  geometric, 67–68
  of jointly distributed random variables, 200
  of linear functions of a random variable, 159–161, 198–199
  measures of variability from, 72–82
  of normal distribution, population variance known, 319–320, 356–365, 373–375
  of normal distribution, population variance unknown, 366–368
  of Poisson probability distribution, 172
  of sampling distribution of sample variances, 287
  weighted, 84–87

Mean square regression (MSR), 509, 510
Mean squares
  between-groups, 655
  within-groups, 655
Measurement levels, 30–31
Measures of central tendency, 63–72
  geometric mean, 67–68
  mean, median, mode, 64–66
  shape of a distribution, 66–67
Median, 64–66, 67
Minimum variance unbiased estimator, 292
Minitab, 91. *See also* Excel
  autoregressive models, 713–716
  confidence intervals using, 341, 342–343, 345
  descriptive measures using, 91
  Durbin-Watson test, 590
  exponential model estimation, 523
  hypothesis testing, 381, 393–394, 400
  lagged dependent variable, 573
  matrix plots, 490–491
  Monte Carlo sampling simulations, 284–287
  for probability distributions, 158, 168–169
  regression analysis using, 433–434
Missing values, 31, 334–335
Mode, 64–66
Model error variance, estimation of, 441
Model specification, 533–535, 556–557
Monte Carlo sampling simulations, 258–264, 284–287
  Minitab, 284–287
Most efficient estimator, 291–293
Moving averages
  explanation of, 693–695
  extraction of seasonal component through, 696–701
  simple centered (2*m* + 1)-point, 695
Multicollinearity, 578–581
  corrections for, 580–581
  indicators for, 579
Multiple comparisons, 658–659
Multiple regression. *See also* Regression
  analysis application procedure and, 533–541
  applications of, 479–480
  confidence intervals and hypothesis tests for individual regression coefficients, 497–506

estimation of coefficients and, 485–491
  explanatory power of multiple regression equation and, 492–496
  introduction to, 478
  least squares procedure, 486–491
  objectives, 480
  prediction and, 515–517
  tests on regression coefficients, 509–513
Multiple regression equation, 492–496
Multiple regression model, 478
  assumptions, 486
  development of, 481–484, 535–536
  dummy variables for, 526–530
  explanation of, 478–484
  model specification, 478–480
  objectives, 480–481
  population, 483
  residuals analysis and, 538–541
  test on all coefficients of, 501
  three-dimensional graphing of, 484
  transformations for nonlinear, 518–524
Multiplication rule of probabilities, 118–120
Mutually exclusive events, 100–101, 121

Nominal data, 30
Nondiversifiable risk, 460
Nonlinear regression models
  logarithmic transformations, 521–522
  quadratic transformations, 519–521
  transformations for, 518–524
Nonparametric tests
  for independent random samples, 632–636
  Kruskal-Wallis test, 662–664
  Mann-Whitney *U* test, 632–634
  normal approximation to the sign test, 627–628
  for paired or matched samples, 623–630
  for randomness, 640–643
  sign test, 623–625, 630
  Spearman rank correlation, 638–639
  Wilcoxon rank sum test, 635–636
  Wilcoxon signed rank test, 626–630

Standard Normal Distribution Table

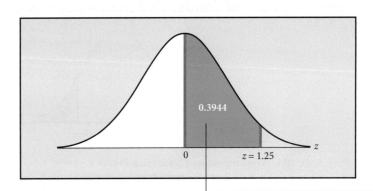

z	0	0.01	0.02	0.03	0.04	0.05	0.06	0.07	0.08	0.09
0.0	0.0000	0.0040	0.0080	0.0120	0.0160	0.0199	0.0239	0.0279	0.0319	0.0359
0.1	0.0398	0.0438	0.0478	0.0517	0.0557	0.0596	0.0636	0.0675	0.0714	0.0753
0.2	0.0793	0.0832	0.0871	0.0910	0.0948	0.0987	0.1026	0.1064	0.1103	0.1141
0.3	0.1179	0.1217	0.1255	0.1293	0.1331	0.1368	0.1406	0.1443	0.1480	0.1517
0.4	0.1554	0.1591	0.1628	0.1664	0.1700	0.1736	0.1772	0.1808	0.1844	0.1879
0.5	0.1915	0.1950	0.1985	0.2019	0.2054	0.2088	0.2123	0.2157	0.2190	0.2224
0.6	0.2257	0.2291	0.2324	0.2357	0.2389	0.2422	0.2454	0.2486	0.2517	0.2549
0.7	0.2580	0.2611	0.2642	0.2673	0.2704	0.2734	0.2764	0.2794	0.2823	0.2852
0.8	0.2881	0.2910	0.2939	0.2967	0.2995	0.3023	0.3051	0.3078	0.3106	0.3133
0.9	0.3159	0.3186	0.3212	0.3238	0.3264	0.3289	0.3315	0.3340	0.3365	0.3389
1.0	0.3413	0.3438	0.3461	0.3485	0.3508	0.3531	0.3554	0.3577	0.3599	0.3621
1.1	0.3643	0.3665	0.3686	0.3708	0.3729	0.3749	0.3770	0.3790	0.3810	0.3830
1.2	0.3849	0.3869	0.3888	0.3907	0.3925	0.3944	0.3962	0.3980	0.3997	0.4015
1.3	0.4032	0.4049	0.4066	0.4082	0.4099	0.4115	0.4131	0.4147	0.4162	0.4177
1.4	0.4192	0.4207	0.4222	0.4236	0.4251	0.4265	0.4279	0.4292	0.4306	0.4319
1.5	0.4332	0.4345	0.4357	0.4370	0.4382	0.4394	0.4406	0.4418	0.4429	0.4441
1.6	0.4452	0.4463	0.4474	0.4484	0.4495	0.4505	0.4515	0.4525	0.4535	0.4545
1.7	0.4554	0.4564	0.4573	0.4582	0.4591	0.4599	0.4608	0.4616	0.4625	0.4633
1.8	0.4641	0.4649	0.4656	0.4664	0.4671	0.4678	0.4686	0.4693	0.4699	0.4706
1.9	0.4713	0.4719	0.4726	0.4732	0.4738	0.4744	0.4750	0.4756	0.4761	0.4767
2.0	0.4772	0.4778	0.4783	0.4788	0.4793	0.4798	0.4803	0.4808	0.4812	0.4817
2.1	0.4821	0.4826	0.4830	0.4834	0.4838	0.4842	0.4846	0.4850	0.4854	0.4857
2.2	0.4861	0.4864	0.4868	0.4871	0.4875	0.4878	0.4881	0.4884	0.4887	0.4890
2.3	0.4893	0.4896	0.4898	0.4901	0.4904	0.4906	0.4909	0.4911	0.4913	0.4916
2.4	0.4918	0.4920	0.4922	0.4925	0.4927	0.4929	0.4931	0.4932	0.4934	0.4936
2.5	0.4938	0.4940	0.4941	0.4943	0.4945	0.4946	0.4948	0.4949	0.4951	0.4952
2.6	0.4953	0.4955	0.4956	0.4957	0.4959	0.4960	0.4961	0.4962	0.4963	0.4964
2.7	0.4965	0.4966	0.4967	0.4968	0.4969	0.4970	0.4971	0.4972	0.4973	0.4974
2.8	0.4974	0.4975	0.4976	0.4977	0.4977	0.4978	0.4979	0.4979	0.4980	0.4981
2.9	0.4981	0.4982	0.4982	0.4983	0.4984	0.4984	0.4985	0.4985	0.4986	0.4986
3.0	0.4987	0.4987	0.4987	0.4988	0.4988	0.4989	0.4989	0.4989	0.4990	0.4990
3.1	0.4990	0.4991	0.4991	0.4991	0.4992	0.4992	0.4992	0.4992	0.4993	0.4993
3.2	0.4993	0.4993	0.4994	0.4994	0.4994	0.4994	0.4994	0.4995	0.4995	0.4995
3.3	0.4995	0.4995	0.4995	0.4996	0.4996	0.4996	0.4996	0.4996	0.4996	0.4997

Dr. William L. Carlson, prepared using Minitab 16.

Upper critical values of Student's t Distribution with ν Degrees of Freedom

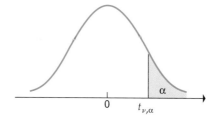

For selected probabilities, α, the table shows the values $t_{\nu,\alpha}$ such that $P(t_\nu > t_{\nu,\alpha}) = \alpha$, where t_ν is a Student's t random variable with ν degrees of freedom. For example, the probability is .10 that a Student's t random variable with 10 degrees of freedom exceeds 1.372.

	PROBABILITY OF EXCEEDING THE CRITICAL VALUE					
ν	0.10	0.05	0.025	0.01	0.005	0.001
1	3.078	6.314	12.706	31.821	63.657	318.313
2	1.886	2.920	4.303	6.965	9.925	22.327
3	1.638	2.353	3.182	4.541	5.841	10.215
4	1.533	2.132	2.776	3.747	4.604	7.173
5	1.476	2.015	2.571	3.365	4.032	5.893
6	1.440	1.943	2.447	3.143	3.707	5.208
7	1.415	1.895	2.365	2.998	3.499	4.782
8	1.397	1.860	2.306	2.896	3.355	4.499
9	1.383	1.833	2.262	2.821	3.250	4.296
10	1.372	1.812	2.228	2.764	3.169	4.143
11	1.363	1.796	2.201	2.718	3.106	4.024
12	1.356	1.782	2.179	2.681	3.055	3.929
13	1.350	1.771	2.160	2.650	3.012	3.852
14	1.345	1.761	2.145	2.624	2.977	3.787
15	1.341	1.753	2.131	2.602	2.947	3.733
16	1.337	1.746	2.120	2.583	2.921	3.686
17	1.333	1.740	2.110	2.567	2.898	3.646
18	1.330	1.734	2.101	2.552	2.878	3.610
19	1.328	1.729	2.093	2.539	2.861	3.579
20	1.325	1.725	2.086	2.528	2.845	3.552
21	1.323	1.721	2.080	2.518	2.831	3.527
22	1.321	1.717	2.074	2.508	2.819	3.505
23	1.319	1.714	2.069	2.500	2.807	3.485
24	1.318	1.711	2.064	2.492	2.797	3.467
25	1.316	1.708	2.060	2.485	2.787	3.450
26	1.315	1.706	2.056	2.479	2.779	3.435
27	1.314	1.703	2.052	2.473	2.771	3.421
28	1.313	1.701	2.048	2.467	2.763	3.408
29	1.311	1.699	2.045	2.462	2.756	3.396
30	1.310	1.697	2.042	2.457	2.750	3.385
40	1.303	1.684	2.021	2.423	2.704	3.307
60	1.296	1.671	2.000	2.390	2.660	3.232
100	1.290	1.660	1.984	2.364	2.626	3.174
∞	1.282	1.645	1.960	2.326	2.576	3.090

NIST/SEMATECH e-Handbook of Statistical Methods, http://www.itl.nist.gov/div898/handbook/, September 2011.